the Elements

by MARY ELVIRA WEEKS

Edited, with a chapter on
Elements Discovered by Atomic Bombardment,

by HENRY M. LEICESTER, Ph.D.
College of Physicians and Surgeons
San Francisco, California

Illustrations collected by F. B. DAINS
Professor of Chemistry
University of Kansas

JOURNAL OF CHEMICAL EDUCATION

SIXTH EDITION
Enlarged and Revised

*Printed in the United States of America by the
Mack Printing Company, Easton, Pa.*

Foreword

*T*he material blessings that man enjoys today have resulted largely from his ever-increasing knowledge of about one hundred simple substances, the chemical elements, most of which were entirely unknown to ancient civilizations. In the luxurious thermæ of the Roman patrician, with all their lavish display of alabaster floors, porphyry walls, marble stairs, and mosaic ceilings, no nickel-plated or chromium fixtures were to be seen; among his artistic golden bowls and goblets no platinum or tantalum objects were ever to be found; with all his spoils of war he could not buy the smallest aluminum trinket.

Even the haughtiest Roman conqueror was earthbound, for he knew no light metal like aluminum or magnesium and no light gas like hydrogen or helium to make lofty flight possible. Without a lantern in his hand, he could not walk along the splendid lava pavements of the city streets at night, for the white glow of the tungsten filament and the crimson glow of the neon tube were lacking. The water that came to him from mountain springs, lakes, and rivers through miles of magnificent aqueducts was a menace to health, for there was no chlorine with which to kill the bacteria. When accident befell him, there was no iodine for the healing of the wound; when he lay gasping for breath, no cylinder of oxygen to save him.

The story of the disclosure, one by one, of the chemical elements has never been told as a connected narrative. The reports of these discoveries and the life stories of the discoverers are recorded for the most part in old chemical journals, biographical dictionaries, old letters, and obsolete textbooks that are seldom read by the busy modern chemist. It is hoped, therefore, that these chapters may not only render tribute to the honored men and women who helped to reveal the hidden chemical elements, but may also serve to acquaint chemists and others with these great achievements.

The task of selecting and eliminating material has been pleasant but difficult. It has frequently happened that two or more men have discovered the same element independently. In other instances various observers have recognized the existence of a new element long before it was actually isolated. In such cases an attempt has been made to relate all important steps in the discovery as fairly and completely as possible without ascribing the honor of discovery to any one person.

If the reader is led through closer acquaintance with the discoverers of the chemical elements to a deeper appreciation of their glorious achievements, the book has not been written in vain.

It is a pleasure to acknowledge the kind assistance given by Dr. E. H. S. Bailey and Dr. Selma Gottlieb Kallis, who read portions of the manuscript, by Dr. F. B. Dains, who made many helpful suggestions as to sources of material and furnished most of the illustrations, by Dr. Max Speter, who read the proof for the fourth edition, and by Dr. Henry M. Leicester, who read the manuscript of the sixth edition and wrote the chapter on "Elements Discovered by Atomic Bombardment."

Grateful acknowledgment is given to Mr. Oren Bingham, who made most of the photographic reproductions for the first edition. The generous coöperation of the library staff and graduate research committee at The University of Kansas, the Edgar Fahs Smith Memorial Library, the former Austro-American Institute of Education, Science Service, and the *Journal of Chemical Education* is deeply appreciated. The publication of valuable illustrations was made possible through the courtesy of the Aluminum Co. of America, the library of the American Philosophical Society, the Army Medical Library, the Bausch and Lomb Optical Co., the Central Scientific Co., Cornell University, the École Supérieure des Mines at Paris, the Fansteel Products Co., the Fisher Scientific Co., the Franklin Institute, Gauthier-Villars et Cie., Harvard University, The Johns Hopkins University, Lehigh University Library, Macmillan and Co., Masson et Cie., the McGraw-Hill Book Co., the Arthur Nemayer Buchdruckerei und Verlag, the Royal Library of Stockholm, the *Scientific American,* the *Scientific Monthly,* and the University of New Hampshire. The author wishes to thank Mr. M. K. Elias and Miss Mary Larson for the Russian and some of the Swedish translations. The kind coöperation of the following persons who assisted in the search for illustrations and other historical material is also acknowledged with pleasure: Dr. Fred Allison, Miss Eva Armstrong, Prof. Modesto Bargalló, Dr. William H. Barnes, Prof. Gabriel Bertrand, Mr. Carl Björkbom, Dr. C. A. Browne, Dr. Otto Brunck, Señor B. J. Caycedo, Dr. Fritz Chemnitius, Dr. F. G. Corning, Dr. Dirk Coster, Mr. James M. Crowe, Dr. Tenney L. Davis, Dr. Claude K. Deischer, Dr. Leonard Dobbin,

Dr. A. S. Eve, Dr. P. V. Faragher, Miss M. Elizabeth Farson, Dr. A. Fleck, Dr. F. Fiala, Mr. Allyn B. Forbes, M. Freymann, Señor A. de Gálvez-Cañero, Dr. Neil E. Gordon, Dr. A. V. Grosse, Dr. W. A. Hamor, Mrs. Gertrude D. Hess, Dr. J. Heyrovsky, Mr. Douglas B. Hobbs, Dr. H. N. Holmes, Dr. B. Smith Hopkins, Sir James C. Irvine, Mme. Y. Khouvine, Dr. Graham Lusk, Dr. L. W. McCay, Dr. and Mrs. H. N. McCoy, Dr. Julius Meyer, Dr. E. Moles, Mr. Julius Nagy, Dr. L. C. Newell, Dr. Gunnar Nilson, Dr. R. E. Oesper, Mr. E. H. Parke, Mr. R. B. Pilcher, Mme. J. Presne, Prof. H. Rheinboldt, Dr. E. H. Riegel, Señor Pablo Martínez del Río, Professor Luigi Rolla, Dr. A. S. Russell, Dr. Stig Rydén, Dr. E. Segrè, Dr. S. E. Sheppard, Dr. H. G. Söderbaum, Prof. L. von Szathmáry, Dr. W. T. Taggart, Dr. L. G. Toraude, Dr. M. W. Travers, Mr. W. D. Trow, Miss Amy Wästfelt, and Mr. T. A. Wertime.

Thoughtful readers and reviewers of earlier editions of this book have also given many helpful suggestions.

MARY ELVIRA WEEKS

Detroit
May, 1956

Contents

Foreword v

1 Elements known to the ancient world 3
    gold, silver, copper, iron, lead, tin, mercury, sulfur,
    carbon

2 Carbon and some of its compounds 75

3 Elements of the alchemists 91
    arsenic, antimony, bismuth, phosphorus

4 More on the discovery of phosphorus 121

5 Some eighteenth-century metals 141
    zinc, cobalt, nickel, manganese

6 Old compounds of hydrogen and nitrogen 183

7 Three important gases 197
    hydrogen, nitrogen, oxygen

8 Rutherford, discoverer of nitrogen 235

9 Chromium, molybdenum, tungsten, uranium 253

10 Contributions of the de Elhuyar brothers 285
    tungsten

11 Tellurium and selenium 303

12 Klaproth-Kitaibel letters on tellurium 321

13 Niobium (columbium), tantalum, vanadium 339

14 Contributions of Charles Hatchett 369
    niobium

15 Contributions of Andrés Manuel del Río 391
    vanadium

16 The platinum metals 407
    platinum, rhodium, osmium, iridium, palladium,
    ruthenium

17 Some old potassium and sodium compounds 455

18 Three alkali metals   473
    potassium, sodium, lithium

19 J. A. Arfwedson and his service to chemistry   495
    lithium

20 Alkaline earth metals, magnesium, cadmium   505
    calcium, barium, strontium, magnesium, cadmium

21 Elements isolated with the aid of potassium and sodium . . .   543
    zirconium, titanium, cerium, thorium

22 Other elements isolated with the aid of potassium and sodium   565
    beryllium, boron, silicon, aluminum

23 Some spectroscopic discoveries   619
    cesium, rubidium, thallium, indium

24 Periodic system of the elements   653

25 Some elements predicted by Mendeleev   671
    gallium, scandium, germanium

26 The rare earth elements   695
    ytterbium, cerium, lanthanum, neodymium, praseo-
    dymium, erbium, terbium, yttrium, scandium, hol-
    mium, thulium, samarium, gadolinium, dysprosium,
    europium, lutetium

27 The halogen family   729
    fluorine, chlorine, bromine, iodine

28 The inert gases   779
    helium, neon, argon, krypton, xenon

29 The natural radioactive elements   803
    radium, polonium, uranium, radon, protactinium,
    actinium, thorium

30 Discoveries by X-ray spectrum analysis   845
    hafnium, rhenium

31 Elements discovered by atomic bombardment   859
    francium, technetium, promethium, astatine, neptu-
    nium, plutonium, americium, curium, berkelium,
    californium, mendelevium, einsteinium, fermium

List of the chemical elements   883

Chronology of element discovery   885

Index   899

Discovery
of the Elements

Hermes Trismegistos

The world of chemical reactions is like a stage, on which scene after scene is ceaselessly played. The actors on it are the elements (1).

What connection do the books show between the fifty or sixty chemical elements and the historical eras? (119).

1

Elements known to the ancient world

Although the ancient conception of an element was quite different from the modern one, a few of the substances now recognized as chemical elements have been known and used since the dawn of history. Although no one knows who discovered these ancient "building-stones of the universe," the writings of Pliny the Elder and Dioscorides and the Hebrew and Hindu Scriptures abound in interesting allusions to the metals, gold, silver, copper, iron, lead, tin, and mercury, and the non-metals, sulfur and carbon.

*T*he chemical elements, those primeval building materials from which Nature has constructed all her varied forms, have been discovered, one by one, through the ages, by patient searchers in many lands. The ancient Greek philosophers Thales, Xenophanes, and Heraclitus believed that all substances were composed of a single element, but they did not agree as to its nature. Thales thought that water was the element which, upon evaporating and condensing, produced all substances. Heraclitus, however, believed that fire was the one fundamental building material.

The conception of four simple substances (earth, air, water, and fire) had its origin in the mind of Empedocles about four hundred and forty years before the birth of Christ, and held sway for many centuries. Every one knows today that neither earth nor air, water nor fire is an element. Earth is the most complex of all, for it can be separated into many chemical compounds, whose natures vary according to the locality from which the soil has been taken. From air can be obtained a number of simple gases, among them nitrogen, oxygen, and argon. Water, also, can be easily decomposed into the two gaseous elements, oxygen and hydrogen; and fire, far from being an element, consists of the incandescent gases or glowing embers of the fuel which is being burned. Simple as these facts may seem to the modern mind, the world's best intellects once debated them and established them.

During the centuries, man's conception of what constitutes a chemical element has undergone many other changes. Aristotle (384–322 B.C.) believed that the properties of substances are the result of the simultaneous presence or blending of certain fundamental properties (*102*). He

3

spoke of "elements" only in the sense of hypothetical bearers of these fundamental properties, not as undecomposable substances that can be detected empirically and isolated. The Aristotelian doctrine was therefore concerned not with what modern chemists call elements but with an abstract conception of certain properties, especially coldness, hotness, dryness, and moistness, which may be united in four combinations: dry-

From Delbrueck's "Antike Porträts"

Heraclitus, 540–475 B.C. Ascetic Greek philosopher and founder of metaphysics. He believed that fire is the primary substance, and that change is the only actuality in Nature.

ness and heat (fire), heat and moisture (air), moisture and cold (water), and cold and dryness (earth) (*102*). Aristotle and his followers believed that all substances are composed of these four elemental states of matter.

In the twelfth century there appeared in certain Latin works alleged to be translations from the Arabic the theory of the principles of metals: namely mercury, which confers metallic properties, and sulfur, which causes the loss of these properties on roasting. Another principle, salt, which imparted refractoriness or "fixity in the fire," was added later by the famous popularizer of medical chemistry, Paracelsus (*85*).

In 1661 Robert Boyle published "The Sceptical Chymist," a book in which he discussed the criteria by which one can decide whether a substance is or is not a chemical element. He concluded that the four Aristotelian elements and three principles commonly accepted in his time cannot be real chemical elements since they can neither compose nor be extracted from substances (85). He stated clearly "I now mean by Elements, as those Chymists that speak plainest do by their Principles, certain Primitive and Simple, or perfectly unmingled bodies; which not being made up of any other bodies, or of one another, are the Ingredients of which all those call'd perfectly mixt Bodies are immediately compounded, and into which they are ultimately resolved: now whether there be any one such body to be constantly met with in all, and each, of those that are said to be Elemented bodies, is the thing I now question" (84). In spite of its clearness, this definition of a chemical element played no important part in the progress of chemistry for more than a century.

In 1789 A.-L. Lavoisier stated in his "Traité Élémentaire de Chimie": "If . . . we attach to the name of element or principle of bodies the idea of the last term to which analysis reaches, then all substances which we have not yet been able by any means to decompose are elements to us—not that we can be sure that these bodies which we regard as simple may not themselves be composed of two or even of a greater number of principles, but since these principles are never separated, or rather, since we have no means of separating them, they act as far as we are concerned in the manner of simple bodies, and we ought not to suppose them compounded until experience and observation shall have furnished the proof" (84). Even since Lavoisier's time however the concept of element has undergone many changes. In his list of elements, for example, he included light and heat (caloric), which of course are now known to be forms of energy. The changing views concerning the definition of a chemical element have been set forth in a scholarly manner by B. N. Menschutkin (82), Tenney L. Davis (84), J. R. Partington, (85), and Marie Boas (103, 105).

The story of the "defunct elements," those so-called "elements" which were later found to be complex, is most interesting, but the present narrative will be confined to the simple substances now recognized by chemists. The curious false elements, considerably more than a hundred in number, were described in a fascinating article by Charles Baskerville (2).

ANCIENT METALS

The chemical elements which were undoubtedly known to the ancient world are the metals: gold, silver, copper, iron, lead, tin, and mercury, and the non-metals: sulfur and carbon. The ancient Jews, as one learns from the Old Testament, were certainly acquainted with the first six.

The six metals mentioned in the Bible are gold, silver, copper, tin, lead, and iron. Eleazar the priest classified them all as substances that can be purified by fire: "the gold, and the silver, the brass, the iron, the tin, and the lead" (Num. **31,** 22). The word *brass* in this passage means *bronze,* an alloy of copper and tin. Isaiah's vision of the new Jerusalem therefore implies knowledge or application of five of these metals. In the Smith-Goodspeed translation, it reads as follows:

> *"Instead of bronze will I bring gold,*
> *And instead of iron will I bring silver;*
> *And instead of wood, bronze,*
> *And instead of stones, iron;*
> *And Peace will I make your government,*
> *And Righteousness your ruler"* (Isa. **60,** 17) (37).

The same metals were also known to Daniel (Dan. **2,** 32–3; **5,** 4). The modern Brazilian Portuguese translation, however, reads copper (*cobre*) instead of bronze in all these passages (88).

In the missing portion of the second book of Esdras which the British Orientalist Robert L. Bensly discovered at Amiens and published in 1875, the angel says (in speaking to Ezra of the earth), "You produce gold and silver and copper and also iron and lead and clay. But silver is more abundant than gold, and copper than silver, and iron than copper, lead than iron, and clay than lead" (II Esdras **7,** 55–6) (37).

The ancient Hindus used these metals also, for Sir Praphulla Chandra Rây quotes from the Charaka: "Gold and the five metals . . . silver, copper, lead, tin, and iron" (3). R. N. Bhagvat of Bombay published in the *Journal of Chemical Education* an interesting article on knowledge of the metals in ancient India and illustrated it with pictures of gold, silver, copper, and iron utensils; an iron furnace; the famous wrought iron pillar near Delhi, weighing about ten tons and believed to date from about the fourth century A.D.; and a copper blast furnace (87). He believed that even in the time of the most ancient Vedas (the most sacred writings of the Hindus), "metals, including iron, were well known and that the craft of metalworking had reached a fairly advanced stage" (87). The Vedic period extended from about 5000 to 4500 B.C.

GOLD

Gold ornaments have been found in Egyptian tombs of the prehistoric stone age, and the Egyptian goldsmiths of the earliest dynasties were skillful artisans. The metal was used as a medium of exchange in the days of Abraham, and is mentioned in Exodus, Deuteronomy, the First Book of Kings, Job, the Psalms, the Proverbs, Isaiah, Lamentations, Haggai, and Zechariah (4). The reference in Genesis to the good gold of Havilah (the sand land) is evidence of the great antiquity of this metal (Gen. **2,** 11–12). Its malleability and ductility were already recognized and utilized when Aaron's vestments were embroidered: "And they did beat the gold into thin plates, and cut it into wires, to work it in the blue, and in the purple, and in the scarlet, and in the fine linen, with cunning work" (Ex. **39**, 3).

In the time of David and Solomon, both precious and useful metals were available in quantities. In charging Solomon to build the Temple, David said, "Of the gold, the silver, and the brass, and the iron there is no number" (I Chron. **22**, 14, 16). The word *brass* in this passage means *bronze* (*37*). Solomon's fleet, manned by his servants and King Hiram's experienced Tyrian sailors, embarked from Ezion-Geber, near Eloth in the land of Edom on the Red Sea, proceeded to Ophir, and returned with four hundred and twenty talents (more than twelve million dollars' worth) of gold (I Kings **9**, 26–8). Nelson Glueck believes that the port city of Ezion-Geber and its successor Elath (*sic*) were located at the north end of the Gulf of 'Aqabah in the Early Iron Age (*89*).

In the prophetic book of Isaiah (as translated by Alex. R. Gordon) stands the promise:

> *"I shall still the pride of the arrogant,*
> *And shall bring low the haughtiness of tyrants;*
> *I shall make man rarer than fine gold,*
> *Mankind more rare than gold of Ophir"* (Isa. **13**, 12) (*37*).

Gold was brought from Ophir, Arabia, Sheba, and (to a lesser extent) from Uphaz (the high country) and Parvaim (Jer. **10**, 9; II Chron. **3**, 6; **9**, 1, 14). When Carsten Niebuhr traveled through Arabia in 1761–63, he stated that the Greeks and Latins had often mentioned the immense quantities of gold produced there. He said, however, "In remote times possibly, when the Arabians were the factors of the trade to India, much of this precious metal might pass through Arabia into Europe; but that gold was probably the produce of the mines of India. At present, at least, there is no gold mine in Arabia . . ." (*90*). The first book of the Maccabees mentions the silver and gold mines of Spain (I Macc. **8**, 1–3).

The metallurgical parables and analogies, like the agricultural ones, express some of the loftiest truths in the Scriptures. Metallurgical processes for the precious metals are described in Malachi, the Psalms, and the Proverbs: "But who may abide the day of his coming? and who shall stand when he appeareth? for he is like a refiner's fire, and like fullers' soap: And he shall sit as a refiner and purifier of silver: and he shall purify the sons of Levi, and purge them as gold and silver, that they may offer unto the Lord an offering in righteousness" (Mal. **3**, 2–3). "For thou, O God, hast proved us: thou hast tried us, as silver is tried" (Ps. **66**, 10). "The fining pot is for silver, and the furnace for gold: but

the Lord trieth the hearts" (Prov. **17**, 3). "As the fining pot for silver
and the furnace for gold; so is a man to his praise" (Prov. **27**, 21). Alex.
R. Gordon translates this as "smelter" instead of fining pot (*37*). The
modern Spanish and Brazilian Portuguese translations, however, use the
word *"crisol,"* or crucible (*88, 91*).

The art of working gold is exceedingly ancient. The two leading
goldsmiths who accompanied Moses through the wilderness were Bezaleel
of the tribe of Judah and Aholiab of the tribe of Dan, who were highly
skilled in metal-working and in many other arts (Ex. **31**, 1–11; **35**, 30–35;
38, 22–3). Moses himself was doubtless familiar with these crafts, for
(according to Luke) he "was learned in all the wisdom of the Egyptians"
(Acts **7**, 22). Isaiah mentioned the goldsmith's art as applied to the construction of idols: "So the carpenter encouraged the goldsmith. . . .
They lavish gold out of the bag, and weigh silver in the balance, and hire
a goldsmith; and he maketh it a god. . ." (Isa. **41**, 7; **46**, 6).

Pliny the Elder (A.D. 23–79) said that grains of gold were found
in the stream-beds of the Tagus in Spain, the Po in Italy, the Hebrus in
Thracia, the Pactolus in Asia Minor, and the Ganges in India (*5*). In
the second century before Christ, a cupellation process was used for refining the metal, and in Pliny's time the mercury process was well
known (*6*).

Vitruvius, who lived in the reign of Augustus, mentioned the use
of mercury to recover finely divided gold. "When gold has been woven
into a garment," said he, "and the garment becomes worn out with age
so that it is no longer respectable to use, the pieces of cloth are put into
earthern pots, and burned up over a fire. The ashes are then thrown
into water and quicksilver added thereto. This attracts all the bits of
gold, and makes them combine with itself. The water is then poured
off, and emptied into a cloth and squeezed in the hands, whereupon the
quicksilver, being a liquid, escapes through the loose texture of the cloth,
but the gold, which has been brought together by the squeezing, is found
inside in a pure state" (*47*).

Paul Bergsøe of Copenhagen has published photographs of many
small golden fishhooks, forceps, nails, tacks, pins, sewing needles, spoons,
trinkets, and ornaments made at Esmeraldas and La Tolita, Ecuador, by
pre-Columbian Indians (*106*). They are composed of gold alloyed with
platinum and silver in varying proportions.

Archaeologists have found that the province of Coclé in Panama is
rich in gold artifacts (*117*). In the spring of 1940 a scientific expedition
from the University of Pennsylvania excavated a pre-Columbian cemetery in this province, about one hundred miles west of Panama City, and
brought back to the Museum a great collection of large repoussé plaques,

a four-inch crocodile with a one-inch emerald set in its back, pendants, nose clips, beads, cuffs, and greaves, all of nearly pure gold. The gold ornaments found on one chieftain weighed one hundred ounces troy. The area from which these objects were excavated was only 54 by 27 feet.

Even on his first voyage, Christopher Columbus was not disappointed in his quest for gold. In a letter to Luis de Santangel, Chancellor of the Exchequer of Aragon, he wrote on February 15, 1493, "Española [Haiti] is a wonder. . . . The harbours on the coast and the number and size and wholesomeness of the rivers, most of them bearing gold, surpass anything that would be believed by one who had not seen them. . . . In this island there are many spices and extensive mines of gold and other metals. The inhabitants have neither iron, nor steel, nor arms. . . .

Pliny the Elder, 23–79 A.D. Roman philosopher. Author of a "Natural History" in 37 books, in which he discussed the astronomy, geology, zoölogy, botany, agriculture, mineralogy, and medicine of his time.

They never refuse anything that they possess . . .; on the contrary, they offer it themselves, and they exhibit so much loving kindness that they would even give their hearts. . . . I forbade that worthless things. . . should be given to them" (*107*).

In a letter describing the second voyage, Dr. Chanca, physician to the fleet of Columbus, wrote that "the Indians beat the gold into very thin plates, in order to make masks of it. . . . It is not the costliness of the gold that they value in their ornaments, but its showy appearance. . . . It appears to me that these people put more value upon copper than gold" (*107*). The gold mines of Cibao in the interior of Haiti [Hispaniola] were discovered by Alonso de Ojeda in 1494 (*108*).

On his fourth voyage, Columbus wrote in 1503 that "in this land of Veragua [Panama] I saw more signs of gold in the first two days than I saw in Española [Haiti] during four years" (*107*).

Gonzálo Fernández de Oviedo y Valdés, "surveyor of the melting shops pertayning to the gold mynes of the firme Land" [Tierra Firma, Panama], said that most of the wrought gold of the Indians was contaminated with copper. He described the mining procedure in detail, and stated that the Indian women were highly skilled in panning gold (*109*). "The Indians," he said, "can very excellently gild such Vessels of Copper and base Gold as they make. . ." (*110*).

In 1534 Pedro Sancho, secretary to Governor Francisco Pizarro, in his report of the conquest of Peru, described the gold and silver artifacts and life-size statues found in Cuzco, the ancient Inca capital. "Amongst other things," said he, "there were sheepe of fine gold very great, and ten or twelve statues of women in their just bignesse and proportion, artificially composed of fine Gold. . ." (*111*).

In 1586 Lopez Vaz, a Portuguese, told Captain Withrington that "The first Land that is inhabited by the Spaniards along the Coast is called Veragua [Panama]; this is the most richest Land of Gold then [sic] all the rest of the Indies: therefore it is inhabited with Spaniards." He added that the Spaniards endured sickness and other hardships for the sake of the gold which they obtained from the rivers with Negro labor (*112*).

In his "Natural and Moral History of the Indies," which was first published in Seville in 1590, Father José de Acosta said that he had found aborigines who had no desire to possess gold, and that the Indians, instead of using gold, silver, or any other metal for money, bartered their products and used the metals only for ornament (*113*). Padre de Acosta also stated that "it is wel knowne by approved histories that the Yncas of Peru did not content themselves with great and small vessels of gold, as pots, cups, goblets, and flagons . . . but they had chaires also and litters of massie golde, and in their temples they had set vppe manie Images of pure gold. . ." (*113*).

Padre A. A. Barba regarded gold as "the most perfect of all inanimate bodies created by Nature." He stated that the city of La Paz was "fertile in gold" and that "during the rainy season, boys find Nuggets in the Streets, especially in that one which descends by the Monastery of the Dominicans towards the river" (*114*). Even in the twentieth century, these ancient gold artifacts are sometimes unearthed. S. K. Lothrop has told in *American Antiquity* how some Peruvian boys of fifteen years and younger found a golden crown, bracelets, and vases at the bottom of a trench formed by a break in an irrigation ditch at Chongoyape (*115*).

In the autumn of 1699 Dr. James Wallace made a voyage to New Caledonia in Darien.   In his account of it in the *Philosophical Transactions* he wrote: "This Country certainly affords Gold enough, for besides that the Natives constantly assure us that they Know several Gold-Mines on this side; besides that, I say, the Plates they Wear in their Noses and the Quantity of Gold that is amongst them is enough to perswade any Man of the Truth of it.   There was one Night aboard here some Indians that had a hundred Ounces of Gold about them" (*116*).

Georgius Agricola used the touchstone and touch needles for examining bullion, coins, and jewelry, but did not test with acid the

From Biringuccio's "Pirotechnia"

An Assay Furnace, 1540

"streak" which the metal left on the black siliceous stone.   Other time-honored tests for gold were its specific gravity, as determined by Archimedes; its resistance to atmospheric oxidation on fusion, as shown in the "trial by fire"; its resistance to the oxidizing power of litharge in cupellation; and its insolubility in acids.   By the early sixteenth century some assayers had become proficient in the "parting" of gold and silver (*118*).

Although assayers were usually not deceived by imitation gold, the "augmentation" of it was more difficult to detect.   Since gold persistently retains some of the mercury used in its amalgamation, absorbs silver from argentiferous lead, and may also absorb copper, alchemists were able to "augment" the weight of their product (*118*).

Gold Ruby Glass.   The ancient Egyptians were masters of the art of adding metallic oxides and minerals to the colorless frit to produce glass of various colors. In their most ancient red glass, the color was usually produced by iron or copper. Gold ruby glass is of much later origin (120). In his *Alchymia*, which was first published in 1595, Andreas Liebau (Libavius) told how to use gold solutions to produce a red color in glass and thus to imitate the ruby (120, 121, 122). Father Antonio Neri and Isaac and Johann Isaac Hollandus, contemporaries of Libavius, prepared ruby glass that was transparent like the carbuncle by adding to the colorless frit a powder prepared by repeatedly treating gold with a mixture of nitric and hydrochloric acids (aqua regia), evaporating to dryness, and heating the residue in a small reverberatory furnace until it became red (120).

In the seventeenth century J. R. Glauber reduced gold solutions with tin. Although the resulting precipitate is known as "purple of Cassius," Johann Kunckel stated that Dr. Andreas Cassius may have learned the secret of it from Glauber (120, 121). With this powder Dr. Cassius prepared ruby glass by a process which Kunckel afterward developed to a high stage of perfection. In his "Vollständiges Laboratorium Chymicum," Kunckel wrote: "It originated in the following manner. There was a doctor of medicine by the name of Cassius, who discovered the Praecipitationem Solis cum Jove (precipitation of gold with tin), to which perhaps Glauber may have given the impulse, on which I offer no opinion. This aforesaid Dr. Cassius tried to introduce it into glass; when, however, he wanted to form it into glass or when it came out of the fire, it was as clear as any other crystal, and he could not bring it to any permanent redness. As a man of curiosity, he may, however, have noticed among the glass-blowers that a color often changes through malaxation [dilution] in the flame of the lamp, wherefore he also tried it, and thus saw the handsomest ruby color. When I learned this, I immediately set to work, but how much trouble I had to discover the composition and how one can get it permanently red, I myself know best" (120, 121, 123). Some fine examples of Kunckel's ruby glass still exist (124).

W. P. Jorissen and J. Postma have shown that J. R. Glauber described the ruby gold in 1659, a quarter of a century before Cassius did (125).

Potable Gold. In the *Kolloid-Zeitschrift*, H. Lösner discussed the history of colloidal gold and quoted several early recipes for the preparation of red gold sols, or potable gold (Trinkgold). Preparations such as this were made by Creiling (1730), Valentin Kräutermann (1717), G. E. Stahl (1744), and George Wilson (126).

In 1746 William Lewis (1714–1781) edited George Wilson's "Compleat Course Chymistry" and published it under the title "A Course of Practical Chemistry." Wilson's recipe for "Aurum potabile, as I prepared it for the chief physician of a great prince, 1692" is to be found in that volume (127). His earlier researches with gold, which were begun in March, 1687, ended "the eleventh of December; when I was treated as the Spanish ambassador was: for the mob taking me for a conjurer, or something worse, broke my glasses and athanor; saying that I was preparing the devil's fire-works, purposely to burn the city and Whitehall. And thus ended this operation" (127).

Wilson's contemporary Nicolas Lémery, however, more distrustful of alchemists, said that "their Aurum potabile, which they crack with so loud, and which they sell at so dear a price, is commonly nothing else but a tincture of some Vegetable or Mineral whose color comes near to that of gold. . . . This same cheat of theirs is none of the least that they use to get by, for in point of Medicins, abundance of people prove extreme credulous . . ." (128). Geoffroy the Elder concluded "that the most valuable and most precious of all Metals is the most useless in Physick, except when considered as an Antidote to Poverty" (129).

The California Gold Rush. Vague references to an Eldorado on an island in the Pacific appeared as early as the sixteenth century (130). Early in 1848 gold was found at Sutter's mill near the present town of Coloma, California. Among the claimants to the honor of this discovery may be mentioned Captain Charles Bennett, James W. Marshall (his partner), and Emma Bonney. By the autumn of 1848 incredible reports had gradually circulated in the United States that the inhabitants of the California Territory, but lately acquired from Mexico, were leaving their customary occupations to pan gold. Verification of these reports led to the great "gold rush of '49," in which adventurous men from all walks of life made the tedious and perilous journey to California by overland trail, around Cape Horn, or across the disease-ridden Isthmus of Panama (130, 131, 277).

In 1859 a party of miners detected gold in Dry Creek, near Denver, Colorado. Before the close of that year, the gulches near Central City were swarming with gold seekers (132).

Gold in Sea Water. Although the presence of gold in sea water has often been reported, Georges Claude estimated the gold content of sea water off the California coast (where one might expect it to be above the average concentration for the ocean as a whole) to be less than 0.1 milligram per cubic meter (133). Gold has been electroplated from sea water, but at a cost five times the value of the metal. Dr. Colin G. Fink found that when a stationary cathode is used, the gold precipitates out rapidly in colloidal form. With a rapidly rotating cathode, it is possible to get a visible deposit of crystalline gold (134).

SILVER

Silver, since it rarely occurs uncombined, did not come into use as early as did gold (29). In Egypt between the thirtieth and fifteenth centuries before Christ, it was rarer and more costly than gold. It must have been used as a medium of exchange long before it was coined, for it is related in Genesis that when Abraham purchased a burial place for Sarah he weighed out the silver in the presence of witnesses (7). Jeremiah, too, weighed out the silver when he purchased the family inheritance, Hanameel's field (Jer. **32**, 9–10).

In the ancient cupellation process of refining gold and silver, the impure metal was heated in a cupel (a shallow, porous cup of bone ash) by means of a blast of air. The base metals, such as lead, tin, iron, and copper, were thus oxidized and absorbed into the porous cupel, leaving a button of unoxidizable, noble metal behind. Unless lead was already present as an impurity, it was added before the cupel was heated. About seven and a half centuries before the birth of Christ, Isaiah referred to this process as follows: "And I will turn my hand upon thee, and purely purge away thy dross, and take away all thy tin" (Isa. **1**, 25). The modern Brazilian Portuguese translation of this verse reads: "voltarei a minha mão sobre ti, e purificarei como com potassa a tua escoria, e tirarei de ti todo o teu estanho" (88).

A century and a half later, Jeremiah described the cupellation process more vividly in his rebuke to backsliding Judah. Although the metallurgical meaning is evident in the Authorized Version, it is brought out still more clearly in the translation by Alex. R. Gordon:

> "I have made you an assayer and tester among my people,
> That you may prove and assay their ways.
> For they are all of them hardened rebels,
> Dealers in slander;
> They are all of them bronze and iron,
> Wholly corrupt.
> The bellows are scorched with the fire,
> The lead is consumed;
> But in vain does the smelter keep on smelting,
> The dross is not drawn out.
> 'Refuse silver,' are they called,
> For the Lord has refused them" (Jer. **6**, 27–30) (37).

The modern Spanish translation interprets the 29th verse differently, however: "Los fuelles soplan furiosamente; de su fuego resulta plomo . . . (The bellows blow furiously; from their fire, lead results . . ."), (91).

Jeremiah also mentioned sheet silver. For the embellishment of an idol, "Silver spread into plates is brought from Tarshish, and gold from Uphaz, the work of the workman, and of the hands of the founder: blue and purple is their clothing: they are all the work of cunning men" (Jer. **10,** 9). The Smith-Goodspeed translation refers to these metals as beaten silver from Tarshish" and "gold from Ophir" (*37*).

In the parable of the dross in the furnace, Ezekiel described the cupellation process in detail: "And the word of the Lord came unto me,

Iron   **Silver**

Seventeenth-century Symbols, from Peters's "Aus pharmazeutischer Vorzeit in Bild und Wort"

saying, Son of man, the house of Israel is to me become dross: all they are brass, and tin, and iron, and lead, in the midst of the furnace; they are even the dross of silver. Therefore thus saith the Lord God; Because ye are all become dross, behold, therefore I will gather you into the midst of Jersusalem, As they gather silver, and brass, and iron, and lead, and tin, into the midst of the furnace, to blow the fire upon it, to melt it;

so will I gather you in mine anger and in my fury, and I will leave you there, and melt you. . . ." Ezek. **22**, 17–22.

Zechariah, too, used a metallurgical analogy to portray the saving of a remnant of the people in Jerusalem: "And it shall come to pass, that in all the land, saith the Lord, two parts therein shall be cut off and die; but the third shall be left therein. And I will bring the third part through the fire, and will refine them as silver is refined, and will try them as gold is tried: they shall call on my name, and I will hear them: I will say, It is my people: and they shall say, The Lord is my God" (Zech. **13**, 8–9). The metallurgical analogies in the Bible were thoroughly discussed and explained by James Napier (1810–1884), a Scottish dyer and chemist who studied under Thomas Graham at Glasgow in the same class with David Livingstone (*92, 93*).

In the New Testament, too, silver plays an important role.

When Paul's teaching of Christ's gospel endangered the livelihood of Demetrius and other silversmiths who made and sold shrines for Diana at Ephesus, they stirred up great commotion among their fellow citizens (Acts **19**, 23–41). In Paul's time, the Ephesians worshipped Diana and "an image which fell down from Jupiter." The latter may have been a meteorite. Among the alchemists, the name and figure of Diana long served as the chemical symbol for silver. According to J. R. Partington, "Egyptian silver . . . was an alloy with gold containing approximately 60 to 92 per cent of silver and 3 to 38 of gold, with occasionally a little copper, and was probably a white natural product, not obtained by smelting an ore." He also stated that the Greeks first worked argentiferous galena for silver in about the seventh century B.C. (*135*).

Jagnaux stated that when the Phœnicians made their first voyage to Spain they found more silver than their ships could carry, and that, for this reason, they weighted their wooden anchors with silver instead of lead (*8*). When the Spaniards conquered Peru they found many silver utensils that had been made by the ancient inhabitants (*9, 28*).

Some Ancient Silver Mines. The gold and silver mines of Spain are mentioned in the Apocrypha. In the days of the Maccabees they were in possession of the Romans: "Now Judas had heard of the fame of the Romans. . . . It was told him also of their wars . . . and what they had done in the Country of Spain, for the winning of the mines of the silver and gold which is there . . ." (*136*).

In 1700 J.-P. de Tournefort visited the Island of Kimolos in the Aegean Sea. "This Island," said he, "by the Greeks call'd Chimoli, took the name of Argentière at the time when the Silver Mines were first discover'd there: there are still to be seen the Work-houses and Furnaces where they used to prepare this Metal" (*137*).

In the first edition of the "Natural History of the West Indies," which Gonzálo Fernández de Oviedo y Valdés wrote for Charles V. in 1525, he stated that Stephen Gómez had recently found silver and copper in northern America (*108*). Oviedo later published a more comprehensive work on the same subject (*109*).

The silver mines of Charcas, Peru, were discovered in 1535, those of Potosí, Peru (now part of Bolivia), in 1545, those of Zacatecas, Mexico, in 1548, and those of Guanajuato, Mexico, in 1550 (*108*). The first coins struck in America were produced in Mexico in 1536 under the viceroyship of Antonio de Mendoza. They were of copper and silver (*108*).

In his "Natural and Moral History of the Indies," Father José de Acosta wrote in 1590: "The Creator hath furnished the West Indies with so great a treasure of silver, as all that which we reade of in antient Histories and that which is spoken of the mines of Spaine, and other provinces, is not comparable to that we see in those partes. . . . The maner to purge and refine siluer [sic] which the Indians have vsed was by melting, in dissolving this masse of mettall by fire, which casts the earthly drosse aparte, and by his force separates silver from lead, tinne from copper, and other mettalls mixt.

"To this end," continued Father de Acosta, "they did build small furnaces in places whereas the wind did commonly blow, and with wood and cole made their refining, the which furnaces in Peru they call *huayras*. Since the Spaniards entred, besides this manner of refining which they vse to this day, they likewise refine silver with qvick-silver, and draw more by this means then [sic] in refining it by fire. For there is some kind of silver mettall found which can by no means be purged and refined by fire, but onely with quicksilver . . ." (*45*).

According to Father de Acosta, "the chief places of the Indies from which they draw silver are New Spaine [Mexico] and Peru; but the mines of Peru farre surpasse the rest; and amongst all others of the worlde, those of Potosí [now in Bolivia]" (*45*).

Father de Acosta then went on to tell how the mines of Potosí were discovered, twelve years after the Spanish conquest of Peru, by an Indian named Hualpa of the province of Cuzco. One day when Hualpa was hunting deer, he had to take hold of a branch in order to climb up a rough slope. In the hole left by the uprooted shrub, Hualpa saw some metal. After it had been assayed at Porco, he worked the rich vein secretly for about two months until another Indian, named Huanca, discovered his secret (*45*). Hualpa then gave Huanca another vein which was equally rich in silver but somewhat more difficult to work than the original Diego Centeno vein. Dissatisfied with this agreement, Huanca revealed the secret to his Spanish master, Villarroel. Thus on April 21,

1545, Huanca and Villarroel became joint owners of the mines of Potosí. The King of Spain claimed one-fifth of their proceeds (45).

At this day," said Father de Acosta, "the most vsuall maner of refining in Potosí is by quickesilver, as also in the mines of Zacatecas, and others of New Spaine. There were in old time, vpon the sides and toppes of Potosí, above six thousand *Huayras,* which are small furnaces where they melt their mettall, the which were placed like lights (a pleasant sight to behold by night) casting a light a farre off like a flame of fire. . . . But at this day there are not above two thousand . . ." (45).

In 1569 the poet Alonso de Ercilla y Zúniga described this ancient process and the hill of Potosí in his poem *Araucana:*

> *"Pues de un quintal de tierra de la mina*
> *Las dos arrobas son de plata fina"* (113),

which may be translated:

> *"For from one quintal of earth of the mine*
> *Two arrobas are yielded of silver fine."*

Of the assay masters, Father de Acosta said, "Their ballaunce and weights are so delicate, and their graines so small, as they cannot take them vppe with the hand, but with a small paire of pincers: and this triall they make by candle light, that no ayre might moove the ballance. For of this little the price of the whole barre dependeth" (45).

In the seventeenth century, Father Alvaro Alonso Barba of Potosí said that some of the mines there had been worked by the Incas and that, since the coming of the Spaniards, the wealth of this hill had been distributed to all parts of the world (46).

Silver Trees. In the eighteenth century, silver solutions were reduced in various ways to form "the tree of Diana," which Erasmus Darwin described as follows:

> *"So the learn'd Alchemist exulting sees*
> *Rise in his bright matrass Diana's trees;*
> *Drop after drop, with just delay, he pours*
> *The red-fumed acid on Potosi's ores;*
> *With sudden flash the fierce bullitions rise,*
> *And wide in air the gas phlogistic flies;*
> *Slow shoot, at length, in many a brilliant mass*
> *Metallic roots across the netted glass;*
> *Branch after branch extend their silver stems,*
> *Bud into gold, and blossoms into gems"* (138).

De la Condamine and Wilhelm Homberg each gave methods of making so-called vegetations of silver and other metals (139, 140). According to Caspar Neumann, "If solution of Silver be diluted with pure water, a considerable quantity of pure Mercury added, and the whole set in a cold place, there will form by degrees a precipitation and crystallization resembling a little tree, with its root, trunk, and branches, called *Arbor Dianæ,* or the philosophic Silver-tree. Lémery gives another method of making an *Arbor Dianæ,* by adding to solution of Silver some warm distilled Vinegar" (*141*). Dr. Neumann also described the formation of a silver tree by spreading silver solution on a glass plate and placing in the center of it a piece of iron or other metal capable of precipitating silver. He added that solutions of other metals also form so-called vegetations, "but none so elegant ones as that of Silver" (*141*).

COPPER

Copper, in the opinion of Berthelot, has been mined for at least five thousand years. He found by analysis that the most ancient Egyptian articles were made of pure copper rather than of its alloys (*10*), (*27*).

The word *copper* appears in the Old Testament only in the passage where Ezra describes the treasure which he weighed out and committed to the twelve priests. Besides the silver and gold were "two vessels of fine copper, precious as gold" (*11*). Leroy Waterman, however, interprets this word as "fine burnished bronze" (*37*) The modern Spanish and Brazilian Portuguese translations also render it as bronze (*88, 91*).

The trade of coppersmith is mentioned in Isaias **41**, 6–7 of Bishop Challoner's revision of the Douai-Reims Bible, which is based on the Latin Vulgate (*94*). The corresponding passage in the Authorized Version is rendered "goldsmith" instead of "coppersmith" (Isa. **41**, 6–7). In his second letter to Timothy, Paul mentioned that "Alexander the coppersmith did me much evil" (II Tim. **4**, 14). Edgar J. Goodspeed translates this, however, as "metal-worker" rather than coppersmith. The widow's mites were probably small copper coins (Mark **12**, 43; Luke **21**, 2) (*37*).

The word "brass" of the Authorized Version of the Old Testament sometimes means *copper* and sometimes *bronze*. The passage in which Moses describes the Promised Land as "a land whose stones are iron, and out of whose hills thou mayest dig brass" is evidently an allusion to copper, which frequently occurs in the uncombined state (Deut. **8**, 9). In the American translation by J. M. Powis Smith and Edgar J. Goodspeed and in the modern Brazilian Portuguese and Spanish translations, it is so interpreted (*37, 88, 91*). This description would hold good for the Lebanon or for the Sinaitic region (*95*). Rabbi Joseph Schwarz wrote in 1845 that "Except in the neighbourhood of Aleppo, no Copper is found anywhere in Palestine. I was, however, told that Northern Galilee

J. B. Scolin, sculp.

Frontispiece to 1733 French Edition of Barba's "Art of the Metals."
The poem mentions that France used to be rich in precious metals, and
questions the necessity of searching for them in the New World.

> *Pourquoi de l'Océan courir les vastes bords.*
> *France, ne trouvez vo.ˢ de l'Or qu'au nouveau Monde.*
> *En Métaux précieux autrefois si féconde*
> *N'avez vous pas toujours vos immenses Trésors.*

and the lower range of Lebanon contain veins of Copper" and that this metal was also obtained on the Egyptian frontier (96).

In 1934 a joint expedition of the American School of Oriental Research, Baghdad, the Hebrew Union College, the American Council of Learned Societies, and the Transjordan Department of Antiquities made a thorough archaeological survey of Edom. Nelson Glueck and his fellow-explorers found copper slag-piles and ruins of ancient smelting furnaces at Kh. (Khirbet) el-Gheweibeh, Kh. el-Jâriyeh, and Kh. Nqeib Aseimer, a great mass of highly cupriferous sandstone at the Wâdi el-Jâriyeh; and a great copper mine at Umm el-'Amad (89). On the surface at Kh. Jâriyeh, at Mene'îyyeh, and at Kh. Nqeib Aseimer, they found good ore of mixed cuprite and malachite.

Since the region is poor in fuel, the furnaces may have been fired with large quantities of dried shrubs, a fuel still used in Palestine and Transjordan for firing crude lime kilns (89). However, since immense quantities of copper were smelted in the 'Arabah (the fissure extending for about 185 kilometers between the Dead Sea and the Gulf of 'Aqabah) in the Early Iron Age, much of the fuel must have been brought in the form of charcoal by caravans of camels and donkeys from the forests of Edom (89). Long before the coming of the Israelites, the Kenites and Edomites worked the ore deposits of the 'Arabah (89). The archaeological evidence shows that this was truly "a land whose stones contain iron, and out of whose hills you can dig copper" (Deut. 8, 9) (37, 89).

Dr. Glueck believes that Solomon's fleet which used to sail from Ezion-Geber to Ophir once every three years for gold, silver, ivory, apes, and peacocks must have carried as export cargo copper from the 'Arabah (89). He believes that the passage should read "Tarshish ships" (going to Ophir) instead of "ships sailing to Tarshish." Since both water and fuel are scarce, the countries of the Near East found it cheaper to import their copper than to work these ancient deposits (89).

In 1934 Rabbi Glueck excavated a site a few miles south of the Dead Sea and discovered King Solomon's copper mines. Four years later he excavated a site near the Gulf of 'Aqabah (the Ezion-Geber of the Bible) and discovered an ancient copper mine that is now being worked by Israeli miners (267, 279). Copper mining and smelting sites have also been found in Sinai (89).

Job's statement that "brass is molten out of the stone" must refer to the smelting of copper from its ore (Job 28, 2). Similarly, the two "mountains of brass" which Zechariah described in the vision of the four chariots must have been mountains of copper or its ore (Zech. 6, 1) (37).

Although the Israelites must have imported their copper, the Egyptians mined this metal even before the time of Cheops who built the great pyramid at Gizeh (97). The "isles of Chittim" probably included Cyprus, famous for its copper mines. "Javan, Tubal, and Meshech," said Ezekiel, "they were thy merchants; they traded the persons of men and vessels of brass in thy market" (Ezek. **27**, 6, 13). Long before the Roman period, copper ore and ingots were exported from Cyprus, and its mines still yield a limited amount of the metal (98). The inhabitants of New Paphos (Old Baffa) on this island worshipped Venus (99). Among the alchemists, Venus symbolized copper. Copper is found in the free state in Egypt, the Lake Superior region of North America, and in many other parts of the world, and can be obtained from malachite ore by a simple process. Knives, axes, spear heads, chisels, and bracelets of this metal have been found in Indian mounds in Wisconsin, Illinois, and neighboring states. Indian tools and excavations for working the copper veins have been discovered in the Ontonagon region of northern Michigan (39). Much of the copper worked by the aborigines came from Isle Royale in Lake Superior (40).

The pre-Columbian Indians of La Tolita on the Esmeraldas coast of Ecuador made small axes, bells, sewing needles, and filigree work by hot-hammering native copper. Paul Bergsøe of Copenhagen has made a thorough study of the gold, platinum, and copper artifacts of this region (41).

Christopher Columbus wrote in 1503, on his fourth voyage to the West Indies, "Some of the people whom I discovered were cannibals. . . . They say that there are great mines of copper in the country, of which they make hatchets and other elaborate articles, both cast and soldered; they also make of it forges, with all the apparatus of the goldsmith, and crucibles" (107).

Stephen Gómez, in his journey down the Atlantic coast from Nova Scotia to Florida in 1525, found copper and silver in the north. In the following year Gonzálo Fernández de Oviedo y Valdés (1478–1557) mentioned Gómez and his discoveries in his work on the natural history of the New World (108).

Coronado, too, saw some primitive copper artifacts. Arriving at last in the fabled Quivira (now part of Kansas) after his remarkable journey from Compostela, Mexico, in search of the gold and silver treasures described by his false guide "the Turk," Don Francisco Vázquez de Coronado wrote King Charles V on October 20, 1541, that "the natives there gave me a piece of copper that an Indian chief wore suspended from his neck. I am sending it to the viceroy of New Spain, for I have not seen any other metal in this region except this and some copper jingle bells which I am forwarding to him" (42). In his treatise on the Coronado expedition, George Parker Winship stated that Indian traders used to carry pieces of copper from the mines on the shores of Lake Superior, from tribe to tribe, as far east as the Atlantic Ocean and as far west as the Rocky Mountains (*43*).

In describing his voyage to northern Virginia with Sir Walter Raleigh, John Brereton wrote in 1602 that he had seen Indians wearing elaborate chains, earrings, and collars of copper, and that some of their arrow heads and skull-shaped drinking cups were made of it (*44*).

Malachite and Azurite. In 1778 the Abbé Felice Fontana (1730–1805) published analyses of malachite and azurite in the *Journal de Physique*. According to Edmund Cullen, "The illustrious Fontana was the first who determined the true nature of the malachites" (*142, 280*).

The British mineralogist Edward Daniel Clarke, in his "Travels in Various Countries of Europe, Asia, and Africa," described a most unusual specimen of malachite. "But of all the surprising articles in natural history I saw in Moscow," said he, "the most worthy of admiration were two specimens, the one of malachite, and the other of Siberian emerald, in the audience chamber of prince Alexander Galitzin. They were placed alone, independent of any cabinet, on two pedestals, opposite a canopy, beneath which the prince and princess sat on days of ceremony. . . . The first, or the mass of green, carbonated copper, commonly called malachite, was not only the largest appearance of that substance ever discovered, but also the most beautiful. It was found in the Siberian mines; and was matchless in every circumstance of form and colour which might interest a naturalist or fulfil the wishes of the lapidary. Its delicate surface, of the most beautiful, silky lustre, exhibited that mammillary undulation, and those conical nodes, which decide the stalactite origin of the mineral. Its interiour, though exquisitely zoned, was entire and compact; and for the mere purpose of cutting into plates, in the hands of jewellers, would have been inestimable. The weight of this enormous mass must have been at least a ton. For this specimen, while I remained in the city, a dealer offered his highness six thousand roubles, which were refused" (*143*).

Verdigris. In ancient times verdigris was used mainly as a medicament but sometimes also as a pigment (*144*). Theophrastus, in his "History of Stones," described a process of manufacturing it by placing copper over the lees of wine (*145*). According to Pedanios Dioscorides of Anazarba, it was made by inverting a brazen vessel over a hogshead of vinegar or by hanging brass plates above the vinegar (*146*).

The Stockholm papyrus (third or fourth century A.D.) gives the following recipe for preparing verdigris for making artificial emeralds: "Clean a well-made sheet of Cyprian copper by means of pumice stone and water, dry, and smear it very lightly with a very little oil. Spread it out and tie a cord around it. Then hang it in a cask with sharp vinegar so that it does not touch the vinegar, and carefully close the cask so that no evaporation takes place. Now if you put it in in the morning, then scrape off the verdigris carefully in the evening . . . and suspend it again until the sheet becomes used up. However, as often as you scrape it off again, smear the sheet with oil as explained previously. The vinegar is [thus rendered] unfit for use" (147).

At Montpellier the manufacture of verdigris was entirely domestic. In most wine farmhouses there was a verdigris cellar operated by the women of the family (148). After the juice had been pressed out, the skins of the grapes were placed in alternate layers on copper plates. As the skins became acidic, they corroded the copper (149).

In Geoffroy the Elder's "Treatise of the Fossil, Vegetable, and Animal Substances that are made use of in Physick," which is based on lectures which he began to deliver in 1709 and which were found in good order among his papers at the time of his death, he stated that "Various Recrements of Copper were prepared by the Ancients and employed in Medicines . . . but the *Aerugo,* or Verdigrease, is the only Recrement now in use. It is a green Rust raised in Copper Plates; the Method of raising it, taken from the Memoirs of the Philosophical Society of Montpelier, is as follows. The Husks, Stones &c. of Grapes, being first dried, and after dipped in some strong Wine, are laid for nine or ten Days in wooden or earthen Vessels, till they begin to ferment. Then being squeezed together with both Hands, they are formed into Balls, which being put into proper earthen Pots, and Wine poured upon them, till about half is covered, the Vessels have a straw Lid thrown over them, and are set in a Wine Cellar; where the Balls are left in Maceration for twelve or fifteen Hours, being turned every four Hours, that the Wine may penetrate every Part of them. Afterwards the Balls being raised about a Finger's breadth above the surface of the Wine, and set upon wooden Bars, the Vessels are shut again, and left in that State for ten or twelve Days more. After which time, the Balls emit a strong and penetrating Scent, and are then fit for dissolving Copper. For this purpose they are broke and bruised with the Hand, that the outer Part of them, which is driest, may be exactly mix'd with the inner, which is still moist with Wine; then they are stratified with Copper Plates in the same Vessels upon wooden Bars, the Plates making always the lowest Stratum, and the Balls the uppermost." . . . "Verdigrease," added Geoffroy, "is used by Painters and other artists, but is seldom prescribed inwardly by Physicians. It is often used outwardly." . . . (129).

In 1798 J.-A. Chaptal described the improvements which had been made in this process since 1750–53, when an account of it had been published in the *Mémoires de l'Académie des Sciences* of Paris. "The copper used," said he, "formerly came, already prepared, from Sweden. Today it is obtained from various smelting-houses established at Saint-Bel, Lyons, Avignon, Bedarieux, Montpellier, etc." (*150*).

Copper in Spring Waters. Geoffroy the Elder was familiar with certain spring waters which contain copper in solution. "There are some Springs of Copper-waters, of which Vitriol is made by boiling, and Copper may be praecipitated from them by means of Iron, which has made some Persons imagine that these Waters turned Iron into Copper. . . . There is a famous Spring of this Kind near the Carpathian Mountains, the Waters of which corrode Iron thrown into it, and in place thereof substitute Copper; so that a Horse-Shoe, for instance, that has lain several Days in this Water shall, when taken out, appear not to be Iron, but Copper" (*129*).

In 1738 Matthew Belius (Bell), a Lutheran pastor at Pressburg, Hungary, observed that the water from a spring at Neusohl had the same property (*151*). "This water," said he, "which seems not to have been known in the time of Georg Agricola, was discovered in the year 1605 during the insurrection of the Botskay, when several miners hid their property and especially their ironware in the mines; and when they took it out again after the retreat of the Botskay [Bocskay] party, they found it coated with a crust of copper" (*151*). The miners used the spring water medicinally, and prepared copper of unusually high quality from the deposit on the iron. Belius realized that this was not an alchemical transmutation of iron into copper and that the spring derived its copper from flowing through chalcopyrite (*151*). They were called "cement-springs" (*152*).

A similar spring in Wicklow, Ireland, was described by John Bond in the *Philosophical Transactions* for 1753. In a letter to Sir Peter Thompson he wrote: "You may remember I had the honour of spending an evening with you in June last, and happen'd to mention a spring in the county of Wicklow in Ireland, which was supposed to have the surprising quality of changing iron into copper. But your constant love of truth and strong aversion to vulgar errors made you doubt the fact. . . . Having soon afterwards occasion to go to Dublin, I went to the spring, which is from thence about 38 miles, and made several experiments on the water, the result of which I beg leave to present you with, hoping it may afford you some satisfaction in explaining that process, of which you so justly doubted the account given by some credulous authors, who mistook it for a real transmutation: a ridiculous doctrine, which destroys the essential qualities of bodies which were impressed by the Great Creator on all material substances. . . .

"As the history of this discovery has already been accurately related in several papers read before the Royal Society," said Bond, ". . . I shall confine myself to the chemical analysis of the water. . . . This water flows from a rich copper mine, and is of a sharp acid taste and light blue colour. It is received and collected in pits, wherein iron bars are put, which, after lying in the water for about three months, are intirely [sic] consumed, and at the bottom of the pits a quantity of copper, greater than that of the iron, is found in the form of coarse sand. This fact is confirmed by profitable experiments often repeated since the discovery, the honour of which is due to Mr. Matthew Johnston, a worthy old gentleman, and one of the proprietors of the mine, who first proposed this method of collecting the copper . . ." (153). Bond made the practical suggestion that "perhaps an easier method may be discover'd of separating copper from its ore by precipitation" (153).

Some Famous Copper Mines. The word *copper* is indicative of its Cyprian origin. Whether the Island of Cyprus was named for the metal or the metal for the island would be difficult to decide (98). Copper was mined at Cyprus in antiquity, especially in the foothills of the Troödos range along the coast from Marium to Soli, and was its most important product (98) Long before the Roman period, copper was exported from Cyprus as ore and as ingots. The copper mines of this island are still productive (98).

The earliest metal implements from Cypriote tombs are not true bronze but are composed of copper containing only a slight admixture of tin, which may have been introduced from the use of a slightly stanniferous copper ore. Part of the ore was purposely left unreduced in the form of copper oxide in order to give greater hardness to the metal (154).

The great copper mine at Falun, Sweden, has been worked for more than seven centuries; its charter is dated 1288. For centuries it was Sweden's greatest source of material wealth (155). In 1734 Emanuel Swedenborg published a Latin treatise "Regnum subterraneum sive minerale de cupro et orichalco," in which he devoted several chapters to this mine. He said that when its "foundations, doors, grottoes, walls, porticoes, halls, and columns were thrown open to their fullest extent, the ore glittering on all sides with a ruddy glow, and almost blinding the eyes with rays of golden colour," the guests "seemed to be, as it were, introduced into the presence of Venus [copper] herself sitting as a bride or newly wedded wife in her most splendidly decorated bridal chamber" (156).

Carl von Linné (Linnæus) described the Falun mine as follows: ". . . Out of the mine a constant smoke ascended. Never has a poet described a Styx, nor a theologian a hell so awful, as that seen here, for upward rises a poisonous, stinging, sulphurous smoke, which taints the air all round, and so corrodes the ground that no plants can grow in the neighbourhood. . . . The drifts are dark with soot, the floor of slippery stone, the passages narrow as if burrowed by moles, on all sides incrusted with vitriol, and the roof drips corrosive vitriolic water . . ." (157). Grateful for his safe return from the mine, awed by its grandeur, and terrified by its hazards, Linné wrote an anthem (157).

According to Ludwig Darmstaedter, the German copper deposits in the Harz were worked as early as the year 968 A.D. In 1450 Nessler, a metallurgist of Joachimsthal, showed that siliceous ores could be worked by roasting them, leaching out the copper vitriol with water, and depositing the copper from this solution on iron (158).

Henry Latrobe stated that the copper mine near the confluence of the Passaic and Hackensack Rivers in New Jersey was discovered in about 1719 by Arent Schuyler (159). "The ore," said Latrobe, "was found where it appeared on the side of the hill; was easily raised; and, as the policy of England, at that time, prohibited the establishment of smelting works or manufactories in her colonies, it was packed in casks, each containing about four hundred pounds, and exported, in its state of ore, to England. . . . At the time when pure copper was sold in England at £75 sterling per ton, the ore of Schuyler's mine was shipped for England, at New York, at £70 sterling per ton. This proves the uncommon richness of the ore, and the small expense of converting it into metal."

Per Kalm, a great Swedish naturalist who visited North America in 1748–51, spoke of a fine copper mine which the Dutch settlers "discovered upon the second river between Elizabeth-town and New York" (160). They had learned of it through the Indians, who smoked tobacco pipes made of copper from this mine.

In 1653 Père Francesco G. Bressani, a Jesuit missionary to New France, stated in his report that "There is a Copper ore, which is very pure, and which has no need of passing through the fire; but it is in places far distant and hard to reach. . . . I have seen it in the hands of the Barbarians, but no one has visited the place . . ." (161).

In 1660 one of the Jesuit fathers (probably Druillettes) met a Christian Indian who had explored the Lake Superior region. The account states that this lake is "enriched in its entire circumference with mines of lead in a nearly pure state; with copper of such excellence that pieces as large as one's fist are found, all refined; and with great rocks having whole veins of turquoise" (162). The "turquoise" was probably amethyst.

The Jesuit explorers of Lake Superior compared it to a bow and arrow, the Canadian shore being the bow, the southern or United States shore the bowstring, and the Keweenaw promontory the arrow. In this promontory were many great deposits of native copper. In 1669–70 they learned that the island most famous for copper was called Minong [Isle Royale]. "Pieces of Copper, mingled with the stones," so runs the Jesuit report, "are found at the water's edge almost all around the Island, especially on the South side; but principally in a certain inlet that is near the end facing the Northeast, toward the offing, there are some very steep clay hills where are seen several strata or beds of red Copper, one over another, separated or divided by other strata of earth or of Rocks. In the water even is seen Copper sand as it were; and from it may be dipped up with ladles grains as large as a nut, and other smaller ones reduced to sand. This large Island is almost all surrounded with Islets that are said to be formed of Copper . . ." (*163*).

Even before 1778, skilled miners were sent from Redruth, Cornwall, to inspect the Lake Superior copper deposits (*164*). The *Medical Repository* for 1802 recorded the failure of an expedition to this region. "Travellers," it said, "have related that there are vast beds of native copper and copper ores of great value on the south side of Lake Superior, within the territory of the United States." A resolution which passed both Houses of Congress in 1800 authorized the President of the United States to employ an agent to ascertain on what terms the mines might be purchased for the government. Because of procrastination this opportunity was lost (*165*).

In 1821 Henry R. Schoolcraft published a report in the *American Journal of Science* on the native copper on the southern shore of Lake Superior. "The first appearances of copper," said he, "are seen on the head of the portage across Keweena [sic] point, two hundred and seventy miles beyond the Sault de St. Marie, where the pebbles along the shore of the lake contain native copper disseminated in particles varying in size from a grain of sand to a lump of two pounds weight. Many of the detached stones at this point are also coloured green by the carbonate of copper, and the rock strata in the vicinity exhibit traces of the same ore. These indications continue to the river Ontonagon, which has long been noted for the large masses of native copper found upon its banks" (*166*). James Douglas, who described the geology of this region in 1874, said that the Calumet Mine had been discovered about thirteen years earlier (*167*).

Copper in Plants and Animals. As early as 1818 C. F. Bucholz detected copper in vegetable ash (*170, 169*). In 1850 F. J. Malaguti and his collaborators detected it in several species of *Fucus* taken near Saint-Malo (*170*). "The normal presence of copper in organized nature being today a fact generally admitted," said they, "one may conclude that if terrestrial plants imbibe this metal from the soil, the *Fucus* must obtain

it from sea water, that is to say, from the medium in which they live"
(*170, 281*). J. G. Forchhammer in 1865 noticed the presence of copper
in the lime salts of marine animals, in the ash of certain seaweeds and
corals, and in *Fucus vesiculosus* (*171*).

Professor Jérôme Nicklès of Nancy pointed out in 1867 an easily
overlooked source of error in some of the early researches on the diffusion
of copper in nature. "Impressed with this wonderful diffusion of a metal
which is found everywhere save in the reagents employed for finding it,
. . . it appeared to me that there was some source of error, and if it was
not in the reagents, it must be found in the apparatus, especially the
apparatus used for the incineration. . . . In fact, the Bunsen burners
are generally of copper. . . . Besides, when such a burner is lighted,
the flame is often seen colored blue by the copper which is volatilized
. . ." (*168*).

In 1847 E. Harless discovered the presence of copper in the blood of
the octopus *Eledone* and the snail *Helix pomatia* (*172, 173*). Investigation of the phenomenon by which the blood and tissues of certain marine
animals turn blue on exposure to air finally led to the discovery that the
blood plasma of such animals contains copper combined with a protein.
Because of its analogy to hemoglobin and its ability to carry oxygen,
L. Fredericq in 1878 named the copper-containing protein in the blood
of *Octopus vulgaris* hemocyanin (*173, 174*).

Small amounts of copper occur in all tissues of the human body.
E. B. Hart, H. Steenbock, J. Waddell, and C. A. Elvehjem of the University of Wisconsin found in 1928 that "iron salts of high purity when fed
at levels of 0.5 milligram of iron six times per week were ineffective in
correcting a progressive anemia in rats confined to a diet of cow's whole
milk; but that an equal amount of iron fed as the ash, or acid extract of
the ash, of dried lettuce, of yellow corn, or of beef liver was very potent
in restoring to normal the hemoglobin of the blood stream" (*175*). Noticing the pale blue color of some of these ashes, they were reminded of the
copper content of hemocyanin and its ability to form oxyhemocyanin.
When they added copper sulfate to the previous diet, their anemic rats
rapidly recovered (*175*).

IRON

Iron articles were probably made by the Egyptians twenty-five or
thirty centuries before Christ, but because the metal is so readily corroded,
iron objects of great antiquity are much rarer than similar ones made of
gold, silver, or copper (*25*). Smelting furnaces for iron were used in
ancient times, but the exact nature of the process is not known.

Of all the ancient allusions to this metal, the Biblical ones are the most interesting. Who can forget Job's eloquent words: "Oh, that my words were now written! Oh, that they were printed in a book! That they were graven with an iron pen . . ." (*13*). The first mention of iron in the Bible is in the fourth chapter of Genesis. It refers to "Tubal-cain, an instructor of every artificer in brass and iron" (Gen. **4**, 22). Theophile J. Meek translates this: "Tubal-cain, the forger of bronze and iron utensils" (*37*).

In a short but remarkable discourse on Hebrew mining, Job states that "Iron is taken out of the earth" (Job **28**, 2). This passage describes the deep shaft, the dark galleries and tunnels through the rock, the underground streams, the beautiful, precious minerals, and the rugged, hazardous life of the miners. The iron stylus mentioned in Job **19**, 24 was one of the most ancient of writing instruments. Iron fishhooks and spears must also have been in use when this book was written: "Canst thou draw out leviathan with an hook? . . . Canst thou fill his skin with barbed irons? or his head with fish spears?" (Job **41**, 1, 7).

In the third chapter of Deuteronomy there appears to be a description of an enormous iron bed: "For only Og king of Bashan remained of the remnant of giants; behold his bedstead was a bedstead of iron; is it not in Rabbath of the children of Ammon? nine cubits was the length thereof, and four cubits the breadth of it, after the cubit of a man" (Deut. **3**, 11). Since the Hebrew cubit was equal to about seventeen and a half inches, this bed must have been about six feet wide by thirteen feet long. Theophile J. Meek interpreted this to mean not a bed, but a sarcophagus, and James Patrick believed that it was made not of iron but of black basalt (*14, 37, 38, 48*). In the following chapter, the land of bondage is compared to an iron furnace: "But the Lord hath taken you, and brought you forth out of the iron furnace, even out of Egypt . . ." (Deut. **4**, 20).

Joshua mentioned the iron chariots of the Canaanites (Josh. **17**, 16). In the days of Saul and Jonathan, there was no smith in all Israel (I Sam. **13**, 19) (*92*). When David was preparing material for the Temple, iron was abundant. "And David prepared iron in abundance for the nails for the doors of the gates, and for the joinings. . . . Now, behold, in my trouble I have prepared for the house of the Lord an hundred thousand talents of gold, and a thousand thousand talents of silver; and of brass and iron without weight; for it is in abundance . . ." (I Chron. **22**, 3, 14). Saws, harrows, and axes of this metal were also used in the time of David (II Sam. **12**, 31).

When Solomon compiled the proverbs, iron tools for sharpening must have been well known: "Iron sharpeneth iron; so a man sharpeneth the countenance of his friend" (Prov. **27**, 17). Amos mentioned iron thresh-ing implements, and Isaiah spoke of cutting down thickets with iron (Amos **1**, 3; Isa. **10**, 34). Hezekiah's workmen who diverted the water from the upper springs of Gihon and allowed it to flow down to supply the city of David used iron tools (II Chron. **32**, 30; Ecclus. **48**, 17) (*37*).

The ancient Hebrews also made iron cooking utensils such as the pan mentioned by Ezekiel (Ezek. **4**, 3). Six centuries before Christ, this metal was an important commodity in the market at Tyre: "Dan also and Javan going to and fro occupied in thy fairs: bright iron, cassia, and calamus, were in thy market" (Ezek. **27**, 19). The American translation by Smith and Goodspeed and the modern Spanish translation render this as "wrought iron," or "hierro forjado" (*37, 91*).

Jeremiah declared that "The sin of Judah is written with a pen of iron . . ." (Jer. **17**, 1).

When King Nebuchadnezzar conquered Jerusalem, he took all the craftsmen and smiths back captive to Babylon (II Kings **24**, 14–16; Jer. **24**, 1). The trade of blacksmith is mentioned several times in the Bible. In the Book of Isaiah, the Lord says: "Behold I have created the smith that bloweth the coals in the fire, and that bringeth forth an instrument for his work . . ." (Isa. **54**, 16). Isaiah also described the construction of a graven image: "The smith with the tongs both worketh in the coals, and fashioneth it with hammers, and worketh it with the strength of his arms . . ." (Isa. **44**, 12). Eccleciasticus wrote: "The smith also sitting by the anvil, and considering the iron work, the vapour of the fire wasteth his flesh, and he fighteth with the heat of the furnace: the noise of the hammer and the anvil is ever in his ears, and his eyes look still upon the pattern of the thing that he maketh; he setteth his mind to finish his work, and watcheth to polish it perfectly" (Ecclus. **38**, 28).

Iron is mentioned also in the New Testament. When Peter, for example, was delivered from the prison of Herod Agrippa I, he passed through "the iron gate that leadeth unto the city" of Antioch, Syria (Acts **12**, 10).

Rabbi Joseph Schwarz wrote in 1845 that iron was found near the town of Dir Al Kamr, in Lebanon, and that the Jews worked the mines and made horseshoes from the metal. Iron was also obtained from the Egyptian frontier (*96*). In their exploration of Edom in 1934, Nelson Glueck and his party of explorers found rich deposits of iron ore at Sabrah, south of Petra (*89*).

The metal must have been in common use in Pliny's day, for he wrote (*12*):

It is by the aid of iron that we construct houses, cleave rocks, and perform so many other useful offices of life. But it is with iron also that wars, murders, and robberies are effected, and this, not only hand to hand, but from a distance even, by the aid of weapons and winged weapons, now launched from engines, now hurled by the human arm, and now furnished with feathery wings. This last I regard as the most criminal artifice that has been devised by the human mind; for, as if to bring death upon man with still greater rapidity, we have given wings to iron and taught it to fly. Let us, therefore, acquit Nature of a charge that belongs to man himself. . . . Nature, in conformity with her usual benevolence, has limited the power of iron by inflicting upon it the punishment of rust; and has thus displayed her usual foresight in rendering nothing in existence more perishable than the substance which brings the greatest dangers upon perishable mortality.

Meteoric Iron. G. W. Wainwright regards some iron beads which he found at Gerzah, Egypt, about fifty miles south of Cairo, as the most ancient pieces of iron known. They date back to 3500 B.C. or earlier. Since they contain 7.5 per cent of nickel, they must have been made from meteoric material (77). Primitive tribes often used meteoric iron for weapons and tools, and, because of its celestial origin, regarded it with great reverence. Under the title "Our Stone-pelted Planet," H. H. Nininger published a scholarly and entertaining history of the most famous meteorites (78).

"The first tolerably accurate narration of the fall of a meteoric stone," said W. T. Brande, "relates to that of Ensisheim, near Basle, upon the Rhine. The account which is deposited in the church was thus: A.D. 1492, Wednesday, 7 November, there was a loud clap of thunder, and a child saw a stone fall from heaven; it struck into a field of wheat, and did no harm, but made a hole there. The noise it made was heard at Lucerne, Villing, and other places; on the Monday, King Maximilian ordered the stone to be brought to the castle, and after having conversed about it with the noblemen, said the people of Ensisheim should hang it up in their church . . ." (176).

Brande also mentioned "the great block of iron at Elbogen in Bohemia; the large mass discovered by Pallas, weighing 1600 Russian pounds, near Krasnoyarsk in Siberia . . . and those noticed by Bruce, Bougainville, Humboldt and others in America, of enormous magnitude, exceeding thirty tons in weight. That these should be of the same source as the other meteoric stones seems at first to startle belief; but when they are submitted to analysis and the iron they contain found alloyed by nickel, it no longer seems credulous to regard them as of meteoric origin. We find nothing of the kind in the earth" (176). The Elbogen meteorite fell in about 1400 A.D. (78).

The great mass of iron which a Cossack found at Krasnoyarsk in 1749 interested Professor P. S. Pallas so much that in 1775 he had it brought to St. Petersburg for investigation. When Torbern Bergman examined it five years later, he concluded that it must be of natural origin. It is frequently mentioned in the literature as the Pallas meteorite (*177*). According to G. A. Wainwright, iron is the only metal known to occur in metallic form in meteorites (*77*).

Smelted Iron. The earliest known finds of smelted iron are from Tell Asmar, Mesopotamia, and Tall Chagar Bazaar in North Syria. One such specimen cannot have been made later than 2700 B.C. and may have been produced as early as 3000 B.C. Since it contains no nickel, it cannot be of meteoric origin (*79*). Although the Hittites developed skill in smelting iron, they kept the process secret. After the fall of their Empire shortly before 1200 B.C., the iron workers were dispersed and the true Iron Age dawned in the Near East. About two centuries later, according to H. H. Coghlan, this craft reached Europe (*79*).

Many Negro tribes of Africa have worked iron for centuries. In his "Mining and Metallurgy in Negro Africa," Walter Cline states that the iron and slag found in the earliest deposits at Zimbabwe give evidence that iron must have been smelted in southeast Africa at least as early as the eighth century A.D. and that by that time the "iron age" in this locality was well advanced (*80*). According to A. F. Cronstedt, the process of making osmund iron was known to the Eskimos, Yakuts, and Ostiaks of Siberia (*81*).

Hematite. Theophrastus of Eresus was familiar with hematite, which he called "the Haematites or Blood-stone, which is of a dense, solid Texture, dry, or, according to its Name, seeming as if form'd of concreted Blood" (*178*). He also knew how to make red ocher from the yellow variety, a process which he attributed to "Cydias, who took the Hint of it, as is said, from observing, in a House which was on fire, that some Ochre which was there, when half burnt, assumed a red Colour. The way of making the factitious is this: They put the Ochre into new earthen Vessels, which they cover with Clay and set in Furnaces; and these, as they grow hot, heat also the Ochre, and the greater Degree of Fire they give, the deeper and more strongly Purple the Matter becomes" (*178*). Dioscorides prepared hematite by heating magnetite (*179*).

Magnetite (The Lodestone). Thales stated in about 585 B.C. that certain iron ores and iron turnings found near Magnesia in Lydia have a strange power of attraction. He called them *magnets* after their place of origin (*180*). Theophrastus said of the lodestone that "the greatest and most evident attractive Quality is in that Stone which attracts Iron. But that is a scarce stone, and found in but few Places" (*178*).

Pyrite, Green Vitriol, and Ocher. In 1579 Matthias Falconer of Brabant founded at Queenborough the first plant in England for converting iron pyrites into copperas (ferrous sulfate, or green vitriol) and brimstone. The pyrite occurred in large quantities in Sheppey and on the Essex shore (*181*). Peter Mundy, who toured Europe in 1639–47, described another process used at "Quinburrow" [Queenborough] for making copperas: After scrap iron had been boiled in "a certain liquor," branches were laid in the hot solution, and as the latter cooled it deposited ferrous sulfate crystals on the branches (*181*).

Charles Hatchett analyzed magnetic pyrite and stated that the discovery of iron in pyrite is comparatively recent. "According to Henckel," said he, "this was first noticed by our countryman Martin Lister, a member of this learned Society [the Royal Society] . . ." (*182*).

When Edward Daniel Clarke visited the great copper mine at Falun, Sweden, he observed great stalactites of green vitriol hanging from the brick roofs of the levels and the wooden ducts for carrying off the water. "The whole of this vitriol," said Clarke, "and all the vitriolic water of the mine are the property of Assessor Gahn. . . . The water of the mine at Fahlun is impregnated with sulphuric acid, holding copper in solution: but in its passage through the works, whenever it comes into contact with iron, for which the sulphuric acid has a greater affinity, a portion of the sulphate of iron being then exposed to evaporation, is gradually concentrated; and either crystallizes, or appears in beautiful transparent stalactites in different parts of the mine. But the product of this deposit is trifling, compared with the quantity of the same salt which is procured from the vitriol-works on the outside of the mine; to which the water of the mine is conveyed by pumps . . ." (*183*).

"Formerly, when the mine was richer," said Clarke, "they made no use of the iron pyrites, which is dug in considerable quantity; but now a work is established for roasting this mineral, and manufacturing red-ochre as a pigment. . . . The process for the peroxidation of the iron is extremely simple: it is obtained from heaps of decomposed sulphurets, or, as they are commonly called, pyrites, which have been long exposed to the action of the atmosphere. Of these, a lixivium is made; in which a yellow mud subsiding, affords the ochre, which is submitted to the action of heat in a long furnace; so contrived, as that the flame, drawn out to considerable length, may act upon the iron oxide, and thus convert it into red ochre" (*183*).

In 1821 John Locke described a pyrite mine and copperas plant at Strafford, Vermont. To facilitate crystallization of the green vitriol, branches of trees were put into the evaporating cisterns as nuclei for the crystals. "The branches," said Locke, "have a fine crop of foliage and fruit composed of beautiful green crystals. . . . Everything about this mineral manufactory is curiously reddened with iron rust. When a dry day succeeds a rain or a shower, the whole mine becomes covered with a white crystalline efflorescence like a hoar frost, and the rain water which runs down into the cavities of the mine becomes so strong a solution as to crystallize. Wherever the solution dribbles from the rocks or leaks from the cisterns, large stalactites are formed so precisely like icicles that they would not be distinguished from them were it not for their green colour . . ." (*184*).

Some Famous Iron Mines. The Cerro de Mercado in Durango, north central Mexico, one of the largest iron ore deposits in the world, was discovered by Gines Vásquez de Mercado in 1552 (*108*).

Herman Boerhaave (1668–1738) said in his "New Method of Chemistry" that "Iron mines are common in most countries of Europe: Norway, Poland, Germany, France, England, &c. abound with them; only America, which is so plentiful in gold and silver mines, has none of iron; and accordingly, the natives prefer a metal of so much use infinitely beyond their own treasures" (*185*). Although the Indians, as Boerhaave stated, did not know how to reduce iron ores, the New England colonists worked the bog iron ore of the Saugus River near Lynn, Massachusetts, as early as 1643 (*186*).

Per Kalm observed in 1748–51 that "Iron is dug in such great quantities in Pennsylvania and in other American provinces of the English that they could provide with that commodity not only England but almost all Europe and perhaps the greatest part of the globe. The ore is here commonly infinitely easier got in the mines than our Swedish ore. For in many places, with a pick-axe, a crow-foot, and a wooden club, it is got with the same ease with which a hole can be made in a hard soil: in many places the people know nothing of boring, blasting, and firing; and the ore is likewise very fusible. Of this iron they get such quantities that not only the numerous inhabitants of the colonies themselves have enough of it, but great quantities are sent to the West Indies. . . . This iron is reckoned better for ship-building than our Swedish iron or any other, because salt water does not corrode it so much . . ." (*187*).

Kalm visited an iron works at Trois Rivières, between Quebec and Montreal, on the St. Lawrence River. "The ore is got," said he, "two French miles and a half from the iron works and is carried thither on sledges. . . . This iron work was first founded in 1737 by private persons who afterwards ceded it to the king; they cast cannon and mortars here of different sizes, iron stoves which are used all over Canada, kettles, etc. . . . They have likewise tried to make steel here, but cannot bring it to any great perfection . . ." (*187*).

The iron ores of the Lake Superior district were first found in commercial quantities near Negaunee, Michigan, in 1844 by Douglas Houghton, state geologist (*188*). Those of northern Minnesota were first reported by J. G. Norwood in 1850. Shipping of iron ores from the Lake Superior district did not begin until four years later. Each of the great deposits was discovered separately. Charles R. Van Hise said in 1903, "Discovered only about ten years ago, in the early nineties, the Mesabi District has today no rival in its production or reserve of iron ore" (*188*).

Long before World War II and the postwar expansion of the steel industry had seriously depleted the vast deposits of high-grade ores that can be mined by relatively cheap open-pit methods, Professor Edward Wilson Davis, a metallurgical engineer at the University of Minnesota, had been studying the possibility of utilizing the taconite, a hard, iron-bearing rock that can be mined and concentrated only with considerable difficulty and expense. Some of the steel companies are already producing great quantities of taconite concentrates from the Mesabi range. This enormous enterprise was recently described in *Reader's Digest* (*189*).

Iron in Vegetable Ash. Geoffroy the Elder believed that the iron detected in the ash of plants had been generated or produced during the ignition. Etienne-François Geoffroy was born in Paris on February 13, 1672, a son of Mathieu-François Geoffroy, a distinguished apothecary. As a boy he listened to the scientific discussions of his father's friends (one of whom was Wilhelm Homberg), worked at the lathe, ground lenses, made models of machines, and studied Italian. When he was twenty years old, his father sent him to Montpellier to study pharmacy. During a visit to England he gained the friendship of Sir Hans Sloane, and in Italy and the Netherlands he met some of the greatest scientists of his time.

Mathieu-François Geoffroy had chosen pharmacy as the career for his elder son Etienne-François and medicine for his younger son. Etienne preferred medicine, however, while Claude-Joseph followed his father's calling and became a famous apothecary and chemist, Geoffroy the Younger.

After receiving his medical degree, Etienne-François studied for ten more years before beginning to practice. He became professor of materia medica at the Collège Royal and professor of chemistry at the Jardin Royal. In 1718 he prepared his famous table of chemical affinities. He died on January 6, 1731, at the age of fifty-eight years. According to B.-B. de Fontenelle, he was gentle, discreet, even-tempered, and sympathetic (*190, 191, 192*).

Using a magnet to test for iron, E.-F. Geoffroy found that he could detect much more of it in a mixture of ignited clay and linseed oil than he could in the original clay, and concluded that iron had been produced or created. Louis Lémery showed in 1706–08, however, that iron can be converted (for example, by treatment with an acid) into a non-magnetic condition. When he heated the clay alone and the mixture of clay and linseed oil to a moderate temperature under identical conditions, the clay yielded a red substance scarcely attracted by the magnet, whereas the mixture of clay and oil yielded a black substance that was much more magnetic. He concluded therefore that the iron must have been present originally in the clay, but in a non-magnetic form which

Georgius Agricola, 1494-1555. German metallurgist. Author of "De Re Metallica," a famous Latin treatise on mining and metallurgy, which has been translated into English by Ex-president and Mrs. Herbert Hoover. See also ref. (278).

From Bugge's "Das Buch der grossen Chemiker"

Geoffroy had failed to detect. Lémery also pointed out that there is no direct relation between the iron content of an ore and its magnetic property (193).

He then went on to show that "iron often fails to show itself even where it is actually present; that the soil contains a great deal of it, and that its ascent in plants takes place very easily. One can scarcely extract it from any substance in which one could not correctly surmise that it was already present; and conjecture will always be opposed to the artificial production of a metal and in favor of its pre-existence."

Lémery concluded that "one does not produce iron merely by making it sensitive to the influence of the magnet . . . and [that] the time for the pleasant hope of the artificial production of the metals has not arrived" (193).

In his researches on iron in plants, Lémery also discovered that by dissolving iron filings in spirit of niter [nitric acid], he could make an "iron plant" or "tree of Mars." When Tsar Peter the Great visited the Academy, Lémery showed him this curious chemical vegetation. The "tree of Diana," or "silver tree," had already been discovered (*194*). Lémery also investigated the physiological properties of iron and introduced into medicine the use of *Ethiops martial*, which came to be known as "black powder of M. Lémery" (*194*).

Louis Lémery, son of the immortal French physician and chemist Nicolas Lémery, was born in Paris on January 25, 1677, and studied at Harcourt College (*194*). Because of the boy's gift of eloquence, his uncle, Louis Lémery, a famous attorney, tried to induce him to study law. Young Louis preferred his father's calling, however, and at the age of twenty-one years received the degree of doctor of medicine. Two years later he entered the Academy to study, first under M. de Tournefort and then under his father Nicolas Lémery.

In 1702 Louis Lémery published his famous "Treatise on Foods." For thirty-three years he served as physician at the chief hospital (l'Hôtel Dieu), where he always attracted a large number of medical students (*194*). Since he worked with extreme facility and since "his knowledge, his office, and his laboratory were everywhere," he was able to write some of his memoirs at the chateau of his royal patient, the Princess of Conti, who provided him a quiet retreat for his scientific research (*194*).

His most fruitful chemical work was done in three fields: the nature of iron and its production, niter and other salts, and the analysis of plants and animals. In 1731 he succeeded Geoffroy the Elder as professor of chemistry at the Jardin Royal. After M. Lémery died on June 9, 1743, Dortous de Mairan said in the eulogy, "He was kind and polished in his conversation, capable of friendship, generous and liberal. Everything that suffered had a claim upon his heart and his property, and he sometimes gave to the poor sums which were exorbitant for one with so modest a fortune" (*194*).

The presence of iron in vegetable ash has been known since the beginning of the eighteenth century. Although iron is not a constituent of the chlorophyll molecule, a plant grown in a culture medium entirely free from it produces no chlorophyll. According to Roscoe W. Thatcher, plants take iron from the soil in the smallest proportion of any of the essential elements. Since ferrous compounds are toxic to plants, only the soluble ferric compounds can be utilized (*195*).

Iron in Animals. William Lewis stated in 1746 in his annotated edition of George Wilson's "Compleat Course of Chymistry," that "red coral calcined in an open fire loses its colour and becomes white; from the calx, iron may be extracted by applying a load stone" (*196*).

Herman Boerhaave said in his "Elements of Chemistry" that "Iron, which seems to be the metal whose earth most closely resembles vegetable and animal earth, also has a great deal of affinity with the bodies of animals and plants, and may perhaps even be digested by them in some way. That is why it is an excellent remedy for various diseases of the human body on which other metals act too violently" (*197*).

Iron in the Blood. According to P.-J. Macquer's "Dictionary of Chemistry," the first scientist to investigate thoroughly the cause of the red color of the blood was Vincenzo Menghini, who found that the red portion of it contains a great deal of iron (*198*).

Vincenzo Menghini, who was born in 1705 in Budrio, Italy, was highly regarded as a practicing physician. From 1737 to the close of his life in 1759 he taught medicine at the University of Bologna. In 1745 he demonstrated the presence of iron in the blood corpuscles. Seeking to establish the presence of it in some dogs which had been fed iron preparations, he burned some blood from a normal dog, expecting to find the ash free from iron. To his surprise he saw that some of the particles were attracted by the blade of a magnetized knife. By a series of precise experiments he proved that this iron was localized in the red corpuscles (*199*). According to Mario Betti, who published a biographical sketch of Menghini, the first person to discover the presence of iron in milk was Luigi Galvani, who, however, did not publish his observation (*199*).

P.-J. Macquer said that "the experiments of this physician [Menghini] are very beautiful and convincing, but M. Rouelle has attained a new degree of accuracy and made other important observations on the salt-like materials contained in the blood, as one can see in the *Journal de Médecine* for July, 1776. According to the observations of this expert chemist, the blood of a healthy person contains—after drying, burning, and calcination of the ash—natrum, or fixed mineral alkali, common salt, digestive salt [potassium chloride] in small quantity, an animal or calcareous earth, iron, and, finally, carbon" (*198*). In order to be sure that the ash contained iron, Rouelle heated it with reducing agents until it was readily attracted by the magnet. In his experiments he used the blood of cattle, horses, calves, sheep, hogs, donkeys, and goats.

After stating that the red color of the blood might be due to the presence of iron, Macquer added: "An observation from practical medicine agrees well with this view; namely that mineral water containing iron, iron itself, and all preparations of this metal, of which at least a considerable part passes into the blood, as the experiments of M. Menghini have shown, are the best remedy one can use for chlorosis, in which disease the red part of the blood is almost entirely decolorized or discolored" (*198*). Macquer realized that the iron was not itself the coloring matter of the blood "but perhaps that which binds this pigment and determines its action" (*198*).

In 1667 the Italian physician Carlo Fracassati published a paper in the *Philosophical Transactions* in which he maintained that the black color of the blood at the bottom of a dish filled with it is caused not by the presence of a "melancholy humour" but by its lack of contact with the air. When he exposed the dark blood to air, it became bright red again (*200*).

Two years later Richard Lower showed that arterial blood acquires its brilliant color through exposure to air in the lungs (*200*). "I have shown," said he, "that the bright red colour of arterial blood is not acquired through any heating in the heart or anywhere else at any time. . . . We must next see to what the blood is indebted for this deep red coloration. This must be attributed entirely to the lungs, as I have found that the blood, which enters the lungs completely venous and dark in colour, returns from them quite arterial and bright . . ." (*201*).

The fact that the lower part of a quantity of blood is black while the surface is red was formerly explained by assuming that the black particles, being heavier, sank to the bottom. In 1759 Giovanni Francesco Cigna, professor of anatomy at the University of Turin, showed that when the dark layers of the blood are successively exposed to the air by removal of the red surface layer, they too become red. At his request Father Giovanni Battista Beccaria tested the effect of a vacuum on blood and found that dark blood remained dark as long as it was kept in a vacuum but became red when subsequently exposed to air (*202*).

William Hewson, in his "Experimental Inquiry into the Properties of Blood," which was published in the *Philosophical Transactions* in 1770, demonstrated experimentally that "There is a difference between the arterial and venous blood in colour; the former is of a florid red like the surface of the Crassamentum [clot], the latter is dark or blackish like the bottom of the crassamentum. This change in its colour is produced as it passes through the lungs, as we see by opening of living animals; and as a similar change is produced by air applied to blood out of the body, it is presumed that the air in the lungs is the immediate cause of this change; but how it effects it, is not yet determined . . ." (*203*). In a footnote Hewson added "That this change is really produced in the lungs, I am persuaded from experiments in which I have distinctly seen the blood of a more florid red in the left auricle than it was in the right . . ." (*202, 203*).

With the early microscopes it was difficult to see the red corpuscles of the blood distinctly, and because they were crowded so closely together, they usually appeared merely as a confused mass. Leeuwenhoek thought they were spherical. Father de la Torre of Naples however believed them to be annular. After diluting the blood with serum,

Hewson was able to observe the separate red corpuscles more distinctly and to note that they were "flat as a guinea," with "a dark spot in the middle" which "was not a perforation" (*204*).

Joseph Priestley found that the constituent of the atmosphere which restores the bright red color to the dark blood is "dephlogisticated air" (oxygen) (*202*). Although Fourcroy and Vauquelin believed that the iron in the blood was combined as a phosphate, it is now known to be present in a far more complex compound, hemoglobin (*205*). M. O. Schultze found that analyses of hemoglobins of different species yielded concordant values of 0.335 per cent of iron (*206*).

In the summer of 1840 Robert Mayer, while performing a simple operation of bloodletting on board a Dutch ship in Java, was so startled by the bright red color of the venous blood that he feared for a moment that he might have opened an artery by mistake (*283*). Although he was unaware of Adair Crawford's experiments on the influence of temperature on the color of venous blood in living animals, which were published in the "Experiments and Observations on Animal Heat and the Inflammation of Combustible Bodies" in 1788, Mayer reasoned that in a hot climate, such as that of Java, the human body needed less internal combustion in order to maintain its temperature. Two years later he formulated the law of the equivalence between heat and work (*283*).

LEAD

The unsurpassed dramatist who wrote the Book of Job mentioned lead as a writing material. In one of his replies to Bildad, Job exclaims: "Oh that my words were now written! oh that they were printed in a book! That they were graven with an iron pen and lead in the rock for ever. For I know that my redeemer liveth . . ." (Job **19**, 23–5) (*13*). Commentators disagree as to the exact manner in which this writing was done, some maintaining that the characters were simply engraved on a lead plate with an iron stylus, whereas others believe that the stylus was used to engrave the rock and that molten lead was afterward poured into the etched marks.

After the pursuing chariots of Pharaoh had been engulfed by the Red Sea, Moses and the children of Israel sang in the anthem of thanksgiving, "Thou didst blow with thy wind, the sea covered them: they sank as lead in the mighty waters" (Ex. **15**, 10). In the time of Ezekiel (nearly six centuries before Christ), lead was brought to the great Tyrian market from Tarshish: "Tarshish was thy merchant by reason of the multitude of all kind of riches; with silver, iron, tin, and lead, they traded in thy fairs" (*15*).

In the time of Zechariah (a century later), lead weights were in use. "And behold, there was lifted up a talent of lead . . ." (Zech. **5**, 7). Ecclesiasticus said of King Solomon, "thou didst gather gold as tin, and didst multiply silver as lead" (Ecclus. **47**, 18).

Lead ores are widely distributed in Nature, and are easily smelted. The Babylonians too engraved inscriptions on thin plates of metallic lead (*10*). The Romans used it extensively for water pipes, writing tablets, and coins. Unfortunately, they also used it for cooking utensils, and lead poisoning was an all-too-frequent result. A few very small lead nuggets, some of which are believed to be of pre-Columbian origin, have been found in Peru, Yucatan, and Guatemala (*41*).

White Lead. Theophrastus (372?–287 B.C.), in his "History of Stones," described the manufacture of "ceruse" (basic lead carbonate, or white lead) as follows: "Lead is placed in earthern Vessels, over sharp Vinegar, and after it has acquired some Thickness of a kind of Rust, which it commonly does in about ten Days, they open the Vessels, and scrape it off, as it were, in a kind of Foulness; they then place the Lead over the Vinegar again, repeating over and over the same Method of scraping it, till it is wholly dissolved; what has been scraped off they then beat to Powder, and boil for a long Time; and what at last subsides to the Bottom of the Vessel is the Ceruse" (*207*). By the time of Dioscorides (first century A.D.) the process had undergone little or no change (*208*).

Dioscorides also described minium, distinguished it from cinnabar, and mentioned its use for the painting and decorating of walls (*208*).

Marcus Vitruvius, architect and engineer under the Emperor Augustus, was familiar with the toxicity of lead and observed that the laborers in the smelters have pale complexions because of their prolonged exposure to lead dust and vapor (*209*).

Some Famous Lead Mines. J.-P. de Tournefort, who visited the Levant in 1700, wrote: "Siphanto, in days of yore, was famed for its rich Gold and Silver Mines; . . . Besides the Mines aforesaid, they have plenty of Lead; the Rains make a plain discovery of this, go almost where you will throughout the whole Island. The Oar is greyish, sleek, and yields a Lead like Pewter" (*210*).

The lead mines of Missouri (formerly known as the lead mines of Louisiana) were discovered in 1720 by Philip Francis Renault and M. La Motte, who afterward worked them by the open-cut method. The famous Burton mine was discovered more than half a century later and was worked wastefully by the Spaniards. In 1797 Moses Austin of Connecticut sank the first shaft, installed a reverberatory furnace, and manufactured shot and sheet lead. When the United States purchased from France in 1803 the vast region formerly known as Louisiana, the lead industry was already well developed.

In about 1819 Henry R. Schoolcraft visited all the lead mines in the Missouri region, traveling on foot and exploring the minerals and geological structures. He found the lead mainly in the form of the sulfide, galena. Zinc sulfide, or sphalerite, was also known to be abundant, but was not appreciated at that early period because satisfactory metallurgical processes were lacking (211). This Tri-state Area (Missouri, Kansas, and Oklahoma) has since become one of the world's leading sources of both lead and zinc.

TIN

Among the spoils of war which the Israelites took from the Midianites were tin and the other five metals known at that time: "And Eleazar the priest said unto the men of war which went to the battle, This is the ordinance of the law which the Lord commanded Moses; Only the gold, and the silver, the brass, the iron, the tin, and the lead, Every thing that may abide the fire, ye shall make it go through the fire, and it shall be clean . . ." (Num. 31, 21–3). Making the metals "go through the fire" probably meant a gentle, brief ignition to remove organic matter without melting the lead and tin (92).

Hebrew metal workers recognized tin as a frequent adulterant of the noble metals: "And I will turn my hand upon thee, and purely purge away thy dross, and take away all thy tin" (Isa. 1, 25). Alex. R. Gordon interprets this to mean "alloy" instead of tin (19). Ezekiel's parable of the dross in the furnace also recognizes tin as a base metal (Ezek. 22, 18–22).

After the Phœnicians began to navigate the western Mediterranean, they brought tin from Etruria, Spain, the mouths of the Loire, the Charente, and the rivers of Brittany, and from Cornwall and the Scilly Islands to supply the demand for bronze in the ancient world (268).

Since cassiterite is the only important ore of tin, it must have been the earliest source of the metal. Although the Cassiterides, or tin islands, vaguely mentioned by classical writers were usually supposed to have been named for the ore, cassiterite may possibly have been named for the islands, just as copper may have been named for Cyprus and bronze for Brundisium (Brindisi, Italy) (62). Some scholars identify the Cassiterides with the Scilly Isles. In speaking of mirrors, Pliny the Elder stated that "the best known to our forefathers were made at Brundisium from a mixture of copper and *stagnum*" (63).

Bronze. Long before metallic tin was known, bronze was in common use. In Mesopotamia, in the Indus valley, and in Egypt, alloys of copper and tin were made thirty centuries before Christ. Between 2100 and 1700 B.C., the Cretans added tin to copper to lower the melting point. According to Wilhelm Witter, at least some of this early bronze must have come from the ancient tin mines in Vogtland, central Germany, which also yielded native copper, azurite, and malachite. The tin concentrates may have been added to the copper ores before smelting, first accidentally and later intentionally, to harden the copper and make it more suitable for casting (*212, 213, 214*).

The composition of Peruvian bronze, according to Hiram Bingham, was not accidental. Pure tin which had evidently been prepared for use in casting was found at Machu Picchu, the mountain citadel of the Incas. The ancient inhabitants of this fortress were highly skilled metallurgists who made bronze implements of varying composition according to the purposes for which they were to be used. No artifacts of pure tin were found there (*64*). Alexander von Humboldt brought home from his American travels a well-forged Peruvian chisel in which the French chemist N.-L. Vauquelin afterward found 94 per cent of copper and 6 per cent of tin (*104*).

In his "Ancient Egyptian Materials and Industries," A. Lucas states that, although tin ore has not been found in Egypt, the earliest known artifacts of this metal, apart from bronze, are a ring and a pilgrim bottle from Egyptian tombs of the eighteenth dynasty (1580 B.C. to 1350 B.C.) (*65*).

Homer's "Iliad" relates how Hephaistos, the lame god of fire, made a shield for Achilles: "And he threw bronze that weareth not into the fire, and tin and precious gold and silver. . . ." Among the many decorations on the shield was a vineyard scene in gold and silver with a fence of tin and a herd of cattle, "and the kine were fashioned of gold and tin. . . ." The greaves were of "pliant tin" (*66*). This may have been a tin alloy, however, rather than the pure metal (*62*).

Herodotus (484–425 B.C.) said in his "History" that he did not know of any "islands called the Cassiterides whence the tin comes which we use. . . . Though I have taken great pains, I have never been able to get an assurance from an eye-witness that there is any sea on the further side of Europe. Nevertheless, tin and amber do certainly come to us from the ends of the earth" (*67*).

In his valuable book entitled "The Cornish Miner," A. K. H. Jenkin mentions some excavations made in 1925 at the famous castle of Chun, near St. Just, which dates back to 300 to 200 B.C. The slag found in the small smelting pits there contained tin. Thus the Cornish tin industry must be more than two thousand years old. The earliest known charter of the Cornish stannaries is dated 1201 (*68*). In Book V of his "Commentaries on the Gallic War," Julius Caesar mentioned the production of tin in the midland regions of Britain (69).

In the first century of the present era, the Latins referred to tin as "plumbum album" to distinguish it from lead, which they called "plumbum nigrum" (16). Pliny and Dioscorides mentioned the use of tin coatings to prevent corrosion of copper vessels (17).

When Hernando Cortés arrived in Mexico in 1519, tin from a mine in Taxco was already in circulation as money (40, 70). "Some small pieces of it," said Cortés, "were found among the natives of a province called Tachco [Tasco, or Taxco], in the form of very thin coins; and continuing my search I discovered that in that province and many others this was used as money; I further learned that it was mined in the province of Tachco, twenty-six leagues from this city [Temixtitán]" (71).*

Captain Robert Heath, a British mathematician, said in his "Natural and Historical Account of the Islands of Scilly," "Several of these islands afford tin, and some also lead and copper. The tin is discoverable by the banks next the sea, where the marks of the ore in some places are visible upon the surface; this I was assured by some very considerable Cornish tinners, in the year 1744. . . . Dionysius Alexandrinus speaks thus of the Hesperides, our present Scilly. . . .

> *Against the sacred Cape, great Europe's head*
> *Th'Hesperides along the ocean spread;*
> *Whose wealthy hills with mines of tin abound,*
> *And stout Iberians till the fertile ground.*

They were called Oestrymnides by Festus Avienus in his poem *De Oris Maritimis,* or *Book of the Coasts,* wherein he writes:

> *The isles Oestrymnides are clustering seen,*
> *Where the rich soil is stor'd with lead and tin.*
> *Stout are the natives, and untam'd in war . . .*
> *They skim remote, the briny swelling flood,*
> *With leathern boats contriv'd of skins and wood"*
> (215, 216).

In the time of Nicolas Lémery (1645–1715), tin was "found in several mines, principally in England, which is therefore called the Isle of Tin. . . . The purest tin," said he, "is that which comes in pigs from Cornwall . . ." (217).

In the seventeenth century Padre A. A. Barba visited tin mines in Bolivia which had been worked by the Incas and later by the Spaniards.

---

* Temixtitán and Tenochtitlán are old Aztec names for Mexico City.

"Also," said he, "in this Parish of San Bernardo, of which I am at present the incumbent, and about a quarter of a league from the Church, there are very rich Tin mines" (*218*).

Tin Dishes. A. S. Marggraf stated in 1746–47 that even the purest tin then obtainable contained arsenic. "That man must have believed tin to be especially harmless for use in human life," said he, "is evident from the great number of vessels of it, such as dishes, plates, pans, tankards, teapots and coffee-pots intended for food and drink, and various utensils used in the preparation of food, as well as the tin-plating of copper and iron receptacles and the many vessels used in chemistry and pharmacy, the tin and tin-plated still-heads, stills, caldrons, basins, cucurbits, tubes, etc.; all this, however, holds only for the pure unadulterated native tin" (*219*).

Many tin alloys containing lead, copper, antimony, and bismuth were also in use in Marggraf's time. He mentioned three kinds of unalloyed tin: "first the Malaga, reputed to be the best, second the English, and third the Saxon and Bohemian" (*219*).

Although tin ewers, plates, saltcellars, tankards, and goblets were in common use in seventeenth-century France, they became less common as the art of enameling developed there. Much tin was then consumed in the manufacture of enamels (*220*).

At the time of the French Revolution, however, tin dishes were still to be seen in wealthy homes and in convents, and many utensils of this metal were used in the preparation of food and pharmaceuticals. The police department therefore commissioned Pierre Bayen, Hilaire-Marin Rouelle, and Charlard to examine the tin to see whether or not it contained anything deleterious to health. Scarcely had the investigation begun, when death deprived Bayen and Charlard of their distinguished collaborator, Rouelle (*220*). When they examined tin from Banka in the East Indies, Malaga in Spain, and Cornwall, England, by Marggraf's method, Bayen and Charlard found them to be free from arsenic and well suited for household use (*220*).

Tin Plating. In 320 B.C., Theophrastus of Eresus mentioned the plating of iron with tin (*221*). In 1820 Samuel Parkes described several processes for this art which, he said, flourished in Bohemia long before it was practiced elsewhere in Europe. "About the beginning of the seventeenth century," said he, "mines of tin were discovered in Saxony, and the Elector had the address to transplant the tin-plate manufactory to his own kingdom. In the year 1665, when Mr. Andrew Yarrington visited these manufactories, they were of such extent as to employ about 80,000 workmen; and the tin-plates were sent to all parts of the civilized world. . . . The art of making tin-plate does not seem to have been practised in England till about 1720. A manufactory was then established at Pontypool, in Monmouthshire, where the art is still practised to a considerable extent . . ." (222).

Timothy Dwight, in his "Travels in New England and New York," described the tinware trade carried on by pedlars in New England, Virginia, North and South Carolina, and Georgia. "Immediately after the late war with Great Britain, which terminated in 1815," said he, "ten thousand boxes of tinned plates were manufactured into culinary vessels in the town of Berlin (Connecticut) in one year." This business afterward declined (223).

The importance of tin, as Dr. F. J. North of the National Museum of Wales pointed out, cannot be correctly judged from the quantities used. Since the days of ancient Rome, it has been applied as an extremely thin protective layer, or tin plate, to other metals to make them more resistant to corrosion and safer as receptacles for foods (224). In 1941 the National Museum of Wales held a special exhibition entitled "Tin through the Ages in Arts, Crafts, and Industry."

MERCURY

"It is a fluid
but does not moisten,
and runs about,
though it has no feet" (225, 226).

"On vermil beds in Idria's mighty caves
The living Silver rolls its ponderous waves" (227).

Mercury was known to the ancient Chinese and Hindus, and has been found in Egyptian tombs dating back to 1500 or 1600 B.C. (10). Dioscorides mentioned its preparation from cinnabar (18), while Pliny gave a method of purifying it by squeezing it through leather, and stated that it is poisonous (6). Earle R. Caley has shown by quotations from Aristotle, Theophrastus, Dioscorides, Pliny the Elder, Vitruvius, and the Leyden Papyrus of the third century A.D. that mercury has been known much longer than most persons realize. He states that cinnabar was probably the only mercury compound known to the ancients and that they used it both as a pigment and as a source of the metal (49). In his "Metallurgic Chemistry," C. E. Gellert (1713–1795) stated that "The only ore of mercury hitherto known is native cinnabar" (50). The most ancient specimen of quicksilver known is probably that which H. Schliemann found in a little cocoanut-shaped amulet in an Egyptian tomb at Kurna dating from the fifteenth or sixteenth century B.C. (51, 52).

Theophrastus, a disciple of Plato and successor to Aristotle, described quicksilver as a useful substance "obtained from native Cinnabar, rubbed with Vinegar in a brass Mortar with a brass Pestle" (53, 54, 55).

"The factitious cinnabar," said Theophrastus, "is from the Country a little above Ephesus; it is but in small Quantities, and is had only from one Place. It is only a Sand, shining like Scarlet, which they collect, and rub to a very fine Powder, in vessels of Stone only, and afterwards wash in other Vessels of Brass, or sometimes of Wood: What subsides they go to work on again, rubbing it and washing it as before" (221, 228).

Theophrastus also said that "one Callius, an Athenian, who belonged to the Silver Mines, invented and taught the making of this artificial Cinnabar. He had carefully got together a great Quantity of this Sand, imagining from its shining Appearance that it contained Gold: But when he had found that it did not, and had had an Opportunity, in his Trials,

From Biringuccio's "Pirotechnia"

Mercury Stills, 1540

of admiring the Beauty of its Colour, he invented and brought into use this Preparation of it. And this is no old Thing, the Invention being only of about ninety Years Date; Praxibulus being at this Time in the Government of Athens" (226, 228).

In the first century A.D., Dioscorides Pedanios of Anazarbus, Cilicia, gave the following process for preparing metallic mercury: "Putting an iron spoon having Cinnabaris in an earthen pot, they cover the Cup, dawbing it about with clay, then they make a fire under with coals; and ye soot that sticks to ye pot, being scrapped off & cooled, becomes

Hydrargyrum [mercury]. It is found also in ye place where Silver is melted, standing together by drops on ye roofs. And some say that Hydrargyrum is found by itself in ye mines. But it is kept in glassen, or leaden, or tinnen, or silver vessels, for it eats through all other matter, and makes it run out" (*18, 56*).

The Chinese alchemist Ko Hung (281–361 A.D.) wrote in the Pao Pu Tzu, "Many do not even know that mercury comes out of cinnabar (*tan sha*). When told, they still refuse to believe it, saying that cinnabar is red, and how can it produce a white substance? They also say that cinnabar is a stone—that stones when heated turn to ashes: and how then can anything else be expected of *tan sha?*" (*57*).

Christophle (Christophe) Glaser, under whom Nicolas Lémery once studied, stated in his "Traité de la Chymie" ("Chymischer Wegweiser") that natural cinnabar "consists of much mercury and some sulfur and earth; these three together make a hard body, a very beautiful red color varying in brightness according to the purity of the ore and the place where it is found. It is brought to us from different localities, as from Transylvania and Hungary and from many places in Germany; the handsomest, however, is found in Carinthia" (*229, 230*).

J. M. Hoppensack stated in 1795 that the mercury mines of Almadén had been worked for at least 2287 years and that cinnabar from them was sent to ancient Rome in the form of powder or sand (*58*). A. de Gálvez-Cañero believed that the Spanish mercury mines have been worked since the third or fourth century B.C. (*28*). In the *Mémoires* of the Académie des Sciences of Paris for 1719, Antoine Jussieu published a first-hand description of the great mine and smelters at Almadén, Spain, which he had visited two years previously (*233*). He was surprised to find that the crops, trees, and inhabitants were not injured by the fumes, and that springs near the mine yielded good potable water. The slaves who worked and ate in the mine however suffered severely from mercury poisoning (*231*).

In his "Natural and Moral History of the Indies," Father José de Acosta said that the Incas labored long in the Peruvian mercury mines without knowing what quicksilver was, seeking only cinnabar, or vermilion, to use as war paint (*59*). The Spaniards discovered the mercury mines of Huancavelica in 1566–67.

Father de Acosta told how Henrique Garces, a native of Portugal, discovered that the red substance *llimpi* with which the Indians used to paint their faces was the same as the Castilian vermilion. After the mines of Palcas in the territory of Guamanga had been discovered in this way, much of the mercury obtained from them was shipped to Mexico to be used in the refining of silver (*232*). Pedro Fernández de Velasco, who had observed this process in Mexico, demonstrated it successfully at Potosí in the year 1571 or 1572 (232).

When he demonstrated de Medina's cold amalgamation process to the Viceroy, the latter offered him suitable reward, ordered him to make the secret known at Potosí (Bolivia), and added that the most important wedding in the world was about to take place: the marriage of Mount Potosí (silver) to Mount Huancavelica (mercury) (60).

A. A. Barba of Bolivia stated in 1640 in his "Arte de los Metales," the first treatise on American metallurgy, that "There was very little use or consumption of Quicksilver before the beginning of this new Silver age in the world, then they only wasted it in Mercury sublimate, Cinabrio, or Vermillion, and the powders made thereof called *Precipitate,* which are also called in Spain the powders of Juanes de Vigo, which have been used to such mischievous purposes that the world was said to have too much of them, although in bulk and quantity then they had but little; but since it hath been used to collect the Silver together out of Oar, which is ground small (an invention which the Ancients had scarcely arrived to, and practised it but very little), it is incredible how great a quantity is consumed by the Founders of Mettals of this Kingdom: for if the abundance of Silver that hath gone out of this Kingdom hath filled the world with riches and admiration, by it may be estimated the consumption and loss of Quicksilver, which after a most extravagant expence thereof at first, being now by good experience regulated within terms of moderation, is found to be equal in weight to the Silver extracted; and very seldom that the wast [sic] is so little . . ." (233).

Baron Alexander von Humboldt, in his "Political Essay on New Spain," gave the following account of the discovery of this mine: "The famous mine of Huancavelica," said he, ". . . is located on Mount Santa Bárbara, south of the city of Huancavelica. . . .   The discovery of the great mercury mine is generally attributed to the Indian, Gonzalo Abincopa, or Navincopa; but it certainly occurred long before the year 1567, for even the Incas used cinnabar [*llimpi*] for their cosmetics, getting it from the mountains of Palcas.   The working of the mine on Mt. Santa Bárbara, for the crown, did not begin until about the month of September in 1570, the year in which Fernández de Velasco introduced Mexican amalgamation into Peru" (234).

The Mexican method referred to by Father de Acosta and Baron von Humboldt was the cold amalgamation, or *patio,* process introduced at Pachuca by Bartolomé de Medina about the middle of the sixteenth century.   As early as March 4, 1552, the governing princess (Princesa Gobernadora) in Valladolid acknowledged an urgent request for mercury to be used in the exploitation of silver (28).   In this process, salt, mercury, and copper sulfate were used. The pulverized mineral, salt brine, and a *magistral* consisting of roasted copper and iron pyrites and mercury were all mixed together on a paved floor. Heat was required only for the last stage of the process—the decomposition of the silver amalgam (*60, 235*).

The hot amalgamation process for silver was invented by Father A. A. Barba (1569–1662) soon after his arrival in Charcas, Bolivia (*28, 236*). His "El Arte de los Metales" was devoted mainly to the metallurgy of silver and gold by amalgamation (*235*). He lived to be ninety-three years old (*237*). Captain William Betagh, in his "Observations on the Country of Peru," gave a detailed description of the hot amalgamation process for silver as practised there in the early part of the eighteenth century (*238*).

Baron von Humboldt mentioned three occurrences of cinnabar in New Granada: the province of Antioquía; Mount Quindiu in the Cordilleras; and a place between Azogue and Cuenca in the province of Quito. "The discovery of the cinnabar of Quindiu," said he, "is owing to the patriotic zeal of the celebrated botanist Mutis," who, in the months of August and September, 1786, had some mine-operators examine, at his expense, the portion of the granitic Cordillera which extends southward from Nevado de Tolima to the Rio Saldaña (*234*). José Celestino Mutis was a scholarly Spanish ecclesiastic and physician who became professor of philosophy, mathematics, and natural history at the University of Santa Fé in Bogota, New Granada (Colombia). His active interest in the flora of South America led him to carry on an extensive correspondence with Linné (Linnæus) (*239*). A description of the Spanish and the Peruvian quicksilver mines was published in the *American Journal of Science* for 1868 (*61*).

Indians living near the old Santa Clara Mission, about fifty miles from the present city of San Francisco, California, used to apply red and yellow pigments from the "Cave of the Red Earth" near there for personal adornment. In 1845 Captain Andrés Castillero of the Mexican Army, who had studied chemistry and metallurgy at the College of Mines in Mexico City, discovered near the Santa Clara Mission an ore in which he easily detected metallic mercury. When Don Manuel Herrera of that College of Mines analyzed specimens of this ore he found an average mercury content of 35.5 per cent and reported that some pieces were practically pure cinnabar. Dr. Henry M. Leicester published an interesting article on the history of the New Almaden Mine in California in the *Journal of Chemical Education* (*100*). When gold was discovered near Sutter's Fort, California, in 1848 the operation of the gold mines that were opened up during the "gold rush of '49" was greatly facilitated by the nearby supply of mercury for amalgamation.

Corrosive Sublimate and Calomel. A method for preparing a rather pure mercurous chloride (calomel) was known to Parisian physicians before 1608 (*83*). Oswald Croll prepared it by a secret process, and Jean Beguin in his "Tyrocinium Chymicum," which was published in 1608, described the process. This "mild sublimate" was made by rubbing corrosive sublimate with as much mercury as could be "killed" or made to combine with it (*240, 241, 242*). Calomel, corrosive sublimate, and vermilion have been manufactured for centuries at Hankow, China (*243*).

Chemists of India prepared both chlorides of mercury as early as the twelfth century (*244*). A detailed description of the process was given in the thirteenth or fourteenth century (*245*). A mixture of common salt, brick dust, alum, Indian aloe, and mercury was heated for three days in a closed earthen pot. The Japanese and Chinese also prepared calomel by similar methods (*244*).

The Freezing of Mercury. Until the middle of the eighteenth century, chemists believed that fluidity was an essential property of mercury. During a blizzard on the twenty-fifth of December, 1759, A. Braune (or Braun) and M. V. Lomonosov of the Academy of Sciences of St. Petersburg thought it would be interesting to see how much farther the temperature could be lowered by artificial means. In the presence of several fellow members of the Academy, they packed a mercury thermometer in a mixture of nitric acid and snow. The mercury fell rapidly and solidified (*246, 282*). Jakob Fries gave a vivid account in Crell's *Annalen* of his experiences with freezing mercury in January, 1787, during a cold spell (*247*). P. S. Pallas also had a similar experience with the natural cold of Siberia (*248, 249*).

ANCIENT NON-METALS

SULFUR

Since sulfur and carbon both occur uncombined in many parts of the world they must certainly have been known to all the ancient peoples.

Although the word *brimstone* originally meant the gum of the gopher tree, it was later used to designate other flammable substances, especially sulfur (*86*). The alchemists used the word sulfur to signify combustibility.

The exact location of Sodom and Gomorrah is difficult to establish. The Biblical account of their destruction reads: "Then the Lord rained upon Sodom and upon Gomorrah brimstone and fire from the Lord out of heaven" (Gen. **19**, 24). In his unsympathetic interpretation of Job's suffering, Bildad set forth the punishment of the wicked, and added that "brimstone shall be scattered upon his habitation" (Job **18**, 15). Ezekiel prophesied a similar upheaval which, he said, was to be accompanied by "a great shaking in the land of Israel, . . . an overflowing rain, and great hailstones, fire, and brimstone" (Ezek. **38**, 19–22).

Biblical writers used the flammability of sulfur to symbolize torment and destruction. In speaking of the condemned Tophet, Isaiah mentioned liquid sulfur: "the breath of the Lord, like a stream of brimstone, doth kindle it" (Isa. **30**, 33).

Although there seems to be no suggestion in the Bible that the Hebrews made any use of sulfur, the Greeks, even in the time of Homer,

Woodcut Showing
Distillation of Sulphur
in 1557

employed it as a fumigant (*72*). After the killing of the wooers in Book XXII of Homer's "Odyssey," Odysseus called to Eurycleia, "Bring sulphur, old nurse, that cleanses all pollution and bring me fire, that I may purify the house with sulphur" (*72*).

Pliny described the Italian and Sicilian deposits in great detail, mentioning the use of block sulfur for medicinal purposes, the bleaching of cloth with sulfur vapor, and the manufacture of sulfur matches and lamp wicks (*19, 73*). Georgius Agricola (*26*) stated that these matches could be ignited by friction on stone and used for lighting candles and dry wood. He also left no doubt as to his opinion of gunpowder when he said: "Sulfur is also made to enter into that powder—execrable invention —which hurls iron, brass, or stone instruments of war of a new kind" (*20*).

It is difficult for the modern chemist to understand the early literature of sulfur, for the name was incorrectly used to designate all combustible substances. In the tenth century, Jabir believed that the metals were compounds of sulfur and mercury; and hence these two elements came to have great significance for the alchemists. Abu Mansur mentioned the use of the former as an antidote for various kinds of metallic poisoning, and Pseudo-Geber told how to prepare milk of sulfur by adding vinegar to alkaline sulfur solutions (34). Some scholars regard the Latin work "Invention of Verity, or Perfection," as a translation of an unknown Arabic treatise by Geber (Abu Musa Jabir ibn Hayyan), who lived in the tenth century A.D. Professor Julius Ruska believed, however, that Geber (Jabir) and Pseudo-Geber (the author of the "Invention of Verity") must have been separated by five centuries of time (35).

The sulfur from which Cortés and his daring conquistadores made their first gunpowder was obtained, so he said, from the rumbling, smoking crater of Mount Popocatepetl (70). In a letter to Charles V, written from Temixtítán on October 15, 1524, he said, "As for sulphur, I have spoken to Your Majesty of that mountain in the province of Mexico which smokes. A Spaniard [Francisco Montaño] descended by means of a rope, seventy or eighty fathoms, and obtained a sufficient quantity to last us in our need; but henceforward there will be no necessity of going to this trouble because it is dangerous and I shall always write to obtain these things from Spain" (76).

Until 1849 there seems to have been no repetition of this exploit. During the eighteen-fifties, however, intrepid miners, or *volcaneros*, used to make the difficult ascent of this mountain. After being lowered by a windlass into the stifling crater, they used to collect about ten 25-pound sacks of sulfur, which they pushed over the rim of the crater and allowed to slide down the steep, snow-covered slope of the mountain. At the Tlamacas rancho the sulfur was purified by distillation (70). Norman J. Harrar described these hazardous operations in the *Journal of Chemical Education*.

In the year 1700, when Joseph-Pitton Tournefort was traveling in the Levant, he noticed the common occurrence of sulfur in volcanic regions near the sea. "Such," said he, "are the famous Vulcanoes [sic] that vomit Flames of Fire; Vesuvius, Stromboli, Mount Aetna, Mountains in Ireland, Fayal, Pic-Teneriffe. In these Islands and on the Coasts of the Terra-firma of America [Panama], there are Fires which have been burning from the beginning of the World. . . . The Sulphur of Milo [the Island of Melos] is very beautiful, and has a greenish shining Cast, which made the Ancients prefer it to that of Italy . . ." (250).

In 1759 Count Vincenzo Masini (1689–1762) of Cesena, Italy, published a patriotic poem on sulfur, in which he described its extraction, purification, and uses. Signor Gino Testi has published extracts from this poem, with explanatory notes (74). In eloquent Italian verses Count Masini gave poetic expression to Giorgio Baglivi's belief that vegetables and animals exert an influence over the formation of the metals and the so-called semi-metals

> ". . . Within the rocks, among the thorns,
> Between the cliffs, sulfur takes root;
> For gold, silver, copper, iron, and sulfur
> Likewise are plants" (74)*

Count Masini also expressed dramatically the relation between sulfur and volcanic action.

The Abbé Lazaro Spallanzani (1729–1799) described the sulfurous fumes of Vulcano, and added that "Above these fumes there is a plain, of no great extent, which one is at first afraid to venture on, from the subterranean noise heard there, and from the shaking of the ground when struck with the foot. . . . On this plain it was that formerly stood the furnaces in which the sulphur of Vulcano was purified. But this useful labour has long since been abandoned . . . nor was it abandoned because the quantity of sulphur obtained was too little . . ., as the vein is very rich and even inexhaustible. The real cause why the inhabitants of Lipari no longer continued this work was that the ground . . . grows hotter the deeper it is dug into . . ., to which is to be added the offensive stench of the sulphureous fumes . . ." (75).

In the latter part of the eighteenth century, A.-L. Lavoisier and his adherents regarded sulfur as an element. As late as 1809, however, Sir Humphry Davy believed that it contained oxygen and hydrogen as essential constituents and that it was similar in composition to the resins (30, 33). Experiments by A. Berthollet, son of C. L. Berthollet, had indicated that sulfur contains hydrogen. From his own experiments with Sicilian sulfur in 1808, Sir Humphry concluded that "the existence of hydrogen in sulphur is fully proved" and that "sulphur, in its common state, is a compound of small quantities of oxygen and hydrogen with a large quantity of a basis that produces the acids of sulphur in combustion . . ." (30). In 1809 Gay-Lussac and Thenard thoroughly established the elementary nature of sulfur (31, 32).

---

* " . . Entro le balze
    Fra dumi, e fra dirupi il zolfo aligna;
    Che piante e vegetabili pur sono
    L'oro, l'argento, il rame, il ferro, il zolfo . . ." (74)

By 1810 Davy had changed his views and suspected "a notable proportion of oxygen in Sicilian sulphur, which is probably owing to the presence of oxide of sulphur. . . . Considering the manner in which sulphur is procured in Sicily, it might be expected to contain oxygen; when taken from the mine, the limestone rock containing it, broken into small fragments, is subjected to heat in a kind of kiln; whilst a small portion of the sulphur is burnt, and ascends into the atmosphere in the form of sulphurous acid gas, the greater part of it melts, sinks, and flows out through an opening designed to give issue. This process I witnessed at the extensive sulphur mines in the neighbourhood of Gujenti [Girgenti, or Agrigentum]; and I believe it is generally in use throughout the sulphur districts" (30).

When Davy allowed "oxymuriatic acid gas" (chlorine) to react with moist sulfur, he obtained hydrogen chloride and oxygen. When he repeated the experiment, using Sicilian sulfur dried over calcium chloride, "no oxygen gas was evolved and not a cubical inch of muriatic [hydrochloric] acid . . . and it was found that between 16 and 17 cubical inches of oxymuriatic acid gas [chlorine] had disappeared; the whole of the sulfur was sublimed in the gas, and the liquor formed was of a tawny-orange colour" [probably sulfur monochloride] (30).

Sulfur in Louisiana and Texas. Prospectors who were boring for petroleum in Louisiana in 1865 discovered a great sulfur deposit beneath a layer of quicksand five hundred feet thick (251). After several companies had failed in all attempts to exploit this sulfur, Herman Frasch in about 1890 began to study the problem. His method of attack is carefully recorded in his address of acceptance of the Perkin Medal in 1912.

"To meet the extraordinary conditions existing in this deposit," said he, "I decided that the only way to mine this sulphur was to melt it in the ground and pump it to the surface in the form of a liquid. . . . At that time, the drilling of a well in an alluvial deposit containing quicksand, etc., was a very tedious task, and it took from six to nine months to get through the alluvial material to the rock–work which we do today in three days. . . . When everything was ready to make the first trial, . . . we raised steam in the boilers, and sent the superheated water into the ground without a hitch. If for one instant the high temperature required should drop below the melting point of sulphur, it would mean failure. . . .

"After permitting the melting fluid to go into the ground for twenty-four hours," continued Mr. Frasch, "I decided that sufficient material must have been melted to produce some sulphur. The pumping engine was started on the sulphur line, and the increasing strain against the engine showed that work was being done. More and more slowly went the engine, more steam was supplied, until the man at the throttle sang out at the top of his voice, 'She's pumping.' A liquid appeared in the polished rod, and when I wiped it off with my finger I found my finger covered with sulphur. Within five minutes the receptacles under pressure were opened, and a beautiful stream of the golden fluid shot into the barrels we had ready to receive the product. . . .   When everything had been finished, the sulphur all piled up in one heap, and the men had departed, . . . I mounted the sulphur pile and seated myself on the very top. It pleased me to hear the slight noise caused by the contraction of the warm sulphur, which was like a greeting from below . . ." (251).

In presenting the Perkin Medal to Mr. Frasch, Dr. C. F. Chandler said, "At present the Louisiana deposit supplies this country with sulphur and might supply large quantities to European countries. Fortunately the company is owned by a few broad-minded and large-hearted men who could not be induced to bring starvation and ruin upon the two hundred and fifty thousand people dependent upon the mining of sulphur in Sicily" (251). Mr. Frasch said that great credit was also due the Italian government for averting unemployment and misery. These great American sulfur deposits also extend into Texas.

Herman Frasch was educated in Germany as an apothecary's apprentice, and came to the United States at the age of sixteen years (274). After spending most of his life in this country and making many notable contributions to chemical engineering, he lived in retirement in France, where he died in 1914 at the age of sixty-two years (252).

Sulfur in Plants. The presence of sulfur in plants was first demonstrated in 1781 by Nicolas Deyeux, who detected it in the roots of the dock (*Rumex patientia*), the cochlearia, and the horse radish (269, 270). Scheele, however, unable to confirm the discovery, thought that the plants which Deyeux had analyzed had perhaps grown near "hepatic air" [hydrogen sulfide] or pyrite (271). Sulfur is now known to be essential for plant growth. In many early plant analyses only the non-volatile sulfur, which appeared as sulfates in the ash, was determined. Modern analytical methods, which prevent volatilization and loss of organic sulfur compounds during the combustion, show that plants require larger amounts of sulfur than was formerly believed (195).

Sulfur in Animals. In 1813 Heinrich August Vogel published in the *Annales de Chimie et de Physique* a paper "On the existence of sulfur in the bile and in the blood" (272). After Cadet and Fourcroy had observed an odor of hydrogen sulfide when bile was treated with hydrochloric acid or distilled, Vogel distilled two kilograms of fresh ox bile from a large glass retort connected to a flask containing a solution of lead acetate. A small precipitate of lead sulfide revealed the presence of sulfur in the bile. He also demonstrated its presence in blood and urine (*272*). The "Encyclopédie Méthodique" (1815) mentioned its presence in albumen, hair, and wool (*273*).

CARBON

That the Biblical word "coals" means charcoal is evident from the proverb "As coals are to burning coals, and wood to fire; so is a contentious man to kindle strife" (Prov. **26**, 21).

In a discourse on the folly of worshipping a wooden idol, Isaiah said, "And none considereth in his heart, neither is there knowledge nor understanding to say, I have burned part of it in the fire; yea, also I have baked bread upon the coals thereof; I have roasted flesh, and eaten it: and shall I make the residue thereof an abomination? shall I fall down to the stock of a tree?" (Isa. **44**, 19).

From Biringuccio's "Pirotechnia"

Manufacture of Wood Charcoal

One of the proverbs uses the figurative expression "heaping coals of fire on an enemy's head" to represent remorse caused by returning good for evil: "If thine enemy be hungry, give him bread to eat; and if he be thirsty, give him water to drink: For thou shalt heap coals of fire upon his head . . ." (Prov. **25**, 21–2). In his letter to the Christians in Rome, Paul urged them to follow this precept (Rom. **12**, 20).

Carbon in the form of lampblack was often mixed with olive oil or balsam gum (*101, 275*) and used as ink. It was carried in an inkhorn suspended from the girdle, as mentioned by Ezekiel six centuries before Christ: "And behold six men came from the way of the higher gate, which lieth toward the north, and every man a slaughter weapon in his hand; and one man among them was clothed with linen, with a writer's inkhorn by his side . . ." (Ezek. 9, 2). Jeremiah, a contemporary of Ezekiel, also mentioned ink (Jer. 36, 18).

Carbon in the forms of charcoal and soot must certainly have been known even to prehistoric races, and in Pliny's time the former was made, much as it is today, by heating wood in a pyramid covered with clay to exclude the air (21). The recognition of carbon, the chief constituent of charcoal, as a chemical element, however, is much more recent. In an interesting article in *Osiris*, entitled "The discovery of the element carbon," Theodore A. Wertime traced the development of this concept (276). In his opinion the identification of carbon as an element was worked out step by step by R.-A.-F. de Réaumur, H.-L. Duhamel du Monceau, Torbern Bergman, C. W. Scheele, C.-L. Berthollet, A.-L. Lavoisier, and others.

Réaumur distinguished between steel, wrought iron, and cast iron, and stated that their characteristic properties "were related to their content of a black combustible material, which he knew to be the chief constituent of charcoal . . ." (276). Duhamel du Monceau, who had studied the charcoal-making process, thought that the "phlogiston" in the wood must be concentrated in the charring process. Bergman believed that the essential differences between wrought iron, steel, and cast iron were caused by a "plumbago" (graphite) precipitate composed of "fixed air" (carbon dioxide) and "phlogiston"* (276). Scheele in 1779 produced "fixed air" by burning graphite with saltpeter and proved that the constituents of graphite ("plumbago") are "aerial acid united with a large quantity of phlogiston," or, as one would say today, that it consists essentially of uncombined carbon (253, 254). In 1783–84 Lavoisier distinguished between hydrogen and matter derived from charcoal, since they form different combustion products (water and "acide charbonneux" (carbon dioxide) respectively). Berthollet showed in 1785 that methane is formed from carbonaceous matter and the "inflammable gas from water" (hydrogen).

In 1787 Guyton de Morveau, Lavoisier, Berthollet, and Fourcroy introduced in their "Méthode de nomenclature chimique" the terms *carbone*, for the element carbon, instead of *charbon* (charcoal) and "acide carbonique" (carbon dioxide) instead of "air fixe" ("fixed air").

---

* "Phlogiston" was a hypothetical principle supposed to escape with the flame during combustion. See also Chapter 7.

According to the "Encyclopædia Biblica," the word diamond as used in the old Testament probably does not refer to the true diamond but more likely to corundum (22, 36). The ancient Hindu scriptures, the Vedas, the Ramayana, and the Mahabharata, make frequent mention of the diamond.

In 1694–95 Cosmus III, Grand Duke of Tuscany, made it possible for Giuseppe Averani and Cipriano Antonio Targioni of Florence to heat a diamond with a large burning glass. The gem was destroyed (255). Various modifications of this experiment were tried in Vienna and Paris (256).

P.-J. Macquer has left us, in his "Dictionary of Chemistry," a fine first-hand account of the scientific history of this gem (255). On July 26, 1771, Macquer and Godefroy de Villetaneuse, in presence of Jean Darcet (1725–1801), Hilaire-Marin Rouelle (Rouelle the Younger), and others, heated a flawless diamond in a refractory capsule in Macquer's wind furnace. When it reached the temperature of melting copper, a flame could be seen surrounding it, and in less than an hour the gem disappeared without leaving a trace (257, 258, 259).

Jewelers and diamond cutters, however, were skeptical. To remove certain flaws, they had often heated diamonds, carefully packed in chalk dust and powdered charcoal, and had never experienced any loss. After several inconclusive experiments had been made by others, Maillard, a famous gem cutter, placed three diamonds, closely packed in charcoal dust, in the bowl of a tobacco pipe, and enclosed it in sheet iron inside a crucible filled with a lining of chalk dust and a fusible sand used for castings. After moistening the mixture with salt water and letting it dry, Maillard heated the crucible in Macquer's furnace. The contents soon became so fluid that it was necessary to allow the furnace to cool.

As Maillard searched among the ash and molten material which had fallen through the grate, the academicians were confident that he would never see his diamonds again. When the airtight, glassy covering was broken away and the crucible opened, the tobacco pipe, the carbon dust, and the three diamonds were recovered intact. Hence it was evident that both heat and air were required for the destruction of the diamond (258, 260).

Pierre-Joseph Macquer, a descendant of the Scottish nobility, was born in Paris in 1718. Although he chose medicine as his profession, he devoted much time and thought to physical science, especially to chemistry. His "Dictionary of Chemistry" gives a comprehensive, scholarly, impartial view of all branches of eighteenth-century chemical technology. In his eulogy, Condorcet said, "The spirit one observes in the works of M. Macquer is the same which directed his conduct. Everything about

Frontispiece to the German translation of
P.-J. Macquer's "Dictionnaire de Chymie," 1788

him was in harmony; that precision of meaning, that moderation in his judgments, that reserve in his assertions was the source of the modesty, tranquility, and kindness which he constantly showed in all the circumstances of his life . . ." (261).

In 1772–73 Lavoisier, Macquer, Cadet, and Mathurin-Jacques Brisson ignited a diamond under a bell jar by means of the great Tschirnhausen burning glass, collected the resulting gas over mercury, added lime water, and obtained a white precipitate of calcium carbonate which proved that the gas must be carbon dioxide (255). According to Macquer, many of these experiments were carried out by Lavoisier alone and at his own expense. "This enthusiastic academician," said he, "gradually conceived several arrangements of crystal glass vessels . . ." and finally used "glass bell jars inverted over dishes, some of which were filled with water, others with mercury, which, upon removal of the air, was allowed to rise to a certain height under the bell jar. The diamonds were laid, uncovered, on supports of hard unglazed porcelain under the bell jars, and could thus be subjected to the ignition point without communicating with the outer air" (255). The details are given in the second part of Lavoisier's physical and chemical researches (23, 262).

In 1799 Guyton de Morveau converted the diamond first into graphite and finally into carbonic acid (carbon dioxide). He did not realize, however, that graphite is merely another allotropic form of carbon, but regarded it as partially oxidized carbon (263, 264).

In 1796 Smithson Tennant proved that equal weights of carbon and diamond, when burned with saltpeter, yielded equal amounts of carbon dioxide (258, 265). Three years later Guyton de Morveau and Louis Clouet produced cast steel by heating a 907-milligram diamond in a small crucible of wrought iron (24, 258, 266). As early as 1704 Sir Isaac Newton stated in his "Optics" that the diamond must be combustible, and in 1772 Lavoisier found this to be true (23). The English chemist Smithson Tennant proved in 1796 that it consists solely of carbon (24).[*]

Because of the great importance of carbon compounds and carbonaceous substances a special chapter will now be devoted to them.

LITERATURE CITED

(1) WINKLER, C., "Ueber die Entdeckung neuer Elemente im Verlaufe der letzten fünfundzwanzig Jahre," *Ber.*, **30**, 13 (Jan., 1897).
(2) BASKERVILLE, C., "The elements: Verified and unverified," *Science*, N. S., **19**, 88–100 (Jan., 1904).
(3) RÂY, P. C., "History of Hindu Chemistry," 2nd ed., Vol. 1, Chuckervertty, Chatterjee and Co., Calcutta, **1904**, p. 25.

---

[*] For a brief mention of attempts to prepare diamonds artificially see p. 768.

(4) Ex. **20:** 23; Deu. **8:** 13; I Ki. **20:** 3; Job **31:** 24; Ps. **19:** 10; Prov. **16:** 16; Isa. **60:** 17; Lam. **4:** 1; Hag. **2:** 8; Zec. **13:** 9.

(5) PLINY THE ELDER, "Natural History," translated by Bostock and Riley, Geo. Bell and Sons, London, **1856,** Book XXXIII, Chap. 21.

(6) *Ibid.,* Book XXXIII, Chap. 32.

(7) Genesis, **23:** 16.

(8) JAGNAUX, R., "Histoire de la Chimie," Vol. 2, Baudry et Cie., Paris, **1891,** p. 372.

(9) THOMSON, THOMAS, "History of Chemistry," Vol. 1, Colburn and Bentley, London, **1830,** p. 53; E. O. VON LIPPMANN, "Entstehung und Ausbreitung der Alchemic," Springer, Berlin, **1919,** pp. 519–30.

(10) STILLMAN, J. M., "The Story of Early Chemistry," D. Appleton and Co., New York City, **1924** pp. 2–7.

(11) Ezra, **8:** 27.

(12) PLINY THE ELDER, "Natural History," ref. *(5)*, Book XXXIV, Chap. 39.

(13) Job **19:** 23–4.

(14) Deu. **3:** 11.

(15) Eze. **27:** 12.

(16) PLINY THE ELDER, "Natural History," ref. *(5)*, Book XXXIV, Chap. 47.

(17) *Ibid.,* Book XXXIV, Chap. 48.

(18) JAGNAUX, R., "Histoire de la Chimie," ref. *(8)*, Vol. 2, p. 366.

(19) THOMSON, THOMAS, "History of Chemistry," ref. *(9)*, Vol. 1, p. 103; PLINY THE ELDER, "Natural History," ref. *(5)*, Book XXXV, Chap. 50.

(20) JAGNAUX, R., "Histoire de la Chimie," ref. *(8)*, Vol. 1, p. 458.

(21) *Ibid.,* Vol. 1, p. 680; PLINY THE ELDER, "Natural History," ref. *(5)*, Book XVI, Chap. 8.

(22) Ex. **28:** 18; **39:** 11; Eze. **28:** 13; Jer. **17:** 1.

(23) JAGNAUX, R., "Histoire de la Chimie," ref. *(8)*, Vol. 1, pp. 664–8; ERNST VON MEYER, "Geschichte der Chemie," 4th ed., Veit and Co., Leipzig, **1914,** p. 371.

(24) THOMSON, THOMAS, "History of Chemistry," ref. *(9)*, Vol. 2, p. 236.

(25) BERTHELOT, P.-E.-M., "Les Origines de l'Alchimie," Steinheil, Paris, **1885,** pp. 227–28.

(26) BILLINGER, R. D., "Assaying with Agricola," *J. Chem. Educ.,* **6,** 349–54 (Feb., 1929).

(27) BERTHELOT, P.-E.-M., "La Chimie au Moyen Âge," Vol. 1, Imprimerie Nationale, Paris, **1893,** p. 364.

(28) DE GÁLVEZ-CAÑERO, A., "La Metalurgia de la Plata y del Mercurio. Bosquejo Histórico," IX Congreso Internacional de Química Pura y Aplicada, Madrid, **1934,** 37 pp.

(29) PARTINGTON, J. R., "Origins and Development of Applied Chemistry," Longmans, Green and Co., London, **1935,** pp. 14–100; see also HERMANN, PAUL, "Conquest by Man," Harper, New York, **1954,** pp. 51–61.

(30) DAVY, J., "The Collected Works of Sir Humphry Davy, Bart.," Smith, Elder and Co., London, **1840,** Vol. 5, pp. 73, 160–8, 216–20, 310–11.

(31) KOPP, H., "Geschichte der Chemie," Fr. Vieweg und Sohn, Braunschweig, **1847,** Vol. 3, pp. 310–11.

(32) GAY-LUSSAC, L.-J. and L.-J. THENARD, "En réponse aux recherches analytiques de M. Davy, sur la nature du soufre et du phosphore," *Ann. chim. phys.,* (1), **73,** 229–53 (Mar. 31, 1810). Read Sept. 18, 1809.

(33) DAVY, H., "Sur la nature de certains corps, particulièrement des alcalis, du soufre, du phosphore, du carbone et des acides réputés simples," *ibid.,* (1), **73,** 5–11 (Jan. 31, 1810).

(34) HOLMYARD, E. J., "The Works of Geber Englished by Richard Russell, 1678," J. M. Dent and Sons, London and Toronto, **1928,** p. 209.

(35) BUGGE, G., "Das Buch der grossen Chemiker," Verlag Chemie, Berlin, **1929,** Vol. 1, pp. 18–31, 60–9. Articles on Jabir and Pseudo-Geber by J. Ruska.

(36)   CHEYNE, T. K. and J. S. BLACK, "Encyclopædia Biblica," The Macmillan
Company, New York, **1899**, Vol. 1, columns 1097–8.

(37)   SMITH, J. M. P. and E. J. GOODSPEED, "The Bible. An American Translation,"
University of Chicago Press, Chicago, **1931**, 418 pp. Translation of Deuteronomy by T. J. Meek.

(38)   WEEKS, M. E., "An exhibit of chemical substances mentioned in the Bible,"
J. Chem. Educ., **20**, 63–76 (Feb., 1943).

(39)   DANA, J. D., "Manual of Mineralogy and Lithology," John Wiley and Sons,
New York, **1880**, 3rd ed., p. 144.

(40)   BROWNE, C. A., "The chemical industries of the American aborigines," *Isis*,
23 (2), 417 (Sept., 1935).

(41)   BERGSØE, PAUL, "The Gilding Process and the Metallurgy of Copper and Lead
among the pre-Columbian Indians," Danmarks Naturvidenskabelige Samfund, Copenhagen, **1938**, Ingeniørvidenskabelige Skrifter, No. A 46, 56 pp.

(42)   HAMMOND, G. P. and AGAPITO REY, "Narratives of the Coronado Expedition,
1540–1542," University of New Mexico Press, Albuquerque, **1940**, p. 188.

(43)   WINSHIP, G. P., "The Coronado Expedition, 1540–1542," U. S. Bu. Am.
Ethnology, Washington, D. C., **1896**, pp. 345, 350, 397, 405, 509, 577, 582.

(44)   BRERETON, JOHN, "A Briefe and True Relation of the Discouerie of the North
Part of Virginia," George Bishop, London, **1602**, p. 9.

(45)   DE ACOSTA, FATHER JOSÉ, "Natural and Moral History of the Indies," The
Hakluyt Society, London, **1880**, Vol. 1, pp. 186–211, 223.

(46)   BARBA, A. A., "El Arte de los Metales," John Wiley and Sons, New York,
1923, pp. 67–9. English translation by R. E. Douglass and E. P. Mathew-
son.

(47)   MORGAN, M. H., "Vitruvius. The Ten Books on Architecture," Harvard
University Press, Cambridge, **1914**, pp. 215–16.

(48)   ISSEROW, SAUL and HUGO ZAHND, "Chemical knowledge in the Old Testa-
ment," *J. Chem. Educ.*, **20**, 327–35 (July, 1943); ZAHND, H., and DOROTHY
GILLIS, "Chemical knowledge in the New Testament," *ibid.*, **23**, 90–7
(Feb., 1946); **23**, 128–34 (Mar., 1946).

(49)   CALEY, E. R., "Mercury and its compounds in ancient times," *ibid.*, **5**, 419–
24 (Apr., 1928).

(50)   GELLERT, C. E., "Metallurgic Chemistry," T. Becket, London, **1776**, p. 57.

(51)   VON LIPPMANN, E. O., ref. (*9*), vol. 1, pp. 600–7.

(52)   SCHELENZ, H., "Geschichte der Pharmazie," J. Springer, Berlin, **1904**, p. 41.

(53)   HILL, JOHN, "Theophrastus's History of Stones," printed for the author,
London, **1774**, 2nd ed., pp. 227–35.

(54)   KOPP, H., ref. (*31*), Vol. 4, p. 172.

(55)   MARTIN, BENJAMIN, "Biographia Philosophica," W. Owen, London, **1764**,
pp. 58–60. Biographical sketch of Theophrastus.

(56)   GUNTHER, R. T., "The Greek Herbal of Dioscorides," Oxford University Press,
Oxford, **1934**, pp. 623–6, 638, 648.

(57)   DAVIS, TENNEY L., "Remarks on the value of historical studies," *Report of
New England Assoc. of Chem. Teachers*, May, 1930, p. 5.

(58)   HOPPENSACK, J. M., "Ueber den Bergbau in Spanien überhaupt und der
Quecksilber-bergbau zu Almadén," Weimar, **1796**, 158 pp. Review in
Ann. chim. phys., (1), **25**, 51–60 (1798).

(59)   DE ACOSTA, FATHER JOSÉ, ref. (*45*), Vol. 1, pp. 185, 214–17. English translation by Edward Grimston, **1604**.

(60)   ARÉVALO, CELSO, "La Historia Natural en España," Unión Poligráfica, Madrid,
1935, pp. 143–9.

(61)   HAWLEY, C. E., "Notes on the quicksilver mine of Santa Bárbara in Peru,"
Am. J. Sci., (2), **45**, 5–9 (Jan., 1868); "Notes on the quicksilver mines of
Almadén, Spain," *ibid.*, (2), **45**, 9–13 (1868).

(62) SAGLIO, E. and E. POTTIER, "Dictionnaire des Antiquités Grecques et Romaines," Librairie Hachette et Cie., Paris, **1877**, Vol. 4, pp. 1457–64. Article on Stannum by Maurice Besnier.

(63) BAILEY, K. C., "The Elder Pliny's Chapters on Chemical Subjects," Edward Arnold and Co., London, **1929**, Part 1, p. 129.

(64) BINGHAM, HIRAM, "Machu Picchu, a Citadel of the Incas," Yale University Press, New Haven, Conn., **1930**, p. 197.

(65) LUCAS, A., "Ancient Egyptian Materials and Industries," Edward Arnold and Co., London, **1934**, 2nd ed., pp. 209–11, 214, 352.

(66) "The Complete Works of Homer," Modern Library, New York, no date, pp. 350–4. The "Iliad," Book 18.

(67) RAWLINSON, G. and M. KOMROFF, "The History of Herodotus," Tudor Publishing Co., New York, **1941**, p. 188; Book III of the Herodotus History.

(68) JENKIN, A. K. H., "The Cornish Miner," George Allen and Unwin, Ltd., London, **1927**, 351 pp.

(69) LODGE, H. C. and F. W. HALSEY, "The Best of the World's Classics," Funk and Wagnalls Co., New York and London, **1909**, Vol. 2, p. 65.

(70) HARRAR, N. J., "Sulfur from Popocatepetl," *J. Chem. Educ.*, **11**, 641 (Dec., 1934).

(71) MACNUTT, F. A., "Letters of Cortes," G. P. Putnam's Sons, New York and London, **1908**, Vol. 2, p. 204. Letter of Cortes to Charles V, Oct. 15, 1524.

(72) "The Complete Works of Homer," ref. (66), pp. 352–3. Book XXII of the "Odyssey."

(73) BAILEY, K. C., ref. (63), Vol. 2, pp. 97–9; Pliny, "Historia Naturalis," Book 35, paragraphs 174–7.

(74) TESTI, GINO, "La chimica dello zolfo in un poema del 1759," *La Chimica nell' Industria, nell' Agricoltura, e nella Biologia*, **6**, 182–5 (May 31, 1930).

(75) PINKERTON, JOHN, "A General Collection of the Best and Most Interesting Voyages and Travels in All Parts of the World," Longman, Hurst, Rees, and Orme, London, **1809**, Vol. 5, pp. 139–40. L. Spallanzani's "Travels in the two Sicilies."

(76) MACNUTT, F. A., ref. (71), Vol. 2, p. 205.

(77) WAINWRIGHT, G. A., "The coming of iron," *Antiquity*, **10**, 5–24 (March, 1936).

(78) NININGER, H. H., "Our Stone-pelted Planet," Houghton Mifflin Co., Boston and New York, **1933**, 237 pp.

(79) COGHLAN, H. H., "Prehistoric iron prior to the dispersion of the Hittite Empire," *Man*, **41**, 74–80 (July, Aug., 1941).

(80) CLINE, WALTER, "Mining and Metallurgy in Negro Africa," George Banta Publishing Co., Menasha, Wis., **1937**, pp. 17–23. Chapter on Negro ironworking in antiquity.

(81) CRONSTEDT, A. F., "Åminnelsetal öfver H. T. Scheffer," Lars Salvius, Stockholm, **1760**, pp. 15–31.

(82) MENSCHUTKIN, B. N., "Historical development of the conception of chemical elements," *J. Chem. Educ.*, **14**, 59–61 (Feb., 1937).

(83) URDANG, GEORGE, "The early chemical and pharmaceutical history of calomel," *Chymia*, **1**, 93–108 (1948).

(84) DAVIS, T. L., "Boyle's conception of element compared with that of Lavoisier," *Isis*, **48**, 82–91 (July, 1931); BOYLE ROBERT, "The Sceptical Chymist," 1st ed., London, **1661**, p. 350; LAVOISIER, A.-L., "Traité élémentaire de chimie," 1st ed., Paris, **1789**, p. 4.

(85) PARTINGTON, J. R., "The concepts of substance and chemical element," *Chymia*, **1**, 109–21 (1948).

(86) FALLOWS, "The Popular and Critical Bible Encyclopedia," Howard-Severance Co., Chicago, Ill., **1907**, Vol. 1, p. 309.

(87) Bhagvat, R. N., "Knowledge of the metals in ancient India," *J. Chem. Educ.*, 10, 659–66 (Nov., 1933); see also Rây, P. R., "Chemistry in ancient India," *ibid.*, 25, 327–35 (June, 1948).

(88) "A Biblia Sagrada, contendo o Velho e o Novo Testamento traduzida segundo os originaes hebraico e grego. Traducção Brazileira," Am. Bible Soc., New York.

(89) Glueck, Nelson, "Explorations in Eastern Palestine. II," *Annual Am. Schools of Oriental Research*, 15, 1–202 (1934–35).

(90) Pinkerton, ref. (75), Vol. 10, p. 199. C. Niebuhr's "Travels in Arabia."

(91) "La Santa Biblia . . . traducida de las lenguas originales y cotejada diligentemente con muchas y diversas traducciones," Am. Bible Soc., New York, 1246 pp.

(92) Napier, James, "Manufacturing Arts in Ancient Times with Special Reference to Bible History," Hamilton, Adams, and Co., London, 1874, 362 pp.

(93) Stephen, Sir Leslie, and Sir Sidney Lee, "Dictionary of national biography," Oxford University Press, 1921–22, Vol. 4, p. 59. Sketch of James Napier.

(94) "The Holy Bible translated from the Latin Vulgate (diligently compared with the Hebrew, Greek, and other editions, in various languages) . . . with annotations by the Rev. Dr. Challoner," D. and J. Sadlier and Co., New York and Montreal.

(95) Hastings, James, "Dictionary of the Bible," Charles Scribner's Sons, New York, 1929, pp. 619–20. Article on Mining and Metals by James Patrick.

(96) Schwarz, Joseph, "A Descriptive Geography of Palestine," A. Hart, Philadelphia, 1850, pp. 318–24.

(97) Singer, Isidore, "The Jewish Encyclopedia," Funk and Wagnalls Co., 1905, Vol. 4, pp. 260–1. Article on Copper by William Nowack.

(98) Hill, Sir George, "A history of Cyprus," University Press, Cambridge, England, 1940, Vol. 1, pp. 8–9, 82.

(99) Pinkerton, ref. (75), Vol. 10, pp. 586–7. R. Pococke's "Travels in the East."

(100) Leicester, Henry M., "The New Almaden Mine. The first chemical industry in California," *J. Chem. Educ.*, 20, 235–8 (May, 1943).

(101) "The Jewish Encyclopedia," ref. (97), Vol. 6, p. 585. Article on Ink by W. Nowack.

(102) Kopp, Hermann, ref. (31), Part 1, pp. 27–31.

(103) Boas, Marie, "An early version of Boyle's Sceptical Chymist," *Isis*, 45, 153–68 (July, 1954).

(104) Browne, C. A., "Alexander von Humboldt as historian of science in Latin America," *ibid.*, 35, 134–9 (Spring, 1944).

(105) Boas, Marie, "Boyle as a theoretical scientist," *ibid.*, 41, 261–8 (Dec., 1950).

(106) Bergsøe, Paul, "The metallurgy and technology of gold and platinum among the Pre-Columbian Indians," Danmarks Naturvidenskabelige Samfund, Copenhagen, 1937, 44 pp.

(107) Major, R. H. "Select Letters of Christopher Columbus," Hakluyt Soc., London, 1870, 2nd ed., pp. 5–7, 55, 57, 201–3.

(108) Aiton, A. S., and L. C. Karpinski, "Chronology of events of scientific importance in North and South America in the sixteenth century," *Archeion*, 22, 382–97 (1940).

(109) Arévalo, Celso, ref. (60), pp. 57–92.

(110) "Hakluytus Posthumus or Purchas his pilgrimes," James MacLehose and Sons, Glasgow, 1906, Vol. 15, pp. 148–53. Extracts from Oviedo's "Summarie and generall historie of the Indies."

(111) *Ibid.*, Vol. 17, p. 432.

(112) *Ibid.*, Vol. 17, p. 250.

(113) Paoli, U. G., "l'Età aurea della metallurgia ispanocoloniale," *Archivio di Storia della Scienza* 8, 200–2 (Jan.–Apr., 1927).

(*114*) BARBA, A. A., ref. (*46*), pp. 64–6.

(*115*) LOTHROP, S. K., "Gold ornaments of Chavin style from Chongoyape, Peru," *Am. Antiquity*, **6**, 250–62 (Jan., 1941).

(*116*) WALLACE, JAMES, "A Voyage to New Caledonia in Darien," Phil. Trans. and Collections to the end of the year 1700 abridged by John Lowthorp, London, **1705**, Vol. 3, pp. 561–4; Phil. Trans. No. 262, p. 536.

(*117*) LOTHROP, S. K., "Archaeological investigation in the province of Coclé, Panama," *Am. J. Archaeology*, (2), **38**, 207–11 (Apr.–June, 1934).

(*118*) KENT, ANDREW, "The early chemistry of gold," *Proc. Roy. Philos. Soc.* (*Glasgow*), **60**, 101–12 (1931–32).

(*119*) Works of R. W. EMERSON, Centenary Ed., Houghton, Mifflin Co., Boston and New York, Vol. II, p. 40; see also BROWNE, C. A., "Emerson and chemistry," *J. Chem. Educ.*, **5**, 269–79 (Mar., 1928); **5**, 391–403 (Apr., 1928).

(*120*) CORNEJO, ALFONSO, "Zur ältesten Geschichte des Goldrubinglases," *Kolloid-Z.*, **12**, 1–6 (Jan., 1913).

(*121*) KOPP, HERMANN, ref. (*31*), Part 4, pp. 216–20.

(*122*) LIBAVII, ANDREAE, "Praxis alchymiæ," Excudebat Joannes Saurius, impensis Petri Kopffii, Francofurti, **1604**, pp. 586–7.

(*123*) KUNCKEL, J., "Vollständiges Laboratorium chymicum," Rüdigersche Buchhandlung, Berlin, **1767**, 4th ed., pp. 596–601.

(*124*) HEINE, AXEL, "Johan Kunchel von Löwenstern," Nielsen and Lydiche (Axel Simmelkiær), Copenhagen, **1912**, 33 pp.

(*125*) JORISSEN, W. P., and J. POSTMA, "Johann Rudolph Glauber, Andreas Cassius en het Purper van Cassius," *Chem. Weekblad*, **24**, 30–3 (Jan. 15, 1927).

(*126*) LÖSNER, H., "Zur Geschichte des kolloiden Goldes," *Kolloid-Z.*, **6**, 1–3 (Jan., 1910).

(*127*) LEWIS, WILLIAM, "A Course of Practical Chemistry," J. Nourse, London, **1746**, pp. 19–22, 415–22.

(*128*) LÉMERY, N., "A Course of Chymistry," Walter Kettilby, London, **1686**, pp. 48–61.

(*129*) GEOFFROY, E.-F., "A Treatise of the Fossil, Vegetable and Animal Substances That Are Made Use of in Physik," W. Innys, R. Manby, *et al.*, London, **1736**, pp. 267–70, 281.

(*130*) WEBSTER, KIMBALL, "The Gold Seekers of '49," Standard Book Co., Manchester, N. H., **1917**, 240 pp.

(*131*) "Ore Deposits of the Western States," Am. Inst. Mining and Metallurgical Engineers, New York, **1933**, pp. 730–84.

(*132*) DOUGLAS, JAMES, "Gold-mines and milling of Gilpin County, Colorado, U. S.," *Quarterly J. Sci.*, N. S., **3**, 13–29 (Jan., 1873).

(*133*) CLAUDE, GEORGES, "Sur la présence de l'or dans l'eau de mer," *Compt. rend.*, **202**, 1885–7 (June 8, 1936).

(*134*) ANON., "Extraction of gold from sea water," *Nature*, **148**, 171 (Aug. 9, 1941).

(*135*) PARTINGTON, J. R., ref. (*29*), p. 46.

(*136*) I. Maccabees, **8**, 1–3.

(*137*) TOURNEFORT, J.-P. DE, "A Voyage into the Levant," D. Midwinter, R. Ware, C. Rivington, *et al.*, London, **1741**, Vol. 1, pp. 152–3.

(*138*) DARWIN, ERASMUS, "The Botanic Garden," J. Johnson, London, **1791**, 2nd ed., Part 1, pp. 70–2, 132–3, 206.

(*139*) DE LA CONDAMINE, "Ueber eine neue Art von metallischen Vegetationen," *Crell's Neues chem. Archiv*, **3**, 196–7 (1785); Mém. de l'acad. roy. des sciences (Paris), **1731**, p. 655.

(*140*) HOMBERG, W., "Abhandlung über die künstlichen Vegetationen," *Crell's Neues chem. Archiv*, **1**, 44–9 (1784); Mém. de l'acad. roy. des sciences (Paris), **1710**, p. 556.

(*141*)   LEWIS, WILLIAM, "The Chemical Works of Caspar Neumann, M.D.," Johnston, Keith, Linde *et al.*, London, **1759**, p. 47.

(*142*)   CULLEN, EDMUND, "Physical and Chemical Essays Translated from the Original Latin of Sir Torbern Bergman," J. Murray, Balfour, Gordon, and Dickson, London, **1784**, Vol. 1, p. 21; *ibid.*, Vol. 2, footnote to p. 438.

(*143*)   CLARKE, E. D., "Travels in Various Countries of Europe, Asia, and Africa," John W. Robbins, Hartford, Conn., **1817**, 5th American ed., part 1, section 1, p. 100.

(*144*)   BECKMANN, JOHANN, "A History of Inventions, Discoveries, and Origins," Henry G. Bohn, London, **1846**, 4th ed., Vol. 1, pp. 171–5.

(*145*)   HILL, JOHN, ref. (*53*), pp. 225, 227–35.

(*146*)   GUNTHER, R. T., ref. (*56*), pp. 629–30.

(*147*)   CALEY, E. R., "The Stockholm papyrus. An English translation with brief notes," *J. Chem. Educ.*, **4**, 979–1002 (Aug., 1927).

(*148*)   HUNT, ROBERT, "Ure's Dictionary of Arts, Manufactures, and Mines," Longmans, Green and Co., London, **1867**, 6th ed., Vol. 3. Article on verdigris.

(*149*)   LEWIS, WILLIAM, ref. (*141*), p. 63.

(*150*)   BELIUS, MATTHEW, "Historisch-physische Beschreibung der Kupfer- oder Cementwasser zu Neusohl, die das Eisen in Kupfer verwandeln," *Crell's Neues chem. Archiv*, **3**, 33–5 (1785); *Phil. Trans.* **40**, 351–61 (Oct., Nov., 1738).

(*151*)   SZATHMÁRY, LÁSZLÓ, "Magyar Alkémisták," Kiadja a K. M. Természettudományi Társulat, Budapest, **1928**, pp. 343–4.

(*152*)   GELLERT, C. E., ref. (*50*), p. 43.

(*153*)   BOND, JOHN, "A letter to Sir Peter Thompson, Knt. F. R. S. containing experiments on the copper springs in Wicklow in Ireland," *Phil. Trans.*, **48**, (1), 90–4 (1753).

(*154*)   MYRES, JOHN L., "Handbook of the Cesnola Collection of Antiquities from Cyprus," Metropolitan Museum of Art, New York, **1914**, p. 471.

(*155*)   "The Fahlun copper mine," *Mentor*, **17**, 62 (Apr., 1929).

(*156*)   BROWNE, C. A., "Historical observations during a recent chemical trip to Europe," *J. Chem. Educ.*, **17**, 54–5 (Feb., 1940); SWEDENBORG, E., "Treatise on copper." English translation by A. H. Searle.

(*157*)   JACKSON, B. D., "Linnæus," H. F. and G. Witherby, London, **1923**. Adapted from the Swedish of Theodor Magnus Fries.

(*158*)   DARMSTAEDTER, LUDWIG, "Handbuch zur Geschichte der Naturwissenschaften und der Technik," J. Springer, Berlin, **1908**, 2nd ed., p. 63.

(*159*)   "Henry Latrobe's description of the Schuyler copper mine in New Jersey," *Medical Repository*, **6**, 319–21 (Nov., Dec., 1802; Jan., 1803).

(*160*)   PINKERTON, JOHN, ref. (*75*), Vol. 13, pp. 498–9. Per Kalm's "Travels in North America."

(*161*)   THWAITES, R. G., "The Jesuit Relations and Allied Documents," Burrows Brothers, Cleveland, Ohio, **1899**, Vol. 38, p. 243; BRESSANI, FATHER F. G., "A Brief Account of Certain Missions of the Fathers of the Society of Jesus in New France," Heirs of Agostino Grisei, Macerata, **1653**.

(*162*)   THWAITES, ref. (*161*), Vol. 45, pp. 219–21. "Relation of What Occurred Most Remarkable in the Missions of the Fathers of the Society of Jesus in New France in the Years 1659–1660," Sebastien Cramoisy, Paris, **1661**.

(*163*)   THWAITES, ref. (*161*), Vol. 54, pp. 153–65.

(*164*)   JENKIN, A. K. H., ref. (*68*), p. 323.

(*165*)   "Failure of the expedition to Lake Superior," *Medical Repository*, **6**, 211–2 (Aug., Sept., Oct., 1802).

(*166*)   SCHOOLCRAFT, H. R., "Account of the native copper on the southern shore of Lake Superior, with historical citations . . .," *Am. J. Sci.*, (1), **3**, 201–16 (1821).

(*167*)   DOUGLAS, JAMES, "The native copper mines of Lake Superior," *Quarterly J. Sci.*, N. S., **4**, 162–80 (Apr., 1874).

(*168*) "Correspondence of Prof. Jérôme Nicklès, dated Nancy, France, Oct. 22, 1867," *Am. J. Sci.*, (2), **45**, 67–8 (Jan., 1868).

(*169*) KOPP, HERMANN, ref. (*31*), Part 4, p. 161.

(*170*) MALAGUTI, F.-J., DUROCHER, and SARZEAUD, "Sur la présence du plomb, du cuivre, et de l'argent dans l'eau de la mer et sur l'existence de ce dernier métal dans les plantes et les êtres organisés," *Ann. chim. phys.*, (3), **28**, 129–57 (Feb., 1850).

(*171*) FORCHHAMMER, GEORG, "On the composition of sea water in the different parts of the ocean," *Phil. Trans.*, **155**, 203–62 (1865).

(*172*) SHOHL, A. T., "Mineral Metabolism," Reinhold Publishing Corporation, New York, 1939, pp. 121–5, 234–53.

(*173*) SEVERY, H. W., "The occurrence of copper and zinc in certain marine animals," *J. Biol. Chem.*, **55**, 79–92 (1923).

(*174*) FREDERICQ, L., *Bull. Acad. roy. Belgique*, (2), **46**, No. 11 (1878).

(*175*) HART, E. B., H. STEENBOCK, J. WADDELL, and C. A. ELVEHJEM, "Iron in nutrition. VII. Copper as a supplement to iron for hemoglobin building in the rat," *J. Biol. Chem.*, **77**, 797–812 (1928).

(*176*) "Report of Mr. Brande's lectures on mineralogical chemistry . . . in . . . 1817," *Quarterly J. Sci.*, **5**, 292–4 (1818).

(*177*) KOBELL, FRANZ VON, "Geschichte der Mineralogie von 1650 bis 1860," J. G. Cotta, Munich, 1864, pp. 636–49.

(*178*) HILL, JOHN, ref. (*53*), pp. 133–4, 163–5, 217–9.

(*179*) KOPP, HERMANN, ref. (*31*), Part 4, pp. 137–40.

(*180*) DARMSTAEDTER, LUDWIG, ref. (*158*), p. 7.

(*181*) TEMPLE, SIR R. C., "The Travels of Peter Mundy in Europe and Asia, 1608–1667," Hakluyt Soc., London, 1925, series 2, Vol. 55, p. 57. Volume 4 of Mundy's Travels.

(*182*) HATCHETT, CHARLES, "An analysis of the magnetical pyrites . . .," *Nicholson's J.*, (2), **10**, 273 (Apr., 1805).

(*183*) CLARKE, E. D., ref. (*143*), Vol. 10, pp. 527–50.

(*184*) LOCKE, JOHN, "Some account of the copperas mines and manufactory in Strafford, Vermont," *Am. J. Sci.*, (1), **3**, 326–30 (1821).

(*185*) BOERHAAVE, HERMAN, "A New Method of Chemistry," T. Longman, London, 1741, 2nd ed., Vol. 1, p. 95.

(*186*) BROWNE, C. A., "Chemistry in old Boston," *J. Chem. Educ.*, **11**, 391–3 (July, 1934).

(*187*) PINKERTON, JOHN, ref. (*75*), Vol. 13, pp. 473, 498, 516–7, 630–1. Per Kalm's "Travels in North America."

(*188*) WIRTH, F. P., "The Discovery and Exploitation of the Minnesota Iron Lands," The Torch Press, Cedar Rapids, Iowa, 1937, pp. 1–27.

(*189*) SPENCE, HARTZELL, "The professor's crazy billion-dollar dream," *Reader's Digest*, **33**, 20–4 (Sept., 1954); Murphy, W. J., "The impossible takes longer," *Chem. Eng. News*, **32**, 4053 (Oct. 11, 1954).

(*190*) "Oeuvres de Fontenelle," Salmon, Libraire-Editeur, Paris, 1825, Vol. 2, pp. 281–9. Eulogy of E.-F. Geoffroy.

(*191*) BUGGE, G., ref. (*35*), Vol. 1, pp. 221–7. Chapter on Geoffroy the Elder by Max Speter.

(*192*) GEOFFROY, E.-F., ref. (*129*), pp. iii–xii.

(*193*) "Neue Aufklärung über die vorgegebene künstliche Entstehung des Eisens, die zuerst von Bechern vorgebracht und von Hrn. Geofroy [sic] vertheidigt wurde, von Hrn. Lémery dem Jüngern," *Crell's Neues chem. Archiv*, **1**, 17–22 (1784); *Abh. k. Akad. Wiss. (Paris)*, 1708, p. 482.

(*194*) "Eloge de M. Louis Lémery," *Mém. Acad. Sci. (Paris)*, 1743, pp. 195–208.

(*195*) THATCHER, ROSCOE W., "The Chemistry of Plant Life," McGraw-Hill Book Co., New York, 1921, p. 11.

(*196*) LEWIS, WILLIAM, ref. (*127*), p. 235.

(197) BOERHAAVE, H., "Elémens de chymie," Chardon, fils, Paris, **1754**, Vol. 5, p. 64.

(198) MACQUER, P.-J., "Chymisches Wörterbuch," Weidmann, Leipzig, **1788**, 2nd German ed. from the 2nd French, Vol. 1, pp. 528–39. Article on Blut.

(199) BETTI, MARIO, "Nel secondo centenario della istituzione della prima cattedra di chimica in Italia (1737–1937)," *Soc. Ital. per il Progresso delle Scienze, Atti della XXVII Riunione*, **6**, 501–10 (Sept., 1939).

(200) THOMSON, THOMAS, "History of the Royal Society," Robert Baldwin, London, **1812**, pp. 123–7.

(201) GUNTHER, R. T., "Early science in Oxford," University Press, Oxford, **1932**, Vol. 9, pp. 153–71. Lower's De Corde, London, **1669**.

(202) PRIESTLEY, J., "Experiments and Observations on Different Kinds of Air," Thomas Pearson, Birmingham, **1790**, Vol. 3, pp. 348–75.

(203) HEWSON, WILLIAM, "Experiments on the blood, with some remarks on its morbid appearances," *Phil. Trans.*, **60**, 368–83 (1770).

(204) HEWSON, WILLIAM, "On the figure and composition of the red particles of the blood, commonly called the red globules," *ibid.*, **63**, (2), 303–23 (1773).

(205) FOURCROY, A.-F. DE, "Système des connaissances chimiques," Baudouin, Paris, **1800** (Brumaire, an IX), Vol. 9, pp. 150–6.

(206) SCHULTZE, M. O., "Metallic elements and blood formation," *Physiol. Rev.*, **20**, 37–67 (Jan., 1940).

(207) HILL, JOHN, ref. (53), 2nd ed., pp. 78, 223–5.

(208) GUNTHER, R. T., ref. (56), pp. 635–7.

(209) DARMSTAEDTER, LUDWIG, ref. (158), p. 30.

(210) TOURNEFORT, J.-P. DE, ref. (137), Vol. 1, pp. 186–7.

(211) Review of H. R. Schoolcraft's "A view of the lead mines of Missouri," *Am. J. Sci.*, (1), **3**, 59–72 (1821).

(212) WITTER, WILHELM, "Woher kam das Zinn in der frühen Bronzezeit?" *Mannus*, **28**, 446–56 (1936); *Neues Jahrb. für Mineralogie, Geologie, und Paläontologie*, Referate II, 733–5 (1939).

(213) PAULY, AUGUST, "Real-Encyclopädie der classischen Altertumswissenschaft," J. B. Metzlerscher Verlag, Stuttgart, **1899**, revised ed., Vol. 3, columns 892–7. Article on Bronze.

(214) GOWLAND, WILLIAM, "Copper and its alloys in early times," *J. Inst. Metals*, **7**, 23–42 (1912).

(215) PINKERTON, ref. (75), Vol. 2, p. 730. Robert Heath's "Natural and historical account of the islands of Scilly."

(216) STEPHEN, SIR LESLIE, and SIR SIDNEY LEE, ref. (93), Vol. 9, pp. 349–50.

(217) LÉMERY, N., "Cours de chymie," Theodore Haak, Leyden, **1716**, 11th ed., pp. 120–1.

(218) BARBA, A. A., ref. (46), pp. 79–80.

(219) MARGGRAF, A. S., "Chymische Schriften," Arnold Wever, Berlin, **1768**, revised ed., part 2, pp. 87–106.

(220) BAYEN, PIERRE, "Opuscules chimiques," A.-J. Dugour and Durand, Paris, an VI, Vol. 2, pp. 213–460.

(221) DARMSTAEDTER, LUDWIG, ref. (158), p. 18.

(222) PARKES, SAMUEL, "A descriptive account of the several processes which are usually pursued in the manufacture of the article known in commerce by the name of tin-plate," *Annals of Philos.*, **15**, 205–7 (Mar., 1820).

(223) DWIGHT, TIMOTHY, "Travels in New England and New York," Timothy Dwight, New Haven, Conn., **1821**, Vol. 2, p. 55.

(224) NORTH, F. J., "Tin through the ages," *Nature*, **148**, 413–4 (Oct. 4, 1941).

(225) WAITE, A. E., "The Hermetic and Alchemical Writings of . . . Paracelsus the Great," James Elliott and Co., London, **1894**, Vol. 1, pp. 136, 254–5, 314.

(226) "Zinc, cadmium, and mercury. A classic of science," *Sci. News Letter*, **19**, 76–7 (Jan. 31, 1931).

(227) DARWIN, ERASMUS, ref. (*138*), pp. 16–7, 68, 95.

(228) HILL, JOHN, ref. (*53*), pp. 227–35.

(229) GLASER, CHRISTOPHE, "Chymischer Wegweiser," Matthäus Birckner, Jena and Helmstädt, **1696**, pp. 264–5.

(230) LEFEVRE, NICOLAS, "Cours de chymie," J.-N. Leloup, Paris, **1751**, 5th ed., Vol. 5, pp. 319–20.

(231) JUSSIEU, A., "Beobachtungen, wie man in den Minen von Almadén in Spanien verfährt, um das Quecksilber zu gewinnen; und über die Krankheiten der Arbeiter in denselben," *Crell's Neues chem. Archiv*, **2**, 22–31 (1784); "Mém. de l'acad. roy. des sciences (Paris)," **1719**, p. 461.

(232) ACOSTA, FATHER JOSÉ DE, ref. (*45*), Vol. 1, pp. 185, 214–7. English translation of Edward Grimston, **1604**.

(233) BARBA, A. A., "The Art of Metals," S. Mearne, London, **1674**, pp. 140–1.

(234) HUMBOLDT, A. VON, "Ensayo político sobre Nueva España," Lecointe, Paris, **1836**, Vol. 3, pp. 204–17.

(235) DIERGART, PAUL, "Beiträge aus der Geschichte der Chemie dem Gedächtnis von G. W. A. Kahlbaum," Franz Deuticke, Leipzig and Vienna, **1909**, pp. 314–24. Chapter by J. R. Carracido, "Procédés découverts par les Espagnols pour l'exploitation des minérais argentifères."

(236) PAOLI, U. G., "Il metallurgista spagnolo Alvaro Alonso Barba da Villa Lepe, 1569–1662," *Archivio di Storia della Scienza*, **3**, 150–68 (1922).

(237) PAOLI, U. G., ref. (*113*), pp. 83–94, 200–2.

(238) PINKERTON, JOHN, ref. (*75*), Vol. 14, pp. 14–9. Capt. Betagh's "Observations on the country of Peru and its inhabitants, during his captivity."

(239) SMITH, SIR JAMES EDWARD, "A Selection of the Correspondence of Linnæus and Other Naturalists," Longman, Hurst, Rees, Orme, and Brown, London, **1821**, Vol. 2, pp. 506–9.

(240) THOMSON, THOMAS, "Calomel," *Annals of Philos.*, **16**, 309–10 (Oct., 1820).

(241) BERGMAN, T., "Schluss der Geschichte von der Vereinigung des Quecksilbers mit Salzsäure," *Crell's Neueste Entdeckungen*, **1**, 76–82 (1781); *K. Svenska Vet. Acad. Handl.*, **34**, 189.

(242) BEGUIN, JEAN, "Tyrocinium chymicum," Apud Baleonium, Venetiis, **1643**, revised ed., pp. 398–405.

(243) SMITH, F. PORTER, "Chinese chemical manufactures," *Am. Chemist*, **4**, 56–9 (Aug., 1873).

(244) RÂY, SIR P. C., ref. (*3*), Vol. 1, pp. 250–61.

(245) DIERGART, PAUL, ref. (*235*), pp. 120–6. Chapter by E. C. van Leersum, "Préparation du calomel chez les anciens Hindous."

(246) Poissonnier, "Versuche über frierende Quecksilber," *Crell's Neues chem. Archiv*, **8**, 176–7 (1791); Hist. Acad. Roy. des Sciences (Paris), **1760**, p. 49.

(247) FRIES, JAKOB, "Ueber das Gefrieren des Quecksilbers in freyer Luft," *Crell's Ann.*, **8**, 318–23 (1787).

(248) MACQUER, P.-J., ref. (*198*), Vol. 5, pp. 14–5.

(249) BAUMÉ, A., "Chymie expérimentale et raisonnée," P.-F. Didot le jeune, Paris, **1773**, Vol. 2, pp. 395–6.

(250) TOURNEFORT, J.-P. de, Ref. (*137*), Vol. 1, pp. 167–8.

(251) "Presentation of the Perkin Medal to Herman Frasch," *Met. Chem. Eng.*, **10**, 73–82 (Feb., 1912).

(252) "Herman Frasch, chemical engineer," *Chem. Eng. News*, **20**, 730 (June 10, 1942).

(253) PELLETIER, CHARLES, and SEDILLOT JEUNE, "Mémoires et observations de Bertrand Pelletier," Croullebois, Fuchs, etc., Paris, 1798, Vol. 1, pp. 146–58.

(254) DOBBIN, L., "The Collected Papers of C. W. Scheele," G. Bell and Sons, London, **1931**, pp. 202–7; Scheele, *K. Vet. Acad. Handl.*, **40**, 238–45 (1779).

(255) Macquer, P.-J., Ref. (*198*), Vol. 2, pp. 14–49.

(256) "Wörtliche Erzählung der Versuche, welche die Herren Darcet und Rouelle in der chemischen Werkstätte des letztern mit Diamanten und Edelsteinen angestellt haben," *Crell's Neueste Entdeckungen in der Chemie*, 8, 242–50 (1783); *Rozier's Observations sur la physique*, etc. 4, (1), 131–58 (1772).

(257) Baumé, A., Ref. (*249*), Vol. 1, pp. 106–16.

(258) Kobell, Franz von, Ref. (*177*), pp. 388–94.

(259) D'Arcet and Rouelle, "Neue Erfahrungen über die Zerstörbarkeit des Diamants in verschlossenen Gefässen," *Crell's Beyträge zu den Chem. Ann.*, 1, part 2, 114–26 (1786); *J. de Méd.*, 39, 50 (Jan.–June, 1772).

(260) Coleby, L. J. M., "The Chemical Studies of P.-J. Macquer," George Allen and Unwin, Ltd., London, 1938, pp. 74–8.

(261) O'Connor, A. Condorcet, and M.-F. Arago, "Oeuvres de Condorcet," Firmin Didot Frères, Paris, 1847, pp. 125–38. Eulogy of Macquer.

(262) Lavoisier, "Premier mémoire sur la destruction du diamant par le feu," *Mém. Acad. des Sci.*, 1772, Part II, p. 564; "Seconde Mémoire . . .," *ibid.*, 1772, Part II, p. 591; "Oeuvres de Lavoisier," Imprimerie Impériale, Paris, 1864, Vol. 2, p. 38.

(263) Brisson, M. J., "Physical principles of chemistry," J. Cuthell and Vernor and Hood, London, 1801, pp. 180–1.

(264) Guyton de Morveau, "Sur le passage du diamant à l'état de charbon ou d'oxide noir de carbone," *Ann. chim. phys.*, (1) 32 (1799). (30 Vendémiaire, an VIIIᵉ.)

(265) Kopp, H., "Geschichte der Chemie," Ref. (*31*), Part 3, pp. 288–92; Part 4, p. 79.

(266) Guyton de Morveau, "De la conversion du fer doux en acier fondu par le diamant," *Ann. chim. phys.*, (1), 31, 328–36 (1799). (30 Fructidor, an VIIᵉ.)

(267) Clark, Blake, "How the Bible is building Israel," *Reader's Digest*, 33, 26–30 (Mar., 1954).

(268) Perrot and Chipiez, "History of Art in Phœnicia and Its Dependencies," Chapman and Hall, London, 1885, Vol. 2, pp. 413–14.

(269) Murray, John, "A System of Chemistry," William Creech, Edinburgh, 1812, 3rd ed., Vol. 2, p. 401.

(270) Deyeux, N., "Observations sur la physique, sur l'histoire naturelle, et sur les arts," *J. de Physique*, 17, 241–2 (1781).

(271) Nordenskiöld, A. E., "C. W. Scheele. Nachgelassene Briefe und Aufzeichnungen," P. A. Norstedt and Sons, Stockholm, 1892, pp. 334–6.

(272) Vogel, H. A., "Sur l'existence du soufre dans la bile et dans le sang," *Ann. chim. phys.*, (1), 87, 215–7 (Aug. 31, 1813).

(273) "Encyclopédie méthodique. Chimie et métallurgie par MM. Fourcroy et Vauquelin," Mme. Veuve Agasse, Paris, 1815, Vol. 6, p. 173. Article on Soufre.

(274) Cunningham, W. A., "Sulfur," *J. Chem. Educ.*, 12, 17–23 (Jan., 1935); 12, 83–7 (Feb., 1935).

(275) Brownlee, W. H., "Discoveries in the Judean wilderness," *Land Reborn*, 5, 8–10 (Dec., 1954).

(276) Wertime, T. A., "The discovery of the element carbon," *Osiris*, 11, 211–20 (1954).

(277) Peattie, Donald and Louise, "California's mother Lode," *Reader's Digest*, 33, 77–81 (Nov., 1954).

(278) Adams, F. D., "The Birth and Development of the Geological Sciences," Dover Publications, Inc., New York, 1954, pp. 183–95.

(279) "The Bible Blueprint of the Holy Land," broadcast on "The Eternal Light" program Jan. 9, 1955 by the National Broadcasting Co.; see also E. Aschner, "Israel's chemical industry," *Chem. Eng. News*, **33**, 4316–23 (Oct. 10, 1955).

(280) PROVENZAL, GIULIO, "Profili Bio-Bibliografici di Chimici Italiani. Sec. XV-Sec. XIX," Istituto Nazionale Medico Farmacologico Serono, Rome, **1937**, pp. 55–62.

(281) *Ibid.*, pp. 153–60.

(282) MENSHUTKIN, B. N., "Russia's Lomonosov," Princeton University Press, Princeton, N. J., **1952**, pp. 67–9.

(283) FARBER, EDUARD, "The color of venous blood," *Isis*, **45**, 3–9 (May, 1954).

Courtesy H. S. van Klooster

Jan Ingenhousz, 1730–1799. Dutch physician and plant physiologist. Court physician to Maria Theresia in Vienna. He showed that only the green parts of plants purify the atmosphere and that they do so only in sunlight. See also ref. (56).

Hence sable Coal his massy couch extends;
And stars of gold the sparkling pyrite blends;
Hence dull-eyed Naphtha pours his pitchy streams,
And Jet uncolour'd drinks the solar beams . . . (54).

2

Carbon and some of its compounds

Since the complete story of carbon would be a history of organic chemistry, asphalt, carbonate rocks, alkaline carbonates, fuels, foods, plant and animal nutrition, photosynthesis, and respiration, the following brief sketch can merely suggest the magnitude of the subject.

*T*heophrastus of Eresus described mineral coal (probably lignite) in about 320 B.C. (*1*) M. E. Cunnington stated that coal was sometimes used as fuel in Great Britain during the Roman period (*2*). It has been mined in the Midland Area (Derbyshire and Notts) since 1257 (*53*), and by the beginning of the seventeenth century it had become one of England's important natural resources (*3*).

In the second decade of the eighteenth century, Dr. Rosinus Lentilius (Linsenbahrdt) (1657–1733) discussed the occurrences of coal. "The best description of coal," said he, "is given by Friedr. Hoffmann (in obs. phys. chem. libr. II. obs. 24). He says that these coals are a loose, porous earth intimately penetrated by a large amount of a subterranean resinous fluid. Their principal constituent is the resin, for when that has been lost, they no longer smoke and burn. . ." (*4*). He also described the destructive distillation of coal.

Per Kalm stated, in the account of his journey to North America in 1748–51, that "Coals have not yet been found in Pennsylvania, but people pretend to have seen them higher up in the country among the natives. Many people, however, agree that they are met with in great quantity more to the north, near Cape Breton" (*5*).

In 1791 a Pennsylvania hunter named Philip Ginther stumbled over an uprooted tree trunk on the summit of Sharp Mountain near the Lehigh Valley and saw in the loosened soil a black rock. Having heard of the presence of "stone coal" in this region, he gave the specimen to Colonel Jacob Weiss, who lived near the present site of Mauch Chunk. After mineralogists of Philadelphia had identified it as anthracite, Colonel Weiss in 1792 founded the Lehigh Coal Mine Company. Because of the cheap and abundant supply of wood and charcoal, the lack of transportation facilities, and the ignorance of the proper method of firing coal, however, there was little demand for it. Blacksmiths in Schuykill County used it successfully, and in 1817 Colonel George Shoemaker sent eight or ten wagonloads of it to Philadelphia. The Fairmount Nail Works, which received several tons of it, spent an entire morning in a vain attempt to fire a furnace with it. "They raked it, and they stirred it up, and poked it, and blew tremendously upon it with blowers." The men gave up hope and went to eat their dinner. "Returning at the usual time, their consternation may be imagined as they beheld the furnace-door red hot, and the fire within seething and roaring like a tempest. . . . Never before had such a fire been seen" (6).

In 1824 an anonymous contributor to the *Aesculapian Register* of Philadelphia wrote as follows: "Much as we are gratified with the vast advantages which we promise ourselves by the introduction of the Lehigh Coal into common use, we already perceive an evil arising from it, which it becomes necessary to counteract.— Unlike the fuel heretofore employed, its ashes afford no alkali that can render them useful in the formation of soap; nor as yet have they probably been sufficiently tested as a manure. Our streets have therefore become their deposit . . ." (7). He believed that until coal could be sold at from 20 to 25 cents a bushel, it would be unable to compete successfully with wood.

ASPHALT AND BITUMEN

The inhabitants of ancient Nineveh used an asphaltic mortar prepared from partially evaporated petroleum (8). In some translations of the Old Testament, this substance is called "pitch" or "slime." When Noah built the ark, he was told to "pitch it within and without with pitch." For building the Tower of Babel, Noah's descendants "had brick for stone, and slime had they for mortar" (9).

Herodotus (484–425 B.C.) mentioned the occurrence of many lumps of bitumen in the River Is, a small tributary of the Euphrates (10). The Babylonians heated this bitumen and used it instead of mortar for cementing together the bricks of their walls and buildings (11). Herodotus also spoke of a well near Susa (the Shushan of the Bible) which yielded bitumen, salt, and oil (11). Cornelius Tacitus, a friend of Pliny the Younger, described the bitumen of the Dead Sea (12). R. J. Forbes states in his book "Bitumen and Petroleum in Antiquity" that the ancients used tar and pitch for waterproofing pottery, for caulking ships, and for making torches, paint for roofs and walls, and lampblack for paints and ink (13).

"Asphalt, or Judaean bitumen, also called funeral gum, amber of Sodom, mountain pitch, or mummy balm, etc.," said A.-F. de Fourcroy, "is a black, heavy, solid, shining bitumen. It is found on the waters of the Asphalt Lake or Dead Sea in Judæa, near which were the ancient cities of Sodom and Gomorrah. The inhabitants, inconvenienced by the odor of this bitumen which collects on the waters, and encouraged by the profit which they gained from it, carefully gathered it" (17).

PETROLEUM

Petroleum has been exported from Persia since the seventh century A.D., and the Baku oil fields have been well known since the ninth and tenth centuries (14). When Marco Polo visited Armenia in the thirteenth century, he observed the thriving petroleum industry: "On the confines towards Georgia," said he, "there is a fountain from which oil springs in great abundance, insomuch that a hundred shiploads might be taken from it at one time. This oil is not good to use with food, but 'tis good to burn, and is also used to anoint camels that have the mange. People come from vast distances to fetch it, for in all the countries round about they have no other oil" (15).

One of the early writers on petroleum was Geoffroy the Elder. "There are few Countries," said he, "in which this oil is not to be found. In the Island of Samos, a kind of it is gathered, called by the Inhabitants by a Name which signifies *Oleum Terræ;* and it is in great Esteem among the Indians. In Italy, near Modena, this Oil is gathered from Springs and Wells; and indeed this whole Dutchy abounds with it, especially at a place called Frumetto. The Inhabitants dig Wells to the Depth of thirty or forty Feet, till the oily Spring is found, and there it is always mixed with Water. The Wells dug at the Foot of the Hill furnish a large Quantity of very red Oil; those near the Top, a white Oil, but in smaller Quantities. There is another Rock in the same Country, near the Apennine Hills, where there is a perpetual Spring of Water, on which this Oil swims of a yellow Colour, and in so great Quantities that twice a Week they gather six Pounds of it at a time. . . . Petroleum easily takes Fire, and it is the Custom in many Places to burn it in Lamps instead of common Oil . . ." (16). Geoffroy also mentioned the presence of petroleum near Beriers, Brittany, and near Clermont in Auvergne.

Father Joseph de la Roche, Récollet Daillon, a French Jesuit missionary, visited some oil springs near Lake Erie in 1627 (18). The Jesuit "Relation of 1656–57," which was edited by Paul le Jeune and published in Paris in 1658, states that "As one approaches nearer to the country of the Cats (Eries), one finds heavy and thick water, which ignites like brandy, and boils up in bubbles of flame when fire is applied to it. It is, moreover, so oily that all our Savages use it to anoint and grease their heads and their bodies" (19). This was probably the oil spring at Cuba, Allegany County, New York.

In 1807–09 Fortescue Cumings made a tour of what was then called "the western country." Near Little Beaver on the Ohio River and on Oil Creek, a branch of the Allegheny River, he saw an oily substance bubbling up from the surface of the water. Zadok Cramer, a Pittsburgh printer who annotated Cumings's report, said that to collect the oil, "The place where it is found bubbling up in the creek is surrounded by a wall or dam to a narrow compass, a man takes a blanket, flannel, or other woollen cloth, to which the oil adheres, and spreading it over the surface of the enclosed pond, presses it down a little, then draws it up, and running the cloth through his hands, squeezes out the oil into a vessel prepared for the purpose; thus twenty or thirty gallons of pure oil can be obtained in two or three days by one man" (20).

In the *American Journal of Science* for 1833 Benjamin Silliman the Elder described an oil spring in Allegany County, New York. "The Oil Spring, or fountain," said he, "rises in the midst of a marshy ground. . . . They collect the petroleum by skimming it like cream from a milkpan. . . . It has then a very foul appearance like very dirty tar or molasses; but it is purified by heating it, and straining it while hot through flannel or other woolen stuff. It is used by the people of the vicinity for sprains and rheumatism and for sores upon their horses. It is not monopolized by anyone, but is carried away freely by all who care to collect it. . . . The history of this spring is not distinctly known. The Indians were well acquainted with it, and a square mile around it is still reserved for the Senecas . . ." (8). Silliman mentioned that petroleum was often sold in the eastern states under the name Seneca Oil. He distilled off the naphtha from some of it and used the distillate to preserve his specimens of sodium and potassium.

Pioneers on the Santa Fe trail used petroleum from some of the pools and streams in Miami County, Kansas, to grease the wheels of their wagons (21). After surveying part of the new townsite of Lawrence, A. D. Searl went to Miami County in 1855 and found oil seeping from the ground near the present site of Paola. The first mention of petroleum in a Kansas newspaper was the following item in the Lawrence *Herald of Freedom* for July 25, 1855: "We learn from R. S. Stevens, Esq. that a valuable petroleum or rock oil has been discovered some eight miles northeast of Paola. He states that it can be collected in the amount of several gallons daily. He had a bottle with him" (21).

More than thirty years before the drilling of the first petroleum well in Ohio, borings for salt sometimes yielded more petroleum than salt (8). Since there was little demand for the oil, this always led to disappointment. The first petroleum well in the United States was drilled by Edwin L. Drake at Titusville, Pennsylvania, in 1859 (*22*). J. T. Henry described this event in his "Early and Later History of Petroleum" as follows:

"Saturday afternoon, August 28th, 1859, as Mr. Smith and his boys were about to quit for the day, the drill dropped into one of those crevices, common alike in oil and salt borings, a distance of about six inches, making the total depth of the whole well 69$^1/_2$ feet. They withdrew the tools, and all went home till Monday morning. On Sunday afternoon, however, "Uncle Billy [Smith] went down to the well to reconnoiter, and peering in could see a fluid within eight or ten feet of the surface. He plugged one end of a bit of a tin rain-water spout, and let it down with a string. He drew it up *filled* with *Petroleum*. That night the news reached the village, and Drake, when he came down the next morning, bright and early, found the old man and his boys proudly guarding the spot, with several barrels of Petroleum standing about . . ." (*8*).

At the very beginning of the twentieth century, when Captain Anthony F. Lucas was drilling for oil near Beaumont, Texas, gas whistled out, and twisted sections of pipe together with sand and rock were forced out by a gigantic geyser of oil. This enormous "Spindletop" gusher opened the great oil era in Texas and the Southwest. The magazine *Life* commissioned the artist Alexandre Hogue to paint this dramatic scene and used the colorful painting as a cover design (*50*).

NATURAL GAS

In 400 B.C., Ktesias of Knidos mentioned the occurrence of natural gas in Karamania, Asia Minor. It provided "perpetual flame" for the fire-worshippers and fuel for their homes (*23*).

The "Records of the Kingdoms South of Mt. Hua (Hua yang kuo chih)," a work on the local history and geography of Szechwan and adjacent regions of China compiled in about 347 A.D., mentions "fire wells" (huo ching) which date from the Han dynasty (206 B.C.–24 A.D.) and states that the natural gas from them was used for the boiling of salt brines and for other purposes (*55*).

In 1783 George Washington made some experiments at Rocky Hill, New Jersey, to test and explain the popular belief that the creek that runs near the bottom of this hill could be "set on fire." Thomas Paine wrote in his report of these experiments: "When the mud at the bottom was disturbed by the poles, the air bubbles rose fast, and I saw the fire take from Gen. Washington's light, and descend from thence to the surface of the water, in a similar manner as when a lighted candle is held so as to touch the smoke of a candle just blown out, the smoke will take fire and the fire will descend and light up the candle. This was demonstrative evidence that what was called setting the river on fire, was setting the inflammable air on fire that arose out of the mud . . ." (*51*). Thomas Paine referred to this flammable natural gas as "carburetted hydrogen."

Some of the houses at Fredonia, New York, were lighted with natural gas as early as 1821 (*18*). Mrs. Almira Hart Lincoln Phelps mentioned in her "Familiar Lectures on Chemistry" that a rivulet running through

Almira Hart Lincoln Phelps, 1793–1884. Principal of the Patapsco Institute at Ellicott's Mills, Maryland. Author of "Familiar Lectures on Chemistry" and "Chemistry for Beginners" and translator of a French dictionary of chemistry. She was the second woman to be elected to the American Association for the Advancement of Science. See ref. (*57*).

the village of Fredonia and another brook near Portland Harbor, both in Chautauqua County, New York, contained "light carburetted hydrogen gas" (methane), bubbles of which kept rising to the surface. The houses at Fredonia and the lighthouse at Portland Harbor were lighted with this natural gas (*24, 57*).

The *American Journal of Science* for 1840 described an amazing phenomenon caused by this kind of gas. At West Town, Chester County, Pennsylvania, the students of the boarding school used to bathe in a mill-pond supplied by Chester Creek. Rising from the creek were countless bubbles of gas from decaying leaves and wood (*25*). "I first visited the place in the year 1834," said Moses Lockwood. "Taking as apparatus a bell-glass furnished with a stop-cock and a taper, and as companion an assistant teacher . . ., we proceeded to the pond, readily filled the receiver, and fired the gas issuing from the stop-cock. We next proposed to burn the bubbles as they arose from the water. On stirring the leaves, the gas ascended in large quantities, affording an admirably successful experiment. No sooner was the lighted taper brought near the surface of the water, than we found ourselves enveloped in flames. . . . We however escaped with but a slight scorching" (25). The article concludes with a sprightly account of how "Master Moses set the river afire" in the presence of the schoolboys.

COAL GAS AND GAS LIGHTING

In 1618 Jean Tardin, a French physician, described a "fire well" near some bituminous coal beds at Grenoble. By heating some of this coal in a closed vessel, he prepared an artificial gas (26, 27).

In the *Philosophical Transactions* for 1667 one finds a description by Thomas Shirley of "A Well and Earth in Lancashire taking Fire by a Candle approached to it." Shirley had visited this gas spring at Wigan, near Warrington, in 1659 and had observed that it gave a flame about eighteen inches high (28). He concluded that the gas must consist of "bituminous or sulphurous fumes" from coal.

In 1688 the Reverend John Clayton, rector of Crofton, at Wakefield, Yorkshire, wrote a letter to the Royal Society describing his recent voyage to the American colony of Virginia (28, 29). He compared the thunder storms of Virginia "with some sulphureous Spirits which I have drawn from Coals, that I could no way condense, yet were inflammable, nay *would burn* after they had passed through Water, and that seemingly fiercer, if they were not overpowered therewith. I have kept of this Spirit a considerable time in bladders, and tho' it appeared as if they were only blown with the Air, yet if I let it forth and *fired it* with a Match or Candle, it would continue burning til all was spent" (28).

Clayton's biographer, Walter T. Layton, believes that the experiments referred to in this letter were made at Wigan, Lancashire, some time before Clayton went to Virginia in 1686. An account of them was published half a century later in the *Philosophical Transactions* for 1739–40 (30). Clayton not only examined the Wigan gas, as Shirley had done, but also obtained coal from the pits nearby and distilled it from a retort. "At first there came over only Phlegm, afterwards a black Oil, and then likewise a Spirit arose, which I could noways condense . . ." (30). Finding that this "spirit" was flammable, he collected and preserved it in bladders. After pricking holes in the bladders, he lighted the escaping gas (26, 31).

Stephen Hales, George Dixon, and Bishop Watson afterward made similar experiments. Professor Minckelers of the University of Louvain distilled gas from powdered coal and lighted his lecture room with it in 1784–85 (26). In 1792 William Murdock lighted his house at Redruth, Cornwall, with gas made by the destructive distillation of coal (28).

J. J. Berzelius drew in his diary a sketch of one of the gas fixtures that he saw on his visit to England in 1818 (52). "It lights up," he said, "far beyond anything I have ever seen with wax light or lamps and has over lamps the invaluable advantage that the light is not so sharp . . ." (52). The diary is also illustrated with diagrams of Fredrick Accum's gas works for illuminating the Royal Mint in London with his "thermolamp" (47).

In January, 1821, Thomas Jarman of Bristol, England, who had recently seen gas lights demonstrated at Yale College, wrote as follows to Benjamin Silliman: ". . . The streets of the city of Bristol . . . were lighted with lamp oil till about two years ago, when a few persons united in forming a company for supplying the city with gas from pit-coal: I was one of that company. . . I have a house in the city . . . in which I use six rooms and an entrance hall . . . and I burn the gas till ten o'clock at night, for £25 a year: this is nearly about what it cost me for candles before; but I have an unvarying and brilliant light in every room, without any trouble but the turning of a key. All the officers and shops (or stores) in Bristol, of any respectability, purchase the light in the same way. . . It is intended, however, to sell the gas by measure; as some abuses have crept in by individuals burning the gas longer than they contract for: a Gas-Meter has been invented. . . I forgot to mention to you that the charcoal and tar produced from the coal at the works are profitable to us . . ." (32).

An anonymous contributor to the *Aesculapian Register* of Philadelphia wrote in 1824: "So far back as Nov. 1818, the following notice respecting gas lights appeared in the *American Daily Advertiser:* 'It appears, from a work recently published in London, that between *nineteen* and *twenty* thousand lamps, lighted with carbonated [sic] hydrogen gas, have been already placed in many of the principal streets of the city. . . The distance to which the subterranean tubes that convey the gas has already extended falls little short of *sixty-five* English miles'" (33). This contributor suggested that Philadelphia's streets ought to be lighted in the same manner, and in 1835 that city finally adopted this improved form of lighting (26).

Further information concerning the history of gas lighting may be found in Dr. C. A. Browne's articles on Fredrick Accum in volume 2 of the *Journal of Chemical Education* (47).

FIRE DAMP AND CHOKE DAMP

Although "fire damp," which is mainly methane, and "choke damp" (carbon dioxide) are frequent causes of mine accidents, Dr. William Brownrigg learned how to make good use of them. In 1741 he communicated to the Royal Society several papers on the gases of coal mines, but preferred to withhold them from publication until he could prepare a comprehensive treatise on the subject His laboratory at Whitchaven was provided with several gas furnaces of his own design and a constant supply of fire damp from the nearby mines. Because of his skill in foretelling explosions by the rapid fall of the barometer, mine operators often consulted him.

He also showed that many mineral waters contain considerable quantities of "air" identical with choke damp. Even at this early date he recognized the acidic nature of carbon dioxide and showed that some of the earths which had been precipitated from the water could be redissolved by the choke damp. He showed that, although "the air from fermenting liquors . . . is . . . a deadly poison when applied to the lungs . . . exactly in the manner of the choak-damp, . . . yet nevertheless this air, when taken inwardly in a convenient quantity of a liquid vehicle, is found to have wonderfully exciting and reviving qualities . . ." (34). For his experiments on choke damp and carbon dioxide Dr. Brownrigg was awarded the Copley Medal.

CARBON IN PLANT AND ANIMAL NUTRITION

Leonardo da Vinci (1452–1519) knew that plants seek air and light and that they can utilize even vitiated air (35, 36). One of the most brilliant discoveries of the eighteenth century was the explanation of the wonderful role of carbon and oxygen in vegetation. The Swiss entomologist Charles Bonnet (1720–1793) observed gas bubbles rising from the leaves of a grapevine immersed in water in the sunshine. Since dead leaves immersed in water containing air also collect bubbles on their surface, he did not understand the nature of this gas nor recognize that it resulted from a life process within the leaves themselves (37, 38, 39).

As early as 1771 Joseph Priestley noticed that this process purified the air, and in 1778 he identified the gas as "dephologisticated air" (oxygen) (40). "I have been so happy," said he, "as by accident to have hit upon a method of restoring air which has been injured by the burning of candles, and to have discovered at least one of the restoratives which nature employs for this purpose. It is *vegetation*. . . . Finding that candles would burn very well in air in which plants had grown a long time, and having had some reason to think that there was something attending vegetation which restored air that had been injured by respiration, I thought it was possible that the same process might also restore the air that had been injured by the burning of candles. Accordingly, on the 17th of August 1771, I put a sprig of mint into a quantity of air in which a wax candle had burned out, and found that, on the 27th of the same month, another candle burned perfectly well in it. . . . This remarkable effect does not depend on anything peculiar to *mint*, which was the plant that I always made use of till July 1772; for on the 16th of that month I found a quantity of this kind of air to be perfectly restored by sprigs of *balm*, which had grown in it from the 7th of the same month" (*40*).

Priestley took some "air made thoroughly noxious by mice breathing and dying in it, and divided it into two parts; one of which," said he, "I put into a phial immersed in water; and to the other (which was contained in a glass jar standing in water) I put a sprig of mint. This was about the beginning of August, 1771, and after eight or nine days, I found that a mouse lived perfectly well in that part of the air in which the sprig of mint had grown, but died the moment it was put into the other part of the same original quantity of air; and which I had kept in the very same exposure, but without any plant growing in it" (*40*).

Priestley soon became interested in the little bubbles which he saw rising from the stalks and roots of plants growing in water. "Few persons, I believe," said he, "have met with so much unexpected good success as myself in the course of my philosophical pursuits. . . . But none of these unexpected discoveries appear to me to have been so extraordinary as that which I am about to relate. . . . In the course of my experiments on the growth of plants in water impregnated with fixed air [carbon dioxide], I observed that bubbles of air seemed to issue spontaneously from the stalks and roots of several of those which grew in the unimpregnated water; and I imagined that this air had percolated through the plant. It immediately occurred to me that if this was the case, the state of that air might possibly help to determine what I was at that time investigating, viz. whether the growth of plants contributes to purify, or to contaminate the air . . . (*40*).

Although Priestley believed that green plants always free the atmosphere from "fixed air" [carbon dioxide], C. W. Scheele thought that they always increase the amount of "fixed air" in the atmosphere. In a letter which he wrote to J. G. Gahn in May, 1772, but forgot to mail Scheele wrote: "In the assertion that Vegetabilia are able to improve again air which is unsuitable for respiration, the English experimenter has certainly gone astray, and the vessels in which these plant experiments were carried out not made tight, for plants would scarcely grow in such air, and insects die as soon as they again reach it, and, in fact, sooner than before" (*41*). From these results it seems probable that Priestley's plants must have been better illuminated than those of Scheele.

When Benjamin Franklin saw some of Priestley's plants flourishing in "highly noxious air," he expressed great satisfaction: "The strong thriving state of your mint in putrid air seems to shew that the air is mended by taking something from it, and not by adding to it. . . . I hope this will give some check to the rage of destroying trees that grow near houses, which has accompanied our late improvements in gardening, from an opinion of their being unwholesome. I am certain, from long observation, that there is nothing unhealthy in the air of woods; for we Americans have every where our country habitations in the midst of woods, and no people on earth enjoy better health, or are more prolific" (*40*).

In presenting the gold medal of the Royal Society to Priestley in 1773, Sir John Pringle said that "these experiments show us plainly that no plant grows in vain, but that every one of them, from the oak in the forest to the grass in the field, is useful to mankind. Even those which seem to have no special use help to keep the atmosphere sufficiently pure for animal life" (*37*). With this inspiring thought in mind, Jan Ingenhousz (1730–1799) began to investigate the gas evolved by plants. In his first paper on the subject, entitled "Experiments upon vegetables, discovering their great power of purifying the common air in the sunshine and of injuring it in the shade and at night," which was published in London in 1779, he proved that green plants exposed to daylight are able to purify the atmosphere from the products of animal respiration. He also showed that both Priestley and Scheele were partly right and partly in error, that the green parts of plants give off oxygen only in the daylight, and that the parts which are not green (such as roots, flowers, and fruits) give off carbon dioxide in darkness. Ingenhousz thus made a clear distinction between respiration and assimilation in plants and showed that plants obtain their carbon not from the soil but from the atmosphere.

When J.-H. Hassenfratz maintained that the plant obtains its carbon from the soil through its roots, Ingenhousz replied that if that were true a large tree could scarcely be expected to find its food in the same spot for hundreds of years (*38*).

Jan Ingenhousz was born at Breda in the Netherlands on December 8, 1730. In the Universities of Löwen, Leyden, Paris, and Edinburgh he received an unusually fine education. When at the age of sixteen years he sought permission to attend medical lectures at Löwen, the Rector expressed doubt as to whether so young a boy could be well enough prepared, especially in Greek and Latin. Seeing a Greek version of the Old Testament lying on a table, Jan asked the Rector to select a passage for him to translate into Latin. To the Rector's astonishment, the boy translated it rapidly and correctly (37).

Ingenhousz spent much of his life in England and Austria. In 1788 he went to France, arrived in Paris on July 14th of that year, and witnessed the fall of the Bastille. Shocked by the terrible disorder, he left Paris the following day, determined to leave the European turmoil and work peacefully in America with his friend Benjamin Franklin. He first returned to the Netherlands, however, because of the death of his brother. Two years later, while in England awaiting passage to America, he received news that made him give up forever all thought of emigrating: Benjamin Franklin had died, and America without Franklin had no more charm for Jan Ingenhousz (37).

Dr. Thomas Young said that Dr. Ingenhousz "was in the habit of collecting the gas from cabbage leaves and of keeping it bottled up in his pocket; and he was prepared with some coils of iron wire fastened into the corks, in order to exhibit the brilliant phenomenon to his friends" (43). In developing these new views of plant nutrition, Ingenhousz was guided in his later years by Lavoisier's great discoveries on the nature of combustion (44).

In 1782–83 Jean Senebier of Geneva, Switzerland, verified many of Ingenhousz's results (39, 45, 46). When he placed plants in the sunshine in water of high carbon dioxide content, they gave off more oxygen than did plants grown in water low in carbon dioxide (35). He recognized also that this abundant production of oxygen by the green parts of the plant was activated not by heat but by light (35, 48).

To stimulate interest in the experimental determination of the different sources of carbon in vegetables, the National Institute of France in 1804 and 1805 offered a generous prize (49).

Théodore de Saussure showed that when a seed begins to germinate it loses carbon as carbon dioxide. Jean-Baptiste Boussingault (1802–1887) then studied a later stage of germination of wheat and clover (trifolium pratense), and found that the process became more complex. As the green parts of the plants developed, a new chemical reaction occurred (42, 45). "The action of the green matter," said Boussingault, "begins to be manifested long before the first phases of germination have entirely ceased; so that during a certain time two opposite forces are at work simultaneously. One of these, as we have seen, tends to discharge carbon from the seed; the other tends to accumulate this element within it. So long as the first of these forces predominates, the seed loses carbon; but with the appearance of the green matter the young plant recovers a portion of this principle; finally, when by the progress of the vegetation the second force surpasses the first in energy, the plant grows, increases, and advances to maturity. . . . The presence of light is indispensable to the manifestation of the chemical force by which the green parts of plants appropriate the gaseous elements of the atmosphere. Germination, on the contrary, may take place in absolute darkness" (45).

Plants are thus able to synthesize innumerable carbonaceous products such as cellulose, starch, sugars, lignin, dextrin, and gums (42). "Plants and animals," said J.-B. Dumas, "come from the air and return to it" (42).

LITERATURE CITED

(1) DARMSTAEDTER, LUDWIG, "Handbuch zur Geschichte der Naturwissenschaften und der Technik," J. Springer, Berlin, 1908, 2nd ed., p. 18.

(2) CUNNINGTON, M. E., "Mineral coal in Roman Britain," *Antiquity,* 7, 89–90 (Mar., 1933); *Gent. Mag.,* 1866 (1), 335; *ibid.,* 1857 (1), 625; *ibid.,* 1843 (1), 303.

(3) MERTON, R. K., "Science in seventeenth-century England," *Osiris,* 4, 360–632 (1938).

(4) LENTILIUS, ROSIN, "Von den Steinkohlen, *"Crell's Neues chem. Archiv,* 1, 301–6 (1784); *Abh. Römisch-Kayserlichen Akad. der Naturforscher,* 1, 235 (1721–25).

(5) PINKERTON, JOHN, "A General Collection of the Best and Most Interesting Voyages and Travels," Longman, Hurst, Rees, and Orme, London, 1812, Vol. 13, p. 405. Per Kalm's "Travels in North America."

(6) ANON., "Coal and the coal mines of Pennsylvania," *Harper's Mag.,* 15, 451–69 (Sept., 1857).

(7) "Lehigh coal," *Aesculapian Register (Philadelphia),* 1, 5 (June 17, 1824).

(8) HENRY, J. T., "The Early and Later History of Petroleum," James B. Rodger, Philadelphia, 1873, pp. 9–12, 20–6, 91, 323–30.

(9) Genesis 6: 14; 11: 3.

(10) DARMSTAEDTER, LUDWIG, Ref. (1), p. 11.

(11) RAWLINSON, G. and M. KOMROFF, "The History of Herodotus," Tudor Publishing Co., New York, 1941, p. 67 (Book I of Herodotus); *ibid.,* p. 262 (Book IV); *ibid.,* p. 346 (Book VI).

(12) FYFE, W. H., "Tacitus. The Histories," Clarendon Press, Oxford, 1912, Vol. 2, pp. 109–10; Tacitus, History, Book 5, Chapter 6.

(13) FORBES, R. J., "Bitumen and Petroleum in Antiquity," E. J. Brill, Leyden, 1936, 105 pp.

(14) LIPPMANN, E. O. VON, "Petroleum im frühen Mittelalter," *Archivio di Storia della Scienza,* 8, 40–1 (Jan.–Apr., 1927).

(15) PARKS, G. B., "The Book of Ser Marco Polo, the Venetian," Book League of America, New York, 1930, p. 25.

(16) GEOFFROY, E.-F., "A Treatise of the Fossil, Vegetable, and Animal Substances That Are Made Use of in Physick," W. Innys, R. Manby, *et al.,* London, 1736, pp, 133–5.

(17) FOURCROY, A.-F. DE, "Système des connaissances chimiques," Baudouin, Paris, Brumaire, an IX, 1801, Vol. 8, pp. 234–56, 241–2.

(18) MILLS, EDMUND J., "Destructive Distillation," Gurney and Jackson, London,
      1892, pp. 108–9.
(19) THWAITES, R. G., "Travels and Explorations of the Jesuit Missionaries in New
      France, 1610–1791," Burrows Brothers Co., Cleveland, Ohio, 1899, Vol. 43,
      pp. 261 and 326.
(20) THWAITES, R. G., "Early Western Travels, 1748–1846," A. H. Clark Co.,
      Cleveland, Ohio, 1904, Vol. 4, pp. 101–2.
(21) HOWES, CECIL, "Kansas oil used by pioneers long before wells were drilled,"
      Kansas City Times, Oct. 13, 1938.
(22) WILSON, C. W., "Foundation and development of the gas industry in America,"
      J. Chem. Educ., 18, 103–7 (March, 1941).
(23) DARMSTAEDTER, LUDWIG, Ref. (1), p. 14.
(24) PHELPS, MRS. A. H. L., "Familiar Lectures on Chemistry for Schools, Families,
      and Private Students," F. J. Huntington and Co., New York, 1838, 448 pp.
(25) LOCKWOOD, MOSES B., "Carburetted hydrogen," Am. J. Sci., 39, 200–1
      (1840).
(26) ROBINS, F. W., "The Story of the Lamp and the Candle," Oxford University
      Press, London, New York, and Toronto, 1939, pp. 116–19.
(27) TARDIN, JEAN, "Histoire naturelle de la fontaine qui brusle près de Grenoble,"
      Tournon, 1618.
(28) LAYTON, W. T., "The Discoverer of Gas Lighting. Notes on the life and work
      of the Rev. John Clayton, D.D., 1657–1725," Walter King Ltd., London,
      1926, 56 pp.
(29) BROWNE, C. A., "Historical observations during a recent chemical trip to
      Europe," J. Chem. Educ., 17, 57–63 (Feb., 1940).
(30) CLAYTON, JOHN, "An experiment concerning the spirit of coals," Phil. Trans.,
      41, 59–61 (1739–40).
(31) CLAYTON, JOHN, "An experiment concerning the spirit of coals," Phil. Trans.
      Abridgment by John Martyn, 9 (3), 395–7 (1747).
(32) JARMAN, THOMAS, "On gas lights," Am. J. Sci., (1), 3, 170–3 (1821).
(33) "Gas lights," Aesculapian Register (Philadelphia), 1, 37–8 (July 15, 1824).
(34) BROWNRIGG, WILLIAM, "On the uses of a knowledge of mineral exhalations
      when applied to discover the principles and properties of mineral waters,
      the nature of burning fountains and those poisonous lakes called averni,"
      Phil. Trans., 55, 218–43 (1765); ibid., 64, 357–71 (1774).
(35) TRIER, GEORG, "Chemie der Pflanzenstoffe," Verlag von Gebrüder Born-
      traeger, Berlin, 1924, pp. 11–21.
(36) LIPPMANN, E. O. VON, "Abhandlungen und Vorträge zur Geschichte der
      Naturwissenschaften," Veit and Co., Leipzig, 1906, pp. 361–2, 368.
(37) WIESNER, JULIUS, "Jan Ingenhousz. Sein Leben und sein Wirken als Natur-
      forscher und Arzt," Carl Konegen, Vienna, 1905, 252 pp.
(38) SACHS, JULIUS VON, "History of Botany, 1530–1860," Clarendon Press, Oxford,
      1890, pp. 491–504.
(39) FUETER, EDUARD, "Grosse Schweizer Forscher," Atlantis Verlag, Zurich, 1939,
      pp. 132–3, 148–9. Biographical sketches of Bonnet and Senebier.
(40) PRIESTLEY, J., "Experiments and Observations on Different Kinds of Air,"
      Thomas Pearson, Birmingham, 1790, Vol. 3, pp. 247–92.
(41) NORDENSKIÖLD, A. E., "C. W. Scheele. Nachgelassene Briefe und Aufzeich-
      nungen," P. A. Norstedt & Söner, Stockholm, 1892, pp. 100–1.
(42) DUMAS, J.-B., and J.-B. BOUSSINGAULT, "Essai de statique chimique des êtres
      organisés," Fortin, Masson et Cie., Paris, 1844, 3rd ed., pp. 1–27, 140.
(43) PEACOCK, GEORGE, "Miscellaneous Works of the Late Thomas Young," John
      Murray, London, 1855, vol. 2, pp. 501–4. Biographical sketch of Jan
      Ingenhousz.
(44) Review of J. Wiesner's "Jan Ingenhousz. Sein Leben und sein Wirken als
      Naturforscher und Arzt," Nature, 75, 3–4 (Nov. 1, 1906).

(45) BOUSSINGAULT, J.-B., "Role of chlorophyll in plants," *Sci. News Letter*, **13**, 377–8 (June 16, 1928).

(46) SENEBIER, JEAN, "Mémoires physico-chymiques sur l'influence de la lumière solaire pour modifier les êtres des trois règnes de la Nature, et surtout ceux du règne végétal," Barthelemi Chirol, Geneva, **1782**; "Recherches sur l'influence de la lumière solaire pour métamorphoser l'air fixe en air pur par la végétation," Geneva, **1783**.

(47) BROWNE, C. A., "The life and chemical services of Fredrick Accum," *J. Chem. Educ.*, **2**, 829–51 (Oct., 1925); **2**, 1008–34 (Nov., 1925); **2**, 1140–9 (Dec., 1925).

(48) BAY, J. C., "Jean Senebier, 1742–1808," *Plant Physiology*, **6**, 189–93 (Jan., 1931).

(49) "Sources of carbon in vegetables," *Nicholson's J.*, (2), **10**, 301 (Apr., 1805).

(50) *Life*, Feb. 10, 1941, p. 41.

(51) BROWNE, C. A., "Thomas Paine's theory of atmospheric contagion and his account of an experiment performed by George Washington upon the production of marsh gas," *J. Chem. Educ.*, **2**, 99–101 (Feb., 1925).

(52) SÖDERBAUM, H. G., "Jac. Berzelius Reseanteckningar," P. A. Norstedt & Söner, Stockholm, **1903**, pp. 94–5, 164–8.

(53) HART, IVOR B., "The Great Engineers," Methuen & Co. Ltd., London, **1928**, pp. 24–6.

(54) DARWIN, ERASMUS, "A Botanic Garden," J. Johnson, London, **1791**, 2nd ed., p. 90.

(55) RUDOLPH, R. C., "A second-century Chinese illustration of salt mining," *Isis*, **43**, 39–41 (Apr., 1952).

(56) VAN KLOOSTER, H. S., "Jan Ingenhousz," *J. Chem. Educ.*, **29**, 353–5 (July, 1952).

(57) WEEKS, M. E. and F. B. DAINS, "Mrs. A. H. Lincoln Phelps and her services to chemical education," *J. Chem. Educ.*, **14**, 53–7 (Feb., 1937).

Sixteenth-century cartoon on alchemy

Penotus [Bernard Gabriel Penot] . . . died a hundred years old wanting but two, . . . and he used to say before he died, having spent his whole life in vainly searching after the Philosophers' stone, that if he had a mortal Enemy he did not dare to encounter openly, he would advise him above all things to give himself up to the Study and Practice of Alchymy (67).

Get what you can, and what you get hold;
'Tis the Stone that will turn all your lead into gold.
   (68).

. . . Surely to alchemy this right is due, that it may be compared to the husbandman whereof Aesop makes the fable; that, when he died, told his sons that he had left unto them gold buried underground in his vineyard; and they digged over all the ground, and gold they found none; but by reason of their stirring and digging the mould about the roots of their vines, they had a great vintage the year following: so assuredly the search and stir to make gold hath brought to light a great number of good and fruitful inventions and experiments . . . (1).

Chemistry began by saying it would change the baser metals into gold. By not doing that it has done much greater things (64).

3

Elements of the alchemists

The alchemists never succeeded in making gold from base metals, yet their experiments, recorded under a mystical and intentionally obscure terminology, gradually revealed metallic arsenic and antimony. Bismuth was discovered by practical miners. Finally, in the latter part of the seventeenth century, the pale light of phosphorus began to illumine the dark secrets of alchemy and to disclose the steady advance of scientific chemistry.

The part played in ancient civilizations by gold, silver, copper, iron, lead, tin, mercury, carbon, and sulfur has already been shown. Certain other elements, although their lineage is not quite so ancient, have nevertheless had a history that extends far back through the centuries. In this group may be mentioned arsenic, antimony, bismuth, and phosphorus; and, strangely enough, these four simple substances have so many characteristics in common that they constitute one of the groups in the system of classification now universally used by chemists. Their early history is so shrouded in uncertainty that only in the case of phosphorus is it possible to assign the honor of discovery definitely to any person. They were brought to light however during the long visionary search by alchemists for the philosophers' stone that would convert base metals into gold and by iatrochemists for the elixir of life that would prolong life indefinitely and through the efforts of miners. Reflecting on the folly of attempts to prepare gold from sulfur and mercury, Leonardo da Vinci wrote in one of his notebooks, "If, however, insensate avarice should drive you into such error, why do you not go to the mines where nature produces this gold, and there become her disciple? She will completely cure you of your folly by showing you that nothing which you employ in your furnace will be numbered among the things which she employs in order to produce this gold. For there is there no quicksilver, no sulphur of any kind, no fire nor other heat than that of nature giving life to our world; and she will show you the veins of the gold spreading through the stone . . ." (69).

91

ARSENIC

"For smelter fumes have I been named.
I am an evil, poisonous smoke . . .
But when from poison I am freed,
Through art and sleight of hand,
Then can I cure both man and beast,
From dire disease ofttimes direct them;
But prepare me correctly, and take great care
That you faithfully keep watchful guard over me;
For else am I poison, and poison remain,
That pierces the heart of many a one." (36) *

The so-called "arsenic" of the Greeks and Romans consisted of the poisonous sulfides, orpiment and sandarac, mined with heavy loss of life by slave labor (2). Both Pliny the Elder and Dioscorides were familiar with orpiment and realgar (sandarac) (70). The latter mentioned that "Arsenicum" and "Sandaracha" occur in the same mines, that sandarac has a "brimstone-like" odor, and that these two ores are roasted in the same manner (71).

No one knows who first isolated the metal, but this honor is sometimes accredited to Albert the Great (Albertus Magnus, 1193–1280), who obtained it by heating orpiment with soap (3). Paracelsus (15), the eccentric and boastful medical alchemist of the sixteenth century, mentioned a process for obtaining metallic arsenic, "white like silver," by heating the so-called "arsenic" of the ancients with egg shells (18, 66). Berthelot believed, however, that metallic arsenic was known much earlier than this, for it is easily reduced from its ores. Since it sublimes easily, and readily forms soft alloys with other metals, and since the arsenic sulfide, realgar, looks very much like the corresponding mercury ore, cinnabar, the alchemists regarded arsenic as a kind of quicksilver. The Pseudo-Democritus gave the following method of reducing the ore: "Fix the mercury obtained from arsenic (sulfide) or from sandarac, throw it on to copper and iron treated with sulfur, and the metal will become white" (3, 17, 23).

Signor Marcello Muccioli published in *Archeion* an article on the knowledge of arsenic possessed by the Chinese in about 1600, as exhibited in the Pen Ts'ao Kan-Mu (or Kang-mu), a 52-volume encyclopedia on materia medica (37). Yoshio Mikami states that this work

---

* *"Mein Nahme heisset Hütten-Rauch/ Und bin ein gifftiger böser Schmauch . . . /*
Da aber Ich verlier den Gifft/ Durch Kunst und rechte Handgriff/ So kan Ich
Menschen und Vieh curiren/ Auss böser Kranckheit offtmals führen/ Doch bereit mit
recht/ und hab gut Acht/ Dass du halst mit mir gute Wacht/ Sonst bin Ich Gifft und
bleibe Gifft/ Das manchems Hertz im Leib absticht" (36).

Albertus Magnus, 1193–1280. German Dominican scholar and alchemist who interpreted Aristotle to the Latin races. Author of "De Mineralibus." He also contributed to mechanics, geography, and biology. See also ref. (63).

was printed in 1590 and that it was the result of thirty years of scholarly labor by its author, Li Shih-chen (38). The Chinese were thoroughly familiar with the poisonous properties of arsenic, and knew how to test whether or not a person had been poisoned by it. They used it to kill mice in their fields and insects in their rice plantations. Chinese persons were sometimes poisoned by drinking beverages which had stood for some time in new tin vessels. The author of the Pen Ts'ao attributed these cases to improper purification of tin prepared from minerals containing arsenic (37). After making erasures in their manuscripts (which were written on yellow paper), ancient Chinese scholars covered them neatly with a yellow varnish containing finely pulverized orpiment. Most of the orpiment was used by artists, however, as a pigment (37).

Rudolf Winderlich, 1876–1951. Advanced-studies adviser at the secondary school at Oldenburg in Oldenburg. Author of excellent textbooks containing valuable notes on the history of chemistry; of the books "Chemie und Kultur," "Chemie für Jedermann," and "Das Ding"; and of many articles in educational journals. Contributor to "Das Buch der grossen Chemiker." See ref. (61).

In 1649 Johann Schroeder published a pharmacopœia in which he gave two methods of obtaining metallic arsenic: (1) by decomposing orpiment, arsenious sulfide, with lime and (2) by reducing arsenious oxide with charcoal.

E.-F. Geoffroy (1672–1731) recognized three kinds of arsenic: orpiment, realgar, and "arsenic properly so called," which was extracted from the cobalt ores of Saxony and Bohemia. "German Cobalt of the Shops, Cadmia Metallica of Agricola," said he, "is a ponderous, hard, fossil Substance, almost black, not unlike Antimony or some Kinds of Pyrites, emitting a strong sulphureous Smell when burnt, often mixed with Copper, sometimes with Silver. It is dug out of Mines in Saxony, near Goslar; in Bohemia, in the Valley of Joachim [Joachimsthal]; and in England in the Mendip Hills, in great Quantities. It has so strong a Corrosive Quality as sometimes to burn and ulcerate the Hands and Feet of the Miners, and it is a deadly Poison for all known Animals. All the three Kinds of Arsenick are extracted from it, and it likewise serves to make Zaffera, used by Potters in giving a blue Colour to their Vessels:

and the *Encaustum Cæruleum,* or that Kind of Blue sometimes used by Painters, and often by Women to mix with Starch for whitening and stiffening Linen" (*72*). The blue color was undoubtedly imparted by the cobalt in the ore.

The metallic nature of arsenic was thoroughly established through the researches of J. F. Henckel (or Henkel), who in 1725 told how to prepare it by sublimation, and of Georg Brandt, who investigated its properties in 1733, noticed its amphoteric nature, and was surprised that "the same substance should dissolve in so many different menstrua" (*16, 21, 76*). Bishop Johan Browall (1744), A.-M. Monnet (1774), and J. H. Pott (1720) also studied it (*3, 22*).

As early as 1738 C.-J. Geoffroy (Geoffroy the Younger) noticed that when most kinds of tin were heated they gave off fumes which seemed to contain arsenic. J. F. Henckel, in his translation of de Respour's "Mineral-Geist," described a test for arsenic in tin. In 1747 A. S. Margraf reported the presence of arsenic in all the specimens of tin which he examined (*73, 74*).

ANTIMONY

"But antimony, like mercury, can best be compared to a round circle without end, . . . and the more one investigates it, by suitable means, the more one discovers in it and learns from it; it cannot be mastered, in short, by one person alone because of the shortness of human life." (*58*)

Antimony, like arsenic, was known to the ancients, but perhaps only in the form of its sulfide, which Oriental women of leisure used to use to darken and beautify their eyebrows (*4*).

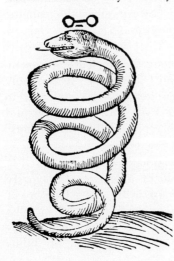

From Peters's "Aus pharmazeutischer Vorzeit in Bild und Wort"

Seventeenth-century alchemistic symbol. Arsenic (*left*) and antimony (*above*). For the history of chemical symbols see ref. (*61*).

In the revised Douai Bible, the account of Jezebel's (Jezabel's) death begins as follows: "And Jehu came into Jezrahel: But Jezabel hearing of his coming in, painted her face with stibic stone . . ." (IV Kings 9, 30). The modern Spanish translation states that Jezebel "se pintó los ojos con antimonio" (81). The authorized English Version does not mention the nature of the cosmetic (II Kings 9, 30). The harmful custom of painting the eyes was condemned by Jeremiah and by Ezekiel (Ezek. 23, 40). Jeremias 4, 30 of the revised Douai Bible reads as follows: "But when thou art spoiled, what wilt thou do? Though thou clothest thyself with scarlet, though thou deckest thee with ornaments of gold, and paintest thy eyes with stibick-stone, thou shalt dress thyself out in vain: thy lovers have despised thee, they will seek thy life." The modern Spanish translation reads: "aunque te pintes los ojos con antimonio" (81). Here, too, the Authorized English Version does not mention the cosmetic, but merely reads: "though thou rentest thy face with painting" (Jer. 4, 30).

The "stibick-stone" was undoubtedly stibnite, or antimonious sulfide. Oriental women used the black, pulverized mineral as an eye paint for increasing the apparent size of the eyes, giving them the staring protruding appearance characteristic of Egyptian portraits. Job's youngest daughter was named Kerenhappuch, which means "horn of eye-paint" (82). "And in all the land were no women found so fair" (Job 42, 14–15). Although T. K. Cheyne questions this interpretation of the name, the Challoner revision of the Douai-Reims Bible gives the Latin names of Job's daughters as follows: "And he called the name of one Dies, and the name of the second Cassia, and the name of the third Cornustibij" (horn of antimony) (83, 84).

Ancient eye paints often contained cupric oxide, lead sulfide, and lampblack. Their most costly constituent, however, was the stibnite, which had to be imported from distant countries (85). The Hebrew word for this eye paint was pûk (85).

Geoffroy the Elder mentioned that "Among the Ancients, Antimony [stibnite] was used to dye the Supercilia and Cilia Black. Accordingly we find in Scripture that the wicked Queen Jezabel [sic], in order to charm the King her Husband, painted her Eyes with Antimony; and the Women who used that Practice are also reproved by the Prophets" (75).

A. Lucas stated that antimony and its compounds were rarely used in ancient Egypt. He mentioned one example of a Nineteenth-Dynasty eye paint consisting of antimony sulfide; the use in the same Dynasty of antimony and lead to color glass yellow; some small beads of metallic antimony, probably made from native metal in the Twenty-second Dynasty (945–745 B.C.); a tablet of metallic antimony which M. Julius

Oppert found at Khorsabad; and a vase of pure antimony which M. Sarzec found at Tello and which M. Berthelot described in the *Comptes rendus* in 1887 (77). Stibnite, or *Stimmi,* is mentioned twice in the Ebers medical papyrus of the sixteenth century B.C. (78).

Berthelot's belief that metallic antimony was known to the ancient Chaldeans was based on his analysis of the most unusual vase that had

From N. LeFevre's "Cours de Chymie," 1751

Calcination of Antimony. *a,* the table; *b,* the mirror, which can be raised or lowered; *c,* the stone or the slab, on which is placed the powdered antimony; *d,* the adept adjusting the mirror and moving the antimony; *e,* the light focused by the mirror.

been brought to the Louvre from the ruins of Tello, and which he found to consist of pure metallic antimony containing only a trace of iron (5, 19). He also quoted the following passage from Dioscorides: "One roasts this ore (antimonious sulfide) by placing it on charcoal and heating to incandescence; if one continues the roasting, it changes into lead" (5). Pliny issued the same warning in his description of the preparation of antimony medicinals, when he said: "But the main thing of all is to observe such a degree of nicety in heating it, as not to let it become lead" (4). Hence it is possible that the Greeks and Romans, like the Chaldeans, knew how to obtain antimony, but since they did not have adequate methods of distinguishing between metals, they applied the indefinite term "lead" to all those that were soft, easily fusible, and black.

Georgius Agricola, in the sixteenth century A.D., was familiar with metallic antimony and an important use of it. "Stibium," said he in his "De natura fossilium," "when smelted in the crucible and refined, has as

Basilius Valentinus. Although the collection of chemical writings attributed to the fifteenth-century Benedictine monk, Basilius Valentinus, contains this alleged portrait, there is no conclusive evidence that such a person ever lived. Although the "Triumphal Chariot of Antimony" and other writings commonly attributed to him are much too modern for the fifteenth century, they are nevertheless of great historical value.

much right to be regarded as a proper metal as is accorded to lead by writers. If, when smelted, a certain portion be added to tin, a bookseller's alloy is produced from which the type is made that is used by those who print books on paper" (39).

Since the alchemists considered natural antimony minerals to be the most suitable raw material for the transmutation of metals into gold, alchemical literature abounds in references to antimony (65). The most famous of the early monographs on this element is the "Triumphal Chariot of Antimony," which first appeared in 1604, in German. Johann Thölde, operator of a saltworks in Frankenhausen, Thuringia, the editor of this work, claimed that it had been written by a fifteenth-century Benedictine monk, Basilius Valentinus (3, 6). Since no conclusive evidence of the existence of this monk has been unearthed, and since the literary style of the "Triumphal Chariot" is much too modern for a fifteenth-century manuscript, many historians of chemistry have concluded that it must have been written in the latter part of the sixteenth century, possibly by Thölde himself. Felix Fritz, however, has concluded from comparison with the "Haligraphia" and other authentic publications of J. Thölde that he cannot have been the author of the "Triumphal Chariot" nor of the other writings attributed to Basilius (40).

In 1707 Nicolas Lémery published his famous "Treatise on Antimony." He was born at Rouen on November 17, 1645. After studying pharmacy there under one of his relatives, he went to Paris in 1666 to complete his education. Dissatisfied with his progress under the unsociable but scholarly Christophe Glaser, demonstrator of chemistry at the Jardin du Roi, he resolved to tour France and learn firsthand from the greatest chemists of his day (43). Dr. Clara DeMilt believed however that Lémery gained many of the ideas presented in his textbook from

Nicolas Lémery, M.D., 1645–1715. French chemist. Author of "Cours de Chymie," one of the textbooks that Scheele studied, and of a treatise on antimony.

Glaser (43). Returning to Paris in 1672, Lémery lectured to groups of students who rebelled against the prevailing ignorance and prejudice of the iatrochemists (41).

When M. Lémery had to choose between the two degrees, Doctor of Medicine or Master Apothecary, he selected the latter first because of its closer relation to chemistry. B.-B. de Fontenelle described his public laboratory in the Rue Galande as "less a room than a cellar, and almost a magic cavern, illumined only by the light of the furnaces; yet the influx of people was so great that there was scarcely enough room for his operations. Even women, carried along by fashion, had the audacity to show themselves at such learned assemblies" (*41*).

Students came from all parts of Europe to live at his boarding school, "and the rooms of the quarter were filled with half-pensioners, who wished at least to eat at his home." His pharmaceutical preparations had a large sale, and the profits from his "bismuth magistery," a cosmetic, were sufficient for all the expenses of his household. In 1675 he published his famous "Cours de Chymie," which, unlike most scientific books, sold out edition after edition "like a work of romance or satire."

When Lémery was received into the Academy of Sciences in 1699, he decided to make a thorough analysis of the mineral known as antimony [stibnite] in a search for useful medicaments. After reading his paper in instalments to the Academy, he finally published it in 1707 as the "Treatise on Antimony." "When I resolved to study antimony thoroughly in all its aspects," said he, "I believed it proper to begin with some reflections on the nature of this compound and the places where it occurs; on the names which were applied to it, and their diversity; on how to select it; and on its medicinal virtues (*41*).

"Antimony," said Lémery, "is a heavy, fragile, black, shining, odorless, insipid, and very sulfurous mineral crystallizing in laminæ or in long needles. It occurs near the metals in many European mines, in Hungary, in Transylvania, in Brittany, in Poitou, and in Avernia. In Latin it is called *antimonium* or *stibium*. The alchemists, who abound in high-sounding names, have called it the *red lion* or *wolf*, because in the fire it devours the greater part of the metals; believing that many metals were derived from it, they have called it *the root of the metals*; because it receives various forms and colors, they have sometimes called it *Proteus*; sometimes *sacred lead*, or *philosophers' lead*, because they believed that, since this mineral devours many metals, it must be related to lead, which combines with many metallic substances (*41*).

"Among the merchants," continued Lémery, "we find two general species of antimony, the unworked mineral and the artificial: the former is taken from the mine loaded or mixed with many rock fragments, which the artisans call *gangue*. . . . This kind of antimony is not very common at the apothecaries' shops because it does not sell well. . . .

"The other kind of antimony," said Lémery, "is that commonly found at the apothecaries'; it is not different from the first except that it has been purified from its stony and earthy constituents. To purify it, the antimony taken from the mine is melted in vessels or crucibles in the fire, then removed by means of a perforated iron ladle to other vessels; the

Frontispiece from Johann Schroeder's Pharmacopœia, 1646

dirt which remains on the strainer is thrown away, and when the antimony has become cold, the vessels are broken open and removed, and it [the antimony] is sent to us in loaves as we see it. The antimony from Poitou is the handsomest and best, because most carefully purified. . ." (41). Before the discovery of stibnite in France, small specimens of it had been imported from Hungary.

By heating a mixture of crude, pulverized stibnite, saltpeter, and "red tartar" to redness in a crucible, Lémery obtained the metal, which fused completely, and condensed on cooling to form a massive, shining solid with the characteristic stellar structure of antimony on its surface (41). This highly specialized investigation led Fontenelle to foresee the great chemical monographs of today. "One might learn from this example," said he, "that the study of a single mixture is almost limitless and that each in particular might have its own chemist" (41).

Du Monstier, the editor of Nicolas Le Fevre's "Cours de Chymie," was more critical of Lémery's work. "A treatise that he published on antimony," said Du Monstier, "found itself exposed to the criticism of persons better informed than he on this mineral. I have been not a little surprised to see with what boldness he gives to sick persons antimony preparations which he devises and risks for the first time. One feels nevertheless on reading it that he has never seen those of Basil Valentine and of Suchten, both Germans whose works are held in high esteem by connoisseurs" (42).

Paul-Antoine Cap's biographical sketch of Lémery, written with the literary elegance of a French classic, opens with an imaginary word picture of Lémery entertaining in his laboratory his cosmopolitan friend Wilhelm Homberg. "At the end of the room, opposite the door," said Cap, "one noticed an immense furnace of solid and massive construction, surmounted by a basket full of instruments and various kinds of apparatus. Retorts and flasks there contended for space with matrasses, siphons, and aludels [earthen subliming pots]. Around this monumental furnace were placed other portable furnaces and polychrests, with their alembics, refrigerants, serpentines, rosaries, athanors, sand baths, and reverberatory furnaces, with their domes, their moor's head stills, and their copper or tin copings. In the center of this great room one saw a large table covered with utensils, urns, scorifiers, two-stage and three-stage glass alembics, and subliming apparatus with long cones arranged in pyramids. A copper lamp suspended from the ceiling swayed in the air, chemical symbols, arithmetical tables, slates streaked with chalk covered the walls of the room, and at each corner, hourglasses of various sizes served for measuring time and regulating the duration of experiments.

"This laboratory," said Cap, "one could judge at a glance, was not that of a sixteenth-century alchemist. One did not recognize here, by the peculiarity of their forms, the bizarre ideas conceived by these men on the nature of elements and mixtures. One saw none of those emblems, allegories, and symbolic figures with the aid of which they thought to hide from the knowledge of the common man their pretended secrets, already so obscure even for the true adepts. Nothing there suggested mystery, charlatanism, or occultism; on the contrary, everything bore the stamp of laborious study, of useful science; everything bespoke the modest scholar who devoted his life, in good faith and unreservedly, to the search for truth" (44).

After the publication of his monograph on antimony, Lémery began to suffer from paralytic strokes and apoplexy, which on June 19, 1715, brought his life to a close. According to B. Le Bovier de Fontenelle, "most of Europe learned chemistry from him, and most of the great chemists, French or foreign, have rendered homage to him by their learning. He was a man of unceasing industry, knowing only the bedside of his patients, his study, his laboratory, and the Academy, and showing that he who wastes no time has plenty of it" (41).

Early Uses of Antimony. Geoffroy the Elder mentioned the use of cups of metallic antimony "which communicate an emetick Quality to Wine which has stood in them for a Night's time" (75). "Besides the Medical Uses of Antimony," said he, "it is employed by several Artificers, to give Silver Sound to Tin, in casting Bells, making Metalline Specula, and Types for Printing, etc. It is likewise used by Goldsmiths in refining Gold, for when melted with that Metal, it destroys all other Metals that can be mixed with it, Silver itself not excepted, and turns them to Dross" (75).

Native Antimony. In 1748 Anton von Svab found that the so-called "arsenical pyrite" from the Sala mine in Sweden was native antimony (76, 79). In a review in 1781 of Torbern Bergman's dissertation on the wet assay of minerals, one finds the statement that "the native antimony (Spiessglaskönig) discovered by von Svab is also found, although but rarely, outside Sweden in a quartzose matrix" (80).

BISMUTH

The Germanisches Museum in Nuremberg preserved a collection of boxes, caskets, chests, and little cupboards decorated in bright colors painted over a background of metallic bismuth (28, 45). In his "History of Bismuth from 1400 to 1800," E. O. von Lippmann stated that one of these was made in about 1480 (46). By 1572 this art had developed into a craft there, and in 1613 its artisans were incorporated into a guild (47).

Edmund Oskar von Lippmann, 1857–1940. Austrian-German historian of chemistry and sugar chemist and technologist. Author of authoritative books on the chemistry and history of sugar, history of the magnetic needle, and history of alchemy and chemistry. Head of the large sugar refinery at Halle. Honorary professor of the history of chemistry at the University of Halle. See also ref. (87).

F. Wibel described a wooden casket in the Museum of Useful Arts at Hamburg, made in 1557. Over a chalk background attached with wax or glue, it has a metallic surface about one millimeter thick, overlaid with gold or amber lacquer. Investigation of this surface proved it to be bismuth. In the latter part of the eighteenth century, bismuth painting was superseded by a cheaper process in which perfected lacquers were applied directly to the wood (47).

In the middle of the fifteenth century the demand for bismuth increased. The early Gutenberg printing presses first used type cut from brass, and later, type cast from metals, such as lead, copper, or tin. In about 1450 a secret method of casting type from a bismuth alloy came into use (46). According to E. O. von Lippmann, the earliest mining publication to mention bismuth is that of Rülein von Kalbe, Burgomaster of Freiberg, who in 1505 referred to "Wysmudertz" as something already well known.

In his "Heaven of the Philosophers," Paracelsus (1493–1541) made a vague allusion to bismuth: "Two kinds of Antimony are found: one the common black, by which Sol [gold] is purified when liquefied therein. This has the closest affinity with Saturn [lead]. The other kind is the white, which is also called Magnesia and Bismuth. It has great affinity with Jupiter [tin], and when mixed with the other Antimony it augments Luna [silver]" (48).

Georgius Agricola, a contemporary of Paracelsus, described the properties of bismuth in much greater detail and told how it was extracted from ores mined near Schneeberg in the Saxon-Bohemian Erzgebirge. In his book "Bermannus," Bermannus says to Nævius, "this which just now I said we called *bisemutum* cannot correctly be called *plumbum candidum* (tin) nor *nigrum* (lead), but is different from both and is a third one" (49). In believing it to be a specific metal, different from all others, Agricola was far in advance of his age, for the idea that bismuth was a kind of lead persisted even into the eighteenth century (7). The miners believed that there were three kinds of lead (ordinary lead, tin, and bismuth) and that bismuth had progressed farthest in its transmutation into silver. When they struck a vein of bismuth they said naïvely and sadly, "Alas, we have come too soon" (7). Since they usually found silver below the bismuth, they called the latter "tectum argenti" or "roof of silver" (24).

In his "De re metallica" Agricola gave several methods of obtaining the metal by simple liquation of the native bismuth or by reduction with charcoal. Pulverized charcoal was placed in a small, dry pit, and a fire of beech wood was kindled over it. When the ore was thrown into the fire, the molten bismuth dripped out of it into the pit. The solidified cakes were later purified in a crucible (24).

After discussing the prevalent belief that the growth of precious stones and metals was governed by the stars, Padre Alvaro Alonso Barba stated in 1640 in his "*Arte de los Metales*": "But this subordination and application is uncertain, as is also the conceit that Mettals are but seven in number, whereas it is very probable that in the bowels of the Earth there be more sorts than we yet know. A few years ago in the mountains of Sudnos in Bohemia was found a Mettal between Tin and Lead, and yet distinct from them both: there are but few that know of it, and 'tis very possible more Mettals also may have escaped the notice of the generality. And if one should admit the subordination and resemblance between Mettals and the Planets, modern experience, by excellent Teliscopes has discover'd that they are more than seven. Gallileo de Galiles [sic!] has written a Treatise of the Satelites of Jupiter, where one may find curious observations of the number and motion of those new Planets" (*50*).

Georgio Baglivi and Father José de Acosta believed that metals grew like plants under the influence of the planets. "Mettalls," said de Acosta, "are (as plants) hidden and buried in the bowels of the earth, which have some conformitie in themselves, in the forme and maner of the production; for that wee see and discover even in them branches and, as it were, a bodie, from whence they grow and proceede, which are the greater veines and the lesse. . .they are engendered in the bowels of the earth, by the vertue and force of the Sunne and other planets, and in long continuance of time they increase and multiply after the manner of plants . . . the rough and barren earth is as a substance and nutriment for mettalls and that which is fertile and better seasoned a nourishment for plants" (*51, 86*).

In the fifth edition of his "Cours de Chymie," Nicolas Lémery confused bismuth with tin. "Bismuth," said he, "is a Sulphureous Marcassite that is found in the Tinn Mines; many do think it is an imperfect Tinn which partakes of good store of Arsenick; its pores are disposed in another manner than those of Tinn, which is evident enough because the Menstruum which dissolves Bismuth cannot intirely dissolve Tinn. There is another sort of Marcassite, called Zinch, that much resembles Bismuth. . . Marcassite is nothing else but the excrement of a Metal, or an Earth impregnated with Metallick parts. The Pewterers do mix Bismuth and Zinch in their Tinn to make it found the better" (*52*).

In the eleventh edition of this work, Lémery said that older writers believed bismuth to be "a natural marcasite or an imperfect tin found in tin mines; but the moderns," said he, "believe with much likelihood that it is a regulus of tin prepared artificially by the English; my thought on this subject is that there is natural bismuth, but that it is rare, and that which is commonly brought us from England is artificial. However that may be, it is certain that excellent bismuth is made with tin, tartar, and saltpetre; some also mix arsenic with it" (*30, 53*).

Even as late as 1713 the "Memoirs of the French Academy" contained the statement that bismuth is composed of a mineral, crude sulfur, mercury, arsenic, and earth; and the pharmacopœias of that time contained recipes for making it (*7*). Lémery, for example, described the following

The Alchemist, by D. Teniers (1610–1690)

method which he said was used in the English tin mines: "The workmen," said he, "mix this tin with equal parts of tartar and saltpetre. This mixture they throw by degrees into crucibles made red hot in a large fire. When this is melted, they pour it into greased iron mortars and let it cool. Afterward they separate the regulus at the bottom from the scoriæ and wash it well. This is the tin-glass which may be called the regulus of tin" (*13*).

Caspar Neumann (1683–1737) clearly recognized bismuth as a specific metal (*31*). "Bismuth," said he, "is extracted from its own proper ore, which is found most plentifully in Saxony, near Schneeberg, and of which some quantities are met with also in Bohemia and in England. Many have affirmed that it is an artificial composition, and accordingly delivered processes for making it; of which processes I tried those which seemed to approach the nearest to probability. . ." By heating "four ounces of English Tin, two ounces of white Arsenic, one ounce of white Tartar, and half an ounce of Nitre, cemented and melted together" he obtained "a Regulus, weighing three ounces and three drams, so much resembling Bismuth as to be easily mistaken for it by one who had not thoroughly examined the appearance of that semi-metal. There are, however, some differences in the structure of the two. . . . In their intrinsic properties they are extremely different: Thus the counterfeit, dissolved in Aqua fortis, forms a bluish coagulum, whilst the solution of the natural Bismuth continues uniform and limpid; the counterfeit, calcined and mixed with sulphur, exhibits nothing of that singular needled structure which the natural assumes in the same circumstances. Since therefore it has been reported that the Bismuth met with in the shops is an artificial production, and since experiment shows that it is capable of being imitated in its external form though not in its qualities, we ought to be upon our guard against such an imposition."

The French chemist Jean Hellot noticed that the tin smelters in Cornwall added natural bismuth, instead of the ingredients recommended in the pharmacopœias, to make the tin hard and brilliant, and in 1737 he obtained by fire assay of a cobalt-bismuth ore a button of the latter metal (7).

In 1753 Claude-François Geoffroy, a son of Claude-Joseph (Geoffroy the Younger), made a thorough investigation of bismuth (7, 20). Since this metal had not yet been introduced into medicine and was used only by pewterers for rendering tin whiter and more sonorous, it had been neglected by most chemists. J. H. Pott, however, had investigated it and published his "Exercitationes chymicæ de Wismutho," and C.-F. Geoffroy first repeated the experiments of this famous German chemist. Although Pott had stated that bismuth loses $3/38$ of its weight when calcined in an open fire, Geoffroy found that the weight increased instead, and that, after the calx had once been formed, no amount of heat caused any further increase.

Knowing that lead behaved similarly, Geoffroy sought for other points of resemblance between the two metals. Although it had long been assumed that lead was the only metal suitable for the cupellation of silver and gold, an artist had informed Charles-François de Cisternay du Fay in 1727 that, if the gold contained certain impurities such as emery it was necessary to cupel it with a large quantity of bismuth. Pott and Geoffroy both found that bismuth can also be used in the cupellation of silver. Although Pott had stated that bismuth is not combustible, Geoffroy saw it burn with its characteristic blue flame (54). He found ten points of similarity between bismuth and lead but nevertheless distinguished clearly between them and closed with the words "In a second Memoir I shall ascertain whether or not this analogy holds on treating these two substances with acids and different salts" (54). Because of his premature death in 1753, C.-F. Geoffroy was unable to complete this second memoir.

In his "Elements of the Art of Assaying Metals," Johann Andreas Cramer pointed out the close association of bismuth with arsenic and cobalt. "Every ore of Bismuth," said he, "as is shewn by the chemical analysis, is reduced to the State of Ore by Arsenick: For this goes out of it by Sublimation. You find in the same Ore that Kind of Earth that gives an azure Colour to Glasses, of which we have already spoken in the Article of Cobalt. Whence it is evident that the Ore of Bismuth may without Impropriety be called Cobalt of Bismuth: The more, because you will find in any ore of Bismuth the same Principles as in Cobalt, only in a different Proportion" (55). This close association of bismuth and cobalt in nature made it difficult for early chemists to distinguish between them (56).

In Cromwell Mortimer's notes to the second English edition of Cramer's work there is a description of an ore sent from Cornwall which was "so very rich of Bismuth that, by only holding a Piece with a Pair of Tongs against a clear Fire, the melting Bismuth will run down as soon and as easy as cheese will drop in toasting" (55).

Torbern Bergman (1735–1784) stated that "Bismuth is either native or mineralized by sulfur, perhaps also by acid air [carbon dioxide]. The first ore was found not in Germany, but in Sweden, especially at Riddarhytta" (80).

When the Swedish mineralogist J. J. Ferber visited Derbyshire in the latter part of the eighteenth century, he found that "Mineralogy in England is still in its cradle, and it is not long since Cornish miners threw away the bizmuth with the refuse, as a substance perfectly useless; and they would have remained in the same error had it not been for Dr. Schlosser of Amsterdam" (57).

PHOSPHORUS*

In the seventeenth century there lived in Hamburg a merchant by the name of Hennig Brand (or Brandt), who was apparently the first man ever to discover an element. Of course, gold and lead and the other metals and non-metals used in ancient civilizations must have been dis-

* See also "More on the Discovery of Phosphorus," Chapter 4, pp. 121–139.

covered by somebody, but these great contributors to human knowledge are as unknown today as is that greatest of all inventors—the man who made the first wheel.

Brand was a soldier in his youth, and it is said that later he became "an uncouth physician who knew not a word of Latin" (8). In spite of this deficiency he married a wealthy wife, who honored him for his scientific attainments. While endeavoring to improve his financial standing, he was lured by the spell of alchemy to search for the King of Metals. No one knows what led this zealous alchemist to hope that in human urine he might find a liquid capable of converting silver into gold, but it is well known that his queer experiments made in the seventeenth century† produced results that were both startling and strangely beautiful. Small wonder that he was delighted with the white, waxy substance that glowed so charmingly in his dark laboratory. The method of obtaining this light-giving element, which is now called phosphorus, Brand kept secret, but the news of the amazing discovery soon spread throughout Germany (9).

There lived at that time a famous chemist, Johann Kunckel (1630–1702), a son of an alchemist in the court of the Duke of Holstein (10). The younger Kunckel studied pharmacy, glass-making, and assaying; worked in the Dresden laboratory of John George II, Elector of Saxony; taught chemistry in the famous medical school at Wittenberg; and later managed the glass-works in Berlin belonging to Frederick William, the Elector of Brandenburg. His last years were spent in the service of King Charles XI of Sweden, who conferred on him the titles, Baron von Löwenstern and Counselor of Metals (10).

One day Kunckel proudly exhibited to a friend in Hamburg—much as a modern chemist might show a specimen of hafnium or rhenium—a phosphorescent substance. To his great surprise, the friend had not only seen this substance before, but offered to take Kunckel to the home of the medical alchemist, Dr. Brand, to see a still more remarkable substance that shines spontaneously in the dark. Brand, they found, had given away his entire supply, but he took Kunckel to the home of a friend to see the wondrous element.

Kunckel, in the heat of excitement, wrote immediately to his friend, Dr. Johann Daniel Krafft of Dresden. The latter, however, proved to be a false friend, for, without replying to Kunckel's letter, he went immediately to Hamburg and bought the secret from Brand for two hundred thalers. Just as the transaction was being made, Kunckel arrived on the scene. All his attempts to learn the secret process failed, but he did find

† Most authors give the date as 1669; J. R. Partington however considers 1674 or 1675 as the correct date.

Courtesy Tenney L. Davis

Johann Kunckel von Löwenstern, 1630–1702. German chemist, pharmacist, and glass technologist who gave an early account of phosphorus and studied the "aurum potabile" or "drinkable gold" of the alchemists (*60*). Counselor of Metals under King Charles XI of Sweden. (The portrait reproduced herewith is the frontispiece of Kunckel's "Ars Vitraria Experimentalis," published during his lifetime in 1679).

out that the new luminous substance, which had come to be known as phosphorus, had been obtained from urine (8).

Kunckel then began experimenting with this fluid, and was finally successful. Like Brand, he refused to reveal the method, giving as his reason the fear that dangerous accidents with phosphorus might become frequent. According to Homberg, Kunckel's process was essentially as follows: Fresh urine was evaporated nearly to dryness, after which the black residue was allowed to putrefy in a cellar for several months. This

Robert Boyle, 1627–1691. English chemist and physicist famous for his researches on gases, his air pump, his early experiments on the mechanical origin of heat, and his independent discovery of phosphorus. One of the founders of quantitative analysis. See also ref. (59) and (88).

material was heated, gently at first and then strongly, with twice its weight of sand, in a retort leading to a receiver containing water. After the volatile and oily constituents had distilled over, the phosphorus began to settle out in the receiver as a white, waxy solid. This was the part of the process which Kunckel thought too dangerous to reveal to the public. To prevent fires and explosions, it was necessary to remove the flame as soon as the phosphorus began to appear, and to keep the receiver closed until it became cold (8).

Kunckel not only prepared phosphorus, but also cast it in molds to obtain the stick phosphorus now familiar to all chemistry students. He also introduced its use as a medicinal, and his famous book on the subject bears the curious title: "Treatise of the Phosphorus Mirabilis, and Its Wonderful Shining Pills" (10). It is pleasant to know that his phosphorus researches were not without reward, for Duke Johann Friedrich of Hanover paid him an annual pension for the rest of his life (9).

According to Thomas Thomson (11), William Homberg purchased Kunckel's secret of making phosphorus by giving in exchange the in-

Ambrose Godfrey Hanckwitz, 1660–1741. In this portrait by George Vertue (1718), the bust of Hanckwitz is shown surrounded by his apparatus. At the left are shown the furnace and receiver used in the manufacture of phosphorus. The molten product was removed with a ladle to the molds in which it was cast into sticks, the entire operation being carried out under water. Flaming phosphorus and the phœnix, emblem of fire and immortality, figure prominently in the foreground.

genious barometer invented by Otto von Guericke, in which a little man comes to the door of his house in dry weather and discreetly retires within as soon as the air becomes moist (35). Homberg had learned of the new "phosphoruses" through Christian Adolph Balduin and Johann Kunckel (Kunkel). He found Balduin's phosphorus to be similar to the Bolognian, but more feebly luminous. "He bought it for some other experiment, but he had to have that of Kunkel, who had a great reputation. He found Kunkel at Berlin, and fortunately the latter was seized with a desire to own Guericke's little prophet. The bargain was soon concluded between the two virtuosos, and the little man was given in exchange for the phosphorus. It was the phosphorus from urine, now well known" (35).

It would be unfair to conclude this brief account of the discovery of phosphorus without mentioning that Robert Boyle, the illustrious English pioneer in pneumatic chemistry, also discovered it independently. He prepared it by a method somewhat resembling that of Kunckel, but, as Boyle himself said, without any previous knowledge of that process. Boyle was a man of such high integrity that one cannot doubt the truth of his statement. Krafft claimed, however, to have communicated his process directly to Boyle (32). Boyle's assistant, Godfrey Hanckwitz, made phosphorus on quite a large scale, and exported it to Europe (12). One of his advertisements reads as follows: "Ambrose Godfrey Hanckwitz, chemist in London, Southampton Street, Covent Garden, continues faithfully to prepare all sorts of remedies, chemical and galenical. . . . For the information of the curious, he is the only one in London who makes inflammable phosphorus, black phosphorus, and that made with acid, oil, and other varieties. All unadulterated. . . . Solid phosphorus, wholesale 50s. an ounce, and retail, £3 sterling, the ounce" (14).

In 1737 a stranger in Paris offered to sell the secret process of making phosphorus to the Academy of Sciences. After accepting the offer, the French government appointed Jean Hellot chairman of a committee to study the process, and his detailed report, published in the Memoirs of the Academy for 1737 and later in P.-J. Macquer's textbook of chemistry, made the process accessible to all chemists (12, 34). The "Dictionnaire de Chymie" published in Yverdon, Switzerland, in 1767 states that "as this process, up to the present, has been more curious than useful, and as, moreover, it is both costly and embarrassing, I have no knowledge whatever that any chemist repeated it then in France except M. Rouelle, who, shortly thereafter, opened his course in chemistry, in which he tried to make phosphorus in presence of his audience. I was present at his first attempt; M. Hellot, who took great interest in this experiment, came also, and followed the process throughout its entire duration. We spent the night there; this first operation failed, to tell the truth, because

GUILLAUME FRANÇOIS ROUELLE

Apothicaire de Paris, ancien Inspecteur général de la Pharmacie de l'Hotel Dieu, Demonstrateur en Chymie au Jardin royal des Plantes, des Academies royales des Sciences de Paris et de Stockholm, et de l'Academie Electoral d'Erfort, né au village de Mathieu à deux lieues de Caen le 16 7bre 1703 et mort à Passy le 3 Aout 1770.

Courtesy Tenney L. Davis

Guillaume-François Rouelle, 1703–1770. Parisian apothecary. Former inspector-general of the pharmacy at the City Hospital. Demonstrator in chemistry at the Royal Botanical Garden. Member of the Royal Academies of Science of Paris and Stockholm and of the Electoral Academy of Erfurt. Born in the village of Mathieu two leagues from Caen September 16, 1703, died at Passy Aug. 3, 1770. (Translated from the French caption on the frame.) See also ref. (62).

of a defect in the retort; but in the following years M. Rouelle succeeded a number of times in making phosphorus in his course" (29, 31). However, phosphorus is no longer prepared by the unpleasant method described above. In 1769 the Swedish scientists Scheele and Gahn (33) found that it is an important constituent of bones, and in the following year Scheele succeeded in isolating it from them (8, 25, 26, 27). It really is strange that phosphorus was discovered so early in the history of chemistry, for the reactions involved in Brand's method are rather complex, and even today this element is not isolated with ease.

LITERATURE CITED

(1) BACON, FRANCIS, "The Advancement of Learning," edited by Wm. A. Wright, 3rd ed., Clarendon Press, Oxford, 1885, p. 36.

(2) PLINY THE ELDER, "Natural History," translated by Bostock and Riley, Geo. Bell and Sons, London, 1856, Book XXXIII, Chap. 22; Book XXXIV, Chap. 55; R. JAGNAUX, "Histoire de la Chimie," Vol. 1, Baudry et Cie., Paris, 1891, pp. 656–8.

(3) JAGNAUX, R., "Histoire de la Chimie," ref. (2), Vol. 1, pp. 656–8.

(4) PLINY THE ELDER, "Natural History," ref. (2), Book XXXIII, Chap. 34; P. C. RÂY, "History of Hindu Chemistry," 1st ed., Vol. 2, Bengal Chemical and Pharmaceutical Works, Calcutta, 1909, p. 54.

(5) JAGNAUX, R., "Histoire de la Chimie," ref. (2), Vol. 2, p. 235; CHUNG YU WANG, "Antimony, Its History, Chemistry, Mineralogy, Geology, Metallurgy, Uses, Preparations, Analysis, Production, and Valuation," Chas. Griffin and Co., London, 1909, pp. 1–5.

(6) STILLMAN, J. M., "The Story of Early Chemistry," D. Appleton and Co., New York, 1924, pp. 372–6; T. L. DAVIS, "Questions for the student of elementary chemistry," J. Chem. Educ., 7, 1141–6 (May, 1930).

(7) JAGNAUX, R., "Histoire de la Chimie," ref. (2), Vol. 2, pp. 331–2; H. KOPP, "Geschichte der Chemie," part 4, F. Vieweg und Sohn, Braunschweig, 1847, pp. 110–2.

(8) JAGNAUX, R., "Histoire de la Chimie," ref. (2), Vol. 1, pp. 634–7; A. C. WOOTTON, "Chronicles of Pharmacy," Vol. 1, Macmillan and Co., London, 1910, pp. 360–7; KUNCKEL VON LÖWENSTERN, "Vollständiges Laboratorium Chymicum," vierte Auflage, Rüdigersche Buchhandlung, Berlin, 1767, pp. 595–609.

(9) POGGENDORFF, J. C., "Biographisch-Literarisches Handwörterbuch zur Geschichte der exakten Wissenschaften," 6 vols., Verlag Chemie, Leipzig and Berlin, 1863–1937. Article on Brand.

(10) THOMSON, THOMAS, "History of Chemistry," Vol. 1, Colburn and Bentley, London, 1830, pp. 233–5; T. L. DAVIS, "Kunckel and the early history of phosphorus," J. Chem. Educ., 4, 1105–13 (Sept., 1927).

(11) THOMSON, THOMAS, "History of Chemistry," ref. (10), Vol. 1, p. 240; L. VON CRELL, "Neues chem. Archiv," Vol. 1, J. G. Müller, Leipzig, 1784, pp. 77–8.

(12) THOMSON, THOMAS, "History of Chemistry," ref. (10), Vol. 1, pp. 285–6.

(13) WOOTTON, A. C., "Chronicles of Pharmacy," ref. (8), Vol. 1, p. 387; H. KOPP, "Geschichte der Chemie," ref. (7), part 4, p. 111.

(14) LAWALL, C. H., "Four Thousand Years of Pharmacy," J. B. Lippincott Co., Philadelphia, 1927, p. 336.

(15) DAVIS, T. L., "Boerhaave's account of Paracelsus and van Helmont," J. Chem. Educ., 5, 671–81 (June, 1928).

(16) KOPP, H., "Geschichte der Chemie," ref. (7), part 4, p. 92.

(17) BERTHELOT, P.-E.-M., "La Chimie au Moyen Age," Vol. 1, Imprimerie Nationale, Paris, 1893, p. 263.

(18) WAITE, A. E., "The Hermetic and Alchemical Writings of Paracelsus," Vol. 1, Elliott and Co., London, 1894, p. 58.

(19) VON LIPPMANN, E. O., "Entstehung und Ausbreitung der Alchemie," Springer, Berlin, 1919, pp. 629–30.

(20) DORVEAUX, PAUL, "Apothicaires membres de l'Académie Royale des Sciences," Revue d'histoire de la pharmacie, 19, 118–26 (1931); ibid., 20, 113–26 (1932); M. E. WEEKS, J. Chem. Educ., 11, 428 (July, 1934).

(21) BRANDT, GEORG, "Observations sur l'arsenic," "Recueil des Mémoires . . . de chymie . . . dans les actes de l'académie d'Upsal et dans les mémoires de l'académie royale des sciences dc Stockholm, publiés depuis 1720 jusqu'en 1760," P. Fr. Didot le Jeune, Paris, 1764, Vol. 1, pp. 1–8; Actes de l'acad. d' Upsal, 3, (1733).

(22) BROWALL, JEAN, "Expériences et remarques sur l'arsenic," Recueil des Mémoires., ref. (21), Vol. 1, pp. 133–48; Mém. de l'Acad. Roy. de Suède, 6 (1744).

(23) O'HANLON, SISTER MARY ELLEN, "Albertus Magnus, the chemist," The Torch, 16, 21–3 (July–Aug., 1932).

(24) HOOVER, H. C. and L. H. HOOVER, "Georgius Agricola. De re metallica translated from the first Latin edition of 1556," Mining Mag., London, 1912, pp. 433–7; see also Sci. Monthly, 81, 253–4 (Nov., 1955).

(25) SPETER, MAX, "History of phosphoric acid. II. Berzelius' views on Gahn's share in the discovery of the composition of bone earth," Superphosphate, 6, 125–6 (July, 1933).

(26) DOBBIN, L., "Collected papers of C. W. Scheele," G. Bell and Sons Ltd., London, 1931, pp. 311–3.

(27) NORDENSKIÖLD, A. E., "Scheeles nachgelassene Briefe und Aufzeichnungen," Norstedt & Söner, Stockholm, 1892, pp. 37–9.

(28) WIBEL, F., "Beiträge zur Geschichte, Etymologie, und Technik des Wismuts und der Wismutmalerei," Z. angew. Chemie, 6, 502–3 (Aug. 15, 1893).

(29) "Dictionnaire de Chymie," Yverdon, 1767, Vol. 2, pp. 621–43. Article on "Phosphore d'Angleterre ou de Kunckel."

(30) MELLOR, J. W., "Comprehensive Treatise on Inorganic and Theoretical Chemistry," Longmans, Green & Co., London, 1929, Vol. 9, pp. 587–8.

(31) LEWIS, WILLIAM, "The Chemical Works of Caspar Neumann, M.D.," Johnston, Keith, Linde, etc., London, 1759, pp. 113, 579–84.

(32) KOPP, H., "Geschichte der Chemie," ref. (7), part 3, p. 329; G. E. STAHL, "Experimenta, observationes, animadversiones CCC numero, chymicæ et physicæ," Ambrosius Haude, Berolini, 1731, pp. 392–4.

(33) SPETER, MAX, "Who discovered the composition of bone-earth: Scheele or Gahn?" Superphosphate, ref. (25), 4, 141–5 (June, 1931).

(34) MACQUER. P.-J., "Elements of the Theory and Practice of Chymistry," A. Millar and J. Nourse, London, 1764, 2nd ed., Vol. 1, pp. 261–7.

(35) "Eloge de M. Guillaume Homberg," Hist. de l'Acad. des Sciences (Paris), 1715, pp. 82 ff.

(36) "Fr. Basilii Valentini chymische Schriften," Gottfried Liebezeit, Hamburg, 1694, part 2, p. 156.

(37) MUCCIOLI, M., "L'arsenic presso i cinesi," Archivio di Storia della Scienza (Archeion), 8, 65–76 (Jan.–Apr., 1927).

(38) MIKAMI, YOSHIO, "A chronology of the sixteenth century. China and Japan," ibid., 23, 222 (Nov. 12, 1941).

(39) HOOVER, H. C. and L. H. HOOVER, ref. (24), pp. 1–3. Quotations from Agricola's "De natura fossilium," p. 180 and "Bermannus," p. 439.

(40) BUGGE, G., "Das Buch der grossen Chemiker," Verlag Chemie, Berlin, 1929, Vol. 1, pp. 125–41. Chapter on Basilius Valentinus by Felix Fritz.

(41) "Eloge de M. Nicolas Lémery," Hist. de l'Acad. des Sciences de Paris, 1715, pp. 73–81; N. LÉMERY, "Trattato dell'antimonio . . .," Gabriel Hertz, Venice, 1732, preface and pp. 1–3, 275–6.

(42) LeFEVRE, NICOLAS, "Cours de Chymie," J.-N. Leloup, Paris, 1751, 5th ed., Vol. 1, pp. vi–vii.

(43) DE MILT, CLARA, "Christopher Glaser," J. Chem. Educ., 19, 58–9 (Feb., 1942).

(44) CAP, P.-A., "Nicolas Lémery, Chimiste," Imprimerie et Fonderie de Fain, Paris, 1839, pp. 2–3.

(45) VON LIPPMANN, E. O., "Abhandlungen und Vorträge zur Geschichte der Naturwissenschaften," Veit and Co., Leipzig, 1913, Vol. 1, pp. 247–8.

(46) VON LIPPMANN, E. O., "Die Geschichte des Wismuts zwischen 1400 und 1800," Julius Springer, Berlin, 1930, 42 pp.

(47) VON LIPPMANN, E. O., "Nachträge zur Geschichte des Wismuts," Chem.-Ztg., 57, 4 (Jan. 4, 1933).

(48) WAITE, A. E., ref. (18), Vol. 1, p. 8.

(49) HOOVER, H. C. and L. H. HOOVER, ref. (24) pp. 1–3.

(50) BARBA, FATHER A. A., "The Art of the Metals," S. Mearne, London, 1674, pp. 29–30, 90–1.

(51) DE ACOSTA, FATHER JOSÉ, "The Natural and Moral History of the Indies," The Hakluyt Society, London, 1880, Vol. 1, pp. 183–4. English translation by Edward Grimston, 1604.

(52) LÉMERY, N., "A Course of Chymistry," Walter Kettilby, London, 1686, 2nd English ed. from the 5th French, pp. 101–2.

(53) LÉMERY, N., "Cours de Chymie," Theodore Haak, Leyden, 1716, 11th ed., pp. 136–7.

(54) GEOFFROY, C.-F. (Geoffroy, fils), "Analyse chimique du bismuth, de laquelle il résulte une analogie entre le plomb et ce sémimétal," Mém. de l'Acad. Roy. des Sciences de Paris, 1753, pp. 296–312; Hist. de l'Acad. Roy., 1753, pp. 190–4.

(55) CRAMER, J. A., "Elements of the Art of Assaying Metals," L. Davis and C. Reymers, London, 1764, 2nd ed., pp. 161–2.

(56) BAUMÉ, A., "Chymie Expérimentale et Raisonnée," P.-F. Didot le jeune, Paris, 1773, Vol. 2, pp. 371–2.

(57) PINKERTON, JOHN, "A general collection of the best and most interesting voyages and travels," Longman, Hurst, Rees, and Orme, London, 1808, Vol. 2, p. 484. J. J. Ferber's "Essay on the oryctography of Derbyshire."

(58) Basilius Valentinus, ref. (36), part 2, p. 314.

(59) REILLY, DESMOND, "Robert Boyle and his background," J. Chem. Educ., 28, 178–83 (Apr., 1951).

(60) HAUSER, ERNST A., "Aurum potabile," ibid., 29, 456–8 (Sept., 1952).

(61) WINDERLICH, RUDOLF, "History of the chemical sign language," ibid., 30, 58–62 (Feb., 1953).

(62) LEMAY, PIERRE and R. E. OESPER, "The lectures of Guillaume François Rouelle," ibid., 31, 338–43 (July, 1954).

(63) DAVIS, TENNEY L., "The advice of Albertus Magnus to the ambitious alchemist," ibid., 6, 977–8 (May, 1929).

(64) "Journals of R. W. Emerson," Centenary ed., Houghton Mifflin Co., Boston and New York, Vol. II, p. 288; see also C. A. BROWNE, "Emerson and chemistry," J. Chem. Educ., 5, 269–79, 391–403 (Mar.–Apr., 1928).

(65) DUFRENOY, M. L., and J. DUFRENOY, J. Chem. Educ., 27, 595–7 (Nov., 1950).

(66) WALKER, FREDERIC, "The iconoclast," ibid., 8, 885–95 (May, 1931).

(67) LÉMERY, N., ref. (52), "A Course of Chymistry," Walter Kettilby, London, 1686, pp. 48–61.

(68) "The Autobiography of Benjamin Franklin and Selections from his Other Writings," Modern Library, New York, 1932, p. 213.

(69) MacCurdy, Edward, "The Notebooks of Leonardo da Vinci," Garden City Publishing Co., Garden City, New York, **1941-2**, p. 143.

(70) Bailey, K. C., "The Elder Pliny's Chapters on Chemical Subjects," Edward Arnold, London, **1932**, Vol. 1, p. 101; Vol. 2, pp. 75–7, 91.

(71) Gunther, R. T., "The Greek Herbal of Dioscorides," Oxford University Press, Oxford, **1934**, pp. 632–3, 642.

(72) Geoffroy, E.-F., "Treatise of the Fossil, Vegetable, and Animal Substances That Are Made Use of in Physick," W. Innys, R. Manby *et al.*, London, **1736**, pp. 163–7.

(73) Kopp, Hermann, ref. (7), Vol. 4, pp. 93–4.

(74) Marggraf, A. S., "Chymische Schriften," Arnold Wever, Berlin, **1768**, revised ed., Vol. 2, pp. 87–112.

(75) Geoffroy, E.-F., ref. (72), pp. 191, 196, 209.

(76) Kobell, Franz von, "Geschichte der Mineralogie von 1650–1860," J. G. Cotta, Munich, **1864**, pp. 536–7, 540, 609–10.

(77) Lucas, A., "Ancient Egyptian Materials and Industries," Edward Arnold and Co., London, **1934**, 2nd ed., pp. 81, 147–8.

(78) Lippmann, E. O. von, ref. (45), Vol. 2, pp. 10–11.

(79) Svab, Anton von, "Berättelse om en nativ regulus antimoni eller spetsglaskung," *Vet. Acad. Handl.*, **10** (1748); "Recueil des mémoires," ref. (21), Vol. 1, pp. 166–72.

(80) "Dissertatio metallurgica de minerarum docimasia humida; quam Præs. M. Torb. Bergmann [sic!] defendet Petr. Castorin," Vestm. Vpsal., **1780**, 4, p. 40; *Crell's Neueste Entdeckungen* **1**, 218–9, 225, 230 (1781).

(81) "La Santa Biblia . . . traducida de las lenguas originales, y cotejada diligentemente con muchas y diversas traducciones," Am. Bible Soc., New York, 1246 pp.

(82) Hastings, James, "Dictionary of the Bible," Charles Scribner's Sons, New York, **1929**, p. 103. Article on Antimony.

(83) "The Holy Bible translated from the Latin Vulgate (diligently compared with the Hebrew, Greek, and other editions, in various languages) . . . with annotations by the Rev. Dr. Challoner," D. and J. Sadlier and Co., New York and Montreal.

(84) Cheyne, T. K. and J. S. Black, "Encyclopædia Biblica," Macmillan Co., New York and London, **1902**, Vol. 2, column 2659. Article on Kerenhappuch by T. K. Cheyne.

(85) *Ibid.*, Vol. 3, columns 3524–5. Article on Paint by Stanley A. Cook.

(86) Adams, Frank Dawson, "The Birth and Development of the Geological Sciences," Dover Publications, Inc., New York, **1954**, pp. 277–328. The origin of metals and their ores.

(87) Oesper, Ralph E., "Edmund O. von Lippmann," *J. Chem. Educ.*, **13**, 535 (Nov., 1936).

(88) More, L. T., "The life and works of the Honourable Robert Boyle," Oxford University Press, London, New York, Toronto, **1944**, 313 pp.

The alchemist. The artist who painted this scene, Joseph Wright of Derby (1734–1797), called it "The Alchymist in search of the philosopher's stone discovers phosphorus and prays for the successful conclusion of his operation, as was the custom of the ancient chymical astrologers." It was first exhibited in 1771, and was engraved by William Pether in 1775.

4

More on the discovery of phosphorus

*Although most accounts of the discovery of phosphorus are based
mainly on the writings of Kunckel von Löwenstern and record
the events essentially as they have just been described, other early
records present a somewhat different story. In 1902 Hermann
Peters, a famous German historian of chemistry and pharmacy,
made a thorough study of the autograph letters of Brand, Krafft,
Kunckel, Homberg, G. W. Leibniz, and others which are preserved in the Royal Library at Hanover, and found that, although
the various accounts differ in many respects, they all agree on one
point: namely, that phosphorus was originally discovered by Dr.
Hennig Brand of Hamburg.   Although most historical records
present Dr. Brand as an almost mythical character and do not
even mention his Christian name, he emerges from these rare old
letters as a real human being.*

In his correspondence with the Abbé Nollet, Raimondo di Sangro
(1710–1771) mentioned the "perpetual lamps" of Saint Augustine (354–
430), which were sometimes found in sepulchers of the early Christians.
Raimondo di Sangro believed that these lamps contained phosphorus, and
Gino Testi considered this obscure point in chemical history worthy of
further investigation (26, 77).

In his "History of the match industry" in the *Journal of Chemical
Education*, M. F. Crass, Jr., quoted Paracelsus's recipe for "the separation
of the elements from watery substances" (28, 29).   Paracelsus's "icicles
which are the element of fire," which he apparently obtained by distillation of urine, may possibly have been elemental phosphorus.   If
that be the case, it is difficult to understand why they aroused so little
interest.

Most authorities agree that the original discoverer of elemental
phosphorus was the seventeenth-century alchemist and physician Hennig
(or Henning) Brand of Hamburg.   Gottfried Wilhelm Leibniz (1646–

EDITOR'S NOTE: Readers who prefer a shorter, yet connected, account of the discovery
of the elements may find it convenient to omit the supplementary information provided in chapters 2, 4, 6, 8, 10, 12, 14, 15, 17, and 19.

1716) was personally acquainted with Brand, corresponded with him regularly for at least four years, and wrote a history of the discovery of phosphorus. According to this great philosopher and mathematician, Brand was living in 1677 at the Michaelisplatz in Hamburg, in the newer part of the city. His wife, Frau Margaretha Brand, was proud of his attainments, and the dates of her letters show that she lived to enjoy the honors which resulted from his epoch-making discovery. A stepson often assisted the doctor in his experiments, and there were other children as well. Although Dr. Brand was something of a spendthrift and borrower, the family must have lived comfortably on their income of 1000 *Reichsthalers* a year. Visionary and impractical though he was, his skill in chemistry won the respect of his contemporaries at a time when iatro-chemistry held the forefront in medical thought. Ambrose Godfrey Hanckwitz once referred to him as "old honest Brandt of Hamburg" (*15*).

When his alchemical experiments revealed the beautiful light-giving element, Brand called it *cold fire* (*"kaltes Feuer"*), or, affectionately, *"mein Feuer."* The luminous substance which Kunckel subsequently exhibited in Hamburg was "Balduin's phosphorus," a phosphorescent calcium nitrate which had been prepared by distilling a solution of chalk in nitric acid (*2, 3, 20*). Brand's "cold fire" interested Kunckel greatly, and when he wrote about it to his friend, Johann Daniel Krafft (or Kraft) of Dresden, the latter also came to Hamburg. They visited Brand and suggested that they might be able to sell his secret to some royal personage for a high price. According to Leibniz, both Kunckel and Krafft learned the secret directly from Dr. Brand at that time (*1, 4*).

The learned Dr. Krafft soon made the new substance known far beyond the walls of Hamburg as he traveled to the Netherlands, to England, and even to northern America (*"dem mitternächtlichen Amerika"*) (*4*). In an attempt to sell the secret process, he exhibited the *cold fire* in the court of the Great Elector, Friedrich Wilhelm of Brandenburg. On April 24, 1676, at nine in the evening, all the candles were extinguished while Dr. Krafft performed before a large assembly a number of experiments with the "perpetual fire." However, he did not reveal the method by which it had been prepared.

In the following spring Dr. Krafft went to the court at Hanover, where G. W. Leibniz was serving as librarian and historian under Duke Johann Friedrich, and exhibited two little phials that shone like glowworms. When Leibniz suggested that a large piece of phosphorus might give enough light to illumine an entire room, Dr. Krafft told him that this would be impractical because the process of preparation was too difficult (*1*). On September 15, 1677, Krafft performed some startling experiments with it before Robert Boyle and several other members of the

Royal Society.   At the request of Robert Hooke, Boyle wrote a detailed report of them.   After the candles had been removed to another room and "the windows closed with wooden-shuts," Krafft's precious little specimen of phosphorus, of the size of two peas, was seen to shine brightly.   When Krafft scattered tiny bits of it on the carpet, Boyle was delighted "to see how vividly they shined. . . .   And these twinkling sparks, without doing any harm (that we took notice of) to the Turky Carpet they lay on, continued to shine for a good while. . . .   Mr. Kraft [sic] also calling for a sheet of Paper and taking some of his stuff upon the tip of his finger, writ in large characters . . . DOMINI, . . . which . . . shone so briskly and lookt so oddly, that the sight was extreamly pleasing, having in it a mixture of strangeness, beauty, and frightfulness . . ." (23).   One hundred and fifty-seven letters from Krafft are still preserved in the library at Hanover.

Gottfried Wilhelm Leibniz, 1646–1716. German mathematician, philosopher, historian, and scientist. Independent discoverer of the differential calculus. He was personally acquainted with Brand and Krafft, and wrote a detailed account of the discovery of phosphorus, including biographical sketches of Brand, Krafft, Kunckel, and Becher.

Courtesy Mathematics Dept.,
The University of Kansas

In July, 1678, Leibniz went to Hamburg and drew up a contract between Duke Johann Friedrich and Dr. Hennig Brand according to which the latter was to correspond regularly with Leibniz and keep him informed about new developments regarding the *"cold fire."* The Duke's part of the contract consisted in the promise to pay ten thalers a month, with the stipulation that sixty thalers, or six months' allowance, would be paid in advance for revealing the secret processes (*"bei Communicirung der Composition und ander bereit habender Curiositäten"*) (1).

Shortly after this, Dr. J. J. Becher went to Hamburg and attempted to engage Brand for the Duke of Mecklenburg-Güstrow. In this, however, he was intercepted by Leibniz, who took Dr. Brand back with him to Hanover and advised Duke Johann Friedrich that it would be best to keep him at the court or send him to the Harz Mountains until the secret processes had been tested. Leibniz thought that Dr. Brand would be able to prepare a large quantity of phosphorus in the mountains and that he might perhaps find the philosophers' stone. Brand did not go to the Harz, however, but remained in Hanover for five weeks, preparing a fresh supply of phosphorus outside the city and showing Leibniz the secret process according to the agreement. The latter also prepared a quantity of phosphorus and sent some of it to the physicist Christian Huygens in Paris, who was studying the nature of light (1, 5). Thus Leibniz was the fourth person to prepare the new element (Brand, Krafft, Kunckel, Leibniz) (1).

Brand, however, was highly dissatisfied with the pay he had received, and wrote angry letters to Leibniz claiming that it was insufficient for his traveling expenses and the care of his family at home. Frau Margaretha Brand also wrote angrily to Leibniz, and her husband berated Krafft for inducing him to place confidence in Leibniz instead of in Dr. Becher. He also accused Krafft of having received one thousand thalers for the phosphorus in England.

On December 24, 1678, Dr. Krafft sent this letter to Leibniz, saying, "Since you mention having received an angry letter from him [Brand], I am sending you mine herewith. You may compare them and see which is the prettier" (1). Nevertheless, Leibniz advised the Duke to deal more liberally with Dr. Brand, partly out of sympathy, and partly to prevent him from selling his secrets to others.

This tactfulness calmed Brand's wrath, and in 1679 he planned another trip to Hanover to prepare phosphorus on a large scale and reveal his other chemical secrets. A weekly salary of ten thalers in addition to board and traveling expenses was agreed upon, and a later letter shows that, on this second trip, Brand worked for Duke Johann Friedrich two months. The last letter from Brand in the Hanover library is dated August 23, 1682, but, according to Leibniz, he was still living ten years later (1, 4). Hermann Peters thought that possibly other letters from Brand may still exist in Hamburg or elsewhere.

Leibniz communicated Brand's method of making phosphorus to Count Ehrenfried Walter von Tschirnhaus (1651–1708) in Paris, and sent him a specimen by request. When Count E. W. von Tschirnhaus (58) published the Brand-Leibniz recipe in the history of the Royal Academy, Colbert recommended him for membership in the French

Academy of Sciences, and on July 22, 1682, he was elected. According to Dr. Peters, this recipe was also published in the fifth edition of Nicolas Lémery's "Cours de Chymie" in 1683 (1).

When Krafft went to England, he exhibited phosphorus in the court of Charles II and showed it to the Honorable Robert Boyle (1, 4, 6, 23). The great English scientist then prepared it by a slightly different method and studied its properties more thoroughly than did any other chemist of the seventeenth century (1).

When Wilhelm Homberg defended Kunckel's claim to the re-discovery of phosphorus after the original secret process had been lost to the world, Leibniz strove to defend the rights of Dr. Brand and stated emphatically that the real discoverer of phosphorus was still living long after Krafft and Kunckel had made the element known, and that he used to complain bitterly about his false treatment (1). Although Krafft published his recipe in 1679, Brand was still living in 1692, and even by 1710 Leibniz had heard no report of his death. A. Godfrey Hanck-witz once paid the following tribute to the great Hamburg chemist:

. . . as all things have their period so has also the *vitalis lucula* (scintilla, spark) by approaching age. By (in the case of) this urosophus Brandt, it daily lessened and wore off, till at last in the midst of his best experiments it e'en quite extinguished. His fine stare fire, which through art he produced, remained for his memory longer with us than himself . . . and shined longer than his *flammula vitæ*, that in time of his best occupation did turn and return to its fiery sphere. His acquaintances and confidents would feign (if wishes would have done it) have retarded his decrease to set it farther off . . . (15).

Robert Hooke and his contemporaries, recalling the animal origin of phosphorus, had several "disputes, whether there were any such thing as *flammula vitæ:* and it was conceived by some that the experiments of phosphorous [sic] plainly proved such a *flammula* as being extracted either immediately out of the blood or mediately out of the urine" (30). The great Dutch physician and chemist Herman Boerhaave (1668–1738), in speaking to his students concerning some of the errors into which chemists had fallen, said "One has therefore made of the human body a laboratory of chemistry. . . . All of these errors have been carried to the point that an otherwise excellent man has dared to propose that the body contains a lighted fire, since chemistry has found the means of extracting the English phosphorus from urine with the aid of fire" (46).

According to Leibniz, Brand was not secretive, but, on the contrary, gave over the process too readily to Krafft and Kunckel in return for some little gifts and the promise of larger payments (1, 4). When Kunckel tried out the process at home, his first attempts were unsuccessful. His complaining letters to Brand brought him no further information, however, for the Hamburg chemist had soon regretted his poor bargain. In the meantime Kunckel experimented by a trial-and-error method, and, since he had seen the process and was familiar with Brand's distillation apparatus, he finally succeeded in correcting his own mistake. He then had the audacity to claim the discovery for himself (1, 4).

In a letter to Brand written from Wittenberg on June 25, 1676, Kunckel asked him directly for the details of preparation, suggesting that the recipe might be worded so obscurely as to be meaningless to others, and assuring him that there would be no danger of any one else opening the letter. He complained because Brand had given some phosphorus to Krafft and the chaplain of the Pest House, and begged him to give no more of it to any one else. Kunckel modified the Brand process a little by adding sand to the urine before distilling. In June, 1676, he told his friend, G. C. Kirchmaier, professor of chemistry at Wittenberg, about the new process, and the latter published a paper on it. Whether Kunckel ever prepared the new element on a large scale or not is not known, but at the end of his history of phosphorus he wrote, "However, I am not making it any more, for much harm can come of it" (2, 3).

Dr. Hermann Peters concluded from a study of these old letters that Kunckel did not rediscover phosphorus, but merely made a little of it by Brand's method, and that, even without Kunckel, phosphorus would have remained known to the world through the efforts of Krafft, Leibniz, and Boyle (1).

In 1726 W. Derham published a book entitled "Philosophical Experiments and Observations of the Late Eminent Dr. Robert Hooke, F.R.S. and Geom. Prof. Gresh and Other Eminent Virtuoso's in His Time," in which he included a detailed description of Brand's process of making phosphorus (20). Under the title "Phosphoros Elementaris, by Dr. Brandt of Hamburgh," Derham wrote:

"Take a Quantity of Urine (not less for one Experiment than 50 or 60 Pails full); let it lie steeping in one or more Tubs, . . . till it putrify and breed Worms, as it will do in 14 or 15 days. Then, in a large Kettle, set some of it to boil on a strong Fire, and, as it consumes and evaporates, pour in more, and so on, till, at last, the whole Quantity be reduced to a Paste . . . and this may be done in two or three Days, if the Fire be well tended, but else it may be doing a Fortnight or more. Then take the said Paste, or Coal; powder it, and add thereto some fair Water, about 15 Fingers high . . .; and boil them together for $1/4$ of an Hour. Then strain the Liquor and all through a Woolen Cloth . . . the Liquor that passes must be taken and boil'd till it come to a Salt, which it will be in a few Hours. Then take off the Caput Mortuum (which you have at any Apothecary's, being the Remainder of Aqua Fortis from Vitriol and Salt of Niter) and add a Pound thereof to half a Pound of the said Salt, both of them being first finely pulverized. And then for 24 Hours steep'd in the most rectify'd Spirit of Wine, two or three Fingers high, so as it will become a Kind of Pap.

"Then evaporate all in warm Sand, and there will remain a red, or reddish, Salt. Take this Salt, put it into a Retort, and, for the first Hour, begin with a small Fire; more the next, a greater the 3d, and more the 4th; and then continue it, as high as you can, for 24 Hours. Sometimes, by the Force of the Fire, 24 Hours proves enough; for when you see the Recipient white, and shining with Fire, and that there are no more Flashes, or, as it were, Blasts of Wind, coming from Time to Time from the Retort, then the Work is finished. And you may, with Feather, gather the Fire together, or scrape it off with a Knife, where it sticks."

Derham said of this phosphorus, "I saw some of it, press'd with a Quill that was cut, and it fired Gun-powder about it. Mr. Concle [Kunckel?] writ also with it on Paper, and the Letters all shined in the Dark. . . . My Author says he had once wrapp'd up a Knob in Wax, at Hanover, and it being in his Pocket, and he busy near the Fire, the very Heat set it in Flame, and burn'd all his Cloaths, and his Fingers also; for though he rubbed them in the Dirt, nothing would quench it, unless he had had Water; he was ill for 15 Days, and the Skin came off. . . ."

The following incident related by Nicolas Lémery illustrates the carelessness of early chemists in handling this dangerously flammable element. "After some Experiments," said he, "made one day at my house upon the Phosphorus, a little piece of it being left negligently upon the Table in my Chamber, the maid making the bed took it up in the bed-clothes she had put upon the Table, not seeing the little piece: the person who lay afterwards in the bed, waking at night . . . , perceived that the coverlid was on fire" (31).

In his article entitled "The aerial noctiluca," Robert Boyle mentioned that "the experienced chymist Mr. Daniel Krafft had, in a visit that he purposely made me, shewn me and some of my friends, both his liquid and consistent posphorus. . . ." In return for some information about "uncommon mercuries, . . . he [Krafft], in requital, confest to me at parting, that at least the principal matter of his phosphorus's was some-what that belonged to the body of man . . ." (6, 19). On September 30, 1680, Boyle's efforts to prepare the luminous element were crowned with success, and two weeks later he deposited his recipe with the secretaries of the Royal Society, who, however, did not open it until after he had died in 1691 (7).

Boyle's assistant, A. G. Hanckwitz or Hanckewitz (1660–1741), was therefore able to develop the process on a commercial scale, improve it, and export phosphorus to the continent (8, 9, 17). Hanckwitz had been brought over from Germany at an early age by his honored master. He later built furnaces and stills in Maiden Lane, and traveled through the

Ambrose Godfrey. According to Ince (Ref. 15) this represents Ambrose Godfrey Hanckwitz, but according to Pilcher (Ref. 22) it is Hanckwitz's son, Ambrose Godfrey (1685–1756). Since the portrait was made from life in 1738 it must represent the son.

Netherlands, France, Italy, and Germany. He founded a famous pharmaceutical firm in London, and so great was his fame that a letter once came to him safely from Berlin addressed simply, "For Mr. Godfrey, famous Chymist in London" (15). He was known in England simply by the name Ambrose Godfrey, the German surname being reserved for formal occasions.

The letters which constitute his correspondence with Sir Hans Sloane from 1721 to 1733 are still preserved in the British Museum (18), and in 1858 Joseph Ince wrote an interesting biographical sketch of Hanckwitz based on correspondence, diaries, and notes (15). According to Caspar Neumann, "Mr. Godfrey himself . . . was once in danger of his life from [phosphorus], his hand being burnt so terribly that for a time he was out of his senses, and for three days lay in exquisite pain, as if his hand had been constantly in a fire" (21). In spite of all his dangerous experiments, this great disciple of Robert Boyle lived to be an octogenarian. He died on January 15, 1741, and was survived by three sons, Boyle, Ambrose, and John Godfrey, all of whom shared their father's interest in science.

Hanckwitz kept his recipe for phosphorus a profound secret, and, even in the article which he published in 1733, forty or fifty years after leaving Boyle's laboratory, gave only an obscure description of the process (8, 10). The sons evidently adopted the same policy, for one of them wrote:

As to the phosphorus made of urine called Kunckel's, we have it described by the Honourable Mr. Boyle, Mons. Homberg, and others. But I shall beg to be excused for not discovering the process how I prepare it, or from giving any farther light into its production than what was done by my father, before the Royal Society, in the year 1733 (16).

Yet only two years after this obscure and vague description of the process was published, the aged Hanckwitz allowed Dr. J. H. Hampe, the court physician, to coax him into revealing the secret (8). Not many years ago Dr. Max Speter found this long-lost recipe in an unexpected place. In the published correspondence of the Counselor of Mines, Johann Friedrich Henckel (or Henkel) of Freiberg (1679–1744), there

Max Speter, 1883–1942. Transylvanian inventor and historian of chemistry. Author of many articles on Boerhaave, Geoffroy the Elder, Marggraf, Black and Lavoisier. Contributor to "Das Buch der grossen Chemiker." In 1929 he found the Boyle-Hanckwitz recipe for phosphorus, after it had been kept secret for more than two centuries (25).

appears a letter from Dr. Hampe written in London on August 29, 1735 (8, 11). In reply to Henckel's inquiries regarding Hanckwitz and the secret process, Dr. Hampe wrote that Boyle's famous assistant was still living, but so forgetful because of advanced age that little could be learned from him. Nevertheless, through diligent questioning of the old man, he had succeeded in getting the essential details of the phosphorus recipe which Henckel had requested. Dr. Hampe asked Henckel to write him about any difficulties that might arise in his attempts to make phosphorus, in order that the aged Hanckwitz might be further questioned if necessary.

From this letter it appears that "the true key" to the process, which consisted in distilling a mixture of solid and liquid excrement, "was, above all else, that everything be done under water; especially while pouring it into the molds and while cutting it, enough water must always be at hand" (8, 11). To avoid the necessity of redistillation, or rectification, Hanckwitz pressed the phosphorus through leather, being carefull to keep it under water. In a second letter written on September 9 of the same year, Dr. Hampe gave Henckel further information about the process. On November 15 he asked Henckel not to divulge the secret to any one else and suggested that they keep each other informed about the experiments with phosphorus (8).

Henckel had learned the details of Kunckel's method of preparing it as early as 1731 from Johann Linck, an apothecary in Leipzig. In his letter of May 29, 1731, Linck stated that a better method was being used in England by Hanckwitz, but that he did not know the details (8, 11).

Hanckwitz, however, like his contemporaries, had entirely incorrect views as to the chemical nature of phosphorus. "Its principal Contexture," said he, "is found to consist of a subtile Acid concentrated by the Salt of Urine, and of a fat depurated Oil. . . . The Phlogistic Part is so slightly connected with the other Principles, that the least Motion, Friction, or Warmth, sets it on fire. . . . Phosphorus may be called an urinous Soap, as it consists of the saline and oleaginous Parts of the Urine. . . . In regard to the Parts whereof Phosphorus consists, it may be considered as the Soot of a deflagrated Oil; and so may every combustible Substance be looked upon as a Kind of Phosphorus, as consisting of inflammable Materials. . . . Phosphorus is more immediately compounded of a Salt tending to the Nature of Sal Ammoniac, of an urinous Salt, of an Acid, and an oily Phlogiston, with a subtile Earth. . . ." He also stated that glowworms "seem to have Phosphorus lodged in their bodies." Hanckwitz claimed that Kunckel, Krafft, and Brand had been able to obtain only "unctuous and opaque" phosphorus, whereas his was "hard, transparent, and glacial" (10).

Another of the early experimenters with phosphorus was the Abbé J.-A. Nollet, who watched Jean Hellot and others demonstrate its properties before the French Academy of Sciences in 1737 (32). The procedure was described in detail in the Memoirs of the Academy of Sciences for that year and later in P.-J. Macquer's "Elements of the Theory and Practice of Chymistry." Even in the eighteenth century, chemists had

From Ferchl's Apotheker-Kalender for 1932
Courtesy Mr. Arthur Nemayer,
Buchdruckerei und Verlag, Mittenwald, Bavaria.

Johann Heinrich Linck, 1675-1735. Leipzig apothecary who communicated Kunckel's method of preparing phosphorus to J. F. Henckel. The "Golden Lion" pharmacy was in possession of the Linck family for three generations, and their museum of natural history and art was known throughout all Germany.

a completely erroneous idea of its nature. "Almost all the Chymists," said Macquer, "consider Phosphorus as a substance consisting of the Acid of Sea-Salt combined with the Phlogiston, in the same manner as Sulphur consists of the Vitriolic Acid combined with the Phlogiston" (33). This conception was based, according to Macquer, on the presence of salt and phlogiston (carbonaceous matter?) in the urine from which phosphorus is prepared and on the fact that phosphoric acid, like hydrochloric, throws down a precipitate with silver nitrate (33).

In 1743 A. S. Marggraf, a student of Henckel, found a much better way of preparing this element from urine (12, 13, 14, 24) and, since the phosphorus business was no longer as profitable as it had been, he promptly published the process. According to Marggraf, the new method had been suggested by Henckel's statement that, when the "calx of lead" was digested with sal ammoniac, potassium carbonate, and old urine, and then distilled, a good grade of phosphorus could be obtained. According to J. Mielcke, the microcosmic salt, $NaNH_4HPO_4 \cdot 4H_2O$, in the urine was converted by heating into sodium metaphosphate, $NaPO_3$. In the meantime the potassium carbonate and carbon reduced the lead chloride and lead oxychloride to lead, after which the carbon and lead reduced the sodium metaphosphate to sodium pyrophosphate and phosphorus (12). Dr. Speter also studied the correspondence between Marggraf and Henckel regarding this interesting method of preparing phosphorus.

Marggraf tried in vain to prepare phosphorus without urine. When he used mixtures of various chlorides with "vegetable coals, and even animal matters such as oil of hartshorn, human blood, etc.," all his attempts failed. When he separated some microcosmic salt from urine, however, mixed the salt with lampblack, and distilled the mixture, "he obtained from it a considerable quantity of very fine phosphorus . . . , whence he concluded that in this Saline matter resides the true Acid that is fit to enter into the composition of phosphorus" (33).

In 1688 Bernhard Albinus (Weiss) mentioned the presence of phosphorus in the ash of mustard and cress (34). In 1743 Marggraf prepared it from wheat and mustard (35). "In order to demonstrate by experiment," said he, "that the vegetables we enjoy every day or occasionally also contain that which is necessary for the production of the phosphorus, I found in Albinus' Dissertation on Phosphorus as well as on page 477 of the celebrated Hofmann's [Friedrich Hoffmann's] notes to Poterius that the seeds of black and white mustard and of cress yield phosphorus. Since I myself, however, still had no experience with it, yet found in Professor Pott's Collegio Mscpto on the first edition of Boerhaave's Chemistry that wheat, rye, and other similar grains yield phosphorus, I made the following experiments . . ." (35).

When Marggraf distilled the seeds of white and black mustard, garden cress, pepper, and wheat, he obtained phosphorus from each of them except the pepper. Although Albinus had added sand, Marggraf found this to be unnecessary. For the sake of economy, Marggraf used pepper from which the essential oil had previously been distilled (35). When he found that microcosmic salt could be reduced to phosphorus, he became curious to know the source of this salt in human urine. Since he found higher concentrations of microcosmic salt and phosphoric acid in the urine in the summer (when people eat more garden products such as mustard and cress), he thought it probable that these might be the source of the microcosmic salt (36). Although the modern chemist has simple qualitative tests for phosphates, Marggraf and his contemporaries were obliged to carry out the much more difficult process of liberating elemental phosphorus in order to detect its presence.

Since plants and animals are able to concentrate phosphorus in their tissues, and since these tissues contain their own reducing agents, E. B. R. Prideaux does not consider it surprising that physicians and pharmacists of the seventeenth and eighteenth centuries first prepared this element from substances of vegetable and animal origin (36).

Lavoisier said that "Phosphorus is met with in almost all animal substances and in some plants which, according to chemical analysis, have an animal nature. . . . The discovery that M. Hassenfratz has made of this substance in wood charcoal would make one suspect that it is commoner in the vegetable realm than has been thought; this much is certain: that, when properly treated, entire families of plants yield it" (37). Apothecary J. K. F. Meyer of Stettin wrote in 1784 that he had observed, several years previously, a permanent green color in the essences he prepared by digesting green herbs in copper vessels. He concluded that phosphates in the leaves had reacted with the copper to form copper phosphate (38).

William Lewis stated in 1759 that the ash of bones and horn resembles chalk and "the earth of the shells of sea-fishes . . . in being easily soluble in nitrous [nitric], marine, and vegetable acids, and not in the vitriolic." The only difference he was able to observe between the calcareous earth from shells and the bone ash was that the latter is "not changeable by fire into Lime: How strongly soever the earth of Bones and Horns be calcined, it continues insipid and gives no manifest impregnation to water" (39).

When J. G. Wallerius analyzed eggs, bone, and other animal substances in 1760, he detected lime, and had a vague idea that they also contain certain other earths. In a footnote to this paper in the *Neues chemisches Archiv*, Crell stated, "Hr. W. did not yet know the nature of the animal earth which the unforgettable Scheele made known to us: that is, that it consists of lime and phosphoric acid" (40). In 1769 C. W. Scheele and J. G. Gahn discovered that phosphorus is an important constituent of bone. Although some historians of chemistry have attributed this discovery to Gahn or Scheele alone, Dr. Max Speter proved from Gahn's own notes that both had a part in it (*41*).

In his *Chemisches Journal* Lorenz von Crell mentioned a rare publication announcing this discovery. "In the medical commentaries of a society of physicians at Edinburgh I found in the first issue of the third part (p. 97 *ff.* of the German translation, Altenb. 1776) a report by Hrn. D. Heinrich Gahn of Stockholm of how one can obtain a phosphorus from the bones of animals and especially from the hartshorn. I searched for a more detailed account of this wonderful discovery of Herr Gahn's. Except for the remark in C. W. Scheele's investigation of fluorspar that it has recently been discovered that *the earth in bones or horns is lime saturated with phosphoric acid,* all my searching was in vain. In the meantime, since this process of working up bones to obtain the phosphorus seemed to me to belong to the masterpieces of chemical decomposition, I repeated the experiment according to the instruction in the aforementioned book, and, to my great pleasure, found it to be true" (*42*). The "Heinrich Gahn" mentioned by von Crell was probably J. G. Gahn's brother, Henrik Gahn, assessor in the medical school.

Even to J. G. Gahn and Scheele, phosphorus was a rarity. When Scheele first read the English translation of his treatise "On air and fire," he found that Johann Reinhold Forster had translated the word *Gran* as *ounces* instead of *grains.* "Nine ounces of phosphorus," said Scheele, "I have never yet seen" (*43*).

Even in the eighteenth century, phosphorus was still regarded as an animal production. "The phosphorus, made of animal parts," wrote C. E. Gellert, "proves the existence of a phlogiston in the animal kingdom" (*47*). Before the true nature of combustion was understood, it was regarded not as a combination of oxygen with the combustible substance but as the escape of a volatile principle called "phlogiston." In 1780 J. G. Gahn found that the "green lead ore" of Breisgau is a natural lead phosphate and thus demonstrated the presence of phosphorus in the mineral kingdom (*48, 49*). This discovery was confirmed by M. H. Klaproth a few years later in his analysis of a "green crystalline cerussite" from the Holy Trinity Mine at Zschopau near the Erzgebirge (*50, 51*). From Klaproth's description of this mineral it was probably pyromorphite.

After mentioning some acids found in only one of the three natural realms, the Swedish chemist Torbern Bergman stated that "Other acids are common to all the kingdoms of nature, as the phosphoric, which has been falsely assigned to the animal kingdom alone; but which has been found, though rarely, in the fossil, and in great plenty in the vegetable kingdom. . . . Of all the acids, that of phosphorus is the scarcest, and has hitherto been found with a spataceous kind of lead only" (*52*). In

Bergman's time the word "fossil" meant mineral or anything dug from the earth.

Many early chemists observed that when ordinary white phosphorus was exposed to light, even in a vacuum, it became red. Although the great Swedish chemist J. J. Berzelius regarded the red substance as a modification of phosphorus, others believed that an oxide had been formed by interaction of the insufficiently dried phosphorus with water. Anton von Schrötter isolated the red substance, made a thorough study

Johan Gottschalk Wallerius, 1709–1785. Swedish chemist, physician, mineralogist, and agriculturist. T. Bergman's predecessor as professor of chemistry, metallurgy, and pharmacy at Upsala. In his analyses of bone and other animal substances in 1760, he detected the calcium but not the phosphorus.

IOANN GOTSCHALK WALLERIUS
Eques Ordin. Reg. Wasae
Primas Chemiae Metall. et Pharm. Professor Ups. MDCCL.
Ac Imp. Nat. Cur. et R.R. Acad. Stock. et Ups. Membrum.
Natus A. MDCCIX.

*Courtesy Edgar Fahs Smith
Memorial Collection*

of its properties, and confirmed Berzelius's opinion. Schrötter found that in an inert atmosphere phosphorus can be transformed from one allotropic form to the other without change of weight (53).

Since the red modification can be handled much more safely than white phosphorus this discovery has been extremely beneficent to workers in the match industry. As early as 1851 von Schrötter prepared matches with it, but they were not easily ignited. H. Hochstätter of Langen, near Frankfort-on-the Main, exhibited successful red phosphorus matches at the London Exhibition of 1872 (54). The Hochstätter matches, according to von Schrötter, "can be struck even upon cloth; they burn quietly, . . . almost without smoke and smell. . . . What is still more important, the workmen during their production are not exposed to danger of any kind soever" (54). In 1856 von Schrötter was awarded the Montyon Prize which had been established by the Paris Academy to honor those who have made notable contributions to hygienic conditions in industry.

Anton Schrötter, the son of an apothecary at Olmütz, Austria, studied medicine, chemistry, and physics, and in 1830 received an appointment in the Technical Institute in Graz, Austria. In 1843 he was called to the Polytechnic Institute in Vienna. After twenty-five years of outstanding service there he was appointed Director of the Mint (55). His last contribution to science was a chapter on "Phosphorus and matches" in Dr. A. W. von Hofmann's "Report on the Development of Chemical Industry During the Last Decade," which was published in Brunswick in 1875–77 (55).

For further details concerning the history of the match industry the reader may consult, for example, the series of articles published by M. F. Crass, Jr., in volume 18 of the *Journal of Chemical Education* in 1941 (28) and Professor László (Ladislaus) von Szathmáry's "History of the Match up to the End of the Nineteenth Century" (56). The early history of the manufacture of phosphorus in America has been described in the *Journal of Chemical Education* in an interesting article by William E. Gibbs and Claude K. Deischer (57).

Gahn was a man of broad interests who "often laid aside the *Philosophical Transactions* or his blow-pipe to read aloud, near the sewing-table in the next room, now a poem by Kellgren, Franzén, Fru Lenngren, Leopold, or Voltaire, now a comedy by Molière or Holberg; or to exhibit a little mechanical or optical masterpiece; or to study the instruments for some household art and present a method of improving them" (44).

During the preparations for his daughter Margareta's wedding, Gahn and his family witnessed a most unusual manifestation of household chemistry. Since the recipe for salting ham with a brine containing sugar and saltpeter had been lost, Fru Gahn trusted to her memory, and made the mistake of adding altogether too much saltpeter and too little water. On the wedding day, when the ham was being boiled in the brine, the terrified, breathless housekeeper came running in to report that the ham had burst into flame and was throwing out flashes of lightning, and that the house was in danger of burning down. The ensuing scene was described by Gahn himself in a letter written to Berzelius on September 20, 1807: "It was really a peculiar and pretty sight: first there rose, over the entire surface of the water in the kettle, bright, flashing sparks, which silently appeared and disappeared; then long and sometimes brilliant and violent streams of flashes were thrown in all directions over the water" (45). "After the kettle had been removed from the fire and left to cool," said Gahn, "I could see that the shining particles were originally small oil-like drops, several of which I quickly caught, and picked up, and found to be actually *phosphorus!*" (45).

The kind assistance of Dr. Max Speter of Berlin, who graciously contributed a number of important references on the early history of phosphorus, is gratefully acknowledged.

LITERATURE CITED

(1)   PETERS, HERMANN, "Geschichte des Phosphors nach Leibniz and dessen Brief-wechsel," *Chem-Ztg.*, **26**, 1190–8 (Dec. 13, 1902).

(2)   KUNCKEL, J., "Vollständiges Laboratorium Chymicum" 4th edition Rüdigersche Buchhandlung, Berlin, **1767**, pp. 605–9.

(3)   DAVIS, T. L., "Kunckel and the early history of phosphorus," *J. Chem. Educ.*, **4**, 1105–13 (Sept., 1927).

(4)   LEIBNIZ, G. W., "Geschichte der Erfindung des Phosphors," *Crell's Neues chem. Archiv*, **1**, 213–18 (1784).

(5)   "Oeuvres Complètes de Christian Huygens," Vol. 8, Soc. Hollandaise des Sciences, The Hague, **1899**, pp. 217, 236, 238, 248–9, 251–2, 256–7, 267; *ibid.*, Vol. 10, **1905**, pp. 688–9, 696–7.

(6)   "The Works of the Honourable Robert Boyle," Vol. 4, A. Millar, London, **1744**, p. 21.

(7)   BOYLE, R., "A phosphorus," *Phil. Trans. Abridgment*, 5th edition, **3**, 353–4 (1749); *Phil. Trans.*, **17**, 583–4 (Jan., 1692).

(8)   SPETER, MAX, "Zur Geschichte des Urin-Phosphors: Das entdeckte Phosphor Rezept von Boyle-Hanckwitz," *Chem.-Ztg.*, **53**, 1005–6 (Dec. 28, 1929).

(9)   SMITH, E. F., "Forgotten chemists," *J. Chem. Educ.*, **3**, 39–40 (Jan., 1926).

(10) HANCKWITZ, A. G., "Some experiments on the phosphorus urinæ . . . with several observations tending to explain the nature of that wonderful chemical production," *Phil. Trans.*, **38**, 58–70 (1733–4); *Phil. Trans. Abridgment*, ref. (7), **9**, 373–9 (1747); *Crell's Neues chem. Archiv*, **3**, 6–14 (1785).

(11) "Mineralogische, Chymische, und Alchemistische Briefe von reisenden und anderen Gelehrten an den chemaligen Chursächsischen Bergrath J. F. Henkel," 3 vols., Waltherische Buchhandlung, Dresden, **1794–95.**

(12) BUGGE, G., "Das Buch der grossen Chemiker," Vol. 1, Verlag Chemie, Berlin, **1929**, pp. 231–4.   Article on Marggraf by Max Speter.

(13) MARGGRAF, A. S., "Verschiedene neue Arten, den Harnphosphorus leichter zu verfertigen, und ihn geschwind aus Phlogiston und einem besondern Harn-salze zusammenzusetzen," *Crell's Neues chem. Archiv*, **3**, 300–3 (1785); No. 187 of Ostwald's Klassiker der exakten Wissenschaften.

(14) SPETER, MAX, "Zur Geschichte des Marggrafschen Urin-Phosphors," *Chem.-techn. Rundschau*, **44**, 1049–51 (Aug. 13, 1929).

(15) INCE, J., "Ambrose Godfrey Hanckwitz," *Pharm. J.*, [1], **18**, 126–30, 157–62, 215–22 (Aug., Sept., Oct., 1858).

(16) INCE, J., "On the discovery of phosphorus," *ibid.*, [1], **13**, 280–2 (Dec., 1853).

(17) GORE, G., "On the origin and progress of the phosphorus and match manu-factures," *Chem. News*, **4**, 16–18 (July 13, 1861).

(18) STEPHEN, L. and S. LEE, "Dictionary of National Biography," Vol. 22, Mac-millan and Co., London, **1890**, pp. 30–1.   Article on Godfrey or Godfrey-Hanckwitz.

(19) "Nitrogen and phosphorus: A classic of science," *Sci. News Letter*, **22**, 102–3 (Aug. 13, 1932).   Reprint of Boyle's "Aerial Noctiluca," ref. (6).

(20) DERHAM, W., "Philosophical experiments and observations of the late eminent Dr. Robert Hooke, F.R.S. . . . and other eminent Virtuoso's in his time," W. and J. Innys, London, 1726, pp. 178–81.

(21) LEWIS, WILLIAM, "The Chemical Works of Caspar Neumann, M.D.," Johnston, Keith, Linde, etc., London, 1759, p. 582.

(22) PILCHER, R. B., "Boyle's laboratory," Ambix, 2, Plate VII (June, 1938).

(23) GUNTHER, R. T., "Early Science in Oxford," Vol. 8, printed for the author, Oxford, 1931, pp. 271–82. Boyle's "Short memorial of some observations made upon an artificial substance that shines without precedent illustration," Sept., 1677.

(24) MACQUER, P.-J., "Elements of the Theory and Practice of Chymistry," 2nd ed., Vol. 1, A. Millar and J. Nourse London, 1764, pp. 273–7.

(25) WEEKS, M. E., "Max Speter, 1883–1942," Isis, 34, 340–4 (Spring, 1943).

(26) TESTI, GINO, "Un punto oscuro di storia della chimica da investigare. L'opera di Raimondo di Sangro," La Chimica nell' Industria, nell' Agricoltura, e nella Biologia, 6, 412–13 (Oct. 31, 1930); Archeion, 13, 67–8 (1931).

(27) VON KLINCKOWSTROEM, CARL GRAF, "Raimondo di Sangro," ibid., 14, 490–1 (1932).

(28) CRASS, M. F., JR., "A history of the match industry," J. Chem. Educ., 18, 116 (Mar., 1941).

(29) WAITE, A. E., "The Hermetic and Alchemical Writings of Paracelsus the Great," Vol. 2, James Elliott and Co., London, 1894, p. 19.

(30) GUNTHER, R. T., "Early Science in Oxford," ref. (23), Vol. 7, pp. 588–9.

(31) LÉMERY, N., "A Course of Chymistry," 2nd English ed. from the 5th French, Walter Kettilby, London, 1686, p. 529.

(32) NOLLET, M. L'ABBÉ, "Leçons de Physique Expérimentale," vol. 4, Frères Guerin, Paris, 1748, pp. 228–36.

(33) MACQUER, P.-J., "Elements of the Theory and Practice of Chymistry," 2nd ed., Vol. 1, A. Millar and J. Nourse, 1764, pp. 261–79.

(34) ALBINUS, B., Dissertatio de Phosphoro Liquido et Solido," Frankfurt-on-the Oder, 1688.

(35) MARGGRAF, A. S., "Chymische Schriften," revised ed., Vol. 1, Arnold Wever, Berlin, 1768, pp. 75–7, 104–5.

(36) FRIEND, J. N., "A Textbook of Inorganic Chemistry," Vol. 6, part 2, Charles Griffin and Co., London, 1934, pp. 4–5. "Phosphorus" by E. B. R. Prideaux.

(37) LAVOISIER, A.-L., "Traité Élémentaire de Chimie," 2nd ed., Vol. 1, Cuchet, Paris, 1793, pp. 224–5.

(38) MEYER, J. K. F., "Ueber die Phosphorsäure in dem grünen harzigten Bestandtheile der Pflanzenblätter," Crell's Ann., 1, 521–2 (1784).

(39) LEWIS, WILLIAM, ref. (21), pp. 493–4.

(40) WALLERIUS, J. G., "Untersuchung der Erden aus Wasser, Pflanzen, und Thieren, drittes Stück; von der Erde aus Thieren," Crell's Neues chem. Archiv, 8, 285–6 (1791); K. Vet. Acad. Handl., 22, 188 (1760).

(41) SPETER, MAX, "Berzelius' views on Gahn's share in the discovery of the composition of bone earth," Superphosphate, 6, 125–6 (July, 1933). In German, French, and English.

(42) VON CRELL, L., "Versuch aus menschlichen Knochen einen Phosphorus zu bereiten," Crell's Chemisches Journal, 1, 23–39 (1778).

(43) NORDENSKIÖLD, A. E., "C. W. Scheele. Nachgelassene Briefe und Aufzeichnungen," P. A. Norstedt and Sons, Stockholm, 1892, p. 318. Letter of Scheele to T. Bergman, Aug. 18, 1780.

(44) JÄRTA, HANS, "Åminnelse-tal öfver Herr Joh. Gottl. Gahn," P. A. Norstedt and Sons, Stockholm, 1832, 51 pp.

(45) SÖDERBAUM, H. G., "Jac. Berzelius Brev," part 9, Almqvist and Wiksells Publishing Co., Upsala, 1922, pp. 18–19. Letter of Gahn to Berzelius, Sept. 20, 1807.

(46) BOERHAAVE, HERMAN, "Élémens de Chymie," Vol. 1, Chardon fils, Paris, 1754, pp. lviii–lix.
(47) GELLERT, C. E., "Metallurgic Chemistry," T. Becket, London, 1776, p. 28.
(48) BERGMAN, TORBERN, "Opuscula physica et chemica," Vol. 2, I. G. Müller, Lipsiæ, 1792, p. 424; "De minerarum docimasia," Upsala, 1780.
(49) "Encyclopédie méthodique. Chimie et métallurgie par M. Fourcroy," Vol. 5, H. Agasse, Paris, 1808, p. 638.
(50) KOBELL, FRANZ VON, "Geschichte der Mineralogie von 1650–1860," J. G. Cotta, Munich, 1864, pp. 536–7, 540, 609–10.
(51) KLAPROTH, M. H., "Ueber die Phosphorsäure im Zschopauer grünen Bleyspathe," Crell's Beyträge zu den Chem. Ann., 1 (part 2), 13–21 (1785).
(52) "Physical and Chemical Essays Translated from the Original Latin of Sir Torbern Bergman," Vol. 3, Mudie, Fairbairn, and J. Evans, London, 1791, pp. 261 and 281.
(53) SCHRÖTTER, A. VON, "Neue Modifikation des Phosphors," Ann., 68, 247–53 (1848); J. prakt. Chem., (1), 51, 155 (1850).
(54) SCHRÖTTER, A. VON, "Phosphorus and matches," Chem. News, 36, 208, 219–21 (Nov. 9–16, 1877).
(55) KOHN, MORITZ, "The discovery of red phosphorus (1847) by Anton von Schrötter (1802–1875)," J. Chem. Educ., 21, 522 (Nov., 1944).
(56) SZATHMÁRY, LÁSZLÓ, "A Gyufa Története a XIX-ik Század Végéig," A Kis Akademia Kiadása, Budapest, 1935, 127 pp.; Nouvelles de la Chimie, No. 23 (Nov., 1936); SZATHMÁRY, LADISLAUS VON, "Stephan Rómer, der Fabrikant, and Johann Irinyi, der Ideeeur-Erfinder des geräuschlos entflammenden Phosphor-Zündholzes von Anno 1836," Z. für das gesamte Schiess- und Sprengstoffwesen, 31, No. 10, 333–7; No. 11, 368–72; No. 12, 1–3 (1936). Translated from Hungarian into German by Max Speter.
(57) GIBBS, W. E. and C. K. DEISCHER, "George Rose: A pioneer in American phosphorus manufacture from 1870 to 1899," J. Chem. Educ., 27, 269–73 (May, 1950).
(58) WINDERLICH, RUDOLF, "Brenngläser als Hilfsmittel chemischen Forschens," Chymia, 2, 37–43 (1949).

Andreas Sigismund Marggraf, 1709-1782. German chemist who distinguished between potash and soda, realized that clay contains the peculiar oxide now known as alumina, recognized magnesia, isolated zinc from calamine, and discovered sugar in the beet.

From Bugge's "Das Buch der grossen Chemiker"

"Knowing how contented, free and joyful is life in the realms of science, one fervently wishes that many would enter their portals." (1).

5

Some eighteenth-century metals

*Among the metals isolated in the eighteenth century may be men-
tioned zinc, cobalt, nickel, and manganese, the last three of which
were discovered in Sweden. The researches of Marggraf, Georg
Brandt, Cronstedt, and Gahn which led to the recognition and
isolation of these elements were scientific contributions of the
first rank, and the personalities of these great men are well worthy
of study and emulation. Other metals of this period will be discussed in later chapters.*

ZINC

*P*liny the Elder and Dioscorides of Anazarbus mentioned that
zinc compounds were used for healing wounds and sore eyes (*41, 42*). In
the latter part of the thirteenth century A.D., Marco Polo described
the manufacture of zinc oxide in Persia: "Kubenan is a large town. The
people worship Mahommet. There is much iron and steel. . . . They
also prepare both *Tutia* (a thing very good for the eyes) and *Spodium;*
and I will tell you the process. They have a vein of a certain earth
which has the required quality, and this they put into a great flaming
furnace, whilst over the furnace there is an iron grating. The smoke and
moisture, expelled from the earth of which I speak, adhere to the iron
grating, and thus form *Tutia,* whilst the slag that is left after burning is
the *Spodium*" (*43*).

Brass. Centuries before zinc was discovered in the metallic form,
its ores were used for making brass.

Strabo of Amasia, Asia Minor (66 B.C.–24 A.D.), said in his geography that only the Cyprian ore contained "the cadmian stone, copper
vitriol, and tutty," that is to say, the constituents from which brass can
be made (*90*). He also mentioned "a stone in the neighbourhood of
Andeira which, when burned, becomes iron, and then, when heated in
a furnace with a certain earth, distils mocksilver [zinc]; and this, with
the addition of copper, makes the mixture, as it is called, which by some
is called mountain-copper [orichalcum, or brass]" (*91*).

The Romans manufactured a copper-zinc alloy which they called
orichalcum or *aurichalcum.* In speaking of copper, Pliny the Elder

said that "The ore is mined as already related, and smelted. The metal is prepared also from a coppery mineral called cadmea. . . . Cyprian copper soon became very cheap when better kinds, more particularly aurichalcum, were found elsewhere . . ." (92). Of the Marian, or Cordovan, copper he said, "It is only surpassed by the Livian in its power of alloying with cadmea, and sesterces and two-as pieces made from it are so fine as to counterfeit aurichalcum." The Latin word *cadmea* refers both to zinc ores and to the volatized zinc oxide (Ofenbruch, or furnace calamine) obtained by roasting them (47). These ores included both the hydrous silicate (calamine) and the carbonate (smithsonite).

William Gowland stated in 1912 that the Romans first made brass in the time of Augustus (20 B.C. to 14 A.D.) (93). They made it by heating a mixture of powdered calamine, charcoal, and granules of copper, keeping the contents of the crucible below the melting point of copper. After the zinc vapor had reacted with the copper, the temperature was raised to melt the brass. This "calamine brass" was manufactured in Europe as late as the nineteenth century. Although James Emerson patented a process in England in 1781 for the manufacture of brass from copper and zinc metals, conservative English metallurgists long preferred the calamine process (93).

Metallic Zinc. Ancient metallurgist probably lost the volatile zinc metal as vapor because their apparatus was not designed for condensing it. E. O. von Lippmann, a great authority on the history of science, searched the writings of Aristotle, Pliny, and Dioscorides in vain for any mention of it, but an idol containing 87.5 per cent of that metal was found in a prehistoric Dacian ruin at Dordosch, Transylvania (2).

According to the *Rasarnava,* which was published in India in the thirteenth century A.D., metallic zinc was prepared by reducing calamine in a closed crucible with organic substances such as lac or wool (94). P. C. Râ011y stated that the Hindu king, Madanapála, recognized zinc as a metal as early as 1374 (3), and it is probable that the art of smelting the ores originated in India and was carried first to China.

A Chinese book entitled "Tien kong kai ou" printed in 1637 describes the metallurgy and uses of this metal (2, 44). As early as the sixteenth century, Europe was importing zinc from China, where the large-scale production of it probably originated (44, 95). In his extended researches on the history of zinc, W. Hommel analyzed a specimen of this metal which had once formed part of the cargo of the East India Company's ship *Götheborg* which sank near Gothenburg, Sweden, in 1745. He found it to be very pure (44). Although small amounts of zinc for medicinal purposes were prepared in India in the thirteenth and four-

Production of Zinc in China as pictured in the Chinese technical lexicon "Tien kong kai ou."

teenth centuries, the technical production of it originated in China in the sixteenth century. Hommel quoted from the 1637 edition of the "Tien kong kai ou" the following description of the process: "One strongly compresses the ore [Lu-kan-shi, or calamine] in clay crucibles having covers well luted with loam. The crucibles are piled up in a pyramid with lump coal between them, and, after being brought to redness, are cooled and broken. The metal is found in the center in the form of a round regulus" (44).

Johann Beckmann, in his "History of Inventions," quoted the following passage from the 1616 Strasburg folio edition of the works of Paracelsus (1493?–1541): "There is another metal, zinc, which is in general unknown. It is a distinct metal of a different origin, though adulterated with many other metals. It can be melted, for it consists of three fluid principles, but it is not malleable. In its colour it is unlike all others, and does not grow in the same manner; but with its *ultima materia* I am as yet unacquainted, for it is almost as strange in its properties as *argentum vivum* [quicksilver]. It admits of no mixture, will not bear the fabrications of other metals, but keeps itself entirely to itself" (47). A similar passage appears in the "Book of Minerals," which forms part of the Latin folio edition of Paracelsus's works published in Geneva in 1658 (96).

In the seventeenth century, miners believed that base metals gradually develop in the mine into the more perfect ones such as silver and gold. J. R. Glauber said that "when the miners sometimes dig up an untimely ore, such as bismuth, cobalt, or zinc, and test it for silver without finding any, they say, we have come too soon . . ." (97). Glauber, however, did not share the general belief in the close relationship between the planets and the metals. "For," said he, "if each planet generated its special metal, it would also undoubtedly choose a special place and would not allow another to come into its nest and interfere with its intention. And if we nevertheless maintain that each planet gives birth to its own metal, to which star should one assign bismuth, cobalt, antimony, and zinc?" (97).

Geoffroy the Elder (1672–1731) described zinc as "a Metallick sulphureous heavy Substance resembling Lead in Colour, fusible and ductile to a certain Degree, being very hard to break, inflammable, and volatile. It seems to have been quite unknown to the Antients, and even the Moderns knew very little about its Nature or Origin till M. Stahl, now First Physician to his Prussian Majesty, explained it in his Dissertation *De Metallurgia*. It is extracted from the Lead Oar of the Mines of Gosselaar [Goslar]. . . . Three substances are separated from it: Lead, Zinch, and a Kind of *Cadmia Fornacea*, which being melted with Copper, makes a Prince's or Bath Metal. . . .   The Pewterers use Zinch in whitening and purifying Tin . . ." (98).

"The Modern *Cadmia, Cadmia Fornacum* of Agricola, Tutia of the shops," continued Geoffroy, "is a Recrement of Calamin, melted with Copper, and not of Copper alone, as was that of the Antients. The official Tutty therefore may be defined as a Sublimation of Calamin from melting Copper to the upper Part or Roof of the Furnace, where it concretes round Iron Rods placed there, into a solid Crust, which is afterwards beat off into Pieces, like the Bark of Trees, of a yellowish Colour, smooth on the inside and sonorous; of a bluish Ash Colour on the outside, and powdered as it were with very small Grains of the same Substance. . . . Tutty is reckoned among the principal Ophthalmick Medicines. . . .   The Pompholyx of our Shops, *Nihil Album* of some Authors, is a fine white Flower, or Soot, which sticks to the Arch of the Furnaces and Covers of the Crucibles in which Calamin and Copper are melted together . . ."(98).

A hundred years before zinc was smelted in Europe, it was being sold there by Portuguese traders who brought it from the Orient (4). G. Agricola mentioned the formation of "zincum" in the furnaces in Silesia (31). Small amounts of metallic zinc were obtained as a by-product of the lead industry at Goslar, Prussia, and G. E. Löhneyss described the process as follows: "The metal *zinc* or *counterfeht* is formed under the smelting furnaces and in the crevices of the wall where the bricks are not well plastered. When the wall is scraped, the metal falls down into a trough placed to receive it. The metal is not much valued, and the workmen collect it only when they are promised Trinkgeld" (2, 18, 28).

Caspar Neumann (1683–1737) gave the following first-hand description of the Goslar zinc works: "The greatest quantities of Zinc come from the East Indies, in large oblong pieces; and from Goslar, commonly in round cakes or loaves. Of the origin of the East-India Zinc we have no certain account: The Goslarian is extracted from the Lead- and Silver-ores of Rammelsberg by a particular contrivance in the structure of the furnace. The Zinc, naturally contained in the ore, separates during the fusion from the other metallic matters, being elevated by the heat in form of fume, which passes into a reservoir made for that purpose in the front wall, over the gutter by which the Lead runs off. The reservoir for the Zinc is inclosed, on the inside, by a large flat stone, only some chinks being left for the fumes to enter; and on the outside, by another stone, which is closely luted, and frequently sprinkled during the process with cold water, to cool and condense the fumes. Each smelting lasts twenty hours, beginning at ten in the forenoon and ending at six next morning. When the fusion of the ore is completed, the workman dextrously strikes the outer stone of the reservoir with an Iron rod, so as to loosen some of the luting at the bottom; upon which the Zinc, collected during the process, runs out like Quicksilver. He continues to tap till nothing more will run; then melts the Zinc again in an iron pot, and casts it into hemi-spherical masses. I have several times been at this work, and kept at it two days and a night together without leaving the furnace.

"Though a part of the Zinc is thus obtained in its metallic form, a part is also dissipated, and a very considerable one adheres to the sides of the furnace in the form of a calx. . . . The produce of Zinc is extremely variable. . . . At Goslar, when the due precautions happen to be neglected, there is not so much Zinc detained as to be worth collect-ing . . ." (33).

Johann Andreas Cramer of Blankenburg (1710–1777), in his "Ele-ments of the Art of Assaying Metals," which was first published in Leyden in 1737, wrote: "Zinc is called in German *Contrafait Spiauter;* whether it is or ever was found native, in the same Form mentioned, is a Secret to me; nor is there any known kind of Ore, out of which this semi-Metal may be melted. . . . Therefore, all the Zink that is prepared in Germany, especially at Goslar, is obtained by sublimation, not by Eliquation, and not got out of any singular Ore, but out of such an intricate and confused Mixture of different Ores that several other Metals and semi-Metals may be separated at the same Time from it. Iron, Lead, and Copper are also contained in it in great Plenty; and are almost all involved in Sulphur and Arsenick. There are no peculiar Sublimations made for the extracting of Zink, but, by a Sort of secondary Operation, it is collected during the Eliquation of the other Metals, especially of Lead. . . .

"However," continued Cramer, "there are besides the Matrixs [sic] of Zink hitherto mentioned, that are found at Goslar, some others which may be called Zink Ores. To this class belongs especially the Lapis Calaminaris, or Calamine, in German *Galmey*, and also native *Cadmia*, to distinguish it from that which is called *Furnace-cadmia*. . . . You can never, by the only Force of Fire, or by the help of the common reducing Fluxes, produce any Zink out of this Stone. However, the Agreeableness of the Flowers of the said Stone with those of Zink, the changing of the red Colour of Copper into the yellow gold Colour (brass), which alteration is effected both by the Calamine and by Zink; and finally, the Production of Zink itself out of the Lapis Calaminaris, to be obtained by several manual Operations, require that we should class it among Zink-Ores. . . . Zink is confounded with Bismuth by several Authors. . . .

"The Dutch bring to Europe in their East India Ships," said Cramer, "a great Quantity of Zink, which is a little more blue than the German Zink, and in every Respect more tenacious. But we know nothing certain either of the Country where the Ore that contains this Zink is digged out or . . . of the Manner in which Zink is obtained out of it. For they say no European is granted the Liberty of entering into those Countries" (*51, 99*).

Johann Kunckel and Georg Ernst Stahl believed that the ore calamine contained a metal that alloys with copper to form brass, and even as late as 1735, the Swedish chemist Georg Brandt thought that calamine could not be reduced to a metal except in presence of copper (*2, 19*). During the years between 1768 and 1781, Richard Watson, Bishop of Llandaff, published his famous chemical essays (*45*). In the one on zinc, he quoted the following passage from page 295 of the French translation of J. F. Henckel's (or Henkel's) "Pyritologia": "One makes, for example, with the calamine, not only iron (in small amounts, to be sure), but also a very large quantity of zinc, which one obtains not only on presenting to it the substance with which it can incorporate itself (that is to say, copper, which is its lodestone), but also this half-metal shows itself simply on addition of a fatty substance which metallizes; it is only necessary to avoid letting this phoenix be reduced to ash, to keep it from burning, and to observe the time and circumstances" (*46*). Henckel prepared metallic zinc by reduction of calamine, but kept the process secret (*29, 47*). As the shining metal came forth from the hard, lusterless ore, he was reminded of the Egyptian symbol of immortality, the phoenix, a fabulous bird which rose to new life from its ashes.

In the introduction to his German translation of P. M. de Respour's "Special Experiments on the Mineral Spirit," Henckel mentioned in 1743 that "In our smelting furnaces at Freyberg we have obtained the essence of zinc [zinckische Wesen] in power but not in form" (*48*). He believed that their failure to obtain "corporal" [metallic] zinc must have been due to the complex nature of their ore, to the construction of their furnaces, and to the long-continued heating, which made it "impossible for the phoenix, even when resurrected from its ash, to withstand the fire" (*48*).

"Nevertheless," said Henckel, "zinc is a metal with regard to its consistency, luster, specific gravity, tenacity, and mercurial fluidity in the fire, but also not a metal with respect to its flammability and complete combustibility, wherein it is entirely different from all other metals" (*48*).

The Flemish metallurgist P. M. de Respour published the first edition of his "Special Experiments on the Mineral Spirit" in 1668, when he was twenty-four years old. He prepared a minute amount of metallic

zinc by gently heating a mixture of zinc oxide and fat on a sandbath for
six or seven days. When he subsequently distilled this mixture, he found
in the retort only a little gray, fuming deposit in which he was unable
to distinguish any metallic particles. When he rubbed it with mercury,
however, and distilled off the latter, he obtained a little metallic zinc
(48).

Bishop Watson stated that, "though Henckel was the first, Dr. Isaac
Lawson was, probably, the second person in Europe who procured zinc
from calamine. . . . Our English writers . . . speak in high terms of
Lawson . . ." (46). Since the Bishop prefaces his description of the
metal with the words "If the reader has never seen a piece of zinc," it
must have been a rarity even in the second half of the eighteenth century (46).

When Lawson observed that the flowers of lapis calaminaris were
the same as those of zinc and that they had the same effect on copper,
he worked tirelessly until he found a method of separating the zinc from
this mineral. He never realized any profit, however, from this discovery (46).

While in Leyden, Dr. Lawson belonged to a scientific club presided
over by the great Swedish botanist Carl von Linné, and became so engrossed in making mineralogical analyses that he gave up attending
lectures. Another of Lawson's Leyden contemporaries who held him in
high esteem was Dr. Herman Boerhaave (49, 50).

Johann Andreas Cramer assisted Dr. Lawson for several years in
his chemical experiments in Leyden. In the preface to the second English
edition of Cramer's "Elements of the Art of Assaying Metals," there is
a fine tribute to Dr. Lawson, who "had resided much longer at Leyden
than those foreigners usually do who go there to qualify themselves for
the Practice of Physick. He then employed himself in the Cultivation
of those arts which he had there been taught; particularly of Chemistry;
and was highly esteemed for his Skill therein, and lived in great Intimacy
with Boerhaave . . . and with several other Men of great Learning, who
resided in that University . . . as also with Linnaeus. . . . Doctor Lawson
afterwards served as Physician to the British Army in Flanders; where,
by his Death, in the year 1745, the World was deprived of the Advantage
of many useful Discoveries. To him we owe several of the Observations
contained in this Work. . ." (51).

In a great research "On the method of extracting zinc from its true
mineral, calamine," A. S. Marggraf in 1746 reduced calamine from Poland,
England, Breslau, and Hungary with carbon in closed retorts, and obtained
metallic zinc from all of them (2, 19, 27). He found the ore from
Holywell to be especially rich in it. He stated that both J. H. Pott and

J. H. Henckel had known how to prepare this metal and keep it from burning.

Marggraf also showed that the lead ores of Rammelsberg contained zinc and that zinc can be prepared from blende, or sphalerite (53). "Who would think," said he, "that this furnace calamine [in Saxony] is derived

Courtesy Virginia Bartow

Richard Watson, Bishop of Llandaff, 1737–1816.
Professor of chemistry, and later professor of divinity,
at Cambridge. Between 1768 and 1781 he published
a collection of chemical essays on water, air, coal, lead,
zinc, salt, saltpeter, and other common substances. He
gave an excellent account of the early history of zinc.

from blende and that this blende contains the zinc earth, for I know of no one who ever thought of it except the aforementioned Herr Professor Pott, who mentioned on page 119 of his treatise on pseudo-galena that pulverized blende, melted with carbon and copper, did not, to be sure, entirely convert the copper to brass, yet made it rather yellow, and therefore correctly concluded that it must contain an earth related to calamine. Still less has anyone, so far as I know, ever yet made known the process of actually preparing zinc from this mineral, which, however, I hope to make clear from the following experiment" (53).

Marggraf was probably unaware that in 1742 Anton von Svab, a step-brother of Emanuel Swedenborg, had distilled zinc from calamine at Vestervik, Dalecarlia, and that, two years later, he had even prepared it from blende (18). Since the vapors rose to the top of the alembic before passing into the receiver, this process was called distillation *per ascensum*. In the fall of 1752 Svab and A. F. Cronstedt developed at government expense the use of Swedish zinc ores in the manufacture of brass, to avoid the necessity of importing calamine. They installed equipment near Skisshyttan for the washing, slow oxidation, decomposition, and calcination of the ore and for distillation of the zinc. Svab showed that blende can be reduced even in the absence of copper (52). In 1755 Cronstedt's share in the work was taken over by Sven Rinman (32, 46, 47). Rinman so improved the metallurgical process that zinc could be smelted not merely in the form of grains or powder, which required subsequent melting and consequent loss of metal, but also in fluid form directly from the ore (81).

Some Famous American Zinc Mines. In 1810 Dr. Archibald Bruce analyzed a new orange-red mineral from Franklin Furnace, Sussex County, New Jersey, and found it to be zinc oxide containing a little manganese. This mineral is now known as zincite (100, 101, 102).

Archibald Bruce was born and educated in New York City. His father, a British army surgeon stationed in New York, always declared that his son should never be educated for the medical profession. The boy's natural inclination led him, however, to study medicine and allied sciences secretly while enrolled in the arts course in Columbia College. His favorite recreation was the collection and study of minerals. After studying abroad for several years he received his degree of doctor of medicine from the University of Edinburgh in 1800. During a two-year tour of France, Switzerland, and Italy, he exchanged American minerals for European specimens and thus built up a valuable collection. After his return to New York in 1803 he engaged in a successful practice of medicine (103). He also served as professor of materia medica and mineralogy in the Medical Institution of the State of New York and Queen's College, New Jersey. Among his friends and correspondents were Mr. Greville of Paddington Green, near London, Count J.-L. Bournon, Sir Joseph Banks, and the Abbé R.-J. Haüy. Dr. Bruce died in New York in 1818 at the age of forty-one years.

Among the remarkable zinc minerals at Franklin Furnace Dr. Bruce also found another new one which was black. When P. Berthier analyzed a specimen of it, he found it to be composed of the oxides of iron, manganese, and zinc. He gave it the name *franklinite* "derived from Franklin, in order to remind us that it was found, for the first time, in a place to which the Americans have given the name of a great man, whose memory is venerated equally in Europe as in the new world by all the friends of science and humanity" (*101*).

A third remarkable and unusual zinc mineral in the Franklin ore body is willemite, the fluorescent zinc orthosilicate which was first characterized in 1829 by Armand Levy, who named it for Willem I of the Netherlands (*102*).

In about 1830 an unsuccessful attempt was made to determine the nature of a peculiar ore from the Saucon Valley near Bethlehem, Pennsylvania. Mr. W. T. Roepper, who afterward became the first professor of mineralogy at Lehigh University, identified it as calamine, zinc hydrosilicate, and produced brass by smelting it with native copper (*110*). The history of early zinc works in the Lehigh Valley has been ably presented in the *Journal of Chemical Education* by R. D. Billinger (*110*).

When Henry R. Schoolcraft visited the lead mines of Missouri in about 1819, he noticed that the zinc sulfide ore sphalerite was also abundant (*111*). Even in the early nineteenth century, the value of sphalerite was not appreciated. In Henry R. Schoolcraft's report on the lead mines of Missouri, which was published in the *American Journal of Science* for 1821, appears the statement: "Zinc is abundant, but as the ore is the sulphuret, it is not very valuable. It is not mentioned that the calamine, which is *the useful* ore of zinc, has been found" (*54*).

Zinc in Plant and Animal Nutrition. As early as 1877 G. Lechartier and F. Bellamy observed the presence of zinc in plants and animals (*104, 105*). Since then its important role in the nutrition of many plants has been demonstrated repeatedly. When some pecan trees growing on a copper-deficient soil in Florida were treated with a copper solution, the only trees which responded favorably were those treated with a certain batch of copper solution which had been stirred up in a galvanized bucket and therefore contained zinc as an unintentional constituent (*106*). Zinc solutions are now used in the treatment of the disease called pecan rosette and of other zinc-deficiency diseases of fruit trees and nut-bearing trees in the western states (*112*).

L. B. Mendel and H. C. Bradley found in 1905 that the snail *sycotypus* contains zinc in the liver and in the oxygen-carrying protein of the blood, hemosycotypin. The three respiratory proteins, hemoglobin of the vertebrates, hemocyanin of the octopus, and hemosycotypin of the snail, are thus analogous. Their oxygen-carrying metals are respectively iron, copper, and zinc (*107, 113*).

Because of the importance of zinc in nutrition, sensitive methods have been devised for determining it in plant and animal materials, soils, and natural waters. The polarographic method has been used with success (*108, 109*).

SOME SWEDISH METALS

In the eighteenth century Sweden outstripped all other countries in the discovery of new elements. It is blessed with a rich supply of rare ores and, moreover, it had a long succession of brilliant chemists and mineralogists whose greatest delight was to investigate these curious minerals. In the century following the accidental discovery of phosphorus, three new metals, cobalt, nickel, and manganese, were discovered by Swedish chemists.

COBALT

> *"Thus with Hermetic art the Adept combines*
> *The Royal acid with cobaltic mines;*
> *Marks with quick pen, in lines unseen portrayed,*
> *The blushing mead, green dell, and dusky glade;*
> *Shades with pellucid clouds the tintless field,*
> *And all the future Group exists conceal'd;*
> *Till waked by fire the dawning tablet glows,*
> *Green springs the herb, the purple floret blows,*
> *Hills, vales, and woods in bright succession rise,*
> *And all the living landscape charms the eyes"* (*62*).

Analyses of blue glass made by the ancients show that the earliest specimens were colored sometimes with cobalt but much more often with copper (*64, 65, 66*). In the tomb of Tut-ankh-Amen were many specimens of dark blue glass, only one of which was found to contain cobalt (*67*). Archaeologists from the University of Pennsylvania discovered in Nippur, Mesopotamia, an authentic specimen of artificial lapis lazuli dating from about 1400 B.C. and sent a sample of it to Professor Neumann of the Higher Technical School of Breslau for analysis. He found that this glass contains a remarkably high cobalt content, namely about 0.93 per cent of cobaltous oxide. Although Neumann and his collaborators had analyzed many antique glasses dating from 1500 B.C. to 800 A.D. this was the first one in which they found cobalt (*114*). R. Winderlich believed that when the Persian ceramist Abulqâsim wrote in his "Book of Gems and Perfumes" in 1301 A.D. that one takes for coloring the glaze "for the Sulaimânî blue . . . for every forty parts of glass frit one part of lâgward [lapis lazuli, or ultramarine]," he must have been speaking of cobalt ores; true lapis lazuli is useless for this purpose (115, 116).

Paracelsus, in his "Book of Minerals," which forms part of the 1658 Latin folio edition of his works, gave only a vague description of cobalt (7). The unknown author of the writings attributed to "Basil Valentine" stated in his treatise "On the great stone of the ancient philosophers" that "Among the minerals are included all metals, ores, marcasite, cobalt (Kobold), talc, zinc, shining pyrites, and stones" (63). P.-E.-M. Berthelot thought, however, that metallic cobalt must have been prepared before the thirteenth century, for the alchemists understood how to roast and reduce ores. They did not, however, know how to refine the metals and distinguish between them (7).

Near the end of the fifteenth century, a troublesome and supposedly worthless mineral, "cobalt," was found in large quantity in the mines on the borders of Saxony and Bohemia (68). The miners disliked it because of the labor of removing it and also because the arsenic in it injured their health. The first glassmaker who really understood the specific ability of these ores to impart a blue color to glass was Christoph Schürer of Platten, Bohemia, who, in about the middle of the sixteenth century, prepared a blue color for pottery at the Eulen smelter in Neudeck (69). On a visit to Schneeberg he collected some pieces of the ore. When he tested them in his glass-furnace, he found that they fused with the vitreous mass and yielded a handsome blue glass. At his plant in Neudeck he prepared the new color, first for the use of local potters and later for shipment to Nuremberg and thence to the Netherlands, where the skilled glass-painters understood better how to use it (68).

The poorer grades were used for making bluing and blue starch for laundry (70). Roasted cobalt ore was soon exported in casks to eight colormills in the Netherlands. When the people of Schneeberg began to remark that the part of the cobalt ore which dropped down while being roasted contained more color than the roasted ore itself, Elector Johann Georg subsidized the development of an extensive cobalt industry there (68). A mixture of roasted cobalt ore and sand, which was added to conceal its nature, was known as Zaffer, Safflor, or Safran. Most of the cobalt ores in the Erzgebirge also contained bismuth, which was easily separated by liquation.

After mentioning calamine, Vannoccio Biringuccio stated in his "Pirotechnia" in 1540: "Another similar half-mineral is Zaffer. It is heavy like metal. It does not melt by itself, but when mixed with vitreous substances it becomes like water and colors them blue. Zaffer is therefore used for coloring glasses blue or for painting glass vessels with a blue color. At the artist's desire, it also serves as a black pigment in these crafts, by taking more of it than is permissible for blue" (71, 85, 151).

The great sixteenth-century French ceramist Bernard Palissy (86) once wrote: "I know no plant nor mineral nor any substance which can tinge stones blue or azure except saphre, which is a mineral earth, extracted from gold, silver, and copper, which has very little color, except gray inclining a little toward the violet. Whenever the said saphre is incorporated with vitreous substances, it makes a marvelously fine azure: hence one may know that all stones having an azure color have taken their tint from the said saphre" (72).

In his "Art of Glass," an English translation of which was published in 1699, Haudicquer de Blancourt, who was especially fond of blue because "it has resemblance to that of the Heavenly Arch and is taken for the Symbol of Generosity," gave specific directions for the preparation of metallic pigments used to tinge glass and "set it off with an unspeakable Beauty" (73). In his chapter on "The way to prepare Zaffer to tinge and colour Glass," he quoted from Christopher Merret's annotated translation of Father Antonio Neri's "L'Arte vetraria":

"Merret speaking of Zaffer, and of the Latin word Zaffera, says it comes from Germany. It is taken by some for a preparation of an Earth to tinge Glass blue, by others for a Stone, and by him for a Secret; asserting that there are but few Authors who make mention of it, and no one that tells us what it is. . . . Merret says Zaffer is a Compound, asserting it is neither Earth nor Stone. . . . That certainly, if it were either of these two, it would have been discovered by the Diligence of those that have treated of it, being of so great use to those who make Glass. Which makes that Author say, the Zaffer is a Secret, whereof the Composition was found out by a German. That if he might give his Conjecture of it, he should think it made of Copper and Sand, and some proportion of Lapis Calaminaris; that the blue Colour it gives seems to be owing to the Brass, as that of Manganese to Iron. That only Minerals can tinge Glass, and that no Materials can be found for that purpose, except Metalline Ones. Wherefore he concludes, that the matter which composes Zaffer can only be either Copper or Brass . . ." (73).

Haudicquer de Blancourt then told how Father Neri prepared Zaffer by heating the ore to redness in the furnace, sprinkling it with vinegar, grinding it, and washing it by decantation with warm water (73, 74). In his "Ars Vitraria Experimentalis" Johann Kunckel explained that the acetic acid used in this process was unnecessary and that the roasting

Bernard Palissy, 1510?–1589. French glassmaker, surveyor, potter, agriculturist, and chemist who was familiar with "zaffer," or cobalt blue.

> *"Who is it in the suburbs here,*
> *This Potter, working with such cheer, . . .*
> *This madman, as the people say,*
> *Who breaks his tables and his chairs*
> *To feed his furnace fires . . .*
> *O Palissy! within thy breast*
> *Burned the hot fever of unrest"* (82, 152)

of the ore served to remove the arsenic, which was then collected, re-sublimed, and sold in the apothecary shops (70).

Pierre Pomet (Pometius), a contemporary of Haudicquer de Blancourt, described Zaffer in the section on minerals in his "History of Drugs": "Safre, or Zafre, is a Mineral of a Bluish or Partridge-Eye Colour, which the English, Dutch, and Hamburgers bring us from the East Indies and especially from Surat. . . . Safre is much us'd by Delft

Ware and Glass Makers, to give a blue Colour to both Sorts of Ware; 'Tis also with Safre that they colour calcin'd Pewter, in order to make the false Stone, which I've noted in the Chapter of Enamels: And lastly, with Safre it is that the azure Colour of Glass is produc'd, as is before observ'd, and of which is made the counterfeit Sapphires" (117).

Georg Brandt, the discoverer of cobalt, was born in the spring of 1694 at Riddarhytta, Vestmanland, where his father, Jurgen Brandt, a former apothecary, operated a copper smelter, an ironworks, and some mines. At an early age Georg began to help his father with his chemical and metallurgical experiments. He studied medicine and chemistry for three years at Leyden under the famous Herman Boerhaave and received his degree of doctor of medicine at Reims in 1726. Although he never carried on a general practice, he was one of the physicians called to the deathbed of Fredrik I (5, 6, 34).

On his way home from the Netherlands he studied mining and metallurgy in the Harz, and in 1727 he was placed in charged of the chemical laboratory at the Bureau of Mines in Stockholm, which was then in poor financial condition. After the laboratory was sold, Brandt and his students Henrik Teofil Scheffer and Axel Fredrik Constedt carried on their epoch-making researches at the Royal Mint, and in 1730 Brandt became assay master of the Mint. Three years later he published a systematic investigation of arsenic and its compounds in which he showed that arsenic is a "semi-metal" and that "white arsenic" [arsenious oxide] is its calx (35).

Brandt's most important contribution to science was his discovery of the element cobalt. Since the mineral which had been used since the sixteenth century for making "Zaffer," or smalt, resembled copper ores in its ability to give blue solutions when dissolved in acids, yet (even in minute amounts) imparted a much deeper blue color to glass than copper compounds do, it was called "cobalt" from the German word *Kobold,* meaning *subterranean gnome.* These little, teasing earth sprites are frequently mentioned in Goethe's "Faust":

Salamander soll glühen	Salamander shall kindle,
Undene sich winden,	Writhe nymph of the wave,
Sylphe verschwinden,	In air sylph shall dwindle,
Kobold sich mühen.	And Kobold shall slave.
Wer sie nicht kennte	Who doth ignore
Die Elemente,	The primal Four,
Ihre Kraft,	Nor knows aright
Und Eigenschaft,	Their use and might,
Wäre kein Meister	O'er spirits will he
Über die Geister. (8)	Ne'er master be. (8)

The Kobolds, according to an ancient German superstition, delighted in destroying the work of the miners, causing them endless trouble; and in mining towns the people used to pray in the churches for deliverance from the power of these malicious spirits (7).

In 1730 or before, Georg Brandt prepared a dark blue pigment from an ore found at the Skilå copper works (Riddarhytta) in Westmanland (39). Specimens of this "färgcobalt" are still preserved in the Cederbaum collection at Oskarshamn. Since the first accurate description of metallic cobalt is to be found in Brandt's dissertation on the half-metals in the *Acta Literaria et Scientiarum Sveciae* for 1735, it has frequently been stated that cobalt was discovered in that year. Nils Zenzén has shown, however, that this issue of the *Acta* was not published until 1739 and that the portion of Brandt's "Diarium Chymicum" which records his researches from the latter part of 1737 to the end of 1738 is merely a Swedish edition of the "Dissertatio de semi-metallis."

According to Zenzén, Brandt stated in his diary for 1741 (which was not edited until 1744): "As there are six kinds of metals, so I have also shown with reliable experiments, in my dissertation on the half-metals which I presented to the Royal Academy of Sciences in Upsala in 1735, that there are also six kinds of half-metals. The same dissertation shows that I, through my experiments, had the good fortune . . . to be the first discoverer of a new half-metal, namely cobalt regulus, which had formerly been confused with bismuth . . ." (39). Zenzén believes, however, that this date must be attributed to Brandt's lack of memory. After separating this metal by fire assay, he named it *cobalt* for the mineral from which he had extracted it. In his "Dissertation on the semi-metals" Brandt stated that six metals and six "half-metals" (mercury, bismuth, zinc, and the reguluses of antimony, cobalt, and arsenic) were then known. By a "half-metal" he meant a substance which resembles the metals in color, weight, and form but which is not malleable. Since most bismuth ores contain cobalt, he gave six ways of distinguishing between these two "semi-metals."

"1. When bismuth is broken with a hammer, it gives a fracture composed of little super-imposed laminae. The regulus of cobalt is more like a true metal. Moreover there is a very great difference in the color of these two metals. . . .

"2. In fusing they do not mingle at all with each other; it is easy to separate them with a stroke of the hammer; for they are attached about as an almond is to its stone; and in this union they seem to be separated by a segment of a circle so that they both appear to form but a single regulus, at one end of which is found the bismuth, or marcasite, and at the other the regulus of cobalt.

"3. The regulus of cobalt, pulverized and calcined, gives when one fuses it with flint and fixed alkali, a blue glass, known under the names *zaffera, sasre,* or *smalt.* Marcasite does not give any smalt. The blue glass which bismuth ore sometimes gives is produced by the cobalt which is almost always found in the ores of this semi-metal.

"4. Bismuth melts easily; when kept fused, it becomes calcined like lead and converted into a yellow powder, which, when melted, gives a glass of the same color as that of lead. . . .

"5. Bismuth amalgamates with mercury; which the regulus of cobalt does not do at all.

"6. Bismuth dissolves in nitric acid and in aqua regia; both solutions are precipitated by pure water in the form of a white powder. When the regulus of cobalt is dissolved in these menstrua, it cannot be precipitated from them except by the alkalies; fixed alkali precipitates it in the form of a powder which, after being washed, remains dark and black; whereas when one precipitates it with volatile alkali, especially if it has been dissolved by aqua regia, it acquires a very red color, which changes to blue, if one exposes it to the fire up to the point of redness" (27).

Brandt later made a more complete investigation of cobalt. He also demonstrated that common salt and soda contain the same (mineral) alkali, whereas saltpeter contains the vegetable alkali (potash). This confirmed the earlier work of Duhamel du Monceau. Brandt encouraged the use of Swedish zinc in the manufacture of brass. In 1748 he demonstrated before Crown Prince Adolf Fredrik and the Royal Swedish Academy of Sciences that gold can be made to dissolve in hot nitric acid in a closed vessel but that when the solution is shaken in presence of air the gold precipitates out (87). Since Brandt prepared his nitric acid from saltpeter and sulfuric acid it probably contained some of the latter. This discovery shed light on some of the alleged transmutations of silver to gold and was an important step in the triumph of pure science over alchemy. In the opinion of C. W. Oseen, "No Swedish chemist did more than Georg Brandt for the combating of alchemy" (87). When Brandt died at Stockholm on April 29, 1768, his death was mourned by the entire scientific world. He was one of the ablest chemists of his time (6).

A. F. Cronstedt once spoke eloquently of "what a Brandt in our time can accomplish in cramped quarters, with broad knowledge and with zeal which even age cannot check. This honored man, whose presence here prevents me from saying what I wish, received chemistry and its instruments (already rusting after Hjärne's death) with newer views in natural science, with thorough mathematical knowledge, and with systematic order such as his master Herman Boerhaave of Leyden had employed. Thereafter, followed only experiments which all scholars could apply to experimental physics and from which husbandry could quickly benefit. The science was presented as clearly as it had formerly been made obscure, and from that day, it has gradually gained the right to instruct the youth in our universities, to the great gain of both parties" (75).

After Anton von Svab and Georg Brandt had died in the same year, Carl von Linné said: "The kingdom and our sciences have now lost in a single year two stars of the first magnitude, Brandt and Svab. The Bureau of Mines and the science of mining have lost their supporting pillars. Men such as these never spring up like mushrooms. So far as I know, Europe has none like them. . . . A king can lose an army, but within a year have another just as good. A king can lose a fleet and within two years have another rigged up, but a Brandt and a Svab cannot be gotten again during his entire reign" (52). The history of the Swedish Academy of Sciences describes Brandt as "frugal, taciturn, and solitary" (76).

In 1776 a Hungarian chemist, Petrus Madács, defended a thesis in which he claimed, as did J. J. Winterl, that cobalt is a compound of iron and arsenic, but admitted that nickel is an element. He distinguished clearly between copper and nickel and stated that "copper and arsenic never give nickel" (77).

Although chemists long disputed the elemental nature of cobalt, perhaps because they were unable to reduce the blue smalt to the metal, Torbern Bergman explained in 1780 that, because of the high coloring power of cobalt, only a small amount of it need be present in smalt. He heated many kinds of cobalt glass with black flux and was able, in each case, to obtain the metal, but only in small amounts (78). He distinguished definitely between nickel and cobalt, stated that nickel never gives a blue glass nor a sympathetic ink nor a red solution in acids and that cobalt never gives a green one, and that pure nickel readily alloys with silver, whereas cobalt does not (78). From experiments with the preparation of smalt and sympathetic ink in the following year, Sven Rinman also concluded that cobalt and nickel are two entirely different metals (79).

In 1736 the brothers Henric and Olof Kalmeter discovered at Los, Färila parish, Hälsingland, a cobalt ore which they at first exported in this form. In 1744, however, a smalt works employing skilled workers from Germany was built there (39).

Shortly before this, Georg Brandt had discovered a new cobalt mineral at the Göran Mine at Bastnäs, near Riddarhytta. "My curiosity," said he, "did not allow me to postpone the chemical investigation until my return to Stockholm; I therefore began it immediately, so far as my instruments permitted" (*118*). When he calcined the mineral strongly, he noticed an odor of sulfuric acid but no sulfur flame, and drew the incorrect conclusion that the ore must be a sulfate. With a simple forge and bellows he prepared metal from it, and on his return to Stockholm he prepared a blue glass by fusing the ore with flint and alkali. Since the ore had a high iron content, the regulus contained more iron than cobalt. He observed that "some cobalt regulus mixed with the iron does not make it brittle even after cooling and that it remains as ductile as before, yet at the same time hard and tenacious. On the other hand I have found that, when arsenic and iron are combined in the form of a regulus, they yield a mass as brittle as chilled cast iron" (*118*).

Brandt published a description of this mineral in the volume of the *Acta* of the Upsala Academy for 1742 and in *Vetenskapsacademiens Handlingarna* for 1746, and mentioned that it contains cobalt, iron, and sulfur, but that, unlike ordinary cobalt glance, it is free from arsenic. When W. von Hisinger made a quantitative analysis of it in 1810, he found it to be cobalt sulfide. This mineral is now known as linnaeite; its formula is Co_3S_4, in which part of the cobalt may be replaced by nickel, iron, or copper.

Sympathetic Ink. Although the discovery of the cobalt sympathetic ink, which remains invisible until warmed, has often been attributed to Jean Hellot, who first made it known publicly, he was not the first person to prepare it. Hellot himself stated that a German artist of Stolberg had shown him a reddish salt which, when exposed to heat, became blue. It had been prepared by dissolving Schneeberg cobalt in aqua regia (*119*). H. F. Teichmeyer of Jena was also familiar with this cobalt ink, perhaps even before Hellot made its composition public in 1737 (*119*).

Johann Beckmann stated, in his "History of Inventions, Discoveries, and Origins," that a German lady mentioned by Pot [J. H. Pott] in his "Observ. Chym. Collectio prima" in 1739 (page 163), published the recipe for this sympathetic ink in 1705 in a book which Pott quotes "under the unintelligible title of D. J. W. in clave" (*119*). Hermann Kopp explained that the author of this "Key to the cabinet of Nature's secret treasury" was Dr. Jacob Waitz, physician in ordinary at Gotha, Germany (*120*). All these early recipes specified the use of bismuth ores. Dr. Johann Albrecht Gesner of Württemberg showed in 1744, however, that this peculiar ink was produced not from the bismuth itself but from the cobalt present in the ore (*120*).

Cobalt in Meteorites. The *Quarterly Journal of Science and the Arts* for 1819 has a note on the discovery of cobalt in meteorites: "M. Stromeyer has discovered cobalt in those masses of matter of meteoric origin; but It is uncertain whether it is constantly present or not.   The mass in which M. Stromeyer has detected it is that at the Cape of Good Hope; but he could find none in the specimen discovered in Siberia by Pallas, nor in that of Ellenbogen [Elbogen] in Bohemia.   Klaproth is the only chemist who had previously observed appearances which justified the opinion that meteoric stones contained cobalt, and the stone in which he remarked it was that which fell at Aichstaedt in 1785" (121).   Smithson Tennant had previously detected the presence of nickel in this meteoric iron which Stromeyer analyzed (122).

Cobalt in Nutrition.   Johan Georg Forchhammer found in his great research on the composition of sea water that marine organisms concentrate the substances necessary for their existence and thus provide the chemist with a delicate indirect means of detecting certain elements which occur in sea water in very minute amounts.   He discovered cobalt, for example, in the ashes of *Zostera marina* and in the fossil sponges of the chalk (123).

M. O. Schultze stated that cobalt is an essential element for the nutrition of sheep and cattle.   Although it is not essential for the growth of the herbage plants, they nevertheless take it up from the soil and make it available for animal nutrition (106).   To prevent anemia, even when the diet contains adequate amounts of iron, a small amount of cobalt (not more than four micrograms per day per kilogram of body weight of sheep) is required (124).   It is an important constituent of vitamin B_{12}.

NICKEL

Axel Fredrik Cronstedt, the discoverer of nickel, was born on December 23, 1722, at Ströppsta, Turinge parish, in the province of Södermanland in Sweden (5).   His father, a lieutenant-general, gave him a good education, and the boy soon demonstrated his ability in physical science and mathematics.   As a child he studied at home under private tutors and became especially interested in mathematics, natural sciences, and drawing.   In J. G. Wallerius' classes in mineralogy and chemistry at Upsala he became acquainted with Sven Rinman, who aroused his enthusiasm for a career in mining.   In 1744–45 Cronstedt visited the most important mines in Sweden, and at the Sala mine gained a first-hand knowledge of the metallurgy of lead and silver.   From 1746 to 1748 he studied assaying and chemistry under Georg Brandt.   He rendered great service to his country as a metallurgist in the Bureau of Mines, and his name will always be honored because of the brilliant manner with which he discovered the useful metal nickel (6, 24).

The history of this metal is similar to that of cobalt. An alloy of nickel called packfong (or paktong) was used by the Chinese long before the metal was known in Europe (7, 23). In Germany a heavy, reddish brown ore, frequently found covered with green spots or stains, was used to color glass green; the miners called it *Kupfernickel* (21). Since *Nickel*, like *Kobold*, means *deceptive little spirit*, the word *Kupfernickel* may be translated, *false copper*. Urban Hiärne, in a work on metals published in

Urban Hiärne, 1641–1724. Swedish physician, mineralogist, and poet. Assessor and later acting president of the Swedish Bureau of Mines. Author of "Regium Laboratorium Chymicum," Stockholm, 1683. In 1694 he mentioned the ore *Kupfernickel*, in which Cronstedt more than half a century later discovered nickel. See also ref. (*84*).

1694, expressed a belief that Kupfernickel was a kind of cobalt or arsenic mixed with copper, but in this view there was only a germ of truth (7, 24). A. F. Cronstedt once said, "Hiärne in his lifetime pursued chemical research most zealously. With all his creative genius and his desire to support Cartesian natural science with chemical arguments and conclusions, he still did not fail to consider the practical use which industry could demand of it. With the support of the authorities, he therefore occupied himself with the testing and investigation of substances from all realms of nature and all parts of the country" (75). With Hiärne, according to Sten Lindroth, "Swedish chemistry attained international fame for the first time" (88).

Although no one had ever succeeded in extracting copper from *Kupfernickel*, J. H. Linck (or Link) stated in 1726 that, since it gives green solutions when dissolved in nitric acid, it must be a cobalt ore containing copper (*24, 80*). When Swedish cobalt miners found a reddish yellow ore which imparted little or no blue color when fused with glass frit, they called it "cobalt which had lost its soul" (*21*).

In 1751 Axel Fredrik Cronstedt investigated a new mineral which he found in the cobalt mine at Los, Färila parish, Hälsingland (*21*). When he began this research he was not yet thirty years of age. In one of his experiments he placed a piece of iron in the acid solution of the ore, expecting to see the copper deposit on it. To his great surprise, he was unable to secure a deposit of any kind, for, as is now well known, niccolite contains no copper (*9*). Upon calcining the green crystals which covered the surface of some weathered Kupfernickel, and reducing the calx, or oxide, by heating it with charcoal, Cronstedt obtained a white metal bearing no resemblance whatever to copper. After studying its physical, chemical, and magnetic properties, he announced in the Memoirs of the Stockholm Academy that he had discovered a new metal, different from all others, for which he proposed the name nickel (*7, 21*).

He said,

This salt or this vitriol, after having been calcined, gives a colcothar or clear, gray residue which, when fused with three parts of black flux, gives a regulus of 50 pounds per quintal. This regulus is yellowish on the outside, but in the fracture it is silver-colored with iridescent colors, and composed of little laminae, quite similar to those of bismuth. It is hard and brittle, only feebly attracted by the magnet; calcination changes it to a black powder; these two properties come from the iron which has passed into the vitriol. This regulus dissolves in aqua fortis, aqua regia, and spirit of salt; it gives on dissolving a: brilliant green color, and there precipitates a black powder which, when heated before the enamelers' blowpipe, gives signs of phlogiston and of the metallic part which it contains . . . (*7, 21*).

The slight magnetization observed by Cronstedt is a property of nickel itself. In 1751 he mixed some Kupfernickel with "black flux," placed the mixture in a crucible, and covered it with a layer of common salt. Upon roasting it he not only reduced the oxide to the metallic state, but melted the metal. "I made many attempts," said he, "to mix whole and half metals for the purpose of preparing a product like it; but without success. I have therefore employed Herr Director Scheffer's rich insight and untiring efforts to the same end, but all his observations have as yet given no clue." Cronstedt therefore concluded that, if no one of the twelve known "whole and half metals" nor any mixture of them could duplicate the properties of the regulus which remained after the removal of the iron and cobalt, he would have to regard it as a new half-metal (*21*). Not until 1754 did he publicly christen it. "The greatest quantity of the new previously described half metal," said he, "is contained in Kupfer-nickel; therefore I retain the same name for its regulus or call it *nickel* for short. For my experiments I have used a massive *Kupfernickel* from the Kuhschacht [Cow Shaft] in Freiberg, Saxony" (*21*). Kupfernickel, or niccolite, is now known to be an arsenide of nickel.

Cronstedt pointed out that nickel and cobalt are closely associated in nature and that the speiss which falls to the bottom of the pots in which cobalt is vitrified in the manufacture of saffre is composed mainly of nickel containing more or less cobalt, iron, sulfur, and arsenic.

Many chemists in Sweden and in other parts of the world immediately accepted Cronstedt's claim to the discovery of a new element, but B.-G. Sage (*22*) and A.-G. Monnet in France believed that his nickel was merely a mixture of cobalt, arsenic, iron, and copper (*7*). As a matter of fact, it was somewhat contaminated with iron, cobalt, and arsenic; and there-

Balthasar-Georges Sage, 1740–1824. French analytical and mineralogical chemist of the phlogistic school. In his "Analyse Chimique," published in 1786, he gave methods of testing and analyzing coal, clay, water, and many minerals.

fore the great pioneer in analytical chemistry Torbern Bergman carried out an elaborate series of experiments by means of which he obtained nickel in a high state of purity. The results he published in 1775 completely confirmed those of Cronstedt, for he showed that no combination of iron, arsenic, cobalt, and copper will duplicate the properties of nickel. Bergman's pupil Johan Arvidsson Afzelius defended these views at Upsala in 1775 (*7, 36*).

Even after this proof, some chemists were very conservative about accepting the new element. William Nicholson, in his "First Principles of Chemistry" published in 1796, gave the following account of it:

This metallic substance has not been applied to any use; and the chief attention of those chemists who have examined it has been directed to obtain it in a state of purity; which, however, has not yet been accomplished. . . . Nickel has been thought to be a modification of iron. . . .   So long as no one is able to produce this metal from pure iron or copper, and to explain in an intelligible way the process by which it can be generated, we must continue to regard it as a peculiar substance, possessing distinct properties.   The general opinions of chemists concur in admitting the force of this reasoning (10).

Cronstedt's fame does not rest alone on his discovery of nickel. One of his greatest contributions to science was the treatise in which he reformed mineralogy and classified minerals not merely according to their external properties, such as form, hardness, and color, but also according to their chemical composition. This treatise was translated into several languages. Berzelius said of him, "Cronstedt, the founder of the chemical system of mineralogy, a man who by his acuteness in that science rose so far above his age that he was never correctly understood by it, used the blowpipe to distinguish between minerals" (11). Ability to use this instrument skillfully and without fatigue and injury to health required, as Berzelius pointed out, an intensive training that few chemists care to undergo (83). Nevertheless, Cronstedt acquired such unusual control over it that he could direct a candle-flame upon a sample no larger than the head of a pin and make it white-hot (11).

Jagnaux stated that Cronstedt and Rinman operated a successful plant for distilling zinc, and that they "were as well versed in metallurgy as in mineralogy" (4). Cronstedt also discovered a zeolite, one of the silicates so widely used for softening water, and wrote a paper on it in 1756. He died in Säters parish near Stockholm on August 19, 1765 (32).

Nickel in Meteorites. Centuries before the discovery of nickel, primitive peoples shaped meteoric iron into implements and swords and appreciated the superiority of this Heaven-sent metal (125). In 1777 J. K. F. Meyer of Stettin noticed that when he added sulfuric acid to some native iron which P. S. Pallas had found in Siberia, he obtained a green solution which became blue when it was treated with ammonium hydroxide. In 1799 Joseph-Louis Proust detected nickel in meteoric iron from Peru (126). This grayish white native iron had been observed by Rubin de Celis. Since it did not rust, it was sometimes mistaken for native silver.

Led by the deep green color of its solutions to suspect the presence in it of copper, Proust passed hydrogen sulfide into an acidic solution of the iron, but obtained no precipitate. Believing that only nickel could produce such an effect, he removed the iron as hydrous ferric oxide and prepared nickel sulfate from the filtrate. These experiments are described in *Nicholson's Journal* for November, 1800: "The native iron of Peru is therefore, according to the experiments made by M. Proust, an alloy of iron and nickel; a new discovery of the most interesting nature. The presence of nickel in this alloy, observes the author, appears to announce that it is the product of art; but when it is considered that there exists a mass of more than 1363 myriagrams (300 quintals) in a plain of more than 100 leagues in circumference, where there is neither mountain nor water, nor scarcely a stone is to be found, the difficulty of the problem still remains in all its force. Lastly, adds M. Proust, if the power of uniting these metals in suitable proportions can be obtained by metallurgists, they will have obtained an alloy which will possess many advantages over other iron, and more particularly that of not being able to rust" (127).

In 1805 James Sowerby received a piece of meteoric iron which Captain Barrow had found "about two hundred miles within the Cape of Good Hope." When Smithson Tennant analyzed it, he found about 10 per cent of nickel in it. Mr. Sowerby had the metal hammered into a sword, which he presented to the Emperor of Russia (128).

Some Famous Nickel Mines and Smelters. The nickel smelting works near Schneeberg in the Saxon Erzgebirge date from 1642. They produced nickel, cobalt, arsenic, and bismuth from the local ores, and refined the nickel-cobalt regulus imported from the Modum works in southern Norway (129).

French explorers worked the La Motte Mine in Missouri for nickel as early as 1719 and during the period from 1830–50 shipped the metal to refiners in England (125). Before the mining of nickel ores on the island of New Caledonia in the Pacific was well developed in about 1877, nickel was so scarce that ores containing as little as one per cent of it could be worked profitably (125). The greatest nickel deposits in the world, those of the Sudbury district of Ontario, Canada, were discovered in about 1856 (23, 125).

Early Nickel Alloys. In 1776 Assessor Gustaf von Engeström, an assay master who had studied under H. T. Scheffer, A. F. Cronstedt, Anton von Svab, and A. S. Marggraf, found that the Chinese alloy *packfong* contained copper, nickel, and zinc. This sonorous, white metal was called *packfong* (white copper) to distinguish it from *tongfong* (red copper). When Engeström and Peter Johan Bladh of the Swedish East India Company tested the untreated metal, they found it to be made from a natural alloy of nickel, copper, and a very little cobalt, which was probably an accidental impurity. This crude metal from complex copper-nickel sulfide ores of Yunnan, southern China, was shipped to Canton in the form of "three-cornered rings" 8 or 9 inches in outer diameter and about $1^1/_2$ inches thick (21, 125). Engeström believed it must have been smelted from nickeliferous copper ores. The natural mixture had a red-

dish color, but in Canton another metal was added to it to make it perfectly white; and many craftsmen worked it up into household utensils
such as spoons, dishes, snuffboxes, lamps, etc. Engeström found by experiment that the metal added at Canton must have been zinc.

He stated that the alloy was suitable for ornamental articles which
would not come into contact with acid or salt and that if the copper,
nickel, and cobalt ores from Riddarhytta, Häkansboda, Tunaberg, etc.

Torbern Bergman, 1735–1784. Swedish
chemist, mineralogist, and editor.
Author of the "Opuscula physica et
chemica," a six-volume treatise. Among
his students were Gahn, the discoverer
of manganese; Hjelm, who isolated
molybdenum; and the de Elhuyar
brothers, who discovered tungsten.

could be made free from arsenic, it ought to be possible to manufacture
the alloy in Sweden. Cobalt, he thought, would serve the same purpose
as the nickel (130). He loved to collect minerals from the East Indies.
Since he was the translator of Cronstedt's mineralogy, his interest in the
metal which Cronstedt discovered is easily understood (131).

In 1816 Hans Peter Eggertz, Baron Johan Nordin, and J. G. Gahn
founded at Falun a small plant for the manufacture of imitation packfong
from the nickeliferous ores of the Slättberg and Kuso mines. This plant
was in operation until 1821, when it was destroyed by fire (132).

Since the middle of the seventeenth century, an alloy known as "white
copper" had been manufactured at Suhl in the Thuringian Forest from
old slag belonging to the copper smelters. In 1823 it was found to contain
copper and zinc. The manufacture of *Argentans* or *Neusilber* (German
silver, or nickel silver) began in 1824 (125, 126). Until 1865 German
silver was almost the only form in which nickel was used commercially.
The first pure malleable nickel was prepared by Joseph Wharton of
Philadelphia (125).

MANGANESE

When Cronstedt died, the man who is conceded to be the discoverer
of manganese was exactly twenty years old.   Johan Gottlieb Gahn was
born at Voxna, an iron-mining town in South Helsingland on August 19,
1745 (5).   Left fatherless at an early age and obliged to earn his living
in the mines, he shared the joys and sorrows of the laborers and learned
mining "on the lowest and wettest level" (17).   He studied mineralogy
under Bergman, became expert in the use of the blowpipe, and, according
to Berzelius, always carried it with him, even on the shortest trips.   When
Gahn demonstrated the presence of copper in certain kinds of paper by
burning a quarter of a sheet, heating the ash with the blowpipe, and
displaying a tiny speck of the red metal, the young Berzelius watched him
with wonder and admiration (11).   J. Nicklès believed, however, that this
copper must have been volatilized from Gahn's burner (40).

Pyrolusite has been used for centuries in the manufacture of glass.
After mentioning the production of blue glass with "zaffer" (a mixture of
roasted cobalt ore and sand), Vannoccio Biringuccio wrote in his "Pirotechnia" in 1540, "There is still another half mineral of the same kind,
so-called Braunstein.   This comes from Germany and is found especially
in Tuscany in Mt. Viterbo and at Salodiana in the neighborhood of Monte-
castello, near Cara.   It is dark rust brown.   It does not melt so that one
can obtain metal from it.   But when one adds vitrifiable substances to it,
it colors them a handsome violet.   The master glass-makers color their
glasses a wonderful violet with it.   The master potters also use it for violet
decorations.   Braunstein, moreover, when mixed with molten glass, has
the special property of purifying it and making it white instead of green or
yellow" (57).   Because of the last-named property, glassmakers used to
call it *sapo vitri,* or glass soap.

E.-F. Geoffroy said that "Magnesia or Manganesia of the Glass-
Makers, the Soap of Glass of Merret, is a fossil, metallick, ferruginous
Substance resembling Antimony in its shining Colour, and very brittle.
Pomet mentions two Kinds of it; one ash-coloured, which is not easy to
be got, and therefore little used; the other black, which is very common.
It is used in making and purifying of Glass; for, by mixing a small Quantity
of it with the Glass, whilst in Fusion, it clears it from any green or bluish
Colours, and makes it more transparent and bright; and it was on that
account that Merret termed it *Sapo Vitri.*   If too great a Quantity of it
be put in, it gives the Glass a purple Colour.   It is used by Potters in
colouring their Vessels black, as the Zaffera, already mentioned, is for
blue.   The same Merret says, the best Manganese is that which is hard,
heavy, sparkling, and blackish, and which being reduced to Powder, turns

Lead black. It is dug in Germany, Italy, Piedmont, and in England, near the Mendip Hills in Somersetshire, famous for Lead Mines. . ." (*133*).

The Berlin glass and porcelain technologist J. H. Pott believed that pyrolusite consisted of phlogiston and an earth somewhat like that in alum (*58*). In 1740 he prepared "chameleon mineral" (potassium permanganate) and other compounds from it and showed that iron is not a constituent of pure pyrolusite (*13*).

The first person to prepare a little metallic manganese was probably Ignatius Gottfried Kaim, who described it in his dissertation, "De metallis dubiis," which was published at Vienna in 1770 (*12*). Although this pub-

Johan Gottlieb Gahn, 1745–1818. Swedish chemist, mineralogist, and mining engineer. Manufacturer of copper, sulfur, sulfuric acid, and red ochre. Discoverer of metallic manganese.

lication is rare and inaccessible, P.-J. Macquer left an abstract of it in his famous chemical dictionary. By heating a mixture of one part of pulverized pyrolusite with two parts of black flux, Kaim obtained a bluish white, brittle metal with countless shining facets of different shapes, showing in the fracture a play of colors from blue to yellow. He claimed that this regulus was free from iron (*59*). This incomplete research attracted little notice.

The mineral was also known by the confusing names "black magnesia" and "manganese." Torbern Bergman knew, however, that it was not a compound of the alkaline earth, magnesia, for he said, "The mineral called black magnesia is nothing other than the calx of a new metal, which must not be confounded with lime nor with magnesia alba." He failed, however, in all attempts to reduce the ore (13, 25), and finally turned the problem over to his friend C. W. Scheele, who in 1774, after experimenting for three years, presented his results to the Stockholm Academy in the form of a paper entitled, "Concerning manganese and its properties." In this epoch-making dissertation he announced the existence of the gaseous element chlorine and paved the way for the discovery of oxygen gas and the metals barium and manganese. Scheele stated that the mineral known as "manganese" was the calx of the metal different from any then known (26).

Although Pott, Bergman, and Scheele all believed in the existence of the metal manganese none of them were able to isolate it. However, in 1774 Gahn (25) lined a crucible with moist charcoal dust, placed in the center a mixture of the pulverized pyrolusite and oil, and covered it with more of the charcoal dust. After luting another crucible to this, he heated them intensely for an hour and, upon opening the apparatus, he found in it a button of metallic manganese weighing about a third as much as the ore from which he had isolated it (13, 30). For the accomplishment of this difficult reduction and for the isolation of this important metal, Gahn deserves high praise.

This discovery, like most of his others, was not published in any scientific journal. In his first attempts, Gahn obtained what Scheele called "reduced pyrolusite . . . combined with much phlogiston and a little iron." On May 16, 1774, Scheele sent him some purified pyrolusite with the suggestion, "I am eagerly waiting to see what kind of result this pure Braunstein will give when you apply your hell-fire to it, and I hope you will send me a little of the regulus as soon as possible" (37). On June 27th of the same year, Scheele thanked Gahn for the manganese regulus ["regulum magnesiae"] and added, "I believe that the Braunstein regulus is a half metal different from other half metals and closely related to iron" (37).

In his notes to H. T. Scheffer's chemical lectures, which were published in 1775, Torbern Bergman stated that a fifteenth metal had recently been added to the fourteen which Scheffer had discussed. Because of its weight, ability to color glass, and its precipitation with ferrocyanides (blodlut), Bergman had suspected that pyrolusite must contain a peculiar metal as an essential constituent. "At the same time," said he, "Hr. J. G. Gahn, without knowing of my reasons, actually brought forth from it by reduction a half metal which in refractoriness approaches nearest to platinum, and which, moreover, does not resemble any of those previously known. . . . Since then, I, too, have obtained the regulus of pyrolusite by reduction, but could not purify it from iron" (38).

In 1785 P. J. Hjelm published in the *Nya Handlingar* of the Swedish Academy of Sciences a detailed description of this reduction. He obtained his specimens from a pyrolusite quarry in Undenas parish in Vermland. After placing a mixture of a known weight of the pulverized sample with a little oil or melted tallow and powdered coal dust or blood charcoal in a large covered crucible lined with a mixture of iron-free clay and coal dust, he applied sufficient heat from his forge to volatilize the oil without allowing it to burst into flame. In less than an hour, he obtained a regulus which weighed more than half as much as the original crude pyrolusite. Assessor Bengt Qvist suggested to him that the metal could be produced more economically in a cast steel furnace or wind furnace (*60*).

J. C. Ilsemann of Clausthal also obtained manganese independently without previous knowledge of the methods used by Gahn and Bergman. Ilsemann reduced 110 pounds of pyrolusite from Ilsefeld by heating it with a mixture of fluorspar, lime, powdered charcoal, and ignited salt, and obtained four and one-half pounds of impure metallic manganese from which he was unable to separate the iron (*61*).

In 1784 Gahn was made assessor at the College of Mines; he also served as deputy to the 1819 Diet, and was known politically as a Liberal (*14*). He was not only a brilliant chemist and mineralogist and a conscientious public official, but also a highly successful business executive. He owned and managed mines and smelters, and introduced new industrial methods; and it was in his sulfuric acid plant that J. J. Berzelius discovered the element selenium. During the American Revolution, when large amounts of pure copper were needed for sheathing ships, Gahn's plant at Stora Kopparberg was able to fill large rush orders (*15*). It is a curious fact that Assessor Gahn bore such a striking resemblance in features, gestures, and intellectual interests to Dr. William Hyde Wollaston, the English scientist who later discovered palladium and rhodium, that he was often called "the Wollaston of Stockholm" (*16*). Berzelius once stated, in fact, that one "would take them for sons of the same father" (*16*). Thomas Thomson, who once visited Assessor Gahn at his home in Falun, said that "his manners were the most simple, unaffected and pleasing of all the men of science" he had ever met, and that "benevolence and goodness of heart . . . beamed in his countenance."

When Edward Daniel Clarke visited Falun, he said that "perhaps in no part of the world" will the traveler "meet with superintendents so well informed . . . at the head of whom is the celebrated Gahn, whose acquirements, and the kindness he has always shewn to strangers, have entitled him to respect and consideration in all the Academical Institutions of Europe. . . . Hospitality in a Swede is what we may always expect; but the attention paid to strangers by Mr. Gahn, especially if their visits had any view to science, was of a more exalted nature. He not only shewed a zeal, as if actuated by a religious duty, to satisfy scientific inquiries; but he did more—he directed them; and himself endeavoured to stimulate the ardour of those with whom he conversed . . . by exciting and then gratifying their curiosity" (55).

At the time of his sixty-eighth birthday, Gahn received a novel congratulatory note from Berzelius, which read: "From Herr Assessor's last letter I was happy to find new support for the doctrine of definite proportions. Herr Assessor was 68 on August 19; the following day (the 20th) I became 34; now $34 \times 2 = 68$, from whence it follows that Herr Assessor is equal to a multiple of me by two . . ." (56).

Gahn, unfortunately, left most of his scientific work unpublished, leaving only a few papers on the blowpipe, on a sensitive balance, and on economy in the operation of smelters. He died in Stockholm on December 8, 1818, at the age of seventy-three years. In a biographical sketch in the *Annals of Philosophy*, one may read this high tribute:

To sum up the whole, we may safely say that he was alike eminent as a practical chemist and mechanic, as a patriot in public, and a friend in private life, as presiding over the interests of the miner and of the farmer, and in fine as the guardian and overseer of the large family of his native poor.* It will not indeed be easy to find another whose talents have been at once more brilliant and more useful, who has been more admired and more loved by his country, than John Gottlieb Gahn (15).

Manganese in Iron Ores. In 1773 Sven Rinman had the iron ores at Dingelvik in Dalsland tested for manganese (89). In the following year P. J. Hjelm defended a thesis, under Torbern Bergman, in which he showed that manganese is a common constituent of bog iron ores, magnetite, and bloodstone (hematite). "On accurate investigation," said he, "of several substances found on trips through the mining regions, Braunstein (pyrolusite) occurred as a rather common accompaniment. When earths, slags, pig iron, etc. were investigated and waters tested, I found traces of it everywhere" (134). In the opinion of A. E. Nordenskiöld, Hjelm may therefore be credited with the discovery of the wide distribution of manganese in nature and the observation that pig iron made from manganiferous iron ores often produces excellent steel (89).

Chameleon Mineral (Potassium Permanganate). J. R. Glauber mentioned in 1659, in his "Teutschlands Wohlfarth," that when pyrolusite is

---

* Assessor Gahn helped to establish the first poorhouse at Falun.

fused with caustic potash and the mass is dissolved in water, the solution is at first purple but changes through blue and red to green. J. H. Pott stated, however, in 1740, in his research on pyrolusite, that a solution obtained in this manner is green at first and that it becomes blue, then red, and finally green again (*134*). In 1774, C. W. Scheele expressed the view that the solution of pyrolusite in potash was actually blue but that it could be colored red by suspended particles of pyrolusite or green by fine particles of yellow iron oxide (*135*).

Even at the beginning of the nineteenth century, chemists still disagreed as to the cause of these remarkable color changes. Christian Friedrich Bucholtz (1770–1818), a nephew of W. H. S. Bucholtz, stated in 1809 that the green solution became red because it absorbed oxygen from the atmosphere (*134, 136*). His scientific career was cut short by prolonged illness, loss of vision, and premature death (137).

M.-E. Chevreul believed that the green and red "chameleons" were in the same stage of oxidation and that they were more highly oxidized than the colorless salts of manganese (*138*). By mixing the green and red solutions in different proportions, he produced all the intermediate shades through green, blue, indigo, purple, and red.

Pierre-François Chevillot and William Frederic Edwards found in 1817 that when they fused pyrolusite in caustic potash out of contact with air, they obtained no chameleon mineral. They also found that the change to the red form took place faster in pure oxygen than in the atmosphere, and that when the pyrolusite was in excess in the fusion mixture, they obtained the red form directly. They concluded therefore that the green solution of the chameleon mineral contained more potash than the red one. In 1818 they prepared similar compounds of sodium, barium, and strontium (*139*). In 1820 J. G. Forchhammer of Copenhagen, in his doctor's dissertation, distinguished two different acids (manganic in the green solution and permanganic in the red one), and in 1830–32 Eilhard Mitscherlich determined the chemical composition of these acids (*140, 141, 150*).

Manganese in Plants. When Scheele warmed some sifted vegetable ashes with spirit of salt (hydrochloric acid) in 1774, he noticed an odor of aqua regia like that obtained when pyrolusite is similarly treated. On investigating the cause of this odor, he found that the ash contained "manganese" (manganese dioxide). "Nevertheless," said Scheele, "I observed very little in the ashes from Serpillum: wood ashes gave more of it" (*142, 147*).

In a letter to Gahn on March 28, 1774, he wrote: "I have also discovered some of this earth [baryta] as well as a little Braunstein [manganese dioxide] in vegetable ash, and am delighted that I have conclusively found in the presence of Braunstein the reason why *alkalia fixa* assumes a blue-green color on calcination" (*143*).

L.-J. Proust detected manganese in the ash of the pine, the fig tree, the calendula, and other plants (*144*). In 1849 Prince Salm-Horstmar found it in the ash of the oat plant (*45*). According to A. T. Shohl, plants store manganese in their leaves and seeds, and use it as an essential element in their nutrition (*146*).

Manganese in Animals. In 1808 A.-F. de Fourcroy and N.-L. Vauquelin detected manganese in the bones of the ox, and three years later they demonstrated its presence in human bones (*148*). In 1830 Ferdinand Wurzer of Marburg detected a small amount of manganese in human blood and published his results in Poggendorff's *Annalen* and in Schweigger's *Journal* (*149*). E. R. Orent and E. V. McCollum proved that manganese is an essential element in animal nutrition (*146*).

LITERATURE CITED

(*1*) MENDELEEV, D., "First Principles of Chemistry," 5th ed., Vol. 1, translated by Kamensky and Greenaway, Longmans, Green & Co., London, **1891**, preface, p. ix.

(*2*) MELLOR, J. W., "Comprehensive Treatise on Inorganic and Theoretical Chemistry," Vol. 4, Longmans, Green & Co., London, **1923**, pp. 398–405. Article on Zinc.

(*3*) RÂY, P. C., "History of Hindu Chemistry," 2nd ed., Vol. 1, Chuckervertty, Chatterjee and Co., Calcutta, **1904**, pp. 157–8; 1st ed., Vol. 2, Bengal Chemical and Pharmaceutical Works, Calcutta, **1909**, pp. 17, 19, and 22.

(*4*) JAGNAUX, R., "Histoire de la Chimie," Vol. 2, Baudry et Cie., Paris, **1891**, pp. 209–11; E. O. VON LIPPMANN, "Entstehung und Ausbreitung der Alchemie," Springer, Berlin, **1919**, pp. 591–600.

(*5*) POGGENDORFF, J. C., "Biographisch-Literarisches Handwörterbuch zur Geschichte der exakten Wissenschaften," 6 vols., Verlag Chemie, Leipzig and Berlin, **1863–1937**. Articles on Brandt, Cronstedt, and Gahn.

(*6*) "Biographie Universelle, Ancienne et Moderne," 85 vols., Michaud Frères, Paris, **1811–62**. Biographical sketch of Brandt by Catteaux.

(*7*) JAGNAUX, R., "Histoire de la Chimie," ref. (*4*), Vol. 2, pp. 318–21; L. GMELIN, Handbuch der theoretischen Chemie," ersten Bandes Zweite Abtheilung, F. Varrentrapp, Frankfurt am Main, **1826**, p. 1193; G. BRANDT, *Act. Upsal.*, **1735**, 33; A. E. WAITE, "Hermetic and Alchemical Writings of Paracelsus," Vol. 1, Elliott and Co., London, **1894**, p. 254.

(*8*) VON GOETHE, J. W., "Faust," part 1, lines 1273–82. Translation from the "Harvard Classics," vol. 19, P. F. Collier and Son, New York, **1909–10**, p. 51.

(*9*) FÄRBER, E., "Geschichtliche Entwicklung der Chemie," Springer, Berlin, **1921**, pp. 63–4.

(*10*) NICHOLSON, W., "First Principles of Chemistry," 3rd ed., C. G. and J. Robinson, London, **1796**, pp. 363–5.

(11) BERZELIUS, J. J., "Die Anwendung des Lötrohrs in der Chemie und Miner-
      alogie," Zweite Auflage, **1828**; F. C. PHILLIPS, "Chemical German," 2nd ed.,
      Chemical Publishing Co., Easton, Pa., **1915**, p. 103; J. J. BERZELIUS, "Om
      Blåsrörets Användande i Kemien och Mineralogien," Nordström, Stockholm,
      1820, pp. 1–8.

(12) VON WURZBACH, C., "Biographisches Lexikon des Kaiserthums Oesterreich,"
      Vol. 57, Hof- und Staatsdruckerei, Vienna, **1889**, p. 89.   Article on J. J.
      Winterl; J. C. KAIM, "Dissertatio de metallis dubiis," Vienna, **1770**, Chap.
      4, pp. 48 ff.

(13) JAGNAUX, R., "Histoire de la Chimie," ref. (4), Vol. 2, pp. 315–16; L. GMELIN,
      "Handbuch der theoretischen Chemie," ersten Bandes zweite Abtheilung,
      ref. (7), p. 882.   See also P. J. HJELM, "Versuche aus dem Braunsteine den
      Braunsteinkönig (Magnesium) zu erhalten," *Crell's Ann.*, **7**, 158–68; 446–57
      (**1787**).

(14) HOEFER, F., "Nouvelle Biographie Générale," Didot Frères, Paris, **1866**.   Bio-
      graphical sketch of Gahn by Guyot de Fère.

(15) "Biographical Account of Assessor John Gottlieb Gahn," *Annals of Phil's.*,
      New Series, **8**, 1–11 (July, **1824**).

(16) SÖDERBAUM, H. G., "Jac. Berzelius Bref," Vol. 1, part 3, Almqvist and Wiksells,
      Upsala, **1912–14**, p. 242; EMILIE WÖHLER, "Aus Berzelius's Tagebuch
      während seines Aufenthaltes in London im Sommer 1812," *Z. angew.
      Chem.*, **18**, 1946–8 (Dec., **1905**).

(17) HOOVER, H., radio address of acceptance of the Saunders Medal.

(18) BERGMAN, T., "Opuscula Physica et Chemica," Vol. 2, Mülleriano, Lipsiae,
      1792, pp. 309–14.

(19) KOPP, H., "Geschichte der Chemie," part 4, F. Vieweg und Sohn, Braun-
      schweig, **1847**, pp. 113–20.

(20) SMITH, E. F., "Forgotten chemists," *J. Chem. Educ.*, **3**, 31–2 (Jan., **1926**).

(21) BERGMAN, T., "Opuscula Physica et Chemica," ref. (18), Vol. 2, pp. 231–3;
      A. F. CRONSTEDT, "Rön och försök gjorde med en malm-art från Los Kobolt-
      grufvor i Färila socken och Helsingeland," *Vet. Acad. Handl.*, **1751**, pp.
      287–92; "Fortsättning af rön och försök gjorde med en malm-art från Los
      Kobolt-grufvor," *ibid.*, **1754**, pp. 38–45; *Crell's Neues chem. Archiv.*, **8**,
      230–3 (**1791**).

(22) SAGE, B.-G., "Mémoires de Chimie," Imprimerie Royale, Paris, **1773**, pp.
      116–26.   "Examen de la Mine de Cobalt d'un gris rougeâtre nommée Kup-
      fernickel."

(23) BALDWIN, W. H., "The story of nickel.   Part 1.   How 'Old Nick's gnomes
      were outwitted," *J. Chem. Educ.*, **8**, 1749–50 (Sept., **1931**).

(24) KOPP, H., Geschichte der Chemie," ref. (19), part 4, pp. 157–9.

(25) BERGMAN, T., "Opuscula Physica et Chemica," ref. (18), Vol. 2, pp. 201–3.

(26) SCHEELE, C. W., "Sämmtliche physische und chemische Werke," translated
      into German by Hermbstädt, 2nd ed., Vol. 2, Rottmann, Berlin, **1793**, pp.
      33–90.

(27) BRANDT, G., "Dissertation sur les demi-métaux," Recueil des Mémoires de
      Chymie, etc., contenus dans les Actes de l'Acad. d'Upsal et dans les Mém.
      de l'Acad. Roy. des Sciences de Stockolm, 1720–60, Vol. 1, P. F. Didot
      le Jeune, Paris, **1764**, pp. 8–25; *Actes de l'Acad. d'Upsal*, **4**, (**1735**).

(28) HOMMEL, W., "Berghauptmann Löhneysen, ein Plagiator des 17.   Jahr-
      hunderts," *Chem.-Ztg.*, **36**, 137–8 (Feb. 3, **1912**).

(29) HENCKEL, J. F., "Abhandlung von dem Zinke," *Crell's Neues chem. Archiv*,
      2, 265 (**1784**); *Physisch-medicinische Abh. Akad. Naturforscher*, **4**, 308
      (1733–6).

(30) NORDENSKIÖLD, A. E., "Scheeles nachgelassene Briefe und Aufzeichnungen," P. A. Norstedt & Söner, Stockholm, 1892, pp. 120–6. Letters of Scheele to Gahn, May 16, 1774, and June 27, 1774.

(31) HOOVER, H. C. and L. H. HOOVER, "Georgius Agricola. De re metallica translated from the first Latin edition of 1556," Mining Mag., London, 1912, pp. 408–10.

(32) "Svenskt biografiskt lexikon," Vol. 9, Albert Bonniers Boktryckeri, Stockholm, 1929, pp. 279–95. Article on Cronstedt by Nils Zenzén.

(33) LEWIS, WILLIAM, "The Chemical Works of Caspar Neumann, M.D.," Johnston, Keith, Linde, etc., London, 1759, pp. 122–3.

(34) "Svenskt biografiskt lexikon," Vol. 5, Albert Bonniers Boktryckeri, Stockholm, 1925, pp. 784–9. Article on Georg Brandt by Sv. Odén.

(35) NORDENSKIÖLD, A. E., "A leaf from the history of Swedish natural science," Nature, 21, 518–21 (Apr. 1, 1880); G. BRANDT, "Observations sur l'arsenic," Recueil des mémoires de chymie . . . dans les actes de l'académie d'Upsal et dans les mémoires de l'académie royale de Stockolm . . . 1720–60, Vol. 1, P. Fr. Didot le Jeune, Paris, 1764, pp. 1–8; Actes de l'acad. d'Upsal, 3 (1733).

(36) BOËTHIUS, "Svenskt biografikst lexikon," ref. (32), Vol. 1, pp. 222–4 (1918); P. J. HJELM, "Åminnelsetal öfver Herr T. O. Bergman," J. G. Lange, Stockholm, 1786, p. 99; TORBERN BERGMAN and J. ARVIDSSON AFZELIUS, "Dissertatio chemica de Niccolo" Upsala, 1775.

(37) NORDENSKIÖLD, A. E., "C. W. Scheele. Efterlemnade bref och anteckningar," P. A. Norstedt and Sons, Stockholm, 1892, pp. 120–6. Cf. ref. (30).

(38) SCHEFFER, H. T., "Chemiske föreläsningar rörande salter, jordarter, vatten, fetmor, metaller och färgning," M. Swederus, Upsala, 1775, p. 390. Annotated by T. Bergman.

(39) ZENZÉN, NILS, "Försök till historik över Cederbaumska mineralsamlingen i Oskarsham," Arkiv för Kemi, Mineralogi och Geologi, 10A, 31–4, 41–6 (1930).

(40) "Correspondence of Prof. Jérôme Nicklès, dated Nancy, France, Oct. 22, 1867," Am. J. Sci., (2), 45, 67–8 (Jan., 1868).

(41) BAILEY, K. C., "The Elder Pliny's Chapters on Chemical Subjects," Vol. 2, Edward Arnold, London, 1932, pp. 25, 37, 166–8.

(42) GUNTHER, R. T., "The Greek Herbal of Dioscorides," Oxford University Press, Oxford, 1934, pp. 623–8, 648.

(43) PARKS, G. B., "The Book of Ser Marco Polo, the Venetian, Concerning the Kingdoms and Marvels of the East," The Macmillan Company, New York City, 1927, Book 1, chap. 21, p. 48.

(44) HOMMEL, W., "Ueber indisches und chinesisches Zink," Z. angew. Chem., 25, 97–100 (Jan. 19, 1912).

(45) BARTOW, VIRGINIA, "Richard Watson, eighteenth-century chemist and clergyman," J. Chem. Educ., 15, 103–11 (March, 1938).

(46) WATSON, R., "Chemical Essays," 2nd ed., Vol. 4, J. Archdeacon, Cambridge, 1786, pp. 1–84.

(47) BECKMANN, JOHANN, "A History of Inventions, Discoveries, and Origins," 4th ed., Vol. 2, Henry G. Bohn, London, 1846, pp. 32–45.

(48) VON RESPUR, P. M. (DE RESPOUR), "Besondere Versuche vom Mineral-Geist, zur Auflösung und Verwandlung derer Metallen," Friedrich Hekel, Dresden and Leipzig, 1743, pp. 178–80 and Section 5 of the Neue Vorrede by J. F. Henkel (or Henckel).

(49) SMITH, SIR JAMES EDWARD, "A Selection of the Correspondence of Linnaeus and Other Naturalists," Vol. 2, Longman, Hurst, Rees, Orme, and Brown, London, 1821, pp. 174–6, 205–6. Letters of J. F. Gronovius and H. Boerhaave.

(50) JACKSON, B. D., "Linnaeus," H. F. and G. Witherby, London, 1923, pp. 142–3, 165–8.

(51) CRAMER, J. A., "Elements of the Art of Assaying Metals," Thomas Woodward and C. Davis, London, 1741, pp. 163–7; ibid., 2nd ed., L. Davis and C. Reymers, London, 1764, pp. iii and iv.

(52) HILDEBRAND, BENGT, "K. Svenska Vetenskapsakademien. Förhistoria, Grundläggning och Organisation," K. Vet. Akad., Stockholm, 1939, pp. 537–9.

(53) MARGGRAF, A. S., "Ueber die Methode den Zink aus seiner wahren Minera dem Galmeysteine hervorzubringen," Crell's Neues chem. Archiv, 4, 280–3 (1785); Abh. königl. Akad. Wiss. (Berlin), 1746, Mém., p. 15; "Chymische Schriften," revised ed., Vol. 1, Arnold Wever, Berlin, 1768, pp. 248–58.

(54) Review of H. R. Schoolcraft's "A view of the lead mines of Missouri," Am. J. Sci., (1), 3, 63 (1821).

(55) CLARKE, E. D., "Travels in Various Countries of Europe, Asia, and Africa," Vol. 10, T. Cadell, London, 1824, pp. 527–8.

(56) SÖDERBAUM, H. G., "Jac. Berzelius Levnadsteckning," Vol. 1, Almqvist and Wiksells Publishing Co., Upsala, 1929–31, pp. 495–7. Letter of Berzelius to Gahn, Aug. 27, 1813.

(57) JOHANNSEN, OTTO, "Biringuccio's Pirotechnia," Friedrich Vieweg und Sohn, Braunschweig, 1925, p. 133.

(58) POTT, J. H., "Chemische Untersuchung des Braunsteins, oder der Magnesia der Glasschmelzer," Crell's Neues chem. Archiv, 3, 289–94 (1785); Abh. königl. Akad. Wiss. (Berlin), 1735–42, p. 40.

(59) MACQUER, P.-J., "Chymisches Wörterbuch," 2nd ed., part 1, Weidmannische Buchhandlung, Leipzig, 1788, pp. 572–4.

(60) HJELM, P. J., "Versuche aus dem Braunsteine den Braunsteinkönig (Magnesium) zu erhalten, und denselben mit einigen andern Metallen zusammen zu schmelzen," Crell's Ann., 7, 158–68, 446–54 (1787); K. Vet. Acad. Nya Handl. (Apr., May, June, 1785), pp. 141–58.

(61) ILSEMANN, J. C., "Versuche über einen ganz reinen strahligten glänzenden Braunstein von Ilsefeld, und den daraus erhaltenen König," Crell's Neueste Entdeckungen, 4, 24–42 (1782).

(62) DARWIN, ERASMUS, "A Botanic Garden," 2nd ed., J. Johnson, London, 1791, p. 48.

(63) "Fr. Basilii Valentini Chymische Schriften," Gottfried Liebezeit, Hamburg, 1694, pp. 209–10. "Von dem grossen Stein der Uhralten Weisen."

(64) KOPP, H., ref. (19), Vol. 4, pp. 150–7.

(65) NEWELL, L. C., "Chemistry in the service of Egyptology," J. Chem. Educ., 10, 262 (May, 1933).

(66) LUCAS, A., "Ancient Egyptian Materials and Industries," 2nd ed., Edward Arnold and Co., London, 1934, pp. 122–4.

(67) CARTER, HOWARD, "The Tomb of Tut-ankh-Amen," Vol. 2, George H. Doran Co., New York, 1927, p. 242. Chapter on "The chemistry of the tomb" by A. Lucas.

(68) BECKMANN, JOHANN, ref. (47), Vol. 1, pp. 109–10, 131–2, 478–87.

(69) "Gmelin's Handbuch der anorganischen Chemie," 8th ed., Vol. 58A, Verlag Chemie, Berlin, 1932, pp. 1–5.

(70) KUNCKEL, JOHANN, "Ars Vitraria experimentalis," Christoph Riegel, Frankfurt and Leipzig, 1689, pp. 45–8.

(71) BIRINGUCCIO, V., ref. (57), pp. 132–3.

(72) DUPUY, ERNEST, "Bernard Palissy," Soc. Française d'Imprimerie et de Librairie, Paris, 1902, pp. 227–8; Palissy, "Des pierres," II, 176; FOSTER, MARY LOUISE, "Bernard Palissy, sixteenth-century scientist," J. Chem. Educ., 8, 1048 (June, 1931).

(73) DE BLANCOURT, HAUDICQUER, "Art of Glass," Smith, Greenwood and Co., London, **1699**, preface and pp. 63–4, 211.

(74) "Art de la Verrerie de Neri, Merret, et Kunckel," Durand and Pissot, Paris, **1752**, pp. 48–52.

(75) CRONSTEDT, A. F., "Åminnelsetal öfver H. T. Scheffer," Lars Salvius, Stockholm, **1760**, pp. 15–31.

(76) HILDEBRAND, B., ref. (52), pp. 533–9.

(77) MADÁCS, PETRUS, "Theoria affinitatum chemicarum . . .," Comitat. Lyptov Physicus Tyrnav, **1776**, p. 29; *Crell's Neueste Entdeckungen*, **2**, 270 (1781).

(78) BERGMAN, T., "Fällungsversuche mit Platina, Nickel, Kobold, und Braunstein," *ibid.*, **8**, 206 (1783); *K. Vet. Acad. Nya Handl.*, **1**, 282–93 (1780).

(79) RINMAN, S., "Fortsetzung von einer grünen Farbe aus dem Kobolde," *Crell's Neueste Entdeckungen*, **10**, 151–63 (1783); *K. Vet. Acad. Nya Handl.*, **2**, 3–13 (1781).

(80) LINCK (or LINK), J. H., "A discourse on the cobaltum or smalt," *Phil. Trans. Abridgment*, **6**, 235–40 (1734); *Phil. Trans.*, **34**, 192 (1726); *Crell's Neues chem. Archiv.*, **2**, 342 (1784).

(81) FORSSTRAND, CARL, "Sven Rinman. Minnesteckning till 200-årsdagen av hans födelse," Hugo Gebers Förlag, Stockholm, **1920**, pp. 25–7, 73–80.

(82) "Complete Poetical Works of H. W. Longfellow," Houghton, Mifflin and Company, Boston and New York, **1902**, pp. 428–9. "Kéramos."

(83) EDELSTEIN, S. M., "An historic kit for blowpipe analysis," *J. Chem. Educ.*, **26**, 126–31 (Mar., 1949).

(84) ÅBERG, BERTIL, "Urban Hiärne—the first Swedish chemist," *ibid.*, **27**, 334–7 (June, 1950).

(85) ZIETZ, J. R., JR., "The Pirotechnia of Vannoccio Biringuccio," *ibid.*, **29**, 507–10 (Oct., 1952).

(86) FOSTER, MARY LOUISE, "Bernard Palissy. Sixteenth-century scientist," *ibid.*, **8**, 1045–59 (June, 1931).

(87) OSEEN, C. W., "En episod i den Svenska kemiens historia," *Lychnos*, **1940**, pp. 73–85.

(88) LINDROTH, STEN, "Urban Hiärne och Laboratorium Chymicum," *ibid.*, **1946-47**, pp. 51–116.

(89) NORDENSKIÖLD, ref. (30), pp. 373–4.

(90) DIERGART, PAUL, "Beiträge aus der Geschichte der Chemie dem Gedächtnis von G. W. A. Kahlbaum," Franz Deuticke, Leipzig and Vienna, **1909**, pp. 132–42. Chapter by Gustav Oppert, "Mitteilungen zur chemisch-technischen Terminologie im alten Indien,"; Strabo's Geography, **3**, 4, 10.

(91) JONES, H. L., "The geography of Strabo," Vol. 6, G. P. Putnam's Sons, New York, **1929**, p. 115; Strabo's Geography, **13**, 1, 56.

(92) BAILEY, Ref. (41), Vol. 2, pp. 25–7, 159–61; Pliny's Historia Naturalis **34**, 1–4.

(93) GOWLAND, WILLIAM, "Copper and its alloys in early times," *J. Inst. of Metals*, **7**, 43–8 (1912).

(94) RÂY, P. C., Ref. (3), Vol. 1. p. 71.

(95) LIPPMANN, E. O. VON, Ref. (4), Vol. 1, pp. 520, 539, 595–6.

(96) WAITE, A. E., "The hermetic and alchemical writings of . . . Paracelsus the Great," Vol. 1, James Elliott and Co., London, **1894**, pp. 136, 254–5, 314.

(97) GLAUBER, J. R., "Opera chymica," revised ed., Thomas Matthias Götzen, Frankfort-on-the Main, **1658**, pp. 354–5.

(98)   Geoffroy, E.-F., "A Treatise of the Fossil, Vegetable, and Animal Sub-
       stances That Are Made Use of in Physick," W. Innys, R. Manby et al.,
       London, 1736, pp. 179–87, 210–14.

(99)   Claus, "Zum Andenken Herrn Johann Andreas Cramer, Herzog. Braun-
       schweig-Lüneburgischen Cammerraths zu Blankenburg," Crell's Ann., 6,
       376–84 (1786).

(100) Murray, John, "A System of Chemistry," 3rd ed., Vol. 3, William Creech,
       Bell and Bradfute, et al., Edinburgh, 1812, p. 564.

(101) Berthier, P., "Analysis of two zinc ores from the United States of America,"
       Am. J. Sci., (1), 2, 319–26 (1820).

(102) Kobell, Franz von, "Geschichte der Mineralogie," J. G. Cotta, Munich,
       1864, pp. 624–6.

(103) "Biographical notice of the late Archibald Bruce, M.D.," Am. J. Sc., (1),
       1, 299–304 (1819).

(104) Willis, L. G., "Bibliography of References to the Literature on the Minor
       Elements and Their Relation to Plant and Animal Nutrition," 3rd ed.,
       Chilean Nitrate Educational Bureau, New York City, 1939, columns 132,
       891–932.

(105) Lechartier, G. and F. Bellamy, "The presence of zinc in animals and
       plants," Compt. rend., 84, 687–90 (1877).

(106) Nichol, Hugh, "What the plant does with its materials," Nature, 150, 13
       (July 4, 1942).

(107) Mendel, L. B. and H. C. Bradley, "The inorganic constituents of the liver
       of the sycotypus," Am. J. Physiol., 14, 313–27 (1905); ibid., 17, 167–76
       (1906).

(108) Kuroda, Kazuo, "Zinc content of the hot springs of Japan," Bull. Chem. Soc.
       (Japan), 15, 88–92 (March, 1940).

(109) Reed, J. F. and R. W. Cummings, "Determination of zinc in plant mate-
       rials," Ind. Eng. Chem., Anal. Ed., 12, 489–92 (Aug., 1940).

(110) Billinger, R. D., "Early zinc works in the Lehigh Valley," J. Chem. Educ.,
       13, 60–2 (Feb., 1936).

(111) Review of H. R. Schoolcraft's "A view of the lead mines of Missouri," Am. J.
       Sci., (1), 3, 59–72 (1821).

(112) Wann, F. B. and D. W. Thorne, "Zinc deficiency of plants in the western
       states, Sci. Monthly, 70, 180–4 (Mar., 1950).

(113) Shohl, A. T., "Mineral Metabolism," Reinhold Publishing Corporation, New
       York, 1939, pp. 32–3, 96, 141, 145, 162–8, 246–7.

(114) Winderlich, Rudolf, "Chemische Kenntnisse der alten Babylonier und
       Ägypter," Aus der Heimat, 47, 116–21 (Apr., 1934).

(115) Winderlich, Rudolf, "A Persian description of the faïence technic at
       Kashan in 1301 A.D.," J. Chem. Educ., 13, 361–2 (Aug., 1936); Ritter,
       H., J. Ruska, F. Sarre, and R. Winderlich, "Orientalische Steinbücher
       und persische Fayence-Technik," German Archaeological Institute, Istan-
       bul, 1935, 70 pp.

(116) Marggraf, A. S., "Chymische Schriften," Ref. (53), Vol. 1, pp. 133–4.

(117) Pomet, Pierre, "The History of Drugs," 3rd ed., J. Bonwicke et al., London,
       1737, p. 368.

(118) Brandt, Georg, "Untersuchung und Beschreibung einer neuen Art des
       Kobaltes," Crell's Neues chem. Archiv, 3, 221–30 (1785); ibid., 5, 45–8
       (1786); Acta Societ. Regiae Sc. Upsal, ann. 1742, Stockholm, 1748; Vet.
       Acad. Handl., 8, 127 (1746). Published in 1752; "Recueil des mémoires
       . . . contenus dans les Actes de l'Acad. Roy. des Sciences de Stockholm
       [sic]," Vol. 1, P.-F. Didot le Jeune, Paris, 1764, pp. 38–50.

(119) Beckmann, Johann, Ref. (47), Vol. 1, pp. 109–10, 131–2, 478–87.

(120) Kopp, Hermann, Ref. (19), Vol. 4, pp. 155–7.

(121) "Cobalt in meteorites," Quarterly J. Sci., 6, 162 (1819).

(122) Stromeyer, F., "Découverte du cobalt dans le fer météorique," Ann. chim. phys., (2), 8, 98–9 (1818).

(123) Forchhammer, J. G., "On the composition of sea water in the different parts of the ocean," Phil. Trans., 155, 203–62 (1865).

(124) Schultze, M. O., "Metallic elements and blood formation," Physiol. Rev., 20, 37–67 (Jan., 1940).

(125) Stanley, R. C., "Nickel. Past and Present," International Nickel Co. of Canada, 1934, pp. 11–22.

(126) Kopp, Hermann, Ref. (19), part 4, pp. 157–9.

(127) "Account of a memoir of M. Proust," Nicholson's J., 4, 356–7 (Nov., 1800).

(128) Merrill, G. P. and W. F. Foshag, "Minerals from Earth and Sky," Vol. 3, Smithsonian Scientific Series, Washington, D. C., 1929, p. 101.

(129) "Nickel at the Vienna Exposition," Am. Chemist, 5, 181 (Nov., 1874).

(130) Engeström, Gustaf von, "Pak-fong, ein chinesisches weisses Metall," Crell's Neueste Entdeckungen, 3, 178–81 (1781); Vet. Acad. Hundl., 37, 35–8.

(131) Zenzén, "Om den Swedenborgsstammen och det Swedenborgska marmorbordet," Svenska Linné-Sällskapets Årsskrift, 14, 95–9 (1931).

(132) Eggertz, V., "Hans Peter Eggertz, Lefnadsteckningar öfver K. Svenska Vetenskaps Akademiens efter år 1854 aflidna ledamöter," Vol. 2, Stockholm, 1878–85, pp. 37–41.

(133) Geoffroy, E.-F., Ref. (98), pp. 178–9.

(134) Hjelm, P. J., "Versuch über die Gegenwart des Braunsteins in den Eisenerzen," Crell's Neueste Entdeckungen, 6, 164–71 (1782); Vet. Acad. Handl., 39, 82–7 (1778).

(135) Dobbin, Leonard, "The Collected Papers of C. W. Scheele," G. Bell and Sons, London, 1931, p. 38.

(136) "Death of C. F. Bucholtz, 1770–1818," Schweigger's Neues Journal für Chemie und Physik, (4), 22, 131–2 (1818).

(137) Thomson, Thomas, "Death of C. F. Bucholtz," Annals of Philos., 13, 72–3 (Jan., 1819).

(138) Chevreul, M.-E., "Note sur la cause des changemens de couleur que présente le caméléon minéral, extraite d'un travail sur le manganèse," Ann. Chim. Phys., (2), 4, 42–9 (1817).

(139) Chevillot and Edwards, "Mémoire sur le caméléon minéral," Ibid., (2), 4, 287–97 (1817); Ibid., (2), 8, 337–58 (1818).

(140) Kopp, Hermann, Ref. (19), Part 4, pp. 88–9.

(141) Mitscherlich, E., "Ueber die Mangansäure, Uebermangansäure, Ueberchlorsäure, und die Salze dieser Säuren," Ann., 2, 5–11 (1832).

(142) Dobbin, Leonard, Ref. (135), pp. 3–16, 46–7, 209–14, 295–304; Scheele, Vet. Acad. Handl., 32, 120–38 (1771); Ibid., 35, 89–116, 177–94 (1774); Scheele, Vet. Acad. Nya Handl., 1, 18–26 (1780); Crell's Ann., 5, 3–17 (1786).

(143) Nordenskiöld, A. E., Ref. (30), pp. 118, 324–5, 399. Letters of Scheele to Gahn, Bergman, and Hjelm.

(144) Thomson, Thomas, "A System of Chemistry," 2nd ed., Vol. 4, Bell and Bradfute et al., Edinburgh, 1804, p. 357.

(145) Fisher, E. A., "Manganese as a fertilizer," Chem. World, 3, 319 (Dec., 1914); Salm-Horstmar, J. Prakt. Chem., 46–7, 193 (1849).

(146) Shohl, A. T., Ref. (113), pp. 243–5.

(147) Kopp, Hermann, Ref. (19), Vol. 3, pp. 345–71; Vol. 4, pp. 82–9.

(148) Fourcroy, A.-F. de and N.-L. Vauquelin, "Experiments on human bones, as a supplement to the paper on the bones of the ox," Nicholson's J., (2), 30, 256–60 (Dec., 1811).

(*149*) "Manganese in human blood," *Phil. Mag.*, (2), **9**, 390 (May, 1831).
(*150*) PETERS, KARL, "Eilhard Mitscherlich und sein Geschlecht," Verlag C. L. Mettcker & Söhne, Jever, **1951**, 31 pp.
(*151*) PROVENZAL, GIULIO, "Profili Bio-Bibliografici di Chimici Italiani.   Sec. XV– Sec. XIX," Istituto Nazionale Medico Farmacologico "Serono," Rome, **1937**, pp. 5–8.
(*152*) MORLEY, HENRY, "Palissy the Potter," New ed. (not dated), Cassell Petter & Galpin, London, Paris, and New York, 320 pp.

William Prout, 1785–1850. English physician, physiologist, and chemist. He proved that the acidity of the gastric juice is due to hydrochloric acid; showed that the molecular weight of any substance is equal to twice its vapor density referred to hydrogen; and put forth the hypothesis that the atomic weights of all of the elements, referred to hydrogen as unity, are integers. See ref. (54).

Ceux qui veulent aujourd'hui faire passer la Chymie pour une science nouvelle montrent le peu de connoissance qu'ils ont de la nature & de la lecture des Anciens (51). Those who try today to pass chemistry off as a new science show how little knowledge they have of the character and literature of the ancients.

6

Old compounds of hydrogen and nitrogen

Although hydrogen gas has been known only since the seventeenth century, many of its compounds have been recognized since much more ancient times. Hydrogen is found everywhere in nature, combined in the forms of water, acids, alkalies, organic compounds, hydrogen sulfide, petroleum, natural gas, marsh gas, asphalt, and coal, as an essential constituent of all living beings, and as water of hydration or as hydroxyl in many minerals. Long before the element nitrogen (nitrogen gas) was discovered, compounds such as sal ammoniac, nitric acid, and saltpeter were well known.

HYDROGEN COMPOUNDS

Vinegar and Pyroligneous Acid. Vinegar (acetic acid) is mentioned several times in the Bible, as, for example, in Proverbs **10**, 26: "As vinegar to the teeth and as smoke to the eyes, so is the sluggard to them that send him." It was known to Theophrastus three centuries before the birth of Christ, and was used in the manufacture of white lead and verdigris and in extracting mercury from cinnabar (*1*).

In the seventeenth century J. R. Glauber, in his "Description of New Philosophical Furnaces," told in detail "how an acid spirit, or vinegar, may be distilled out of all vegetables, as hearbs, woods, roots, seeds, etc." (*2*). "Now this spirit," said he, "(being rectified) may commodiously be used in divers Chymical operations, for it doth easily dissolve animal stones, as the eyes of Crabs, the stones of Perches and Carps, Corals also and Pearls, etc. as doth vinegar of wine. By means thereof are dissolved the glasses of metals, as of tin, lead, antimony, and are extracted and reduced into sweet oyles." Glauber's "vinegar of woods" is now known as pyroligneous acid.

Johann Rudolf Glauber was born in 1604, the son of a barber-surgeon in Karlstadt, Franconia. In his youth he earned his living at Vienna by making mirrors. At the age of twenty-one years he discovered the medicinal value of sodium sulfate, which has since been known as *Glauber's salt*. Later, in Amsterdam, he bought a large house which had formerly belonged to an alchemist, and converted it into a fine laboratory equipped with furnaces and apparatus of his own design. The German edition of his "New Philosophical Furnaces" was published in Amsterdam during the years 1648 to 1650, and in 1651 English and Latin editions appeared (52).

At about the same time Glauber established wine presses at Wertheim and Kitzingen. An admirer who translated Glauber's "Furni Novi Philosophici" into English said in his preface: "I therefore present you with a rich Cabinet of nature's unvaluable Jewels; But know, that it hath many doors, the one whereof as being shut to many, but not to all, I have opened with an English key . . ." (2). Glauber, he said, "is carryed upon the wings of Fame throughout the whole world. His Fame all know is great, and flyes high, but his worth surmounts his Fame. He is a Philosopher and Chymist indeed" (2).

In 1655 or 1656 Glauber returned to Amsterdam, where Samuel Sorbière visited him in 1660. Glauber was living in a mansion with four large, magnificent laboratories at the rear, where five or six men were employed. A progressive illness, which may have been caused by prolonged study of poisonous compounds, brought Glauber's life to a close in 1670 (53).

J. G. Gahn of Falun, Sweden, was a manufacturer of vinegar, and in 1816 J. J. Berzelius entered into partnership with him and with H. P. Eggertz in the manufacture of sulfuric and nitric acids, white lead and pigments, soft soap, mustard, and vinegar at Gripsholm (3). When Gahn was perfecting his process for the manufacture of vinegar he received valuable help from his wife. In a letter to Berzelius on February 19, 1804 he wrote: "I congratulate you on your success in making vinegar. My wife, who is always dabbling in vinegar-making for the household, has always made the same observation as Herr Doctor in regard to the difference between wooden and large stone containers: always quicker and stronger vinegar in the latter." One of the ingredients of Fru Gahn's vinegar was a herring (4).

Aqua Fortis (*Nitric Acid*). The preparation of nitric acid, or aqua fortis, was described in the Latin treatise "De inventione veritatis," of the 13th- or 14th-century alchemist Pseudo-Geber (5). From the thirteenth to the sixteenth centuries, Oriental chemists prepared it by distilling a mixture of copper vitriol, saltpeter, and alum (6). Raimundo Lulio (Raymond Lully, 1235–1315) substituted cinnabar for the alum. Albert the Great, Georgius Agricola, J. R. Glauber, and the author of the writings attributed to "Basil Valentine" also described the preparation of this acid. Because of the danger involved in its preparation, it had only limited application until, in the sixteenth century, there arose great demand for it for the parting of gold and silver (6). In the eighteenth century, an improved process of manufacturing sulfuric acid by the oxidation of sulfur with saltpeter greatly lowered the price of oil of vitriol (sulfuric acid), and in turn made possible the manufacture of nitric acid directly from saltpeter and sulfuric acid (7).

Because of its relation to saltpeter, P.-J. Macquer regarded nitric acid as a kind of sulfuric acid modified by its passage through animal and vegetable substances. "In 1750," said he, "the Royal Academy of Sciences at Berlin proposed an account of the generation of Nitre as the subject for their prize, which was conferred on a Memoir wherein this last opinion was supported by some new and very judicious experiments" (8). Macquer stated that "the Nitrous [nitric] Acid is never found but in earths and stones which have been impregnated with matters subject to putrefaction . . ." (8).

Oil of Vitriol (Sulfuric Acid). Geber, Vincent de Beauvais (who wrote the "Speculum naturale" in the middle of the thirteenth century), and Albert the Great all mentioned a "spirit" which could be prepared by strongly heating alum (9). This must have been sulfuric acid. The unknown author of the works of "Basil Valentine" gave detailed descriptions of the preparation of this acid by two methods: first, by distillation of calcined iron vitriol and, second, by heating a mixture of stibnite (antimonious sulfide), sulfur, and nitric acid (aqua fortis). The former process yielded a fuming sulfuric acid containing excess sulfur trioxide. In his "Alchymia," Andreas Libavius (Liebau) showed in 1595 that the acids prepared from green vitriol, blue vitriol, and sulfur are identical (9).

The first industrial preparation of sulfuric acid from green vitriol (ferrous sulfate), according to Hermann Kopp, was by Johann Christian Bernhardt in 1755 (9, 10). A fuming sulfuric acid known as Nordhausen oil of vitriol was manufactured at Nordhausen, Thuringia, from partially dehydrated green vitriol (11).

The manufacture of sulfuric acid by burning sulfur with saltpeter was a British discovery. "English artisans," said Guyton de Morveau in the "Encyclopédie Méthodique," "have been credited with the invention of this method, and far be it from me to dispute it; only those who have never actually engaged in it are unaware that it is also an invention to adapt to a large-scale factory manipulations whose principle formerly existed in books; but it is also fair to make known how near theory itself had come to this accomplishment. [Louis] Lémery had already taught that one could extract vitriolic acid from sulfur by mixing it with $1/16$ of its weight of niter or saltpeter, and detonating this mixture with a hot iron in the center of a large stoneware vessel at the bottom of which

water had been placed; the liquid, filtered and concentrated by evapo
ration, bore the name of *oil of sulfur*" (*11*).

Hermann Kopp found the earliest mention of the British process in
Robert Dossie's "Elaboratory laid open" in 1758. Dossie spoke only of
glass receptacles for the acid (*9*). In his "Institutes of Experimental
Chemistry" in the following year, he stated that this process had greatly
lowered the price of oil of vitriol and had made possible the use of this
acid in the preparation of aqua fortis (nitric acid) from saltpeter (*7*).

In 1746 Dr. John Roebuck (1718–1794), of Birmingham, and Samuel
Garbett substituted lead chambers, each about six feet square, for the
glass globes introduced six years previously by Joshua Ward (*22*), an
improvement which cut down the cost of producing the acid to one-
fourth of its former amount (*12, 13*). Three years later, after the
substitution of sulfuric acid for sour milk in the old process of bleaching
had created a demand for the acid, Roebuck and Garbett erected a
sulfuric acid plant at Prestonpans, on the east coast of Scotland (*14*).
Since a salt industry also flourished there, Prestonpans was named for
the salt pans.

When Berzelius visited Paris in 1818, he inspected a lead-chamber
plant in which sulfuric acid was made by burning sulfur with saltpeter,
the daily output being 300 pounds. The acid was condensed first in
a lead caldron and then in a platinum boiler. This plant had three pairs
of lead chambers and two small platinum kettles, each of which had a
capacity of from 2 to $2^{1}/_{2}$ gallons. The cost of the two platinum kettles
was 9000 francs (*15*).

Aqua Regia. Geber described the preparation of nitric acid (aqua
fortis) in his "De inventione veritatis," and added that, if one adds sal
ammoniac to this acid it becomes a more powerful solvent (*5, 16*).
Raymond Lully (Raimundo Lulio) and Albert the Great (St. Albert)
prepared it in the same way. By the time the writings attributed to
"Basil Valentine" were published, hydrochloric acid (acid of salt) was
known; this work describes the preparation of aqua regia by mixing
three parts of hydrochloric acid with one part of nitric acid (*16, 17*). J. R.
Glauber prepared it from common salt and nitric acid and from saltpeter
and hydrochloric acid (*18*).

Hydrochloric Acid ("Acid of Salt") . Although hydrochloric acid
was well known to Libavius in 1595, J. R. Glauber stated in the middle
of the following century that it was the most expensive and most difficult to prepare of all the acids (*16*). In his "Description of the New
Philosophical Furnaces," Glauber gave the following method for preparing "spirit of salt": "Mix salt and vitrial or allome [vitriol or alum]
together, grinding them very well in a mortar. . . . Then cast this

mixture into the fire with an Iron ladle, *viz.*, so much of it as will be sufficient to cover the coals, and then with a great fire the spirits come forth into the receivers. . . . There can by this way distill no spirit of vitriol or allome . . . the reason of this is because these spirits are far more heavy than the spirit of salt, neither can they ascend so great a height . . . because in this furnace the spirit of allome and vitriol [sulfuric acid] cannot be made unless a pipe go out of the furnace near the grate." Glauber stated that his spirit of salt "dissolveth all metals and minerals (excepting silver)" (2).

P.-J. Macquer (1718–1784) said in his "Elements of the Theory and Practice of Chymistry" that "the Acid of Sea-Salt is so called because it is in fact obtained from such Sea-Salt as we use in our kitchens. It is not certainly known in what this Acid differs from the vitriolic and the nitrous [sulfuric and nitric], with regard to its constituent parts" (8).

Free Hydrochloric Acid in the Stomach. On December 23, 1823, Dr. William Prout (1785–1850) discovered the existence of free hydrochloric acid in the stomach. In the *Quarterly Journal of Science and the Arts* for 1824 one may read: "The following are the proofs of the existence of free muriatic [hydrochloric] acid which Dr. Prout has laid before the Royal Society. The contents of a stomach having been digested in distilled water, the solution obtained was divided into four equal parts. One of these, evaporated to dryness, burnt, and examined in the usual way, gave the quantity of muriatic acid in combination with fixed bases. A second, being previously saturated with an alkali, was treated in a similar way, and gave the whole quantity of muriatic acid in the stomach. A third, carefully neutralized with a known solution of alkali, gave the quantity of free acid. The fourth was reserved for any required experiment. In this way Dr. Prout ascertained that the unsaturated muriatic acid in the stomach was always considerable . . ." (19, 55).

Hydrogen in Plants and Animals. J.-B. Boussingault showed that plants can decompose water, liberating oxygen and fixing the hydrogen, and that they are thus able to build up oils and waxes high in hydrogen (20). With J.-B. Dumas he pointed out that "if the animal realm constitutes an immense apparatus for combustion, the vegetable kingdom, on the other hand, constitutes an immense apparatus for reduction, in which reduced carbonic acid leaves its carbon, in which reduced water leaves its hydrogen, in which reduced oxide of ammonium and nitric acid leave their ammonium or their nitrogen" (20).

To appreciate the important and delicate role played by hydrogen in animal life, one need only recall that the pH of the blood plasma never varies much from 7.4 (hydrogen ion concentration 3.98×10^{-8}), the extreme pH limits compatible with life being 6.9 on the acid side and 7.8 on the alkaline side (21).

NITROGEN COMPOUNDS

Sal Ammoniac. In the tenth century A.D., Abu Musa Jabir ibn Hayyan prepared by distillation of blood or hair a volatile product which he called "sal ammoniac from blood" or "sal ammoniac from hair." This was probably "salt of hartshorn," or ammonium carbonate (23).

Sal ammoniac was probably first introduced from Persia (56). In the "Invention of Verity, or Perfection," which has been attributed to Pseudo-Geber, the preparation of sal ammoniac from human urine, perspiration, common salt, and "soot of woods" is described (24, 25).

Alvaro Alonso Barba, in his "Arte de los Metales," the first edition of which was published in Madrid in 1640, discussed the occurrence, properties, and uses of sal ammoniac as follows: "Among all the Salts that Nature alone produceth, the scarcest, but of greatest vertue, is the Salt-Ammoniac; they call it vulgarly Armoniac, and from the name conclude that it comes from Armenia, but that is not the true name of it, but Ammoniac, which in Greek signifies Salt of the sand: and underneath the sand (of the Seashore, I suppose), it is found congealed in little pieces by its internal heat and the continued burning of the Sun, baked so much that it is made the bitterest to taste of all kind of Salt. Goldsmiths use it more than the Physicians. It is one of those they call the four spirits, because the fire will convert them into smoak, and so they fly away: the other three are, 1. Quicksilver, 2. Sulphur, 3. Saltpeter. It hath a particular property to cleanse and colour Gold, and is put into the composition of that *Aqua-fortis* that dissolves it [aqua regia]" (26).

Robert Boyle stated in 1661, in his "Sceptical Chymist," that sal ammoniac is composed of muriatic (hydrochloric) acid and the volatile alkali (ammonia) and told how to separate the "urinous and common salts" (27). In 1716 Geoffroy the Younger demonstrated the composition of sal ammoniac and prepared it by sublimation (28, 29). In the same year, the Jesuit missionary Father Sicard described its preparation at Damiré or Damayer, one mile from the City of El Mansura in the Nile Delta. In twenty-five large laboratories and several smaller ones, it was sublimed in glass vessels from the soot of the burned dung of camels and cows, to which, he said, had been added salt and urine. Lemere, the French consul at Cairo, described the process in 1719 for the Academy of Sciences in Paris, but made no mention of salt or urine (29, 30, 31).

When it was learned that the Egyptians did not add salt, scientists were at a loss to find the source of the muriate (chlorine) in the sal ammoniac. The first satisfactory explanation was given by Fredrik Hasselqvist (a student of Linné who made a scientific journey through Egypt and Palestine in 1749–52) in his first-hand description of the manufacturing process. According to Hasselqvist, Egyptian laborers spent the spring months of each year collecting and drying the dung of horses, donkeys, camels, cattle, buffaloes, sheep, and goats. In Egypt most of the wells are brackish and much of the vegetation is rich in salt. When domestic animals assimilate these plants, they excrete some of the sodium chloride. Egyptian manufacturers were therefore able to prepare sal ammoniac without adding salt.

Since the annual floods of the Nile abundantly enriched the soil, large quantities of animal manures could be diverted to this manufacturing process without impoverishing Egyptian agriculture. As the dung was burned, the soot from it was collected and heated in glass flasks in a brick furnace. "They make the fire gentle at first," said Hasselqvist, ". . . they increase the heat gradually till they bring it to the highest degree, which the workmen call hell-fire, and continue it so for three days and three nights together. When the heat is come to its due degree, the smoke shews itself with a sourish smell that is not unpleasant; and in a little time the salt sticks to the glasses and covers the whole aperture . . ." (32). When the flasks were broken, a rounded cake of sublimed sal ammoniac was removed from each of them. Hasselqvist inspected plants such as this at Rosetta, Gizeh, and other places in the Delta, each of which had its glassworks for manufacturing and remaking them from the broken glass (32, 33).

E.-F. Geoffroy stated that sal ammoniac, because of its volatility and the manner in which it used to be prepared, was often called the *heavenly eagle*, the *flying little bird*, the *solar salt*, or the *mercurial soot* (43). Herman Boerhaave believed that, since Vesuvius and other volcanoes eject sal ammoniac, "it is therefore necessary to class this salt with the fossils, although it is believed that that which is now being brought to us is an animal production" (75). By the word "fossil" Boerhaave and his contemporaries meant a mineral, or substance dug from the earth.

In 1759 Robert Dossie corrected the false belief that sal ammoniac was found in the earth in Oriental countries only where the caravans had rested. "But I know it to be an undoubted fact," said he, "that sal Ammoniacus is sublimed in a considerable quantity out of the chinks or cracks of the earth, in the Sulfiterra (solfatara), near Naples . . . and it is certain, as the salt so sublimed must be raised from vast caverns which lie deep in the earth, its origin cannot be ascribed to the urine of camels, in caravans; nor indeed to any other circumstance in which the parts of animals or vegetables have any concern" (35).

Ammonia. Raimundo Lulio (Raymond Lully) mentioned caustic ammonia in the thirteenth century (36). Johann Kunckel (or Kunkel) von Löwenstern (1630–1702) described it in his posthumously published "Vollständiges Laboratorium Chymicum" (37). He prepared it by adding lime to sal ammoniac (38).

Saltpeter or Niter. "Salt-peter," said P.-J. Macquer, ". . . signifies the Salt of Stone; and in fact Nitre is extracted from the stones and plaister in which it forms . . ." (8). In the chemical works of the unknown monk "Basil Valentine," which were edited by Johann Thölde, saltpeter is described as "a wonder-salt" with an infernal spirit concealed in an ice-like form.

> *"Mein Form ist schlecht ein lauter Eyss/*
> *Darin findst du ein höllschen Geist" (39).*

In 1624 a proclamation was issued in Cambridge, England, for "the preservation of Grounds for making of Salt-Peeter," making it illegal to pave dovecots or cellars (except the part used for wine or beer) with stone, brick, or floor-boards or to lay the same with "lime, sand, gravel, or anything that would stop the growth of the Mine of Saltpeter" (40).

J. R. Glauber was probably the first to form artificial niter beds. By throwing putrefiable matter of both vegetable and animal origin into pits and adding wood ashes, he obtained in due time a "saltpeter earth" from which he extracted a solution which, on evaporation, yielded crystals of this salt. Glauber believed that the function of the putrid material was merely "to draw the niter from the air" (41).

In 1717 Louis Lémery stated that saltpeter was usually obtained from the earth and refuse piles near old lime-plastered walls and in stables and churchyards. To explain its origin, John Mayow postulated the existence of a hypothetical "saltpeter" in the atmosphere. When Mariotte exposed to the air of an upper room some "saltpeter earth" (earth from which all the saltpeter had previously been leached out), however, he was unable to prepare even a gram of saltpeter. When he placed the same earth in the cellar, it soon became covered with saltpeter. Lémery placed three earthen vessels containing respectively lime, potassium carbonate, and leached "saltpeter earth" on pedestals, and exposed them to the moist air of a dark cellar whose walls and floor were covered with saltpeter. Even after two years, however, he found not a trace of saltpeter in any of the three vessels. By frequently moistening the contents with animal substances, however, he soon prepared a considerable quantity of it (42).

Étienne-François Geoffroy, 1672–1731. French physician and chemist known as "Geoffroy the Elder." Professor of chemistry at the Jardin du Roi and physician to the King of France. He is most famous for his table of chemical affinities.

To distinguish saltpeter from sodium carbonate (the "niter," or natrum, of the ancients) E.-F. Geoffroy called it "the niter of the moderns. . . . Since no Salt-petre is obtainable," said he, "except from Earths impregnated with the urinous Salts of Animals or Vegetables, it is doubted by some whether this Salt be of a Mineral or Animal Original. This we leave to be determined by others, but we chuse to follow the Example of the Generality of Chemists, in ranking it among Minerals, because it is extracted immediately from the Earth, and cannot be obtained from the Urine and Faeces of Animals without Earth" (43).

His contemporary Dr. Herman Boerhaave said that "Modern niter, or saltpeter, forms octagonal crystals: it is a semi-fossil extracted from a bitter nitrous earth; it melts in a moderate fire; it gives off very little water; it is rather fixed; when it is melted, it bursts into flame with all inflammable matter; it dissolves in $6^{1}/_{2}$ (parts) of water" (34).

After mentioning the use of saltpeter in gunpowder, Boerhaave wrote: "May it please Heaven that men, no longer ingenious in finding means of destroying one another, may cease from cruelly waging war on each other and no longer employ to their own destruction the beautiful inventions of a science in itself so salutary. Therefore I feel compelled to remain silent regarding several other discoveries more dangerous and more detestable" (34).

A small saltpeter refinery was in operation in Dijon, France, as early as 1725. Itinerant saltpeter-makers, authorized by the government to collect earth from the stables and cellars of the inhabitants, also demanded from them free lodging and wood for heating their evaporating kettles (44). In the latter part of the eighteenth century Lavoisier greatly improved the French saltpeter industry (45). In 1778 Guyton de Morveau, Jean-Baptiste Courtois, and others founded a plant at Dijon for the artificial production of saltpeter, which was unable to compete with the cheap product from India. During the French Revolution, however, J.-B. Courtois found the business lucrative. His son, Bernard, while scarcely more than a child, began to help in the plant and to show an intelligent interest in the process.

To convert the alkaline earth nitrates into saltpeter, Bernard and his father added wood ashes. Since much of the potash from the ashes was wasted by reacting with salts other than nitrates, they conceived the idea of using, instead of wood ashes, the cheaper ash of sea-weeds, especially *Fucus* and *Laminaria* from the coasts of Normandy and Brittany. The resulting sodium nitrate was then economically converted to potassium nitrate by treatment with wood ashes. The ash of these algae contains sodium, potassium, magnesium, and calcium as chlorides, bromides, iodides, carbonates, and sulfates, but was then valued only for its alkali content (*44*).

Volume 1 of the *American Journal of Science* contains a first-hand description, by Dr. Samuel Brown, of the niter caves of Kentucky, which have been known since the beginning of the nineteenth century (*46*). R. N. Maxson described these caves in the *Journal of Chemical Education* for November, 1932 (*47*).

Chilean Nitrate. Chile saltpeter, or sodium nitrate, was probably known to the South American Indians before the coming of the Spaniards (*48*). The first Englishman to visit the nitrate coast (then part of southern Peru) was Sir Francis Drake in 1578. Eight years later, Lopez Vaz, a Portuguese, told Captain Withrington that "Peru . . . hath many mines of gold and more of silver, as also great store of copper and tinne-mines with abundance of salt peter and brimstone to make gun-pouder" (*48, 49, 50*). The Indians near Lima used to purify the nitrate and covert it into gunpowder for use in the mercury mines at Huancavelica and in their fireworks. In the nineteenth century, Chile saltpeter was shipped to Europe for manufacturing rockets for saint-day displays in Catholic countries (*48*).

LITERATURE CITED

(*1*) HILL, JOHN, "Theophrastus's History of Stones," 2nd ed., printed for the translator, London, 1774, pp. 225, 227–35.

(*2*) GLAUBER, J. R., "A Description of New Philosophical Furnaces," Richard Coats, London, 1651–2. Preface by J. F., the English translator, also pp. 10–13, 31, 76–8, 96–7.

(*3*) SÖDERBAUM, H. G., "Jac. Berzelius. Levnadsteckning," Vol. 2, P. A. Norstedt and Sons, Stockholm, 1929–31, pp. 54–7.

(*4*) *Ibid.,* Vol. 1, p. 187.

(*5*) BUGGE, GÜNTHER, "Das Buch der grossen Chemiker," Vol. 1, Verlag Chemie, Berlin, 1929, pp. 60–9. Chapter on Pseudo-Geber by Julius Ruska.

(*6*) KOPP, HERMANN, "Geschichte der Chemie," Vol. 3, F. Vieweg and Son, Braunschweig, 1847, pp. 225–32.

(*7*) DOSSIE, ROBERT, "Institutes of Experimental Chemistry," Vol. 1, J. Nourse, London, 1759, p. 334.

(*8*) MACQUER, P.-J., "Elements of the Theory and Practice of Chymistry," 2nd ed., Vol. 1, A. Millar and J. Nourse, London, 1764, pp. 28–9, 32, 241.

(*9*) KOPP, HERMANN, ref. (*6*), Vol. 3, pp. 303–9.

(*10*) MACQUER, P.-J., "Chymisches Wörterbuch," German translation from the 2nd French ed., Vol. 6, Weidmannische Buchhandlung, Leipzig, 1790, pp. 763–92.

(*11*) "Encyclopédie méthodique," Vol. 1, Panckoucke, Paris, 1786, pp. 353–97.

(*12*) STEPHEN, L. and S. LEE, "Dictionary of National Biography," Vol. 17, Oxford University Press, London, 1921–2, pp. 93–5. Article on John Roebuck by Francis Espinasse.

(*13*) *Ibid.,* Vol. 20, pp. 783–5. Article on Joshua Ward by E. I. Carlyle.

(*14*) MACTEAR, JAMES, "On the growth of the alkali and bleaching-powder manufacture of the Glasgow district," *Chem. News,* 35, 14–17 (Jan. 12, 1877).

(15) SÖDERBAUM, H. G., "Jac. Berzelius. Reseanteckningar," P. A. Norstedt and Sons, Stockholm, 1903, pp. 171–3.

(16) KOPP, HERMANN, Ref. (6), Vol. 3, pp. 348–53; Vol. 4, pp. 82–9.

(17) "Fr. Basilii chymische Schriften," revised ed., part 1, Gottfried Liebezeit, Hamburg, 1694, pp. 281–2.

(18) GLAUBER, J. R., "Opera chymica," T. M. Götzen, Frankfort-on-the Main, 1658, p. 52. Second part of the Pharmacopaeae Spagyricae.

(19) "On muriatic acid in the stomach," Quarterly J. Sci., 17, 181 (1824).

(20) DUMAS, J.-B. and BOUSSINGAULT, J.-B., "Essai de statique chimique des êtres organisés," 3rd ed., Fortin, Masson et Cie., Paris, 1844, pp. 5, 27–8, 140.

(21) SHOHL, A. T., "Mineral Metabolism," Reinhold Publishing Corporation, New York, 1939, pp. 28 and 282.

(22) "Taschen-Buch für Scheidekünstler und Apotheker," Hoffmann Buchhandlung, Weimar, 1782, pp. 109–21.

(23) BUGGE, G., "Das Buch der grossen Chemiker," Vol. 1, Verlag Chemie, Berlin, 1929, p. 28. Article on Dschabir (Jabir or Geber) by J. Ruska.

(24) HOLMYARD, E. J., "The Works of Geber, Englished by Richard Russell, 1678," J. M. Dent and Sons, London and Toronto, 1928, pp. 205–6.

(25) DARMSTAEDTER, ERNST, "Die Alchemie des Geber," Julius Springer, Berlin, 1922, pp. 105–6.

(26) BARBA, A. A., "The Art of Metals," S. Mearne, London, 1674, pp. 29–30, 90–1.

(27) BOYLE, ROBERT, "The Sceptical Chymist," J. M. Dent and Sons, London (undated reprint), p. 47.

(28) GEOFFROY THE YOUNGER, "Beobachtungen über die Natur und Mischung des Salmiaks," Crell's Neues chem. Archiv, 2, 60–79, 157–67 (1784); Mém. de l'Acad. des Sciences (Paris), 1716, 1720, 1723.

(29) "Anzeige an die Akademie über den Salmiak, usw. von Lemere, Consul in Cairo, den 24sten Junii, 1719," Crell's Neues chem. Archiv, 2, 61–5 (1784).

(30) BECKMAN, JOHANN, "A history of Inventions, Discoveries, and Origins," 4th ed., Vol. 2, Henry G. Bohn, London, 1846, pp. 402–7.

(31) "Recueil des mémoires de chymie . . . contenus dans les Actes de l'Acad. d'Upsal et dans les mémoires de l'Acad. Roy. des Sciences de Stockolm [sic] . . . ," P.-F. Didot le jeune, Paris, 1764, pp. 227–36 (M. C. Leyel on sal ammoniac); LEYEL, Vet. Acad. Handl., 13 (1751).

(32) HASSELQVIST, F., "Iter Palaestinum eller resa till Heliga Landet," Lars Salvius, Stockholm, 1757, pp. 540–3; "Voyages and Travels in the Levant," L. Davis and C. Reymers, London, 1766, pp. 304–7.

(33) "Recueil des Mémoires," ref. (31), pp. 237–43. F. Hasselqvist on Sal ammoniac.

(34) BOERHAAVE, H., "Elémens de chymie," Vol. 1, Chardon fils, Paris, 1754, pp. 88, 90, 215.

(35) DOSSIE, ROBERT, ref. (7), Vol. 1, pp. 319, 354.

(36) DARMSTAEDTER, LUDWIG, "Handbuch zur Geschichte der Naturwissenschaften und der Technik," 2nd ed., J. Springer, Berlin, 1908, p. 55.

(37) Ibid., p. 158.

(38) KUNKEL VON LÖWENSTERN, JOHANN, "Vollständiges Laboratorium Chymicum," 4th ed., Rüdigersche Buchhandlung, Berlin, 1767, p. 459.

(39) "Fr. Basilii Valentini Chymische Schriften," ref. (17), pp. 157–8.

(40) GUNTHER, R. T., "Early Science in Cambridge," University Press, Oxford, 1937, p. 219.

(41) MASSEY, JAMES, "A treatise on saltpetre," Memoirs Lit. and Philos. Soc. (Manchester), 1, 184–223 (1789).

(42) LÉMERY, L., "Ueber den Salpeter," Crell's Neues chem. Archiv, 1, 159–75 (1784); Hist. de l'Acad. Roy. des Sciences, 1717.

(43) GEOFFROY, E.-F., "Treatise of the Fossil, Vegetable, and Animal Substances That Are Made Use of in Physick," W. Innys, R. Manby, et al., London, 1736, pp. 96–7, 123.

(44) TORAUDE, L.-G., "Bernard Courtois et la découverte de l'iode," Vigot Frères, Paris, 1921, 164 pp.

(45) GRIMAUX, E., "Lavoisier, 1743–1794," Félix Alcan, Paris, 1888, pp. 82–96.

(46) BROWN, SAMUEL, "On a curious substance which accompanies the native nitre of Kentucky and of Africa," Am. J. Sci., 1, 146–8 (1819).

(47) MAXSON, R. N., "The niter caves of Kentucky," J. Chem. Educ., 9, 1847–64 (Nov., 1932).

(48) DONALD, M. B., "History of the Chile nitrate industry," Annals of Sci., 1, 29–47, 193–216 (1936).

(49) "The History of Lopez Vaz, a Portugall, Taken by Captaine Withrington at the River of Plate, Anno 1586. Purchas his pilgrimes," Vol. 17, James MacLehose and Sons, Glasgow, 1906, p. 283.

(50) HAKLUYT, RICHARD, "The Principal Navigations, Voyages, Traffiques, and Discoveries of the English Nation," Vol. 8, J. M. Dent and Co., London (undated reprint), p. 199. "A discourse of the West Indies and South Sea, written by Lopez Vaz, a Portugal."

(51) LE FEVRE, NICOLAS, "Cours de chymie," 5th ed., Vol. 1, J.-N. Leloup, Paris, 1751, p. 1.

(52) ARMSTRONG, EVA V. and C. K. DEISCHER, "Johann Rudolf Glauber (1604–70)," J. Chem. Educ., 19, 3–8 (Jan., 1942).

(53) JORISSEN, W. P., "Iets over Glauber's Amsterdamschen Tijd," Chem. Weekbl., 15, 268–71 (1918).

(54) GLASSTONE, SAMUEL, "William Prout (1785–1850)," J. Chem. Educ., 24, 478–81 (Oct., 1947).

(55) PROUT, WILLIAM, "Chemistry, Meteorology, and the Function of Digestion Considered with Reference to Natural Theology," William Pickering, London, 1834, 499–500.

(56) RUSKA, JULIUS, Z. angew. Chemie, 41, 1321 (1928).

Antoine-Laurent Lavoisier. Bronze medal by Abel Lafleur honoring the memory of Lavoisier, founder of modern chemistry, on the bicentenary of his birth. It reads: "He is perhaps the most complete, the greatest man that France has produced in the Sciences" (J. B. Dumas).

"*The generality of men are so accustomed to judge of things by their senses that, because the air is invisible, they ascribe but little to it, and think it but one remove from nothing.*" (1)

7

Three important gases

> *Chemists of the eighteenth century were intensely interested in "air," which they prepared by fermentation, by heating various chemical compounds, and by allowing substances of vegetable and animal origin to putrefy. Gradually the idea dawned that, as Priestley expressed it, there are "different kinds of air," and that Cavendish's "inflammable air from metals" is quite different from Daniel Rutherford's "noxious air" and from Scheele's "fire air." The preparation and recognition of the three gases, hydrogen, nitrogen, and oxygen, required true genius. For further information about Rutherford see pp. 235–51.*

*I*n the latter part of the seventeenth century, Johann Joachim Becher and Georg Ernst Stahl advanced a peculiar theory of combustion that held sway over the minds of chemists for nearly a hundred years. They maintained that everything that can be burned contains a substance, phlogiston, which escapes in the form of flame during the combustion, and until Lavoisier overthrew this theory in 1777, practically all chemists believed that a metal consists of its calx, or oxide, and phlogiston. It was in this period of chemical history that the gases hydrogen, nitrogen, and oxygen were discovered.

HYDROGEN

Hydrogen was observed and collected long before it was recognized as an individual gas. The statement of Paracelsus (1493–1541) that *"Luft erhebt sich und bricht herfür gleichwie ein Wind"** has often been cited erroneously as an allusion to this gas (2, 37). Van Helmont, Boyle, Mayow, and Stephen Hales all had some slight acquaintance with hydrogen. In his "New experiments touching the relation betwixt flame and air," which were ready for publication in 1671, Robert Boyle dissolved iron in dilute hydrochloric or sulfuric acid and prepared hydrogen in the form of "inflammable solution of Mars [iron]" (44).

* "Air rises and breaks forth like a wind."

"Having provided a saline spirit [hydrochloric acid]," said Boyle, ". . . we put into a vial, capable of containing three or four ounces of water, a very convenient quantity of filings of steel, which were not such as are commonly sold in shops to chemists and apothecaries (those being usually not free enough from rust) but such as I had a while before caused to be purposely filed off from a piece of good steel. This metalline powder being moistened in the vial with a little of the menstruum, was afterwards drenched with more; whereupon the mixture grew very hot, and belched up copious and stinking fumes; which whether they con-

Georg Ernst Stahl, 1660–1734. German chemist, physician, and professor. Co-founder of the phlogiston theory of combustion.   Author of "Fundamenta Chymiae Dogmaticae et Experimentalis."   He distinguished between potash and soda and recognized that alum contains a peculiar earth different from all others.

From Bugge's "Das Buch der grossen Chemiker"

sisted altogether of the volatile suphur of the Mars, or of metalline steams participating of a sulphureous nature, and joined with the saline exhalations of the menstruum, is not necessary to be here discussed.   But whencesoever this stinking smoke proceeded, so inflammable it was, that on the approach of a lighted candle to it, it would readily enough take fire and burn with a blueish and somewhat greenish flame at the mouth of the vial for a good while together; and that, though with little light, yet with more strength than one would easily suspect" (*44*).

Nicolas Lémery described it in 1700 in the Mémoires of the Paris Academy (*2*).   In the 1686 English edition of his "Course of Chymistry," which was based on the fifth French edition, there is no mention of the evolution of any flammable or explosive gas when "vitriol of Mars" is prepared by dissolving iron in dilute sulfuric acid.   At that time, Lémery

Johann Joachim Becher, Med. Doct.
wie auch
Röm. Kayserl. Majestät Cammer. und
Commercien-Rath etc.

Krugner sen. sc. Lip.

Courtesy Dr. Claude K. Deischer, Edgar Fahs Smith Memorial Collection

Johann Joachim Becher, 1635–1682. German chemist and physician. Founder of the phlogiston theory. His experiments on minerals are described in his "Physica Subterranea." Stahl summarized his views on combustion in a book entitled "Specimen Becherianum."

merely observed that "the liquor heats and boils considerably" (45). In the eleventh French edition, however, which was published in 1716, a year after Lémery's death, the same preparation is described as yielding "white vapors which will rise to the top of the neck of the matrass; if one presents a lighted candle to the mouth of this vessel, the vapor will immediately take fire and at the same time produce a violent, shrill fulmination" (45). In this reaction Lémery believed he had found the cause of thunder and lightning.

Hermann Kopp stated in his "Geschichte der Chemie" that at the beginning of the seventeenth century Turquet de Mayerne (1573–1655) noticed the flammability of the gas evolved from a mixture of iron and sulfuric acid and was the first to make this observation (2). Brief accounts of the life and work of Turquet de Mayerne may be found also in Dr. Charles H. LaWall's "The Curious Lore of Drugs and Medicines" (64) and Dr. Victor Robinson's "The Story of Medicine" (65).

The name most closely associated with the early history of hydrogen is that of Mr. Henry Cavendish. Although he was a descendant of the

Henry Cavendish, 1731–1810. English chemist and physicist. This is the Alexander portrait. The likeness of Cavendish in W. Walker's engraving of British scientists was taken from the drawing by Tomlinson (46). Cavendish was the first to distinguish hydrogen from other gases and was an independent discoverer of nitrogen.

Dukes of Devonshire and the Dukes of Kent, he was born at Nice; for his mother, Lady Anne Cavendish, had gone to France for the benefit of the mild climate. The date of his birth is given as October 10, 1731. The unfortunate death of Lady Cavendish two years later, and the consequent lack of maternal affection in the young child's life may account in some degree for the abnormal shyness and ungregariousness of the man. At the age of eleven years Henry Cavendish entered Dr. New-come's school at Hackney, and from 1749 to 1753 he attended Cambridge University. Although he lacked only a few days of the necessary residence requirements, he left Cambridge without receiving a degree (3).

From Edward Smith's "Life of Sir Joseph Banks"

Lady Banks   Sir Joseph Banks
(From a Wedgwood cameo, attributed to Flaxman.)

Sir Joseph Banks, 1743–1820. English naturalist and collector of plants and insects. President of the Royal Society from 1778–1820. His collections of books and natural history specimens were bequeathed to the British Museum. **Lady Banks** used to assist him in giving frequent receptions for the scientists of London.

During his father's lifetime Cavendish lived on a meager allowance, but, upon his father's death in 1783, he received an enormous inheri-tance. Not long after this an aunt died, leaving him another large legacy. Thus he became, as Biot said, "the richest of all the learned and the most learned of all the rich" (4). Since Cavendish lived very modestly, the interest on his money accumulated until, at the time of his death, he was the largest depositor in the Bank of England (5).

It may be said without exaggeration that, of all great personages of scientific history, Mr. Henry Cavendish was the most singular. He was shy and awkward among strangers, and to him all men were strangers. The only social contacts he ever made were at the meetings of the Royal

Society and at the Sunday evening receptions which Sir Joseph Banks was accustomed to give for the scientists in London. Cavendish spoke falteringly in shrill tones and was unable to converse with more than one person at a time; yet, because of his broad knowledge and clear reasoning, the members of the Royal Society all recognized him as a superior. Dr. Thomas Thomson in his well-known "History of Chemistry" cites a striking example of Cavendish's extreme fear of publicity. Dr. Jan Ingenhousz once brought as his guest to the home of Sir Joseph Banks a distinguished Austrian scientist, whom he introduced to Cavendish with extravagant praise. The foreign guest, in turn, became profuse in his flattery of Cavendish, stating that he had come to London with the express purpose of meeting such a distinguished scientist, whereupon Cavendish, at first embarrassed, then utterly confused, darted through the crowd to his waiting carriage (5).

A few scientists, however, knew how to overcome his extreme diffidence, and of these perhaps the most successful was Dr. W. H. Wollaston. "The way to talk to Cavendish," said he, "is never to look at him, but to talk as it were into vacancy, and then it is not unlikely but you may set him going" (6).

In spite of his love of solitude, Cavendish was not lacking in interest in the researches carried out by others. He presented young Humphry Davy with some platinum for his experiments, and went occasionally to the Royal Institution to see his brilliant experiments on the decomposition of the alkalies (6). Sir Humphry said later in his eulogy of Cavendish,

. . . Upon all subjects of science he was luminous and profound; and in discussion wonderfully acute. . . . His name will be an object of more veneration in future ages than at the present moment. Though it was unknown in the busy scenes of life, or in the popular discussions of the day, it will remain illustrious in the annals of science, which are as imperishable as that nature to which they belong; and it will be an immortal honour to his house, to his age, and to his country (7).

Cavendish dressed like an English gentleman of a bygone day. He wore a cocked hat and a gray-green coat with a high collar and frilled cuffs. His costume and personality are well depicted in the famous Alexander portrait, sketched hastily at a dinner without Cavendish's knowledge. Cavendish had three residences: one near the British Museum, furnished mainly with books and apparatus; another in Dean Street, Soho, containing his main library, which he generously placed at the disposal of all scholars who wished to use it; and a third dwelling known as Cavendish House, Clapham Common. This suburban home at Clapham, his favorite residence, he converted almost entirely into workshops and laboratories (8).

Although many historians of chemical progress mention Cavendish as the discoverer of hydrogen, he himself made no such claim and prefaced his remarks on the explosibility of a mixture of hydrogen and air with the words, ". . . it has been observed by others. . . ." He was, however, the first to collect gases over mercury (*41*) and distinguish hydrogen

From Thorpe's "Scientific Papers of the Hon. Henry Cavendish"

Cavendish's House at Clapham

from other gases by the descriptive term, "inflammable air from the metals." His accurate description of its properties and his methods of obtaining the pure gas from different sources were scientific contributions of the first rank. He had, however, the mistaken idea that the hydrogen came from the metal rather than from the acid (*9*). He at first identified hydrogen with phlogiston, but later thought it was a compound of phlogiston and water.

Cavendish's death was as lonely as his life. He lived to the age of seventy-nine years, and then, one day, feeling the approach of death, he asked an attendant servant to leave the room and not return until a

Photograph by Bachrach

Harold Clayton Urey, 1893– . Professor of chemistry at the Institute for Nuclear Studies at the University of Chicago. In 1931 Dr. Urey and his collaborators discovered deuterium, the heavy isotope of hydrogen. He has carried out notable researches on the entropy of gases and on the properties and separation of isotopes and has studied the chemical evidence of the earth's origin.

specified time. When the servitor returned, he found his great master dead (*10*). Mr. Henry Cavendish was given the honor of a public funeral and burial in All Hallows Church near the tomb of his philanthropic ancestor, Elizabeth Hardwicke. He lived a blameless life, unselfishly devoted to the advancement of science. His researches included electricity, astronomy, meteorology, and chemistry, and he was also well versed in mathematics, mining, metallurgy, and geology. He was a great scientist in the fullest sense of the word.

In December, 1931, H. C. Urey, F. G. Brickwedde, and G. M. Murphy of Columbia University detected, in the residue from a large amount of liquid hydrogen that had been allowed to evaporate down, two very faint lines near the Balmer lines in the spectrum of ordinary atomic hydrogen (*81*). By application of quantum mechanics they showed that the measured separations of these faint lines from the more intense lines of hydrogen must be due to a hydrogen atom of mass two, which they named deuterium.

In July, 1932, Professor Urey and Dr. Edward W. Washburn of the U. S. Bureau of Standards found that when water is separated into its constituents electrolytically, *i. e.*, when a current of electricity is passed through water containing a little sulfuric acid to make it conduct the current, the water remaining in the container becomes heavier and heavier (*62*). Dr. Urey and his collaborators found that this increase in weight is caused by the presence of deuterium. Since deuterium is twice as heavy as ordinary hydrogen, its discovery convincingly disproved the idea that isotopes of a given element (atomic species of the same atomic number but different atomic weights) necessarily have identical chemical properties and are inseparable by chemical means. Deuterium and hydrogen are easily separated.

The history of tritium, the extremely rare hydrogen isotope of mass three, has been reported in the *Journal of Chemical Education* (*81*).

NITROGEN

The discovery of nitrogen was announced in a doctor's dissertation by Daniel Rutherford, uncle of Sir Walter Scott (*11, 40*). He was a son of Dr. John Rutherford, one of the founders of the Medical School at Edinburgh, and was born in that city on November 3, 1749. Preparatory to entering his father's profession, he graduated from the Arts course at the University of Edinburgh, and on September 12, 1772, he received the degree of doctor of medicine. His dissertation was the result of a research suggested and directed by the famous Scottish chemist, Dr. Joseph Black. Dr. Black had noticed that when a carbonaceous substance was burned, a certain amount of air remained even after the "fixed air" (carbon dioxide) had all been absorbed by caustic potash. He therefore gave to Rutherford the problem of studying the properties of this residual "air" (*12, 38*).

Rutherford found that when a mouse was left in a confined volume of air until it died, one-sixteenth of the volume disappeared; and that when the remaining air was treated with alkali, it, in turn, lost one-eleventh of its volume. After thus removing the carbon dioxide ("fixed, or mephitic, air") and most of the oxygen, he studied the properties of the residual gas. He found it very difficult "to completely saturate air with phlogiston" (to remove all the oxygen), for after a mouse had died in it, a candle would burn feebly, and after the flame had flickered out, the candle wick or phosphorus would continue to glow.   His best results

Joseph   Black,   1728–1799. Scottish   chemist,   physicist, and physician.   Professor of chemistry at Glasgow.   He clearly   characterized   carbon dioxide ("fixed air") as the gas which makes caustic alkalies mild,° and distinguished between magnesia and lime. He discovered the latent heats of   fusion   and   vaporization, measured the specific heats of many substances, and invented an ice calorimeter.

Courtesy Lyman C. Newell

were obtained by burning phosphorus in the confined air.   Since the residual gas did not support life, he called it "noxious," or injurious, air He did not realize, however, that his "noxious air," or nitrogen, as it is now called, is the constituent of the atmosphere that remains after removal of the oxygen and carbon dioxide.   He thought that the "noxious air" was atmospheric air that had taken up phlogiston from the substance that had been burned.   According to Rutherford, ". . . this conjecture is confirmed by the fact that air which has served for the calcination of metals is similar, and has clearly taken away from them their phlogiston." He thought that the "mephitic air" obtained by burning carbonaceous material contained less phlogiston than the "noxious air" remaining after combustion of phosphorus.   Rutherford's epoch-making thesis, *Dissertatio Inauguralis de Aere fixo dicto, aut mephitico,* is preserved in the British

° The Belgian chemist Jan Baptist van Helmont (1577–1644) has shown that when must undergoes fermentation a kind of air which he called "gas sylvestre" and which is identical with the non-respirable gas given off by burning charcoal escapes (70), but considered it a transformation product of water (71).   He was the first to use the word *gas.*

Jan Baptist van Helmont, 1577–1644. Belgian physician and chemist who made a detailed study of carbon dioxide (gas silvestre) and understood its preparation by the burning of charcoal or other carbonaceous organic material, by fermentation of beer and wine, and by action of vinegar on shells and limestone. See also ref. (86).

Museum (*12*, *39*) and at the University of Edinburgh and has been translated into English.

After completing his medical course, Dr. Rutherford traveled for three years in England, France, and Italy. Upon returning to Edinburgh in 1775 he began his medical practice, and never again engaged in chemical research. Eleven years later he accepted the chair of botany at Edinburgh, but continued to practice medicine. He served for a time as president of the Royal College of Physicians of Edinburgh. Dr. Rutherford had a pleasant disposition, and displayed true loyalty and friendship toward his honored teacher, Dr. Black (*12*).

Although most authorities agree that Dr. Rutherford was the discoverer of nitrogen, it would be unfair to disregard the work of Scheele, Cavendish, and Priestley. Scheele obtained nitrogen at about the same time by absorbing the oxygen of the atmosphere in liver of sulfur or a mixture of sulfur and iron filings (*13*). One of Cavendish's papers, written before 1772 and marked in his handwriting "communicated to Dr. Priestley," describes his method of preparing "burnt air" by passing atmospheric air repeatedly over red-hot charcoal, and then removing the carbon dioxide by absorbing it in caustic potash. He studied the properties of nitrogen carefully, as shown by this accurate description: "The specific gravity of this air was found to differ very little from that of common air; of the two it seemed rather lighter. It extinguished flame, and rendered common air unfit for making bodies burn in the same manner as fixed air, but in a less degree, as a candle which burnt about 80″ in pure common air, and which went out immediately in common air mixed with $^6/_{56}$ of fixed air burnt about 26″ in common air mixed with the same portion of this burnt air" (*14*). It is probable that Rutherford was unacquainted with Priestley's earlier work on nitrogen (*38*, *39*).

The elementary nature of nitrogen was long disputed by some chemists. In 1840 J. Lawrence Smith presented a thesis for the doctorate entitled "The Compound Nature of Nitrogen" (*66*). In his "Simple Bodies of Chemistry," David Low, as late as 1848, expressed a belief in the compound nature of nitrogen, based on the curious reasoning that, since ammonia is derived from the organic kingdom, it must contain carbon, and that therefore nitrogen must consist of carbon and oxygen (*49*).

E. T. Allen of the Geophysical Laboratory in Washington, D. C., considered W. F. Hillebrand's observation that nitrogen is an essential constituent of uraninite the "first discovery of that element in the primitive crust of the earth" (*63*).

OXYGEN

"When Air's pure essence joins the vital flood,
And with phosphoric Acid dyes the blood,
Your Virgin Trains the transient Heat dispart,
And lead the soft combustion round the heart;
Life's holy lamp with fires successive feed,
From the crown'd forehead to the prostrate wood,
From Earth's proud realms to all that swim or sweep
The yielding ether or tumultuous deep.
You swell the bulb beneath the heaving lawn,
Brood the live seed, unfold the bursting spawn;
Nurse with soft lap, and warm with fragrant breath
The embryon panting in the arms of Death;
Youth's vivid eye with living light adorn,
And fire the rising blush of Beauty's golden morn" (50).

Many books have been written about the discovery of oxygen. The Orientalist Heinrich Julius Klaproth, a son of the famous German chemist Martin Heinrich Klaproth, found a reference to this gas in a Chinese book written by Mao-Khóa about the middle of the eighth century after

Leonardo da Vinci, 1452–1519. (From a drawing in red chalk by himself. In the Royal Library, Turin.) Italian artist, sculptor, anatomist, and scientist of the first rank. Pioneer in mechanics and aëronautics. The first European to recognize that the atmosphere contains at least two constituents.

From Jean Paul Richter's "Leonardo"

Christ. Mao-Khóa believed that the atmosphere is composed of two substances: Yânn, or complete air (nitrogen), and Ȳne, or incomplete air (oxygen). Ordinary air can be made more perfect by using metals, sulfur, or carbon to rob it of part of its Ȳne. He said that when these substances burn in air, they combine with Ȳne, which, according to Mao-Khóa, never occurs free, but is present in certain minerals and in saltpeter, from which it can be driven out by heating (*15, 34*). Signor Muccioli (*36*), however, has questioned the authenticity of this Chinese manuscript.

The first European to state that air is not an element was the versatile artist-scientist, Leonardo da Vinci (1452–1519). Leonardo, keen observer that he was, noticed that air is consumed in respiration and combustion, but that it is not *completely* consumed (*15, 35, 57*). He described clearly and strikingly the intimate relation between combustion and respiration in the words "Where flame cannot live no animal that draws breath can live" (*58*).

In 1630 Jean Rey noticed the increase of weight of tin on calcination, and believed that it "comes from the air, which in the vessel has been rendered denser, heavier, and in some measure adhesive, by the vehement and long-continued heat of the furnace: which air mixes with the calx . . . and becomes attached to its most minute particles: not otherwise than water makes heavier sand which you throw into it and agitate, by moistening it and adhering to the smallest of its grains" (*82, 83, 84, 85*).

In 1756 the great Russian chemist and poet M. V. Lomonosov heated metals in airtight sealed glass vessels and found that without the admission of outside air the weight of the metal remained constant (*87*). He concluded that the increase in weight of a metal on calcination is caused by its combination with the air. He denied the existence of phlogiston, for since the sealed retort containing the metal did not change weight when heated, the metal could not have lost phlogiston. These quantitative experiments of Lomonosov were not published however but were preserved in the archives of the Academy of Sciences of St. Petersburg. When Lavoisier made similar experiments about eighteen years later and obtained the same results, he observed that only *part* of the air in the sealed retort united with the metal, hence that air is composed of two gases (*87, 88*).

Robert Hooke (*16*), in his famous book "Micrographia" published in 1665, gave a complete theory of combustion. He thought that air contains a substance (oxygen) that exists in solid form in saltpeter, and a larger quantity of an inert substance (nitrogen). Dr. John Mayow, when only thirty-three years of age, explained combustion by saying that air contains a *Spiritus nitro-aereus* (oxygen), a gas that is consumed in respiration and burning, with the result that substances no longer burn in the air that is left. He thought that his *Spiritus* was present in saltpeter, and stated that it existed, not in the alkaline part of the salt, but in the acid part. According to Dr. Mayow, all acids contain the *Spiritus*, and all animals absorb it into their blood as they breathe (*17*). T. S. Patterson, however, who has made an exhaustive study of Dr. Mayow's writings, believes that his contributions to the theory of combustion have been greatly over-estimated (*18, 80*).

The first person to prepare oxygen by heating saltpeter was Ole Borch, but he did not know how to collect it (*19*). He stated in 1678 that it did not burn but that it made charcoal burn very vigorously (*51*). In his "Prominent Danish Scientists," V. Meisen shows a facsimile of the introduction to Borch's "Nitrum non inflammari," which was published in volume five of Thomas Bartholin's "Acta Medica:" "In a little book *Naturalis Historia Nitri* (Authore Guilielmo Clarcke Anglo, Francofurti et Hamburg 1675.8°. p. 13), a man of learning says: 'Saltpetre is ignitible, because experience shows that if a small piece of it is cast into a fire, it

From Gunther's "Early Science in Oxford," Vol. 7

Robert Hooke's Home, Montague House, which afterward became the first home of the British Museum.

is ignited at once and burns, leaving a rest of lime or ash. It catches fire suddenly and blazes lively; and it burns downwards, whereas ordinarily fire always burns upwards.' In numberless experiments I have however found nothing of the kind . . ." (*52*). William Clarke's "Treatise on the Natural History of Nitre" was first published in London in 1670. A Latin translation of it was issued in 1675. Borch was a great physician, botanist, chemist, philologist, and historian of science who bequeathed all his property to the University of Copenhagen for the erection and maintenance of Borch's Collegium, a dormitory for students deserving of financial aid (52). Stephen Hales also prepared oxygen from saltpeter and collected it over water, but thought he had ordinary air; he did not believe in the existence of a "vivifying spirit" in the atmosphere (19).

In April 1774, there appeared in Abbé Rozier's *Journal de Physique* a remarkable paper by Pierre Bayen, a pharmacist who later became a medical inspector in the armies of the French Republic. In discussing his experiments with mercuric oxide, Bayen stated that, when mercury is

John Mayow, 1641–1679, English chemist and physician, who died quite young. Famous for his early researches on combustion and respiration. His theory of combustion was described in his tract entitled "De Sale Nitro et Spirito Nitroaereo" in 1674 (48).

Courtesy E. R. Riegel

calcined, it does not lose phlogiston, but combines with a gas and increases in weight. He thus rejected the phlogiston theory three years before it was proved false by Lavoisier (20).

Bayen, however, like all his predecessors who had handled oxygen, neglected to make a thorough study of its properties and failed to recog-

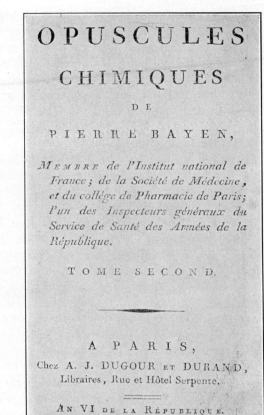

Title Page of Bayen's "Opuscules Chimiques"

OPUSCULES

CHIMIQUES

D E

P I E R R E   B A Y E N,

MEMBRE de l'Institut national de France; de la Société de Médecine, et du collége de Pharmacie de Paris; l'un des Inspecteurs généraux du Service de Santé des Armées de la République.

T O M E   S E C O N D.

A   P A R I S,

Chez A. J. DUGOUR et DURAND, Libraires, Rue et Hôtel Serpente.

AN VI DE LA RÉPUBLIQUE.

nize it as a new substance. As Patterson says, he ". . . cannot therefore be regarded as having discovered it, and this applies with greater force to other unconscious preparations of oxygen by Hales and possibly by Robert Boyle, and, of course, still more strongly to the vague speculations of Hooke and Mayow" (*18*).

Most chemists agree that the actual discovery of oxygen was made independently at about the same time by Priestley in England and Scheele in Sweden. Priestley's results, to be sure, were published before those of Scheele, but Scheele's publisher had been inexcusably negligent. The question of priority is discussed in a thorough manner in Dr. S. M. Jörgensen's book, "Die Entdeckung des Sauerstoffes," which was translated from Danish into German by V. Ortwed and Max Speter. The general problem of duplication in the history of chemical discoveries was ably presented by Dr. Paul Walden in the *Journal of Chemical Education* (*59*).

Joseph Priestley was born in Fieldhead, a tiny hamlet near Leeds, on March 13 (old style), 1733, and was therefore about one and one-half years older than that other great pioneer in pneumatic chemistry, Mr. Henry Cavendish. Although Priestley and Cavendish had similar scientific interests, their lives and personalities offered the greatest possible contrast. Since Priestley's mother died when he was only six years old, he was entrusted to the care of an aunt, Mrs. Keighley, of whom he afterward said that she "knew no other use of wealth, or of talents of any kind, than to do good" (21).

At the age of nineteen years he was sent to the Dissenting Academy at Daventry to be educated for the liberal ministry. After completing the three-year course, he ministered to congregations at Needham Market and later at Nantwich, but with small success. In 1761 he received an appointment as teacher of languages in the Dissenting Academy at Warrington, and taught Latin, Greek, French, Italian, oratory, and civil law. Although these subjects were only distantly related to the science in which he later won undying fame, Priestley's scientific spirit manifested itself even here—he encouraged absolute freedom of speech among his students.

Even when struggling with poverty at Nantwich, Priestley loved to make experiments; and from his meager salary he purchased an air-pump and an electrical machine. In about 1766 an event occurred that caused him to devote the rest of his life to scientific research, namely his introduction to the great American statesman and scientist Benjamin Franklin. In a visit to London Priestley mentioned to Franklin his intention of writing a history of electricity, provided the necessary books could be obtained. "This he readily undertook," Priestley wrote in section 80 of his Memoirs, "and my friends assisting him in it, I set about the work, without having the least idea of doing anything more than writing a distinct and methodical account of all that had been done by others" (79). In the course of this purely literary endeavor Priestley made some original experiments with his electrical machine in order to settle disputed points (67).

Not long after this meeting with Benjamin Franklin, Priestley accepted a pastorate at Leeds. Since the parsonage happened to be located next door to the Jakes and Nell Brewery, the Reverend Mr. Priestley had a convenient source of "fixed air" for his experiments. He soon discovered the pleasant taste of water charged with this gas, and recommended the refreshing beverage to his friends. Dr. William Brownrigg had previously made the same discovery (22, 47).

Since Priestley found that some gases can be collected over water while others require mercury (41), he concluded that there must be different kinds of "airs." On August 1, 1774, he heated mercuric oxide

The Stuart Portrait of Joseph Priestley, 1733–1804

"Oh what an active brain had he,
And clear discriminating mind.
Through life his great desire was this:
To bless and elevate mankind"(54).

with a burning glass, liberated a gas, "dephlogisticated air" (oxygen), and collected it over water.   In an atmosphere of this gas, substances burned more brilliantly than in air.   Five years later he tested the respirability of his "dephlogisticated air" by mixing it with nitric oxide over

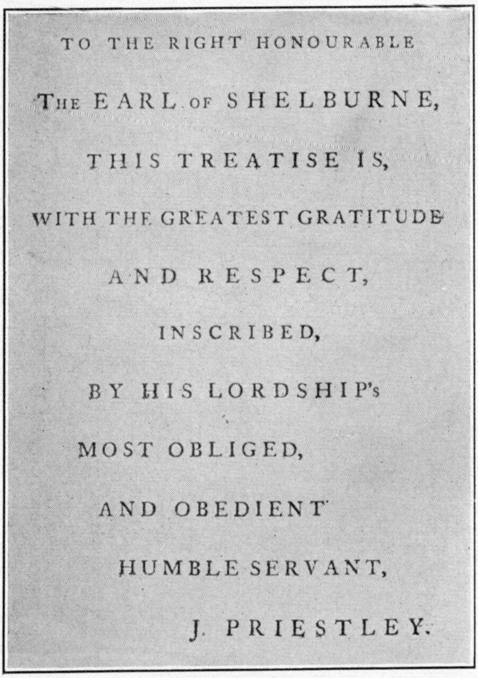

TO THE RIGHT HONOURABLE

THE EARL OF SHELBURNE,

THIS TREATISE IS,

WITH THE GREATEST GRATITUDE

AND RESPECT,

INSCRIBED,

BY HIS LORDSHIP's

MOST OBLIGED,

AND OBEDIENT

HUMBLE SERVANT,

J. PRIESTLEY.

Dedication of Priestley's "Experiments and Observations on Different Kinds of Air," 1774.

water.   He found that much more nitric oxide was required to render a given volume of "dephlogisticated air" unfit for a mouse to breathe than for an equal volume of atmospheric air.   His description of the experiment is charmingly naïve:

My reader will not wonder that, after having ascertained the superior goodness of dephlogisticated air by mice living in it, and the other tests above mentioned, I should have the curiosity to taste it myself. I have gratified that curiosity by breathing it, drawing it through a glass syphon, and by this means I reduced a large jar full of it to the standard of common air. The feeling of it to my lungs was not sensibly different from that of common air, but I fancied that my breast felt peculiarly light and easy for some time afterwards. Who can tell but that, in time, this pure air may become a fashionable article in luxury? Hitherto only two mice and myself have had the privilege of breathing it (24).

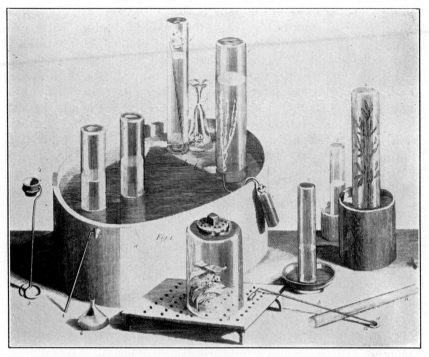

From Priestley's "Experiments and Observations on Different Kinds of Air," 1774 and 1790
See references (9) and (22)

Priestley's Apparatus for Studying the Composition of the Atmosphere. Fig. 1, *a*, Earthenware pneumatic trough, 8" deep; *bb*, flat stones, which in his later wooden trough were replaced by a shelf for holding the jars; *cc*, jars, $10" \times 2^{1}/_{2}"$, for collecting gases; *d*, tall beer glass containing enough air to sustain a mouse for from 20 to 30 minutes, and "something on which it may conveniently sit, out of reach of the water." The mouse was introduced by passing it quickly through the water; *e*, gas generator heated by a candle or a red-hot poker. Fig. 2, "Pots and tea-dishes" to slide under the gas-filled jars when removing them from the trough. Fig. 3, Receiver for keeping the mice alive. It was open at top and bottom, except for plates of perforated tin, the lower of which stood on a wooden frame to permit circulation of air. To avoid chilling the mice, this receiver was kept on a shelf over the kitchen fireplace. Fig. 4, Cork for closing a phial of solid or liquid which must be transferred, without wetting the contents, to a jar of gas in the pneumatic trough. Fig. 5, Wire stand for supporting a gallipot inside a jar of gas. Fig. 6, Funnel for "pouring air" into a glass jar by displacement of water. Fig. 11, Glass cylinder for admitting a candle to test the ability of the gas to support combustion. Fig. 12, *a*, Wax candle, bent for introducing it into a vessel, with the flame upward; *b*, wire; *c*, candle to be held under a jar standing in water. It was removed the instant the flame was extinguished, to avoid contamination of the gas in the jar with smoke.

In the preface to the 1790 edition of his "Experiments and Observations on Different Kinds of Air" Priestley wrote: "And it will not now be thought very assuming to say, that, by working in a tub of water, or a bason of quicksilver, we may perhaps discover principles of more extensive influence than even that of *gravity* itself . . ." (*68*).

Inspired by Priestley's illuminating experiments with oxygen, carbon dioxide, and other gases, the great Spanish physicist, historian, and poet, Father José de Viera y Clavijo (1738–1799), praised him in a long poem. Although the following prose translation of an excerpt from it cannot render justice to the poetry, it nevertheless illustrates an early intellectual bond between the scientists of Spain, Italy, England, and the United States of America.

> *"If by His mandate Torricelli*
> *Poised air's vast sea in slender tube,*
> *Newton with his wondrous prism*
> *Dawn's seven rays dissected out,*
> *Jove's thunder and Heaven's ether*
> *Yielded to Franklin's rod,*
> *God also guided Priestley when He said:*
> *Take thou this earth, take from it the fixed air"* (*53*).*

From 1772 to 1779 Priestley served as literary companion to Lord Shelburne. His most important chemical experiments, culminating in the discovery of oxygen, were made during this period, and his book entitled "Experiments and Observations on Different Kinds of Air" was therefore affectionately dedicated to Lord Shelburne. In 1780 Priestley became minister to a large metropolitan congregation in Birmingham. Here he was contented in his ministry and happy in his association with such men as James Watt, Josiah Wedgwood, and Erasmus Darwin at the meetings of the Lunar Society, which met on the first Monday evening after each full moon in order that the members might find their way home through the unlighted streets. At Birmingham he completed his six-volume work on "Different Kinds of Air," which was later abridged to three volumes.

The struggles of the American and French revolutionists aroused Priestley's sympathy, and he was no dissembler. On July 14, 1791, about

---

* *Si él hizo á Torricelli que pesase*
En tubo estrecho el mar de la atmosfera;
Que Newton con un prisma disecase
Los siete rayos de la luz primera;
Que Franklin con su barra le robase
El rayo á Jove, el Eter á la esfera;
También guió á Priestley, quando le dixo:
Toma esa tierra, saca el Ayre fixo . . ." (*53*).

Frontispiece of Priestley's "Observations on Different Kinds of Air," 1774 and 1790
See references (9) and (22)

Priestley's Laboratory. Fig. **7,** Apparatus for expelling gas from solids. The fireplace was used for heating a gun barrel containing dry sand which had previously been ignited. The open end of the gun barrel was luted to the stem of a tobacco pipe leading to a trough of mercury. Fig. **8,** *a,* Trough containing an inverted cylinder, *b,* of mercury; *c,* a phial containing substances from which a gas may be liberated; *d,* glass trap to intercept moisture. Fig. **9,** Bladder for transferring gases. It contained a bent glass tube at one end and at the other a one-hole cork to admit a funnel. After the gas had been admitted, the bladder was tied tightly with string. Fig. **10,** *a,* Apparatus for impregnating a fluid with gas; *b,* bowl containing a quantity of the same fluid; *c,* phial containing chalk, cream of tartar, or pearlash, and dilute sulfuric acid for generating carbon dioxide; *d,* flexible leather tube, which permitted Priestley to shake the gas generator, *c.* Fig. **13,** Siphon. Fig. **14,** Evacuated bell jar. Fig. **15,** Apparatus for measuring small quantities of gas in his experiments with "nitrous air" (nitric oxide). *a,* Small glass tube; *b,* wire; *c,* sharply bent, thin plate of iron for withdrawing the wire. This little apparatus was introduced under water into a jar of nitric oxide, and when the wire was withdrawn, nitric oxide took its place. Priestley measured the lengths of the columns of air, of nitric oxide, and of the resulting nitrogen peroxide after admixture. Fig. **16,** Apparatus for taking the electric spark in any kind of gas. *a,* Mercury column; *b,* brass knob. Figs. **17, 18,** and **19** are different forms of apparatus for taking the electric spark in gases. Fig. **19** represents a mercury-filled siphon containing an iron wire, *aa,* in each leg. Any gas which was introduced would rise to *bb,* the upper part of the siphon. The mercury basins could be made part of an electric circuit.

eighty persons had a dinner at a Birmingham hotel in observance of the second anniversary of the fall of the Bastille. A mob shattered the windows with stones. Although Priestley did not attend the dinner, his political views were well known. The fanatics broke up the meeting at the hotel, surged through the streets of Birmingham, burned Priestley's church, home, and library, and shattered his apparatus. Even then their thirst for violence was not satiated, and furious rioting continued for three days. Before the dragoons were at last able to disperse the mob and restore order, the homes and churches of many dissenters had become charred ruins (23).

With the aid of friends, the Priestley family escaped without personal injury. After three unhappy years in London, they finally succeeded in collecting a small indemnity from the British Government, and emigrated to America (23). In the first volume of his "Discourses on the Evidence of Revealed Religion," in the dedication to his successor at Hackney, the Reverend Thomas Belsham, Priestley wrote in March, 1794: "I have no where known, or heard of, such studious and orderly young men as those of the New College at Hackney. . . . I think myself peculiarly happy in leaving my congregation, and especially my classes of young persons, under your care. . . . Happy shall I think myself if, in any future destination, I can find, or form, a sphere of exertion of a similar kind; that I may be in America, what I shall leave you here . . ." (61).

In the dedication of the second volume of these "Discourses" to John Adams, Vice-president of the United States, Priestley wrote in May, 1796: "It is happy that, in this country, religion has no connection with civil power, a circumstance which gives the cause of truth all the advantage that its best friends can desire. . . . I cannot conclude this address without expressing the satisfaction I feel in the government which has afforded me an asylum from the persecution which obliged me to leave England, persuaded that, its principles being fundamentally good, instead of tending, like the old governments of Europe, to greater abuse, it will tend to continual melioration. Still, however, my utmost wish is to live as a stranger among you, with liberty to attend without interruption to my favourite pursuits; wishing well to my native country, as I do to all the world, and hoping that its interest, and those of this country, will be inseparable, and consequently that peace between them will be perpetual" (61).

In 1785, nine years before his arrival in the United States, Priestley had been elected to foreign membership in the American Philosophical Society. His famous chemical researches carried out in England were often discussed in early meetings of that Society (67). After his arrival in Pennsylvania Priestley participated actively in the affairs of the

From Zekert's "Carl Wilhelm Scheele. Sein Leben und seine Werke"
Stralsund, the Birthplace of Scheele*

Society, sometimes attended its meetings, and "was considered for president but declined in favor of Mr. [Thomas] Jefferson" (67). Priestley's last days were spent in the peaceful town of Northumberland, Pennsylvania, where he worked without interference at his beloved experiments (33). He died on February 6, 1804, and was buried in the Quaker cemetery at Northumberland.

On the one hundredth anniversary of the discovery of oxygen, a large audience assembled in Birmingham for the unveiling of a statue of Joseph Priestley, and an eloquent eulogy and biographical sketch was delivered by Thomas Huxley (25). At the same time the scientists of Leeds assembled at Priestley's birthplace and the chemists of America gathered at his grave near the banks of the Susquehanna to honor his memory (26). The meeting in Pennsylvania was memorable not only because it marked the centennial of the discovery of oxygen but also because it resulted in the founding of the American Chemical Society.

Carl Wilhelm Scheele was born on December 9 (or 19), 1742, in Stralsund, then the capital of Swedish Pomerania. The discrepancy in the date may perhaps be explained by the fact that at that time the Julian calendar was still in use (72). His lineage was entirely German, as is clearly evident from the genealogy published by Professor Otto Zekert (73) and from the fact that Scheele usually wrote in German. He was the seventh child in a family of eleven, and, since the family was not as rich in worldly goods as in children, he was apprenticed at the age of fourteen years to an apothecary named Martin Anders Bauch, owner of the Unicorn Pharmacy in Gothenburg. Like other pharmacists of his time, Bauch prepared his own medicines from the crude drugs and was well versed in chemistry. In his laboratory were to be found many inorganic salts, the mineral acids, a few ores, rock-crystal, phosphorus, sulfur,

* Reproduced by kind permission of Mr. Arthur Nemayer, Buchdruckerei und Verlag, Mittenwald, Bavaria.

benzoic acid, and camphor.   His chemical library included the works of
H. Boerhaave, N. Lémery, J. Kunckel, and Caspar Neumann (27).   The
fourteen-year-old apprentice soon developed a passion for reading chemical books critically and repeating the experiments described in them.   His
memory for chemical facts was so great that, after reading a book through
once or twice, he had no need to consult it again.

After working and studying at the Unicorn Pharmacy for eight years
Scheele served for three years (1765–68) as clerk at the Spotted Eagle
Pharmacy at Malmö, which was owned by Peter Magnus Kjellström.
There he met the famous apothecary and chemist Anders Jahan Retzius,
who, recognizing young Scheele's genius for experimentation in physical

**Youthful Portrait of Carl Wilhelm
Scheele, 1742–1786.**[*]   Swedish
pharmacist and chemist.   Independent discoverer of oxygen.   He discovered arsenic acid, distinguished
between nitric and nitrous acids,
demonstrated the presence of tartaric, citric, malic and gallic acids
in plants, and discovered lactic and
uric acids in the animal realm.

*From Zekert's "C. W. Scheele.
Sein Leben und seine Werke"*

science, persuaded him to keep a record of his experiments.   Even during
the Malmö period Scheele was engaged in the isolation and investigation
of gases (74).

From 1768 to 1770 he served as clerk at the Gilded Raven Pharmacy
in Stockholm, which was owned by Johan Scharenberg.   His reason for
leaving his conscientious, exacting work in the prescription department

[*] Reproduced by kind permission of Mr. Arthur Nemayer, Buchdruckerei und Verlag,
Mittenwald, Bavaria.

there was that it left him no time for experimentation. He always considered his chemical research as a sideline however and never neglected his duty in the pharmacy (75).

Two of his earliest papers were rejected by the Stockholm Academy, possibly because of the unmethodical style in which they were written. The editor who refused them was Torbern Bergman, who afterward became Scheele's lifelong friend (27). In 1770 Scheele accepted a position in C. L. Lokk's pharmacy, the Arms of Uppland, at Upsala. One day Lokk noticed that saltpeter which has been fused for some time remains neutral, but evolves red fumes when treated with vinegar. Assessor Gahn, the famous mineralogist who discovered manganese, was unable to explain the change, and Bergman, the illustrious professor of chemistry at Upsala, could give him no help. Scheele, however, readily explained that there are two "spirits of niter," or, as one says today, two acids, nitric and nitrous.

Gahn and Scheele became close friends, and much of their correspondence has been preserved. It was through Gahn that Scheele made the acquaintance of Bergman. When Scheele explained that potassium nitrate is converted by fusion into the deliquescent salt, potassium nitrite, Bergman became deeply interested in the young chemist, and they, too, formed a lasting friendship. Bergman received much of his practical instruction from Scheele, while Scheele's intellectual interests were broadened by his long association with the scholarly Bergman (27, 69).

In spite of many offers from universities, Scheele never exchanged the practice of pharmacy for an academic career. The pharmacies of his day were quiet centers of original research, and as Scheele himself once said to Assessor Gahn, " . . . To explain new phenomena, that is my task; and how happy is the scientist when he finds what he so diligently sought, a pleasure that gladdens the heart" (28).

His most brilliant discoveries were made at the Lokk pharmacy. His notebooks, which have since been edited and published by Baron Nordenskiöld, show that he prepared oxygen in 1771 and 1772, that is to say, at least two years before Priestley did. Scheele made it by heating silver carbonate, mercuric carbonate, mercuric oxide, niter, and magnesium nitrate, and by distilling a mixture of manganese dioxide and arsenic acid. When oxygen is prepared by heating silver or mercuric carbonate, the carbon dioxide must be absorbed in caustic alkali.

The results of these experiments were discussed in the book, "Fire and Air," which Scheele sent to his publisher, Swederus, near the end of 1775, but the book did not appear until 1777. In August, 1776, Scheele, exasperated at the delay, wrote dejectedly to Bergman, "I have thought for some time back, and I am now more than ever convinced, that the greater number of my laborious experiments on fire will be repeated, possibly in a somewhat different manner, by others, and that their work will be published sooner than my own, which is concerned also with air. It will then be said that my experiments are taken, it may be in a slightly altered form, from their writings. I have Swederus to thank for all this" (29). Scheele's discovery of oxygen was anticipated, as he had feared, but he is universally recognized as an independent discoverer of that gas.

When the English edition of Scheele's "Fire and Air" appeared, it was provided with notes by English chemists. The translator Johann Reinhold Forster mentioned in a letter to Scheele that some of these

Sigismund Friedrich Hermbstädt, 1760–1833. Professor of chemistry and pharmacy at the School of Medicine and Surgery in Berlin, later professor of chemistry and technology at the University of Berlin. He was one of the first chemists in Germany to adopt Lavoisier's views on combustion. Author of books on dyeing, bleaching, tanning, soap-making, and beet sugar. Editor of the complete works of C. W. Scheele.

Courtesy Edgar Fahs Smith

chemists had disagreed with some of his conclusions. Forster added however: "Your adversaries are people who do not lack courtesy, kindness, moral character, nor knowledge; hence a discussion, nobly carried on, cannot be anything but useful to the realm of truth" (72).

In his handsomely illustrated "Pictorial Life History of the Apothecary Chemist Carl Wilhelm Scheele" Professor George Urdang, Director of the American Institute of the History of Pharmacy, wrote: "The authority which Scheele enjoyed was so great, and his honesty and simplicity of character so obvious and disarming, that none of the usual scientific jealousies and quarrels ever touched him" (72).

In 1776 Scheele became a provisor of the pharmacy at Köping, a little town on the north shore of Lake Mälar. The owner, Heinrich Pohl, had died, leaving the shop to his young widow. Instead of finding the prosperous business he had expected, Scheele met the discouraging task of freeing the estate from heavy debt (27), but he finally placed the business on a sound financial basis and purchased it from the widow Pohl. By 1782 his name was known to all European scientists, and his financial condition permitted him to build a new home and a well-equipped laboratory. One of his sisters and Mrs. Pohl kept house for him.

The last years of his life were filled with intense suffering from rheumatism. When he realized that death was near, he married the widow Pohl in order that the estate which he had struggled so hard to save might return to her. He died three days later on May 21, 1786, at the age of forty-three years. His entire life had been devoted to chemistry, and in one of his letters to Gahn one may read, *"Diese edel Wissenschaft ist mein Auge"*[*] (30).

A scholarly volume of Scheele's manuscripts from 1756 to 1777, in which many gaps were filled and Scheele's difficult abbreviations were interpreted, was published by C. W. Oseen in 1942 (76). This publication is in German, the language in which Scheele usually wrote. On the 150th anniversary of Scheele's death Bengt Hildebrand published in *Lychnos,* the annual of the Swedish History of Science Society, a comprehensive review of the vast literature devoted to Scheele and his work (77).

Scheele was a phlogistonist to the end of his life, and thought that phlogiston was similar to the imponderable ether of the physicists and that hydrogen was a compound of phlogiston and "matter of heat." It has been shown that certain seventeenth-century chemists were ahead of most eighteenth-century scientists in their understanding of the composition of the atmosphere and the nature of combustion and respiration. Even the three men who had contributed most toward an understanding of the atmosphere—namely, Cavendish, Priestley, and Scheele—clung to the end of their days to the outgrown phlogiston theory.

The great French scientist, Lavoisier, would have liked very much to be considered an independent discoverer of oxygen, but he himself may have felt the weakness of his claim. He wrote in his "Mémoire sur l'Existence de l'Air dans l'Acide Nitreux," read on April 20, 1776, "Perhaps, strictly speaking, there is nothing in it of which Mr. Priestley would not be able to claim the original idea; but as the same facts have conducted us to diametrically opposite results, I trust that, if I am reproached for having borrowed my proofs from the works of this celebrated philosopher, my right at least to the conclusions will not be contested" (31). In his remarkable paper "On the Nature of the Principle That Combines with Metals during Their Calcination and Increases Their Weight," which he had read during the Easter season of 1775, he had announced that this

[*] "This noble science is my eye."

Courtesy H. S. van Klooster

Lavoisier in His Laboratory. Experiments on the respiration of a man doing work. Reduced facsimile of a drawing by Mme. Lavoisier. She is shown at the right preparing a record of the experiment. This illustration appeared in the biography of Lavoisier by Édouard Grimaux (Paris, 1888).

principle is simply "the purest and most salubrious part of the air; so that if the air which has been fixed in a metallic combination again becomes free, it reappears in a condition in which it is eminently respirable and better adapted than the air of the atmosphere to support inflammation and the combustion of substances" (*32*).

This was the death blow to the phlogiston theory (*56*). Although Lavoisier discovered no elements himself, he was the first to assert that

M. and Mme. Lavoisier. In 1777 Lavoisier gave quantitative proof of the incorrectness of the phlogiston theory. Shortly after Priestley and Scheele discovered oxygen, Lavoisier gave the true explanation of combustion and respiration. Berthollet, Guyton de Morveau, Fourcroy, and Klaproth were among the first to accept the new views. See also ref. (*60*).

From Grimaux's "Lavoisier"
From the Painting by David

oxygen is an element. Moreover, his correct explanation of combustion so revolutionized the entire science of chemistry that, under the new stimulus, many new elements were discovered soon after his tragic death on the guillotine. For this great service scientists will always honor the name of Antoine-Laurent Lavoisier.

Although Lavoisier completely renounced phlogiston as a material substance, he nevertheless retained in his list of chemical elements two unweighable, immaterial ones—light and "caloric"—which in the opinion of Boris N. Menschutkin "presented an unmistakable likeness to the *principle phlogiston,* as conceived by Stahl" (*78*).

Late in the eighteenth century, while the number of adherents to the phlogiston theory was dwindling and the antiphlogistians were gain-ing ground, Vasiliǐ Vladimirovich Petrov of the Medico-Surgical Academy of St. Petersburg, Russia, began to carry out some decisive experiments to confirm or disprove the new doctrine of combustion.   In 1797, when

A **Statue of Lavoisier** which formed part of the French Exhibit at the San Francisco Exposition in 1915.

the Medico-Surgical Academy received an important consignment of physical apparatus, he set out to answer experimentally the following questions:

"1.   Can natural combustible bodies burn in an airless place?

"2.   Can metallic calces be formed in an airless place or not?

"3.   Can perfect acids [oxides], resulting from the oxidation of simple bodies, be obtained in an airless place or not?

"4.   If products can be obtained in the preceding cases in an airless place, will they be heavier than the materials used in the experiments?" (78).

Petrov spent several years on these experiments and published the results in three books and in papers between 1801 and 1812.

When he focused a burning glass upon natural substances, such as wood, cotton, or paper, in a closed glass jar from which the air had been pumped out, they emitted smoke but no flame.   To make certain that no air had been retained in the pores of the combustible substances or in the glass, Petrov carefully measured the quantity of pure oxygen required to burn an equal quantity of wood in a cylinder placed in a pneumatic trough. He found this quantity to be thousands of times as great as the amount of oxygen retained in the wood or in the jar. He even burned dry chips of wood in a perfect Torricellian vacuum. Since all of the substances that he had burned in a vacuum contained oxygen, as shown by Lavoisier, Petrov's experiments lent further support to the new theory of combustion.

In his experiments to answer his second and third questions Petrov found that in presence of warm sunlight phosphorus will burn for a few seconds in the imperfect vacuum produced by the air pump, but that in a perfect Torricellian vacuum it will neither burn nor glow. He also observed that in a perfect vacuum neither phosphorus nor sulfur will form an oxide.

Since all of his experiments completely confirmed the new views on combustion, Petrov and the Russian chemists of his time were all anti-phlogistians (78). Since Petrov's papers were printed only in Russian, his work has not received from chemists in other parts of the world the attention it deserves.

V. V. Petrov was born in the town of Oboyan (Government of Kursk) in 1761. He was the son of a priest and was educated in the theological college of Kharkov and at the Higher Pedagogical Institute of St. Petersburg, where he graduated in 1788. For some years he taught mathematics and physics at Barnaul, Siberia, and later in St. Petersburg. Having been elected professor of mathematics and physics at the newly established Medico-Surgical Academy of St. Petersburg in 1795, he assembled "the richest physical cabinet of his time in Russia" (78). He continued his experimental work and meteorological observations until the time of his death in 1834. His work was commemorated some years ago by the Institute of the History of Science and Technology (Academy of Sciences, U.S.S.R.).

LITERATURE CITED

(1) BOYLE, R., "Memoirs for a General History of the Air," Shaw's Abridgment of Boyle's Works, Vol. 3, 1725, p. 61; SIR W. RAMSAY, "The Gases of the Atmosphere," Macmillan & Co., London, 1915, p. 10.

(2) KOPP, H., "Geschichte der Chemie," part 3, Vieweg und Sohn, Braunschweig, 1845, pp. 260–1; part 1, p. 111; R. JAGNAUX, "Histoire de la Chimie," Vol. 1, Baudry et Cie., Paris, 1891, pp. 385–6.

(3) WILSON, G., "The Life of the Honourable Henry Cavendish Including Abstracts of His More Important Scientific Papers," printed for the Cavendish Society, London, 1851, p. 17.

(4)   "Biographie Universelle, Ancienne et Moderne," 85 vols., Vol 7, Michaud
        Frères, Paris, **1813**, p. 456.   Biographical sketch of Cavendish by Biot.
(5)   Thomson, Thomas, "History of Chemistry," Vol. 1, Colburn and Bentley,
        London, **1830**, pp. 336–8.
(6)   Wilson, G., "The Life of the Honourable Henry Cavendish," ref. (3), pp.
        168–9.
(7)   Davy, Dr. John, "Memoirs of the Life of Sir Humphry Davy, Bart.," Vol. 1,
        Longman, Rees, Orme, Brown, Green, and Longman, London, **1836**, p. 221.
(8)   Wilson, G., "The Life of the Honourable Henry Cavendish," ref. (3), pp.
        163–4.
(9)   Ibid., pp. 25–7; Alembic Club Reprint No. 3.   H. Cavendish, "Experiments
        on Air," University of Chicago Press, Chicago, **1906**, pp. 13–25; J. Priestley,
        "Experiments and Observations on Different Kinds of Air," Vol. I, Thomas
        Pearson, Birmingham, **1790**, pp. 5 and 270; T. E. Thorpe, "Scientific Papers
        of the Honourable Henry Cavendish, F.R.S.," Vol. 2, University Press, Cam-
        bridge, **1921**, pp. 9–10; H. Cavendish, Phil. Trans., **74**, 119–53 (1784).
(10) Wilson, G., "The Life of the Honourable Henry Cavendish," ref. (3), pp.
        182–5.
(11) Ramsay, Sir W., "Life and Letters of Joseph Black, M.D.," Constable and Co.,
        London, **1918**, p. 51.
(12) Ramsay, Sir W., "The Gases of the Atmosphere," ref. (1), pp. 61–7.
(13) Jagnaux, R., "Histoire de la Chimie," ref. (2), Vol. 1, p. 550; Alembic Club
        Reprint No. 3.   H. Cavendish, "Experiments on Air," ref. (9), pp. 26–7; C.
        W. Scheele, "Sämmtliche physische und chemische Werke," translated into
        German by Hermbstädt, Vol. 1, zweite unveränderte Auflage, Mayer and
        Müller, Berlin, **1891**, pp. 186–7.
(14) Wilson, G., "The Life of the Honourable Henry Cavendish," ref. (3), p. 28,
        British Assoc. Report, **1839**, pp. 64–5; Alembic Club Reprint No. 3.   H.
        Cavendish, "Experiments on Air," ref. (9), p. 49; H. Cavendish, Phil.
        Trans., **75**, 372–84 (1785).
(15) Jörgensen, S. M., "Die Entdeckung des Sauerstoffes," translated from Danish
        into German by Ortwed and Speter.   Ferdinand Enke, Stuttgart, **1909**, pp.
        3–11.
(16) Alembic Club Reprint No. 5, "Extracts from Micrographia," University of
        Chicago Press, Chicago, **1902**, pp. 43–7.
(17) Jörgensen, S. M., "Die Entdeckung des Sauerstoffes," ref. (15), pp. 8–9;
        E. Riegel, "Four eminent chemists who died before their time," J. Chem.
        Educ., **3**, 1103–5 (Oct., 1926).
(18) Patterson, T. S., "John Mayow—in contemporary setting," Isis, **15** [3], 539
        (Sept., 1931).
(19) Jörgensen, S. M., "Die Entdeckung des Sauerstoffes," ref. (15), pp. 12–14.
(20) Jörgensen, S. M., "Die Entdeckung des Sauerstoffes," ref. (15), pp. 30–3; P.
        Bayen, Rozier's Jour. de Physique, **3**, 285 (Apr., 1774); P. Bayen, "Opus-
        cules Chimiques," Vol. 1, Dugour et Durand, Paris, An VI de la République,
        p. li (Éloge by Parmentier); ibid., p. 228.
(21) Thorpe, T. E., "Essays in Historical Chemistry," Macmillan & Co., London,
        1894, p. 30.
(22) Priestley, J, "Experiments and Observations on Different Kinds of Air," J.
        Johnson, London, **1774**, pp. 25–34.
(23) Thorpe, T. E., "Essays in Historical Chemistry," ref. (21), pp. 34–5.
(24) Jagnaux, R., "Histoire de la Chimie," ref. (2), Vol. 1, p. 399; J. Priestley,
        "Experiments and Observations on Different Kinds of Air," Vol. 2, Thomas
        Pearson, Birmingham, **1790**, pp. 161–2.   See also, ibid., pp. 102–87.
(25) Huxley, T., "Science and Education: Essays," D. Appleton & Co., New York
        City, **1897**, pp. 1–37.

(26) THORPE, T. E., "Essays in Historical Chemistry," ref. (21), p. 28.

(27) Ibid., pp. 56–65.

(28) SCHEELE, C. W., "Nachgelassene Briefe und Aufzeichnungen," edited by Nordenskiöld, Norstedt & Söner, Stockholm, 1892, p. 151. Letter of Scheele to Gahn, Dec. 26, 1774.

(29) Ibid., p. 264.

(30) Ibid., p. 165.

(31) "Oeuvres de Lavoisier," Vol. 2, Imprimerie Impériale, Paris, 1862, p. 130.

(32) Ibid., Vol. 2, p. 127.

(33) SMITH, E. F., "Priestley in America," P. Blakiston's Son and Co., Philadelphia, 1920, 173 pages; C. A. BROWNE, "A Half Century of Chemistry in America," The American Chemical Society, Easton, Pa., 1926, pp. 3–16; S. A. GOLDSCHMIDT, "The birth of the American Chemical Society at the Priestley house in 1874," J. Chem. Educ., 4, 145–7 (Feb., 1927); W. H. WALKER, "History of the Priestley house and the movement for its preservation," J. Chem. Educ., 4, 150–7 (Feb., 1927); C. A. BROWNE, "Priestley's life in Northumberland and discussion of the Priestley relics on exhibition in the museum," J. Chem. Educ., 4, 159–71 (Feb., 1927); L. C. NEWELL, "One of Priestley's first letters written from Northumberland, Pa.," J. Chem. Educ., 4, 173–5 (Feb., 1927); T. L. Davis, "Priestley's last defense of phlogiston," J. Chem. Educ., 4, 176–83 (Feb., 1927); C. A. BROWNE, "Joseph Priestley as an historian of science," J. Chem. Educ., 4, 184–99 (Feb., 1927).

(34) KLAPROTH, H. J., "Sur les connaissances chimiques des Chinois dans le VIII. Siècle," Mémoires de l'Acad. de St. Petersbourg, 2, 476–84 (1810).

(35) VON LIPPMANN, E. O., "Abhandlungen und Vorträge zur Geschichte der Naturwissenschaften," Veit and Co., Leipzig, 1906, Vol. 1, p. 361.

(36) MUCCIOLI, M., "Intorno ad una Memoria di Giulio Klaproth sulle 'Conoscenze Chimiche dei Cinesi nell VIII Secolo,'" Archeion, Archiv. di Storia della Scienza, 7, 382–6 (Dec., 1926).

(37) DOBBIN, L., "Paracelsus and the discovery of hydrogen," J. Chem. Educ., 9, 1122–4 (June, 1932); M. E. WEEKS, ibid., 9, 1296 (July, 1932).

(38) WEEKS, M. E., "Daniel Rutherford and the discovery of nitrogen," ibid., 11, 101–7 (Feb., 1934); Rev. Sci., 72, 441–9 (July, 1934).

(39) McKIE, D., "Daniel Rutherford and the discovery of nitrogen," Sci. Progress, 29, 650–60 (Apr., 1935); L. DOBBIN, "Daniel Rutherford's inaugural dissertation. Crum Brown's translation," J. Chem. Educ., 12, 370–5 (Aug., 1935).

(40) WEEKS, M. E., "Some scientific friends of Sir Walter Scott," J. Chem. Educ., 13, 503–7 (Nov., 1936).

(41) SPETER, MAX, "Wer hat zuerst Quecksilber als Sperrflüssigkeit beim Auffangen von Gasen verwendet?" Schweizerische Apotheker-Ztg., 58, 123–4 (Feb., 1920).

(42) SPETER, MAX, "Lavoisier und seine Vorläufer," F. Enke, Stuttgart, 1910, pp. 48–51. Chapter on Pierre Bayen.

(43) SPETER, MAX, ibid., pp. 55–72, 96–108. Chapter on John Mayow; "John Mayow und das Schicksal seiner Lehren," Chem.-Ztg., 34, 946–7, 953–4, 962–4 (Sept., 1910).

(44) "The Works of the Hon. Robert Boyle," Vol. 3, A. Millar, London, 1794, pp. 255–6; ibid., vol. 5, p. 111.

(45) LÉMERY, N., "A Course of Chymistry," Walter Kettilby, London, 1686, pp. 145–6; ibid., Theodore Haak, Leyden, 1716, pp. 184–6.

(46) SMITH, H. M., "Eminent men of science living in 1807–8," J. Chem. Educ., 18, 203–5, 226 (May, 1941); W. WALKER, "Memoirs of the Distinguished Men of Science of Great Britain Living in the Years 1807–8," W. Walker and Son, London, 1862, p. 38.

(47) PRIESTLEY, J., ref. (9), Vol. 1, pp. 4–5.

(48) McKie, D., "John Mayow, 1641–79," *Nature*, **148**, 728 (Dec. 13, 1941).

(49) Low, David, "The Simple Bodies of Chemistry," 2nd ed., Longman, Brown, Green, and Longmans, London, **1848**, p. 85.

(50) Darwin, Erasmus, "A Botanic Garden," 2nd ed., J. Johnson, London, **1791**, pp. 39–40.

(51) Jörgensen, S. M., ref. (15), p. 12.

(52) Meisen, V., "Prominent Danish Scientists," Levin and Munksgaard, Copenhagen, **1932**, pp. 33–5.

(53) Sempere, J., "Ensayo de Una Biblioteca Española de los Mejores Escritores del Reynado de Carlos III," Vol. 6, Imprenta Real, Madrid, **1789, pp.** 155–8.

(54) "The Priestley centennial," *Am. Chemist*, **5**, 43 (Aug., Sept., 1874). Poem by James Aiken.

(55) See also Oesper, R. E., "An excerpt from Lavoisier's laboratory journal," *J. Chem. Educ.*, **18**, 85–6 (Feb., 1941).

(56) French, Sidney J., "The chemical revolution. The second phase," *ibid.*, **27**, 83–9 (Feb., 1950).

(57) Reti, Ladislao, "Leonardo da Vinci's experiments on combustion," *ibid.*, **29**, 590–6 (Dec., 1952).

(58) MacCurdy, Edward, "The Notebooks of Leonardo da Vinci," Garden City Publishing Co., Inc., Garden City, New York, **1941–42**, p. 382.

(59) Walden, Paul, "The problem of duplication in the history of chemical discoveries," *J. Chem. Educ.*, **29**, 304–7 (June, 1952).

(60) Duveen, Denis, "Antoine Laurent Lavoisier and the French Revolution," *ibid.*, **30**, 60–5 (Feb., 1954).

(61) Priestley, Joseph, "Discourses on the Evidence of Revealed Religion," J. Johnson, London, **1794**, pp. iv–vi; "Discourses Relating to the Evidence of Revealed Religion Delivered in Philadelphia, 1796," J. Johnson, London (printed in Philadelphia), **1796**, pp. v–vi, viii.

(62) Selwood, P. W., "Heavy water," *J. Chem. Educ.*, **18**, 515–20 (Nov., 1941).

(63) Allen, E. T., "Pen portrait of W. F. Hillebrand, 1853–1925," *ibid.*, **9**, 80 (Jan., 1932).

(64) LaWall, Charles H., "The Curious Lore of Drugs and Medicines," Garden City Publishing Co., Garden City, New York, **1927**, pp. 264–71.

(65) Robinson, Victor, "The Story of Medicine," Tudor Publishing Co., New York, **1931**, pp. 311–12.

(66) Browne, C. A. (Editor), "A Half-Century of Chemistry in America, 1876–1926," Am. Chem. Soc., Philadelphia, **1926**, p. 76. Article on Mineral Chemistry by Edgar F. Smith.

(67) Bronk, Detlev W., "Joseph Priestley and the early history of the American Philosophical Society," *Proc. Am. Philos. Soc.*, **86**, 103–7 (Sept. 25, 1942).

(68) Priestley, Joseph, "Experiments and Observations on Different Kinds of Air," Vol. 1, Thomas Pearson, Birmingham, **1790**, p. xxiv.

(69) Winderlich, Rudolf, "Carl Wilhelm Scheele. Zur 200. Wiederkehr seines Geburtstages," *Aus der Heimat*, **55**, 157–62 (Dec., 1942).

(70) Nordenskiöld, Erik, "The History of Biology," Tudor Publishing Co., New York, **1935**, p. 139.

(71) Browne, C. A., "A Source Book of Agricultural Chemistry," Chronica Botanica Co., Waltham, Mass., **1944**, pp. 44–5, 135–9.

(72) Urdang, George, "Pictorial Life History of the Apothecary Chemist Carl Wilhelm Scheele," American Institute of the History of Pharmacy, Madison, Wis., **1942**, 71 pp.

(73) Zekert, Otto, "Carl Wilhelm Scheele. Sein Leben und seine Werke," Part 1. Gesellschaft für Geschichte der Pharmazie, **1931**, pp. 1–33.

(74) NORDENSKIÖLD, A. E., "Carl Wilhelm Scheele. Efterlemnade Bref och An-
        teckningar," P. A. Norstedt and Sons, Stockholm, 1892, 490 pp.
(75) FREDGA, ARNE, "Carl Wilhelm Scheele. Minnesteckning," K. Svenska Veten-
        skapsakademi, Stockholm, 1943, 23 pp.
(76) OSEEN, C. W., "Carl Wilhelm Scheele. Manuskript, 1756–1777. Tolkning,"
        K. Svenska Vetenskapsakademi, Stockholm, 1942, 173 pp.
(77) HILDEBRAND, BENGT, "Scheeleforskning och Scheelelitteratur," Lychnos, 1936,
        pp. 76–102.
(78) MENSCHUTKIN, B. N., "Vasilii Vladimirovich Petrov and his physicochemical
        work," Isis, 25, 391 8 (Sept., 1936).
(79) WALKER, W. CAMERON, "The beginnings of the scientific career of Joseph
        Priestley," Isis, 21, 81–97 (Apr., 1934).
(80) GUERLAC, HENRY, "The poets' nitre," Isis, 45, 243–55 (Sept., 1954).
(81) EIDINOFF, M. L., "The search for tritium—the hydrogen isotope of mass three,"
        J. Chem. Educ., 25, 31–4 (Jan., 1948).
(82) REY, JEAN, "The Increase in Weight of Tin and Lead," Alembic Club Reprint
        No. 11, Wm. F. Clay, Edinburgh, 1895, pp. 36–7.
(83) GRIMAUX, EDOUARD, "Lavoisier, 1743–1794," Félix Alcan, Paris, 1888, pp.
        104–5.
(84) "Encyclopédie méthodique. Chimie et métallurgie," Vol. 4, H. Agasse, Paris,
        1805 (An XIII), pp. 244–5.
(85) McKIE, D., "Antoine Lavoisier. The Father of Modern Chemistry," J. B.
        Lippincott Co., Philadelphia, 1935, pp. 195–8, 223.
(86) VAN KLOOSTER, H. S., "Jan Baptist van Helmont," J. Chem. Educ., 24, 319
        (July, 1947).
(87) MENSHUTKIN, B. N., "Russia's Lomonosov," Princeton University Press, Prince-
        ton, N. J., 1952, pp. 118–21.
(88) SPETER, MAX, ref. (42), pp. 52–5. Chapter on M. V. Lomonosov.

Daniel Rutherford, 1749–1819. Scottish physician, botanist, and
chemist. Discoverer of nitrogen. Professor of botany at Edinburgh.
President of the Royal College of Physicians of Edinburgh.

*. . . Prosecuting medical studies at the University
of Edinburgh, he early discovered the existence of a
gaseous fluid, now known as nitrogen gas . . . (1).*

8

Rutherford, discoverer of nitrogen

Although the statement that nitrogen was discovered in 1772 by Daniel Rutherford appears in most histories of chemistry, this Scottish scientist has remained almost unknown to chemists. Nevertheless, the life story and personal character of Dr. Rutherford emerge from the correspondence of his distinguished nephew, Sir Walter Scott, in a most pleasing manner. Both Dr. Rutherford and his father served as physicians to the Scott family, and the great novelist's allusions to them combine admiration, sincere affection, and pardonable family pride.

*D*r. Rutherford served as professor of botany at the University of Edinburgh from 1786 to 1819, and was thus contemporary with Joseph Black, Charles Hope, and John Robison. He invented an ingenious maximum and minimum thermometer which is described in many modern textbooks of physics. The tragic circumstances surrounding his sudden death were described by Sir Walter in numerous letters to members of his family.

In his doctor's thesis Rutherford made a clear distinction between nitrogen and carbon dioxide which most of his contemporaries had failed to observe. Henry Cavendish, however, had made this distinction somewhat earlier, but had failed to publish his results. The names of Priestley and Scheele are also intimately connected with the discovery of nitrogen.

The correspondence of Sir Walter Scott, his family genealogy, and the ten-volume biography by his son-in-law, J. G. Lockhart, contain frequent allusions to Scott's grandfather, Dr. John Rutherford, one of the founders of the medical school at the University of Edinburgh, and to his uncle, Dr. Daniel Rutherford, who is usually regarded as the discoverer of the element nitrogen. In the genealogy of the Scott family one may read:

By his first wife, Jean Swinton, Professor John Rutherford had a son, John, who died young, and a daughter Anne, who married* Walter Scott, writer to the Signet, and became the mother of Sir Walter Scott Bart. He married, secondly, on the 9th August, 1743, Anne M'Kay, by whom he had five sons and three daughters. . . . Daniel Rutherford, second son of Professor John Ruther-

* A facsimile of the marriage contract is to be found in ref. (4).

ford, was born on 3rd November, 1749. Prosecuting medical studies at the University of Edinburgh, he early discovered the existence of a gaseous fluid, now known as nitrogen gas . . . (1).

Sir Walter Scott gave some of the same facts in the following passage from his autobiography:

In [April, 1758] my father married Anne Rutherford, eldest daughter of John Rutherford, professor of medicine in the University of Edinburgh. He was one of those pupils of Boerhaave to whom the school of medicine in our northern metropolis owes its rise, and a man distinguished for professional talent, for lively wit, and for literary acquirements. Dr. Rutherford was twice married. His first wife, of whom my mother is the sole surviving child, was a daughter of Sir John Swinton of Swinton, a family which produced many distinguished warriors during the middle ages, and which, for antiquity and honourable alliances, may rank with any in Britain. My grandfather's second wife was Miss Mackay, by whom he had a second family, of whom are now [1808] alive, Dr. Daniel Rutherford, professor of botany in the University of Edinburgh, and Misses Janet and Christian Rutherford, amiable and accomplished women . . . (2).

As might be expected, the Rutherfords, both father and son, served as physicians to the Scott family. When Sir Walter was only eighteen months old, his right leg became paralyzed, and, after the best physicians had failed in their attempts to restore the use of it, his grandfather, Dr. John Rutherford, had him sent to live in the country (3, 4). During a serious illness in later life, Scott "submitted without a murmur to the severe discipline prescribed by his affectionate physician [Dr. Daniel] Rutherford . . ." (5).

John Rutherford was born in the Manse of Yarrow, Scotland, on August 1, 1695, was educated at the grammar school at Selkirk, and studied anatomy, surgery, and materia medica in London and later in Leyden under Herman Boerhaave. After receiving his medical degree from the University of Reims in 1719, he went to Edinburgh to engage in private practice. In November, 1724, he applied, with three other members of the College of Physicians, for the keeping of the college garden, which had fallen into disuse. With the consent of the town council, the four physicians raised medicinal plants there and, in order to prepare drugs for the apothecaries' shops, set up a chemical laboratory at their own expense. Two years later Dr. Rutherford was appointed Professor of the Practice of Medicine in the medical school which he had helped to found. He used Boerhaave's "Aphorismi de Cognoscendis et Curandis Morbis" as a textbook, and for many years delivered clinical lectures in the Edinburgh Infirmary. He resigned in 1765, and died in 1779 at the age of eight-four years (6, 7).

According to Florence MacCunn, both Sir Walter Scott and his mother inherited their "homely features and look of good-tempered shrewdness" from "old Dr. Rutherford, whose homely, heavy, sensible face hangs in the rooms of the Edinburgh College of Physicians" (8).

According to Lockhart, Dr. Daniel Rutherford "inherited much of the general accomplishments, as well as the professional reputation, of his

Herman Boerhaave, 1668–1738. Dutch physician, anatomist, chemist, and botanist. The Edinburgh Medical School was founded by pupils of Boerhaave while he was still in his prime. John Rutherford, father of Daniel Rutherford, was one of his devoted disciples. See also ref. (*42*).

father" (9). He was keenly interested in the classics, in English literature, and in mathematics, and his graduation thesis, like that of his celebrated professor, Dr. Joseph Black, clearly revealed the existence of a new gas. Just as Black's dissertation, *De humore acido a cibis orto, et magnesia alba*,* published on June 11, 1754, together with his "Experiments upon Magnesia Alba, Quicklime, and Some Other Alcaline Substances" (1755), had clearly characterized the gas "fixed air" now known as carbon

* The acid humor arising from food, and magnesia alba.

dioxide (43), Rutherford's thesis, *Dissertatio inauguralis de aere fixo dicto, aut mephitico,*[*] dated September 12, 1772, made clear the existence of nitrogen (phlogisticated air) as distinct from carbon dioxide.

Although Stephen Hales had prepared nitrogen by absorbing the oxygen from a confined volume of atmospheric air, he had failed to recognize it as a new substance (10). Henry Cavendish was evidently the first person to distinguish nitrogen from other kinds of suffocating incombustible gases, but he had failed to publish his results. In a paper marked in his handwriting "communicated to Dr. Priestley," he had written:

I am not certain what it is which Dr. P[riestley] means by mephitic air, though from some circumstances I guess that what he speaks of . . . was that to which Dr. Black has given the name of fixed air. The natural meaning of mephitic air is any air which suffocates animals (& this is what Dr. Priestley seems to mean by the words), but in all probability there are many kinds of air which possess this property. I am sure there are 2, namely, fixed air, & common air in which candles have burnt, or which has passed thro' the fire. Air which has passed thro' a charcoal fire contains a great deal of fixed air, which is generated from the charcoal, but it consists principally of common air, which has suffered a change in its nature from the fire. As I formerly made an experiment on this subject, which seems to contain some new circumstances, I will here set it down.

I transferd some common air out of one receiver through burning charcoal into a 2nd receiver by means of a bent pipe, the middle of which was filled with powdered charcoal & heated red hot, both receivers being inverted into vessels of water, & the 2nd receiver being full of water, so that no air could get into it but what came out of the first receiver & passed through the charcoal. The quant. air driven out of the first receiver was 180 oz. measures, that driven into the 2nd receiver was 190 oz. measures. In order to see whether any of this was fixed air, some sope leys was mixed with the water in the bason, into which the mouth of this 2nd receiver was immersed; it was thereby reduced to 166 oz.,[†] so that 24 oz. meas. were absorbed by the sope leys, all of which we may conclude to be fixed air produced from the charcoal; therefore 14 oz. of common air were absorbed by the fumes of the burning charcoal, agreeable to what Dr. Hales and others have observed, that all burning bodies absorb air . . . (11).

With characteristic thoroughness Cavendish had passed the 166 ounces of residual air back again through fresh burning charcoal into another receiver. After another treatment with the soap lye there remained 162 ounces of a gas which he described as follows:

[*] Inaugural dissertation on the air called fixed or mephitic.
[†] The number **168** given in the British Association Reports is evidently a misprint.

The specific gravity of this air was found to differ very little from that of common air; of the two it seemed rather lighter. It extinguished flame, & rendered common air unfit for making bodies burn, in the same manner as fixed air, but in a less degree . . . (11).

Sir Walter Scott, 1771–1832. Scottish novelist and poet. His writings contain many interesting allusions to his uncle, Dr. Daniel Rutherford. Scott's circle of friends included Dr. William Hyde Wollaston, Sir David Brewster, Dr. John Davy, Sir Humphry Davy, and Joseph Black.

In a paper read before the Royal Society in March, 1772 (six months before Dr. Rutherford's thesis was published), Priestley mentioned these experiments, but failed to record Cavendish's clear interpretation of them.

The Honourable Mr. Cavendish favoured me [said he] with an account of some experiments of his, in which a quantity of common air was reduced from 180 to 162 ounce measures, by passing through a red-hot iron tube filled with the dust of charcoal. This diminution he ascribed to such a destruction of common air as Dr. Hales imagined to be the consequence of burning. Mr. Cavendish also observed, that there had been a generation of fixed air in this process, but that it was absorbed by sope leys (*12*).

In the same paper Priestley stated:

Air thus diminished by the fumes of burning charcoal not only extinguishes flame, but is in the highest degree noxious to animals; it makes no effervescence with nitrous air, and is incapable of being diminished any further by the fumes of more charcoal, by a mixture of iron filings and brimstone, or by any other cause of the diminution of air that I am acquainted with. This observation, which respects all other kinds of diminished air, proves that Dr. Hales was mistaken in his notion of the absorption of air in those circumstances in which he observed it. For he supposed that the remainder was, in all cases, of the same nature with that which had been absorbed, and that the operation of the same cause would not have failed to produce a farther diminution; whereas all my observations not only shew that air, which has once been fully diminished by any causes whatever, is not only incapable of any farther diminution, either from the same or from any other cause, but that it has likewise acquired new properties, most remarkably different from those which it had before, and that they are, in a great measure, the same in all the cases . . . (*12*).

Priestley also observed that "lime-water never became turbid by the calcination of metals over it," and that "when this process was made in quicksilver, the air was diminished only one-fifth; and upon water being admitted to it, no more was absorbed" (*12*). He stated that this "air in which candles, or brimstone, had burned out . . . is rather lighter than common air" (*12*). Thus Priestley recognized, even at this early date, some of the most important properties of the gas now known as nitrogen.

Although the only copy of Rutherford's thesis which Sir William Ramsay was able to find is in the British Museum, Dr. Leonard Dobbin found a copy of it in the Edinburgh University Library and has published Crum Brown's English translation of it in the *Journal of Chemical Education* (*40*). Although Ramsay stated in the first edition of "The Gases of the Atmosphere" that this dissertation "precedes Priestley's and Scheele's writings by a year or two," he corrected this in the second edition to read: ". . . Priestley had nearly anticipated Rutherford; and indeed, he speculated on the nature of the residual gas, left after combustion and absorption of the fixed air produced" (*13*). Although Rutherford referred in his thesis to Priestley's experiments on the effect of vegetation on the atmosphere, he was evidently unfamiliar with those on nitrogen (*14, 15*).

Dr. Black had noticed that when a carbonaceous substance is burned in air in such a manner that the fixed air can be absorbed in caustic alkali, a portion of the air remains. He had therefore assigned to his student,

Daniel Rutherford, the investigation of this residual air in partial fulfill-
ment of the requirements for the degree of doctor of medicine.

The dissertation begins with an appropriate quotation from Lucretius
and a review of the researches of Black and of Cavendish on fixed air.
Rutherford then described his own experiments in which he had found
that a mouse, left in a confined volume of atmospheric air until it died,
had consumed $1/16$ of the air, and that treatment of the remaining air
with alkali had caused it to lose one-eleventh of its volume. He found

From Gentleman's Magazine, 1799

Stephen Hales, 1677–1761. British clergyman, biologist, chemist, and inventor. His most important researches were on blood pressure, circulation of sap,
respiration, and ventilation.

that the residual air extinguished the flame of a candle and that the wick
would continue to glow in it for only a short time. He also discovered that
air depleted by passage over ignited charcoal is identical with air vitiated
by respiration. When he burned a metal, phosphorus, or sulfur in the
atmosphere, however, he found that the residual gas contained no *mephitic*

air [carbon dioxide], but that it had undergone "a singular change" (*14*). After burning a candle or suffocating a mouse in a confined volume of air, and absorbing the resulting *fixed air*, or carbon dioxide, in caustic alkali, Rutherford concluded from careful study of the residual gas that . . . healthy and pure air by being respired, not only becomes partly mephitic [poisonous], but also suffers another change in its nature. For after all *mephitic air* [carbon dioxide] is separated and removed from it by means of a caustic lixivium, that which remains does not thence become more healthful; for although it makes no precipitate of lime from water, yet it extinguishes fire and life no less than before (*16*).

Rutherford also believed that "pure air is not converted into mephitic air by force of combustion, but that this air rather takes its rise or is thrown out from the body thus resolved" (*15*). He concluded, in other words, "that that unwholesome air is composed of atmospheric air in union with, and, so to say, saturated with, phlogiston" (*15*). After pointing out the distinction between this new "noxious air" [nitrogen] and "mephitic air" [carbon dioxide], the air evolved by the action of acids on metals, and the air from decaying flesh, Rutherford added that he was unable to state with certainty anything regarding the composition of mephitic air or to explain its inability to support life. He believed, however, that it was possibly generated from the food, and expelled as a waste product from the blood by means of the lungs (*14*).

Certain experiments [said he] appear to show . . . that it consists of atmospheric air in union with phlogistic material: for it is never produced except from bodies which abound in inflammable parts; the phlogiston ever appears to be taken up by other bodies, and is hence of value in reducing the calces of metals. I say from phlogistic material, because as already mentioned, pure phlogiston, in combination with common air, can be seen to yield another kind of air . . . (*15*).

Sir William Ramsay believed that Rutherford "may well be credited with the discovery of nitrogen" and that his thesis on mephitic air "was an advance, though not a great one, in the development of the theory of the true nature of air" (*15*). B. B. Woodward believed, however, that "all the facts and views recorded by Rutherford are to be found in Priestley's memoir published in the *Philosophical Transactions* for 1772 (p. 230 *et passim*), and read six months before the publication of Rutherford's tract; but Priestley's exposition is less methodical and precise" (*14*). Both Rutherford and Priestley believed the new gas to be atmospheric air saturated with phlogiston, and neither of them regarded it as an element (*14*).

In his "Lectures on the Elements of Chemistry," Dr. Joseph Black made the following statement about the discovery of nitrogen:

Scarcely inferior to vital air in importance is the *faul air* of Dr. Scheele, which I mentioned on the same occasion, as that noxious portion of atmospherical air which remains when the vital air has been absorbed by the *hepar sulphuris* [product of heating potassium carbonate with sulfur] (*17*). I must here observe, that this portion of our atmosphere was first observed in 1772 by my colleague Dr. Rutherford, and published by him in his inaugural dissertation. He had then discovered that we were mistaken in supposing that all noxious air was the fixed air which I had discovered. He says, that after this has been removed by caustic alkali or lime, a very large proportion of the air remains, which extinguishes life and flame in an instant. Soon after this Dr. Priestley met with this noxious air, which was produced in a variety of experiments, in which bodies were burned, or putrefied, or thickened in certain cases, or metals calcined, or minerals effloresced, &c.&c. In all these cases, he thought that he had reason to believe that phlogiston had quitted the substances under consideration—had combined with the air,—and had thus vitiated it. Now saturated with phlogiston, the air could take no more, and therefore extinguished flame. He called all these processes *phlogisticating processes,* and the air thus tainted *phlogisticated air* (*18*).

According to Dr. Black, it was Scheele who proved that the diminution of bulk which accompanied the vitiation of the air by these combustion processes

. . . was owing to a real abstraction of all the vital air which the atmospheric air contained. For when any of these "*phlogisticating processes*" of Dr. Priestley were performed in vital air, it was *totally* absorbed (*19*). The remainder therefore, when the experiment was made in common air, was considered by him as a primitive air, unchanged in its properties. He called it *faul air,* which may mean either *rotten* air, because it is produced in vast abundance by putrefying bodies, or simply *foul air, i. e.,* tainted occasionally, when the phlogiston is more than will saturate the vital air.

Dr Black also mentioned Berthollet's preparation of nitrogen by pouring nitric acid on fresh muscle fiber and Fourcroy's discovery of this gas in the swimming bladders of carp, bream, and other fish (*20*). He said that, although the discoverers of the element had called it by various names—*phlogisticated, foul,* or *mephitic air,* or *choke-damp* (*Stickstoff*)— the name *nitrogen* had been suggested by "Mr. Chaptal and other chemists of the first rank," after Cavendish had prepared niter by sparking the new gas with oxygen in presence of caustic potash (*21*). The French name *azote* was suggested by Lavoisier because of the inability of the gas to support life (*18, 22, 23, 24*). Although Lavoisier (*25*) had mentioned nitrogen in his list of elements, Sir Humphry Davy doubted its elementary nature as late as 1808–09 and attempted to decompose it (26).

After his graduation, young Dr. Rutherford studied in Paris, Italy, and London for three years before returning to Edinburgh to practice medicine. During his stay in Paris, he declined an invitation to a party at which Prince Charles Edward was expected, saying that, out of respect for the honor of a fallen house, he wished to avoid the spectacle of seeing the prince intoxicated (1).

Since Max Speter (27, 41) mentioned that John Mayow in his "Tractatus Quinque" anticipated Lavoisier (28) in the belief that all acids contain oxygen, it is interesting to know that Dr. Rutherford also made the same error. A note by John Robison in his edition of Black's "Lectures on the Elements of Chemistry" reads as follows:

I cannot omit mentioning in this place, that my colleague, Dr. Daniel Rutherford read, in the year 1775, to the Philosophical Society of Edinburgh, a dissertation on nitre and nitrous acid, in which this doctrine is more than hinted at or surmised. By a series of judiciously contrived experiments, he obtained a great quantity of vital air from nitric acid; about one-third of that quantity from the sulphuric acid, as contained in alum; and a small quantity (and this very variable and uncertain) from the muriatic acid. The manner in which it came off from the compounds, in various circumstances, led him to think that the different quantities obtained did not arise from the different proportions in which it was contained in those acids, but merely in the different forces with which it was retained. He therefore concluded that vital air was contained in all acids, and thought it likely that it was a *necessary* ingredient of an acid; and seeing that it was the *only* substance found, as yet, in them all, he thought it not unlikely that it was *by this that they were acid*, and he points out a course of experiments which seems adapted to the decision of this question. I was appointed to make a report on this dissertation; and I recollect stating as an objection to Dr. Rutherford's opinion, "that it would lay him under the necessity of supposing that vitriolic acid was a compound of sulphur and vital air," which I could not but think an absurdity. So near were we at that time to the knowledge of the nature of the acids (29).

Mayow's "Tractatus Quinque" was published in 1674, Dr. Rutherford's communication was read in 1775, and Lavoisier's statement that oxygen is an essential constituent of all acids is contained in a paper read on November 23, 1779.

In 1786 Rutherford was appointed successor to John Hope, the professor of botany at the University of Edinburgh, and in the same year he was married to Harriet Mitchelson of Middleton (1). With pardonable family pride, Sir Walter Scott once said that Dr. Rutherford "ought to have had the chemistry class, as he was one of the best chemists in Europe;

From Kay's Portraits

John Hope, 1725–1786. Predecessor of Daniel Rutherford as professor of botany and *materia medica* at the University of Edinburgh. Dr. Hope had the plants in the Botanical Garden arranged according to the Linnæan system. In the above portrait he is shown instructing one of the workmen. His son, Thomas Charles Hope (1766–1844), was Rutherford's contemporary as professor of chemistry at Edinburgh.

but superior interest assigned it to another, who, though a neat experimentalist, is not to be compared to poor Daniel for originality of genius. . ." (*30*). Bower's "History of the University of Edinburgh" states that the discovery of nitrogen "entitles Rutherford to rank very high among the chemical philosophers of modern times" and that "the reputation of his discovery being speedily spread through Europe, his character as a chemist of the first eminence was firmly established, and much was augured from a young man in his twenty-second year having distinguished himself so remarkably" (*30*).

Sir R. Christison, one of Dr. Rutherford's botany students, said, on the other hand,

Tradition had it in my student years that he was disappointed at not being made assistant and successor to Black in 1795, when that office was given to Dr. Charles Hope; and he again, son of the botanical predecessor of Rutherford, was said to have preferred to step into his own father's University shoes rather than into those of Dr. Black. However that may have been, Hope highly distinguished himself in his Chemical Chair; while Rutherford, in that of Botany, which he filled for thirty-four years, always seemed to lecture with a grudge, and never contributed a single investigation to the progress of the science which he taught. . . . His lectures, however, were extremely clear, and full of condensed information, his style was beautiful, and his pronunciation pure and scarcely Scotch (*31*).

Because of hereditary gout, Dr. Rutherford was unable to take his botany students on field trips, and Sir R. Christison thought that that important duty ought to have been entrusted to the head gardener (*31*).

I. B. Balfour also thought it strange that Dr. Rutherford should have been chosen to teach botany, and stated in the "Makers of British Botany" that "Rutherford was a chemist, and I have not discovered in any references to him expressions that he was at this period of his life interested in plants otherwise than as objects for his experiments in relation to the chemistry of the atmosphere" (*32*). Nevertheless, the botanical garden developed under Rutherford's administration into one of the best in the world, and the plants of Scotland were carefully recorded by the head gardeners (*32*).

Dr. Rutherford was a fellow of the Philosophical (later the Royal) society of Edinburgh, and contributed to its *Transactions* a description of a thermometer for reading maximum and minimum temperatures (*33, 34*). The portion of the instrument designed for reading minimum temperatures is a horizontal tube filled with alcohol in which is immersed a small glass rod with a knob at each end. As long as the temperature keeps falling, the concave surface tension film of the alcohol drags this little rod back with it, but when the temperature rises, the expanding alcohol moves past the rod, leaving it stationary. The portion of the thermometer used for reading maximum temperatures consists of a horizontal tube containing a thread of mercury which pushes a small bar of iron ahead of it as long as the temperature keeps rising (*34*). Dr. Rutherford also made experiments to improve the air pump (*33*).

He published an octavo volume called "Characteres Generum Plantarum," and collaborated with James Hamilton and James Gregory in

From Kay's Portraits

Cartoon Showing a Controversy in 1817 over the Founding of a Chair of Comparative Anatomy. The Candidate, Dr. Barclay, is shown astride the elephant's skeleton. His opponent, Dr. Thomas Charles Hope (center foreground), has his anchor firmly grounded in "the strontian." This is an allusion to the research in which he distinguished between baryta and strontia. The scene is laid at the entrance to the old College of Edinburgh.

writing "A Guide for Gentlemen Studying Medicine at the University of Edinburgh" (*14*). He was a member of the Linnæan Society and of the Aesculapian, Harveian, and Gymnastic Clubs (*14*).

Dr. and Mrs. Rutherford had two sons and three daughters, but in 1805 the elder son, John, a boy of seventeen, was lost in the shipwreck of an East Indiaman commanded by John Wordsworth, a brother of the famous poet. After his words of sympathy to William Wordsworth, Scott wrote, ". . . The same dreadful catastrophe deprived me of a near relation, a delightful and promising youth, the hope and pride of his parents. He had just obtained a cadetship, and parted from us all in the ardor of youthful hope and expectation, leaving his father (a brother of my mother) almost heartbroken at his departure. . ." (*35*). Fourteen years later Scott said, when writing to his son at the time of Dr. Rutherford's death, "Since you knew him, his health was broken and his spirits dejected, which may be traced to the loss of his eldest son . . ." (*30*).

Scott's correspondence with his aunt, Miss Christian Rutherford, shows that he found in his uncle's family ". . . more than one kind and strenuous encourager of his early literary tastes." Nevertheless, his youthful habit of reading at breakfast often brought forth good-natured protest from the doctor (9).

In December, 1819, Scott suffered the tragic loss of three of his nearest relatives within scarcely more than a week (30, 36). On the twelfth, his mother, who had been in excellent health and spirits in spite

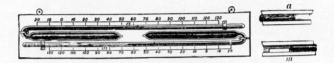

Rutherford's Maximum and Minimum Thermometer.   *a,*
Index of minimum thermometer; *m,* Index of maximum
thermometer.

of her advanced age of eighty-seven years, was suddenly stricken with such a severe attack of paralysis that Dr. Daniel Rutherford felt certain that she could not live more than a few days.

But [said Scott in a letter to his brother in Canada], "this heavy calamity was only the commencement of our family losses. Dr. [Daniel] Rutherford, who had seemed perfectly well and had visited my mother upon Tuesday the fourteenth, was suddenly affected with gout in his stomach, or some disease equally rapid, on Wednesday the fifteenth, and without a moment's warning or complaint, fell down a dead man, almost without a single groan. You are aware of his fondness for animals; he was just stroking his cat after eating his breakfast, as usual, when, without more warning than a half-uttered exclamation, he sunk on the ground, and died in the arms of his daughter Anne. Though the Doctor had no formed complaint, yet I have thought him looking poorly for some months; and though there was no failure whatever in intellect, or anything which approached it, yet his memory was not so good, and I thought he paused during the last time he attended me, and had difficulty in recollecting the precise terms of his recipe. Certainly there was a great decay of outward strength.

We were very anxious about the effect this fatal news was likely to produce on the mind and decayed health of our aunt, Miss C. Rutherford, and resolved, as her health had been gradually falling off ever since she returned from Abbotsford, that she should never learn anything of it until it was impossible to conceal it longer. But God had so ordained it that she was never to know the loss she had sustained, and which she would have felt so deeply. On Friday the 17th December, the second day after her brother's death, she expired, without a groan and without suffering, about six in the morning. . . . It is a most uncommon and afflicting circumstance, that a brother and two sisters should be taken ill the same day—that two of them should die without any rational possibility of the survivance of the third—and that no one of the three could be affected by learning the loss of the other. The Doctor was buried on Monday 20th, and Miss Rutherford this day (Wednesday 22nd), in the burial-place adjoining to and surrounding one of the new Episcopal chapels [St. John's Chapel], where Robert Rutherford [son to the professor of botany] had purchased burial-ground of some extent . . . and in this new place I intend to lay our poor mother when the scene shall close . . . (37).

Scott once paid the following tribute to his uncle: "Dr. Rutherford was a very ingenious as well as an excellent man, more of a gentleman than those of his profession too often are, for he could not take the back-stairs mode of rising in it, otherwise he might have been much more wealthy . . ." (30). This kindly Scottish physician is remembered today for his maximum and minimum thermometer and for the brilliant research in which he clearly distinguished between carbon dioxide and nitrogen (38, 39).

LITERATURE CITED

(1) ROGERS, C., "Genealogical Memoirs of the Family of Sir Walter Scott, Bart. of Abbotsford," Roy. Historical Soc., London, 1877, pp. lv–lviii.

(2) LOCKHART, J. G., "Memoirs of the Life of Sir Walter Scott," Vol. 1, Adam & Charles Black, Edinburgh, 1862, p. 14.

(3) LOCKHART, J. G., ref. (2), Vol. 1, pp. 19–21.

(4) "Catalogue of the Scott Centenary Exhibition," Edinburgh University Press, Edinburgh, 1872, p. 149.

(5) LOCKHART, J. G., ref. (2), Vol. 1, p. 173.

(6) ROGERS, C., ref. (1), p. lii.

(7) GRANT, SIR ALEXANDER, "The Story of the University of Edinburgh during Its First Three Hundred Years," Vol. 1, Longmans, Green & Co., London, 1884, pp. 308–15.

(8) MacCUNN, F., "Sir Walter Scott's Friends," Wm. Blackwood & Sons, Edinburgh and London, 1910, p. 12.

(9) LOCKHART, J. G., ref. (2), Vol. 1, p. 188.

(10) CLARK-KENNEDY, A. E., "Stephen Hales, D.D., F.R.S.," University Press, Cambridge, 1929, pp. 101–10.

(11) HARCOURT, V., "Presidential address," Brit. Assoc. Reports, 9, 3–68 (Aug. 1839). A reprint of Cavendish's paper on nitrogen is included.

(12) PRIESTLEY, J., "Observations on different kinds of air," Phil. Trans., 62, 147–256 (1772). Read Mar. 5, 12, 19, 26 (1772).

(13) RAMSAY, SIR W., "The Gases of the Atmosphere," 1st ed., Macmillan & Co., London, 1896, p. 62; ibid., 2nd ed., 1915, p. 63.

(14) LEE, SIR SIDNEY, "Dictionary of National Biography," Vol. 50, The Macmillan Co., New York City, 1897, pp. 5–6. Article on Daniel Rutherford by B. B. Woodward.

(15) RAMSAY, SIR W., ref. (13), 2nd ed., pp. 62–8.

(16) GRANT, SIR ALEXANDER, ref. (7), Vol. 2, pp. 382–4.

(17) SCHEELE, C. W., "Nachgelassene Briefe und Aufzeichnungen," Nordenskiöld edition, P. A. Norstedt & Söner, Stockholm, 1892, p. 80. Letter of Scheele to J. G. Gahn, Nov., 1775.

(18) BLACK, JOSEPH, "Lectures on the Elements of Chemistry," Vol. 2, Wm Creech, Edinburgh, 1803, pp. 105–8.

(19) DOBBIN, L., "The Collected Papers of Carl Wilhelm Scheele," G. Bell & Sons, London, 1931, pp. 116–7.

(20) FOURCROY, A.-F., "Recherches pour servir à l'histoire du gaz azote ou de la mofette, comme principe des matières animales," Ann. chim. phys., [1], 1, 40–7 (1795); "Observations sur le gaz azote contenu dans la vessie natatoire de la carpe; deux nouveaux procédés pour obtenir ce gaz," ibid., [1], 1, 47–51 (1795).

(21) Alembic Club Reprint No. 3, "Experiments on Air. Papers published in the Philosophical Transactions by the Honourable Henry Cavendish, F.R.S.," Wm. F. Clay, Edinburgh, 1893, pp. 39–52; H. CAVENDISH, Phil. Trans., 75, 372–84 (1785). Read June 2, 1785.

(22) BLACK, JOSEPH, ref. (18), Vol. 1, pp. 395–6.

(23) BLACK, JOSEPH, ref. (18), Vol. 1, p. lv.

(24) "Oeuvres de Lavoisier," Vol. 1, Imprimerie Impériale, Paris, 1864, p. 63; "Nitrogen and phosphorus. Classic of science," Sci. News Letter, 22, 102–4 (Aug. 13, 1932).

(25) "Oeuvres de Lavoisier," ref. (24), Vol. 1, pp. 135–7.

(26) DAVY, H., "The Bakerian lecture. An account of some new analytical researches on the nature of certain bodies," Phil. Trans., 99, 55–6, 103–4 (1809). Read Dec. 15, 1808.

(27) SPETER, MAX, "John Mayow und das Schicksal seiner Lehren," Chem.-Ztg., 34, 946–7, 953–4, 962–4 (Sept. 1910); Alembic Club Reprint No. 17, University of Chicago Press, Chicago, Ill., 1908, pp. 31–2. Translation of Mayow's "Tractatus Quinque Medico-Physici."

(28) "Oeuvres de Lavoisier," ref. (24), Vol. 1, p. 57; ibid., Vol. 2, pp. 248–60. Paper read Nov. 23, 1779. Presented Sept. 5, 1777.

(29) BLACK, J., ref. (18), Vol. 2, p. 213 (note 6) and p. 732.

(30) LOCKHART, J. G., ref. (3), Vol. 6, pp. 157–9. (Letter of Sir W. S. to his son, Cornet Walter Scott); BOWER, "History of the University of Edinburgh," Vol. 3. 1830, pp. 260–1. Quoted by Lockhart.

(31) GRANT, SIR ALEXANDER, ref. (7), Vol. 2, pp. 382–4.

(32) OLIVER, F. W., "Makers of British Botany," Cambridge University Press, Cambridge, 1913, pp. 290–1. Chapter by I. B. Balfour on "A sketch of the professors of botany in Edinburgh from 1670 until 1887."

(33) POGGENDORFF, J. C., "Biographisch-Literarisches Handwörterbuch der exakten Wissenschaften," Vol. 2, Verlag Chemie, Leipzig and Berlin, 1863–1937, p. 726. Article on Daniel Rutherford.

(34) EDSER, E., "Heat for Advanced Students," Macmillan & Co., London, 1911, pp. 18–9; R. T. GLAZEBROOK, "Heat," Cambridge University Press, Cambridge, 1914, p. 25; T. PRESTON, "Theory of Heat," 2nd ed., Macmillan & Co., London, 1904, p. 113.

(35) DOUGLAS, DAVID, "Familiar Letters of Sir Walter Scott," Vol. 1, Houghton Mifflin Co., Boston, 1894, p. 27.

(36) LOCKHART, J. G., ref. (2), Vol. 6, pp. 160–1; D. DOUGLAS, ref. (35), Vol. 2, pp. 66 and 69–70. (Letters of Sir Walter Scott to Wm. Laidlaw, to J. B. Morritt, and to Joanna Baillie.)

(37) LOCKHART, J. G., ref. (2), Vol. 6, pp. 164–8. (Letter of Sir Walter to his brother, Thomas Scott.)

(38) WEEKS, M. E., "The discovery of the elements. IV. Three important gases," J. Chem. Educ., 9, 219–21 (Feb. 1932).

(39) "DAN. RUTHERFORD über die mephitische Luft," Vol. 12, Crell's Neueste Entdeckungen in der Chemie, Weygandsche Buchhandlung, Leipzig, 1784, pp. 187–96.

(40) DOBBIN, L., "Daniel Rutherford's inaugural dissertation.   Crum Brown's translation," *J. Chem. Educ.*, **12**, 370–5 (Aug., 1935).

(41) SPETER, MAX, "Lavoisier und seine Vorläufer," F. Enke, Stuttgart, **1910**, pp. 56–72, 96–108.   Chapter on John Mayow.

(42) ATKINSON, E. R., "Samuel Johnson's Life of Boerhaave," *J. Chem. Educ.*, **19**, 103–8 (Mar., 1942).

(43) NEAVE, E. W. J., "Joseph Black's lectures on the elements of chemistry," *Isis.* **25**, 372–90 (Sept., 1936).

J. L. H. Börjeson's Statue of Carl Wilhelm Scheele. Scheele discovered tungstic and molybdic acids, and was the first to distinguish between graphite and molybdenite.

"Les laboratoires sont les temples de l'avenir, de la richesse et du bien-être; c'est là que l'humanité grandit, se fortifie et devient meilleure." (1)°

"It is to a general diffusion of a knowledge of chemistry, next to the Virtue of our countrymen, that we are to look for the firm establishment of our Independence" (71).

° "Laboratories are the temples of the future, of wealth, and of welfare; in them humanity grows greater, stronger, and better."

9

Chromium, molybdenum, tungsten, uranium

The publications and correspondence of Bergman and Scheele contain interesting allusions to the de Elhuyar brothers, to Hjelm, and to the early history of the metals tungsten and molybdenum which they discovered. The presence of a new metal in pitchblende was recognized by Klaproth in 1789, but it remained for Peligot half a century later to isolate uranium. Chromium, now the most familiar element of the group, was the last to be discovered when the immortal French chemist Vauquelin finally isolated it in 1798 from a Siberian mineral. For further information about tungsten see pp. 284–301.

*D*uring the last two decades of the eighteenth century, investigations were made which foreshadowed the discovery of chromium, molybdenum, tungsten, uranium, tellurium, chlorine, titanium, and beryllium; but some of these elements were not actually isolated until much later. For the sake of simplicity, only the closely related elements, tungsten, molybdenum, uranium, and chromium, will be considered in this chapter.

TUNGSTEN (WOLFRAM)

Tungsten and tungstic acid were first recognized in the minerals wolframite and scheelite. As early as 1761, J. G. Lehmann analyzed the former, without recognizing, however, that it contained two metals which were then unknown, tungsten and manganese. When he fused it with sodium nitrate and dissolved the melt in water, he obtained a green solution which became red (sodium manganate and permanganate). Addition of a mineral acid caused the precipitation of a soft, spongy, white "earth (tungstic acid)" which, after long standing in contact with the solution, became yellow. He concluded, however, that the wolframite from Zinnwald must be "a mineral consisting mainly of a glassy earth, much iron, and a trace of zinc" and that it is related to a mineral used by glassmakers, "*magnesia vitriariorum*," or pyrolusite (58).

Lampadius' Laboratory at Freiberg, 1800. Many of the most eminent mineralogical chemists in Europe were educated at the Freiberg School of Mines. The de Elhuyar brothers, who discovered tungsten, and A. M. del Río, who discovered vanadium ("erythronium"), received part of their training there, and F. Reich and H. T. Richter, the discoverers of indium, and Clemens Winkler, the discoverer of germanium, were members of the teaching staff.

In 1779 Peter Woulfe examined this mineral and concluded that it must contain something new. "The Spar of the Germans," said he, "is commonly called white tin ore. . . . This is supposed by several to be rich in tin; but the Saxon mineralogists assert that it contains none. The only experiment I made with it was to digest it in a powdered state with acids, by which means it acquires a rich yellow colour, like turbith mineral [basic mercuric sulfate]; the acid of salt answers best for this experiment. This is the only substance I know of which has this property" (65).

There is found in Sweden a white mineral which used to be called *tungsten,* or *heavy stone,* and which is now known as scheelite (20). In 1781 Scheele gave the following description of it: "The constituents of this variety of stone seem probably to be still unknown to chemists. Cronstedt enumerates it amongst the ferruginous varieties of stone, under the name of *Ferrum calciforme, terra quadam incognita intime mixtum.* That which I used for my experiments is pearl-coloured and taken from the iron mine of Bitsberg" (56). He decomposed the mineral with aqua fortis (nitric acid) and found that it contained lime and a white acidic powder similar to molybdic acid but differing from it in the following respects:

"(1) The acid of molybdaena is volatile and melts in the fire, which does not occur with acid of tungsten. (2) The first-named acid has a stronger affinity for phlogiston, which is seen from its union with sulphur and the change it undergoes on calcination with oil. (3) *Calx molybdaenata* does not become yellow with acid of nitre and is dissolved by it quite easily. With tungsten the contrary occurs. (4) *Terra ponderosa molybdaenata* is soluble in water, but not the same variety of earth united with our acid; and (5) acid of molybdaena has a weaker attraction for lime than our acid" (*56*).

Thinking, because of its high specific gravity, that scheelite might contain the alkaline earth baryta, Torbern Bergman analyzed it, but found instead an *acidic* oxide (tungstic acid). In 1781 he concluded that both tungstic and molybdic acids must be related to white arsenic and that therefore it ought to be possible to prepare metals from them. Since Bergman himself could not find time to test this hypothesis, he expressed the hope that someone else would make the necessary experiments (*57*).

In the meantime two Spanish chemists, the de Elhuyar* brothers, discovered in wolfram, a dark brown mineral (wolframite) then supposed to be an ore of tin and iron, an acid (wolframic) which they found to be identical with tungstic acid (*2, 21, 25, 37, 38*).

Don Fausto de Elhuyar was born in 1755 at Logroño, Spain. With his elder brother, Don Juan José, he went to Freiberg to study chemistry and mineralogy at the School of Mines, and Don Juan José later went to Upsala to work for half a year in Bergman's famous laboratory (*21, 41*). The Swedish professor mentioned him in his diary. "Mr. de Luyarte, from Spain," said he, "came with Mr. de Virly to Upsala on the same errand [to study], where they not only privately went through an entire course in higher chemistry, but also, with others, went to private lectures in assaying, each passing excellent tests. They remained until the end of the term" (*27, 39*).

In a letter to Bergman dated July 5, 1782, Scheele mentioned a visit which these chemistry students had recently paid him: ". . . The foreign gentlemen," he said, "stayed with me two days; I found real pleasure in talking with them about chemical matters; moreover they were not inexperienced in that field" (*3*).

In 1783 the brothers collaborated in a research on tungsten and wolfram, and found that both these ores contained the tungstic acid that Scheele had reported. The first metallic tungsten was prepared not from

---

* The name was also spelled Luyarte, de Luyart, and d'Elhuyart. In Spanish books it is spelled *de Elhuyar*. The brothers themselves did not agree as to the spelling.

scheelite but from wolframite (*spuma lupi*) from Zinnwald. "We know no Spanish name for this mineral," wrote the de Elhuyar brothers in 1783, "nor do we know that it has been found in our country" (*58*). The possibility of obtaining a new metal by reducing tungstic acid had already been suggested by Bergman and Scheele. The apparatus used by the de Elhuyar brothers was very simple. An intimate mixture of tungstic acid and powdered charcoal was heated strongly in a luted crucible (*22*). After cooling the crucible, they removed from it a dark brown, metallic button, which crumbled easily in their fingers, and when they examined

Fausto de Elhuyar. President of the Mining Tribunal and Director General of Mines of New Spain. For more than thirty years he directed the College of Mines of Mexico.

Courtesy Dr. Moles and Mr. de Gálvez-Cañero

the powder with a lens, they saw metallic globules of tungsten, some of which were as large as the head of a pin (*2, 26*). On April 2, 1784, Scheele wrote to Bergman, "I am glad that Mr. Luyarte has obtained a tungsten regulus. I hope he has sent you specimens of it" (*4*).

The de Elhuyar brothers afterward went to America and in 1788 Fausto became Director of Mines of Mexico. Don Juan José died in Bogotá, Colombia, but at the outbreak of the Revolution Don Fausto returned to Spain. His reason for leaving Mexico may be inferred from the note found at the end of one of Andrés del Río's papers:

The preceding analysis only too plainly shows the wretched state of our laboratory in Mexico, after having been for thirty years under the direction of so distinguished a chemist as M. Elhuyar, the discoverer of wolfram and cerium[!]. It is true that under the old government, this savant found himself obliged to become a man of business, undoubtedly much against his inclination; for it is impossible that he who has once imbibed a taste for science can ever abandon it (*5*).

Torbern Bergman wrote in 1784: "In connection with tungsten I would like to mention that the bright-colored species from Riddarhyttan, which Herr Cronstedt cites, does not belong to the tungstens. At any rate, all those which I myself have collected on the spot or received from others show an entirely different behavior: Herr Director de Elhuyar indeed carried out at Upsala an analysis in the wet way which yielded per hundredweight besides 24 iron and 22 silica nothing but lime" (94). Bergman was referring here to the "Director of all of the smelting works in New Granada," hence not to Don Fausto but to Don Juan José de Elhuyar.

After returning to Spain Fausto served on the General Council of Public Credit, was made Director General of Mines, drew up the famous mining law of 1825, and planned the School of Mines of Madrid. After a long, eventful, and useful life, he died in Madrid on January 6, 1833 (6).

In 1785 Rudolf Erich Raspe, author of "The Adventures of Baron Münchausen," showed that the metal obtained from scheelite is identical with that from wolframite and that it hardens steel (59). In an investigation of two refractory specimens of scheelite, he succeeded in reducing them to a "regulus which contains only a little iron and is unusually hard, strong, and refractory. It cuts glass like good hardened steel and is therefore well suited for the manufacture of all kinds of hard tools, for the improvement of several iron- and steel manufactures, even perhaps for the pouring of anchors in a single operation." He also prepared a fine yellow pigment from the mineral.

When he compared a regulus from wolframite with one from scheelite, he found that the former contained more iron and that "it has almost the same color as the scheelite regulus and is, if I be not mistaken, one and the same thing. Only yesterday I began the experiments with wolframite, which I regard as a kind of crystallized scheelite and which, according to a report in the newspapers, Don Luyarte [de Elhuyar] and another Spaniard have recently announced as containing a new metal" (59). J. Hawkins said that Raspe obtained his wolframite from "Poldice" [Poldise], Cornwall and his scheelite from Entral (60). Wolframite is now known to be a ferrous manganous tungstate of the composition (Fe, Mn)WO_4; scheelite is calcium tungstate, $CaWO_4$.

Rudolf Erich Raspe was born in 1737 in Hanover and educated in the natural sciences and philology at Göttingen and Leipzig. Benjamin Franklin met both Raspe and Baron von Münchausen on his visit in Hanover (61). Raspe was brilliant and versatile, but extravagant and dishonest. After he had pawned some valuable medals which he had stolen from the museum at Cassel, the police described him as a red-haired man, attired alternately in a gold-embroidered red suit, and suits of black, blue, and gray. After his arrest at Clausthal, he escaped in the night and embarked for England, where for the rest of his life he earned his living by tutoring and translating. He was also employed for a time in the mines of Cornwall and Ireland. He died at Mucross, Ireland, in 1794 (62, 95).

When M. H. Klaproth analyzed some supposed specimens of scheelite and wolframite from Poldise, Cornwall, in 1786, he found that the former had not been correctly identified but that the wolframite was genuine. He was unable to reduce tungstic acid to a metal, even in a smelting furnace or in the kilns of the Royal Porcelain Works (72).

As late as 1800, F. C. Gren wrote: "It is still questionable whether the oxyd of wolfram is reducible to a reguline metal. No chemist has yet succeeded in obtaining a pure regulus of it, at least of some magnitude. Whenever the experiment was attempted, the result, upon examination with the glass, was always found to be a mere congeries of small metallic globules" (63).

Nicholson's Journal for the same year contained a brief account of Guyton de Morveau's attempt to fuse tungsten: "Guyton, in a fire urged by the blast of three pipes to 185 degrees of the pyrometer, obtained a well rounded piece of 35 grammes. But it broke in the vice, and exhibited a central portion, which was only agglutinated, and soon acquired a purple colour by exposure to the air . . . and he concludes from the infusibility and brittleness of this metal that it affords little promise of utility in the arts, except in metallic alloys, or by virtue of the property which its oxide possesses, of affording fixed colours, or giving fixity to the colours of vegetables" (64). The tungsten lamp filaments, tungsten contact points, high-speed steel, and cutting tools tipped with hard diamond-like tungsten carbide (Widia) so indispensable to modern life have all resulted nevertheless from the great discovery made so long ago by the de Elhuyar brothers in Spain. Tungsten, in the opinion of W. P. Sykes, "has a value to civilization extremely large in proportion to the small amount in pounds used as lamp filaments. This, however, is sufficient to save the people of the United States alone some three billions of dollars each year as compared with the expenditures which would be required to produce the same level of illumination with carbon filament lamps" (93).

MOLYBDENUM

Native molybdenum disulfide is a soft, black mineral that looks much like graphite. In fact, until the latter part of the eighteenth century, both were sold under the same name: *Molybdän*, or *molybdenum*. German writers used to call molybdenite "Wasserbley," a name suggestive of lead.

Although Johann Heinrich Pott knew that it is not a lead mineral, he confused it with graphite, "Reissbley," and believed that it contained lime, iron, and sulfuric acid (50).

In 1754 Bengt (Andersson) Qvist, a friend of A. F. Cronstedt and Sven Rinman, investigated a mineral which he described as follows: "At one locality of the Bispberg there is found a light, roughly pointed, loose,

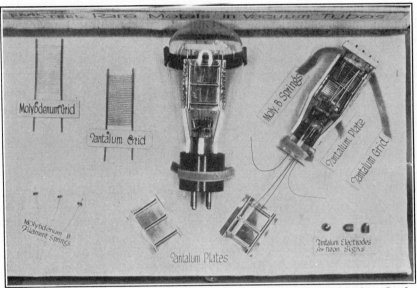

Courtesy Fansteel Products Co., Inc.

Vacuum Tube Showing the Use of Tantalum and Molybdenum

glistening molybdenite [Wasserblei] consisting of flexible lamellae which are not firmly coherent and which for the most part succeed one another in the form of regular pyramids. . . . In the muffle it gave off dense black fumes and a suffocating sulfurous odor; at the same time appeared small yellow "flowers" like snowflakes, which crystallized in masses of rather elastic filaments or lamellae" (51).

Qvist observed that the calx was yellow while hot but glistening white when cold. He obtained positive tests for iron and copper, and found that "on digestion, it gave no sweetness to distilled vinegar" (an indication that molybdenite is not a lead mineral). In one specimen from England he detected tin. He concluded that "it is evident from several experiments that the molybdenite itself contains something specifically metallic in addition to those just mentioned" (51).

On December 19, 1777, Scheele wrote to J. G. Gahn: "You doubtless have there in your mineral collection some foliated *molybdaena* like the enclosed sample. I received some in the summer from Assessor Hoffgaard; I find something peculiar in it. Please be so good as to send me a little of it by mail. On some better occasion I shall describe my experiments" (52).

Scheele kept this promise, and on May 15th of the following year wrote Gahn as follows: "I now have the pleasure of giving you a short report of my experiments with *molybdaena*. Professor Bergman, Assessor Rinman, and B. Hermelin [Samuel Gustav Hermelin] all sent me some of it" (52).

In 1778 Scheele published his analysis of the so-called "lead ore" (molybdenite), then known as *molybdaena*. "I do not mean the ordinary lead ore," said he, "that is met with in the apothecaries' shops, for this is very different from that concerning which I now wish to communicate my experiments to the Royal Academy. I mean here that which in Cronstedt's "Mineralogy" is called *molybdaena membranacea nitens* and with which Qvist and others probably made their experiments. The kinds I had occasion to submit to tests were got in different places, but they were all found to be of the same nature and composed of the same constituents" (53).

Because of its softness, Scheele had to devise an ingenious method of pulverizing the mineral. "Now since it does not permit of being ground to fine powder by itself, on account of its flexible lamellae, some fragments of vitriolated tartar [potassium sulfate] were also placed in the glass mortar occasionally, when it was at last transformed to a fine powder" (53). Scheele then washed the powder by decantation with hot water to remove the potassium sulfate. By adding nitric acid to the mineral several times and evaporating to dryness, he succeeded in decomposing it so completely that only a white powder remained, which he named *terra molybdaenae*.

Bengt Qvist had already shown that the mineral is volatile in the open fire and that it contains sulfur, and Scheele found that "earth of molybdaena is of an acid nature." He examined it "by the method of reduction with black flux and charcoal and with glass of borax and charcoal, but it was in vain; I did not perceive anything in the least metallic" (53). Scheele showed that graphite and the molybdenum mineral are two entirely different substances. Although nitric acid has no effect on graphite, it reacts with the mineral "molybdenum," or molybdenite, to give sulfuric acid and a peculiar white solid, which he named molybdic acid (2, 23). Bergman suggested to Scheele that molybdic acid must be the oxide of a new metal, and since the latter chemist did not have a furnace suitable for the purpose, he asked his friend Hjelm to attempt the reduction of the ore (7).

Peter Jacob Hjelm was of about the same age as Scheele, for he was born on October 2, 1746, at Sunnerbo Härad. He probably met the latter in Upsala, for their correspondence began shortly before Scheele went to Köping (7). At Scheele's suggestion Hjelm tried to reduce molybdic acid with carbon, and in order to get very intimate contact between the two reagents, he stirred the pulverized acid with linseed oil to form a

Torbern Olof Bergman, 1735–1784. Swedish chemist, pharmacist, and physicist. He was among the first to investigate the compounds of manganese, cobalt, nickel, tungsten, and molybdenum. He was an "immediate forerunner of Haüy" in the history of theoretical crystallography (68).

paste. When he heated the mixture strongly in a closed crucible, the oil became carbonized, and the carbon reduced the molybdic acid to the metal, which became known as molybdenum (2, 24).

On September 28, 1781 Scheele wrote to Torbern Bergman, "I am pleased that Herr Hjelm has reduced molybdic acid" (8). On November 16, 1781, Scheele wrote to Hjelm,

. . . I gladly excuse your delay in writing, for I know you are now very busy. I rejoice that we now have another new half-metal, molybdaenum. I think I can already see the French seeking to deny the existence of this new half-metal, since they are not the discoverers of it. What about Meyer? Here we have another new half-metal, and it is fine that Meyer and Bergman have discovered it at almost the same time. Who then deserves the honor of being called its discoverer? If you want to read Meyer's article on it in German, I shall mail it to you. But molybdaena it certainly is not, although it seems to resemble it in many respects. Enclosed herewith is my entire supply of *acido molybdaenae,* which, to be sure, is made with saltpeter, but not with saltpeter in the fire. The acidum enclosed in paper is the same acid that I fused in a crucible. If you prepare a regulus from it, I beg you, because of its rarity, to send me some of it, even if it is only a grain. I have no molybdaenum (8).

The other "half-metal" referred to in the preceding letter was "hydro-siderum," a false element which Apothecary Johann Karl Friedrich Meyer of Stettin, Scheele, and M. H. Klaproth later proved to be a phosphate of iron (73, 74, 41). In another of his letters to Hjelm Scheele said, "As far as I can judge of your work, it does you all credit" (9). Although this correspondence shows that Hjelm must have isolated molybdenum as early as the fall of 1781, his first paper on it was not published until much later.

Justus Christian Heinrich Heyer, in the account of his own researches on molybdenite, stated in 1787 that he had been unable to find from the literature how Hjelm had prepared the metal (75). Heyer repeated Scheele's synthesis of molybdenite by heating a mixture of molybdic acid and flowers of sulfur in a glass retort (75). In 1790, after both Scheele and Bergman had died, Hjelm wrote:

"At the request of the late Scheele and Bergman, I tried to prepare a metal from yellow molybdic acid, using the same acid which the former himself sent me. I first fused ox blood several times with the vegetable alkali; then, when I wanted to reduce the acid, I added to it an equal amount of microcosmic salt, and a little tartar or black flux from which I had often smoked off some grease. I placed the entire mixture, some-times also covered with common salt, in a luted crucible, and exposed it for several hours to the heat of a good wind furnace. If one wishes to reduce a new portion of acid again, one uses the glass produced in the foregoing operation, as it might then be less inclined to attack the earth of molybdenum itself and to dissolve it.

"The small regulus I obtained from the meager supply of earth brought forth the description of it to be found in Herr Bergman's paper on the blowpipe. The traces of sulfur and iron present in the reguluses I attribute to the molybdic earth which I received, for my fluxes were perfectly pure; the former were therefore only a kind of crude metal in which, however, the metallic nature is fundamental. Several writers, including Herr [Bertrand] Pelletier, Sage, Ilsemann, and Heyer, assume this: yet they have not engaged in the actual reduction" (42).

Hjelm prepared purified molybdic acid and obtained a pure regulus, which he examined with the microscope. In an unsuccessful attempt to fuse the molybdenum, he raised the temperature of the wind-furnace with "fire-air" (oxygen) obtained by adding two pounds of crude pyrolusite to the fire (24).

He published papers on the composition of coal, wood, charcoal, steel, pyrolusite, molybdenite, and spring waters, on the arts of purifying lead, hardening copper, and burning bricks, on the working of saltpeter and indigo, on resuscitation of patients with suspended animation, and on the porphyry industry at Elfdal, East Dalarne (54).

In 1782 Hjelm was made Assay Master of the Royal Mint at Stockholm, and twelve years later he became Director of the Chemistry Laboratory at the Bureau of Mines. He died in that city on October 7, 1813 (7).

Edward Daniel Clarke, who visited him in 1799, described him as "a most intelligent man and very able chemist, of the name of Hjelm,

Martin Heinrich Klaproth, 1743–1817. German chemist and pharmacist. The most distinguished German mineralogical and analytical chemist of his time. His careful analyses led to the discovery of uranium and zirconium and verified the discovery of tellurium and titanium. He also made pioneer researches on ceria.

who permitted us to see the collection of minerals belonging to the Crown. . . . Mr. Hjelm was employed, at the time of our arrival, in making what he called Spa Water, that is to say, water impregnated with carbonic acid gas, by the usual process of agitating the fluid in a receiver containing the gas collected from the effervescence of limestone when exposed to the action of an acid. Mr. Hjelm used the sulphuric acid and powdered marble. He showed to us a very great chemical curiosity; namely, a mass of chromium in the metallic state, nearly as large as the top of a man's thumb. We could perceive, however, that the Swedish chemists, celebrated as they justly are, carry on their works in the large way: the furnaces used by Mr. Hjelm, in the Royal Laboratory, were of the size of those in our common blacksmiths' shops; and the rest of his apparatus was on a similar scale" (55).

Professor Hjelm was one of Scheele's best friends, and their correspondence is still treasured by the Stockholm Academy of Sciences. Hjelm's diary is now in possession of the Royal Library at Stockholm (7). When Scheele wrote to Hjelm, *"Es ist ja nur die Wahrheit, welche wir wissen wollen, und welch ein herrliches Gefühl ist es nicht, sie erforscht zu haben"** (10), he knew that he was expressing the latter's feelings as well as his own.

In 1785 B. Pelletier proved that the ore mineralogists used to call "molybdenum" is a sulfide of that metal (28). The molybdic acid obtained by Scheele does not exist as such in the mineral, but was produced when he oxidized the molybdenum sulfide with nitric acid.

In 1790 Baron Ignaz von Born announced in *Crell's Annalen* that Anton Rupprecht, professor at the Mining Academy in Selmeczbánya, Hungary, had prepared molybdenum (67).

Although molybdenite was for several years the only known source of molybdenum, the Abbé F. X. Wulfen in 1785 described a lead mineral from Carinthia which had previously been regarded as lead tungstate, and when M. H. Klaproth analyzed a specimen of it from Bleyberg in 1792–94, he found it to be lead molybdate (76). Two years later, Charles Hatchett examined a larger specimen of it and confirmed Klaproth's conclusion. This mineral is now known as wulfenite.

Molybdenum is a much softer, more ductile metal than tungsten, and is indispensable for the filaments, grids, and screens required in radio broadcasting. Hence this great modern industry rests upon the researches that gave so much intellectual pleasure to Hjelm and Scheele.

URANIUM

When R. T. Gunther of Oxford University was excavating the Imperial Roman Villa on Cape Posilipo on the Bay of Naples he discovered a richly colored glass mosaic mural which for archaeological and historical reasons he believed to date from approximately 79 A.D. A specimen of the pale green glass from it which was analyzed at Oxford University in 1912 was found to contain more than one per cent of an oxide of uranium. After a careful study of the evidence, Earle R. Caley concluded that the addition of a uranium mineral to the glass was probably intentional and that the date 79 A.D. may be "taken as fixing the approximate time of the first use of uranium glass and the approximate time of the first use of any kind of a material containing uranium" (69).

The early history of uranium is closely associated with the name of

---

* "It is only the truth that we want to know, and isn't it a glorious feeling to have discovered it?"

Martin Heinrich Klaproth, a German chemist who was born in Wernigerode in the Harz on December 1, 1743. When he was eight years old,
the family became impoverished by a serious fire. Since there was
little money left for the education of the three Klaproth boys, little Martin
Heinrich earned his tuition by singing in the church choir. After receiving a little instruction in Latin at Wernigerode, he was apprenticed
at the age of sixteen years to an apothecary. After five years of apprenticeship, he worked for four years in public laboratories at Quedlinburg

Valentin Rose the Younger, 1762–1807.[*]
German chemist and apothecary who was
educated by Klaproth, collaborated with
him in his researches, and verified all his
analyses before publication. Rose demonstrated the presence of chromium in
a species of serpentine. He was the
father of Heinrich Rose, the chemist, and
Gustav Rose, the mineralogist. His father, Valentin Rose the Elder, was the
discoverer of the low-melting alloy, Rose's
metal.

From Ferchl's "Von Libau bis Liebig"

and at Hanover, and at Easter time in 1768 he became an assistant in
Wendland's laboratory in Berlin "at the sign of the Golden Angel in the
street of the Moors" (*11, 40*).

In 1770 he became an assistant to the famous chemist, Valentin Rose,
who, however, died only a few months later. Although Klaproth was
only twenty-seven years old when this emergency arose, he met all the
responsibilities of his new position. He not only carried on Rose's duties
for nine years, but acted as a father to his two fatherless sons, providing
carefully for their education. The younger boy unfortunately died in
childhood, but the older one, Valentin Rose the Younger, shared Klaproth's
love for nature, and collaborated with him in many researches. It was
Rose's task to repeat and verify all Klaproth's experiments before the

[*] Reproduced by courtesy of Mr. Arthur Nemayer, Buchdruckerei und Verlag,
Mittenwald, Bavaria.

results were published (11). Klaproth afterward purchased the Flemming laboratory on Spandau Street. His marriage to Sophie Christiana Leckman led to a happy family life. They had four children, and the only son, Heinrich Julius, became a famous Orientalist.

Martin Heinrich Klaproth made many brilliant contributions to analytical and mineralogical chemistry (33), and was a pioneer in the chemical investigation of antiquities such as Greek, Roman, and Chinese coins, ancient glasses, and prehistoric metallic objects (70). His papers are assembled in his "Beiträge zur chemischen Kenntniss der Mineralkörper," a six-volume work. Although he never discovered an element in the sense of isolating it for the first time, his analytical work foreshadowed the discovery of uranium and zirconium and verified the discovery of tellurium and titanium.

Pitchblende. Early chemists and mineralogists believed that pitchblende was an ore of zinc and iron. When M. H. Klaproth first recognized in 1789 that it contained an unknown metal, he sketched its history as follows: "Of late, seventeen metallic substances have been acknowledged as distinct metals, each of a nature peculiar to itself. The design of this essay is to add one to that number, the chemical properties of which will be explained in the sequel. The particular fossil by the decomposition of which I have discovered this new metallic substance is the black, or *pitch*-blende (*pseudo-galena* of many) as it has been hitherto called. In the meantime I shall continue to use that appellation, till, in the progress of this essay, the necessity of giving it a new name will be conspicuous. This fossil is found at Joachimsthal in Bohemia, and at Johann Georgenstadt, in the metalliferous mountains of Saxony (77).

"Only a few writers," continued Klaproth, "appear to have been formerly acquainted with this mineral. . . . Werner, to whom its fracture, hardness, and gravity sufficiently indicated that it could not be a blende, has transferred it from the class of zinc-ores to that of the ores of iron, calling it *Eisen-pecherz;* though only *ad interim,* until its proper place should be ascertained by chemical analysis. A subsequent conjecture of his, that this fossil might, perhaps, contain the metallic radical of *tungsten,* or *Wolfram,* was thought to be supported by actual experiments made at Schemnitz. But this pretended fact is contradicted by the result of the following examination" (77).

Klaproth mentioned two kinds of pitchblende, the first of which was a brownish black, opaque, brittle, massive, resplendent kind with a conchoidal fracture, found in the mines or galleries at Joachimsthal, Saxon Edelleutstolln, and Hohe Tanne.

"The second variety," said he, "to which belongs the greatest part of pitch-blende that occurs at Johann-Georgenstadt, is greyish black, and exhibits various degradations, from the glittering to the dull or dim. At that place it is obtained in the mine Georg Wagsfort, in larger or smaller masses, between strata of schistose mica [Glimmerschiefer]; which is nearly in a state of decay. . . . It has also been met with there in the mine Neujahrsmaassen, between alternate strata of the fibrous iron-stone" (77).

When Klaproth dissolved some pitchblende in nitric acid and neutralized the acid with potash, he obtained a yellow precipitate which dissolved in excess potash. Klaproth concluded correctly that the mineral must contain a new element, which he named in honor of the new planet, Uranus, which Herschel had recently discovered (12). He then attempted to obtain metallic uranium just as Hjelm had prepared metallic molybdenum. By strongly heating an oil paste of the yellow oxide in a charcoal crucible, he obtained a black powder with a metallic luster, and thought he had succeeded in isolating metallic uranium (29). For over fifty years the elementary nature of his product was accepted by chemists, but in 1841 Peligot showed that this supposed uranium metal was really an oxide.

When the University of Berlin was founded, Klaproth was sixty-seven years old, yet he was appointed as the first professor of chemistry, and served in that capacity until his death on January 1, 1817 (13). Thomas Thomson mentioned as his most characteristic personal traits: pure love of science, intellectual integrity, unselfishness, modesty, friendliness, kindness, a sense of humor, religious feeling, freedom from superstition, neatness, and precision (14).

In 1823 J. A. Arfwedson reduced the green oxide of uranium (then believed to be the lowest oxide) with hydrogen, and obtained a brown powder which he took to be the metal, but which is now known to be uranous oxide, UO_2 (15, 30). In 1841 Peligot, on analyzing anhydrous uranous chloride, UCl_4, found that 100 parts of this chloride apparently yielded about 110 parts of its elements uranium and chlorine. His explanation of this seemingly impossible result was that the uranous chloride reacts with water in the following manner:

$$UCl_4 + 2H_2O = UO_2 + 4HCl$$

Since uranous oxide cannot be reduced with hydrogen or carbon, it had always been mistaken for metallic uranium.

Peligot then heated the anhydrous chloride with potassium in a closed platinum crucible. This was heroic treatment for the platinum, to be sure, for the reaction was violent enough to make crucible and contents white-hot. However, since he took care to place the small crucible inside a larger one and to remove his alcohol lamp as soon as the reaction had started, Peligot avoided being injured by the pieces of potassium thrown out of the crucible. When the violent reaction sub-

From Ferchl's "Von Libau bis Liebig"

The Rose Pharmacy in Berlin. *   Valentin Rose the Elder (1735–1771), his son Valentin Rose the Younger (1762–1807), and his grandson Heinrich Rose (1795–1864) all rendered distinguished service to chemistry and pharmacy.

sided, he heated the crucible strongly to remove the excess potassium and to make the reduced uranium coherent. After cooling it, he dissolved out the potassium chloride, and obtained a black metallic powder with properties quite different from those formerly attributed to metallic uranium (*15, 31*). He was evidently the first person to isolate this metal.

* Reproduced by courtesy of Mr. Arthur Nemayer, Buchdruckerei und Verlag, Mittenwald, Bavaria.

Eugène-Melchior Peligot was born on February 24, 1811, at Paris. He studied at the Lycée Henri IV and at the Central School of Arts and Manufactures, but was obliged to leave school for financial reasons. In 1832, however, good fortune dawned for him, and he was admitted to the laboratory of the École Polytechnique to study under J.-B. Dumas. A few years later he was collaborating with Dumas in important researches in organic chemistry.

For thirty-five consecutive years Peligot occupied the chairs of analytical chemistry and glassmaking at the Central School of Arts and Manufactures, and during this time he wrote an important treatise on each of these subjects. He also lectured to large, sympathetic audiences at the Conservatoire des Arts et Métiers, and taught a course in agricultural chemical analysis at the National Agronomic Institute.

Eugène Peligot, 1811–1890. Professor of analytical chemistry and glassmaking at the Central School of Arts and Manufactures in Paris. Director of assays at the Paris Mint. Professor of agricultural chemical analysis at the National Agronomic Institute. The first to isolate the metal uranium.

He was employed at the Mint for forty years, first as assayer, then as verifier, and finally as Director of Assays. His residence was at the Mint also, and it was there that he died in 1890. According to Tissandier, "his life, always calm and methodical, was entirely consecrated to the science that he loved with passion and to his family that he cherished no less" (*34*). He must have been a man of broad interests, for he published papers on such varied topics as: water analysis, the chemical composition of the sugar beet and sugar cane, chemical and physiological studies of silkworms, the composition of Bohemian glass, and researches on uranium and chromium (6).

ADVERTISEMENT.

THE merits of KLAPROTH, in Chemical Ana-lysis, are so eminently established with men of science throughout Europe, that it would seem im-proper to enlarge on the most consummate skill and accuracy with which he performed his experiments, as well as on his laudable candour in stating their results.

On this confideration, it is hoped that the tranf-lation of his Analytico-chemical Effays, &c. which is here offered to the patronage of the English Chemifts, will meet with their kind approbation.—It may be neceffary to add, that all the Effays of the Author relating to this fubject, and which, in the German original, were publifhed in two volumes, are, for the accommodation of the public, compriz-ed in this fingle Volume.

Whenever Mr. Klaproth, as he has given hopes to the Tranflator, fhall give another collection of his laft and neweft Effays, they will be immediately rendered into Englifh.

☞ If fome typographical errors, and a few other miftakes which unfortunately have efcaped the moft careful attention, fhould create fome difficulty in the fenfe, the reader is requefted to refer to the errata in the laft page.

Translator's Preface to the English Edition of Klaproth's "Analytical Essays towards Promoting the Chemical Knowledge of Mineral Substances"

Uranium in Mineral Waters. In 1929 A. Pereira-Forjas demonstrated the presence of uranium in the mineral water from Cambres, Corredoura, Portugal. He detected it spectroscopically in the water itself, not in the residue (78, 79). M. Herculano de Carvalho found that the uranium in five springs near Caria, Casteleiro, Portugal, after separation of the radium, amounted to 10^{-6} gram per liter (80).

CHROMIUM

Nicolas-Louis* Vauquelin, the discoverer of the metal chromium, was born on May 16, 1763, in a little Normany village called St. André

* In the *Annuaire* of the Académie des Sciences the names are given thus, not in the reverse order.

d'Hébertot.* As a child he worked in the fields with his father, who struggled hard to feed and clothe his large family. The boy made surprisingly rapid progress in the village school and in the religious studies taught him by the curé, who was very fond of him (16). At the age of fourteen years, young Vauquelin became a laboratory assistant and dishwasher in an apothecary shop in Rouen, and somewhat later he went to Paris with a letter of introduction from his old curé at St. André d'Hébertot to the prior of the order of Prémontré. His two best friends during his early struggles in Paris were this venerable prior and Mme. Aguesseau, the owner of the estate on which the elder Vauquelin worked as a peasant (16).

Nicolas-Louis Vauquelin, 1763–1829. French analytical and mineralogical chemist and apothecary of the Revolutionary Period. Professor at the École Polytechnique and at the School of Mines. Assayer at the Paris Mint. In 1797 he discovered chromium and in 1798 beryllium.

During his first three years in the city, the boy worked in various apothecary shops, and in his leisure moments studied Latin and botany. One of these pharmacies was owned by M. Cheradame, a cousin of the famous chemist, Antoine-François de Fourcroy. When M. Cheradame told Fourcroy about young Vauquelin's fondness for chemistry, Fourcroy immediately engaged the boy as his assistant and took him home. Fourcroy's unmarried sisters treated the young assistant with all gentleness and kindness, and on one occasion he owed his recovery from a serious illness to their motherly care, an act of kindness which he never forgot.

* Also spelled Saint-André des Berteaux.

Vauquelin continued his study of physics, chemistry, and philosophy, and assisted Fourcroy in teaching a course at the Athenaeum. He was diffident about speaking in public, but as soon as he became acquainted with his new students, he always taught with pleasure and enthusiasm and soon endeared himself to them.

One of the stirring events of the Revolution was Vauquelin's rescue, from the mob, of an unfortunate Swiss soldier who had escaped from the Tuileries massacre. Because of his participation in the Revolution, Vauquelin had to leave Paris in 1793; however, after serving as pharmacist in a military hospital for a few months, he returned to Paris to teach chemistry at the Central School of Public Works, which afterward became the École Polytechnique. He later became an inspector of mines and professor of assaying at the School of Mines, where he also lived. Out of gratitude to Fourcroy's sisters, who continued to keep house for him even after the death of their brother, Vauquelin placed most of the apartment at their disposal, and both the sisters lived with him until they died (*16, 35*).

The first analysis of the Siberian red lead (crocoite or crocoisite) which M. V. Lomonosov (1711–1765) had described was made by Johann Gottlob Lehmann in 1766 (*43, 96*). He was highly esteemed as director of the Prussian mines and as a lecturer in Berlin. In 1761 he became professor of chemistry and director of the Royal Museum in St. Petersburg, and was commissioned by Catherine II to make extensive mineralogical trips throughout the Russian Empire. He described the Siberian red lead in a letter to the Comte de Buffon in 1766. At that time it was found only at a smelter fifteen versts from Ekaterinenstadt (Marxstadt). In his chemical investigation of it, Lehmann dissolved it in hydrochloric acid, noticed the emerald-green color of its (reduced) solution, and found that the mineral contained lead. He concluded that it must be "a lead mineralized with a selenitic spar and iron particles" (*44*). In 1767 his life was suddenly cut short by the bursting of a retort in which he was heating some arsenic (*45*).

In 1770 P. S. Pallas described the Beresof gold mines near Ekaterinburg (Sverdlovsk), Siberia. On the 25th and 26th of June of that year he wrote: "The Beresof pits include four mines, which have been worked since 1752." The Beresof mine also yielded copper, lead, and silver. "A very remarkable red lead mineral is also exploited there," said Pallas, "which has never been found in any other mine of the Empire or elsewhere. This lead ore is heavy, of varying color (sometimes like that of cinnabar), and semi-transparent. . . . One also finds small irregular, tortuous pyramids of it attached like little rubies to quartz. When pulverized, it gives a handsome yellow guhr which could be used in miniature painting. . . . It is difficult today to procure enough of it for large-scale assays, for the part of the mine where this lead ore is found is seldom worked, for lack of air. . . . Five hundred workmen are now employed in these mines . . ." (46).

Peter Simon Pallas (1741–1811) was a native of Berlin. He was broadly educated in medicine, natural sciences, and modern languages, which he studied in Berlin, Halle, Göttingen, the Netherlands, and England. From 1768 until 1774 he made extended journeys at the request of Catherine II and suffered great privations in order to study the natural history of Siberia, the Altai Mountains, the lower Volga region, and the southern part of European Russia (47, 48, 49).

In 1797–98 N.-L. Vauquelin analyzed crocoite and gave a detailed account of its history. "All the specimens of this substance which are to be found in the several mineralogical cabinets in Europe," said he, "were obtained from this [Beresof] gold mine; which indicates that it was

Antoine-François de Fourcroy, 1755–1809. French chemist of the Revolutionary Period. Defender of Lavoisier's views on combustion. In collaboration with Lavoisier, Guyton de Morveau, and Berthollet he carried out a reform of chemical nomenclature. Fourcroy prepared and analyzed many reagents and medicinals.

formerly abundant; but it is said that for some years past it has become very scarce, and that at present it is bought for its weight in gold, especially if pure and regularly formed. The specimens which do not possess the regular figure, or are broken into fragments, are appropriated to painting, in which art this substance is of high value for its beautiful orange-yellow colour, its unchangeableness in the air, and the facility with which it can be levigated with oil" (36).

"The beautiful red colour, transparency, and crystalline figure of the Siberian red lead," continued Vauquelin, "soon induced mineralogists and chemists to make enquiries into its nature. The place of its discovery, its specific gravity, and the lead ore which accompanies it produced an immediate suspicion of the presence of that metal; but, as lead had never been found in possession of the characteristic properties of this Siberian ore, they thought, with justice, that it was mineralised by some other substance; and Lehmann, who first subjected it to chemical

Peter Simon Pallas, 1741–1811. German scientist who made extensive scientific journeys to study the natural history of Russia and Siberia. He described the Beresof gold mines and the "Siberian red lead" (crocoite) in 1770.

The Naturalist's Library, Vol. 9

analysis, asserted, in a Latin dissertation printed at Petersburgh in 1766 . . . that the mineralisers were arsenic and sulphur" (36). When Vauquelin and Macquart analyzed it, they found it to consist of lead peroxide, iron, and aluminum. Bindheim of Moscow reported, however, that it

Fourcroy Autograph from his "Système des Connaissances Chimiques."

Cet ouvrage est mis sous la sauve-garde de la loi.

Tous les exemplaires sont signés par l'Auteur et l'Imprimeur.

contained molybdic acid, nickel, cobalt, iron, and copper. To settle this question Vauquelin in 1797 repeated the analysis (32).

"My labours (said Vauquelin) have not been without their recompense; and I hope to prove in the following paragraphs that all which has hitherto been asserted with regard to the mineraliser of the Siberian red lead is entirely destitute of foundation; that it contains neither arsenic, as Lehmann pretended; nor the molybdic acid and the three or four metals as announced by Bindheim; nor iron nor clay, as Macquart and myself imagined; but a new metal, possessing properties entirely unlike those of any other metal . . ." (*36, 81*). When Vauquelin boiled the

Dedication of the German Edition of Scheele's Works Edited by Hermbstädt

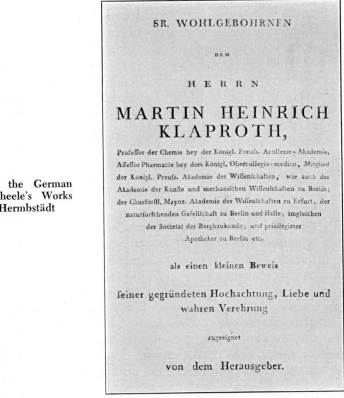

SR. WOHLGEBOHRNEN

DEM

H E R R N

MARTIN HEINRICH KLAPROTH,

Profeffor der Chemie bey der Königl. Preufs. Artillerie-Akademie, Affeffor Pharmacie bey dem Königl. Obercollegio-medico, Mitglied der Königl. Preufs. Akademie der Wiffenfchaften, wie auch der Akademie der Künfte und mechanifchen Wiffenfchaften zu Berlin; der Churfürftl. Maynz. Akademie der Wiffenfchaften zu Erfurt, der naturforfchenden Gefellfchaft zu Berlin und Halle; imgleichen der Societat der Bergbaukunde; und privilegirter Apotheker zu Berlin etc.

als einen kleinen Beweis

feiner gegründeten Hochachtung, Liebe und wahren Verehrung

zugeeignet

von dem Herausgeber.

pulverized mineral with two parts of potassium carbonate, he obtained lead carbonate and a yellow solution containing the potassium salt of an unknown acid. This solution gave a beautiful red precipitate when added to the solution of a mercuric salt and a yellow precipitate when added to a lead solution. He noticed also that when he isolated the new acid and added stannous chloride, the solution became green (reduction of chromic acid to a chromic salt) (*17*).

In 1798 Vauquelin succeeded in isolating the new metal. After removing the lead in the Siberian red lead by precipitation with hydrochloric acid, he evaporated the filtrate to obtain the chromium trioxide, which he put into a charcoal crucible placed inside a large earthen one filled with charcoal dust. After heating it intensely for half an hour, he allowed it to cool. The inner crucible was found to be filled with a network of gray, interlacing metallic needles which weighed one-third as much as the original chromium trioxide that had been reduced. Because of its many colored compounds Fourcroy and Haüy suggested the name *chromium* for the new metal (*17, 36*).

Vauquelin taught for a time at the Collège de France and at the Jardin des Plantes, and in 1811, upon the death of his old friend and teacher, M. Fourcroy, he became his successor as professor of chemistry in the School of Medicine. In 1828 the Department of Calvados, in which his native village of St. André d'Hébertot is situated, appointed him as one of its deputies. He discharged the duties of this office with honor, striving always for the best interest of his beloved Republic. Although his early days were spent in poverty and toil, he became a man of broad culture, took pleasure in music and literature, and frequently quoted his favorite authors, Horace and Virgil (*16*).

M. Chevallier, one of his students, recalled an incident that well illustrates Professor Vauquelin's kindness. In 1808 Bonaparte ordered the arrest and deportation of all Spaniards living in Paris. One of the sixty who were seized and taken to the prefecture of police was a young man who had recently come to study under Professor Vauquelin and who had no other protector in Paris. Vauquelin started out before six o'clock next morning, dressed in the uniform worn on formal occasions by members of the Institute, went to the police station, and succeeded in having the boy released. The young Spaniard, who was named Mateo José Buenaventura Orfila, afterward made a great name for himself in chemistry (*16, 35, 66*).

Sir Humphry Davy once gave the following amusing description of Vauquelin's home life:

Vauquelin was in the decline of life when I first saw him in 1813—a man who gave me the idea of the French chemists of another age; belonging rather to the pharmaceutical laboratory than to the philosophical one; yet he lived in the Jardin du Roi. Nothing could be more singular than his manners, his life, and his ménage. Two old maiden ladies, the Mademoiselles de Fourcroy, sisters of the professor of that name, kept his house. I remember the first time that I entered it, I was ushered into a sort of bed-chamber, which likewise served as a drawing-room. One of the ladies was in bed, but employed in preparations for the kitchen; and was actually paring truffles. Vauquelin wished some immediately to be dressed for my breakfast, and I had some difficulty to prevent it . . . (18).

This was, to be sure, an unusual way of receiving a fashionable English gentleman, but perhaps if Sir Humphry had known the pleasing story of Vauquelin's gratitude to the two old ladies who had befriended him in youth, he would not have been so critical.

Vauquelin in France and Klaproth in Germany were the outstanding analytical chemists of their day, and were, in fact, two of the greatest

Mathieu - Joseph - Bonaventure Orfila, 1787–1853. Spanish chemist who studied under Vauquelin in Paris. The founder of modern toxicology. Professor of toxicology, medical chemistry, and forensic chemistry in Paris.

analysts of all time. According to Thomson, Vauquelin was "by far the most industrious of all French chemists" (19). He died in his native district at the Château des Berteaux on November 14, 1829.

Among the other early investigators of crocoite (Siberian red lead) were Count Apollos Apollosovich Musin-Pushkin* (1760–1805), Tobias Lowitz (Tovii Egorovich Lovits) (1757–1804), and M. H. Klaproth (82). Count Musin-Pushkin's analyses were made with portable equipment during one of his mineralogical journeys (82).

This handsome mineral has also been found in Brazil, Hungary, the Philippine Islands, Arizona, and Tasmania. The Academy of Natural Sciences of Philadelphia has some superb specimens of it from Dundas, Tasmania.

* In the literature one often finds this name transliterated as Moussin-Puschkin.

Chromium in the Emerald and the Ruby. When Vauquelin analyzed a Peruvian emerald in 1798 he found that its green color was caused by the presence in it of a small amount of chromium. By boiling some of the coloring matter from the emerald with concentrated nitric acid, evaporating the solution to dryness, and adding caustic potash to the residue, he obtained a yellow solution which when treated with lead nitrate solution "immediately regenerated the red lead of Siberia" (*83*).

The red color of the ruby is also caused by the presence in it of a trace of chromic oxide, which distinguishes this costly gem from common crystalline corundum (alumina). Thus chromic oxide, according to F. H. Pough, "is the most valuable commodity in the world when purchased in the form of a ruby" (*84*). A beautifully illustrated article on synthetic rubies appeared in the *Journal of Chemical Education* for June, 1931 (*85*).

Chromite. In a letter to *Scherer's Journal*, dated St. Petersburg, November 12, 1798, Count Musin-Pushkin wrote: "You already know that Mr. Lowitz and Mr. Klaproth have independently discovered chromium combined with iron in a fossil I sent them. This ore looks like the black uranium ore (pitchblende), but has a more metallic luster" (*87*). In the same year Mining Superintendent von Soymonof had found some of this mineral in the northern part of the Ural Mountains. When Lowitz analyzed it, he concluded that it must be iron chromate (*88*).

Tobias Lowitz (Toviï Egorovich Lovits) was born at Göttingen in 1757. When he was ten years old, his father was called to St. Petersburg as a professor of mathematics and member of the Imperial Academy of Sciences (*92*). After serving as an apprentice in the Royal Apothecary in St. Petersburg, and after further study in chemistry and pharmacy at Göttingen, Tobias Lowitz finally became a member of the Russian Academy of Sciences as successor to M. V. Lomonosov. He carried out many successful researches on the adsorption of dissolved substances by wood charcoal, crystallography, freezing-mixtures, and other branches of analytical, physical, and organic chemistry. In 1789, in the course of some experiments on crystallization, he discovered glacial acetic acid (*86*). While studying chromium he lost his left hand in a laboratory accident. After a long illness he died at St. Petersburg in 1804.

In 1799 Citizen Tassaert, a Prussian chemist who had been working for several years at the School of Mines of Paris, discovered chromium in an iron mineral found at the Carrade Villa near Gassin in the department of du Var. He too regarded the mineral as a chromate of iron (*89*). Since chromium had previously been detected in the "red lead of Siberia" (crocoite), in the emerald, and in the ruby, the chrome-iron mineral analyzed by Tassaert and by Lowitz was the fourth substance found to contain this recently discovered metal.

Fourcroy predicted that this mineral would give chemists the opportunity to make a more thorough study of the properties of chromium and perhaps to discover compounds of it which, because of their rich and varied colors, would be useful in painting and in the manufacture of glass and enamel (90). He also encouraged study of the chromium alloys. The chrome-iron ore is now known as chromite. It is not a chromate, but has the spinel composition, $Fe(CrO_2)_2$.

Chromium in Meteorites. In 1817 André Laugier detected chromium and sulfur in the great Pallas meteorite from Siberia. Earlier analysts had reported only iron and nickel (91).

Chromium has taken its place among the world's useful metals, and stainless steel, chromium-plated hardware and automobile trimmings, and artistic chromium jewelry now bear witness to the importance of Vauquelin's discovery.

LITERATURE CITED

(1)   VALLERY-RADOT, R., "Life of Pasteur," English translation by Mrs. Devonshire, Doubleday, Page and Co., New York, 1926, p. 152.

(2)   JAGNAUX, R., "Histoire de la Chimie," Vol. 2, Baudry et Cie., Paris, 1891, pp. 344–5.

(3)   NORDENSKIÖLD, A. E., "C. W. Scheele's nachgelassene Briefe und Aufzeichnungen," Norstedt & Söner, Stockholm, 1892, pp. 362–3.

(4)   Ibid., p. 370.

(5)   DEL RÍO, A. M., "Analysis of an alloy of gold and rhodium from the parting house at Mexico," Annals of Phil., 10, 256 (Oct., 1825).

(6)   POGGENDORFF, J. C., "Biographisch-Literarisches Handwörterbuch zur Geschichte der exakten Wissenschaften," 6 vols., Verlag Chemie, Leipzig and Berlin, 1863–1937. Articles on de Elhuyar and Peligot.

(7)   NORDENSKIÖLD, A. E., "Scheele's nachgelassene Briefe und Aufzeichnungen," ref. (3), pp. 373–4.

(8)   Ibid., pp. 332, 399–400.

(9)   Ibid., p. 389. Letter of Mar. 13, 1780.

(10) Ibid., p. 381.

(11) THOMSON, THOMAS, "History of Chemistry," Vol. 2, Colburn and Bentley, London, 1931, pp. 192–3; FERGUSON, ELSIE G., "Bergman, Klaproth, Vauquelin, and Wollaston," J. Chem. Educ., 17, 555–62 (Dec., 1940).

(12) FÄRBER, E., "Geschichtliche Entwicklung der Chemie," Springer, Berlin, 1921, p. 65.

(13) BUGGE, G., "Das Buch der grossen Chemiker," Vol. 1, Verlag Chemie, Berlin, 1929, p. 334.

(14) THOMSON, THOMAS, "History of Chemistry," ref. (11), Vol. 2, pp. 197–8.

(15) JAGNAUX, R., "Histoire de la Chimie," ref. (2), Vol. 2, pp. 322–4.

(16) "Biographie Universelle, Ancienne et Moderne," 85 vols., Michaud Frères, Paris, 1813. Article on Vauquelin by Chevallier.

(17) JAGNAUX, R., "Histoire de la Chimie," ref. (2), Vol. 2, pp. 317–8.

(18) DAVY, DR. JOHN, "Memoirs of the Life of Sir Humphry Davy, Bart.," Smith, Elder and Co., London, 1839, p. 166.

(19) THOMSON, THOMAS, "History of Chemistry," ref. (11), Vol. 2, p. 212.

(20) SCHEELE, C. W., "Sämmtliche physische und chemische Werke," translated into German by Hermbstädt, zweite unveränderte Auflage, Vol. 2, Mayer and Müller, Berlin, 1793, pp. 291–302.

(21) BERGMAN, T., "Opuscula Physica et Chemica," Vol. 6, Libraria I. G. Mülleriana, Lipsiae, 1790, pp. 108–9.

(22) GMELIN, L. "Handbuch der theoretischen Chemie," ersten Bandes zweite Abtheilung, dritte Auflage, Varrentrapp, Frankfurt am Main, 1826, p. 789.

(23) SCHEELE, C. W., "Sämmtliche physische und chemische Werke," ref. (20), pp. 185–200.

(24) HJELM, P. J., "Versuche mit Wasserbley, zur Darstellung desselben in metallischer Gestalt," Crell's Ann., 13, 39–45 (1790); "Versuche mit Wasserbley und Wiederherstellung seiner Erde," ibid., 15, 179–85, 248–80, 353–63, 429–48 (1791).

(25) KLAPROTH, M. H. and F. WOLFF, "Dictionnaire de Chimie," Klostermann Fils, Paris, 1811, Article on "Scheelium."

(26) D'ELHUYAR, F. and J. J., "A Chemical Analysis of Wolfram and Examination of a New Metal Which Enters into Its Composition," translated from the Spanish by Ch. Cullen. Preface by Bergman. London, 1785. German translation by Gren (Halle, 1786).

(27) Bergman's Autobiography, translated by H. N. Barham and A. E. Pearson from original manuscript in Upsala Univ. Library, x.2551.

(28) LAGRANGE, COUNT J.-L., "Notice des Travaux de Bertrand Pelletier," Ann. chim. phys., 27, 199–200 (1797); CHARLES PELLETIER and SEDILLOT JEUNE, "Mémoires et observations de chimie de Bertrand Pelletier," Vol. 1, Croullebois, Fuchs, Barrois and Huzard, Paris, 1798 (an VI), pp. 146–224. "Mémoire sur l'analyse de la plombagine et de la molybdène."

(29) KLAPROTH, M. H., "Chemische Untersuchung des Uranits, einer neuentdeckten metallischen Substanz," Crell's Ann., 12, 387–403 (1789).

(30) ARFVEDSON, J. A., "Recherches sur l'Urane," Ann. chim. phys., [2], 29, 148–75 (1825).

(31) PELIGOT, E., "Sur le poids atomique de l'Urane," Compt. rend., 12, 735–7 (1841); "Recherches sur l'Urane," ibid., 13, 417–26 (1841); "Recherches sur l'Uranium," Ann. chim. phys., [3], 5, 5–47 (May, 1842); [3], 12, 549–74 (Dec., 1844).

(32) VAUQUELIN, N.-L., "Mémoire sur une nouvelle substance métallique contenue dans le plomb rouge de Sibérie, et qu'on propose d'appeler Chrôme, à cause de la propriété qu'il a de colorer les combinaisons où il entre," Ann. chim. phys., [1], 25, 21–31, 194–204 (Jan., 1798).

(33) MEYER, R. "M. H. Klaproth, ein deutscher Chemiker des 18. Jahrhunderts," Z. angew. Chem., 34, 1–3 (Jan. 4, 1921).

(34) TISSANDIER, G., "Eugène Peligot," La Nature, [1], 18, 521–2 (April 26, 1890).

(35) DAINS, F. B., "John Griscom and his impressions of foreign chemists in 1818–19," J. Chem. Educ., 8, 1288–310 (July, 1931).

(36) VAUQUELIN, N.-L., "Memoir on a new metallic acid which exists in the red lead of Siberia," Nicholson's J., 2, 145–6 (July, 1798); "Analysis of the red lead of Siberia, with experiments on the new metal it contains," ibid., 2, 387–93 (Dec., 1798).

(37) WEEKS, M. E., "The scientific contributions of the de Elhuyar Brothers," J. Chem. Educ., 11, 413–9 (July, 1934).

(38) DE GÁLVEZ-CAÑERO, A., "Apuntes biográficos de D. Fausto de Elhuyar," Boletín del Instituto Geológico y Minero de España, Vol. 53, Gráficas reunidas, Madrid, 1933, 253 pp.

(39) VON CRELL, L., "Zum Andenken Torbern Bergmanns," Crell's Ann., 7, 74–96 (1787).

(40) DANN, G. E., "Pharmaziegeschichtliches aus den Vorstudien zur Biographie Klaproths," Pharmazeutische Ztg., 72, 549–52 (May 7, 1927).

(41) HJELM, P. J., "Åminnelse-tal öfver Herr Torbern Olof Bergman," J. G. Lange Stockholm, **1786**, pp. 54–5, 86.

(42) HJELM, P. J., "Versuche mit Wasserbley, zur Darstellung desselben in metallischer Gestalt," *Crell's Ann.*, **13**, 39–45, 140–50 (1790).

(43) KOPP, H., "Geschichte der Chemie," Vol. 4, Fr. Vieweg und Sohn, Braunschweig, **1847**, p. 81; P. I. VALDEN, "Science and Life," Part 1, Petrograd, **1918**, pp. 81–3 (In Russian); *Mineralogical Abstracts*, **2**, 483 (1925).

(44) VON KOBELL, FRANZ, "Geschichte der Mineralogie von 1650–1860," J. G. Cotta, Munich, **1864**, pp. 611–2.

(45) "Allgemeine deutsche Biographie," Vol. 18, Duncker and Humblot, Leipzig, **1883**, pp. 140–1; J. C. POGGENDORFF, "Biographisch-Literarisches Handwörterbuch der exacten Wissenschaften," 6 vols., Verlag Chemie, Leipzig and Berlin, **1863–1937**, Vol. 1, columns 409–10. Articles on J. G. Lehmann.

(46) GAUTHIER DE LA PEYRONIE, "Voyages de M. P. S. Pallas en différentes provinces de l'Empire de Russie et dans l'Asie septentrionale," Vol. 2, Maradan, Paris, **1789**, pp. 225–37.

(47) POGGENDORFF, J. C., ref. (45), Vol. 2, column 348.   Article on P. S. Pallas.

(48) SMITH, E. C., "P. S. Pallas, 1741–1811," *Nature*, **148**, 334–5 (Sept. 20, 1941).

(49) GAUTHIER DE LA PEYRONIE, ref. (46), Vol. 1, p. iii.

(50) POTT, J. H., "Chemische Untersuchung des Wasserbleyes," *Crell's Neues chem. Archiv*, **3**, 284–8 (1785); Abh. königl. Akad. Wiss. (Berlin), **1735–42**, p. 29.

(51) QVIST, BENGT, "Untersuchung vom Wasserbleye," *Crell's Neues chem. Archiv*, **8**, 238–49 (1791); Abh. K. Schwed. Akad. (Stockholm), **1754**, p. 192.

(52) NORDENSKIÖLD, A. E., ref. (3), pp. 200–4, 332–6, 399–400.

(53) DOBBIN, L., "Collected Papers of C. W. Scheele," G. Bell and Sons, London, **1931**, pp. 186–94; C. W. Scheele, *K. Vet. Acad. Handl.*, **39**, 247–55 (1778).

(54) "Mynt-Guardien Petter Jacob Hjelms biographie," *ibid.*, **1813**, pp. 280–3.

(55) CLARKE, E. D., "Travels in Various Countries of Europe, Asia, and Africa," Vol. 9, T. Cadell, London, **1824**, pp. 203–5.

(56) DOBBIN, L., ref. (53), pp. 225–9; C. W. SCHEELE, *K. Vet. Acad. Nya Handl.*, **2**, 89–95 (1781).

(57) BERGMAN, T., "Vom Schwersteine," *Crell's Ann.*, **1**, 44–8 (1784).

(58) KOPPEL, I., "Beitrag zur Entdeckungsgeschichte des Wolframs," *Chem.-Ztg.*, **50**, 969–71 (Dec. 25, 1926).

(59) "Vom Hrn. Raspe in Cornwall," *Crell's Ann.*, **3**, 546–9 (1785).

(60) "Letter from J. Hawkins in Braunschweig," *ibid.*, **4**, 340–1 (1785).

(61) VAN DOREN, CARL, "Benjamin Franklin," Viking Press, New York, **1938**, p. 357.

(62) "Biographie Universelle," Vol. 37, L. G. Michaud, Paris, **1824**, pp. 119–20; "Allgemeine Deutsche Biographie," ref. (45), Vol. 23, pp. 2–3.   Biographical sketches of R. E. Raspe.

(63) GREN, F. C., "Principles of Modern Chemistry," Vol. 2, T. Cadell, Jun. and W. Davies, London, **1800**, p. 422.

(64) "Infusibility of tungsten," *Nicholson's J.*, **4**, 191–2 (July, 1800).

(65) WOULFE, PETER, "Experiments on some mineral substances," *Phil. Trans.*, **69**, 26–7 (1779).

(66) PRELAT, C. E. and A. G. VELARDE, "La química en los 'Eléments de Chimie' de Orfila," *Chymia*, **3**, 77–93 (1950); FLETCHER, H. G., JR., "The history of nicotine," *J. Chem. Educ.*, **18**, 303–8 (July, 1941).

(67) *Crell's Chem. Annalen*, **1790** (II), p. 3 and **1791** (I), p. 3.

(68) HOOYKAAS, R., "Torbern Bergman's crystal theory," *Lychnos*, **1952**, pp. 21–54.

(69) CALEY, EARLE R., "Earliest known use of a material containing uranium," *Isis*, **38**, 190–3 (Feb., 1948).

(70) CALEY, E. R., "Klaproth as a pioneer in the chemical investigation of antiquities," *J. Chem. Educ.*, **26**, 242–7 (May, 1949); "Early history and literature of archaeological chemistry," *ibid.*, **28**, 64–6 (Feb., 1951).

(71) SMITH, EDGAR F., "Chemistry in America," D. Appleton and Co., New York and London, **1914**, p. 36.   (Quoting Thomas P. Smith, 1798).

(72) KLAPROTH, M. H., "Untersuchung des . . . Wolframs aus Cornwall," *Crell's Ann.*, **6**, 502–7 (1786).

(73) "Das vermeyntliche neue Metall, das Wassereisen, vom Erfinder, Hrn. Hofapotheker Meyer, selbst berichtigt," *ibid.*, **1**, 195–7 (1784).

(74) "Von dem Wassereisen, als einem mit Phophorsäure verbundenen Eisenkalke; vom Hrn. Assessor Klaproth in Berlin," *ibid.*, **1**, 390–9 (1784).

(75) HEYER, J. C. H., "Versuche mit Wasserbley," *Crell's Ann.*, **8**, 21–44 (1787); **8**, 124–39 (1787).

(76) KLAPROTH, M. H., "Analytical Essays Towards Promoting the Chemical Knowledge of Mineral Substances," T. Cadell, Jr., and W. Davies, London, **1801**, pp. 532–40.

(77) KLAPROTH, M. H., Ref. (76), pp. 476–95; "Chemische Untersuchung des Uranits, einer neuentdeckten metallischen Substanz," *Crell's Ann.*, **12**, 387–403 (1789). Read Sept. 24, 1789.

(78) "Gmelin's Handbuch der anorganischen Chemie," 8th ed., Vol. 55, Verlag Chemie, Berlin, **1936**, pp. 1–12. History and occurrence of uranium.

(79) PEREIRA-FORJAZ, A., "Spectrochimie des eaux minérales portugaises. L'eau de Cambres," *Compt. rend.* **189**, 703–4 (Oct. 28, 1929).

(80) HERCULANO DE CARVALHO, "Présence de l'uranium dans les eaux minérales. Rapport de cet élément avec le radium," *Compt. rend.*, **191**, 95–7 (July 16, 1930).

(81) VAUQUELIN, N.-L., *J. des Mines*, No. 34, p. 737.

(82) MOUSSIN-PUSCHKIN, COUNT APOLLO, "Sur la mine de plomb rouge de Sibérie," *Ann. chim. phys.*, (1), **32**, 67–79 (1799). (30 Vendémiaire, an VIII⁸.)

(83) VAUQUELIN, N.-L., "Analyse de l'émeraude de Pérou," *Ann. chim. phys.*, **26**, 261–2 (1798).

(84) POUGH, FREDERICK H., "Gem for May," *Natural History*, **47**, 275 (May, 1941); "Gem for July," *ibid.*, **48**, 23 (July, 1941).

(85) WADE, F. B., "Man-made gems," *J. Chem. Educ.*, **8**, 1015–26 (June, 1931).

(86) DIERGART, P., "Beiträge aus der Geschichte der Chemie dem Gedächtnis von G. W. A. Kahlbaum," Franz Deuticke, Leipzig and Vienna, **1909**, pp. 533–44. Article by Paul Walden, "Tobias Lowitz, ein vergessener Physico-Chemiker."

(87) MOUSSIN-PUSCHKIN, GRAF APOLLO, "Correspondenz," *Scherer's Allg. J. der Chemie*, **2**, 210 (1798).

(88) MEDER, P., "Beschreibung einiger neuen russischen Mineralien," *Crell's Ann.*, **29**, 497–8 (1798).

(89) TASSAERT, "Chemische Zerlegung des chromiumsauren Eisens (chromiate de fer) von der Bastide de la Carrade," *Crell's Ann.*, **33**, 355–61 (1800); *Ann. chim. phys.*, **31**, 220–4 (1799). (30 Thermidor, an VIII⁸.)

(90) FOURCROY, A.-F. DE, "Sur la découverte du chromate de fer," *Ann. chim. phys.*, (1), **32**, 223–4 (1799). (30 Brumaire, an VII⁸.)

(91) LAUGIER, A., "Expériences propres à confirmer l'opinion émise par des naturalistes sur l'identité d'origine entre le fer de Sibérie et les aérolithes," *Ann. chim. phys.*, (2), **4**, 363–6 (1817).

(92) LEICESTER, HENRY M., "Tobias Lowitz. Discoverer of basic laboratory methods," *J. Chem. Educ.*, **22**, 149–51 (Mar., 1945).

(93) SYKES, W. P., "Metallurgy of tungsten and molybdenum," *Ibid.*, **17**, 190–2 (Apr., 1940).

(94) BERGMAN, T., "Mineralogiska Anmärkningar," *Vetenskapsacademiens Nya Handlingar*, **5**, 109–22 (Apr., May, June, 1784).

(95) ADAMS, F. D., "The Birth and Development of the Geological Sciences," Dover Publications, Inc., New York, **1954**, pp. 187–8.

(96) MENSHUTKIN, B. N., "Russia's Lomonosov," Princeton University Press, Princeton, N. J., **1952**, p. 156.

Fausto de Elhuyar, 1755–1833, as he appeared while studying in Vienna before going to Mexico. At this period he was already famous because of the research at Vergara in which he and his brother liberated the element now known as tungsten (wolfram). This portrait was bequeathed to the Mining Council by Don Fausto's daughter, Doña Luisa de Elhuyar de Martinez de Aragón.

10

Contributions of the de Elhuyar brothers

Although Don Fausto de Elhuyar and his brother, Don Juan José, achieved undying fame by their isolation of the element now known as tungsten (wolfram), only meager accounts of their contributions have been recorded in the English language, and even in Spanish and Spanish-American journals it is difficult to find more than brief mention of Don Juan José. This Castilian literature, however, contains a wealth of information about the scientific activities of Don Fausto, and the observance of the centenary of his death brought forth new biographical material.

*I*n the latter part of the eighteenth century the Count of Peña-florida, with the approval of King Charles III, founded in the Basque provinces a patriotic organization known as "The Basque Society of Friends of their Country" (*Sociedad Vascongada de Amigos del País*). In the early days of its existence, this learned society, consisting of studious men of the nobility and clergy, used to meet every evening in the week. On Mondays they discussed mathematics; on Tuesdays they made experiments with Abbé Nollet's electrical machine or with their air pump from London or discussed the physical theories of the day, such as Franklin's views on electricity; on Wednesdays they read history and translations by members of the society; on Thursdays they listened to music; on Fridays they studied geography; on Saturdays they conversed on current events; and on Sundays they again listened to music. According to a contemporary writer, Don Juan Sempere y Guarinos (*1*):

The two most glorious monuments of the *Sociedad Vascongada* are the Seminary of Vergara and the House of Mercy of Vitoria. . . . This Seminary was the first in Spain in which virtue was united with the teaching of the sciences most useful to the state. Vergara was the first town in which chairs of chemistry and metallurgy were founded.

Soon after this Seminary was founded in 1777, two brilliant and promising youths of Basque and French lineage, Don Juan José de Elhuyar y de Zubice (1754–1796) and his younger brother, Don Fausto, were commissioned to study abroad. Don Juan José was sent by the King to master the science of metallurgy and Don Fausto was chosen by the Count of Peñaflorida to study mineralogy at the expense of the Society of Friends of their Country and become the first professor of that subject at the new Seminary (2).

Don Fausto was born at Logroño in northern Spain on October 11, 1755, and was educated in Paris under the best masters. While the gifted

Courtesy Dr. Moles and Mr. de Gálvez-Cañero

The Seminary of Vergara. It was here that Don Juan José and Don Fausto de Elhuyar carried out their remarkable analysis of wolframite, which resulted in the isolation of a new metal, "wolfram," or tungsten. Among the professors at this Seminary were L.-J. Proust, François Chabaneau, and Fausto de Elhuyar.*

young Louis-Joseph Proust (3), who later defended the law of definite proportions so valiantly against C.-L. Berthollet, taught chemistry at Vergara, Don Fausto and Don Juan José went to Freiberg, where in 1778 they enrolled as students in the Royal School of Mines, studied subterranean geometry, mining, metallurgy, and machine construction, and became ardent disciples of the great mineralogist Abraham Gottlob Werner. Don Juan José profited from December 1781 to July 1782 by a brief course of study at Upsala under the celebrated Torbern Bergman.

* Even in Spanish literature, the spelling of this name varies. See also the footnotes which Professor A. Sanromá Nicolau added to his excellent translation of "Discovery of the Elements" (24).

From F. G. Corning, "A Student Reverie"

Abraham Gottlob Werner, 1750–1817. Professor of geognosy at the Freiberg School of Mines. Because his followers believed in the aqueous origin of rocks, they were called Neptunists. Among his distinguished students were the de Elhuyar brothers, Baron Alexander von Humboldt, and A. M. del Río, the discoverer of vanadium (erythronium).

When Don Fausto took up his teaching duties at Vergara just after the Christmas vacation in 1781,* he was already famous because of his achievements in northern Europe. He soon published papers on the manufacture of tin plate, the mines of Somorrostro, the ironworks of Biscaya, and the working of copper mines.

Soon after devoting themselves to laboratory research in Vergara, the de Elhuyar brothers analyzed a specimen of wolframite from a tin mine in Zinnwald and separated from it an insoluble yellow powder

* The author wishes to correct a statement in Reference 8. Elhuyar taught at Vergara *before* going to Mexico, not after his return.

which they called wolframic acid and which they later showed to be identical with tungstic acid.   Since these Spanish chemists were the first to reduce wolframic acid, Dr. E. Moles of the University of Madrid and Dr. Fages y Virgili pointed out that the metal ought to be called by the name *wolframium* (*wolfram*) which the de Elhuyar brothers gave it.   Although this name (4) has been changed in some languages to forms derived from *tungstein,* the accepted international symbol, W, still bears witness that the metal was first obtained from wolframite, not from *tungstein* (scheelite).

Although the isolation of this metal has sometimes been erroneously credited to Don Fausto alone, the original paper published in 1783 in the *Extractos de las Juntas Generales* of the Royal Basque Society under the title "Chemical Analysis of Wolfram and Examination of a new Metal which Enters into its Composition" bore the names of both brothers. Because of the great importance of this memoir it was soon translated into French, English, and German (5).

Dr. Fages and Dr. Moles both pointed out that, in isolating the new metal, the de Elhuyar brothers did much more than merely confirm the hypothesis of Torbern Bergman.   Instead of analyzing tungstic acid intentionally prepared to test this hypothesis, as has so often been stated, they analyzed *wolfram* without any preconceived ideas.   Dr. Fages stated that, after the de Elhuyar brothers had discovered the acid in wolframite:

. . . their great enlightenment and erudition, supporting their great genius, caused them to suppose that the earth encountered, completely new to them and to almost all chemists, might be the same that Scheele had discovered a few months before in another mineral, entirely independently . . . (4, 6).

The de Elhuyar brothers concluded from their analysis that wolframite is composed of wolframic acid combined with iron and manganese. Their method of obtaining the metal by reduction of tungstic (wolframic) acid with charcoal has been described in other papers (4, 6, 7, 8).   As late as 1786 the great analytical chemist Martin Heinrich Klaproth admitted that all his own attempts had failed and that "up to the present only Hr. Elhuyar has succeeded in getting the metal" (9).

Although the de Elhuyar brothers were unsuccessful in their attempts to synthesize wolframite, they foreshadowed modern methods of mineral synthesis (3).   They also devised an ingenious method of determining the specific gravity of solids, and their values for wolframite, tungsten trioxide, and metallic tungsten were surprisingly accurate (2).   Their dissertation on wolframite, published three-quarters of a century before Thomas Graham founded the science of colloid chemistry, contains a clear description of a wolframic (tungstic) acid sol (2).   Spanish writers have commented on the lucid and refined style of this great memoir, which though written in the phraseology of the phlogistonists, exhibits scientific concepts and technic which are astonishingly modern. In the French translation of it, the de Elhuyar brothers modestly admit that no use has yet been found for the new metal, but add that "we must not conclude from this that it is entirely useless" (3).

In the meantime, events in the western hemisphere had caused King Charles to make new plans for the de Elhuyar brothers. As early as 1774 Don Joaquín de Velázquez Cárdenas y León had presented a plan for the establishment of a school of mines at Mexico City which had received the King's approval. However, the realization of the plan had unfortunately been deferred by the death in 1786 of this distinguished Mexican scientist. In order to fulfill his cherished hope of developing the mines of America, King Charles sent Don Juan José to New Granada (Colombia) and Don Fausto to Hungary and Germany to prepare himself for the exacting duties of Director General of Mines of Mexico (2, 6).

The former served for many years as professor of mineralogy, successfully administered technical commissions of great responsibility, and developed the mines of New Granada. Early in the spring of 1786 Don Fausto collaborated with François Chabaneau, professor of chemistry at Vergara, in some remarkable researches on platinum. In a letter written in Vergara on March 17th of that year to Don Juan José, who was then living in Bogotá, Colombia, Don Fausto gave a clear description of their process for making pure platinum malleable. In his bibliography of Spanish science, Menéndez y Pelayo mentions a paper on locating veins of mercury which Don Juan José published in the same year (10).

Don Juan José was a highly esteemed friend of the great Spanish botanist, Don José Celestino Mutis, who once said proudly, "I have been the instrument for the glorious acquiring of the two learned D'Elhuyar [sic] brothers and the rapid introduction of Baron Born's new mining process" (11). In 1932 the Republic of Colombia celebrated the bicentenary of the birth of this great Spanish botanist (12). According to Dr. Fages, many documents preserved with the famous Mutis collection at the Botanical Garden in Madrid show that the services of Don Juan José in New Granada were no less useful to Spain that those of his younger brother in Mexico. Don Juan José de Elhuyar died on September 20, 1796, in the Santa Ana mine at Bogotá, without ever revisiting his native land (6, 11).

Don Juan Fages y Virgili stated long ago that many Spanish writers had wrongly attributed the discovery of tungsten (wolfram) solely to Don Fausto whereas foreign writers gave the credit to both brothers. "As for me," he continued, "I find no fact which would make me assume that Don Fausto was the competent and brilliant one and that Don Juan José played only a secondary part. Perhaps a thorough examination would lead one to think not just the opposite, but that in the work on wolfram Don Juan José played a larger part than did Don Fausto" (25). This too is the opinion expressed by Dr. Stig Rydén of the Ibero-American Institute of Gothenburg, Sweden, in his excellent booklet "Don Juan José de Elhuyar in Sweden (1781–1782) and the discovery of tungsten," which was published in 1954 in honor of the bicentenary of the birth of Don Juan José (26). Although it was difficult to decide from the early literature which of the brothers studied in Sweden, Dr. Arthur P. Whitaker (27) and Dr. Stig Rydén (26, 28) have proved convincingly that Don Juan José (not Don Fausto) studied there under Torbern Bergman in 1781–82. Much of the confusion that previously existed was caused by Don Juan José's habit of signing his name merely as "de Luyarte Espagnol" (de Luyarte Spaniard). The fact that the two brothers did not agree on the spelling of the surname is mentioned on page 255 of this book. By correspondence with a descendant of Don Juan José, Mr. Bernardo J. Caycedo of Bogotá, Dr. Rydén learned that Don Juan José died on September 20, 1796 (not in 1804), and that he preferred the name tungsten which Bergman gave to the new metal rather than wolfram. Mr. Caycedo is writing a biography of his distinguished ancestor.

On May 22, 1783, while the de Elhuyar brothers were still engrossed in their famous experiments on wolframite, the King had issued his "Royal Ordinances for the Direction, Management, and Government of the Important Body of Mining in New Spain and of its Royal General Tribunal (13)." In the spring of 1786 Don Fausto de Elhuyar was sent to Hungary and Germany to study the new method of amalgamation which Counselor Born had established in Schemnitz and Freiberg. Because of Born's useful discovery of a method of extracting noble metals from ores by means of mercury and of separating the silver from the mercury by pressing the latter through leather the Austrian poet Aloy's Blumauer dedicated the following poem* to him:

> *Die Schätze, die bisher nur allzutheuer*
> *Sich die Natur von uns bezahlen liess,*
> *Und die der Mensch ihr nur durch Gift und Feuer*
> *Und durch Gewalt mit lahmer Hand entriss,*
> *Die schenkt sie dir—zum sichern Unterpfand,*
> *Dass du ihr Liebling bist—auf einen Druck der Hand (23).*

* The following is an approximate prose translation:

Treasures which Nature hitherto
Has yielded but too dearly,
And which mankind from her has snatched
Only with risk through poison, fire, and force,
On you she doth bestow—as certain pledge
That you her minion are—
At a pressure of the hand.

On July 18, 1786, the Marquis of Sonora wrote as follows to Don Fausto, who was then in Vienna:

The King has deigned to appoint Your Excellency as Director General of the Royal Assembly of Mines of Mexico with a salary of 4000 pesos, and by his Royal command I give you this order for your satisfaction, and that, well informed on the new method of amalgamation that Mr. Born invented, you may return to those realms at your earliest convenience in order to go to New Spain and fill that office with the intelligence and knowledge which the discharge of your obligation demands and which His Majesty expects from your application, proficiency, and zeal (13).

After a year and a half in Hungary and Germany, Professor Elhuyar spent a few months in Vienna studying the mines of the surrounding region and the metallurgy of many metals and enjoying the brilliant social life of the city. Before returning to Spain he married a German lady of distinguished lineage, Juana Raab de Moncelos, who, in the middle of June, 1788, set sail with him from Cadiz for New Spain (11, 21).

When the frigate *Venus* cast anchor at Vera Cruz on September 4th of that year, the new Director General of Mines disembarked and went immediately to Mexico City. After a solemn and colorful ceremony in the Royal Palace, he entered at once into his new duties.

A few months later, as a first step in the construction of a chemical laboratory, assay furnaces were built in the patio of the college building. According to Director Elhuyar's plan, the students admitted were to range in age from fifteen to twenty years and were to wear a prescribed blue uniform with red collar and cuffs and gold buttons decorated with the signs for gold, silver, and mercury. On Sundays and church holidays they were expected to attend the church functions, both morning and afternoon, and to call on the mining officials "in order to learn the usages of polite society (13)." As an incentive to scholarship, the Director arranged that prizes for good conduct and industry should be awarded with great solemnity. These consisted of ornaments to be worn in the buttonhole (13). The School of Mines was officially opened on New Year's Day, 1792, with an impressive ceremony in the Church of San Nicolás. It was the first scientific institution to be erected on Mexican soil (14).

The new Director of Mines made a thorough experimental study of the "patio," or cold amalgamation, process of separating silver from its ores. Although this empirical process invented by Bartolomé de Medina had been used for more than two centuries, no satisfactory explanation of the chemical reactions involved had yet been given. L.-J. Proust, who was then teaching in the Academy of Artillery at Segovia, reviewed these

Don Andrés Manuel del Río,[*] **1764–1849.** Professor of mineralogy, French, and Spanish at the School of Mines of Mexico. Member of the American Philosophical Society. He discovered the element vanadium (erythronium), but later confused it with chromium. This portrait belongs to the School of Mines of Mexico.

[*] The author wishes to thank Señor Pablo Martínez del Río, head of the Extension Dept. of the National University of Mexico, for his kind assistance in locating this portrait.

remarkable experiments of Elhuyar in volume one of the *Anales del Real Laboratorio de Química* in 1791.   The late Señor J. R. Mourelo once stated that ". . . the glory of both [Bartolomé de Medina and Alvaro Alonso Barba] shines and scintillates more brightly in that of . . . the famous mining engineer, Don Fausto Elhuyar, in whom appears completed . . . the magnificent work of those eminent miners . . ." (*15*).

Courtesy F. B. Dains

Baron Alexander von Humboldt, 1769–1859.   German naturalist and traveler.   Author of "Kosmos" and "Political Essay on New Spain."   Friend of Fausto de Elhuyar and A. M. del Río.

Since a royal order, transmitted through the Viceroy of Mexico, had decreed that Werner's theory of the formation of veins be taught to the students, the brilliant young Don Andrés Manuel del Río was sent to Mexico to introduce the most approved mining methods which he had learned at Freiberg (*13*).   Although del Río had declined the professorship of chemistry, he accepted that of mineralogy, and took with him on the warship *San Pedro Alcántara* a quantity of equipment for the School of Mines.   Soon after his arrival in Mexico City in December, 1794,

Don Fausto de Elhuyar asked him to translate Werner's book on the theory of formation of veins into Spanish (13).

When Señor Elhuyar's nine-year term as Director was about to expire in 1797, his colleagues and students requested that he be reappointed for another nine years, or for life, or for whatever period might meet with Royal favor (13). The report stated that ". . . this Royal Seminary is persuaded that in this kingdom there is no other subject of the merit and circumstances so suited to this institution . . . as Sr. D. Fausto Eluyar [sic]." The officers of the school felt that no one else "would recognize the character and genius of the [Mexican] people." The association of mining engineers from all parts of Mexico also voted unanimously for his reappointment, and the request was granted (13).

In the meantime Don Fausto made many inspection trips to mining centers, supervised the installation of pumps of his own invention, and for several months taught the chemistry course, because of the illness of Don Luis Lindner. Under his leadership the prestige of the school increased, and students came from distant parts of Mexico to obtain a broad cultural foundation as well as a practical knowledge of mining. In April, 1798, the King ordered that some of the most promising youths be selected by examination to become directors and mining engineers in the viceroyships of Peru and Buenos Aires and the provinces of Quito, Guatemala, and Chile, and to establish safe, economical methods for the exploitation of the precious metals (13).

After Baron Alexander von Humboldt had visited Mexico in 1803, he wrote that "no city of the new continent, without excepting those of the United States, presents scientific establishments so large and substantial as the Capital of Mexico. I shall mention . . . the School of Mines, directed by the learned Elhuyar . . ." (16).

The Baron also stated that

. . . a European traveler would be surprised to meet in the interior of the country, near the California boundary, young Mexicans reasoning on the decomposition of water in the operation of amalgamation in the open air. The School of Mines has a chemical laboratory, a geological collection classified according to Werner's system, and a physical laboratory, in which are to be found not only valuable instruments of Ramsden, Adams, Lenoir, and Luis Berthoud, but also models made in the same capital with the greatest precision and of the best wood in the country. The best mineralogical work which Spanish literature possesses, the manual of mineralogy arranged by Señor del Río according to the principles of the Freiberg School, where the author studied, has been printed in Mexico (16).

The Baron also mentioned A.-L. Lavoisier's "Elements of Chemistry," the first Spanish edition of which was published in Mexico. J.-A.-C.

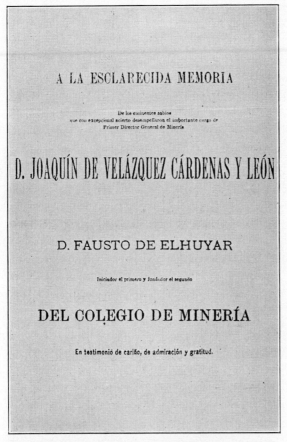

A LA ESCLARECIDA MEMORIA

De los eminentes sabios
que con excepcional acierto desempeñaron el importante cargo de
Primer Director General de Minería

D. JOAQUÍN DE VELÁZQUEZ CÁRDENAS Y LEÓN

D. FAUSTO DE ELHUYAR

Iniciador el primero y fundador el segundo

DEL COLEGIO DE MINERÍA

En testimonió de cariño, de admiración y gratitud.

Dedication of the History of the College of Mines of Mexico (Ref. *13*). *Translation:* "To the illustrious memory of the eminent scientists who filled with exceptional ability the important office of First Director General of Mining, D. Joaquín de Velázquez Cárdenas y León and D. Fausto de Elhuyar, the former the initiator and the latter the founder of the College of Mines. In testimony of affection, admiration, and gratitude."

Chaptal's textbook of chemistry was also used at the Mining Academy, but in 1820 it was superseded by that of M.-J.-B. Orfila (*13*).

Professor Elhuyar often ordered instruments for the School of Mines through von Humboldt, who selected and purchased them without any commission. In return for this courtesy he gave the Baron much valuable information for his "Political Essay on New Spain" (*13, 16*). Von Humboldt later presented to European museums numerous specimens of Mexican minerals which this Spanish scientist had given him.

The School of Mines in Mexico City

Two of de Elhuyar's most famous papers were entitled "Suggestions on Coining in New Spain" and "Memoir on the Influence of Mining on the Agriculture, Industry, Population, and Civilization of New Spain" (*17, 18*). In his "History of Mexico" (*19*), H. H. Bancroft extolled the former treatise as follows:

With regard to the mint and coinage I find the work of Fausto de Elhuyar, entitled Indigaciones sobre la Amonedación en la Nueva España, Madrid, 1818, to be extremely useful. His researches were conducted with great care, and supply a concise and correct history of the mint from its establishment down to the 10th of August, 1814, when he laid before the mining tribunal of Mexico, of which he was director, the results of his labors. In this book, which consists of 142 pages, he gives an account of the different coins struck off and the modifications which they experienced at different periods, also of the new system when the administration was assumed by the government. He moreover considers with attention the causes by which the interests of the mining industry suffered, and suggests remedies.

During the war of independence, the once prosperous mining industry of Mexico passed through such a serious depression that all courses at the School of Mines were suspended, with humane provision, however, for those of its employees who had no other source of income. Don Fausto de Elhuyar relinquished his authority, and thus, after thirty-three years of service, his directorship came to a close on October 22, 1821. The history of the School of Mines (*13*) by the distinguished mining engineer, Santiago Ramírez, contains a wealth of information about Elhuyar's services to Mexico.

After returning to Madrid, Professor Elhuyar was made a member of the General Council of Public Credit (*13*), served on many government commissions, wrote his famous treatise on the influence of mining in New Spain (*17*), drew up the new mining law known as the Royal Decree of July 4, 1825, and was made Director General of Mining* (*20, 22*). He planned the School of Mining Engineering of Madrid and organized and developed the mining industry of his native land, which he served devotedly to the end of his life. One of the reforms which he advocated was the eight-hour day (*2*).

In spite of his many positions of influence and responsibility, Professor Elhuyar lived in modest circumstances, devoting all his energy to intellectual rather than material pursuits. He died at Madrid on January 6, 1833, at the age of seventy-seven years. Although the centenary of Elhuyar's death was observed on *February* 6, 1933, the death certificate which Señor de Gálvez-Cañero discovered in the records of

* Although standard Spanish and German encyclopedias state that Don Fausto de Elhuyar also became Secretary of State, Dr. Fages (*6*) pointed out that this is incorrect.

San Sebastián parish in Madrid states that Don Fausto died on *January 6th* as the result of a fall (*11*).

In 1892 the Mexican government under Porfirio Díaz, the former students of the Mining Academy, and the leading mining companies arranged a mining exposition and a series of public functions throughout

Courtesy Dr. Moles and Mr. de Gálvez-Cañero

Fausto de Elhuyar, Director General of Mines of Spain.
The centenary of his death was observed in 1933 at the School of Mining Engineering of Madrid.

the year to commemorate the centennial anniversary of the founding of the Seminary. All the scientific organizations in the country participated, and the German musical society, the *Orfeón Alemán*, gladly cooperated out of gratitude for the honors which the Seminary had bestowed on Baron von Humboldt. In each arch of the magnificent college building appeared a flag-draped escutcheon bearing an honored name, and foremost among these were Joaquín de Velázquez Cárdenas y León, Fausto de Elhuyar, and Andrés Manuel del Río (14).

On February 6, 1933, the Spanish Society of Physics and Chemistry, the Geological and Mining Institute of Spain, and the Association of Mining Engineers met at the School of Mining Engineering of Madrid to observe the one-hundredth anniversary of the death of Don Fausto de Elhuyar. Eloquent and scholarly addresses on the various phases of his services to science were delivered by Señores Bermejo, Hauser, Gálvez-Cañero, Enrique Moles, Novo, and López Sánchez Avecilla, and three portraits* of him were displayed by Señor de Gálvez-Cañero, who published in 1933 a beautifully illustrated biography based on authentic documents and correspondence. Plans were announced for the publication of some of Don Fausto's papers in a series of Spanish scientific classics, and the Elhuyar Prize of 1000 pesetas was awarded to Don Fernando González Núñez for his revision of the atomic weight of chromium (2).

Acknowledgment

The writer is deeply grateful to Professor E. Moles, Mr. A. de Gálvez-Cañero y Alzola, Dr. F. G. Corning, Señor Pablo Martínez del Río, and Dr. F. B. Dains for the use of the illustrations accompanying this chapter. It is also a pleasure to acknowledge the valuable help obtained from the literature on the history of Spanish chemistry which Dr. Moles, Mr. de Gálvez-Cañero, Dr. Stig Rydén, and Mr. Bernardo J. Caycedo so kindly contributed.

LITERATURE CITED

(1) SEMPERE, J., "Ensayo de una biblioteca española de los mejores escritores del Reynado de Carlos III," Imprenta Real Madrid, 1789, Vol. 5, pp. 151–77.

(2) "El primer centenario de D. Fausto de Elhuyar," Anales soc. españ. fís quím., 31, 115–43 (Mar. 15, 1933).

(3) Ateneo científico, literario, y artístico de Madrid, "La España del Siglo XIX," Librería de D. Antonio San Martín, Madrid, 1886, Vol. 2, pp. 412–52. Chapter on the history of the physical sciences by Mourelo.

(4) MOLES, E., "Wolframio, no tungsteno. Vanadio o eritronio," Anales soc. españ. fís. quím., [3], 26, 234–52 (June, 1928).

(5) ELHUYAR, J. J. and F., "Análisis químico de volfram y examen de un nuevo metal que entra en su composición," Extractos Real Soc. Bascongada, 1783, pp. 46–88; Mémoires Acad. Toulouse, 2, 141–68 (1784); English translation by CHARLES CULLEN, G. Nicol, London, 1785; German translation by F. A. C. GREN, Halle, 1786.

---

* Señor Bermejo, president of the Spanish Society of Physics and Chemistry, also mentioned that there is a statue of Fausto de Elhuyar at the Faculty of Sciences of Saragossa.

(6)   "Discursos leídos ante la Real Academia de Ciencias en la recepcíon pública del Ilmo, Sr. D. Juan Fages y Virgili," Madrid, **1909**, 118 pp. Address on "The chemists of Vergara."

(7)   KOPPEL, I., "Beitrag zur Entdeckungsgeschichte des Wolframs," *Chem.-Ztg.*, **50**, 969–71 (Dec. 25, 1926).

(8)   WEEKS, M. E., "The discovery of the elements. V. Chromium, molybdenum, tungsten, and uranium," *J. Chem. Educ.*, **9**, 459–61 (Mar., 1932); *ibid.*, Mack Printing Co., Easton, Pa., **1933**, pp. 50–2.

(9)   KLAPROTH, M. H., "Untersuchung des angeblichen Tungsteins und des Wolframs aus Cornwall," *Crell's Ann.*, **6**, 507 (1786).

(10)   MENÉNDEZ, M., "La ciencia española," 3rd ed., Vol. 3, A. Perez Dubruli, Madrid, **1888**, pp. 395–6.

(11)   DE GÁLVEZ-CAÑERO, A., "Apuntes biográficos de D. Fausto de Elhuyar y de Zubice," *Boletín del Instituto Geológico y Minero de España*, Vol. 53, Gráficas reunidas, Madrid, **1933**, 253 pp.

(12)   Anuario Acad. Ciencias, Madrid, pp. 180–1 (1932); "Century-old collection yields new plant species," *Sci. News Letter*, **24**, 135 (Aug. 26, 1933).

(13)   RAMÍREZ, S., "Datos para la historia del Colegio de Minería," Government publication for the Sociedad científica Antonio Alzate, Mexico City, **1890**, 494 pp.

(14)   RAMÍREZ, S., "El centenario del Colegio de Minería," *Sociedad científica Antonio Alzate, Memorias y revista*, **6**, 177–242 (1892–93).

(15)   MOURELO, J. R., "Un libro famoso," *Revista acad. ciencias* (Madrid), **29**, 9–52 (Sept., 1932). Review of BARBA, A. A., "El Arte de los Metales," **1640**.

(16)   HUMBOLDT, A., "Ensayo político sobre Nueva España," 3rd ed., Vol. 1, Librería de Lecointe, Paris, **1836**, pp. 232, 236–8; *ibid.*, Vol. 2, p. 85; C. A. BROWNE, "Alexander von Humboldt in some of his relations to chemistry," *J. Chem. Educ.*, **21**, 211–15 (May, 1944).

(17)   ELHUYAR, F., "Indigaciones sobre la amonedación en Nueva España," Imprenta de la calle de la Greda, Madrid, **1818**, 146 pp.; "Memoria sobre el influjo de la minería en la agricultura, industria, población, y civilización de la Nueva España," Imprenta de Amarita, Madrid, **1825**, 154 pp.

(18)   RAMÍREZ, S., "Noticia histórica de la riqueza minera de México," Secretaría de Fomento, Mexico, **1884**, 768 pp.

(19)   "The Works of Hubert Howe Bancroft," Vol. 11, A. L. Bancroft and Co., San Francisco, **1883**, p. 679.

(20)   MOROS, F. A., "Minerales y mineralogistas españoles," *Revista Real acad. ciencias* (Madrid), **21**, 299 (1923–24).

(21)   ARNAIZ Y FREG, ARTURO, "D. Fausto de Elhuyar y de Zubice," *Revista de Historia de América* (México), No. 6, 75–96 (Aug., 1939).

(22)   WHITAKER, A. P., "More about Fausto de Elhuyar," *Revista de Historia de América* (México), No. 10, 125–30 (Dec., 1940).

(23)   "Gedichte von Aloy's Blumauer," part 1, Salomo Lincke, Leipzig, **1801**, p. 53.

(24)   WEEKS, M. E., "Historia de los Elementos Químicos," Manuel Marín, Barcelona, **1949**, pp. 132, 133, 144. Translated by A. Sanromá Nicolau.

(25)   "Discursos leídos ante la Real Academia de Ciencias Exactas, Físicas y Naturales en la recepción pública del Ilmo. Sr. D. Juan Fages y Virgili el día 27 de Junio de 1909," Establecimiento Tipográfico y Editorial Pontelos, Madrid, **1909**, p. 92.

(26)   RYDÉN, STIG, "Don Juan José de Elhuyar en Suecia (1781–1782) y el descubrimiento del tungsteno," Insula, Madrid, **1954**, 69 pp.

(27) WHITAKER, ARTHUR P. "Las misiones mineras de los Elhuyar y la Ilustración," *Revista Chilena de Historia y Geografía, Santiago de Chile,* No. 120, pp. 136–7 (1952); *The Hispanic American Historical Review,* 31, 4 (1951). Cited in ref. (26).

(28) RYDÉN, STIG, "Kungliga Baskiska Sällskapet av Vänner till Hembygden," Reprint from *Med Hammare och Fackla,* XX, 1–74 (1953–54)

Jöns Jacob Berzelius, 1779–1848. Professor of chemistry and medicine at the Stockholm Medical School. He determined the atomic weights of most of the elements then known, discovered selenium and the earth ceria, and isolated silicon, thorium, and zirconium. Among his students may be mentioned Wöhler, Heinrich and Gustav Rose, Mosander, Sefström, and Arfwedson.

"The chymists are a strange class of mortals impelled by an almost insane impulse to seek their pleasure among smoke and vapour, soot and flame, poisons and poverty; yet among all these evils I seem to live so sweetly, that may I die if I would change places with the Persian King." (1)

11

Tellurium and selenium

It has been shown in preceding chapters that a number of elements including zinc, cobalt, nickel, manganese, hydrogen, nitrogen, oxygen, tungsten, molybdenum, and chromium were recognized and isolated during the eighteenth century. The story of tellurium, its discovery by Baron Müller von Reichenstein, and its confirmation by Klaproth remains to be told. Although selenium properly belongs in the early part of the nineteenth century, it is so closely related to tellurium both chemically and historically that it seems best to introduce it at this point. The scientific contributions and correspondence of Klaproth and of Berzelius furnish detailed information about these two great discoveries, and the "Early Recollections of a Chemist" by Friedrich Wöhler present an unforgettable picture of the great Swedish master.

TELLURIUM*

*T*he discoverer of tellurium, Franz Joseph Müller, was born on July 1, 1740, in Nagyszeben (Sibiu, or Hermannstadt) in the Transylvanian Alps (*14*). After studying law and philosophy in Vienna, he attended the School of Mines at Schemnitz (Selmeczbánya, or Štiavnica Baňská), where he became intensely interested in mining, mineralogy, chemistry, and mechanics. At the age of twenty-eight years he became a surveyor in Hungary, and two years later he served so efficiently on a committee which managed the mines and smelters in the Banat that he was appointed surveyor and director of the mines. In 1775 he went to the Tyrol as mine captain and acting superintendent, and under Joseph II he became chief insepector of all the mines, smelters, and saltworks in Transylvania (*2*).

In 1782 Müller extracted from a bluish white ore of gold (called *aurum problematicum, aurum paradoxum,* or *aurum album*) a metal which A. von Rupprecht thought to be antimony. Müller's paper announcing

* See also Chapter 12, pp. 319ff.

303

From Dr. Richard Bright's "Travels through
Lower Hungary," 1818

Schemnitz (Selmeczbanya, or Štiavinca Baňskà). Franz Joseph Müller, the discoverer of tellurium, was educated at the Schemnitz School of Mines.

the discovery was entitled, "An Experiment with the Regulus Thought to Be Metallic Antimony Occurring in the Mariahilf Mine on Mt. Fazebay near Salatna."* Upon careful examination of the regulus, he decided in 1783 that although it bore some resemblance to antimony, it must be a new metal, different from all others. Seeking confirmation of his discovery, he sent a tiny specimen to Torbern Bergman; but, with such a small sample, the latter could do no more than prove that it was not antimony (*3, 11*).

Müller's important discovery seems to have been overlooked for fifteen years, but on January 25, 1798, M. H. Klaproth read a paper on the gold ores of Transylvania before the Academy of Sciences in Berlin. He reminded his hearers of the forgotten element, and suggested for it the name *tellurium*, meaning *earth*, by which it has ever since been known (*3*). It is hard to understand why so many historians of science credit him with the discovery of tellurium. Klaproth, who was never desirous of undeserved honors, stated definitely that the element had been discovered by Müller von Reichenstein in 1782 (*11, 14*).

* "*Versuch mit dem in der Grube Mariahilf in dem Gebirge Fazebay bei Salantna vorkommenden vermeinten gediegenen Spiessglaskönig.*"

Klaproth isolated tellurium from the gold ore by the following method. After digesting the pulverized ore with aqua regia, he filtered off the residue and diluted the filtrate slightly with water. When he made the solution alkaline with caustic potash, a white precipitate appeared, but this dissolved in excess alkali, leaving only a brown, flocculent deposit containing gold and hydrous ferric oxide. Klaproth removed this precipitate by filtration and added hydrochloric acid to the filtrate until it was exactly neutral. A copious precipitate appeared. After washing and drying it he stirred it up with oil and introduced the oil paste into a glass retort, which he gradually heated to redness. When he cooled the apparatus, he found metallic globules of tellurium in the receiver and retort (3, 11).

The discovery of tellurium was by no means the only service that Müller von Reichenstein performed for the glory of his country. Kaiser Joseph appointed him acting governor (*Gubernialrath*) and raised him to the hereditary nobility with the title of Freiherr (Baron) von Reichenstein. For sixteen years he was a courtier in Vienna, but in 1818 he asked permission to retire. Although he was exempted from making reports, he was still asked to attend all the council meetings, in order that the state might continue to receive his valued advice on mining and metallurgy. The cross of the Order of St. Stephen was awarded to him for distinguished services to his country and he was also elected to membership in the Mining Society, the *Gesellschaft naturforschender Freunde* (Society of Scientific Friends) at Berlin, and in the Mineralogical Society at Jena (2). After serving his country for sixty-two years and publishing many contributions to chemistry and mineralogy, Müller von Reichenstein died in Vienna at the venerable age of eighty-five years (4).

According to Paul Diergart, Paul Kitaibel, professor of botany and chemistry at the University of Pest, discovered tellurium independently in 1789 and wrote a paper on it (5, 14, 15). This will be discussed in the next chapter.

Natural Tellurides in the United States. F. A. Genth believed that the name sylvanite usually comprised two distinct minerals, "graphic tellurium," for which he retained the name sylvanite, and the "Weisstellur" and "Gelberz," which he believed to be mechanical mixtures of different species (24). In 1819 both tellurium and tungsten were found in some of the ores from Ephraim Lane's bismuth mine at Huntington, Connecticut (25). The first discovery of a natural telluride in the United States was made in 1848 by Dr. C. T. Jackson. His final analysis of an ore from the Whitehall Mine in Spotsylvania County, near Fredericksburg, Virginia, identified it as tetradymite, bismuth telluride (24, 26). In 1857 W. P. Blake reported the occurrence of tellurium in an ore from Georgetown, California (24, 27).

From "Jac. Berzelius, Selbstbiographische Aufzeichnungen,"
Kahlbaum Monographs, Heft 7

Youthful Portrait of Berzelius? Left an orphan early in his life, he was educated by his stepfather. Berzelius studied at the Linköping Gymnasium and later at the University of Upsala, where he received the degree of Doctor of Medicine. He was a student of Ekeberg, the discoverer of tantalum. Although H. G. Söderbaum used this portrait as the frontispiece to "Jac. Berzelius. Reseanteckningar" (Travel Notes), Arne Holmberg stated that there is some doubt as to its authenticity. See ref. (20).

SELENIUM

The discoverer of selenium was the illustrious Swedish chemist, Jöns Jacob Berzelius, who was born in Wäfversunda, a village in Östergötland, on August 20, 1779. When he was four years old his father died of tuberculosis. Two years later his mother married Anders Ekmarck, pastor of a German congregation at Norrköping, whom Berzelius described long

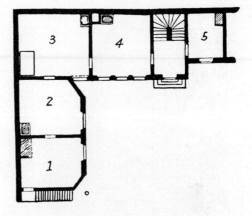

Second-Floor Plan of Ber-
zelius' Laboratory and
Dwelling House. 1—Kit-
chen-Laboratory. 2—Lab-
oratory. 3—Bedroom. 4—
Parlor. 5—Not used by
Berzelius.

after in his autobiography as "a man of exemplary virtue, of more than
ordinary learning, and gifted with a rare disposition for the rearing of
children. He had been married before and had two sons and three
daughters. He was also a good father to his stepchildren (Jöns Jacob and
his sister Flora Christina)" (*21*). When Ekmarck was called to be pastor
at Ekeby and Rinna in the Linköping diocese and imparted the news to
his wife as a glad surprise, the shock to her nervous system, while she
was nursing their very young child, was so great that in a few days "she
was no longer among the living." This tragedy so affected Jöns Jacob,
who was then about eight years old, that throughout his entire life he
dreaded any sort of surprise (*22*).

After receiving his early education first at the school in Linköping
and then under his stepfather and under tutors, Berzelius studied medicine at Upsala, and at the age of twenty-two years he received his medical
degree. Johan Afzelius, a nephew of Torbern Bergman, was then the
professor of chemistry, and A. G. Ekeberg, who discovered tantalum at
about the time of Berzelius' graduation, was an assistant.

In the same year Berzelius was appointed adjunct in medicine and
pharmacy without salary at the celebrated surgical school of Stockholm,
which he served with honor and distinction for the rest of his life. During
part of the time he also lectured at the Military College and at the Medico-
Surgical Institute at Stockholm. Berzelius, unlike other chemistry professors of his time, enlivened his lectures with many striking demonstra-
tions. His fame as a teacher soon spread throughout Europe, with the
result that brilliant ambitious students of chemistry made Stockholm their
Mecca. Eilhard Mitscherlich, Friedrich Wöhler, C. G. Gmelin, C. G.
Mosander, L. F. Svanberg, N. G. Sefström, and the Rose brothers, Heinrich
and Gustav, all received their inspiration from the great Swedish master.
(*23*).

Gustav   Magnus,   1802–1870. German chemist and physicist. One of Berzelius' distinguished students. He was one of the first chemists to investigate tellurium. He contributed to mineralogical chemical analysis, physiological and agricultural chemistry, and chemical technology, and devised a simple process for recovering selenium from the slime in the lead chambers of sulfuric acid plants. He also carried out important researches in mechanics, hydrodynamics, heat, optics, electricity, and magnetism.

A pencil sketch by Magnus's brother, Eduard. From Hofmann's "Zur Erinnerung an vorangegangene Freunde"

A vivid picture of Berzelius and an understanding of his sympathetic attitude toward his students may be obtained by reading the "Early Recollections of a Chemist," by Friedrich Wöhler:

With a throbbing heart [says Wöhler] I stood before Berzelius's door and rang the bell. A well-dressed, dignified gentleman with florid and healthy complexion let me in. It was Berzelius himself. He welcomed me very cordially, informed me that he had been expecting me for some time, and wished me to tell him of my journey—all this in the German language, with which he was as familiar as with French and English. This first day he took me to the Caroline Institute, where he gave his lectures to medical students, but which were also attended by officers of the army and several of his friends, and which I regularly visited afterwards to accustom my ear to the language. This afforded me opportunity to admire his calm and clear delivery and his skill in performing experiments. In this institute was also the laboratory for medical students, which was presided over by Mosander (6).

Berzelius determined the atomic weights of nearly all the elements then known, and was the first chemist to determine them accurately. (19). He referred his atomic weights to oxygen, which, however, he allowed to equal 100, instead of 16 as in our present system. In his little laboratory that looked like a kitchen and in which the sandbath on the stove was never allowed to cool, Berzelius discovered the important elements: selenium, silicon, thorium, cerium, and zirconium (18).

About a hundred miles northwest of Stockholm there lies among barren hills the famous old mining-town of Falun (or Fahlun). The average tourist might not have been greatly interested in the smoky old town with its grimy, little wooden houses, its sickly vegetation, and its odor of sulfuric acid fumes, but the chemist would recall its important rôle in the early history of selenium. Berzelius and Assessor Gahn owned shares in a sulfuric acid plant at Gripsholm that used as raw material pyrite from the mine at Falun.

In the summer of 1817 Berzelius spent several weeks at Gripsholm with J. G. Gahn and Hans Peter Eggertz, working out technical details in the manufacture of sulfuric and nitric acids, vinegar, mustard, soft soap, and pigments. On September 23 he wrote to Trolle-Wachtmeister, "We found tellurium at Gripsholm. Guess where? In the sulfuric acid; but the quantity is very small." On the same day (7) he wrote as follows to Dr. Marcet: "In a sulfuric acid factory here, in which Gahn and I bought shares, we have recently found tellurium in the form of sulfur mixed with sulfuric acid. In plants of this kind, part of the burning sulfur vaporizes without being oxidized, and precipitates in the acid. It is in this deposit at the bottom of the lead chamber that we have found the tellurium. The sulfur we use is produced from pyrite from the Fahlun Mine, where tellurium, however, has never been found. In Fahlun the odor of burning tellurium blended with that of sulfur dioxide has sometimes been detected, although Gahn never succeeded in pointing out any trace of a tellurium-bearing fossil in the Fahlun Mine" (28).

On February 6th of the following year Berzelius wrote again to Dr. Marcet, telling him that they had been mistaken about the tellurium (8):

I have just examined it more carefully here at Stockholm [wrote Berzelius] and have found that what Mr. Gahn and I took for tellurium is a new substance, endowed with interesting properties. This substance has the properties of a metal, combined with that of sulfur to such a degree that one would say it is a new kind of sulfur. Here are some of its properties. . . . If one sublimes it in a large vessel, it is deposited in the form of flowers of a cinnabar red, which are nevertheless not oxidized. During its cooling it keeps for some time a certain degree of fluidity, such that one can shape it between the fingers and draw it into threads. . . . When one heats this new substance with a flame, it burns with an azure blue flame, and gives a very strong odor of radishes; it was this odor that made us think it was tellurium.

The similarity to tellurium has given me occasion to name the new substance selenium. . . . In the hope of pleasing you and Mr. Wollaston, I am enclosing a little thread of selenium, which will surely be broken before arriving, but some of it will always remain. The paper in which it is wrapped has been colored by a sublimation of selenium which took place when, in my absence, the fire was stirred up too much in order to evaporate a solution of ammonium selenate (8).

The following long quotation from Berzelius not only gives the details of this remarkable discovery, but also serves as a splendid example of his vividly clear literary style:

They use at Falun [he said] for the manufacture of sulfur, pyrites occurring at various places in the copper mine. The pyrites are often mixed with galena, blende, and several foreign substances. The pyrites are placed on a layer of dry wood, in long, horizontal furnaces, the upper part of which is covered with earth and decomposed pyrites; the fumes pass from these furnaces into horizontal tuyeres, the fore part of which is of brick and the rest of wood. The wood is lighted below, and the heat causes the excess sulfur to distil from the lower layer of the pyrite; the gaseous sulfur is carried by the current of warm air, and is finally deposited as flowers in the tuyeres. . . .

When this distilled sulfur is used for manufacturing sulfuric acid by burning it, a red, pulverulent mass is deposited at the bottom of the lead chamber. This fact was observed long ago by Mr. Bjuggren, who then owned a sulfuric acid plant at Gripsholm. He found that this does not occur when another kind of sulfur is used; and as he had learned from a chemist that the red material must contain arsenic, he no longer used sulfur from Falun.

Since this plant has been purchased by Gahn, Eggertz and myself [continued Berzelius], the Falun sulfur has been burned there continually. The red sediment which forms in the acid liquid always remained at the bottom of the chamber, and consequently increased in thickness to the depth of a millimeter. The operation by which the sulfur is acidified in this plant differs from that usually employed in that the sulfur is not mixed with potassium nitrate. Flat

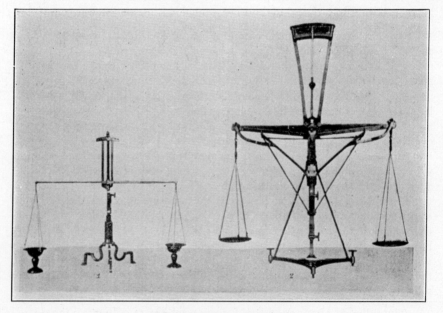

Balances Used by Berzelius

From Guinchard's "Sweden," Vol. 2

The Falun Mine Is the Oldest Copper Mine in Sweden. It was worked in the 13th century, and has been run almost continually ever since. Its present output of copper is small, but iron pyrite is still produced. The pyrite from this mine was the first source of selenium. Gahn, the discoverer of manganese, and Sefström, the discoverer of vanadium, lived in Falun.

glass vessels containing nitric acid are placed on the bottom of the tank and the sulfurous acid gas, in decomposing the nitric acid, produces the nitrous gas necessary for the complete acidification of the sulfur. . . .

Berzelius then explained how he and Assessor Gahn had been misled into thinking that they had found tellurium in the sulfuric acid:

In the glass vessels containing the nitric acid [said he] there is found, after the complete decomposition of the nitric acid, a concentrated sulfuric acid at the bottom of which is deposited a red, or sometimes brown powder. This powder aroused our attention and led us to make a special examination of it. The quantity resulting from the combusion of 250 kilos of sulfur did not exceed 3 grams. The principal mass was sulfur; it could be lighted and burned like this substance; but it left a copious ash which, when heated with a blowpipe, gave a strong odor of decayed radishes or cabbage, analogous to that which Klaproth says is produced when one treats tellurium in the same manner. . . .

The appearance of a substance as rare as tellurium in the Falun sulfur led me to try to isolate it, in order to obtain more exact and certain ideas regarding it. I therefore had the whole mass at the bottom of the lead chamber removed. While still wet it had a reddish color, which, upon desiccation, became almost yellow. It weighed about four pounds. It was treated with aqua regia added in sufficient quantity to render the mass pulpy, and was finally digested at a moderate temperature. It gradually changed color, the red disappeared, and

Alexandre Marcet, 1770–1822. Swiss physician and chemist. Lecturer on chemistry at Guy's Hospital, London. Friend of Berzelius, Wollaston, and Tennant. He carried out a number of researches in physiological chemistry. In collaboration with Berzelius he studied the properties of carbon disulfide.

the mass became greenish yellow. After 48 hours of digestion, water and sulfuric acid were added, and it was filtered. The filtrate had a deep yellow color. The mass remaining on the filter had not visibly diminished in volume; it consisted principally of sulfur mixed with lead sulfate and other impurities.

The final steps in the isolation of the new element were described by Berzelius as follows:

A small quantity of filtrate [said he] was taken to study the method of separating the substance supposed to be present; it was precipitated with ammonium hydroxide. The precipitate, well washed and dried, mixed with potassium and heated at the end of a barometer tube, decomposed with ignition. Placed in water, a part dissolved, and the liquid acquired the orange color of strong beer, very different from the red wine color given by the hydrotelluride of potassium. The liquid did not cover the silvery pellet which always rises to the surface of the hydrotelluride of potassium; but after a few hours, it became turbid and deposited red flakes, the quantity of which was increased by the addition of nitric acid. The precipitate was preserved, and when a part of the filter on which the red precipitate had been collected was lighted at a candle flame, it gave the edges of the flame an azure blue color, meanwhile exhaling a strong odor of putrid cabbage. A portion of very pure tellurium, precipitated in the same manner from a solution of the hydrotelluride of potassium, had a gray color, gave a greenish color to the edge of the flame, and produced no perceptible radish odor. . . .

Berzelius then proved that the odor of impure tellurium is caused by the presence in it of small amounts of the new substance:

Upon examining more carefully the purified tellurium which served for my earlier experiments with the oxide of tellurium and hydrogen telluride gas [said he] I found that it produced no odor, either when one heated it with the blowpipe or upon conversion to the oxide, and that the only way to make it produce such an odor was to heat it in a glass tube closed with the finger, until the vaporized metal escaped through a hole in the softened glass. It then burned in this hole with a blue flame, giving an odor entirely analogous to that of the red substance. . . . These experiments seemed to me to prove that the red substance could not be tellurium, but that tellurium itself contains varying amounts of it according to the care with which it has been purified. . . .

Berzelius continued his experiments and soon realized that he was dealing with a new element:

The brown material, insoluble in water, examined more carefully [said he], was recognized to be the cause of the peculiar odor we mentioned above; and by means of some experiments which we shall report soon, it was found that it was a combustible, elementary substance hitherto unknown, to which I have given the name selenium, derived from Selene (the moon), to recall its analogy with tellurium. According to its chemical properties, this substance belongs between sulfur and tellurium, although it has more properties in common with sulfur than with tellurium (9, 17).

Since Klaproth had named tellurium for the earth, Berzelius thought it appropriate to name the sister element for the earth's satellite. The results of his investigation of selenium and its compounds were published in 1818 in the *Annales de Chimie et de Physique*.

In an attempt to trace selenium to its original mineralogical source in nature, Berzelius investigated the Falun pyrite, but found that it contained only 0.15 per cent of the new element. He then recalled that Jan (Johan) Afzelius had sent Assessor Gahn a specimen of a "Swedish tellurium ore," which gave off a radish-like odor when heated with the blowpipe. Since Berzelius had never been able to detect tellurium in this ore, it now occurred to him that it might be a selenium mineral. Upon request, Afzelius sent him a specimen of it. Berzelius found it to be a double selenide of silver and copper containing about 26 per cent of selenium.

Although Afzelius refused to tell where he had found the mineral, W. Hisinger said that it must have come from a deserted mine at Skrikerum in the North Kalmar district. Berzelius then found specimens of it from this locality in the collections of the Bureau of Mines. Since it had been found at an opportune time, *i. e.*, in time to be mentioned in his original paper on selenium, he named the mineral *eucairite*. In the same collection he also found a still richer selenium mineral, a copper selenide which is now known as berzelianite (28).

In a letter to Hisinger on May 25, 1818, Berzelius wrote, "A thousand

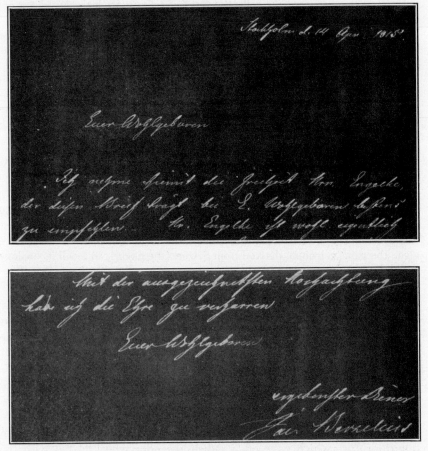

Reproduced by kind permission of the Edgar F. Smith Memorial Collection
in the History of Chemistry, University of Pennsylvania

Berzelius Autograph Letter. (*Translation of Letter, Part of Which is Reproduced Above.*)   Letter of Introduction written by Berzelius for Mr. Engelke to Herr E. L. Schubarth Ph.D., M.D., Professor Extraordinary of Chemistry at the University of Berlin and teacher of chemistry at the Technical Institute in Berlin.

Stockholm, Apr. 14, 1815.

Dear Sir:

I herewith take the liberty to commend to you heartily Mr. Engelke, the bearer of this letter. Mr. Engelke is, to be sure, really neither a scientist nor a technologist; he is employed, however, in our local Commercial College, where, because of exceptional general knowledge and great eagerness to fulfil his duties properly, he will in time take a higher place. The object of his present journey is to study the various industries in foreign countries from the point of view of political economy, and indeed I could recommend him to no other than yourself with greater hope that he would receive sound guidance in these things. I should therefore deem it a great favor if you would have the kindness to receive my friend Engelke so that he may have an opportunity to see and learn the things corresponding to the purpose of his journey.

I beg you to give my best regards to [*name illegible*] and, if there is an opportunity, to introduce Mr. Engelke to him.

With most profound respect, I have the honor to remain, Sir,

Your humble servant,   JAC. BERZELIUS

thanks for the information about the selenium ore.   I went right up to the Bureau of Mines, looked in their Skrickerum (*sic*) collection, and found there a good little specimen of the fossil I called *eucairite* (from eukairos, which came in the nick of time); there was also a calcite penetrated here and there by a black fossil which I found to be a selenide of copper with only a trace of silver. . . .   Svedenstjerna also had in his collection some specimens from Skrickerum, including the calcite penetrated by copper selenide" (*29*).

Berzelius's textbook of chemistry was translated into German by Wöhler and was later translated into several other languages.   Berzelius also published each year, beginning in 1821, a report on progress in physics and chemistry called the "Jahresbericht über die Fortschritte in der Physik und Chemie."

His students and friends adored him.   Although Friedrich Wöhler spent only a few months in Stockholm, his contact with the great master influenced the whole course of his life.   Their frequent exchange of intimate letters lasted many years, to be interrupted at last only by the death of Berzelius.   Berzelius' correspondence with Dr. Alexandre Marcet, Sir Humphry Davy, Dr. W. H. Wollaston, and others was also extensive.

He did not marry until late in life.   On January 29, 1836, he wrote, "Yes, my dear Wöhler, I have now been a benedict for six weeks.   I have learned to know a side of life of which I formerly had a false conception or none at all" (*10*).   The bride was more than thirty years younger than Berzelius, but their married life proved to be most happy.   On the wedding day King Charles Jean of Sweden honored him in a gracious and appropriate manner.   As Berzelius entered his bride's home just before the ceremony, his father-in-law handed him a letter, saying that the King wished to have it read aloud to the guests.   The letter, which was written in French, announced that Berzelius, because of his eminent services to Sweden, was to be given the dignity and title of Baron (*10, 16*).

Selenium in Chile.   In about 1861 Ignaz Domeyko, a Polish naturalist who became professor of mineralogy, geology, and physics at the University of Santiago, Chile, discovered a deposit rich in selenides "in the province of Mendoza, eleven leagues southwest of the capital of this name, at the place called Cacheuta, at the lower part of the Andes."   The minerals included selenides of silver, copper, iron, cobalt, and lead, the percentage of selenium varying between 22.4 and 30.8 per cent (*30*).

Crookesite. In 1866 Baron Nils Adolf Erik Nordenskiöld found among the collections at the Royal Museum in Sweden a rare mineral from Skrikerum, which C. G. Mosander had regarded as a copper selenide. When Baron Nordenskiöld analyzed it, he found it to be a selenide of copper, silver, and thallium. Because it was the first mineral of which the recently discovered element thallium was shown to be an essential constituent, he named it crookesite in honor of Sir William Crookes, the discoverer of thallium (*31*). Although crookesite is very rare, selenium and thallium are often found associated in nature, and both of these elements, so different in chemical properties, were originally discovered in the same source, namely the slime in the lead chambers of sulfuric acid plants using seleniferous and thalliferous pyrite.

Other Sources of Selenium. In 1820 Leopold Gmelin prepared pure selenium from the fuming sulfuric acid of Graslitz [Kretzlitz] in Bohemia, and in the following year Buch and Wöhler showed that this selenium came originally from the particles of iron pyrites dispersed in the alum shale from which the sulfuric acid had been prepared.

New occurrences of selenium were found in rapid succession. J. E. F. Giese of Dorpat, Pleischl of Prague, B. Scholz of Vienna, W. Meissner, J. G. Children, and H. von Meyer all found it in the deposits from various kinds of sulfuric acid. Pleischl detected it in the molybdenite of Schlaggenwald; F. Stromeyer, in the volcanic sal ammoniac from the Lipari Islands; R. Brandes, in the volcanic sal ammoniac of Lanzarote Island (*32*). Stromeyer and J. F. Hausmann, DuMénil, J. B. Trommsdorff, J. K. L. Zincken, and Heinrich Rose detected its presence in several minerals (*33, 34*).

In 1823 Johann Karl Ludwig Zincken (1790–1862) detected selenium in some ores from Zorge and Tilkerode in the eastern part of the Harz, and in 1825 Heinrich Rose analyzed them quantitatively. By heating them in a current of chlorine gas, Rose converted all the metals to chlorides and separated the selenium chloride, which was the only volatile chloride present, from the non-volatile chlorides of the metals (*34*). He found these minerals to be selenides of lead, copper, cobalt, and mercury.

On a visit to the Harz in 1830 Berzelius saw Zincken's supply of $8^1/_2$ kilograms of selenium, cast in ingots, ready to be sold at four louis d'or per ounce. In hoping that perhaps Zincken might like to present some selenium to him as its discoverer, Berzelius was disappointed. Zincken did give him some fine selenium minerals however (*35*). Eilhard Mitscherlich also complained of Zincken's unwillingness to share his selenium with other chemists who wished to investigate its properties (*36*).

In 1828 A. M. del Río published in the *Philosophical Magazine* an analysis of two new minerals containing zinc, mercury, sulfur, and selenium. These specimens had been found by José Manuel Herrera at Culebras, Mexico, near the mining district of El Doctor (37). Del Río also mentioned this discovery in his "Elements of Mineralogy" (38).

In 1826 Carl Kersten of Göttingen detected selenium in the capillary cuprite or so-called copper bloom from Rheinbreitenbach on the Rhine, which Councilor Hausmann had presented to him (39). He also found this element to be present in the earthy ferruginous cuprite (tile ore) from the same locality (39).

In a postscript to Kersten's article in *Schweigger's Journal,* Dr. Fr. W. Schweigger-Seidel mentioned that "the efforts of mineralogists and chemists to locate selenium have nowhere been crowned with such success as in our Fatherland. This is shown, among other things, by the circumstance that busts and pictures from Prague of the great Swedish chemist, cast in selenium, can be offered for sale to his many admirers" (39). According to Dr. Arne Holmberg, who has published a handsome volume devoted to the portraits of Berzelius, these selenium medallions were made by J. B. Batka, a pharmacist of Prague (20).

Selenium Poisoning. Some soils, especially in the North Central and Great Plains regions of the United States, unfortunately contain selenium. Many plants, when grown in such soils, become toxic to domestic animals (40, 41). In 1917 Th. Gassmann showed that plants can take up selenium from the soil (42). According to Annie M. Hurd-Karrer, "animals are far more sensitive to selenium than are plants. Plants absorb relatively large amounts without visible injury, and yet may kill animals. The reverse is true of boron. Plants may take up enough of this element to be fatally injured, yet they are harmless to animals" (41).

Henry G. Knight, Chief of the United States Bureau of Chemistry and Soils, characterized selenium as "the first element discovered in the soil that seems to serve no useful purpose whatsoever, even in extremely small quantities, in the economy of life except for those plants—"selenium-lovers"—which apparently grow and thrive only on seleniferous soils. To domestic plants and especially to domestic animals, it is decidedly a health hazard" (43). O. A. Beath observed in 1932–34 that the two-grooved vetch (*Astragalus bisulcatus*) grown in certain soils had an offensive garlic odor and was more toxic and more highly seleniferous than similar specimens which lacked the odor. He found that twenty-eight species of *Astragalus,* and certain other plants as well, accumulate high concentrations of selenium in their tissues and thus serve as indicators for detecting seleniferous soils" (44).

Uses of Selenium. Selenium is now used instead of manganese for decolorizing glass, and its principal uses are in the glass and ceramics industry. The metallic form of the element is a non-conductor of elec-

318   DISCOVERY OF THE ELEMENTS

tricity in the dark, but has a conductivity proportional to the intensity
of the light falling on it. This peculiar behavior made possible the construction of the very sensitive photoelectric selenium cell. The first
photophone using such a cell for transmitting speech by means of a
beam of light was devised by Alexander Graham Bell in 1880. Although
modern sound films are made with photoelectric cells of the alkali metal
type, the early development of talking pictures, phototelegraphy, and
television owed much to the element that Berzelius discovered in the
slime of his sulfuric acid plant (*12, 13*).

LITERATURE CITED

(*1*)   BECHER, J. J., "Acta Laboratorii Chymica Monacensis, seu Physica Subter-
        ranea," **1669**; H. E. HOWE, "Chemistry in Industry," 3rd ed., Vol. 1, The
        Chemical Foundation, Inc., New York, **1926**, frontispiece.
(*2*)   VON WURZBACH, C., "Biographisches Lexikon des Kaiserthums Oesterreich,"
        60 vols., Hof- und Staatsdruckerei, Vienna, **1891**. Article on Müller,
        Freiherr von Reichenstein, Franz Joseph.
(*3*)   JAGNAUX, R., "Histoire de la Chimie," Vol. 1, Baudry et Cie., Paris, **1891**, pp.
        500–4.
(*4*)   POGGENDORFF, J. C., "Biographisch-Literarisches Handwörterbuch zur Ge-
        schichte der exakten Wissenschaften," 6 vols., Verlag Chemie, Leipzig and
        Berlin, **1863–1937**. Article on Müller von Reichenstein, Franz Joseph.
(*5*)   DIERGART, P., "Tellur und Brom in der Zeit ihrer Entdeckung," *Z. angew.
        Chem.*, **33**, 299–300 (Nov., 1920).
(*6*)   WÖHLER, F., "Early recollections of a chemist," translated into English by
        Laura R. Joy. *Am. Chemist*, **6**, 131–6 (Oct., 1875); "Jugend-Erinnerungen
        eines Chemikers," *Ber.*, **8**, 838–52 (1875).
(*7*)   SÖDERBAUM, H. G., "Jac. Berzelius Bref," (Vol. 1, part 3), Almqvist and Wik-
        sells, Upsala, **1912–1914**, pp. 157–8.
(*8*)   *Ibid.*, Vol. 1, part 3, p. 161.
(*9*)   BERZELIUS, J. J., "Recherches sur un nouveau corps minéral trouvé dans le
        soufre fabriqué à Fahlun," *Ann. chim. phys.*, **9**, 160–6 (1818).
(*10*) WALLACH, O., "Briefwechsel zwischen J. Berzelius und F. Wöhler," Vol. 1,
        Verlag von Wilhelm Engelmann, Leipzig, **1901**, pp. 642–3.
(*11*) KLAPROTH, M. H., "Extrait d'un Mémoire de Klaproth sur un nouveau métal
        nommé Tellurium," *Ann. chim. phys.*, **25**, 273–81, 327–31 (1798); "Abstract
        of a memoir of Klaproth on a new metal denominated tellurium," *Nichol-
        son's J.*, **2**, 372–6 (Nov., 1798).
(*12*) RANKINE, "Telephoning by light," *Nature*, **104**, 604–6 (Feb. 5, 1920).
(*13*) FRIEND, J. N., "A Textbook of Inorganic Chemistry," Vol. 2, part 2, Chas.
        Griffin and Co., London, **1931**, pp. 297–8 and 301–2.
(*14*) VON SZATHMÁRY, L., "Paul Kitaibel, the Hungarian Chemist," *Magyar Gyógys-
        zerèsztud. Társaság Értesitöje*, No. **4**, 1–35 (1931); "Concerning the polemics
        which led to the discovery of tellurium," *ibid.*, No. **1**, 1–11 (1932). In
        Hungarian; summaries in German.
(*15*) WEEKS, M. E., "The discovery of tellurium," *J. Chem. Educ.*, **12**, 403–9 (Sept.,
        1935).
(*16*) SÖDERBAUM, H. G., "Jöns Jacob Berzelius, Autobiographical Notes," Williams
        and Wilkins Co., Baltimore, **1934**, 194 pp. English translation by Olof
        Larsell.
(*17*) BERZELIUS, J. J., "Undersökning af en ny mineralkropp funnen i de orenare
        sorterna af det vid Fahlun tillverkade svaflet," *Afh. i. Fysik, Kemi och
        Mineralogi*, **6**, 42–144 (1818).

(*18*)   WINDERLICH, RUDOLF, "Jöns Jacob Berzelius," *J. Chem. Educ.*, **25**, 500–05 (Sept., 1948).
(*19*)   MacNEVIN, W. M., "Berzelius. Pioneer atomic weight chemist," *J. Chem. Educ.*, **30**, 207–10 (Apr., 1954).
(*20*)   HOLMBERG, ARNE, "Berzelius-porträtt," Royal Acad. of Sciences of Sweden, Stockholm, **1939**, pp. 1–2.
(*21*)   SÖDERBAUM, H. G., "Jac. Berzelius. Själfbiografiska anteckningar," Royal Swedish Acad. of Sciences, Stockholm, **1901**, 246 pp.
(*22*)   SÖDERBAUM, H. G., "Jac. Berzelius. Levnadsteckning," Vol. 1, Royal Swedish Acad. of Sciences, Uppsala, **1929**, p. 18.
(*23*)   RHEINBOLDT, HEINRICH, "A via e obra de Jöns Jacob Berzelius," *Selecta Chimica*, **9** (1950) and **10** (1951), 142 pp.
(*24*)   GENTH, F. A., "Contributions to mineralogy," *Am. J. Sci.*, (2), **45**, 306–20 (May, 1868).
(*25*)   "Discovery of tungsten and tellurium," *ibid.*, (1), **1**, 312, 316, 405 (1819).
(*26*)   JACKSON, C. T., "Discovery of tellurium in Virginia," *Am. J. Sci.*, (2), **6**, 188 (1848); (2), **10**, 78 (1850).
(*27*)   BLAKE, W. P., "Note on the occurrence of telluret of silver in California," *Am. J. Sci.*, (2), **23**, 270–1 (1857).
(*28*)   SÖDERBAUM, H. G., Ref. (22), Vol. 2, pp. 84–5, 92–7.
(*29*)   SÖDERBAUM, H. G., Ref. (7), Vol. 11, p. 16; Vol. 8, pp. 54–5.
(*30*)   "Enciclopedia universal ilustrada Europeo-americana," Vol. 18, part 2, Hijos de J. Espasa, Barcelona, no date given, p. 1821. Biographical sketch of I. Domeyko.
(*31*)   NORDENSKIÖLD, A. E., "Die Selenmineralien von Skrikerum," *J. prakt Chem.*, **102**, 456–8 (1867); *Oefvers. af Akad. Förhandl.*, **1866**, p. 361.
(*32*)   VAUQUELIN, N.-L., "Ueber das Vorkommen des Iodin in dem Mineralreiche. Nachschrift des Dr. Meissner," *Schweigger's J.*, (4), **45**, 26–32 (1825). Iodine and selenium in volcanic sal ammoniac.
(*33*)   STROMEYER, F., "Selenium in the sulphur of the Lipari Isles," *Annals of philos.*, n.s., **10**, 233–4 (Sept., 1825).
(*34*)   ROSE, HEINRICH, "Analysis of the seleniurets of the Eastern Harz," *Annals of philos.*, n.s., **10**, 284–92 (Oct., 1825).
(*35*)   SÖDERBAUM, H. G., Ref. (22), Vol. 3, pp. 18–19.
(*36*)   SÖDERBAUM, H. G., Ref. (7), Vol. 13, p. 195. Letter of E. Mitscherlich tc Berzelius, Nov., 1832.
(*37*)   DEL RÍO, A. M., "Analysis of two new mineral substances, consisting of bi-seleniuret of zinc and sulphuret of mercury, found at Culebras in Mexico,' *Phil. Mag.*, (2), **4**, 113–15 (Aug., 1828).
(*38*)   DEL RÍO, A. M., "Elementos de orictognosia," 2nd ed., John Hurtel, Philadelphia, **1832**, pp. 484–5.
(*39*)   KERSTEN, CARL, "Ueber ein neues Vorkommen des Selens," *Schweigger's J.*, (4), **47**, 294–7 (1826); "Nachschrift des Dr. Fr. W. Schweigger-Seidel," *ibid.*, (4) **47**, 297–309 (1826).
(*40*)   WOODS, L. L., "Selenium, the new enigma," *J. Chem. Educ.*, **17**, 483–4 (Oct., 1940).
(*41*)   HURD-KARRER, ANNIE M., "Selenium Absorption by Plants, and Their Resulting Toxicity to Animals," Ann. Rept. Smithsonian Inst. for **1935**, pp. 289–302.
(*42*)   GASSMANN, TH., "Die quantitative Bestimmung des Selens in Knochen- und Zahngewebe und im Harn," *Hoppe-Seyler's Z. physiol. Chem.*, **98**, 182–9 (1917); "Zum Nachweis des Selens in Menschen-, Tier-, und Pflanzenorganismus," *ibid.*, **108**, 38–41 (1919).
(*43*)   KNIGHT, H. G., "Selenium and its relation to soils, plants, animals, and public health," *Sigma Xi Quarterly*, **25**, 1–9 (Mar., 1937).
(*44*)   TRELEASE, S. F., "Bad earth," *Sci. Monthly*, **54**, 12–28 (Jan., 1942).

Paul Kitaibel, 1757–1817. Hungarian chemist and botanist who anticipated Klaproth in his researches on tellurium. The original discoverer of this element, however, was Müller von Reichenstein.

12

Klaproth-Kitaibel letters on tellurium

Some letters of Klaproth and Kitaibel which have been carefully preserved in the Hungarian National Museum at Budapest for more than a century shed new light on the early history of the element tellurium and reveal the characters of Baron Franz Joseph Müller von Reichenstein, who discovered it in the gold ores of Transylvania, of Paul Kitaibel, who rediscovered it, and of Martin Heinrich Klaproth, who named it and made it known to the scientific world. Since Professor Ladislaus von Szathmáry's excellent articles (1) on this subject are in the Hungarian language and not readily accessible to most chemists, an English translation of the Klaproth-Kitaibel correspondence is presented here. The original letters of both are in German.

*T*he gold mines of Nagyág were discovered by accident. A Roumanian peasant, Juon Armenian (or Armindján), who used to pasture his pig in the Nagyág forest, reported to Baron Ignaz von Born's father that he had seen flames breaking through a crevice, which had led him to believe that there must be a rich deposit of metal there. After years of searching, Born found a black, leafy ore which he at first mistook for pyrite but which proved to be rich in gold. He and his partner, Wildburg, opened the shaft on April 8, 1747, and named it the "Conception of Maria"; the Roumanians, however, called it the "Gypsy Shaft," for a Gypsy who lived nearby used to repair the miners' tools. Although the Born family had no difficulty in extracting the gold, they were unable to determine the composition of the ore, which, because of its rarity, was highly prized by collectors. This ore was found also at Zalatna and Offenbánya, and later in the Börzsöny Mountains (*1*).

Baron Ignaz Edler von Born was born at Karlsburg, Transylvania, on December 26, 1742, received his elementary education at Hermannstadt and Vienna, and was for sixteen months a member of the Jesuit order. After extended travels in several European countries, he returned to his mother country and devoted the rest of his life to natural science,

From Szathmáry, "Magyar Alkémisták"

Ignaz Edler von Born, 1742–1791. Distinguished Transylvanian metallurgist, mineralogist, and mining engineer.
Kitaibel found tellurium in a mineral which von Born had
incorrectly designated as argentiferous molybdenite.

mineralogy, and mining.   On one of his scientific trips through a mine, he suffered an injury from which he never fully recovered.   Because of his kind and generous nature and his outstanding reputation as a scholar, Baron von Born had a large circle of scientific disciples.   He was an active member of the Masonic Order, and founder of its important but short-lived periodical *Physikalische Arbeiten der einträchtigen Freunde in Wien* (Physical Researches of the Harmonious Friends in Vienna), of which only two volumes were ever published.   Baron F. J. Müller von Reichenstein's first papers on tellurium were published in this rare periodical (*13*).   Baron von Born's greatest contribution to mining was

Professor Ladislaus von Szathmáry. Hungarian historian of chemistry and editor.   Author of many articles and books on the history of alchemy, iatrochemistry, pure and applied chemistry, and pharmacy.   In Hungarian his name is written: Szathmáry László.

his improved hot amalgamation process of extracting precious metals from ores.

One of Baron von Born's intimate friends was the famous world traveler Georg Forster.   An entry in Forster's diary for July 31, 1784, depicts Born's social circle as "a society of seventeen lively, vivacious, friendly people bound together by love and friendship, whose custom it is to scatter the seeds of enlightenment, to resist prejudices, and, above all, to speak and think candidly.   Since it was Ignatius Day, the name day of our dear Born was being celebrated. . . . ' The love which everyone here has for him is indescribable.   He is a father among truly loving and beloved children" (*14*).

In the latter part of the eighteenth century, a skillful Hungarian chemist, Colonel Joseph Ramacsaházy, examined the gold ores of the Börzsöny Mountains and was hampered in his analyses by the presence of a troublesome unknown substance. In describing this ore he used the alchemistic term "unripe gold," and on January 30, 1781, he made a contract with another chemist, Matthew Böhm, to "ripen" it. Böhm deceived him, however, and was deported from Hungary. (This information was generously contributed by Professor von Szathmáry, who obtained it from the Record Office in Budapest.)

Courtesy Prof. L. von Szathmáry

Tellurium Medallion. A very rare tellurium medallion bearing on one side the inscription "Tellurium from Nagyág, 1896" and on the other the words "Royal Hungarian Smelter at Selmeczbánya [Schemnitz]." The diameter is 43 mm., the thickness 5.5 mm. One of these medallions is owned by the Hungarian National Museum, another by the University of Sopron [Ödenburg].

At the Maria Loretto shaft near Zalatna in the Facebaj Mountains (lower Fejér County), another white, leafy gold ore known as *Spiessglaskönig* or *argent molybdique* presented similar difficulties. When Professor Anton von Rupprecht of Selmeczbánya (Schemnitz) roasted the mineral gently on charcoal, he found that the metallic residue, when treated with mercury, gave no trace of vermilion (red mercuric sulfide). Since the mineral had a metallic luster, gave no test for sulfur, and behaved in many respects like antimony, von Rupprecht concluded that it must be native antimony.

This view, however, was opposed by a distinguished contemporary. Baron Franz Joseph Müller von Reichenstein was born at Nagyszeben (Sibiu, or Hermannstadt) in the Transylvanian Alps on July 1, 1740.* After receiving his elementary education in his native city, he went to Vienna to study philosophy and law. Later he became so deeply interested in mining, metallurgy, and chemistry that in 1763 he entered the famous School of Mines of Selmeczbánya, or Schemnitz (which is now known as Štiavnica Banská, Czechoslovakia). Here he studied under the capable leadership of N. J. Jacquin (1).

Upon returning to Transylvania, he served on a mining commission to reorganize the neglected mines of his native country, and later became director of mines in the Banat. When he succeeded in putting the mines on a paying basis, Maria Theresia entrusted him with similar

Selenium Medallion. A selenium medallion bearing a portrait of Berzelius. The diameter is about 45 mm. This medallion was cast at the Selmeczbánya smelter and is now in possession of the University of Sopron. It is extremely rare and has unfortunately been broken.

Courtesy Prof. L. von Szathmáry

responsibilities in the Tyrol. In 1775, although successfully established as a mining official in the little Tyrolian town of Schwatz, he preferred to return to his own country. King Joseph II gratified this desire by sending him to Transylvania on special commissions, and in 1778 appointed him as provincial commissioner.

During his travels Müller amassed a splendid mineral collection, which he arranged according to Born's system. When he set to work in his poorly equipped laboratory at Nagyszeben to examine the ore which von Rupprecht believed to be native antimony, he made slow progress. On September 21, 1782, however, he published a statement (2) to the effect that the mineral in question was not native antimony, but bismuth

---

* This statement may serve as a correction to page 65 of the first and second editions of "The Discovery of the Elements." Dr. Speter and Professor von Szathmáry kindly informed me that Baron von Reichenstein was born in Nagyszeben, not in Vienna, and that he at first mistook the tellurium not for antimony but for bismuth.

sulfide. When the ore was melted with niter and tartaric acid, it did not yield antimony. It colored the flame blue and formed an amalgam with mercury, whereas antimony would have failed to give these reactions.

In the following year, however, he concluded that the mineral contained neither bismuth sulfide nor antimony, that the gold was an essential constituent of it, and that it contained an unknown metal. In an investigation lasting three years and consisting of more than fifty tests, he determined the specific gravity of the mineral and noted the radish odor of the white smoke which passed off when the new metal was heated, the red color which the metal imparts to sulfuric acid, and the black precipitate which this solution gives when diluted with water (3).

Müller also sent a very small specimen of the new substance to Torbern Bergman, who regularly corresponded with him and whom he considered to be "the greatest chemist of the present century." In the reply dated April 13, 1784, Bergman confirmed Müller's results, mentioned Elhuyar's recent discovery of tungsten, commented on the surprising increase in the number of known metals, and added, "I am waiting impatiently for your parcel so that I may work with larger amounts." Unfortunately, Bergman was never able to work with this larger specimen, for he died in July of the same year. Twelve years later, Müller, desirous of still further verification, sent a specimen to Martin Heinrich Klaproth, the leading analytical chemist of Germany, who analyzed it and completely confirmed the discovery of the new metal (4). In his report before the Academy of Sciences in Berlin on January 25, 1798, Klaproth named the metal *tellurium* and mentioned that the original discoverer of it was Müller von Reichenstein.

When Müller was promoted to the office of aulic councilor he regretfully left Transylvania for Vienna. He was later pensioned with the order of St. Stephen. He died in Vienna on October 12, 1825 (or 1826?). Although Baron von Reichensten's wife, Margaretha von Hochengarten, was German, and although he spent much of his life among German people and received many honors from the Austrians, his descendants still live in his native land of Transylvania.

In 1789 the famous Hungarian scientist Paul Kitaibel discovered tellurium independently. He was born on February 3, 1757, at Nagy-Márton (Mattersdorf), and attended the academy at Raab in order to prepare himself for the University of Buda. After serving under Professor J. Winterl as adjunct in chemistry and botany (5, 6), he received his medical degree in 1785.

Four years later young Dr. Kitaibel found a new element in an ore from Deutsch-Pilsen which Baron von Born had regarded as argentiferous

molybdenite.   At the suggestion of Abbé Estner* and Mine Captain
Haidinger,† he also investigated the *aurum problematicum* and found
that it contained the same new element as that in the molybdic silver.
When he sent an account of his researches to Klaproth for criticism, the
latter gave a most favorable written report, but evidently gave no further
thought to the matter.   Müller von Reichenstein later presented Klaproth
with his supply of *aurum problematicum*, and Klaproth reported the ex-

Courtesy Dr. F. Fiala

**The Former School of Mining and Forestry at Schemnitz,
or Selmeczbánya.**   Schemnitz, or Štiavnica Baňskà, Czechoslovakia, where Müller von Reichenstein, the discoverer of
tellurium, was educated.   When Austria-Hungary was divided in 1918, the collections, the library, the archives, and
most of the portable equipment at the former Schemnitz
School of Mines were taken to the University of Sopron in
Hungary.   Transylvania, with its historic mines of gold and
tellurium, became part of Roumania.

istence of the new metal, tellurium, *giving full credit to the original discoverer, Müller von Reichenstein,* but failed to mention Kitaibel's work
on the "molybdic silver."   Since Kitaibel was unaware of the researches
of Müller von Reichenstein and had been led to the *erroneous* conclusion
that Klaproth had claimed the discovery, he defended his priority over
the latter in the following letter to Johann Georg Lenz, professor of
mineralogy at Jena (7):

* Abbé Franz Joseph Anton Estner (1739–1803).   Mineralogist at Vienna.
† Karl Haidinger (1756–1797).   Austrian mineralogist and mining engineer.   Father
of the famous mineralogist, Wilhelm Karl von Haidinger.

March, 1800.

I received yesterday the diploma which the Mineralogical Society at Jena intended for me and which you were so kind as to send me. I hasten to give you my heartiest thanks and to ask you to express my gratitude to the famous Society for this honor and to assure it that I shall strive to the best of my ability to live up to your mutual aims. At present, to be sure, I am so occupied with the duties of my office, traveling, and botanical work that I scarcely have time to think of other activities, and my field is not so much mineralogy as botany and chemistry; however, since I hope to find much worthy of notice on my trips

Courtesy Dr. F. Fiala

"Belházy." The building at Štiavnica Baňskà, Czechoslovakia, which in the eighteenth century housed the chemical and mineralogical laboratories of the former Schemnitz School of Mines. Müller von Reichenstein, the discoverer of tellurium, and A. M. del Río, the discoverer of vanadium, both attended this school

now about to be taken at public expense, and since the chemical analysis of mineral products not yet sufficiently well known will be no less welcome to the Society than the external characteristics of the same, I yet hope, when time permits, to accomplish some things suited to your aims.

On this occasion I learned that the news has been brought to Jena that I had discovered tellurium before Klaproth and that this famous chemist had appropriated my discovery to himself. The whole matter stands as follows:

About twelve years ago, the professor of natural history, Piller,* who died here, gave me a little piece of ore from Deutsch-Pilsen in the Hont region, saying that it was argentiferous molybdenite and that I might determine the silver content. In some experiments that I made with it, I found, to be sure, that it

* Mathias Piller (1733–1788), professor of natural history at Buda.

did contain silver (8), but it was evident also that the remainder was certainly not molybdenite, but a new metal. After some time, I found the same mineral listed in Born's Catalogue as molybdic silver.

When Abbé Estner came here to appraise the collection of natural history specimens left by Piller, and I learned that this very expert mineralogist was working on a *Mineralogy*, I told him what I had found out experimentally about the so-called molybdic silver and what I believe it to be. At his request, I repeated my previous experiments with the few fragments of this mineral which I still had, compiled [the results], and sent them to him in Vienna. The sagacious mineralogist and Mine Captain Haidinger, who had an opportunity to read my article, wrote me after a time that they believed that the Transylvanian gold ores (*aurum graphicum, aurum problematicum*) contain the same metal which I had found in Born's molybdic silver; I wished to investigate the matter more thoroughly and found indeed that the metal which was combined with the gold in the ore possessed all the properties found for that in the ore from Pilsen, which I immediately reported to Abbé Estner.

Some time after this, Klaproth's analysis of the molybdic silver appeared. To my no slight surprise, I found there the statement that this contains bismuth. Mr. Klaproth then came to Vienna, and Abbé Estner gave him my paper to read, which was returned to me with a very favorable utterance regarding my chemical work. After this, Mr. Klaproth announced his discovery of tellurium. From this it can certainly be surmised with some foundation that this famous chemist was led to this discovery through my work, yet it cannot be proved; and even if the documents which I possess were sufficient for this, yet I would not do it. Mr. Klaproth, with whom I had the honor to become personally acquainted in Berlin a year and a half ago, is my friend, who, it is to be hoped, will himself, when he announces his corrected analysis of the molybdic silver, state to the public that I discovered the aforementioned new metal in this mineral before he did. If he does not do this, Abbé Estner will do it when he comes to this subject in the edition of his *Mineralogy*. Then one may judge from Klaproth's behavior as one will; as long as I shall not have been the cause of it, it will not trouble me. But until then I must ask that no public use of information on this matter, either from my family or from friends, shall be made; the circumstances of my office demand this.

I cherish the hope that some time I may merit your highly desired friendship, and remain, Sir, your most respectful and obedient servant,

K[itaibel].

The following is a translation of the "very favorable utterance" of Klaproth to which Kitaibel referred in the preceding letter:

Vienna, Aug. 1, 1796.

I have read both of the present chemical articles which Abbé Estner kindly communicated to me with so much the greater pleasure because these give praiseworthy evidence that the author of them is a thoroughly practical chemist. The first of these, concerning molybdic silver, is not, to be sure, in entire agreement with my results; but this is easily explained, for my results for these constituents refer only to the individual specimen which I analyzed. . . .

Klaproth.

[The portion of the report here omitted refers to Kitaibel's paper on hydroferrocyanic acid and Prussian blue.]

One day as Klaproth was reading C. M. Wieland's *New German Mercury,* he ran across the following disconcerting statement (9):

The discovery of the new metal tellurium, which has already, in the first volume of the *Zeitschrift für Ungarn,* been claimed by Professor von Schedius[*] for our energetic fellow-countryman *Kitaibel* (adjunct at the Hungarian University at Pest) will also soon be claimed for Mr. Kitaibel in the second volume of the *Annalen der Jenaischen Gesellschaft für die gesammte Mineralogie.* Mr. Klaproth in Berlin, who has hitherto been regarded in Germany as the discoverer, was merely led by some of Kitaibel's articles which he read on a visit to Vienna to the further investigation of the new metal, which he named tellurium. Suum cuique!

As a result of this unjust accusation Klaproth wrote to Kitaibel as follows:

Berlin Sept. 2, 1803.

Highly esteemed Colleague: It gives me special pleasure to address you by this title, for on February 22nd of this year the Society of Scientific Friends of this place elected you as a foreign member. The sending of the diploma has up to the present been delayed merely because Professor Willdenow,[†] who is taking charge of it, wishes to include a few books at the same time. In the meantime, they are ready, as Count von Waldstein[‡] has noted in the preface to Volume 4B of our *New Publications.*

In proportion as this occasion, like all other opportunities for friendly correspondence with foreign friends and members of our Society, has been pleasant and welcome to me, just so deeply do I regret that this my first letter to you also concerns at the same time an unpleasant matter. Only within the last few days have I seen the fourth issue for 1803 of Wieland's *New German Mercury,* in which, to my greatest astonishment, I find myself accused, under the heading:

[*] Ludwig von Schedius (1768–1847). Hungarian writer, editor, cartographer, and humanitarian.
[†] Karl Ludwig Willdenow (1765–1812). German botanist who studied chemistry under Klaproth.
[‡] Franz de Paula Adam Graf von Waldstein (1759–1823). Austrian botanist and philanthropist.

"Further News of Hungary's Most Recent Literature and Culture," of down-right theft; in other words, of having robbed you of the discovery of tellurium!! You, my dear colleague, will understand that I can by no means allow this insult to my honor and staining of my reputation to pass unnoticed.

To be sure, I do remember that a chemical paper was handed to me in Vienna with the request for my opinion of it, which resulted favorably. How-ever, as far as the subject matter of it is concerned, this I have completely for-gotten, and the person who could inform me is Estner, who is now dead. But, on my honor, and by all that an honest man holds sacred, I assure you that that paper did not have the slightest influence on my chemical experiment with tellurium.

Long before my trip to Vienna, I had worked on this investigation, using a specimen which had been sent here by the late Mr. von Fichtel* to Mr. Sieg-fried†; I am also indebted to Mr. Müller von Reichenstein, who was then in Zalathna, for voluntarily sending me his supply of tellurium ores, which enabled me to carry my earlier investigations farther.

I urgently request and expect a prompt and obliging reply in order to learn whether you yourself will be so good as to arrange that a *public denial* of this accusation of plagiarism made against me may be made as soon as possible; which I shall regard as valuable evidence, not so much of your own love of truth, which I by no means question, as of your friendly and fraternal attitude toward me.

With the best regards of all the regular members of our Society, I have the honor to be, Sir,

Your obedient friend and colleague,

(Signed) Klaproth.
Royal Chief Counselor of Medicine and Sanitation

Kitaibel replied as follows:

Sept. 19, 1803.

Highly Esteemed Colleague:

I received your letter [of September 2nd, 1803] only day before yesterday. Pleased though I was at first to see your esteemed name signed to it, yet all the more deeply was I disconcerted over the real occasion for it: partly because I now truly believe that you have been unjustly insulted; partly because your de-mand places me in an embarrassing situation from which I do not know how to extricate myself. In order to enable you yourself to judge of this matter and of what can be done to ease your mind, I must make you better acquainted with all the details, which perhaps you do not yet correctly know.

I discovered tellurium in 1789 in Born's so-called molybdic silver. The following year I mentioned it verbally to Mr. Estner and after some time sent

* Johann Ehrenreich von Fichtel (1732–1795). Hungarian mineralogist.
† Friedrich Wilhelm Siegfried (1734–1809). German mineralogist.

him at his request a written article on the experiments I had made with this metal. He and Mine Captain Haidinger expressed to me the opinion that the metal I had discovered probably lay hidden also in the [nagyagite] "Transylvanian gray gold" (as Born called the ores containing this tellurium), whereby I was led to find this metal also in the aforementioned ores, of which Estner and Haidinger immediately received notice. The announcement of this discovery was delayed by circumstances which need not be mentioned here.

Then you came to Vienna, obtained from Estner my article on the investigation of the so-called silver molybdenite and another one on hydroferrocyanic acid prepared in the free state, for your opinion, and Estner sent me your written verdict with the information that he had also communicated to you my report on the metal which lay hidden in Transylvanian gold ores and had requested you to investigate the matter further. I rejoiced over this all the more because I had good reason to hope that, when you announced your investigation, you would mention my work.

When I came to Vienna in the following year, your discovery of tellurium was just being read, and Estner said that he was greatly surprised that you had made absolutely no mention of my report which had been communicated to you. It was also mentioned in presence of others, wherefrom I suspected no consequences whatever. After a long time I was also questioned verbally about the details of the affair, and a foreigner also sent me a written inquiry. Without knowing how they had learned of the matter, I answered according to my knowledge and belief. I now see, to be sure, that it would have been better if I had suppressed what I knew; but you see, too, that we were both wrong, you, in that you did not mention what you had learned of my discoveries through Mr. Estner; and I, in that I mentioned what I knew.

You will understand that it is now difficult to set matters right. I cannot say that you knew nothing of my experiments; my article dated by Estner, your written statement, and Estner's letter prove the contrary. If you were to say that you had forgotten about it and had already made the discovery earlier, I and many others would not doubt it, but this would not sufficiently vindicate you before all men; although no one would have doubted your discovery if you had previously said that you had made it before your trip to Vienna. If I were to say that the details of the matter were other than what I have just written, and which are already known, I would be contradicting myself and speaking falsely.

Under such circumstances I do not know what you mean by a *public denial* which you demand of me. I can give you a statement that my two papers . . . which Abbé Estner gave you in Vienna for your verdict were not concerned with the tellurium of the Transylvanian gold ore but with Born's molybdic silver and free hydroferrocyanic acid; I can add that I believe that you discovered tellurium without knowing anything about my researches, if that will satisfy you. If you can with justice demand more, I ask you to mention it and you will always find . . . me ready to do everything which your honor demands and mine permits, for I willingly believe you. That you forgot the contents of my paper, that you discovered tellurium without knowing anything about this, and that, although the premises are true and give cause for detrimental consequences, you were unjustly insulted.

I remain, however, with best regards, Sir,

Your devoted and respectful friend,

K[itaibel].

Klaproth replied as follows:

Berlin, Oct. 4, 1803.

Highly esteemed Colleague:

I am greatly indebted to you for your obligingly prompt reply to my last letter. I must confess, however, that its contents by no means fulfilled my expectations as completely as I had hoped. In the meantime I ask you to pardon me if I am wrong [in believing] that there still remains in your mind some doubt as to the truth of my explanation: *that the article which Estner communicated to me in Vienna has not had the slightest influence on my experiments with tellurium.* Only now does your present letter recall to my mind that I have been concerned with the subject of molybdic silver; but, as regards what you said about it, even at this moment I remember not a single syllable, and I all the more regret that you did not publish this work of yours long ago. I boldly and confidently ask all my friends, here and abroad, who know me better, if it is in any way compatible with my character to be a plagiarist and if they cannot attest on the contrary that discoveries which belong to me have reached the public through others, without my being able to claim them. Yes, indeed. Even today I would rather have made a dozen fewer discoveries than to bear for a moment the slightest suspicion that I could seize the literary property of others.

I believe I have already mentioned in my preceding letter that, several years before my trip to Vienna, perhaps in 1785 to 1786, I had already worked with the so-called *auro problematico* which the late Mr. von Fichtel had sent here to my honored friend, Treasurer Siegfried, and that I was guided by the experiments which Mr. Müller von Reichenstein had made and had described in the *Physical Researches,* and whose belief that it contains a new metal I found to be well grounded; to which conclusion the beautiful criterion previously announced by M. v. R., the red color which this metal imparts to sulfuric acid, was also of special value. Several of my friends here and members of my audience at that time can and will testify to this.

Now just what have I done? Nothing, except to carry out a few little experiments in addition to those published by Mr. M. v. R. on the ore which he himself supplied. But I must almost surmise that you have not seen my complete paper on tellurium. Otherwise you could not possibly retain the *error* that I . . . [have claimed] the discovery. Nowhere have I said that; on the contrary, I have expressly and emphatically explained that the credit for the discovery belongs to Mr. Müller von Reichenstein. Can one more definitely observe the *suum cuique?* Now since I have never claimed the discovery, it is now as clear as day that I cannot have robbed anyone of this honor. I shall now leave it to you, esteemed colleague, as to what course you may deem best to give complete satisfaction as soon as possible for my publicly insulted honor which, to this day, suffers blamelessly, without compelling me to appear in my own defense; for I hate scholastic feuds like sin. If this be done to my satisfaction, as I have occasion to hope that it will, it will incomparably increase my esteem and respect for you as a friend and colleague whose zeal and services in one of the most beautiful branches of natural since I gladly recognize and honor.

With highest esteem, I remain, Sir,

Your obedient friend and colleague,

(Signed) Klaproth.

Thoroughly convinced of Klaproth's integrity, Kitaibel promptly published the following explanation (*10*): (Since the circumstances which gave rise to the unjust charge against Klaproth were stated in detail in the preceding letters, they may be omitted here).

Pest, Oct. 18, 1803.

. . . The correct conclusion to be drawn really amounts to this: that I discovered tellurium in a misunderstood and hitherto uncertain ore at a time when the individuality of this metal and its existence in the Transylvanian gold ores had not been publicly confirmed through the excellent researches of Mr. Klaproth, and more than this I did not wish to claim for myself, as can be seen from the *Zeitschrift von und für Ungarn,* volume 1, page 275 ff.   For Mr. Klaproth has himself pointed out in volume 3, page 16 of his *Beyträge* that the credit for the original discovery of tellurium belongs to Mr. Müller von Reichenstein, aulic counselor [Hofrath].

However, further inferences have been made and conclusions drawn from the aforementioned circumstances that Mr. Klaproth had borrowed from me the discovery of tellurium, which I hereby declare on the following grounds to be highly unjust and false: In the first place, Mr. Klaproth's blameless character is a security that he, who had no need for such a despicable means of increasing his great deserts and his most widespread renown, was incapable of any such action; in the second place, his researches on tellurium and tellurium ores are so extensive that they could not have been carried out so completely in the short time in which they appeared after his departure from Vienna; in the third place, there is considerable difference between Mr. Klaproth's researches and my own, not only in the success of a few experiments, but also in the completeness of their execution. I found, for example, that tellurium is precipitated from nitric acid by water and that the concentrated sulfuric acid from this metal becomes at first brown, then red, and finally, after continued heating, becomes colorless again. Mr. Klaproth's investigation, on the contrary, left mine far behind in completeness, hence the two cannot be compared; finally, Mr. Klaproth could certainly not borrow from me a discovery which belongs neither to him nor to me (NB. For [the statement]: "Mr. Klaproth has himself already pointed out in volume 3, page 16 of his *Beyträge* that the credit for the original discovery of tellurium belongs to Mr. Müller von Reichenstein, aulic counselor" has been mentioned here on page 461!), as Abbé Eder° has so correctly observed in the *Zeitschrift von und für Ungarn,* volume 2, page 90.

Paul Kitaibel, Professor.

Professor Kitaibel's love for botany was stimulated by his opportunity to arrange the rich herbarium of Counselor Mygind, a friend of Linné. In 1793, after a scientific tour of Croatia, he returned to Pest to join the staff of the school of pharmacy. After managing the botanical garden for a time, he became a professor of botany and chemistry, giving no lectures, however, but spending most of his time on scientific expeditions. In 1795 and 1796 he studied the chalybeate spring at Bardiov [Bartfeld, or Bártfa] and the flora of the Carpathians, and with Count Franz Adam von Waldstein explored the territory around the Sea of Marmora. On a visit to Berlin he met K. L. Willdenow, who later named a genus of malvaceæ *Kitaibelia* in his honor. He also explored the beautiful shores of Lake Balaton (the Plattensee, famous for its delicious fish), the fertile Banat, and most of Hungary.

Kitaibel published a number of books and articles on the flora and mineral waters of Hungary, and according to Professor L. von Szathmáry (*11*), was the first to prepare solid bleaching powder and use it for bleaching textiles.

Unfortunately, most of Kitaibel's work was never published, but his manuscripts preserved at the Hungarian National Museum in Budapest show that he was an ingenious designer of chemical apparatus, such as a salt-evaporating pan which utilized the heat of the fuel gas on the countercurrent principle; a device for the saturation of mineral water with carbon dioxide; apparatuses for vacuum filtration and for the distillation of water; and an improved lime kiln and brick kiln (*12*).

Kitaibel died at Budapest on December 13, 1817, at the age of sixty-three years; Klaproth's life had come to a close on New Year's Day of the same year. One of their younger contemporaries wrote for the botanical journal *Flora* a memorial article entitled "Some Flowers on the Grave of Paul Kitaibel" (*5*), in which appears the following characterization: "Honest and outspoken, expressing his opinion openly among his friends, and brandishing the lash of the satyrs, he disdained (although sought out because of the kindnes of his disposition, the extent of his knowledge, and the force of his intellect) all vain social formalities. . . ."

Kitaibel's valuable library was purchased by the National Museum of Budapest, which still treasures the letters which have here been cited.

° Joseph Karl Eder (1760–1810). Transylvanian historian and mineralogist.

Although this intimate correspondence refers to a disconcerting and embarrassing situation in their lives, it casts no shadow on the reputation of either Klaproth or Kitaibel. Their names, on the contrary shine all the more brightly today because they refrained from the bitter polemics of the printed page and settled their serious misunderstanding through the exchange of these restrained and courteous letters.

The author is deeply indebted to Dr. Max Speter of Berlin and to Dr. L. von Szathmáry of Budapest for the use of their notes and of the Klaproth-Kitaibel correspondence, for their many gracious and helpful suggestions, and for the reading of the manuscript; and to Dr. František Fiala, Director of the State Museum of Mines of Štiavnica Bañská, for his kindness in sending photographs and information regarding the former School of Mines of Schemnitz. It is also a pleasure to acknowledge the assistance received from the Graduate Research Fund of the University of Kansas for translations from the Hungarian, which were made by Mr. Julius Nagy of Chicago.

LITERATURE CITED

(1) SZATHMÁRY, LÁSZLO, "Paul Kitaibel, the Hungarian chemist," *Magyar Gyógyszerésztud. Társaság Értesítöje*, No. 4, 1–35 (1931); "Concerning the polemics which led to the discovery of tellurium," *ibid.*, No. 1, 1–11 (1932).

(2) MÜLLER, F. J., "Über den vermeintlichen natürlichen Spiessglaskönig," *Physikalische Arbeiten der einträchtigen Freunde in Wien*, 1 (1), 57–9 (1783).

(3) MÜLLER, F. J., "Versuch mit dem in der Grube Mariahilf in dem Gebirge Facebaj bei Zalatna vorkommenden vermeinten gediegenen Spiessglaskönig," *Physikalische Arbeiten der einträchtigen Freunde in Wien*, 1 (1) 63–9 (1783); 1 (2), 49–53 (1784); 1 (3), 34–52 (1785).

(4) VON WALDSTEIN, WALDAUF, "Ueber den eigentlichen Entdecker des Tellurerzes," *Vaterländische Blätter für den österreichischen Kaiserstaat*, 1, 515–16 (Oct. 3, 1818).

(5) SCHULTES, "Einige Blumen auf das Grab Paul Kitaibel's," *Flora*, 14, 149–59 (1831).

(6) VON WURZBACH, C., "Biographisches Lexikon des Kaiserthums Oesterreich," Vol. 11, Kaiserlich-königliche Hof- und Staatsdruckerei, 1864, pp. 337–9. This lexicon also contains biographical sketches of Born, Fichtel, Haidinger, Müller von Reichenstein, Piller, Rupprecht, Schedius, and Waldstein.

(7) DÖBLING, H., "Die Chemie in Jena zur Goethezeit," Gustav Fischer, Jena, 1928, 220 pp.

(8) KLAPROTH, M. H., "Analytical Essays towards Promoting the Chemical Knowledge of Mineral Substances," Cadell and Davies, London, 1801, pp. 218–20. (Klaproth found no silver in this ore.)

(9) "Fortgesetzte Nachrichten über Ungarns neueste Literatur und Kultur," *Der neue deutsche Merkur*, Stück 4, 298–9 (1803).

(10) KITAIBEL, P., "Erklärung," *Gehlen's Allgem. J. der Chemie*, 1, 460–1 (1803).

(11) VON SZATHMÁRY, L., "Paul Kitaibel entdeckt den Chlorkalk," *Chem.-Ztg.*, 55, 645 (Aug. 22, 1931); *ibid.*, 55, 784 (Oct. 10, 1931). "Kitaibel felfedezi a klórmeszet," *Különlenyomat, a Természettudományi Közlöny*, 1930. évi márc. 1-i számából.

(*12*)   SZATHMÁRY, L. VON, "Einige chemisch-physikalische Apparate des ungarischen Chemikers Paul Kitaibel (1757–1817)," *Chem. Apparatur,* **19,** 49–50 (Mar. 10, 1932).

(*13*)   WURZBACH, C. VON, Ref. (*6*), Vol. 2, pp. 71–4.   Article on Ignaz Edler von Born.

(*14*)   ZINCKE, PAUL, and ALBERT LEITZMANN, "Georg Forster's Tagebücher," B. Behr's Verlag, Berlin, **1914,** p. 147.

Charles Hatchett, 1765–1847.
English chemist and manufacturer. Discoverer of niobium.
Most of his researches were in
analytical and mineralogical
chemistry.

It is impossible that he who has once imbibed a taste
for science can ever abandon it (1).

13

Niobium (columbium), tantalum, vanadium

Although the metals niobium, tantalum, and vanadium were recognized very early in the nineteenth century, the difficult task of preparing them in a pure state is an achievement of recent years. In 1801 the English chemist Charles Hatchett discovered a new element "columbium" in a specimen of columbite which had an interesting connection with the history of New England. In the same year A. M. del Río, a professor of mineralogy in Mexico, examined some "brown lead from Zimapán," and announced the discovery of a new metal, erythronium. In the following year Berzelius' professor, A. G. Ekeberg, analyzed some tantalite from Finland and found in it an element very similar to Hatchett's columbium. Although Dr. Wollaston believed that columbium (niobium) and tantalum are identical, Heinrich Rose and Marignac proved that they are two distinct elements. In 1831 Sefström found in some soft iron from Eckersholm a metal, vanadium, which Wöhler proved to be identical with del Río's erythronium.

NIOBIUM

*T*he element columbium (niobium) was discovered in 1801 by the English chemist Charles Hatchett,* who was born in London in 1765. As a young man in his thirties he engaged actively in chemical research, and published in the *Philosophical Transactions* an analysis of lead molybdate from Carinthia and the results of some experiments on shell and bone (2), and in *Nicholson's Journal* an analysis of an earth from New South Wales called "Sydneia, or Terra Australis" (31).

The discovery on which his fame rests was announced before the Royal Society on November 26, 1801, in a paper entitled "Analysis of a Mineral from North America containing a Metal hitherto Unknown" (3). This mineral, now known as columbite, is a black rock found in New England, and the specimen Hatchett analyzed had an interesting history.

Governor John Winthrop the Younger (30, 46, 52) used to take great pleasure in examining minerals, and his manner of collecting them is best described in the quaint words of an early American poet:

* See also Chapter 14, pp. 368–389.

John Winthrop the Younger, 1606–1676. First governor of Connecticut. Alchemist, manufacturing chemist, and physician. His grandson sent the columbite from which Charles Hatchett later isolated the metal columbium.

From Waters' "A Sketch of the Life of John Winthrop the Younger"

Sometimes his wary steps, but wand'ring too,
Would carry him the Chrystal Mountains to,
Where Nature locks her Gems, each costly spark
Mocking the Stars, spher'd in their Cloisters dark.
Sometimes the Hough, anon the Gardners Spade
He deigned to use, and tools of th' Chymick trade (47).

On one of these expeditions he may have found in a spring near his home at New London, Connecticut, the rock fragment of columbite which his grandson sent to Sir Hans Sloane (1660–1753) in London (4).*

The original, historic specimen of columbite is preserved in the British Museum (67). A portion of it was used by Charles Hatchett in 1802 in his famous research which culminated in the discovery of columbium. In 1809 Dr. W. H. Wollaston obtained permission to detach another portion of it for an investigation, from which he incorrectly concluded that columbium and tantalum are identical (68).

Since columbite is a very complex mineral indeed, containing niobic, tantalic, titanic, and tungstic acids, zirconia, thoria, ceria, and yttria, Hatchett must have possessed great analytical ability in order to discover in it the new element, columbium. Although the greatest chem-

* See also Chapter 14, pp. 371–380.

Edgar F. Smith Memorial Collection, University of Pennsylvania

Autograph Letter of Charles Hatchett. William Thomas Brande (1788–1866), Davy's successor at the Royal Institution, was Charles Hatchett's son-in-law. The English edition of Brande's "Manual of Chemistry" was dedicated to Hatchett.

ists in Europe held for more than forty years the erroneous opinion that columbium and tantalum are identical, Marignac and Heinrich Rose finally proved that they are two distinct elements. Thus Hatchett was correct in concluding that he had found a new metal in columbite (53).

A.-F. de Fourcroy said in 1799 that the most industrious chemist in England was Charles Hatchett, whose father, the King's saddle-maker, had offered him an annual income of 3000 pounds sterling and a seat in Parliament if he would renounce this science. "Charles Hatchett," said Fourcroy, "preferred the study of chemistry, and found the means to continue its cultivation. The analysis of minerals is what occupies and pleases him the most; he is very clever at it; one can rely on his experiments. A few hours of work in his laboratory suffice for his enjoyment and instruction. This is not, by any means, the kind of continuous research we know among the French chemists" (69).

Sir Hans Sloane, 1660–1753. Founder of the British Museum. Physician, pharmacist, traveler, and collector of books, manuscripts, coins, medals, gems, antiquities, and natural history specimens. His asbestos specimens were purchased from Benjamin Franklin (63).

It is to be regretted that a man of such great ability should have given up his scientific research early in life. Thomas Thomson said of him in 1830, ". . . unfortunately this most amiable and accomplished man has been lost to science for more than a quarter of a century; the baneful effects of wealth, and the cares of a lucrative and extensive business having completely weaned him from scientific pursuits" (5). In 1845 Berzelius, writing to Wöhler, expressed a similar opinion: "On my previous visit here in Karlsbad," said he, "I made the personal acquaintance of your king as Prince of Cumberland. He asked me if I knew a number of English chemists, and upon my replying that I knew Davy, Wollaston, Tennant, and Marcet, he shook his head and indicated that

I had forgotten the foremost one, namely, Hatchett. He seemed greatly pleased that I also knew him, however did not want to believe that he had given up chemistry and become a coach-maker as his father's successor" (6). Hatchett retired to his estate at Roehampton, near London, and died at Chelsea on March 10, 1847.

He never succeeded in isolating niobium, and in fact the element eluded chemists for more than six decades. In 1864, however, C. W. Blomstrand reduced niobium chloride by heating it strongly in an atmosphere of hydrogen (48), and saw the shining steel-gray metal.

Henri Moissan, 1852–1907. Professor of Chemistry at the *École de Pharmacie*, and at the Sorbonne. The first to isolate fluorine and make a thorough study of its properties. With his electric furnace he prepared artificial diamonds and many rare metals. He brought about a revival of interest in inorganic chemical research.

In 1901 Henri Moissan pulverized some American columbite, mixed with it some sugar charcoal, compressed the mixture, and heated it from seven to eight minutes in his electric furnace, using a current of one thousand amperes under fifty volts. After volatilizing all the manganese and part of the iron and silicon, he obtained a melt containing niobium and tantalum combined with carbon.

After preparing niobic acid by Marignac's method, he mixed eighty-two parts of it with eighteen of sugar carbon, moistened the mixture slightly with turpentine, and pressed it into the form of a cylinder, which he heated in his electric furnace, using six hundred amperes under fifty volts. A violent reaction took place in accordance with the equation:

$$Nb_2O_5 + 5C = 2Nb + 5CO.$$

After cooling the mixture out of contact with the nitrogen of the air, he found a well-fused ingot with a metallic fracture (*49*). Moissan's niobium contained a small amount of combined carbon, and was so inert and refractory that he believed the element to be a non-metal resembling boron and silicon.

From 1904 to 1910 C. W. Balke (*7, 18, 55*) analyzed many niobium and tantalum compounds and determined the atomic weights of both metals. In 1906 Werner von Bolton of the Siemens & Halske Company

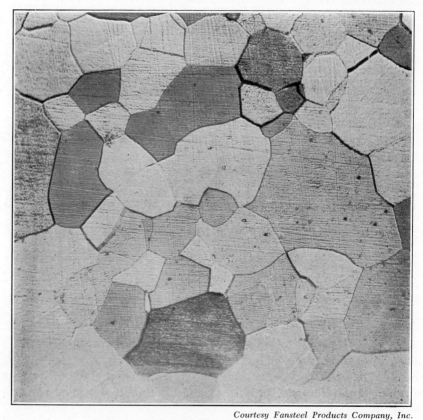

Courtesy Fansteel Products Company, Inc.

Photomicrograph of Niobium.   Approximately 300×.

prepared a niobium regulus by an alumino-thermic method and purified it by repeated melting in a vacuum electric furnace (*17, 18*). For twenty-three years this little specimen in Germany continued to be the only piece of pure niobium in the world, but in May, 1929, Dr. Balke exhibited before the American Chemical Society some highly polished sheets and rods of this rare metal. Because less energy is required to remove an electron from its surface than from that of any other refractory metal, niobium is used in vacuum tubes for high-power service (56).

TANTALUM

Since minerals which contain niobium almost invariably contain also the closely related element, tantalum, it is small wonder that chemists at first confused the two elements. The discoverer of tantalum was the Swedish chemist and mineralogist Anders Gustaf Ekeberg. He was born at Stockholm on January 16, 1767, the son of Joseph Erik Ekeberg, a

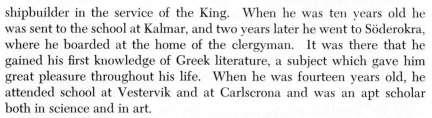

Anders Gustaf Ekeberg, 1767–1813. Swedish chemist, mineralogist, poet, and artist. Professor of Chemistry at Upsala when Berzelius was a student there. The discoverer of tantalum. He was one of the first chemists to investigate yttria.

shipbuilder in the service of the King. When he was ten years old he was sent to the school at Kalmar, and two years later he went to Söderokra, where he boarded at the home of the clergyman. It was there that he gained his first knowledge of Greek literature, a subject which gave him great pleasure throughout his life. When he was fourteen years old, he attended school at Vestervik and at Carlscrona and was an apt scholar both in science and in art.

He graduated from the University of Upsala in 1788, presenting a thesis on *Oils Extracted from Seeds,* and traveled, on salary, through Germany. Soon after his return to Upsala in 1790 he wrote a beautiful poem on the peace recently concluded between Sweden and Russia.

In 1794, after publishing his first contribution to chemistry, he began his teaching career at Upsala where he soon distinguished himself as an analytical chemist and proponent of Lavoisier's new system of chemical nomenclature (64). In 1795 he published with Pehr Afzelius a brochure in which modern names for such elements as hydrogen, nitrogen, and oxygen were introduced for the first time into the Swedish language. When Berzelius was studying medicine at the University of Upsala (1796–1802) Ekeberg, who in the opinion of Anton Blanck was at that time Sweden's foremost chemist, was serving as demonstrator in Torbern Bergman's old laboratory. In the autumn of 1798 Ekeberg gave lectures on the theory of combustion. For the *Litteratur Tidning* published at the University of Upsala he wrote excellent articles on "The present state of chemical science" and on "The advantages which medicine gains from the most recent discoveries in chemistry" (64).

Ekeberg suffered throughout his life from physical handicaps. A severe cold in childhood made him partially deaf for the rest of his life, and in 1801, when a flask exploded in his hand, he lost the sight of one eye (9).

When the royal family visited Upsala in November of that year, an elaborate chemical exposition was held in their honor. A poem of three stanzas, which Ekeberg had composed and written with invisible ink, appeared in blue letters when the King warmed the paper. It began as follows:

> That in our land the sciences' pure light
> Is mingled not with flash and gleam of sword,
> Oh Monarch, 'tis thy work. Accept our hearts' oblation.
> May we, too, celebrate, with joyous visages,
> The long-awaited hour when Peace the world doth greet (57).°

Ekeberg became deeply interested in the wonderful minerals to be found at Ytterby and Falun, and made excellent analyses of a number of them. In 1802 he analyzed a specimen of tantalite from Kimito, Finland, and another mineral, yttrotantalite, from Ytterby. The specimen of tantalite was presented to him by Geyer, Director of Mines, who had discovered it in 1746 and regarded it as a problematical variety of tin garnet (Zinngraupen). Director Geyer found it near the Brokärn estate at Kimito, Åbo, Finland, on a mountain on the shore of the Baltic. Mine surveyor Nils Nordenskiöld afterward described this locality as follows: "Near the Skoyböle estate, three quarters of a mile from the Kimito

---

° At Wetenskapers rena Dag
Ej blandades hos oss med blixtarne af swärden,
Det är ditt werk, Monark, vårt hjertas offer tag!
Wi fire, jemwäl wi, med glädjens anletsdrag
Dem länge drögda stund, då Freden hälsar werlden.

church, there are two prospectors' openings which, according to the statements of older Finnish mineralogists, bear a kind of irregular stanniferous garnet; hence the locality also has retained the name *tin-mine of Kimito*.

"The openings," said Nordenskiöld, "are rather old and are said to have been first begun on the word of a rod-bearer [who said] that toward the east it would yield silver. Afterward, the spherical mica and tantalite which occur there attracted the notice of mineralogists. The openings lie about half a mile from the manor, back in the forest, in a swampy region, on a low mountain. They are cut into an east-west stratum, consisting of a matrix of mica, red albite, and quartz. . . . The tantalite

Heinrich Rose, 1795–1864. German analytical chemist and pharmacist. Son of Valentin Rose the Younger. His comparative study of American columbite and Bavarian tantalite proved that columbium (niobium) and tantalum are two distinct metals.

formerly existed at the surface in greater quantities, but has now so far disappeared that tantalite at this locality may correctly be considered one of the rarest of fossile" (*70*).

Ekeberg found the yttrotantalite in the same place as the gadolinite at Ytterby, Sweden. He found that both contained a hitherto unknown metal. Because it had been such a tantalizing task to trace it down, Ekeberg named it *tantalum* (*32*).

In 1809 Dr. Wollaston analyzed both columbite and tantalite (*10*). His conclusion that niobium and tantalum are identical was accepted by chemists until 1846, when Heinrich Rose (a grandson of Valentin Rose the Elder and son of the Rose whom Klaproth educated) questioned it. Rose had made a thorough study of the columbites and tantalites from America and from Bodenmais, Bavaria, and had extracted from them two acids which he called niobic (columbic) and pelopic acids. He found later, however, that the latter was not the acid of a new metal, as he had at first supposed, but that it contained niobium (columbium) in a lower state of oxidation. Rose stated that niobic and hyponiobic acids are both different from tantalic acid (*11*).

Thomas Thomson, 1773–1852. Scottish chemist and editor. The first distinguished advocate of Dalton's atomic theory. Author of a two-volume "History of Chemistry" characterized by its scientific accuracy and beautiful literary style (*59, 60*).

Although niobic and tantalic acids are extremely difficult to separate, Marignac finally succeeded, not only in separating them, but also in showing that niobium is both tri- and pentavalent, whereas tantalum always has a valence of five. The separation is based on the insolubility of potassium fluotantalate in comparison with potassium fluo-oxyniobate (*12, 20*). In the United States the element discovered by Hatchett used to be known as *columbium*, but in Europe most chemists prefer to use the name *niobium* which Heinrich Rose gave it.

Ekeberg's later years were made less fruitful by continued illness.

The few papers which he published contained the results of the analyses of minerals such as gadolinite, the topaz, and an ore of titanium. In his analysis of the mineral water of Medevi he was assisted by an obscure young student who was destined to bring great glory to the University of Upsala. The discovery of such a student as Berzelius was a far greater honor for Ekeberg than his disclosure of the rather rare element, tantalum.

Berzelius warmly defended Ekeberg's claim to the discovery of this element. In the autumn of 1814 he wrote to Thomas Thomson objecting to an alteration which had been made in an English translation of one of his memoirs. Berzelius had used the word *tantalum,* and Thomson had evidently substituted the word *columbium,* whereupon Berzelius wrote, "Without wishing to depreciate the merits of the celebrated Hatchett, it is nevertheless necessary to observe that tantalum and its properties in the metallic as well as in its oxidized condition were not known at all before Mr. Ekeberg."

Berzelius went on to explain the differences between Ekeberg's tantalum oxide and the columbium oxide prepared by Hatchett:

Mr. Ekeberg received from a friend who had visited England [said he], a little portion of the columbic acid of Mr. Hatchett, and when the experiments of Mr. Wollaston came to his knowledge he examined that acid in a scrupulous manner. He recognized in it a large amount of tungstic acid which had given to the oxide its properties of reacting acid as well as those of combining with the alkalies and of coloring microcosmic salt. These observations of Mr. Ekeberg have gained still more weight by the discovery of a new fossil[*] that Mr. Gahn and I have just made near Falun, which fossil possesses the general properties of Mr. Hatchett's columbite, and in the analysis of which we have found oxide of tantalum combined with tungstic acid. . . .

Now, then [continued Berzelius], it is clear that the columbic acid of Mr. Hatchett, having been composed of oxide of tantalum and tungstic acid, which communicated to it a part of its specific properties, it is clear, I say, that Mr. Hatchett shares the discovery of tantalum in almost the same manner as MM. Fourcroy and Vauquelin share with Mr. Tennant the honor of having discovered osmium ("Thomson's System," Ed. IV, Vol. 1, p. 200), and I suppose that you will not refuse to render the same justice to the work of the Swede Ekeberg that you have just rendered to the Englishman Tennant.[†]

As for the name of the metal [said Berzelius], I do not think that the author of the discovery ought to count for much. For example you do not say menaccanite instead of titanium;[‡] moreover Mr. Hatchett gave this name after the place where it was thought the fossil had been found; now it is not good practice

[*] A tantalite from Broddbo.
[†] See Chapter 16, p. 436–440.
[‡] See Chapter 21, pp. 545–51.

to name elementary substances in chemistry after the places where they have first been found; not to mention the fact that the place where columbite was found is still doubtful, in the same degree as it is not certain that it comes from America. The name tantalum having none of these inconveniences and involving a beautiful meaning of a few properties of this particular metallic body, I have felt compelled to choose it by preference. The reason for the name tantalum (derived from the story of Tantalus) is still more valid if one adds that metallic tantalum, reduced to the finest powder, is not attacked by any acid, not even by aqua regia, concentrated and boiling (13).

In his reply to this letter on November 5, Thomson explained that he had known very little about Ekeberg's experiments and that his only reason for changing Berzelius' nomenclature had been to make the article more intelligible to English readers. He then added:

I regret that it never has been in my power to make experiments on either of these substances (columbite or tantalite). Ekeberg supplied me with a good many specimens, but the ship containing them and all my Swedish collection, which I valued highly, was sunk in the Baltic, and all my property lost. Your fact about the new mineral like columbite [sic] is very interesting. I shall insert what you have told me in the next number of my journal. It is all unknown here (14).

On March 29, 1815 Dr. Marcet wrote to Berzelius:

. . . Dr. Wollaston made some time ago in my presence a little experimental inquiry on wolfram and tantalite and columbite, by which it appeared that Hatchett's columbite did not contain any tungsten, and that therefore he did not make the mistake you suspected he had made. If you are curious to have the details, I shall send them to you (15).

The biographical sketch in *Vetenskapsacademiens Handlingar* pictures Professor Ekeberg as a man of slender build, afflicted with tuberculosis, deafness, and partial blindness which had resulted from a laboratory explosion. "With a naturally animated and energetic temperament he combined a charming benevolence which spread over his countenance and, together with the lines of suffering so evident in his later years, awakened tender sympathy and concern. His manner inspired confidence. He was a gifted teacher and devoted friend" (71).

Ekeberg died at Upsala on February 11, 1813, at the early age of forty-six years. In a letter to Dr. Marcet (16), Berzelius paid the following tribute to his gifted teacher: "Ekeberg has just died after a long, sad, hectic illness. He was one of the most lovable of men, he had sound knowledge, and an irresistible propensity for work. He was a good chemist and mineralogist, a good poet and an excellent artist."* Ekeberg

* "Ekeberg vient de mourir après une maladie hectique longue et malheureuse. Cet homme était des plus aimables; il possédait des connaissances solides et un penchant irrésistible pour le travail. Il était bon chimiste et minéralogue, heureux poëte et très bon peintre."

had a kind, friendly, merry spirit that frequently soared above poverty and suffering, and his love of literature and art was a constant solace to him.

Tantalum can be separated from niobium by recrystallization of the double potassium fluorides. In the commercial process the ore is fused with caustic soda. The insoluble sodium niobate, sodium tantalate, and

Laboratory Equipment Made from Tantalum

Courtesy Fansteel Products Company, Inc.

iron tantalate are filtered off from the soluble sodium salts, and the iron is removed by treatment with hydrochloric acid. The niobic and tantalic acids are treated with hydrofluoric acid and enough potassium fluoride to convert the tantalum into the double fluoride, K_2TaF_7, which is then recrystallized from water containing a little hydrofluoric acid (7).

After Werner von Bolton of Charlottenburg succeeded in 1903 in refining the metal, it soon acquired a limited use as filaments (34). It was found, moreover, that surgical and dental instruments made from it can be sterilized by heating or by immersion in acids without damage to the tantalum. Since the price was almost prohibitive, however, Dr. Balke set to work in Chicago to make the metal on a commercial scale.

Tantalum for Watch Cases
Courtesy Fansteel Products Company, Inc.

Using as his raw material a rich tantalum ore from the desolate Pilbarra region of western Australia, he finally succeeded in February, 1922, in preparing a tantalum ingot which was passed repeatedly through a rolling mill to produce a flawless piece of sheet metal (8, 19).

Tantalum is now made into spinnerets for the manufacture of rayon, into electrodes for the neon signs that give our Great White Ways a ruddier light, and into fine jewelry with iridescent colors.   Its most interesting use, however, depends on its peculiar electrochemical behavior caused by the insolubility of its oxide in acid solution.   When an alternating current is passed through a vessel containing sulfuric acid, a bar of lead, and a bar of tantalum (or of niobium), it becomes a direct current (7, 19).   Thus, because direct current was needed in the early

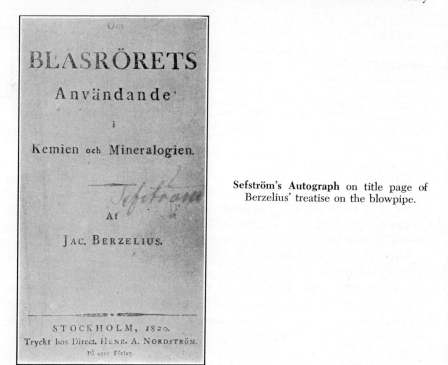

Sefström's **Autograph** on title page of Berzelius' treatise on the blowpipe.

days of radio reception, Ekeberg's tantalizing metal, in the form of radio rectifiers, "B" battery eliminators, and trickle chargers, entered into the home life of thousands upon thousands of families.   It has also been used successfully for the manufacture of standard analytical weights (62).

VANADIUM

In 1801, the year in which Hatchett discovered niobium, Andrés Manuel del Río, a professor of mineralogy in Mexico, examined a specimen of brown lead from Zimapán and concluded that it contained a new metal similar to chromium and uranium.   Very little has been written concerning the personal life of del Río.*   He was born in Madrid on

* See Chapter 15, pp. 390–405.

November 10, 1764, studied at Freiberg and at Schemnitz, and finally became a professor in the School of Mines (Colegio de Minería) in Mexico City, where he taught for about fifty years (1795–1849) (2, 50, 51).

It was there that he discovered a new metal which, because of the red color that its salts acquire when heated, he named *erythronium* (44). Upon further study, however, he decided that he was mistaken, and that the brown lead from Zimapán was merely a basic lead chromate containing 80.72 per cent of lead oxide and 14.80 per cent of chromic acid (12). His paper therefore bore the modest title, "Discovery of chromium in the brown lead of Zimapán" (21). In 1805 Collet-Descotils confirmed del Río's analysis (22), and for twenty-five years no more was heard of the new element, erythronium.

In his textbook of mineralogy published in Philadelphia in 1832, however, del Río said that "the metal in the brown lead is not chromium but vanadium, the very same (el mismo mismísimo) which I called *pancromo* and *eritrono* on page 61 of my translation [of 'Karsten's Tables, Mexico,' 1804]" (72).

In 1820 del Río went to the Spanish court to plead for Mexican independence. His paper (1) on the "Analysis of an alloy of gold and rhodium from the parting house at Mexico" was published in the *Annals of Philosophy* in October, 1825. The closing years of his long useful life were spent in Mexico, where he died on March 23, 1849.

In 1831 the Swedish chemist Nils Gabriel Sefström discovered a new element in iron from the Taberg mine in Småland. Sefström was born on June 2, 1787, at Ilsbo Socken, Norra Helsingland (2). He studied medicine, and received his medical degree at the age of twenty-six years. After four years of practice in a hospital, he became a professor of chemistry and science at the Caroline Institute of Medicine and Surgery, and from 1820 to 1839 he taught chemistry at the newly erected School of Mines at Falun (2, 54).

It was there that he made the remarkable discovery that Berzelius described so charmingly to Wöhler in his letter of January 22, 1831:

In regard to the sample which I am sending with this, I want to tell the following anecdote: In the far north there lived in olden times the goddess Vanadis, beautiful and lovable. One day some one knocked at her door. The goddess remained comfortably seated and thought: let the person knock again; but there was no more knocking, and the one who had knocked went down the steps. The goddess was curious to see who it might be that was so indifferent to being admitted, sprang to the window, and looked at the one who was going away. Alas! she said to herself, that's that fellow Wöhler. Well, he surely deserved it; if he had been a little more concerned about it, he would have been admitted. The fellow does not look up to the window once in passing by. . . .

After a few days some one knocked again at the door; but this time the knocking continued. The goddess finally came herself and opened the door. Sefström entered, and from this union vanadium was born. That is the name of the new metal, whose former name suggesting Erian, meaning wool (whence Erianae was educated, since Minerva taught human beings to spin wool), has been rejected. The Herr Professor guessed correctly that the lead mineral from Zimapán contains vanadium and not chromium. Sefström himself proved with the little specimen belonging to the professor that it is vanadium oxide.

Nils Gabriel Sefström, 1787–1845. Swedish physician and chemist. Professor at the Caroline Institute of Medicine and Surgery and at the School of Mines in Stockholm. In 1831 he discovered vanadium, an element that proved to be identical with del Río's "erythronium."

Vanadium [continued Berzelius] is a thing which is very hard to find. It is related to everything with which it forms compounds in definite proportions, even to silica, so that only now have I been able to obtain it pure. In Sefström's vanadium oxide which he brought with him are found phosphoric acid, silica, alumina, zirconia, and ferric oxide, of whose presence we had no suspicion, but which we, because of ambiguous results, had to remove, one after another; so that in the three weeks which Sefström spent in working with me, we confined ourselves almost entirely to the task of finding these impurities and of thinking out ways of removing them. Sefström had to go home, but left me so much vanadium that I have been in no embarrassment over the continuance of the investigation. I shall send the Herr Professor some of it later, when I see about how much I can spare; but now in the midst of the research I need all I have (23).

Berzelius then consoled Wöhler for his failure to discover vanadium, saying it required more genius to synthesize urea than to discover ten new elements (*58*, *61*). "I have mailed to Poggendorff," he continued, "a little paper on vanadium by Sefström. I have also engaged Sefström to present it to the Academy so that his name alone may be linked with the discovery, which would not be the case if the first paper on it appeared under his and my name together. Thus it also becomes possible to announce the discovery sooner than if we had to wait for the conclusion of my research, which surely connot be completed so quickly" (*23*).

Two weeks later Wöhler replied:

A thousand thanks, dear professor, for your kind letter with the beautiful story about the goddess Vanadis, which gave me great pleasure, although, frankly, it vexed me a little, though only at first, to have made no visit to the beautiful one. Even if I had charmed her out of the lead mineral, I would have had only half the honor of discovery, because of the earlier results of del Río on erythronium. But Sefström, because he succeeded by an entirely different method, keeps the honor unshared. As soon as I know the intimate relations of the metal, and you have sent me a little of it, I will analyze the lead mineral. . . .

Anticipatory as it may seem [continued Wöhler] yet, because of the slowness of the mails, it is time to ask whether, when I publish a notice of the mineral, I ought to give its earlier history, the supposed discovery by del Río of a new metal in it, the refutation by Descotils? that Humboldt brought it with him, etc.? I would not want in the least to take away from Sefström anything of his priority of discovery, especially since such indecision is repugnant in cases like this; on the other hand one must not expose one's self to the charge by the public or especially by one's opponents that one through partisanship concealed earlier claims. In any case Humboldt shall be named, since he alone brought it with him, and with that the rest seems unavoidably linked. Do not laugh at me because of my diplomatic question . . . (*23*).

The keenness of Wöhler's disappointment is more definitely expressed in his letter to Liebig of January 2, 1831, in which he wrote:

. . . at the moment I am interested only in the new Swedish metal, vanadium, discovered by Sefström, but really by Berzelius. *Ich war ein Esel* not to have discovered it before in the brown lead ore from Zimapán, Mexico. I was engaged in analyzing it and had already found in it something new when, in consequence of hydrogen fluoride vapor, I became ill for several months (*24*).

The cast iron in which Sefström discovered vanadium had been prepared from ore from the mine at Taberg, Småland. When Daniel Tilas described this hill in 1760, he stated that iron had been smelted there since 1610 and that the supply of it was still almost inexhaustible (*74*). C. Beijell analyzed this ore in 1760 and found that it contained from 21 to 31.5 per cent of iron, that it was free from sulfur and arsenic, and that good, serviceable iron could be prepared from it (*75*).

From Thomas Thomson's "Travels in Sweden During the Autumn of 1812"

Taberg, Småland, Sweden. Sefström discovered vanadium in iron from the Taberg mine.

Thomas Thomson, in his "Travels through Sweden in the Autumn of 1812," quoted Johann Friedrich Hausmann's description of this great hill of iron ore. "The ironstone of Taberg," wrote Hausmann in 1811, "on the southeast and east side, is quite irregular; partly from the many loose blocks, and partly from the way in which it has been blown up by gunpowder. It is more valuable on account of its tractability and the absence of every hurtful ingredient than on account of the great quantity of iron which it yields. This varies from 21 to 32 per cent. In the hopes of finding richer ore, a shaft was driven into the mountain; but these hopes not being realized, the labour was soon abandoned. . . . Taberg, which has been wrought since the year 1621, supplies all the furnaces in the district, to the number of fifteen, with ore. That it will continue to furnish a source of riches to the latest posterity must be evident from the slightest view of its colossial [*sic*] mass" (*76*).

Thomson wrote in 1813: "The uppermost bed, which cannot be less than 370 feet thick, has been wrought as an iron ore these 250 years. The method is simply to blast it with gunpowder and let it fall to the bottom of the hill, from which it is taken to iron-furnaces in the neighbourhood" (*76*).

For a description of Sefström's method of isolating vanadium, it is necessary to quote again from the correspondence of Berzelius, this time from a letter to Dulong. On January 7, 1831, he wrote:

I must tell you of the discovery of a new metallic substance, of which this letter contains some preparations. . . . The discovery was made by Mr. Sefström, director of the School of Mines at Falun who, wishing to examine a kind of iron remarkable for its extreme softness, found in it, in extremely small quantity, a substance whose properties appear to differ from those of bodies hitherto known, but the quantity of which was so infinitely small that too much expense would have been necessary in order to extract enough of it to permit of closer examination. This iron was taken from the Taberg mine in Småland, which however contains only traces of the new body, but Mr. Sefström, having found that the cast iron contained more of it than the wrought iron, concluded that the scoria formed during the conversion of the cast iron to malleable iron ought to contain larger quantities of it. This proved to be true. Mr. Sefström extracted portions of it which sufficed for studying it, and during his Christmas vacation came to see me, to finish with me the study of "the stranger (*nouveau débarqué*)" (25).

Sefström's own account of the discovery is also of great interest:

It is several years [said he], since Rinman, the manager of the mine, in order to discover easily whether an iron was brittle, gave a method which depends on the circumstance that such an iron, when attacked by muriatic [hydrochloric] acid, gives a black powder. Having occasionally treated in this manner an iron which was not brittle, and finally some iron from Eckersholm, I was greatly surprised to recognize in the latter the reaction of a brittle iron, although the iron from Taberg passes for the most flexible and tenacious that we have. I did not then have the leisure to investigate the nature of the black powder; but in April, 1830, I resumed my experiments to see if it contained phosphorus or any other substance, which was for me not without importance.

I dissolved a considerable quantity of iron in muriatic acid [Sefström then continued] and I noticed that, while it was dissolving, a few particles of iron, mainly those which deposit the black powder, dissolved more rapidly than the others, in such a way that there remained hollow veins in the midst of the iron bar. Upon examining this black powder, I found silica, iron, alumina, lime, copper, and, among other things, uranium. I could not discover in what condition this substance was, because the small quantity of powder did not exceed two decigrams, and, moreover, more than half of it was silica. After several experiments I saw that it was not chromium, and the comparative tests that I made proved to me that it certainly was not uranium. I had sought to compare the highest degrees of oxidation, but I must remark that vanadium is found partly in the lower degree (26).

In one of his letters Berzelius mentioned to Wöhler an unfortunate accident: ". . . As Sefström came home to Falun," said he, "to take up there the study of the vanadium alloy, a student spilled about one lot (ten grams) of dissolved vanadium oxide in such a way that none of it could be saved. Now he has nothing with which he can work, and must repeat the entire preparation process on the slag" (27).

In May, 1830, a careful comparison of vanadium and uranium was made in Berzelius' laboratory. It was found that vanadium forms two series of compounds, the vanadic and the vanadous, but Berzelius and Sefström did not succeed in isolating the metal.

Sir Edward (T. E.) Thorpe, 1845–1925. English chemist famous for his research on the specific volumes of liquids in relation to their chemical constitution, and for his work on the oxides of phosphorus and the compounds of vanadium done in collaboration with Sir Henry Roscoe. Author of excellent textbooks of chemistry and of biographies and essays in historical chemistry.

From 1820 to 1845 Sefström edited *Jernkontorets Annaler* (Annals of the Iron Corporation), and in 1826 he was awarded the gold medal of the Manufacturing Association for his services to this journal (54). Among his many contributions to it were papers on the composition of refinery slag, analyses of clay used in the iron industry, analysis of a highly titaniferous iron ore, improvements in the manufacture of Swedish iron, analysis of the mine water at Falun, and the history of iron mining in Sweden. In a report on one of his foreign journeys, written for *Jernkontorets Annaler*, Sefström said: ". . . I know of no other process which has so many niceties, which is so sensitive to outside influences, presents such a wealth of highly interesting phenomena, and offers such an extensive field for pleasant research as the preparation of bar iron in the hearth. Medicine, in which I was engaged for several years, is also a great field for investigation; but I have had just as many interesting conversations with thoughtful smiths . . . as I ever had among my medical acquaintances . . ." (54, 65).

Sefström died at Stockholm on November 30, 1845 at the age of fifty-eight years, as the result of a paralytic stroke. The anonymous biography in *Vetenskapsakademiens Handlingar* mentioned his large stature and towering height, the frankness and uprightness of his charac-

Andrés Manuel del Río, 1764–1849. Spanish-Mexican scientist. For half a century he was professor of mineralogy at the School of Mines of Mexico.

ter, and his tireless perseverance, and added that he gave to Swedish mining "a new direction, namely the scientific, and thus lighted in Sweden a new miners' lamp, which will never be extinguished" (*66*).

After N. G. Sefström had discovered vanadium in a soft cast iron from Eckersholm, Sweden, no mineral containing it as an essential constituent was known until Wöhler analyzed the specimen of "brown lead from Zimapán" which del Río had sent to Europe by Baron Alexander von Humboldt (*73*). Wöhler's researches (*45*) proved that he had been correct in believing that the ore del Río had analyzed in 1801 really contained vanadium instead of chromium (26). This mineral is now known as vanadinite, $PbCl_2 \cdot 3Pb_3(VO_4)_2$.

The final step in the discovery of vanadium was accomplished by the English chemist, Sir Henry Enfield Roscoe, who was born in London on January 7, 1833. When he was nine years old the family moved to

Sir Henry Enfield Roscoe, 1833–1915. Professor of Chemistry at the University of Manchester. Collaborator with Bunsen in researches in photochemistry. Author of excellent textbooks and treatises on pure and applied chemistry.

From Thorpe's "The Right Honourable Sir Henry Enfield Roscoe"

Liverpool. One of his first schoolmasters reported that "Roscoe is a nice boy, but he looks about him too much, and does not know his irregular verbs" (36). His mother, who evidently did not object seriously to this habit of "looking about," encouraged him to make chemical experiments at home and allowed him to transform one of the rooms into a laboratory.

At the age of fifteen years the boy entered University College, London, where he studied under Thomas Graham and Alexander William Williamson. After graduating in 1853 with honors in chemistry, he went to Heidelberg to study quantitative analysis in the old monastery that had been transformed into a laboratory for Robert Bunsen. After passing his doctor's examination *summa cum laude,* he collaborated with Bunsen in the famous researches on the chemical action of light. During their long friendship Roscoe received from the great German master one hundred twenty-six letters, which he carefully preserved and finally presented in bound form to the Bunsen-Gesellschaft (38).

When only twenty-four years old, Roscoe succeeded Edward Frankland as professor of chemistry at the University of Manchester. In the winter of 1862, when thousands of employees in the cotton mills of Lancashire were thrown out of work because of the Civil War in America, Roscoe, in an effort to relieve the mental depression of the unemployed, instituted a series of popular "Science Lectures for the People." Roscoe, John Tyndall, Thomas Huxley, and other noted scientists addressed large and appreciative audiences each week for eleven consecutive winters, and the printed lectures were afterward sold for a penny all over the world

Carl Friedrich Rammelsberg, 1813–1899. German chemist, mineralogist, and crystallographer who demonstrated the isomorphism of sulfur and selenium crystals obtained from carbon disulfide solutions of these elements, and showed that the vanadates are isomorphous with the phosphates. He also determined the crystal forms of many organic compounds, and wrote textbooks on crystallography, metallurgy, and mineralogical and analytical chemistry.

(39). In his teaching Roscoe emphasized the need of liberal culture as a basis for technical training (28).

In about 1865 he found that some of the copper veins of the Lower Keuper Sandstone of the Trias in Cheshire contained vanadium (37) and that one of the lime precipitates from this ore contained about two per cent of it. It was from this unpromising material that Roscoe and Sir Edward Thorpe laboriously prepared the pure vanadium compounds needed for a thorough study of the element.

When Roscoe investigated them he found that vanadium is a tri- and pentavalent element of the phosphorus group. He also discovered that what Berzelius had taken for the metal was really the mononitride, VN, and that most of the vanadium compounds studied by the Swedish chemists had contained oxygen.

On August 26, 1867, Roscoe wrote to Thorpe saying,

. . . I want you very much to stay with me till April to settle the vanadium and light matters and help me in London with my lectures. . . . I have at last found out about vanadium. The acid is V_2O_5 like P_2O_5. The chloride $VOCl_3$ like $POCl_3$ and the solid chlorides $VOCl_2$, $VOCl$, etc. This explains the isomorphism of the vanadate of lead and the corresponding phosphate and lots of other points. It becomes very interesting now . . . (40).

On September 12 of the same year Roscoe wrote again to his assistant:

Please ask Joseph [Heywood] to send me per book-post *Pogg. Ann.*, vol. 98, in which volume is Rammelsberg's paper on the isomorphism of vanadates and phosphates. There is no doubt in my mind that vanadic acid is V_2O_5, and it will be *exceedingly* interesting to work out the vanadates, which must all be explained as phosphates. The ordinary white NH_3 salt is NH_4VO_3 (like $NaPO_3$) and is a metavanadate. The bi-vanadates can also be explained, but all need re-preparation and analysis. Did I tell you that we have now got V_2O_5, V_2O_4, V_2O_3, V_2O_2 (I wish we had V also!), $V_2O_2Cl_6$, $V_2O_2Cl_4$, $V_2O_2Cl_2$, or $VOCl_3$, $VOCl_2$, $VOCl$? At St. Andrews I saw Professor Heddle; he has a crystal half apatite and half vanadinite, and he threw out the suggestion long ago that vanadic acid is V_2O_5 . . . (40).

Five days later Roscoe sent Thorpe a detailed report of his experiments on the oxides of vanadium and said in conclusion, "The thing above all others necessary for us now is to get the *metal*" (40).

Roscoe's first paper on the subject was the Bakerian Lecture read before the Royal Society on December 19, 1867. On February 14, 1868, with Sir Edward Thorpe as his assistant, he gave a demonstration lecture at the Royal Institution in which he proved that the lemon-colored chloride to which Berzelius had assigned the formula VCl_3 actually contains oxygen. When the audience saw him pass the vapor from a few grams of this chloride, together with pure hydrogen gas, over red-hot carbon, and watched him test the resulting gas for carbon dioxide by passing it into clear baryta water, it was convinced that Berzelius' formula must be incorrect. Roscoe proved by analysis that the lemon-colored chloride is an oxychloride now known as vanadyl chloride, $VOCl_3$ (12, 29).

When he began his researches on vanadium, its compounds were listed at £35 per ounce, and the metal itself was unknown. After all attempts at direct reduction of the oxides had failed, Roscoe attempted to reduce vanadium dichloride, VCl_2, with hydrogen. Rigorous exclusion of oxygen and moisture was necessary, and, since vanadium metal reacts violently with glass and porcelain, the chloride was placed in platinum boats inside a porcelain tube. The tube itself could not be made of platinum because of the porosity of that metal at red heat.

When he heated the tube, hydrochloric acid gas came off in "torrents," and continued to be evolved in decreasing quantity for from forty to eighty hours. When it finally ceased to come off, the tube was cooled and the boat was found to contain "a light whitish grey-colored powder, perfectly free from chlorine." When Roscoe examined this powder under the microscope, he found that it reflected light powerfully and that it consisted of "a brilliant shining crystalline metallic mass possessing a bright silver-white lustre." Roscoe's paper announcing the isolation of metallic vanadium was read before the Royal Society on June 16, 1869 (33).

While studying at Heidelberg, Sir Edward Thorpe read in a French periodical on popular science that the Copley Medal had been awarded to Sir Henry E. Roscoe. His letter of congratulation brought the following reply:

In the first place let me thank you for your letter and congratulations upon the great French discovery! Many of these Parisian wonders have after all turned out myths—and this last is, I believe, no exception—the expression "Medaille de Copley" is, so far as I am aware, the French (and bad French, too!) for the "Bakerian Lecture." I am, however, none the less obliged to you for your good wishes on this occasion, and for all the valuable help which in many ways you gave me (41).

Roscoe's textbooks of chemistry were unusually successful, passed through edition after edition, and were translated into Russian, Italian, Hungarian, Polish, Swedish, modern Greek, Japanese, Urdu, Icelandic, Bengali, Turkish, Malayalam, and Tamil. His autobiography (42) was written with great charm, and the "Treatise on Chemistry" by Roscoe and Schorlemmer is familiar to all chemists.

Sir Henry's last years were spent on his beautiful estate at Woodcote in southern England. Here Lady Roscoe took endless pleasure in the cultivation of flowers and flowering shrubs and in entertaining her husband's distinguished guests. "My father," said Miss Roscoe, "delighted to bring foreigners, and the more heterogeneous they were the more he was pleased. I remember one luncheon party of late years, consisting of a Chinaman, a Japanese, a Czech, a German, and our three selves, and the Occidentals were much the quietest of the party" (43).

After enjoying a serene old age, Sir Henry E. Roscoe died suddenly on December 18, 1915, during an attack of angina pectoris.

In 1927 J. W. Marden and M. N. Rich of the research staff of the Westinghouse Lamp Company obtained metallic vanadium 99.9 per cent pure by heating a mixture of vanadic oxide, metallic calcium, and calcium chloride in an electric furnace for an hour at a temperature of about 1400° Fahrenheit. When the resulting mass was cooled and stirred into cold water, beads of pure metallic vanadium separated out (35).

The alloy ferrovanadium is used extensively in the steel industry. The presence of small amounts of vanadium profoundly alters the properties of steel, greatly increasing its toughness, elasticity, and tensile strength. Thus the metal that Sefström and Berzelius named for the ancient Swedish goddess of beauty has come to play an important utilitarian role in the construction of locomotive frames, driving axles, and large shaftings for electrical machinery.

Patronite. An important commercial deposit of vanadium is the patronite of Peru, an impure sulfide containing free sulfur. This ore was first found in 1905 at Minasragra near Cerro de Pasco, Peru, 16,000 feet above sea level, and was named for its discoverer, Señor Antenor Rizo-Patron (77, 78). Vanadium is also obtained as a by-product from the exploitation of Colorado carnotite for radium and uranium (77).

Vanadium in Plants and Animals. In 1899 Charles Baskerville detected vanadium in the ashes of certain peats (77, 79). M. Henze discovered in 1911 that the blood of certain tunicates contains an organic compound of vanadium (77, 80). He noticed that the blood corpuscles of the ascidian *Phallusia mamillata* contain a chromogen which becomes yellow-green to blue on standing. After separating the corpuscles with a centrifuge, he dissolved this chromogen in distilled water. By adding acetone to the resulting brown solution, he precipitated the chromogen and afterward separated it with a centrifuge. On burning it, and fuming the ash with nitric acid, he obtained an orange-red residue of vanadic acid anhydride. In a quantitative analysis made on a very small portion of the chromogen, Henze found that it contained more than 15 per cent of vanadium pentoxide (80). The vanadium was later found to be localized in specialized green cells, the vanadocytes. As a result of researches at the Zoological Station in Naples, Professor D. A. Webb of Cambridge University concluded that the vanadium chromogen is not a respiratory pigment (81).

LITERATURE CITED

(1) DEL RÍO, A. M., "Analysis of an alloy of gold and rhodium from the parting house at Mexico," *Annals of Phil.*, [2], **10**, 256 (Oct., 1825).

(2) POGGENDORFF, J. C., "Biographisch-Literarisches Handwörterbuch zur Geschichte der exakten Wissenschaften," 6 vols., Verlag Chemie, Leipzig and Berlin, **1863–1937**. Articles on Hatchett, del Río, and Sefström.

(3) HATCHETT, C., "Outline of the properties and habitudes of the metallic substance lately discovered by Charles Hatchett, Esq., and by him denominated columbium." *Nicholson's J.*, [2], **1**, 32–4 (Jan., 1802); *Crell's Ann.*, **37**, 197–201, 257–70, 352–64 (1802).

(4) "New metal columbium," *Nicholson's J.*, **14**, 181 (June, 1806).

(5) THOMSON, THOMAS, "History of Chemistry," Vol. 2, Colburn and Bentley, London, **1831**, p. 231.

(6) WALLACH, O., "Briefwechsel zwischen J. Berzelius und F. Wöhler," Vol. 2, Verlag von Wilhelm Engelmann, Leipzig, **1901**, p. 544.

(7) BALKE, C. W., "Metals of the tungsten and tantalum groups," *Ind. Eng. Chem.*, **21**, 1002–7 (Nov., 1929); C. W. BALKE and EDGAR F. SMITH, "Observations on columbium," *J. Am. Chem. Soc.*, **30**, 1637–68 (Nov., 1908); C. W. BALKE, "The atomic weight of tantalum," *ibid.*, **32**, 1127–33 (Oct., 1910).

(8) "American chemical industries. Fansteel Products Co., Inc.," *Ind. Eng. Chem.*, **22**, 1409–12 (Dec., 1930).

(9) "Biographical account of Mr. Ekeberg, assistant professor of chemistry at Upsala," *Annals of Phil.*, [1], **4**, 241–3 (Oct., 1814); Kongl. Vetenskaps Academiens Handlingar, **1813**, p. 276.

(10) WOLLASTON, W. H., "On the identity of columbium and tantalum," *Nicholson's J.*, **25**, 23–8 (Jan., 1810).

(11) ROSE, H., "On a new metal, pelopium, contained in the Bavarian tantalite," *Phil. Mag.*, [3], **29**, 409–16 (Nov., 1846); Obituary of H. Rose, *J. Chem. Soc.*, **17**, 437–40 (*Proc.* of Mar. 31, 1864).

(12) JAGNAUX, R., "Histoire de la Chimie," Vol. 2, Baudry et Cie., Paris, **1891**, pp. 341–5.

(13) SÖDERBAUM, H. G., "Jac. Berzelius Bref," Vol. 3, part 6, Almqvist and Wiksells, Upsala, **1912–1914**, pp. 18–20.

(14) *Ibid.*, Vol. 3, part 6, p. 25.

(15) *Ibid.*, Vol. 1, part 3, p. 123.

(16) *Ibid.*, Vol. 1, part 3, p. 40.

(17) GILES, "Observations on niobium, tantalum, and titanium," *Chem. News*, **95**, 1–3, 37–9 (Jan. 4 and Jan. 25, 1907); W. VON BOLTON, "Das Niob, seine Darstellung und seine Eigenschaften," *Z. Elektrochem.*, **13**, 145–9 (Apr., 1907).

(18) "Rare Metals," Fansteel Products Co., N. Chicago, **1929**, pp. 7–22.

(19) BALKE, C. W., "The production and uses of ductile tantalum," *Chem. Met. Eng.*, **27**, 1271–3 (Dec. 27, 1922).

(20) DE MARIGNAC, J.-C. G., "Recherches sur les combinaisons du niobium," *Ann. chim. phys.*, [4], **8**, 5–75 (May, 1866); "Recherches sur les combinaisons du tantale," *ibid.*, [4], **9**, 249–76 (Nov., 1866).

(21) DEL RÍO, A. M., "Discovery of chromium in the brown lead of Zimapán," *Gilb. Ann.*, **71**, 7.

(22) COLLET-DESCOTILS, H.-V., "Analyse de la mine brune de plomb de Zimapán, dans le royaume du Mexique, envoyée par M. Humboldt, et dans laquelle M. del Río dit avoir découvert un nouveau métal," *Ann. chim. phys.*, [1], **53**, 268–71 (1805).

(23) WALLACH, O., "Briefwechsel zwischen J. Berzelius und F. Wöhler," ref. (6), Vol. 1, p. 336.

(24) VON HOFMANN, A. W., "Zur Erinnerung an Friedrich Wöhler," *Ber.*, **15**, 3170 (Dec., 1882); A. W. VON HOFMANN and EMILIE WÖHLER, "Justus Liebig's und Friedrich Wöhler's Briefwechsel," Vol. 1, F. Vieweg und Sohn, Braunschweig, **1888**, pp. 38–9.

(25) SÖDERBAUM, H. G., "Jac. Berzelius Bref," ref. (13), Vol. 2, part 4, pp. 98–9.

(26) SEFSTRÖM, N. G., "Sur le vanadium, métal nouveau, trouvé dans du fer en barres de Eckersholm, forge qui tire sa mine de Taberg dans le Småland," *Ann. chim. phys.*, **46**, 105–11 (1831).

(27) WALLACH, O., "Briefwechsel zwischen J. Berzelius und F. Wöhler," ref. (6), Vol. 1, pp. 340–1.

(28) SCHUSTER and SHIPLEY, "Britain's Heritage of Science," Constable and Co., London, **1917**, pp. 149–50.

(29) ROSCOE, H. E., "On vanadium, one of the trivalent group of elements," *Phil. Mag.*, [4], **35**, 307–14 (Apr., 1868).

(30) "Alchemy in old New England," *J. Chem. Educ.*, **8**, 2094 (Oct., 1931); L. C. NEWELL, "Colonial chemistry. I. New England," *ibid.*, **2**, 161–4 (Mar., 1925).

(31) HATCHETT, C., "An analysis of the earthy substance from New South Wales, called sydneia, or terra australis," *Nicholson's J.*, **2**, 72–80 (May, 1798).

(32) EKEBERG, A. G., "Of the properties of the earth yttria, compared with those of glucine; of fossils, in which the first of these earths is contained; and of the discovery of a new substance of a metallic nature (tantalium)," *Nicholson's J.*, **3**, 251–5 (Dec., 1802).

(33) ROSCOE, H. E., "Researches on vanadium. Part II," *Phil. Mag.*, [4], **39**, 146–50 (Feb., 1870).

(34) FANSTEEL PRODUCTS CO., INC., "Metallic tantalum," *J. Chem. Educ.*, **2**, 1168–9 (Dec., 1925); W. VON BOLTON, "Das Tantal, seine Darstellung und seine Eigenschaften," *Z. Elektrochem.*, **11**, 45–51 (Jan. 20, 1905).

(35) "Vanadium new member of world's metal family," *J. Chem. Educ.*, **4**, 686 (May, 1927); J. W. MARDEN and M. N. RICH, "Vanadium," *Ind. Eng. Chem.*, **19**, 786–8 (July, 1927).

(36) THORPE, T. E., "The Right Honourable Sir Henry Enfield Roscoe," Longmans, Green and Co., London, **1916**, p. 18.

(37) *Ibid.*, p. 123.

(38) *Ibid.*, p. 26.

(39) *Ibid.*, pp. 38–9.

(40) *Ibid.*, pp. 125–30.

(41) *Ibid.*, p. 129.

(42) ROSCOE, H. E., "The Life and Experiences of Sir Henry Enfield Roscoe," Macmillan, London, **1906**, 420 pp.

(43) THORPE, T. E., "The Right Honourable Sir Henry Enfield Roscoe," ref. (36), pp. 199–200.

(44) VON HUMBOLDT, A., *Gilb. Ann.*, **18**, 118 (1804).

(45) WÖHLER, F., *Pogg. Ann.*, **21**, 49 (1831).

(46) BROWNE, C. A., "Some relations of early chemistry in America to medicine," *J. Chem. Educ.*, **3**, 268–70 (Mar., 1926).

(47) WATERS, T. F., "A Sketch of the Life of John Winthrop the Younger, Founder of Ipswich, Massachusetts, in 1633," printed for the Ipswich Historical Soc., **1899**, p. 76. Poem on Winthrop by B. Tompson.

(48) BLOMSTRAND, C. W., "Über die Säuren der Tantalgruppe-Mineralien," *J. prakt. Chem.*, **97**, 37–50 (Heft 1, 1866); *Oefversigt af Akad. Forh.*, **21**, 541 (1864).

(49) MOISSAN, H., "Nouveau traitement de la niobite; préparation et propriétés de la fonte de niobium," *Compt. rend.*, **133**, 20–5 (July, 1901).

(50) DEL RÍO, A. M., "Elementos de Orictognosia," "Elémens d'Orictognosie ou de la connoissance des Fossiles, disposés suivant les principes de Werner, à l'usage du Collège royal des mines du Mexique," Imprimerie de Zúñiga et Ontiveros, Mexico City, **1795**. Review in *Ann. chim. phys.*, [1], **21**, 221–4 (Feb., 1797).

(51) WEEKS, M. E., "The scientific contributions of Don A. M. del Río," *J. Chem. Educ.*, **12**, 161–6 (Apr., 1935); "The scientific contributions of the de Elhuyar Brothers," *ibid.*, **11**, 413–9 (July, 1934).

(52) "Selections from an ancient catalogue of objects of natural history formed in New England more than 100 years ago by John Winthrop, F.R.S.," *Am. J. Sci.*, [1], **47**, 282–90 (1844); C. A. BROWNE, "The three hundredth anniversary of chemical industries in America," *Ind. Eng. Chem., News Ed.*, **12**, 427–8 (Dec. 10, 1934).

(53) WEEKS, M. E., "The chemical contributions of Charles Hatchett," *J. Chem. Educ.*, **15**, 153–8 (Apr., 1938).

(54) WEEKS, M. E., "Nils Gabriel Sefström. The sesquicentennial of his birth," *Isis*, **29** (1), 49–57 (July, 1928); S. G. SJÖBERG, "Nils Gabriel Sefström and the discovery of vanadium," *J. Chem. Educ.*, **28**, 294–6 (June, 1951).

(55) ANON., "Balke- Pater et filius." *Ind. Eng. Chem., News Ed.*, **16**, 276 (May 10, 1938).

(56) BALKE, C. W., "Columbium and tantalum," *Ind. Eng. Chem.*, **27**, 1166–9 (Oct., 1935).

(57) SÖDERBAUM, H. G., "Jac. Berzelius. Levnadsteckning," Vol. 1, Almqvist and Wiksells Publishing Co., Upsala, **1929**, p. 141.

(58) HEYL, P. R., "The lingering dryad," *Am. Scientist*, **31**, 78–87 (Jan., 1943). Centenary of urea synthesis.

(59) KLICKSTEIN, H. S., "Thomas Thomson. Pioneer historian of chemistry," *Chymia* **1**, 37–53 (1948).

(60) COWARD, H. F., "John Dalton (1766–1844)," *J. Chem. Educ.*, **4**, 23–37 (Jan., 1927).

(61) WARREN, W. H., "Contemporary reception of Wöhler's discovery of the synthesis of urea," *J. Chem. Educ.*, **5**, 1539–53 (Dec., 1928).

(62) THORNTON, WILLIAM M., JR., "Tantalum as a material for standards of mass," *J. Chem. Educ.*, **16**, 157–60 (Apr., 1939).

(63) VAN DOREN, CARL, "Benjamin Franklin." Viking Press, New York, **1938**, p. 53.

(64) BLANCK, ANTON, "Berzelius som Medicine Studerande," *Lychnos*, **1948–1949**, pp. 168–205.

(65) SEFSTRÖM, N. G., "Utur Professor Sefströms Berättelse om dess sista utländska resa," *Jern-Kontorets Annaler*, **26**, 372–421 (1842).

(66) ANON., "Biografi öfver Nils Gabriel Sefström," *K. Vet. Akad. Handl.*, **1845**, pp. 459–70; *Jern-Kontorets Annaler*, new series 1, Suppl. 1–10 (1846); *Post-och Inrikes Tidningar*, **1846**, 219–20.

(67) "A Guide to the Mineral Gallery," 14th ed., British Museum, London, 1937, p. 37.

(68) SWEET, JESSIE M., "Sir Hans Sloane: Life and mineral collection," *Natural History Magazine*, **5**, 115–16 (July, 1935).

(69) FOURCROY, A.-F. DE, "Anecdotes sur la culture de la chimie en Angleterre et sur quelques chimistes anglais," *Ann. chim. phys.*, (1), **32**, 200–1 (1799, 30 Vendémiaire, an VIIIᵉ).

(70) NORDENSKIÖLD, NILS, "Beiträge zur Mineralogie Finlands. IV. Mineralogische Beschreibung des Tantalitbruches Kimitto [*sic*] in Finland," *Schweigger's J.* (4), **31**, 367–9 (1821).

(71) "Academie-Adjuncten och Chemie-Laboratorn i Upsala, Mag. And. Gust. Ekebergs biographie," *K. Vet. Acad. Handl.*, **1813**, pp. 276–9.

(72) DEL RÍO, A. M., "Elementos de orictognosia . . .," 2nd ed., Juan F. Hurtel, Philadelphia, 1832, pp. 483–5.

(73) WITTICH, E., "El descubrimiento del vanadio," *Boletín Minero*, **13**, 4–15 (Jan., 1922); POGGENDORFF, *Pogg. Ann.*, **21**, 49 (1830).

(74) TILAS, DANIEL, "Das Eisenbergwerk Taberg in Småland," *Crell's Neues chem. Archiv*, **8**, 280–1 (1791); *K. Vet. Acad. Handl.*, **22**, 15 (1760).

(75) BEIJELL, C., "Proben vom Gehalte des Eisenerzes am Taberge," *Crell's Neues chem. Archiv*, **8**, 281–2 (1791); *K. Vet. Acad. Handl.*, **22**, 28 (1760).

(76) THOMSON, THOMAS, "Travels through Sweden in the autumn of 1812," Robert Baldwin, London, 1813, pp. 286–95.

(77) FRIEND, J. N., "A textbook of inorganic chemistry," Vol. 6, part 3, Charles Griffin and Co., London, **1929**, pp. 9–13.

(78) HILLEBRAND, W. F., "The vanadium sulphide, patronite, and its mineral associates from Minasragra, Peru," *Am. J. Sci.*, (4), **24**, 141–51 (1907).

(79) BASKERVILLE, CHARLES, "The occurrence of vanadium, chromium, and titanium in peats," *J. Am. Chem. Soc.*, **21**, 706–7 (1899).

(80) HENZE, M., "Untersuchungen über das Blut der Ascidien," *Z. physiol. Chem.*, **72**, 494–501 (1911).

(81) WEBB, D. A., "Observations on the blood of certain ascidians, with special reference to the biochemistry of vanadium," *J. Exptl. Biol.*, **16**, 499–523 (1939).

Charles Hatchett. This portrait was lithographed by Day and Haghe from the painting by Thomas Phillips, and published in 1836 by Thomas Mc-Lean.

14

Contributions of Charles Hatchett

Unlike most chemists Charles Hatchett spent all his life in luxurious surroundings. He was born on January 2, 1765,[*] the son of a famous coach builder of Long Acre, London, who in 1771 built at Chelsea a mansion called "Belle Vue House" (1, 2, 3).

Most of his scientific research was done during the decade 1796 to 1806. His first paper in the *Philosophical Transactions* described his analysis of the Carinthian lead molybdate (4). "The celebrated Scheele," said he, "in 1778 read before the Academy of Sciences at Stockholm an essay in which he proved . . . that the mineral called *Molybdaena* was composed of sulfur and a peculiar metallic substance, which, like arsenic and tungsten, was liable by super-oxygenation to be converted into a metallic acid which in its properties differed from any other that had been previously discovered." Hatchett mentioned the confirmatory researches of B. Pelletier, P. J. Hjelm, and "Mr. Islmann" [J. C. Ilsemann], and added: "But the existence of this substance was known to be only in that mineral which Scheele had examined." This lead mineral from Carinthia had been described by the Abbé F. X. Wulfen and by N. J. Jacquin. For several years it was believed to be lead tungstate, but Klaproth proved it to be lead molybdate. Since Klaproth had had an insufficient amount of the mineral, Hatchett made a complete analysis of it and investigated the properties of molybdic acid.

In the following year Hatchett was made a Fellow of the Royal Society. In 1798 he analyzed "an earthy substance," *sydneia*, which Josiah Wedgwood had found in New South Wales and another specimen of it provided by Sir Joseph Banks (5). This, according to Wedgwood, was composed of "a fine white sand, a soft white earth, some colourless micaceous particles, and some which were black." Hatchett found it to consist "of siliceous earth, alumine, oxide of iron, and black lead or graphite" and concluded "that the Sydneian genus, in future, must be omitted in the mineral system."

[*] Most authors state that Hatchett was born "in about 1765." The 1935 "Annuaire" of the Académie des Sciences, however, in its list of members and correspondents, gives the definite date, January 2, 1765. This annual gives the date of his death as March 10, 1847, instead of February 10.

In the same year, he analyzed the water of the Mere of Diss (6). Benjamin Wiseman of Diss, Norfolk, had noticed that flint stones, calcareous spar, slate, and pottery left in this water from the summer of 1792 to August, 1795, acquired a metallic stain. He sent some of the water and some of the coated objects to the President and Council of the Royal Society, who forwarded them to Charles Hatchett for analysis. Although the deposit contained pyrite, the water, according to Hatchett, did not hold in solution any sulphur and scarcely any iron; it has not therefore been concerned in forming the pyrites, but it appears to me that the pyritical matter is formed in the mud and filth of the Mere; for Mr. Wiseman says . . . that 'the Mere has received the silt of the streets for ages.' Now . . . sulphur is continually formed, or rather liberated, from putrefying animal and vegetable matter, . . . and this most probably has been the case at Diss. . . ."

In the following year Sir Everard Home interested Mr. Hatchett in the chemical composition of dental enamel (7, 8). Since the tooth of the elephant is composed of three different structures, Sir Everard wished to know whether the materials themselves were different or only differently arranged." Hatchett showed that the enamel was composed of calcium phosphate. "The enamel," said he, "has been supposed not a phosphate but a carbonate of lime. This error may have arisen from its solubility in acetous acid or distilled vinegar; but the effects of the acetous acid are in every respect the same on powdered bone as on the enamel" (8).

Hatchett then investigated the composition of shell and bone. "When it is applied to the cuttle-bone of the shops . . . ," said he, "the term bone is here misapplied . . . for this substance in composition is exactly similar to shell, and consists of various membranes hardened by carbonate of lime, without the smallest mixture of phosphate" (8).

Mr. Hatchett observed that the external skeleton of crustaceans and the egg shells of birds contain more calcium carbonate than calcium phosphate but that in bones the phosphate predominates. " It is possible," said he, ". . . that some bones may be found composed only of phosphate of lime: and that thus shells containing only carbonate of lime and bones containing only phosphate of lime will form the two extremities in the chain. . . ."

In 1800 he published a paper which won the approbation and interest of Sir Humphry Davy (9, 10). "Mr. Hatchett," said he, "has noticed in his excellent paper on zoöphytes that isinglass is almost wholly composed of gelatine. I have found that 100 grains of good and dry isinglass contain more than 98 grains of matter soluble in water. . . ." Dr. John Bostock (1774–1846) also praised this paper. "The term mucus," said he, "had been generally employed in a vague and unrestricted sense until Mr. Hatchett . . . attempted to assign to it a more appropriate and definite meaning. He conceives that jelly and mucus are only modifications of the same substance . . . he considers it to be entitled to the appellation of mucus when it is soluble in cold water and cannot be brought to a gelatinous state . . . the ideas which I have formed of the nature of jelly and mucus . . . differ materially from those of Mr. Hatchett . . . Mr. Hatchett . . . speaks of the white of the egg as consisting of pure albumen, but I believe that in this particular he will be found not perfectly accurate. . . ." Dr. Bostock had found it to contain also a small amount of a substance incapable of coagulation (11).

William Thomas Brande, 1788–1866. British chemist and mineralogist. Successor to Sir Humphry Davy at the Royal Institution. Son-in-law of Charles Hatchett. Author of Brande's "Manual of Chemistry." Lecturer on mineralogical chemistry.

Soon after the turn of the century, Mr. Hatchett became interested in William Thomas Brande, a young apothecaries' apprentice who had recently moved to Chiswick. He encouraged the boy to collect and classify ores and rocks, and presented him with some of his duplicate specimens; the boy, in turn, sometimes assisted Mr. Hatchett in analyzing minerals (1). Brande's first scientific paper was published in *Nicholson's Journal* when he was only sixteen years old. When he became Sir Humphry Davy's successor at the Royal Institution, Brande increased the mineral collection and used it in his lectures. He later married Charles Hatchett's daughter.

Hatchett's greatest achievement was probably his discovery of the metal niobium (12). While he was arranging some minerals at the British Museum, one of them attracted his attention. From Sir Hans

Sloane's catalogue he found that it had been sent by "Mr. Winthrop of Massachusetts."

Early accounts of the discovery of columbite differ in several important respects. While examining some minerals in the British Museum, half a century after the death of its founder, Sir Hans Sloane, Charles Hatchett became interested in a small, dark, heavy specimen which bore some resemblance to the "Siberian chromate of iron" on which he was then making some experiments.

Dedication Page from Brande's "Manual of Chemistry," Third Edition, London, 1830

Courtesy Franklin Institute

"Upon referring to Sir Hans Sloane's catalogue," said Hatchett before the Royal Society on November 26, 1801, "I found that this specimen was only described as 'a very heavy black stone, with golden streaks' which proved to be yellow mica; and it appeared that it had been sent with various specimens of iron ores to Sir Hans Sloane by Mr. Winthrop of Massachusetts. The name of the mine, or place where it was found, is also noted in the catalogue; the writing, however, is scarcely legible: it appears to be an Indian name (Nautneague); but I am informed by several American gentlemen that many of the Indian names (by which certain small districts, hills, etc., were forty or fifty years ago distinguished) are now totally forgotten, and European names have been adopted in the room of them. This may have been the case in the present instance; but, as the other specimens sent by Mr. Winthrop were from the mines of Massachusetts, there is every reason to believe that the mineral substance in question came from one of them, although it may not now be easy to identify the particular mine" (12).

Sir Hans Sloane, 1660–1753. British physician and collector. Editor of the *Philosophical Transactions.* President of the Royal Society. The books, pictures, coins, and specimens which he bequeathed to the nation became the nucleus of the British Museum. The specimen of columbite in which Hatchett discovered niobium was from this collection.

Printed by C. Hullmandel
From T. Faulkner's "Historical and topographical description of Chelsea" 1829

In the following January, *Nicholson's Journal* stated that "the mineral was sent with some iron ores to Sir Hans Sloane by Mr. Winthrop of Massachusetts [sic], and there is therefore every reason to believe that it came from some of the iron mines in that province [sic]" (12).

In the fall of the same year, the *Medical Repository* made a preliminary announcement of Hatchett's discovery of "a metal in an ore lately brought from North-America. . . . We have no particular information from what spot or region the mineral was procured" (36).

Courtesy New York Historical Society

Samuel Latham Mitchill, 1764–1831. Professor of "chemistry, natural history, agriculture, and the other arts depending thereon" at Columbia College, New York City. Editor of the *Medical Repository,* a journal devoted to the general progress of science. See ref. (*50*).

After reading Hatchett's paper in the *Philosophical Transactions* (*12*), Samuel Latham Mitchill, editor, published an abstract of it in his *Medical Repository* (*36, 50*). In commenting on the name "Nautneague" he said, "From the same place, it is probable, more of the like ore can be obtained. This is particularly desirable, as Mr. Hatchett has had so small a piece to work upon, and no other specimen but the half which he reserved for the museum is known to exist. We hope the gentlemen of Massachusetts, who respect Mr. Winthrop's memory and are acquainted with the scope and direction of his researches, will find out the mine and procure more samples of this singular mineral. We think this matter would not be unworthy of that excellent institution the Historical Society" (*36*).

"No complete disoxydation of it," continued Mitchill, "has as yet been effected. The pure metal, therefore, has not been seen, even by Mr. Hatchett himself. And if this discerning experimenter had succeeded in freeing the metal from its oxygen, the quantity he worked upon was so very small that it would have been impossible to have gratified many of the curious by presents. At this time it is not known what quantity may exist in nature, nor to what economical uses it may be applied.

"While we express our hopes that the whole history of this Columbian mineral will soon be made known, we sincerely deplore the afflicting and untimely death of our friend and countryman, Mr. Thomas P. Smith, from whose industry, acuteness, and zeal in chemical (and, indeed, almost the whole circle of physical) researches, Mr. Hatchett informs the Royal Society he had anticipated important aid in this inquiry" (*36*).

In his annual oration before the Chemical Society of Philadelphia in 1798, this youthful chemist voiced his conviction that "The only true bases on which the *Independence* of our country can rest are *Agriculture* and *Manufactures*. To the promotion of these nothing tends in a higher degree than Chemistry. . . . It is to a general diffusion of a knowledge of this science, next to the *Virtue* of our countrymen, that we are to look for the firm establishment of our *Independence*" (*47*). In the return journey from England, Thomas P. Smith died "in consequence of the bursting of a gun" at the age of only twenty-five years (*36*). Mrs. Gertrude D. Hess, assistant librarian, kindly searched the manuscripts of the American Philosophical Society by and pertaining to Thomas P. Smith, but was unable to find there any mention of columbite.

In the spring of 1805 the *Medical Repository* published an article entitled "Place where the ore of columbium was found" (*37*). "It has been ascertained," the article stated, "that the specimen of this metal [*sic*] upon which the experiments were made, as mentioned in our *Med. Rep. Hex. i*, vol. vi., p. 322, was taken from a spring of water in the town of New London, in the State of Connecticut. The fountain is near the house in which Governor Winthrop used to live, and is about three miles distant from the margin of salt water, at the head of the harbour. This is the spot heretofore called Nautneague; which is in Connecticut and not in Massachusetts. By the politeness of Francis B. Winthrop, Esq., of New York, the manuscript papers of his ancestor, relative to this place and to the minerals he carried to Hans Sloane, have been sent to the Historical Society of Massachusetts. By their care, we hope, every interesting particular concerning this substance and the place where it was originally found will be made known to the public. It will then be easy for gentlemen to visit the spot and to collect other specimens of this singular ore" (37).

In the same year A.-L. Millin published in his *Magasin Encyclopé-dique* what seems to be a rather inaccurate French translation of the preceding article. He said he had obtained the information from M. Valentin, a physician and skilful physicist and naturalist of Marseilles (38).

The "Mr. Winthrop of Massachusetts" referred to by Charles Hatchett was John Winthrop (1681–1747), grandson of the first governor of Connecticut and great grandson of the first governor of Massachusetts. He was a Fellow and very active member of the Royal Society. Like his paternal grandfather, who had been one of the original Fellows of this Society, he liked to collect natural objects. The Journal Book of the Royal Society for June 27, 1734, stated that "Mr. Winthrop presented several curiosities from New England, as contained in the following list. . . . These curiosities are a part of a large collection shewn at several meetings during the subsequent winter, and the whole cata-logue to which these numbers refer is entered after the minutes of the day" (39). Sir Hans Sloane was then President of the Royal Society (40).

In 1844 Benjamin Silliman and Benjamin Silliman, Jr., published this historic list in their *American Journal of Science* and remarked in a foot-note "it has been supposed that the original specimen on which Mr. Hatch-ett made the discovery of *columbic acid* was sent in this invoice, and that some hint as to the locality from whence it came might be had" (39). The only entry the Sillimans could find in this list, however, that corre-sponded at all with Hatchett's description of columbite was "No. 348. A black mineral, very heavy, from the inland parts of the country." They concluded that "we must therefore rest content probably in ignorance of the exact locality of that interesting specimen, although mineralogists have, on what evidence does not appear, considered New London as the locality" (39).

Berzelius even doubted the American origin of columbite. In a letter to Thomas Thomson in the autumn of 1814 (see page 349), he stated that "Mr. Hatchett gave this name after the place where it was thought the fossil had been found; now it is not good practice to name elementary substances in chemistry after the places where they have first been found; not to mention the fact that the place where columbite was found is still doubtful, in the same degree as it is not certain that it comes from America."

In his "Report on the Geological Survey of the State of Connecticut," Dr. Charles Upham Shepard said of columbite: "The State of Connecticut furnished the first sample of this ore to science. . . . The chinastone quarry at Middletown has furnished the most extraordinary specimens of columbite yet described in the world. A single group of crystals obtained at this place weighed fourteen pounds. . . . It is also found in small quantity at Haddam. . . . The first sample was sent by Governor Winthrop to Sir Hans Sloane, and was deposited with the collection of the gentleman in the British Museum, where it was examined by Mr. Hatchett, and afterwards by Dr. Wollaston. The specimen was supposed to have been found near New London, which was the residence of Governor Winthrop; but as the ore has not been rediscovered in that vicinity, it is more probable that it was obtained from the region of Middletown" (41).

Since Sir Hans Sloane was only sixteen years old when Governor Winthrop died, Shepard's statement that the columbite had been sent to Sloane by Governor Winthrop is probably erroneous. Hatchett's remark in 1801 that many Indian names (such as Nautneague) which were used "forty or fifty years ago . . . are now totally forgotten" implies that he understood that the original specimen of columbite must have been labeled in about the middle of the eighteenth century (12). He referred to the sender, moreover, not as "Governor" Winthrop but as "Mr." Winthrop.

In his "Chemistry in Old Philadelphia" Edgar F. Smith stated that "Hatchett found . . . a new element in a mineral of the Royal Society Collection which had been sent in from Haddam, Connecticut, and been called there *columbite* by Governor Winthrop" (42).

In an article on the life and mineral collection of Sir Hans Sloane, Jessie M. Sweet states that "The only specimen which fortunately is still in the Mineral Collection is the original fragment of columbite (B. M. 60309), of which a brief account may be given here. Sloane describes it in the catalogue of 'Metalls,' No. 2029, as: A very heavy black stone with golden streaks . . . from Nautneague. From Mr. Winthrop" (40).

Miss Sweet adds that when John Winthrop (1681–1747) was elected a Fellow of the Royal Society in 1734, "he presented more than six hundred specimens (mostly minerals), together with a manuscript catalogue of them, to the Society. . . . Many of these specimens appear to have been incorporated into the Sloane collection, as several entries in the Winthrop

and Sloane manuscript catalogues are identical, and the columbite probably came from Winthrop at that time" (*40*).

Miss Sweet also stated that "it was surmised that 'Nautneague' was
another name for Naumeaug (now New London, Connecticut), and
the specimen was believed to have been found in a spring of water,
near the house of Governor Winthrop. . . . The columbite is figured and
described in James Sowerby's "Exotic Mineralogy," 1811–1820, vol. 1, p. 11
and plate 6, and compares favourably with Sloane's description, but
now the specimen has no longer any 'golden streaks' " (*40*).

**John Winthrop, 1681–
1747.** The specimen of
columbite which Hatchett
analyzed had been sent to
the Royal Society by this
John Winthrop, a grandson
of John Winthrop, first governor of Connecticut. This
portrait was reproduced
from a copy in the collections of the Massachusetts
Historical Society. Volume
40 (1737–38) of the *Philosophical Transactions* was
dedicated to him by Crom-
well Mortimer, Secretary
of the Royal Society.

Courtesy Massachusetts Historical Society

In 1940 Dr. C. A. Browne wrote Mr. Allyn B. Forbes of the Massachusetts Historical Society for information regarding the manuscript
paper which Francis B. Winthrop of New York is said to have sent to
this Society. According to *Nicholson's Journal* for 1806, this manuscript
referred to the mineral which F. B. Winthrop's "ancestor" had given Sir
Hans Sloane and to the place where it was found (*43*). However, no
trace of such a document could be found. Francis B. Winthrop (1754–

1817) was a grandson of John Winthrop (1681–1747) and great-great-grandson of the first governor of Connecticut (*44*).

The Massachusetts Historical Society has preserved a commonplace book which originally belonged to John Winthrop (1681–1747). In it there is a letter which Francis B. Winthrop wrote to his brother Thomas L. Winthrop of Boston on September 10, 1803, describing the spring at New London in connection with their grandfather. "I think you must

To the Honourable

JOHN WINTHROP Efq;

Fellow of the ROYAL SOCIETY.

S I R,

I Beg Leave to make this Addrefs to you in Confideration of thofe excellent Virtues and rare Accomplifhments, with which you are endowed both as a Gentleman and a Scholar. Your great Knowledge of the true and moft fecret Branches of Philofophy, which has been for many Generations handed down in your honourable Family ; your profound Skill in all mineral Affairs, particularly in Metallurgy, which you have likewife inherited from your noble and truly learned Anceftors, of which you have given ample Proofs by thofe curious Collections of *American Minerals*, wherewith you have enriched the *Mufeum's* both of the *Royal Society*, of which you are an illuftrious Orna-

A   ment

DEDICATION.

ment as well as worthy Member, and of their learned and moft eminent Prefident the Honourable Sir *Hans Sloane* Baronet : Your perfonal Acquaintance with our ingenious *Latin* Author Dr. *Cramer*, who cannot but greatly approve of my dedicating to you a Tranflation of his excellent Book on the docimaftic Art ; thefe, Sir, have been the Motives, for which I could not more juftly, nor more judicioufly fhelter this my new Performance under any other Name, than yours.

However, Sir, I fhall always take it as a fingular Favour done me, if you will be pleafed to accept this Tender of my Refpect, as a Teftimony of the vaft Efteem and fincere Friendfhip, wherewith I have the Honour to be,

S I R,

Your moft obedient,

And moft humble Servant,

London,
May 3, 1741.

Dedication of the English Translation of J. A. Cramer's "Elements of the Art of Assaying Metals," London, 1741. It refers to John Winthrop (1681–1747), grandson of the first governor of Connecticut.

remember this spring," said he, "It is about three miles from the sea, which answers to the distance in the memo of articles presented to the Royal Society" (*45*).

In the letters of Governor John Winthrop the Younger, published with the Winthrop Papers of the Massachusetts Historical Collections, there is no mention of columbite. His interest in minerals, despite the difficulty of collecting them, is expressed, however, in a letter to Sir

Robert Moray on August 18, 1668. "I have been very inquisitive," wrote the Governor, "after all sorts of minerals, wch this wildernesse may probably affoard; but indeed the constant warrs, wch have continued amongst the Indians since I came last over, hath hindred all progresse in searching out such matters. . . . Those shewes of minerals, wch we have frō the Indians doe only demonstrate that such are in reality in the country, but they usually bring but small pieces, wch are found accidentally in their huntings, sticking in some rock or on the surface of the earth, on the side of some hill, or banke of a river . . ." (46).

From the existing evidence, it seems impossible to prove conclusively whether columbite was discovered by John Winthrop the Younger, first governor of Connecticut, and bequeathed to his grandson, John Winthrop (1681–1747), or whether it was originally discovered by the grandson. It is possible, however, that this question may some day be settled by the finding of hitherto unknown documents.

Hatchett fused the ore with potassium carbonate. When he took up the melt with boiling water, a brown residue remained. When nitric acid was added to the yellow filtrate, a copious white precipitate was thrown down. "The preceding experiments shew," said he, "that the ore which has been analyzed consists of iron combined with an unknown substance and that the latter constitutes more than three fourths of the whole. This substance is proved to be of a metallic nature by the coloured precipitates which it forms with prussiate of potash and with tincture of galls; by the effects which zinc produces when immersed in the acid solutions; and by the colour which it communicates . . . to concrete phosphoric acid, when melted with it . . . ." He mentioned that it retained oxygen tenaciously and that the oxide was acidic. Although the specimen Hatchett analyzed was very small, he hoped to get more soon from "a gentleman now in England (Mr. Smith, Secretary to the American Philosophical Society)." This was evidently Thomas P. Smith, who died in 1802.

Hatchett named the new metal *columbium* and stated that its "olive green prussiate and the orange-coloured gallate . . . may probably be employed with advantage as pigments." He also described his unsuccessful attempts to reduce the oxide to the metal. From his careful use of Lavoisier's new nomenclature, it is evident that Hatchett was not a phlogistonist.

In 1798 the Committee of Privy Council for considering the state of the coinage reported that the gold coin was suffering considerable losses in weight, and requested Henry Cavendish and Charles Hatchett to examine it "to ascertain whether this loss was occasioned by any defect" (13). Their experiments were begun near the end of 1798 and completed in April, 1801. At Cavendish's request the report was made

by Hatchett alone.   Hatchett stated, however, ". . . At all times I was
favoured with his valuable advice; and the machines to produce friction,
as well as the dies were entirely contrived by himself. . . ."

Hatchett studied the binary alloys of gold with arsenic, antimony,
zinc, cobalt, nickel, manganese, bismuth, lead, tin, iron, platinum, copper,
and silver, and confirmed the prevailing opinion that of these metals only
copper and silver are suitable for alloying gold for coinage.   He concluded
"that gold made standard by silver and copper is rather to be preferred
for coin . . ." and added that "there is commonly some silver in the gold

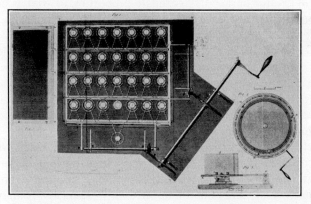

(Phil. Trans., 1803)

**Apparatus Designed by Henry Cavendish and Used by
Charles Hatchett for Determining the Comparative Wear of
Gold When Alloyed by Various Metals.**   Two frames, one
above the other, each carrying twenty-eight coins, rubbed
the upper coins backward and forward over the ones below.
Each of the smaller concentric circles represents a coin.   To
avoid the formation of furrows, the direction in which the
coins rubbed against each other was made to vary continually.

which is sent to the Mint."   He also stated, not without humor, that "our
gold coin suffers but little by friction against itself; and the chief cause
of natural and fair wear probably arises from extraneous and gritty
particles; . . . the united effect of every species of friction to which they
may be subjected, *fairly and unavoidably,* during circulation . . . will
by no means account for the great and rapid diminution which has been
observed in the gold coin of this country. . . ."   He added that the study
of alloys had not kept pace with the rapid progress of chemistry and
that "Few additions have been made to the compound metals employed
by the ancients."

In 1804 Hatchett published an analysis of a "triple sulphuret of lead, antimony, and copper." James Smithson (1765–1829), founder of the Smithsonian Institution, disagreed with his conclusions. "It is not probable," said he, "that the present ore is a direct quadruple combination of the three metals and sulphur and that these, in their simple states, are its immediate component parts; it is much more credible that it is a combination of the three sulphurets of these metals . . ." (14, 15).

At the same time Hatchett became interested in lac (16). Geoffroy the Younger and J.-A.-C. Chaptal had regarded it as a kind of wax, but F. C. Gren and A.-F. Fourcroy believed it to be a true resin. Hatchett concluded "that although lac is indisputably the production of insects, yet . . . the greater part of its aggregate properties, as well as of its component ingredients, are such as more immediately appertain to vegetable bodies. . . ."

In 1804 he analyzed a strongly magnetic specimen of pyrite (17) to determine whether the magnetic polarity was inherent in the iron sulfide or whether minute particles of "the ordinary magnetical iron ore" [magnetite] were interspersed in it. Although he could find no previous mention of magnetic iron sulfide, Hatchett proved experimentally "that the three inflammable substances, carbon, sulphur, and phosphorus . . . possess the property of enabling iron to retain the power of magnetism. . . ."

He continued the study of bitumens which he had begun in 1798 and strengthened the evidence "that bituminous substances are derived from the organized kingdoms of nature, and especially from vegetable bodies." He analyzed a "schistus" (18) which Sir Joseph Banks had discovered near a geyser near Reykum, Iceland, and found it to consist of water, oily bitumen, mixed gas, charcoal, silica, oxide of iron, and alumina.

When Sir James Hall (1761–1832) read of this work, he recalled his own experiments on "the effects of compression in modifying the effects of heat," and concluded that "the changes which, with true scientific modesty, he [Hatchett] ascribes to an unknown cause, may have resulted from various heats acting under pressure of various force" (19). Sir James subjected the theories of the geologists to the test of chemical experiment and showed that when limestone is heated under pressure, it is not converted into quicklime but into crystalline marble.

After analyzing some specimens from a pitch lake of Trinidad, Hatchett concluded that "a considerable part of the aggregate mass at Trinidad was not pure mineral pitch or asphaltum, but rather a porous stone of the argillaceous genus, much impregnated with bitumen. The specimens he analyzed, however, were not representative of the lake as a whole" (20).

In 1804 William Nicholson, the editor, chose Mr. Hatchett and Edward Howard to serve with him on a committee to judge Richard Chenevix's alloy of platinum and mercury which Chenevix believed identical with palladium, the new metal which had been announced anonymously by W. H. Wollaston. Hatchett saw with his own eyes some of the experiments made by the enthusiastic but misguided Chenevix.

During the years 1805 and 1806 Hatchett published three papers on an artificial tanning agent (21). He mentioned the researches of Nicolas Deyeux (1745–1837), Armand Seguin (1767–1835), and Sir Humphry Davy on the natural tanning agents, and added that R. Chenevix had "observed that a decoction of coffee-berries did not precipitate gelatine unless they had been previously roasted; so that tannin had in this case either been formed or had been developed from the other vegetable principles by the effects of heat."

Hatchett treated various kinds of wood, coal, and coke with nitric acid and found that "a substance very analogous to tannin . . . may at any time be produced by exposing carbonaceous substances, whether vegetable, animal, or mineral, to the action of nitric acid." He also "converted skin into leather by means of materials which, to professional men, must appear extraordinary, such as deal sawdust, asphaltum, common turpentine, pit coal, wax candle, and a piece of the same sort of skin. . . ."

Dr. John Bostock tried unsuccessfully to use Hatchett's artificial tan as a test for "jelly" [gelatine]. Although it had been stated "on the highest authority, that of Mr. Hatchett and Mr. Davy . . . that isinglass consists of nearly pure jelly," Dr. Bostock found that isinglass from the shops contained a certain amount of insoluble matter which he believed to be coagulated albumen. Dr. G. Melandri of Milan also investigated Hatchett's tannin.

M.-E. Chevreul, near the beginning of his surprisingly long career, studied Hatchett's papers and prepared some of the "tannin." Hatchett had found that pit coal which contained no resinous substance was dissolved completely by nitric acid and converted into the artificial tannin, whereas any resinous matter remained undissolved. When Chevreul treated pit coal with nitric acid, however, evaporated the solution, and poured it into water, "a yellow matter separated, which was much more abundant than what remained in solution, and had no property that rendered it similar to resins . . . yet I do not allow myself," said Chevreul, "the least reflection on the labours of that celebrated English chemist, as I am too fully aware that different modes of operating and the different varieties of the bodies examined . . . may produce a variation in the results. . . ." Chevreul found that the water-soluble substance which precipitated gelatine copiously was "a compound of nitric acid and carbonaceous matter . . ." (22). These artificial tannins have since been identified as picric acid and other nitro derivatives of phenols (23).

Thomas Thomson said in 1810, "Till lately the analysis of vegetable substances was almost entirely overlooked by British chemists; but the fineness of the field has now begun to attract their attention. Experiments of great importance have been published by Davy, Chenevix &c and above all by Hatchett . . ." (24).

Michel-Eugène Chevreul, 1786–1889. French chemist and psychologist who made notable contributions to the chemistry of fats and oils, soap, candles, and dyes. He lived to be almost one hundred and three years old, sound and active in mind and body. When he investigated Hatchett's artificial tanning agents, Chevreul was only twenty-four years old (twenty-one years younger than Hatchett). See refs. (48, 49, and 52).

On February 21, 1809, Hatchett became a member of the famous Literary Club which had been founded in 1764 by Dr. Samuel Johnson and Sir Joshua Reynolds (51). As treasurer of the club, Hatchett prepared a brief historical account of it, which appears in Boswell's "Life of Johnson" (25). The club also included, among others, Edmund Burke, Oliver Goldsmith, David Garrick, Edward Gibbon, Adam Smith, Sir Joseph Banks, Sir Charles Blagden, Sir Humphry Davy, Dr. W. H. Wollaston, Sir Walter Scott, Sir Thomas Lawrence, and Dr. Thomas Young.

Hatchett also took an active part in the *Animal Chemistry Club,* which met alternately at his home and that of Sir Everard Home. Once every three months, Sir Benjamin Brodie, Sir Humphry Davy, W. T. Brande, Mr. John George Children, and a few others dined with the two hosts and discussed their researches in physiological chemistry (*26, 27, 28*). According to Sir Benjamin Brodie, "they were very rational meetings, in which a good deal of scientific discussion was mixed up with lively and agreeable conversation. The society continued to exist for ten or eleven years, but during the latter part of the time, some other members were added to it, and it degenerated into a mere dinner club. Hatchett, who had now inherited a considerable fortune on the death of his father, had ceased to work in chemistry (in spite of the remonstrance of Sir Joseph Banks, who used to say to him in his rough way that 'he would find being a gentleman of fortune was a confounded bad trade'), but he had previously laid up a large store of knowledge, abounded in the materials of conversation, and was a delightful companion . . ." (*28*).

Hatchett was one of the "educated men, with the sagacity for which this nation is famous" who helped to entertain Berzelius in 1812 (*29*). Since Berzelius understood little of what the English chemists were saying, he had a dull time at Hatchett's dinner party. It was there nevertheless, that he first made the acquaintance of Dr. Alexandre Marcet.

In his travel diary Berzelius wrote, "Hatchett himself is a very agreeable man of about forty to forty-five years. His father was a rich coachmaker, and the son, although a famous chemist at the time of his father's death, has continued to carry on the business. He is in very good circumstances, and lives in Roehampton on a little estate built in a fine Italian style and excellently maintained. . . . Close by his Italian villa he has a very well-equipped laboratory, but for a long time he has not worked" (*30*).

When the English translation of Berzelius' treatise on the composition of animal fluids appeared, Dr. Marcet wrote, "Your great memoir is an honour to us. Hatchett, however, complains that, when you hunted in his grounds, you didn't even cite him; but I have explained to him, as best I could, the haste in which you found yourself and your necessity of abstaining from reference work."

"I am very sorry," replied Berzelius, ". . . . but if you take this matter up with him again, tell him that I am absolutely ignorant of any work of his on these subjects other than that of the testaceae. . . ." Berzelius also explained that he had confined himself almost entirely to a description of his own work. Dr. Marcet replied, "I gave your little compliment to Hatchett, who seemed entirely satisfied with it, and sends you his best regards. You will see on consulting *Thomson* [Thomas Thomson, "A system of chemistry," 1810] that he has written more than once on animal substances" (29).

In 1813 Hatchett published in the *Annals of Philosophy* a method of separating iron and manganese (31). This paper was in the form of a letter to Thomas Thomson, the editor, and was dated "Mount Clare, Roehampton, Sept. 25, 1813." A. F. Gehlen had used succinic acid to separate these two metals, Professor J. F. John had used oxalic acid, but Hatchett simply precipitated the ferric hydroxide from a neutral solution containing ammonium chloride, leaving the manganese in solution.

In 1817 he described a method of renovating musty "corn" [wheat] by floating off the damaged grain with boiling water and carefully drying the rest (32).

In his history of Chelsea (33), Thomas Faulkner has left a contemporary description of Hatchett's fine home, Belle Vue House. "This capital mansion," says Faulkner, "was built by Mr. Hatchett's father in 1771; and the weeping willow opposite to the house, reckoned one of the finest trees of its kind in England, was planted by him in 1776; it commands beautiful views of the Thames and the distant Surrey Hills." In the house were paintings by several great masters, a portrait of Mrs. Hatchett by Gainsborough, a large organ, a collection of manuscript and printed music, and some Mongol idols collected by Hatchett's friend Peter Simon Pallas, the famous traveler. "The Library," said Faulkner, "is extensive, and contains many valuable editions of the Greek and Latin Classics, together with a numerous series of Historical Works, and the voluminous Transactions and Memoirs of the Royal Society and other similar learned Institutions of Europe."

In December, 1818, Dr. Marcet wrote to Berzelius, "Wollaston, [Sir William] Congreve, and Hatchett are hard at work, but up to the present haven't produced anything." Three years later he wrote: "Hatchett is taking care of his money and paying court to personages with grand titles; but is no longer doing anything in chemistry, and I do not even know that he is showing much interest in what others are doing" (29). He must have retained some interest, however, for on September 15, 1823, he was elected as a correspondent for the chemical section of the *Académie des Sciences*. In 1836 Hatchett published a quarto brochure on "The spikenard of the ancients." He died at his home, Belle Vue House, Chelsea, on February 10, 1847, at the age of eighty-two years.

In 1821 the Reverend J. J. Conybeare (1779–1824) named an Australian mineral in honor of "the eminent chemist to whom we are indebted for the most valuable contributions towards the history and analysis of this class of mineral substances"; this form of mineral tallow is still known as *hatchettine* or *hatchettite*. He found later, however, that it was identical with the substance W. T. Brande had referred to as *mineral adipocere* (*34*).

In 1877 the American mineralogical chemist J. Lawrence Smith named a mineral from North Carolina, a columbate of uranium, *hatchettolite,* because Hatchett's discovery of columbium (niobium) "was clear, precise, and well made out, and has never been controverted" (*35*).

The author wishes to thank Dr. C. A. Browne and Mr. Allyn B. Forbes for kindly placing at her disposal their correspondence on the history of columbite, and Mrs. Gertrude D. Hess for examining the papers which Thomas P. Smith bequeathed to the American Philosophical Society.

LITERATURE CITED

(*1*) STEPHEN, LESLIE and SIDNEY LEE, "Dictionary of National Biography," Vol. 25, Smith, Elder and Co., London, **1891**, p. 153. Article on Hatchett by Gordon Goodwin.

(*2*) Anonymous obituary of Charles Hatchett, *Gentlemen's Mag.*, n. s., **28**, 214–5 (Aug., 1847).

(*3*) FAULKNER, THOMAS, "A Historical and Topographical Description of Chelsea and Its Environs," Vol 1, T. Faulkner, Chelsea, **1829**, pp. 89–92.

(*4*) HATCHETT, CHARLES, "An analysis of the Carinthian molybdate of lead . . . ," *Phil. Trans.*, **86**, 285–339 (1796).

(*5*) HATCHETT, CHARLES, "An analysis of the earthy substance from New South Wales, called sydneia, or terra australis," *ibid.*, **88**, 110–29 (1798); *Nicholson's J.*, **2**, 72–80 (May, 1798).

(*6*) HATCHETT, CHARLES, "Analysis of the water of the Mere of Diss," *Phil. Trans.*, **88**, 572–81 (1798); *Nicholson's J.*, **3**, 80–4 (May, 1799).

(*7*) HOME, SIR EVERARD, "Some observations on the structure of the teeth of graminivorous quadrupeds . . . ," *Phil. Trans.*, **89**, 243–7 (1799).

(*8*) HATCHETT, CHARLES, "Experiments and observations on shell and bone," *Phil. Trans.*, **89**, 315–34 (1799); *Nicholson's J.*, **3**, 500–6 (Feb., 1800); *ibid.*, **3**, 529–34 (March, 1800).

(*9*) HATCHETT, CHARLES, "Chemical experiments on zoöphytes," *Phil. Trans.*, **90**, 327–402 (1800).

(*10*) DAVY, SIR H., "An account of some experiments on the constituent parts of some astringent vegetables," *Nicholson's J.*, [2], **5**, 259 (Aug., 1803).

(*11*) BOSTOCK, JOHN, "Observations and experiments for the purpose of ascertaining the definite characters of the primary animal fluids . . ." *Nicholson's J.*, [2], **11**, 251, 254 (Aug., 1805).

(*12*) HATCHETT, CHARLES, "An analysis of a mineral substance from North America containing a metal hitherto unknown," *Phil. Trans.*, **92**, 49–66 (1802). Read Nov. 26, 1801. *Nicholson's J.*, [2], **1**, 32–4 (Jan., 1802).

(*13*) HATCHETT, CHARLES, "Experiments and observations on the various alloys, the specific gravity, and on the comparative wear of gold," *Phil. Trans.*, **93**, 43–194 (1803); *Nicholson's J.*, [2], **5**, 286–303 (Aug., 1803); *ibid.*, [2], **6**, 145–61 (Nov., 1803).

(*14*) HATCHETT, CHARLES "Analysis of a triple sulphuret of lead, antimony and copper from Cornwall," *Phil. Trans.*, **94**, 63–9 (1804).

(*15*) SMITHSON, JAMES, "On the composition of the compound sulphuret from Huel Boys . . . ," *Nicholson's J.*, [2], **20**, 332–3 (Suppl., 1808).

(16) HATCHETT, CHARLES, "Analytical experiments and observations on lac," *Phil. Trans.*, **94**, 191–218 (1804); *Nicholson's J.*, [2], **10**, 45–55 (Jan., 1805); *ibid.*, [2], **10**, 95–102 (Feb., 1805).

(17) HATCHETT, CHARLES, "An analysis of the magnetical pyrites; with remarks on some of the other sulphurets of iron," *Phil. Trans.*, **94**, 315–45 (1804); *Nicholson's J.*, [2], **10**, 265–76 (Apr., 1805); *ibid.*, [2], **11**, 6–17 (May, 1805).

(18) HATCHETT, CHARLES, "Observations on the change of some of the proximate principles of vegetables into bitumen; with analytical experiments on a peculiar substance which is found with the Bovey coal," *Phil. Trans.*, **94**, 385–410 (1804); *Nicholson's J.*, [2], **10**, 181–200 (March, 1805); *ibid.*, **2**, 248–53 (Sept., 1798).

(19) HALL, SIR JAMES, "Account of a series of experiments showing the effects of compression in modifying the effects of heat," *Nicholson's J.*, [2], **14**, 118 (June, 1806); *ibid.*, [2], **14**, 201–2 (July, 1806).

(20) NUGENT, NICHOLAS, "Account of the Pitch Lake of the Island of Trinidad," *ibid.*, [2], **32**, 209 (July, 1812).

(21) HATCHETT, CHARLES, "On an artificial substance which possesses the principal characteristic properties of tannin," *Phil. Trans.*, **95**, 211–24, 285–315 (1805); *ibid.*, **96**, 109–46 (1806); *Nicholson's J.*, [2], **12**, 327–31 (Suppl., 1805); *ibid.*, [2], **13**, 23–36 (Jan., 1806); *ibid.*, [2], **15**, 15–31 (Sept., 1806); *ibid.*, [2], **15**, 86–98 (Oct., 1806).

(22) CHEVREUL, M. E., "Tanning substances formed by the action of nitric acid on several vegetable matters," *Nicholson's J.*, [2], **32**, 360–74 (Suppl., 1812); *Ann. chim. phys.*, [1], **73**, 36–66 (1810).

(23) WOLESENSKY, EDWARD, "Investigation of synthetic tanning material," Bureau of Standards Technologic Paper No. 302 (1925), pp. 6–7.

(24) THOMSON, THOMAS, "A System of Chemistry," 4th ed., Vol. 5, Bell and Bradfute, Edinburgh, **1810**, p. 180.

(25) BOSWELL, JAMES, "Life of Samuel Johnson, LL.D.," Vol. 2, edited by J. W. Croker, George Bell and Sons, London, **1876**, pp. 325–9.

(26) HOLMES, TIMOTHY, "Sir Benjamin Collins Brodie," T. Fisher Unwin, London, **1898**, pp. 46 and 61–2.

(27) Anonymous obituary of W. T. Brande, *J. Chem. Soc.* (London), **19**, 509–11 (1866).

(28) HAWKINS, CHARLES, "The Works of Sir Benjamin Collins Brodie, with an Autobiography," Vol. 1, Longman, Green, Longman, Roberts, and Green, London, **1865**, pp. 55–8.

(29) SÖDERBAUM, H. G., "Jac. Berzelius Bref," Vol. 1, part 1, Almqvist & Wiksells, Upsala, **1912–1914**, p. 42. Berzelius to Berthollet, Oct., 1812; *ibid.*, Vol. 1, part 3, p. 19. Marcet to Berzelius, Jan. 25, 1813; *ibid.*, p. 45. Marcet to Berzelius, May 5, 1813; *ibid.*, p. 58. Berzelius to Marcet, June 30, 1813; *ibid.*, p. 66. Marcet to Berzelius, July 28 and Aug. 4, 1813; *ibid.*, p. 183. Marcet to Berzelius, Dec., 1818; *ibid.*, pp. 231–2. Marcet to Berzelius, Jan. 15, 1822.

(30) BERZELIUS, J. J., "Reseanteckningar," P. A. Norstedt & Söner, Stockholm, **1903**, pp. 23–4, 29, and 38.

(31) HATCHETT, CHARLES, "On the method of separating iron from manganese," *Annals of Philos.*, **2**, 343–5 (Nov., 1813); J. F. JOHN, *ibid.*, **2**, 172–3 (Sept., 1813).

(32) HATCHETT, CHARLES, "A description of a process by which corn tainted with must may be completely purified," *Phil. Trans.*, **107**, 36–8 (1817). Letter to Sir Joseph Banks.

(33) FAULKNER, THOMAS, "A Historical and Topographical Description of Chelsea and its Environs," Vol. 1, T. Faulkner, Chelsea, **1829**, pp. 89–92.

(34) CONYBEARE, J. J., "Description of a new substance found in ironstone," *Annals of Philos.*, **17**, 136 (Feb., 1821); *ibid.*, **21**, 190 (March, 1823).

(35) SMITH, J. LAWRENCE, "Examination of American minerals. No. 6—Description of columbic acid minerals from new localities in the United States, embracing a reclamation for the restoration of the name columbium to the element now called niobium . . . ," *Am. J. Sci.*, [3], **13**, 359–69 (May, 1877).

(36) "New American metal," *Medical Repository*, **6**, 212 (Aug., Sept., Oct., 1802); "Hatchett's analysis of the American mineral substance containing a metal hitherto unknown," *ibid.*, **6**, 323–4 (Nov., Dec., 1802, Jan., 1803).

(37) "Place where the ore of columbium was found," *ibid.* (2), **2**, 437 (Feb., Mar., Apr., 1805).

(38) MILLIN, A.-L., "Nouvelles littéraires. Etats-Unis d'Amérique," *Magasin Encyclopédique*, **6**, 388–9 (1805).

(39) "Selections from an ancient catalogue of objects of natural history, formed in New England more than one hundred years ago by John Winthrop, F. R. S.," *Am. J. Sci.* (1), **47**, 282–90 (1844); *Journal Book of the Roy. Soc.*, **15**, 451–87 (June 27, 1734).

(40) SWEET, JESSIE M., "Sir Hans Sloane: Life and mineral collection," *Natural History Mag.*, **5**, 115–6 (July, 1935).

(41) "A report on the Geological Survey of the state of Connecticut by Professor Charles Upham Shepard, M.D., . . . with extracts and remarks by the editor [B. Silliman]," *Am. J. Sci.* (1), **33**, 162–3 (1838).

(42) SMITH, EDGAR F., "Chemistry in Old Philadelphia," J. B. Lippincott Co., Philadelphia, **1919**, pp. 14–22.

(43) "New metal columbium," *Nicholson's J.*, **14**, 181 (June, 1806).

(44) BROWNE, C. A., "Scientific notes from the books and letters of John Winthrop Jr. (1606–1676), first governor of Connecticut," *Isis*, **11**, 325–42 (1928).

(45) Letter of Allyn B. Forbes to C. A. Browne, Apr. 5, 1940. Quoted by permission.

(46) "Collections of the Massachusetts Historical Society," series 5, Vol. 8, Boston, **1882**, pp. 126–7.

(47) SMITH, EDGAR F., "Chemistry in America," D. Appleton and Co., New York and London, **1914**, p. 36.

(48) WEEKS, M. E. and L. O. AMBERG, "M.-E. Chevreul. The fiftieth anniversary of his death," *J. Am. Pharm. Assoc., Sci. Ed.*, **29**, 89–96 (Feb., 1940).

(49) LEMAY, PIERRE and R. E. OESPER, "Michel Eugène Chevreul (1786–1889)," *J. Chem. Educ.*, **25**, 62–70 (Feb., 1948).

(50) HALL, C. R., "A chemist of a century ago," *ibid.*, **5**, 253–7 (Mar., 1928). (Samuel L. Mitchill.)

(51) SWAINE, D. J., "Samuel Johnson's interest in scientific affairs," *J. Chem. Educ.*, **25**, 458–9 (Aug., 1948).

(52) SARTON, GEORGE, "Hoefer and Chevreul (with an excursus on creative centenarians)," *Bull. History of Medicine*, **8**, 419–45 (Mar., 1940).

From J. Höffner's "Schloss Tegel"

Baron Alexander von Humboldt, 1769–1859. German naturalist and traveler. His "Narrative of Travels to the Equinoctial Regions of America between 1799 and 1844" and his "Political Essay on the Kingdom of New Spain" are a rich source of information on the history of chemistry in Latin America. He introduced the Peruvian fertilizer guano to European agricultural chemists. Because of the breadth of his interests he had an unusually clear understanding of the interrelationships of the various branches of science.

15

Contributions of Andrés Manuel del Río*

Although A. M. del Río, the eminent discoverer of the element now known as vanadium, spent most of his active life in Mexico and a few years in Philadelphia, his services to chemistry and mineralogy are not as widely known and appreciated by American scientists as they deserve to be. He was a schoolmate and honored friend of Baron Alexander von Humboldt and a worthy colleague of Don Fausto de Elhuyar, first director of the School of Mines of Mexico.

Andrés Manuel del Río y Fernández was born on Ave María Street in Madrid on November 10, 1764,† and received his preliminary training at the College of San Isidro. At the age of fifteen years he completed his courses in Latin, Greek, literature, and theology and received his Bachelor's degree from the famous University of Alcalá de Henares, which, two centuries before, had rivaled Salamanca. When Don José Solano held a public contest in experimental physics, the young graduate in theology distinguished himself so highly that the King provided for his further education at the Mining Academy of Almadén. Because of del Río's enthusiasm for mining and subterranean geometry, the Minister of the Indies, Don Diego Gardoqui, selected him to study in France, England, and Germany at government expense (1).

He studied chemistry in Paris under Jean Darcet and attended lectures in medicine and natural history. In 1789 he enrolled at the Royal School of Mines in Freiberg, Saxony, where great things were expected of him because of the enviable records made previously by his fellow countrymen Don Juan José and Don Fausto de Elhuyar. He, too, soon felt the charm of A. G. Werner's teaching of geognosy and mineralogy. One of del Río's intimate friends at the Freiberg Academy was his schoolmate, Baron Alexander von Humboldt, who later renewed the friendship in Mexico. Del Río also studied subterranean geometry,

* Presented before the Division of History of Chemistry at the Cleveland meeting of the A. C. S., Sept. 11, 1934.
† Although the year of del Río's birth has frequently been given as 1765, Ramírez (Ref. 1) obtained the above date from the birth certificate.

analytical chemistry, and metallurgy at the Royal School of Mining and Forestry at Schemnitz, Hungary (Štiávnica Bańská, Czechoslovakia).

In 1791 Señor del Río visited the metallurgical industries of England. During a second sojourn in France, he was associated with Lavoisier, and in the troublous days of 1793, he, too, almost fell prey to the fury of the revolutionists. According to Ramírez (1), del Río disguised himself as a water carrier and escaped to England. Although offered the directorships of several mining enterprises, he declined them.

In 1793 a royal order decreed that Werner's theory of the formation of veins be taught at the School of Mines of Mexico recently founded by Don Fausto de Elhuyar (2). The professorship of mineralogy was therefore offered to Señor del Río, who had previously declined that of chemistry. Early in August, 1794, he set sail from Cadiz on the warship San Pedro Alcántara, taking with him a servant and a supply of apparatus for the School of Mines. Eleven weeks later he disembarked at Vera Cruz (3).

After arriving at Mexico City, del Río immediately arranged the mineral collections and planned his course in oryctognosy, which included mineralogy, geognosy, and paleontology and which began on April 27, 1795. The new world spread forth before him so many objects of scientific inquiry that he afterward wrote with enthusiasm: "Each step of the traveler in this Republic discovers to him something new" (4).

In 1795 he published the first edition of his "Elements of Oryctognosy" (5), which von Humboldt regarded as "the best mineralogical work which Spanish literature possesses" (6), and which Santiago Ramírez (7) called "a monumental work, which . . . will be an object of veneration and consultation by the mineralogists of our country and for all those who . . . are occupied in studying the mineralogy of our native country."

Del Río's paper on the best method of sinking mine shafts was printed for use in all the mines of Mexico, and his article on the relations between the composition of a mineral and the materials of which the vein is composed was published in the supplement to the *Gaceta de México* on January 18, 1797 (1, 3).

The most outstanding achievement of del Río's long, useful life was his discovery in 1801 of the metal now known as vanadium. He found that the brown lead mineral, *Plomo pardo de Zimapán* (8), from the

---

Enrique Moles, 1883–   . Distinguished Spanish chemist and pharmacist. Professor of Inorganic and Physical Chemistry in the Faculty of Chemical Sciences at Madrid. His papers on non-aqueous solutions, molecular volumes and additivity, inorganic complexes, and atomic weight determinations were published in the leading journals of Spain, England, France, Italy, and the Netherlands. See also ref. (31).

Courtesy R. E. Oesper

Cardonal Mine in Hidalgo contained what he believed to be a new metal. Because its salts are of varied colors, he at first called it *panchromium*, but because its salts with alkalies and earths become red on heating or on treatment with acids, he later changed the name to *erythronium* (*1, 9, 10*).

When von Humboldt visited Mexico in 1803, del Río gave him several specimens of the brown lead ore. Von Humboldt sent some of them to the *Institut de France* with an explanatory letter giving del Río's analysis and his conclusions regarding the close resemblance of the new metal to chromium and uranium. A more detailed description addressed to Chaptal was lost in a shipwreck (*10*).

Since the properties of erythronium closely resembled those which Fourcroy had ascribed to the recently discovered metal chromium, del Río lost confidence in the importance of his discovery and concluded that his supposed new element was, after all, nothing but chromium (*11*). In a note to his translation of Karsten's "Mineralogical Tables" he wrote (*7, 9, 12*): ". . . but, knowing that chromium also gives by evaporation red or yellow salts, I believe that the brown lead is a yellow oxide of chromium, combined with excess lead also in the form of the yellow oxide."

Dr. Ernst Wittich, German Ambassador to Mexico, pointed out that Baron von Humboldt was also led into the same error, for the specimen in the *Museum für Naturkunde* in Berlin is labeled in the Baron's handwriting: "Brown lead ore from the veins of Zimapán in northern Mexico. Lead chromate. M. del Río thought he had discovered a new metal in it, which he named erythronium, then panchromium; later he realized that it was ordinary chromium." The label was later corrected by Gustav Rose to read: *"Vanadiumbleierz"* (vanadium lead ore) (*29*).

Another circumstance which helped to shake del Río's confidence in his own work was the analysis of this mineral which H.-V. Collet-Descotils, a friend of Vauquelin, published in 1805 (*13*). When Collet-Descotils concluded that the supposed new metal was merely chromium, del Río warmly defended his own prior claim to the "discovery" of *chromium* in the brown lead ore (*14*).

The details of N. G. Sefström's discovery of vanadium in soft iron from the Taberg Mine in Småland, Sweden, and of F. Wöhler's proof of the identity of erythronium and vanadium have already been related (*14, 15, 16*). Dr. Enrique Moles emphasized the fact that del Río's own excessive modesty and scientific caution led him to renounce the discovery of the new element before the analysis of Collet-Descotils had been published.

Unaware of the shipwreck which had prevented Humboldt from giving full publicity to the discovery of erythronium, del Río wrote in

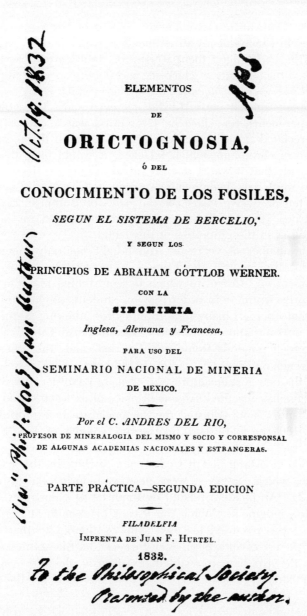

ELEMENTOS

DE

ORICTOGNOSIA,

Ó DEL

CONOCIMIENTO DE LOS FOSILES,

SEGUN EL SISTEMA DE BERCELIO,

Y SEGUN LOS

PRINCIPIOS DE ABRAHAM GÓTTLOB WÉRNER.

CON LA

SINONIMIA

Inglesa, Alemana y Francesa,

PARA USO DEL

SEMINARIO NACIONAL DE MINERIA

DE MEXICO.

———

Por el C. ANDRES DEL RIO,

PROFESOR DE MINERALOGIA DEL MISMO Y SOCIO Y CORRESPONSAL
DE ALGUNAS ACADEMIAS NACIONALES Y ESTRANGERAS.

———

PARTE PRÁCTICA—SEGUNDA EDICION

———

FILADELFIA
IMPRENTA DE JUAN F. HURTEL.

1832.

Title Page of del Río's "Elements of Oryctognosy" written
according to the system of Berzelius and the principles of
A. G. Werner

1832 in his "Elements of Oryctognosy": "When he left Mexico, I gave him
. . . a copy in French of my experiments in order that he might publish
them. If he had judged them worthy of public attention, they would
have excited the curiosity of chemists, and *the discovery of the new metal
would not have been delayed for thirty years,* which is the objection now
unjustly made against me. He did not even show Descotils the copy
of my experiments, for, since he [Descotils] was a chemist, he would
have appreciated them better, would have repeated them, and with his
knowledge of chromium, which I lacked, it would have been easy for
him to decide that it was a distinct metal" (*7, 17*). Since at that time
chromium must have been a novelty even in Europe and since it often
required ten or twelve years for the news of European discoveries to
reach Mexico (*22*), de Río should not be criticized for having been
uninformed as to the properties of this metal.

For a number of years del Río taught not only mineralogy and
mining, but also Spanish and French, and served as one of the editors
of the *Gaceta de México,* to which he contributed many articles, both
literary and scientific. In order that his students might "be proud of a
country that offers so many opportunities for admiring Nature," del Río
added to his translation of Karsten's "Mineralogical Tables" a number of
descriptions of minerals from "this America" and "the other America."
Since a French reviewer (*5*) had criticized him in 1797 for not completely
adopting the new nomenclature proposed by Lavoisier, del Río wrote in
1804, "Usage has accepted *oxígeno* in place of *arcicayo, oxido* in place of
cayo . . . and I have adjusted the nomenclature in conformity with it"
(*9*). In 1805 he published the second volume of his "Elements of
Oryctognosy."

In 1809 he established at Coalcomán, Michoacán, the first ironworks
in Mexico, which, however, were destroyed during the insurrection of
1811 (*1, 3*). An incident related by Ramírez (*1*) illustrates the fairness
of del Río's judgment. When the master blacksmith at the Coalcomán
ironworks, who regarded his own skill as superior to that of del Río,
asked for the use of an experimental furnace, del Río granted the request.
Although the experiments resulted disastrously, del Río's report merely
stated: "Pillado did not succeed very well, but these are the first experiments."

Von Humboldt, who was greatly interested in del Río's pumping
engine, described it as follows: "This engine, which is the first of this kind
constructed in America, is much superior to those in the mines of Hungary;
it was constructed according to the estimates and plans of Señor del
Río, professor of mineralogy of Mexico, who has visited the most famous
mines of Europe and who possesses most thorough and varied erudition;

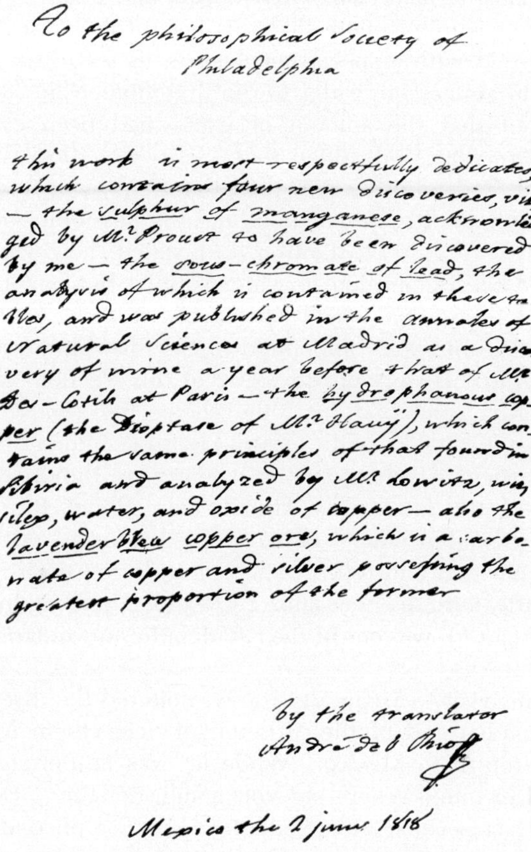

To the philosophical Society of
Philadelphia

this work is most respectfully dedicated
which contains four new discoveries, viz,
— the sulphur of manganese, acknowledged by Mr. Proust to have been discovered
by me — the sous-chromate of lead, the
analysis of which is contained in these tables, and was published in the Annales of
natural Sciences at Madrid as a discovery of mine a year before that of Mr
Des-Cotils at Paris — the hydrophanous copper (the Dioptase of Mr. Haüy), which contains the same principles of that found in
Sibiria and analyzed by Mr. Lowitz, viz,
silex, water, and oxide of copper — also the
lavender bleu copper ore, which is a carbonate of copper and silver possessing the
greatest proportion of the former

by the translator
Andrés del Rio

Mexico the 2 june 1818

Courtesy Am. Philosophical Soc.

In a presentation copy of his translation of Karsten's "Mineralogical Tables," del Río wrote as follows: "To the Philosophical Society of Philadelphia this work is most respectfully dedicated, which contains four new discoveries, *viz.*—the *sulphur of manganese,* acknowledged by Mr. Proust to have been discovered by me—the *sous-chromate of lead,* the analysis of which is contained in these tables, and was published in the Annales of Natural Sciences at Madrid as a discovery of mine a year before that of Mr. Des-Cotils at Paris—the *hydrophanous copper* (the Dioptase of Mr. Haüy), which contains the same principles of that found in Siberia and analyzed by Mr. Lowitz, *viz.,* silex, water, and oxide of copper—also the *lavender bleu copper ore,* which is a carbonate of copper and silver possessing the greatest proportion of the former, by the translator André del Río, Mexico the 2 June 1818."

and Mr. Lachaussée, an artisan native of Brabant, a man of marked ability, built it. . . . It is unfortunate that this beautiful engine, whose throttle valve is provided with a special mechanism, is set up in a place where it is difficult to get enough water to run it continuously. . . ." The Baron then explained that the amount of water had been estimated in an unusually rainy year, and added that "Señor del Río, when he arrived in New Spain, had no other aim than that of proving to Mexican mine operators the effect of such machines and the possibility of making them in this country . . ." (6). Ramírez (1) stated, however, that del Río had predicted the diminution of water supply, but had been unable to prevent the deforestation which had caused it.

In 1820 deputies were appointed to the Spanish court. H. H. Bancroft stated in his "History of Mexico" that this election "took place with no little disorder" and that ". . . the choice fell almost exclusively on ecclesiastics and lawyers, with a sprinkling of soldiers, merchants, and men of no particular calling, among whom were three natives of Spain" (18). One of the latter was Andrés Manuel del Río, who pleaded earnestly for the independence of his adopted country. Although Elhuyar resigned his position and returned to Spain during the struggle, del Río was in sympathy with the new cause (19) and, according to Maffei and de la Rua Figueroa (1), was one of the few deputies to vote for absolute independence.

During his visit to Spain, del Río was offered the directorship of the mines of Almadén and of the Museum of Sciences in Madrid, but he preferred to return to Mexico. While he was in Bordeaux, Señora de Elhuyar said to him, "Where are you going, del Río? Don't you know that Mexico has become independent?" "Yes," replied del Río, "and I am going home to my country" (1). Because of his loyal friends and eager, intelligent students, his splendid collection of minerals from both hemispheres, the undiscovered wonders of the new world, and the charm of his virtuous Mexican wife, del Río had come to regard Mexico as his homeland. Perhaps another incentive for his return was the impressive structure for the School of Mines which had been completed in 1813, and which Mr. Beulloch, a contemporary English traveler, described as follows (20):

"The edifice in which it is located excels in its dimensions and in the beauty of its architecture all those in Europe destined for the same purpose. It was erected at great cost [1½ million pesos] and amply provided with everything necessary for the mine owners and other rich inhabitants." Earthquakes soon damaged the noble structure to such an extent that by 1830 extensive repairs were needed. The architect took the high building apart, placed the stately columns in the patio, and put them back in place without losing a single piece (7).

Courtesy Dr. Harold Hibbert of McGill University

John Dalton, 1766–1844. English Quaker chemist. Teacher of mathematics and physics at New College, Manchester. In his "New System of Chemistry" he showed how his atomic theory can be used to explain the laws which govern chemical combination. He also made careful meteorological observations and described color-blindness (daltonism).
See also ref. (*32*).

In 1821 del Río published an analysis of a gold-rhodium alloy from the smelting house in Mexico which was similar to the gold-palladium ingot previously reported by Joseph Cloud, director of the Philadelphia Mint (*21*). Three years later he published a translation of Berzelius's "New mineral system" (*22*). He served for some time on a committee appointed to inspect the money and improve working conditions at the Mint.

In acknowledgment of his allegiance, the new government, which expelled most Spaniards from Mexico in 1828, made an exception in the case of del Río. Nevertheless, he preferred to share the fate of his fellow-countrymen and therefore spent four years of voluntary exile in Philadelphia. In the preface to the second edition of his "Elements of Oryctognosy," published in Philadelphia in 1832 at the expense of the Mining Tribunal of Mexico, he wrote:

"Knowing by experience the happy disposition of Mexican youth for the study of these sciences, I wish in the last third of my life to consecrate to it the limited product of my efforts, immeasurably happy if I can some day be useful to a country where I have lived for thirty-five years, receiving every kind of distinction. If the result is not proportional to my high aim, it will at least be admitted that I aspire to manifest in the only manner possible to me my gratitude for the distinguished favors with which the Mexicans have honored me; my only merit is to be thankful" (*17*).

In his unassuming devotion to his teaching duties, del Río resembled John Dalton. One day in 1841, when a student knocked at the door of his classroom to announce a distinguished visitor, del Río asked the messenger to have the visitor wait for him. When the bell rang at the close of the class period, del Río greeted Señor Calderon de la Barca, minister plenipotentiary from the Court at Madrid. His Excellency, moreover, was not offended at the delay (*1*).

Del Río belonged to many scientific organizations of France, Germany, Great Britain, Mexico, and Spain, and was an active member of the American Philosophical Society and president of the Geological Society of Philadelphia. From 1830 to 1834 he attended the meetings of the American Philosophical Society, took part in the discussions, donated books which are st'll in possession of the Society's library, and presented papers for publication.

The translation of Karsten's Tables contains in del Río's handwriting the following note of presentation: "To the Philosophical Society of Philadelphia, this work is most respectfully dedicated, which contains four new discoveries—the *sulphur of manganese*, acknowledged by Mr. Proust to have been discovered by me—the *sous-chromate of lead* . . . the *hydrophanous copper* . . . also the *lavender* . . . *copper ore*." This note was written in 1818, but in 1827 del Río wrote: "I thank Sr. Breithaupt for . . . believing me the first discoverer of manganese sulfide . . . I am indeed [discoverer] of that of los Mijes in the state of Oajaca [Oaxaca]; but we must be just. Sr. Proust discovered that of Transylvania two years before" (22). Del Río added that at that time many European discoveries were not known in Mexico until ten or twelve years after publi-

A LA MEMORIA DEL DISTINGUIDO SABIO

EL EXPERTO MINERO Y CELEBRE
MINERALOGISTA

D. ANDRES MANUEL DEL RIO

CUYA MERECIDA FAMA LO DESIGNO
PARA SER EL

INTRODUCTOR DE LAS CIENCIAS NATURALES

EN NUESTRA PATRIA

CUYO ACENDRADO AMOR A MEXICO LO HACE FIGURAR ENTRE
NUESTROS MAS ILUSTRES COMPATRIOTAS;
Y EN CUYAS OBRAS CIENTIFICAS HAN BEBIDO LA INSTRUCCION NUESTRAS
GENERACIONES DE MINEROS,

DEDICA COMO UN HOMENAJE

ESTE INSIGNIFICANTE TRABAJO

EL MAS RESPETUOSO DE SUS ADMIRADORES,

Dedication Page of "The Mineral Wealth of Mexico and Its Present State of Development," which S. Ramírez wrote for the New Orleans Exposition of 1884. *Translation:* "To the memory of the distinguished scientist, expert mine operator, and celebrated mineralogist, D. Andrés Manual del Río, whose well deserved fame designated him to be the introducer of the natural sciences into our country, whose stainless love for Mexico makes him figure among our most illustrious fellow citizens, and from whose scientific books our generations of mine operators have imbibed instruction, this unimportant work is dedicated as a tribute by the most respectful of his admirers."

cation. In the second edition of his "Elements of Oryctognosy," del Río wrote: "In a work such as this little can be called one's own: only a few articles belong to me, such as the manganese sulfide of Oaxaca, the brown lead of Zimapán, the mercury iodide of Casas Viejas, the blue silver of Catorce, and the zinc selenide of Culebras" (17).

His requests for a small specimen of "sulphuret of silver" and other minerals for analysis were granted by the Philosophical Society. At its meetings he must have met A. D. Bache, F. Bache, Robert Hare, Joseph Henry, G. W. Featherstonhaugh, and other contemporary American scientists. Ramírez (1) mentions a process of purifying mercury which del Río had learned from Professor Hare of Philadelphia.

In 1830 del Río read a paper on Becquerel's method of reducing silver ores (23). His paper (24) on the crystals developed in vermiculite by heat begins: "A pupil of the celebrated Werner, I have always been more of a Neptunian than a Plutonist, notwithstanding the many crystallizations produced in the dry way. A new instance which has come under my observation in the crystals of vermiculite has contributed materially to change my opinions. . . ."

Dr. Meigs had heated a specimen of vermiculite in a candle flame and had shown del Río the worm-like filaments which shoot out from it. Under the blowpipe, the Mexican scientist obtained from it oblique prisms nearly an inch long, which were also "crooked and worm-like." Vermiculite is a hydrous silicate generally produced by alteration of mica.

Between 1835 and 1837 several polemical articles by del Río and Charles U. Shepard, the well-known American mineralogist and collector of meteorites, appeared in the *American Journal of Science* (25).

In 1834 del Río was given the chair of geology in addition to that of mineralogy. Before returning to Mexico, he purchased for the Mining Seminary a splendid collection of shells and fossils collected by a Polish naturalist who had recently died in Philadelphia. In 1841 he published a manual of geology describing the fossil flora and fauna of the various rocks, with special emphasis on those found in Mexico (7, 26). Two years later del Río, then about seventy-eight years of age, served on a committee to study the manufacture of porcelain and determine whether or not the raw materials were available in the Republic. Their report, which was highly praised by the Bureau of National Industry, was published in *El Siglo XIX* on May 10, 1843, and a porcelain works was established at Puebla (3).

Two years later del Río was still serving as professor of mineralogy, but in the following year he asked for a substitute in order that he might complete the supplement to his textbook, which was to include discussions of the most recent discoveries made in Europe and the United States. According to Señor Ramírez (7), this was published in 1849 (27). In spite of failing eyesight, del Río continued, almost to the close of his life, to contribute to the literary and scientific periodicals of Mexico, yet in spite of his illustrious services, he was reduced to poverty in his old age (28). On March 23, 1849, he suffered a fatal cerebral attack.

Del Río's colleague, Don Joaquín Velázquez de León, said in his eulogy: "I still seem to see him leaving this college at the close of the day's teaching, with his book under his arm (for he used to say *that the support of science does not dishonor anyone*); surrounded at the doorway of the institution by the unfortunate and the destitute, sharing with them his meager salary, and returning to aid those who were already waiting for him at the doors of his home" (*1*). In 1877 a rich mining region of Chihuahua was named in his honor *the Andrés del Río canton*, with Batopilas as its capital (*7*).

In honor of del Río on the occasion of the centenary of his death, Professor Modesto Bargalló of the National Polytechnic Institute of Mexico City published an interesting detailed description of a copy of the "Elementos de Orictognosia" (Part 1, 1795) containing many corrections and addenda in del Río's handwriting (*30*). Professor Bargalló has just published a handsomely illustrated volume on mining and metallurgy in Spanish America during the Colonial epoch (*33*).

It is a pleasure to acknowledge the kind assistance of Miss Eva Armstrong of the Edgar Fahs Smith Memorial Library, the library of the American Philosophical Society, Dr. E. Moles and Señor A. de Gálvez-Cañero of Madrid, and Dr. F. B. Dains.

LITERATURE CITED

(*1*) MAFFEI, E. and R. R. FIGUEROA, "Apuntes para una biblioteca española de libros . . . relativos al conocimiento y explotación de las riquezas minerales," Imprenta de J. M. Lapuente, Madrid, **1872**, 2 vols., 529 and 693 pp.; J. VELÁZQUEZ DE LEÓN, "Elogio fúnebre del Sr. D. Andrés del Río," Vol. 2, El Album Mexicano, Imprenta de Cumplido, Mexico, **1849**, pp. 219–25; S. RAMÍREZ, "Biografía del Sr. D. Andrés Manuel del Río," *Boletín de la Soc. Mexicana de Geografía y Estadística*, [4], **2**, 205–51 (1890).

(*2*) WEEKS, M. E., "The scientific contributions of the de Elhuyar brothers," *J. Chem. Educ.*, **11**, 413–9 (July, 1934).

(*3*) RAMÍREZ, S., "Datos para la historia del Colegio de Minería," government publication for the Alzate Society, Mexico, **1890**, 494 pp.

(*4*) DEL RÍO, A. M., "Analysis of two new mineral substances, consisting of bi-seleniuret of zinc and seleniuret of mercury, found at Culebras in Mexico," *Phil. Mag.*, [2], **4**, 113–5 (Aug., 1828).

(*5*) DEL RÍO, A. M., "Elementos de orictognosia," Vol. 1, Imprenta de Zúñiga y Ontiveros, Mexico, **1795**, 172 pp.; *ibid.*, **1805**, Vol. 2, 200 pp.; Vol. 1 reviewed in *Ann. chim. phys.*, [1], **21**, 221–4 (Feb., 1797).

(*6*) VON HUMBOLDT, A., "Ensayo político sobre Nueva España," 3rd ed., Vol. 1, Librería de Lecointe, Paris, **1836**, pp. 232, 236–8; Vol. 3, pp. 117–8.

(*7*) RAMÍREZ, S., "Noticia histórica de la riqueza minera de México," Secretaría de Fomento, Mexico, **1884**, 768 pp.

(*8*) "Zimapán, the Leadville of Mexico," *Modern Mexico*, **13**, 30–1 (Sept., 1902).

(*9*) DEL RÍO, A. M., "Tablas Mineralógicas Dispuestas según los Descubrimientos Más Recientes e Ilustradas con Notas por D. L. G. Karsten," Zúñiga y Ontiveros, Mexico, **1804**, pp. 60–62; RAMON DE LA QUADRA, "Introducción á las tablas comparativas de las substancias metálicas," *Anales ciencias naturales* (Madrid), **6**, 46 (May, 1803).

(10) WITTICH, E., "Zur Entdeckungsgeschichte des Elementes Vanadium," *Technik-Industrie und Schweizer Chem.-Ztg.*, **16**, 4–5 (Jan. 31, 1933).

(11) DE FOURCROY, A.-F., "Système des connaissances chimiques," Vol. 5, Baudouin, Paris, **1800** (Brumaire, an IX), pp. 107–13.

(12) DEL RÍO, A. M., "Discurso de las vetas," *Gaceta de México*, Nov. 12, 1802; *Anales de las Ciencias Naturales* (Madrid), **7**, 31 (Feb., 1804). These references taken from E. MOLES, Ref. (15).

(13) COLLET-DESCOTILS, H. V., "Analyse de la mine brune de plomb de Zimapán, dans le royaume du Mexique, envoyée par M. Humboldt, et dans laquelle M. del Río dit avoir découvert un nouveau métal," *Ann. chim. phys.*, [1], **53**, 268–71 (1805); J. L. GAY-LUSSAC, "Biographical account of Hippolyte-Victor Collet-Descotils," *Annals of Philosophy*, **9**, 417–21 (1817); *Ann. chim. phys.*, [2], **4**, 213 (Feb., 1817).

(14) WITTICH, E., "El descubrimiento del vanadio," *Boletín Minero*, **13**, 4–15 (Jan., 1922); see also del Río's autograph letter reproduced on page 397.

(15) MOLES, E., "Wolframio, no tungsteno. Vanadio o eritronio," *Anales soc. españ. fís. quím.*, [3], **26**, 234–52 (June, 1928).

(16) WEEKS, M. E., "The discovery of the elements," *J. Chem. Educ.*, **9**, 873–82 (May, 1932); *ibid.*, 2nd ed., Mack Printing Co., Easton, Pa., **1934**, pp. 87–98.

(17) DEL RÍO, A. M., "Elementos de Orictognosia," 2nd ed., John Hurtel, Philadelphia, **1832**, pp. 484–5.

(18) BANCROFT, H. H., "The Works of Hubert Howe Bancroft," Vol. 12, A. L. Bancroft and Co., San Francisco, **1885**, p. 699.

(19) DE GÁLVEZ-CAÑERO, A., "Apuntes Biográficos de D. Fausto de Elhuyar," Gráficas reunidas, Madrid, **1933**, pp. 107–68.

(20) BEULLOCH, "Viage a México en 1828," Vol. 2, El Album Mexicano, Imprenta del Cumplido, Mexico, **1849**, p. 492; See also: T. A. RICKARD, "Journeys of Observation among the Mines of Mexico," Dewey Publishing Co., San Francisco, **1907**, pp. 30–1.

(21) DEL RÍO, A. M., "Analysis of a specimen of gold found to be alloyed with rhodium," *El Sol*, Dec. 11, 1824; *Am. J. Sci.*, **11**, 298–304 (1826); *Ann. chim. phys.*, [2], **29**, 137–47 (1825); *Annals of Philosophy*, [2], **10**, 251–6 (Oct., 1825); E. F. SMITH, "Chemistry in Old Philadelphia," J. B. Lippincott Co., Philadelphia, **1919**, pp. 86–90.

(22) DEL RÍO, A. M., "Nuevo Sistema Mineral de Señor Bercelio del Año de 1825," Imprenta del Aguila, Mexico, **1827**, 28 pp.

(23) DEL RÍO, A. M., "Silver ores reduced by the method of Becquerel," *Trans. Am. Phil. Soc.*, N. S., **4**, 60–2 (1834). Read Nov. 5, 1830.

(24) DEL RÍO, A. M., "On the crystals developed in vermiculite by heat," *ibid.*, **5**, 137–8 (1837). Read Nov. 1, 1833.

(25) SHEPARD, C. U., "Reply to 'Observations on the treatise of mineralogy of Mr. C. U. Shepard,' by Andrés del Río . . .," *Am. J. Sci.*, **27**, 312–25 (1835); A. M. DEL RIO, *ibid.*, **30**, 384–7 (1836); *ibid.*, **31**, 131–4 (1837).

(26) DEL RÍO, A. M., "Manual de geología extractado de la lethaea geognóstica de Bronn con los animales y vegetales perdidos . . .," Ignacio Cumplido, Mexico, **1841**.

(27) DEL RÍO, A. M., "Suplemento de adiciones y correciones de mi Mineralogia impresa en Filadelfia en 1832," Tipografía de R. Rafael, Mexico, **1849**.

(28) MOLES, E., "Discurso leído en el acto de su recepción. Del momento científico español 1775–1825," Acad. ciencias exactas, físicas, y naturales de Madrid, C. Bermejo, Madrid, **1934**, pp. 97–105.

(29) WITTICH, E., "Zur Entdeckungsgeschichte des Elementes Vanadium," *Forschungen und Fortschritte*, **9**, 38–9 (Jan. 20, 1933).

(30) BARGALLÓ, M., "Homenaje a Don Andrés Manuel del Río y Fernández en ocasión del primer centenario de su muerte (1849–1949)," *Ciencia*, **10**, 270–8 (1950).

(31) OESPER, RALPH E., "Enrique Moles," *J. Chem. Educ.*, **13**, 368 (Aug., 1936).

(32) DUVEEN, D. I. and HERBERT S. KLICKSTEIN, "John Dalton's 'Autobiography,' " *ibid.*, **32**, 333–4 (June, 1955).

(33) BARGALLÓ, MODESTO, "La mineria y la Metalurgia en la América española durante la época colonial," Fondo de Cultura Económica, Mexico and Buenos Aires, **1955**, 442 pp.

Don Antonio de Ulloa, 1716–
1795.   Spanish mathematician,
naval officer, and traveler. The
log of his voyage to Peru published in 1748 contains a description of platinum.

*A successful pursuit of science makes a man the
benefactor of all mankind and of every age (1).*

16

The platinum metals

*The earliest scientific descriptions of platinum are those of Dr.
Brownrigg and Don Antonio de Ulloa in the middle of the
eighteenth century. Rhodium, palladium, osmium, and iridium
were discovered in 1803 and 1804, the first two by Dr. Wollaston
and the others by his friend, Smithson Tennant. Thomson's "History of Chemistry" and Berzelius' correspondence and diary
present a pleasing picture of these two great English chemists.
Ruthenium, the Russian member of the platinum family, was discovered much later by Karl Karlovich Klaus, whose life story was
beautifully told by Professor B. N. Menschutkin of the Polytechnic Institute of Leningrad.*

PLATINUM

*W*hen platinum was first introduced into Europe in the eighteenth century, mineralogists and chemists agreed that it must be a
new metal. In 1790, however, Father Angelo Maria Cortenovis (1727–
1801), an Italian antiquarian of the Barnabite order, concluded from a
study of the Greek and Latin classics that this metal must have been
known to the ancients and that it must be identical with the *electrum* of
the Greeks (*96*). E. O. von Lippmann explained, however, that *electrum*
was the same as the Egyptian *asem*, an alloy of gold and silver (*97*).
M. H. Klaproth's analysis of "electrum, a native alloy of gold and silver"
from Schlangenberg, Siberia, showed that this natural electrum contained
64 parts of gold to 36 of silver (*98*).

When M. Berthelot analyzed some metal detached from a metallic
casket from Thebes, he found it to be an alloy of platinum that was more
resistant to reagents than the pure metal. The hieroglyphics on the
casket showed that it had been dedicated to Queen Shapenapit, daughter
of King Psamnetik I (seventh century B.C.) (*99*). Berthelot believed
that it had been prepared from a native alluvial ore containing iridium
and gold. Alfred Lucas, in his "Ancient Egyptian Materials and Industries," referred to this as the only known occurrence of the intentional
use of platinum in ancient Egypt (*100*).

Although Pliny the Elder's description of a heavy white substance

407

found in the sands of Portugal and Galicia has been construed by J. S. C. Schweigger, F. A. Moros, and others as a reference to platinum, it is far more likely that this was a tin ore (*101, 102, 103*). Neither Hermann Kopp nor L. von Crell believed that Pliny could possibly have been referring to platinum (*41, 104*).

Although platinum occurs as grains and nuggets in the alluvial sands of many rivers, there is only slight evidence of its use by ancient peoples. The pre-Columbian Indians, however, near the place now known as La Tolita, Esmeraldas, Ecuador (*39*), produced white alloys of gold and platinum, from which they made many little artifacts, some of which are now preserved in the University of Pennsylvania Museum in Philadelphia and the Danish National Museum in Copenhagen. Since plati-

Julius Caesar Scaliger, 1484–1558. Italian physician, scholar, and poet. In 1557 he made a brief allusion to a refractory metal which was probably platinum. His son Joseph Justus Scaliger was a famous philologist.

num cannot be melted with any primitive source of heat, Paul Bergsøe (*40*) believes that a little gold was mixed with the grains of platinum in order to seal them together as the gold was melted, and that the sintered mass was then subjected to alternate heating and hammering.

Less than half a century after Balboa had "stood silent on a peak in Darien," facing the unknown ocean, a famous Italian scholar and poet, Julius Caesar Scaliger, or della Scala, recorded the presence there of an unknown noble metal. In 1557 he made what is probably the first definite allusion to platinum. Girolamo Cardano (1501–1576), in his well-known work "On Subtlety," had defined a metal as "a substance which can be melted and which hardens on cooling." In his "Exotericarum exercitationum liber quintus decimus de subtilitate ad Hieronymum Cardanum," Scaliger pointed out that such a definition would exclude mercury and also another metal, found between Mexico and Darien, "which no fire nor any Spanish artifice has yet been able to liquefy" (41, 54).

Because of conflicting accounts, it is difficult to learn the truth about Scaliger's early life (13). One of his numerous children, Joseph Justus, became a noted philologist (106). In an essay on Joseph Scaliger, Mark Pattison gave some striking glimpses of the father (107). In another eulogy of the great philologist, Dominicus Baudius said that the elder Scaliger was "of greatness unexampled, had he not become the father of a son greater than himself . . ." (108).

Part of J. C. Scaliger's "Poetics," which had a striking influence on Ben Jonson, has been translated into English by F. M. Padelford (118). An autographed manuscript of his commentaries on Aristotle's "De Historia Animalium" was bequeathed to the University of Leyden by Joseph Scaliger, who requested in his will that the wax portrait of his father be "put in a safe place where it cannot be handled and damaged by too much contact . . ." (108).

Charles Wood, a metallurgist and assayer, found in Jamaica some platinum from Cartagena [Colombia], and in 1741 took some of it to his relative, Dr. Brownrigg. After preparing a thorough and accurate description of the metal and its properties, Dr. Brownrigg in 1750 presented these specimens to the Royal Society of London. The exhibit included the ore as found in Nature, the purified metal, the fused metal, and a sword with a pummel made partly of platinum (2).

Don Antonio de Ulloa, in the log of his famous voyage to South America, which was published in 1748, gave a brief but definite description of platinum (55, 71). He was born on January 12, 1716, at number 1 Almirante Street in Seville. While still a young child, he began to study mathematics at the Colégio Mayor de Santo Tomás. At the age of fourteen years, he entered service on the galleon San Luis, which set sail from Cadiz under the command of the Marqués de Torre-Blanca. After visiting the ports of Porto Bello and Havana, the storm-tossed fleet ended its journey and anchored at Cadiz in September, 1732 (112).

At that time, the Academy of Sciences of Paris, greatly interested in the shape and dimensions of the earth, was preparing to send two expeditions, one to Lapland and the other to Ecuador, to measure degrees of meridian. In this undertaking Louis XV sought the aid of his relative Philip V of Spain. Because of their demonstrated ability, Don Antonio de Ulloa and Don Jorge Juan y Santacilia, respectively nineteen and twenty-one years of age, were promoted to the rank of frigate lieutenants. Setting sail on May 28, 1735, they cast anchor at Cartagena on July 9th and waited for the French academicians. After studying at Porto Bello, they passed through the Chagres River of Panama to Cruces. On December 29th they arrived at Panama. In Guayaquil, Ecuador, Don Antonio took advantage of an unavoidable delay to study the Guayaquil purple and the cacao plantations. Proceeding by way of the volcanic region of Chimborazo, the expedition arrived at Quito on May 29th. After the astronomical measurements had finally been made, Don Antonio embarked on the French frigate *Notre Dame de la Délivrance,* which was captured by the British at Louisburg, Cape Breton. The English naval officers treated him with the utmost courtesy and kindness, however, preserved his scientific records, and guaranteed him a safe passage to England.

When he petitioned the Admiralty for the return of his papers, says Don Antonio de Ulloa, they "unanimously, and with pleasure, granted the contents of my memorial, nobly adding that they were not at war with the arts and sciences, or their professors." Upon his arrival in London, de Ulloa was introduced to Martin Folkes, the president of the Royal Society, and to many other distinguished men and was elected to membership in that society (*32*).

In 1746 de Ulloa returned to Madrid, and, with Jorge Juan, prepared for publication the memorable "Historical Account of the Voyage to South America," which was published in 1748 (*35, 55, 56*). In the preface to his "Astronomical and Physical Observations," Jorge Juan said that Ulloa regarded platinum as a peculiar metal and anticipated that there must be special mines of it as there are of gold and silver (*55*).

De Ulloa described it as follows: "In the district of Chocó are many mines of Lavadero, or wash gold . . . several of the mines have been abandoned on account of the platina; a substance of such resistance that, when struck on an anvil of steel, it is not easy to be separated; nor is it calcinable; so that the metal, inclosed within this obdurate body, could not be extracted without infinite labour and charge . . ." (*56, 57*).

De Ulloa and Jorge Juan sent a dozen copies of this log to members of the Royal Society of London. On December 19, 1748, William Watson (later Sir William) wrote as follows: "Only last Wednesday I was delighted to receive the copies of your book which you intended for me and your other friends, for which I sincerely thank you. . . . On Thursday Mr. Folkes did not fail to present . . . the copy marked for the Royal Society. . . . The Society voted its special thanks to you both for the gift of a book so charged with curious, choice, and interesting information" (*58*).

Unfortunately, de Ulloa's many activities did not leave him time for a thorough investigation of the new metal. After studying the sciences and useful arts of several European countries, he returned to Spain and reorganized the Schools of Medicine and Surgery, established the textile industry, and developed the mercury mines of Almadén.   In 1758 he was sent to Peru to superintend the mercury mines of Huancavelica.

When the Treaty of Fontainebleau gave Spain authority over Louisiana, Charles III in 1765 ordered Don Antonio to take possession. When he arrived at New Orleans in a heavy storm, the colonists gave him "a respectful, but cold and somber, greeting" (59).   In his "History of Louisiana," Albert Phelps explained: "He was cold, reserved, and proud, but the source of his dignity—his reputation as a man of learning and science—was all unknown to Louisiana, and therefore his assumption of authority, unsupported by any appearance, was taken to be mere

Sir William Watson, 1715–1787.   British physician, naturalist, and electrician who contributed many original papers and summaries of the work of others to the *Philosophical Transactions.*   In 1750 he communicated Dr. William Brownrigg's paper on platinum to the Royal Society. This portrait was engraved by Thorn-thwaite after a painting by Abbott.

arrogance or pretention" (60).   Another historian stated that "his scientific spirit, as often happens, led him to waste his time on trifling details" (59).

When his fiancée arrived from Peru, they were married at the Balize at the mouth of the Mississippi by the chaplain of the vessel which had brought her.   This unceremonious procedure, together with de Ulloa's prolonged absence from New Orleans, brought fresh criticism from the colonists, and he was soon dismissed (34).   N.-J. Thiery de Menonville, a contemporary French botanist and traveler, said, "I have heard much fault found with Don Uloa [sic], but all the subjects of complaint that were alledged against him were charges of familiarity unworthy of his rank, and a shabby meanness in his domestic concerns.   He has never given room for anyone acusing him of injustice or cruelty   , his excessive patience made him to be despised and dismissed" (61).

After serving for a time as commander of the fleet, de Ulloa returned to Spain. Joseph Townsend, a contemporary traveler, gave the following description of his visit to de Ulloa at Cadiz: "For my part, . . . I chiefly associated with Spaniards. Among these the principal was Don Antonio Ulloa, the well known companion of D. Georg Juan. . . . I found him perfectly the philosopher, sensible and well informed, lively in his conversation, free and easy in his manners. . . . This great man, diminutive in stature, remarkably thin and bowed down with age, clad like a peasant, and surrounded by his numerous family of children, with the youngest, about two years old, playing on his knee, was sitting to receive morning visitors. . . .

"The room was twenty feet long by fourteen wide, and less than eight feet high. In this I saw dispersed confused, chairs, tables, trunks, boxes, books, and papers, a bed, a press, umbrellas, clothes, carpenters' tools, mathematical instruments, a barometer, a clock, guns, pictures, looking-glasses, fossils, minerals, and shells, his kettle, basons, broken jugs, American antiquities, money, and a curious mummy from the Canary Islands. . . . When I went to take my leave of him, on quitting Cadiz, he presented me with his Natural History of South America, a work highly deserving to be translated" (62).

De Ulloa died on León Island near Cadiz on July 5, 1795. According to J. Sempere y Guarinos, he brought to Spain the first knowledge of electricity and artificial magnetism, and used a solar reflecting microscope, such as he had seen in England, to demonstrate the circulation of the blood in the appendages of fish and various insects. From his journeys, Ulloa brought back a knowledge of the cinnamon and rubber trees and of improvements in the arts of printing and binding. He also established the first cabinet of natural history and the first metallurgical laboratory in Madrid (58).

About two years after the log of de Ulloa's voyage had been published, Sir William Watson and Dr. William Brownrigg contributed to the *Philosophical Transactions* a more detailed description of platinum. William Brownrigg was born at High Close Hall, Cumberland, on March 24, 1711. He studied medicine in London and later in Leyden under H. Boerhaave, B. S. Albinus, and W. J. s'Gravesande, and began to practise in Whitehaven (2, 63, 64).

A paper read by Watson before the Royal Society on December 13, 1750, contained an excerpt from a letter, dated Whitehaven, December 5th of the same year, in which Dr. Brownrigg had mentioned some experiments which a friend of his had made on "the semi-metal called Platina di Pinto" (sic!), a substance which he had not found mentioned by any writer on minerals (65). Dr. Brownrigg regarded it as strange that such a simple substance "among the metalline tribe" should have remained unknown to naturalists. He pointed out that the principle, long accepted by assayers, that gold and silver may be purified from all other substances by cupellation, did not apply to the new "semi-metal," for it, like gold, "resists the power of fire and the destructive force of lead."

XXXIII. 1. I take the freedom to inclofe to you an account of a *Several Pa-* femi-metal called *Platina di Pinto*; which, fo far as I know, hath not *pers concern-* been taken notice of by any writer on minerals. Mr *Hill*, who is one *ing a new* of the moft modern, makes no mention of it. Prefuming therefore that *Semi Metal,* the fubject is new, I requeft the favour of you to lay this account before *communicated* the R. S. to be by them read and publifhed, if they think it deferving *to the* Royal thofe honours. I fhould fooner have publifhed this account, but wait- *Society by Mr* ed, in hopes of finding leifure to make further experiments on this body *Wm Watfon,* with fulphureous and other cements; alfo with Mercury, and feveral *496. p. 584.* corrofive *menftrua*. But thefe experiments I fhall now defer, until I *Nov. &c.* learn how the above is received. The experiments which I have related *1750. Read* were feveral of them made by a friend, whofe exactnefs in performing *Dec. 13. 1750.* them, and veracity in relating them, I can rely on: however, for grea- *Extract of a* ter certainty, I fhall myfelf repeat them. *Will. Brown-*
   rigg, M. D. F. R. S. *to* Wm. Watfon, F R. S. *Dated* Whitehaven, Dec. 5, 1750.

2. Although the hiftory of minerals, and other foffil fubftances, hath *Memoirs of a* been diligently cultivated, efpecially by the Moderns; yet it muft be *Semi-metal* acknowledged, that, among the vaft variety of bodies which are the *called Platina* objects of that fcience, there ftill remains room for new inquiries. *di Pinto, found* No wonder that, among the great, and almoft inexhauftible varieties *Weft Indies,* of falts, ores, and other concretes, new appearances, and mixtures be- *Ibid. p. 585.* fore unknown, fhould daily be difcovered: but that, among bodies of a more fimple nature, and particularly among the metalline tribe, feve- ral diftinct fpecies fhould ftill remain almoft wholly unknown to Natu- ralifts, will doubtlefs appear more ftrange and extraordinary. Gold is ufually efteemed the moft ponderous of bodies; and yet I have feen, in the poffeffion of the late Profeffor *s'Gravefande*, a metal- line fubftance, brought from the *Eaft-Indies*, that was fpecifically hea-   vier

Facsimile Page from Volume X of the *Philosophical Transactions Abridgment* showing William Watson's description of platinum and a letter from Dr. Brown- rigg on the same subject.

He added that this "platina" had been presented to him about nine years before by "a skilful and inquisitive metallurgist [*Mr. Charles Wood*] who met with it in Jamaica, whither it had been brought from Carthagena" (Colombia). Dr. Brownrigg believed it probable that "there is great plenty of this semimetal in the Spanish West Indies, since trinkets made of it are there very common." He mentioned its high melting point and its refractoriness toward borax and other saline fluxes. "But the Spaniards," said he, "have a way of melting it down, either alone or by means of some flux; and cast it into sword-hilts, buckles, snuff-boxes, and other utensils."

In about 1730, "Don Jorge de Villalonga, first viceroy of Santa Fé, was given a guard for his rapier and some buckles of platina, but was assured that it had not been sufficiently joined or made to coalesce and

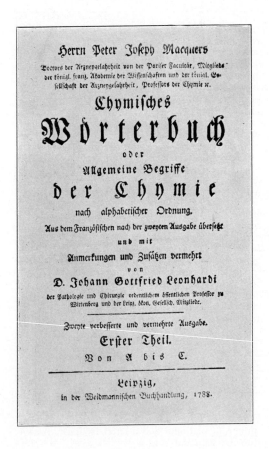

Title Page of the German Edition of Macquer's Chemical Dictionary. Pierre-Joseph Macquer, 1718–1784, was one of the first chemists to investigate platinum.

that it was a brittle metal, but much heavier than the gold with which it was associated in the mines of the province of Cítaro in the district of Chocó" (66).

Sir William Watson said that he had seen this substance mentioned by no other author except de Ulloa. On February 13, 1750, Dr. Brownrigg wrote again to Watson, explaining that the experiments he had mentioned in his previous letter had been made by Mr. Charles Wood, who "was not ambitious of appearing in print," but had permitted Dr. Brownrigg to report his results to the Royal Society.

Dr. Brownrigg was always extremely modest about his discoveries, and preferred to live in comparative obscurity in Cumberland rather than to accept the wider opportunities of London. For his experiments on choke damp and carbon dioxide, Dr. Brownrigg was awarded the Copley Medal (*113*). In 1772 he and Benjamin Franklin stilled with oil the stormy Derwent Lake (*114*). Franklin once visited him at the paternal estate at Ormathwaite, where Dr. Brownrigg was spending his old age in retirement (*115*). He died at Ormathwaite on January 6, 1800. A writer in *Gentleman's Magazine* said of him, "The poor and the rich

Antoine Baumé, 1728–1804. French pharmacist and chemist. Author of a "Chymie expérimentale et raisonnée" in which he discussed chemical apparatus, chemical affinity, fire, air, earth, water, sulfur, gypsum, alum, clay, niter, gunpowder, borax, arsenic, glass, porcelain, and the common acids, alkalies, metals, and ores used in 1773. His hydrometer scale is still used. He was one of the first chemists to investigate platinum.

had everywhere somewhat for which they thanked him, and health seemed only one of the blessings which he had to dispense" (*64*).

Sir William Watson was a distinguished physician, naturalist, and physicist. He was born in London on April 3, 1715, studied at the Merchant Taylors' School, and became apprenticed to an apothecary. He contributed to the *Philosophical Transactions* a large number of original papers and many reviews of the work of other scientists. His long series of brilliant experimental researches on electricity brought him great renown. For many years he served as physician to the Foundling Hospital in London. He was knighted in 1786 and died on May 10th of the following year.

The most distinguished chemists in Europe soon became intensely interested in platinum.   Among those who published papers on it may be mentioned: H. T. Scheffer (*42*), T. Bergman, and J. J. Berzelius in Sweden; William Lewis in England; A. S. Marggraf in Germany; and P.-J. Macquer, A. Baumé, Count G.-L. Leclerc de Buffon, L.-B. Guyton de Morveau, Romé Delisle, A.-L. Lavoisier, and B. Pelletier (*43*) in France.

In 1752 H. T. Scheffer published a detailed scientific description of platinum, or "white gold," as he called it, and, with the aid of arsenic, succeeded in fusing it (*42*).   Henric Theophil Scheffer was born in Stockholm on December 28, 1710, where his father was secretary to the Royal Board of Mines.   After serving an apprenticeship under Georg Brandt, he established his own laboratory and made trips to the mines to learn firsthand the close connection between smelting and assaying.

Bertrand Pelletier, 1761–1797. French chemist and pharmacist who investigated the arsenates, phosphates, and phosphides of many metals, studied the action of phosphorus on platinum, and devised new methods for making soap and refining metal for clocks.   He served as inspector of the hospitals in Belgium.   His son, Joseph Pelletier (1788–1842), and Joseph Caventou discovered quinine, cinchonine, strychnine, and brucine.   See also ref. (*89*).

In his eulogy, A. F. Cronstedt told the members of the Swedish Academy of Sciences how Scheffer became interested in platinum: "In his time," said Cronstedt, "a new metal happened to be discovered, which had evidently not been found in two thousand years, and it was most fitting that the first investigation of such a rare substance should fall to this man who was worthy of it.

"Your literary member, Herr Rudensköld [Ulrik Rudenschöld, 1704–1765], brought this honor to him and to us; for no sooner had Mr. Watson in London let Herr Bose [Georg Matthias Bose, 1710–1761] in Wittenberg know that something resembling a metal of unknown properties had been brought over from America, under the name of *Platina di Pinto,* until Herr Rudensköld arranged to get some of it through his acquaintances in Spain.

"The little bit that came," said Cronstedt, "he handed over to Scheffer, who, driven by his customary zeal, soon solved the mystery of its nature, and showed in a paper that it was a peculiar metal, different from all others, almost infusible when alone, just as noble as gold, and less pliable. He anticipated Mr. Lewis, who made experiments on a greater quantity of it and later published the results of them in the *Transactions of the British Scientific Society* [*Philosophical Transactions of the Royal Society* (*67*)]; but during the investigation neither was aware of the other's manipulations and conclusions, wherefore each of them established a special property in addition to what they in all other respects found to be identical.

"Our Scheffer," said Crondstedt, "who rejoiced over this incontrovertible evidence, found, however, an error in denoting the specific gravity of the many alloys which Mr. Lewis prepared from platinum and other metals; wherefore he corrected them in the *Handlingar* of this Society in a manner which bears witness that the love of truth did not turn the head of the person who found it" (*68*).

Scheffer died on August 10, 1759. As Crondstedt said, "he sought diligently to follow the path that leads to the right goal after death; for he could not harbor the false doctrine that gold, which hinders and leads astray, or panaceas alleged to prolong life can serve as remuneration for piety" (*68*).

In 1772 Baron Carl von Sickingen made extended researches on platinum and rendered it malleable by alloying it with silver and gold, dissolving the alloy in aqua regia, precipitating the platinum with ammonium chloride, igniting the ammonium chloroplatinate, and hammering the resulting finely divided platinum to make it cohere (*69*). His researches on this subject were not published until 1782 (*70*). Two years later F. C. Achard prepared the first platinum crucible by fusing platinum with arsenic and volatilizing off the arsenic (*69*).

The Marqués de los Castillejos presented the Basque Society of Friends of their Country with a large quantity of platinum. The *Extractos* of this Society published William Lewis's dissertation on this metal with the editorial note: "The Commission has made several tests according to this information and has succeeded in applying the use of this metal to the adornment of the handles of several razors and knives, giving it by admixture various tints of golden or yellow color" (*66*). After a thorough investigation of this metal at the Vergara Seminary, Pierre-François Chabaneau (or Chavaneau) succeeded in making pure platinum malleable (*66*).

Professor James Lewis Howe, author of an excellent bibliography of the metals of the platinum group, and Louis Quennessen, head of the firm of Des Moutis and Company, platinum refiners, have reviewed Chabaneau's contributions (71, 72, 73). Chabaneau was born at Nontron, Dordogne, in 1754. An uncle, a monk of the order of St. Anthony, encouraged him to study theology. Although Chabaneau was brilliantly successful in his studies, metaphysical speculations were so distasteful to him that he antagonized his teachers and was expelled from the school.

His penniless condition aroused the sympathy of the Abbé La Rose, director of a Jesuit college at Passy, who offered him the chair of mathematics. Although he scarcely knew arithmetic, Chabaneau, then only seventeen years old, was compelled by dire need to accept this unsuitable position. Studying by firelight every night in preparation for the next day's teaching, he mastered arithmetic, algebra, and geometry, and soon became deeply interested in physics, natural history, and chemistry.

At the age of twenty years he began to give a course of public lectures. Among his auditors were the sons of the Count of Peñaflorida, who had sent them to France to study and to select professors for the recently founded Vergara Seminary. They finally induced Chabaneau to go to Vergara to teach French and physics.

Don José Celestino Mutis mentioned in 1774 two portrait medallions of the King made by Don Francisco Benito, engraver at the Royal Mint in Santa Fé (Colombia). One of these was made of an alloy containing equal parts of copper and platinum, the other of pure platinum (74). Two letters of Don Fausto de Elhuyar, long preserved with the Mutis manuscripts at the Botanical Garden in Madrid, show that he collaborated with Chabaneau in the researches on platinum. Writing from Vergara to his brother Don Juan José in Bogotá on March 17, 1786, Don Fausto described their process in detail, and estimated the value of platinum as less than that of silver. From the other letter, written from Paris to Don Juan José on May 19th of the same year, it is evident that Chabaneau and the two Elhuyar brothers kept this process secret (75, 76).

Soon after this, King Charles III created for Chabaneau a public chair of mineralogy, physics, and chemistry at Madrid, lodged him in one of the royal palaces, and provided him with a valuable library and a luxurious laboratory (72, 73).

The Marqués de Aranda had the government turn over its entire supply of platinum to Chabaneau for his difficult and puzzling researches. When Chabaneau removed the gold, mercury, lead, copper, iron, etc., he thought he had a single metal, platinum. As a matter of fact, however, he was still dealing with six metals, for rhodium, palladium, osmium, iridium, and ruthenium had not yet been discovered.   Small wonder that he oftentimes became discouraged by contradictory results. Sometimes the platinum was malleable and at other times it was brittle (alloyed with iridium); sometimes it was incombustible and non-volatile and at other times (when an osmium alloy happened to be present) it burned and volatilized.

When Chabaneau began to work on other subjects, the patient Marqués de Aranda encouraged him to turn again to the great research on "white gold."   Even when Chabaneau finally lost his temper and destroyed his apparatus and preparations, the Marqués still urged him

José Celestino Mutis, 1732–1808. Spanish botanist, physician, and ecclesiastic who devoted his life to studying the natural history of northern South America.   He investigated the cinchona (or chinchona) forests of Colombia (New Granada) and collaborated with Don Juan José de Elhuyar in developing its mines.   He stated that the gold in the ores of Chocó cannot be separated from the platinum except by amalgamation (87).

not to lose confidence.   Three months later, the Marqués found on a table in his home a ten-centimeter cube of metal.   Attempting to pick it up, he said to Chabaneau, "You are joking.   You have fastened it down."   The little ingot weighed 23 kilograms; it was malleable platinum!   Although the Marqués de Aranda had previously handled platinum only in the spongy form, Chabaneau had compressed a very pure platinum sponge, while hot, at the moment of its formation, and hammered it, while white hot, until it cohered.

The King, who had often come to the laboratory to watch the progress of the experiments, had a commemorative medal struck in platinum, and granted Chabaneau a life pension on condition that he remain in Spain. The letters-patent bearing the date 1783 established Chabaneau's priority in this discovery (72).

Realizing that the very infusibility of platinum would lend value to objects made from it, Chabaneau and Don Joaquín Cabezas purified it, worked it, and carried on a lucrative business in the sale of platinum ingots and utensils. Thus began what Don Juan Fages y Virgili has called "the platinum age in Spain" (66). In 1799 Clavijo Fajardo, director of the Royal Laboratory of Natural History, asked the Minister for forty pounds of purified platinum and three arrobas (1 arroba = 25 pounds) of the native platinum grains for the use of Don Luis (Joseph-Louis) Proust for making crucibles and other utensils, and the government granted even more of it than was requested (66). Thus in a single laboratory in Madrid, "forty-six kilograms of platinum in grains and eighteen and one-half of the same purified were brought in in one day, that is to say, more platinum than we possess today [1909] in all the official laboratories in Spain" (66). Some of the platinum extracted from the gray sand which Don Antonio de Ulloa had brought from America was made into a magnificent communion cup for the chapel of the Royal Palace in Madrid (77). In other parts of the world, too, platinum was then relatively abundant. In 1808 Fredrick Accum sold some platinum to Professor William Peck of Harvard University for about 7 cents a gram ("$1/2$ oz. pure platina in slips 4 shillings") (90).

Late in life Chabaneau renounced his pension in order to seek rest and restoration of his health near his native village. He died in 1842 at the age of eighty-eight years. Jules Delanoue, a contemporary, described him as "a fine-looking old man, with pleasing and regular features, bearing much resemblance to those of our good and lamented Béranger. His conversation was charming and always instructive. Friend and contemporary of Volney, of Cabanis, of Lavoisier, he was nourished upon their ideas and imbued with their spirit, and they were pleasingly reflected in his conversation" (72, 73).

When Chabaneau took some of his ingots to Paris, M. Jeanety made from them some beautiful pieces of jewelry and became so interested that he gave up his craftmanship in gold and silver to devote all his time to the working of platinum (78). In the Jeanety process, objects were fashioned from a platinum-arsenic alloy and heated to expel the arsenic (91). Guyton de Morveau, Sir Joseph Banks, and some of the scientists in Sweden and the Netherlands ordered from him their platinum crucibles and ingots. Jeanety also made platinum snuffboxes, watchchains, spoons, toothpick boxes, blowpipes, and a set of buttons (78, 79). The prices were lower than for the corresponding articles in gold.

In reporting Jeanety's process to the French Bureau of Consultation in 1792, C.-L. Berthollet and Bertrand Pelletier stated that the gold from the Novitá and Citaría mines north of Chocó was separated from the platinum by sorting or by amalgamation. Since platinum could be used to alloy and adulterate gold, and since such alloys resisted parting, the Spanish government ordered that the platinum be thrown into the rivers. "The Chocó gold," said Berthollet and Pelletier, "is then sent to be coined in the two mints at Santa Fé, to those in Bogotá and Popayán, where any platinum which may have remained with the gold is again sorted out. Royal officers guard it, and when there is a certain quantity of it, they come with witnesses to throw it into the Bogotá River two leagues from Santa Fé and into the Cauca River one league from Popayán. The platinum always occurs in little grains; some of them, however, are quite large; there is even one in the cabinet of the Vergara Academy of the size of a pigeon's egg" (78).

An article on the platinum mines of Colombia published in volume 6 of the *Medical Repository* states that "Three hundred pounds of platina were imported into New York in October, 1802, from the Island of Jamaica. But it was not a native production of that place. It was brought from the continental dominions of Spain. As the exportation of platina is prohibited by the government, this quantity was smuggled off in small parcels. In the course of certain secret mercantile transactions, these different collections found their way from the Spaniards to a British subject, who brought to this market the above-mentioned quantity, which is but a part of what he had gathered together. Such a quantity of the rarest of the metals, and of one which is believed to be peculiar to America, and known to Europe only about the middle of the eighteenth century, afforded an excellent opportunity of examining its condition when offered for sale as an article of commerce" (116).

Dr. Samuel Latham Mitchill, editor of the *Medical Repository*, carefully examined and described this metal and added that "Baron Carendeffez has subjected parcels of this platina to a great many experiments, which he intends to publish at large. . . . The mines in the Island of Chaco [Chocó, Colombia] afforded it: These are in Terra Firma, about three hundred miles up the River Magdalena, and south-west some distance from Santa Fé, and are reckoned among the most pure and productive in America. The platina is found among the gold, and the grains of the two metals are washed from the sands together, and afterwards separated. All the platina, as well as all the gold, is deposited in the adjoining custom-house, and kept by the king's officers. It is not certainly known what becomes of the platina. For though it is reported that the policy of the government directs it to be thrown away, and committed to the currents of deep rivers, yet there is a belief that the whole quantity collected is transported to Spain. All commerce in platina is forbidden under penalty of death: consequently none can be procured but by smuggling, and at very great risk. The first cost, fees to assistants, and extraordinary hazards in this contraband trade amounted to so much that the owner of this parcel said it stood him in forty dollars a pound" (116).

In 1818 French and English journals contained a description of an enormous platinum nugget weighing 1 pound, 9 ounces, and 1 dram, which had been found by Justo, a Negro slave of Don Ignacio Hurtado, proprietor of the Condoto gold mine at Novitá, Chocó. It was sent with the Mutis collections to the King of Spain, who deposited it in the Royal Museum at Madrid (117).

William Lewis believed that platinum may have been the substance used by alchemists for "augmenting" gold. "These properties," said he, "together with the place where it is found, and the prohibition said to be laid upon its exportation by the King of Spain, afford sufficient grounds to presume that the *Smiris Hispanica* of the alchemists, employed for augmenting gold, was no other than this Platina or some mineral containing it; more especially as Becher expressly declares that this augmentation was really an abuse; that the Gold so augmented was pale and brittle; and that though it stood all the established tests of perfect Gold, yet it would not bear amalgamation with Quicksilver, the Mercury retaining the Gold and throwing out the *Smiris* in form of a reddish powder. Platina mixed with Gold is thrown out in the same manner; though it is not easy by this method to obtain a perfect separation" (105).

Alexander von Humboldt stated in 1826 that platinum "has not yet been discovered north of the isthmus of Panama on the North American continent. Platina in grains is found only in two places in the known world, that is to say, in Chocó, a province in the kingdom of New Granada, and near the coasts of the Southern Sea in the province of Barbacoas between the second and sixth degrees of north latitude. . . . The placers which at present yield platina are located south of the threshold (*umbral*) which separates the headwaters of the Río Atrato from those of the Río San Juan. . . . It is absolutely false that platinum has ever been found near Cartagena, at Santa Fé de Bogotá, on islands of Puerto Rico or the Barbadoes, or in Peru, even though these localities have been mentioned in excellent and well-known works . . ." (109).

Humboldt obtained much of this information from Don Joaquín Acosta, a well-informed young army officer of the Republic of Colombia. In July, 1826, just as his "Political Essay on New Spain" was ready for the press, Humboldt learned that J.-B. Boussingault had found round grains of platinum in the gold-bearing *pacos* (reddish silver ores) of the veins of Santa Rosa and the Osos, ten leagues northwest of Medellín (109).

A. D. Lumb stated in 1920 in his monograph on the platinum metals that Colombia is the second largest producer of platinum in the world; that the principal source of supply is at the head of the San Juan River, which enters the Pacific Ocean north of Buenaventura, the richest deposits occurring in the tributaries of the San Juan; that platinum is also obtained from the Upper Atrato River, which flows northward to the Caribbean Sea (Gulf of Darien); and that the area including the watersheds of the San Juan and Upper Atrato Rivers is known as the Chocó district (110).

Although the discovery of platinum in Chocó is usually attributed to the eighteenth-century explorer Don Antonio de Ulloa, J.-B. Boussingault believed that the first Spanish gold-seekers of the sixteenth century could not have failed to observe the peculiar "white gold" which settled out with the true gold in the panning process (111). Don José Celestino Mutis of Bogotá also stated that platinum was known in New Granada even before de Ulloa described it (74).

When J.-B. Boussingault had charge of the metallic mines of Colombia, the Congress of that country voted that a platinum equestrian statue of Simón Bolívar be erected in Bogotá. Charged with the duty of executing this order, Boussingault drew up a report showing that the production of all the mines in the country would be insufficient for this purpose and that it would be impossible to cast a statue from this refractory metal. On the advice of a superior official, he withheld the report, however, and, to shield the lawmakers from embarrassment, merely agreed to carry out the commission to the best of his ability. When the Congress had had time to forget about the statue of Bolívar, the two kilograms of platinum which had been carefully saved were made into the apparatus for the laboratory of chemical engineering (80).

In 1774 Joseph Priestley wrote: "Nothing would be easier than to augment the force of fire to a prodigious degree by blowing it with dephlogisticated air [oxygen] instead of common air. . . . Possibly platina might be melted by means of it" (95). In 1801 Robert Hare, then only twenty years old, described before the Chemical Society of Philadelphia his oxyhydrogen blowpipe, with which he could fuse platinum. Two years later he reported to the American Philosophical Society that he had succeeded in volatilizing this metal (81). Hare's student, Joachim Bishop, later founded the American platinum refining industry (82). It was not until after the experiments of Wollaston, however, that the working of platinum became easy (3).

William Hyde Wollaston, the son of an Episcopal clergyman, was born as East Dereham, Norfolkshire, England, on August 6, 1766. His childhood was not a lonely one, for he had fourteen active brothers and sisters. After studying at Cambridge, he received his medical degree at

Robert Hare, 1781–1858. Professor of chemistry at the University of Pennsylvania. At the age of twenty years he invented the oxy-hydrogen, or compound, blowpipe, with which he fused and volatilized platinum and other refractory substances. He was most ingenious in devising chemical apparatus.

the age of twenty-seven years. Although he practiced his profession for a time at Bury St. Edmunds,* he retired in 1800 and went to live in London, in order that he might devote all his time to physical science (*4, 88*).

* John Winthrop the Younger once attended grammar school at this place.

For half a century after its discovery platinum had few uses because of the difficulty of working it.   Dr. Wollaston found, however, that spongy platinum becomes malleable when strongly compressed and that it can be annealed and hammered.   This process made possible the widespread use of the metal for laboratory apparatus, and the income from it enabled Wollaston to retire from his medical practice at the early age of thirty-four years and devote the rest of his life to scientific research. He specified the exact composition of the aqua regia which would dissolve the platinum without dissolving the iridium, and the proper method of expelling the ammonium chloride without making the fine particles of platinum cohere.   The pulverizing was done with the hands and with a wooden mortar and pestle, for harder surfaces burnished the platinum so that it could not be welded.   The powder was then thoroughly washed with water, and, while still wet, strongly compressed in a mould, heated in a wind furnace, and struck, while hot, with a heavy hammer.

On April 22, 1813, Berzelius wrote from Stockholm to Dr. Alexandre Marcet of London:

When you see Dr. Wollaston give him a thousand compliments from me and then ask him if it would be possible to have a little malleable platinum, not separated from its natural alloy with palladium, rhodium, etc., to make a crucible.   The crucibles I have bought recently from Cary are of a metal noticeably purer than those which I formerly had, and for that very reason infinitely more susceptible to attack by other substances (5).

About two weeks later Dr. Marcet replied:

Wollaston laughs at the idea that you want him to get you some impure platinum.   He asks me to suggest that you alloy pure platinum with a little silver, as the surest means of increasing its durability (6).

On February 24, 1829, Berzelius wrote to Eilhard Mitscherlich, "Wollaston's death grieves me.   His specifications for making platina pliable were circulated at the same time as the news of his death.   As I got iridium to cohere in an analogous manner, I was struck all the more by his simple method, went out into the laboratory, where I had a wet filter with platina on it, partly washed, which I pressed in a vice, dried, and ignited over a spirit lamp in a small platina crucible, and got it so coherent that it could no longer be broken with the fingers and could easily be cold-hammered.   That's as far as I have yet gone.   That was ten minutes' work, then I had to let it wait for a better time" (83).

That Berzelius made good use of Wollaston's process is evident from his letter to F. Wöhler written on May 1, 1829:

We are now re-casting all our old soldered platinum crucibles by Wollaston's method of making platinum pliable; it goes like a dance.   I think Wollaston must have laughed inside over the many elaborate methods which have been used in vain for this purpose, when his is so simple. It seems that by heating the bottom of the crucible glowing hot in Sefström's forge, the formation of bubbles can be entirely prevented (7).

In preparing solid platinum from its powder, Wollaston foreshadowed modern methods of powder metallurgy, by which the powders of refractory metals, such as tungsten, molybdenum, tantalum, and columbium, can be fabricated into useful articles (84, 86).

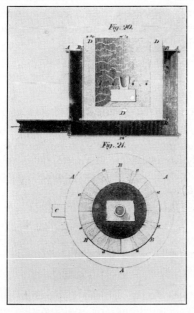

N. G. Sefström's Portable Eight-Blast Forge. Fig. 20. Vertical section. Fig. 21. Transverse section. a . . . a are the eight conical tuyères from the bellows. With small pieces of dust-free wood charcoal as fuel, Sefström melted platinum in this forge.

From Berzelius' "Lehrbuch der Chemie"

The technical working of massive platinum should be ascribed, however, to Thomas Cock, a brother-in-law of the platinum-refiner P. N. Johnson, rather than to Wollaston. Cock worked out the process in William Allen's laboratory at Plough Court and, at Allen's request, communicated it to Wollaston (51). According to G. Matthey, P. N. Johnson was the first to manufacture platinum on a commercial scale and the first to prepare a large and perfect sheet of the pure metal. James Lewis Howe has stated that Chabaneau's process was rediscovered by Knight and possibly also by Cock (72).

Apollos Apollosovich Musin-Pushkin (1760–1805) of St. Peters-

A Page from Sefström's Laboratory Notes. Translation: Cinchona reactions. 5 lbs. cortex Peruvian, first quality, with the sea captain Ripa from Amsterdam, belongs to Mazer and Co. Board of Health, minutes for Sept. 16, 1816. Bark very fine dark gray. Infusion clear, quite weak quinine taste, gave with iron solution a dark green precipitate. Antimony tartrate, very weak opalescence. Infusion of nutgalls, very heavy white precipitate like that of gelatin and nutgalls. Gelatin solution, faint opalescence. It is *no good.* Stockholm, Sept. 22, 1816. N. G. Sefström, M.D., Adjunct in Chemistry.

* The writer is deeply grateful to Miss Mary Larson of the Zoölogy Department at the University of Kansas and to Mr. Einar Bourman for the translation of this letter from the Swedish and for assistance in securing Swedish illustrations.

burg investigated platinum between the years 1797 and 1805. He prepared platinum amalgam by triturating mercury with ammonium chloroplatinate or by triturating platinum sponge powder with a fivefold amount of mercury (91). He then produced malleable platinum by placing this amalgam in a wooden mold, heating the mold to volatilize the mercury, and keeping the platinum metal white hot for two hours or more. The wooden molds were burned.

In his lectures in 1817, W. T. Brande stated that platinum "may be considered as the exclusive product of South America" (46). In 1819, however, a white metal was observed in the gold placers on the eastern, or Siberian, slopes of the Urals, south of Ekaterinburg (Sverdlovsk) (69). In 1822 I. I. Varvinskiĭ, director of the Gold-smelting Laboratory of Ekaterinburg, showed that it contained platinum, and V. V. Liubarskiĭ, an assayer of St. Petersburg, later proved it to be osmiridium. In 1824 platinum was discovered north of Ekaterinburg in the Urals (36).

In 1826, thus two years before Wollaston disclosed his secret process, P. G. Sobolevskiĭ and V. V. Liubarskiĭ of St. Petersburg devised a cheap method of preparing malleable platinum from the spongy metal resulting from the calcination of ammonium chloroplatinate. Early in the following year they demonstrated their method publicly before the Mining Cadet Corps and the Scientific Committee on Mining and Salt Industries. For this invention they received gifts from Emperor Nicholas I. Their method was essentially the same as Wollaston's secret process (91).

When Alexander von Humboldt, Gustav Rose, and Christian Gottfried Ehrenberg made a scientific expedition to Russia in 1829 the Russian Minister of Finance E. F. Kankrin made arrangements for their comfort and security. Humboldt made important observations on the gold- and platinum-bearing alluvial deposits of the Urals (92). Professor B. N. Menschutkin published in the *Journal of Chemical Education* an excellent historical sketch of the Russian platinum (36).

In 1828 the Russian government authorized the coinage of large amounts of Siberian platinum acquired from Count Demidoff (85). The following notice appeared in *Philosophical Magazine* in December of that year: "A letter from Professor Breithaupt to Dr. Schweigger-Seidel, an extract from which is given in a late Number of the Jahrbuch der Chemie &c., confirms the statement, some time since made by the newspapers, that the Russian Government had resolved to coin a large sum in Siberian platina. It appears that Count Demidoff, the proprietor of the locality where the platina was discovered, has disposed of to the Government the quantity of that metal which had been collected. He has sent four young Russians, destined for official situations in Siberia, to be educated at the Mining Academy of Freyberg" (85).

Between the years 1828 and 1845 a total of 14,600 kilograms of platinum was coined in three-, six-, and twelve-ruble denominations (36). In 1846 the platinum coins were withdrawn from circulation.

PALLADIUM

As early as 1700, or more than a century before palladium was discovered, Brazilian miners became familiar with a natural alloy which they called *prata* (silver), *ouro podre* (worthless, or spoiled gold), or *ouro branco* (white gold) (44). In about 1780 a silver-white gold bar at the Sabará smelting-house broke into several pieces under the impact of the die. This gold had come from St. Anna dos Ferros, near Itabira do Dentro, Minas (44). In 1798 José Vieira do Couto mentioned several localities in Brazil where a silver-white "platinum" was to be found. This was probably the alloy palladium-gold.

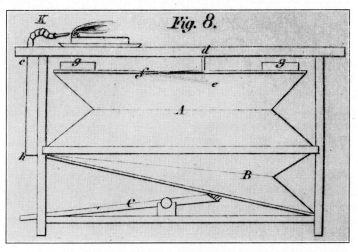

From Berzelius' "Lehrbuch der Chemie"

Bellows Used with Sefström's Forge

In 1803 Dr. Wollaston succeeded in separating two new metals from platinum. He dissolved the crude metal in aqua regia, evaporated off the excess acid, and added a solution of mercurous cyanide, drop by drop, until a yellow precipitate appeared. When this substance was washed and ignited, a white metal remained. By heating the yellow precipitate with sulfur and borax he also succeeded in obtaining a button of the new metal, which he named *palladium* in honor of the recently discovered asteroid, *Pallas* (6).

The first knowledge that the London public received of this discovery was an anonymous handbill offering the metal for sale. The humorous and pathetic story of the young Irish chemist, Richard Chenevix (8), who believed the new metal to be fraudulent and who tried to prove that it was a platinum amalgam, has been told in the *Journal of Chemical Education* by White and Friedman (21) and by Desmond Reilly (130).

After considerable polemics, Chenevix' claim that the palladium was merely an amalgam of platinum was disproved, and Dr. Wollaston wrote in 1804: "Notwithstanding I was aware that M. Descotils had ascribed the red colour of certain precipitates and salts of platina to the presence of a new metal; and although Mr. Tennant had obligingly communicated to me his discovery of the same substance, as well as of a second new metal, in the shining powder that remains undissolved from the ore of platina; yet I was led to suppose that the more soluble parts of this mineral might be deserving of further examination, as the fluid which remains after the precipitation of platina by sal ammoniac presents appearances which I could not ascribe to either of those bodies or to any other known substance" (120). Dr. Wollaston added that "the metallic substance which was last year offered for sale by the name of Palladium is contained (though in very small proportion) in the ore of platina" (120).

N.-L. Vauquelin paid eloquent tribute to the excellence of these researches: "Though Dr. Wollaston operated on only one thousand grains of the ore of platinum, and had at the most only six or seven grains of each of the new metals at his disposal, yet he recognized their principal properties, which does infinite honour to his sagacity; for the thing appears at first view incredible. For my part, though I employed sixty marcs [15 kilograms] of platinum ore, I found it very difficult to separate exactly the palladium and rhodium from the platinum and the other metals which exist in that ore, and especially to obtain them perfectly pure" (45).

At Dr. Wollaston's suggestion palladium was alloyed with gold and used "for the graduated part of the great astronomical circle erected at the Royal Observatory by Mr. Troughton" (46). Dr. Wollaston emphasized the desirability of using palladium weights for precise work. A set of them which once belonged to Thomas Thomson has been described in the *Journal of Chemical Education* (47).

In 1809–10 Joseph Cloud, chemical director of the Philadelphia Mint, discovered an alloy of gold and palladium in two ingots of gold from Brazil (48, 49). The following account of this discovery is to be found in *Nicholson's Journal* for 1812: "In 1807 about 820 ounces of gold bullion were brought into the mint of the United States. They consisted of 120 small ingots, each stamped on one side with the arms of Portugal and the inscription *Río das Montis*, and on the other with a globe. The fineness of each ingot too was marked on it. Among these were two differing from the others so much in colour that Mr. Cloud preserved one, weighing 3 oz. 11 dwts., 12 grs., to examine it . . ." (49).

Eugen Hussak stated that the inscription on these ingots was not "Río das montis," but Río dos Mortes," which is near S. João del Rey (44). Although native gold usually contains some silver, copper, or other metals, Cloud found this ingot to be alloyed only with palladium (49). Although this alloy contained no easily oxidizable metal, silver, nor platinum, Cloud obtained from it a button of palladium. Since palladium had previously been obtained only from impure platinum, some chemists may still have believed with Richard Chenevix that it must be an alloy of platinum. Cloud's isolation from the platinum-free ingots of a metal which proved to be identical with Dr. Wollaston's palladium afforded strong evidence that the latter must be an individual metal and not an alloy of platinum (50).

Although neither Couto nor Cloud had been certain whether the palladium-gold was a natural alloy or an artificial alloy of native palladium with native gold, Berzelius in 1835 analyzed some of the natural "ouro podre" which the geologist E. Pohl of Vienna had sent him from Capitania Porpez or [Goyaz], Brazil, and found it to consist of about 86 per cent of gold, 10 per cent of palladium, and 4 per cent of silver (44, 121).

When the gold bars from Gongo-Soco, Brazil, first began to come to England, the Mint refused to accept them because of their brittleness. The famous platinum refiner Percival Norton Johnson assayed them, however, detected the palladium, and perfected a process for refining and toughening the Brazilian gold (51, 52). In 1837 he presented specimens of palladium-gold, palladium ammonium chloride, and palladium metal to W. A. Lampadius of the Freiberg School of Mines. According to Lampadius, "Palladium has not been separated from the Brazilian gold until the last four years, but since that time Mr. Johnson, who had worked on palladium a great deal with the late Wollaston, has given the owners of the aforementioned gold mine a method of parting by means of which the gold is produced pure, and the separated palladium put to many other uses. . . . The palladium thus produced, alloyed with 20 per cent silver, is now used in London as metal for dentists, also for making scales for sextants and other astronomical instruments. Alloyed with copper, it gives a composition which makes steel more elastic. Even earlier, a watchmaker, Bennet, specified an alloy of 24 palladium, 44 silver, 72 gold, and 92 copper for bearings for chronometers" (52).

Johnson separated the palladium from an enormous quantity of the Gongo-Soco gold, and in 1845 supplied the Royal Geological Society of

London with a sufficient quantity of this metal for the casting of the Wollaston Medal (*44*). Johnson was always considerate of the miners, and sincerely devoted to their welfare. He spent much of his time and fortune on the schools which he erected near the mines (*51*).

In 1809 Wollaston demonstrated the presence of grains of native palladium and native platinum in a Brazilian alluvial gold ore presented to him by the Portuguese ambassador, H. E. Chev. de Souza Coutinho. Wollaston was led to this discovery by the observation that some of the grains, although they looked like platinum, dissolved faster in aqua regia (*44, 122, 123*). In 1825 Alexander von Humboldt also reported the occurrence of native palladium in Brazil (*109*).

RHODIUM

W. H. Wollaston discovered rhodium in 1803–04 in crude platinum ore. Although he did not definitely state the source of this ore, it must have come from South America; the Russian platinum ores had not yet been discovered. "Since the platina to be procured in this country," said Wollaston, "generally contains small scales of gold intermixed, as well as a portion of the mercury which the Spaniards employ for the separation of the gold, the platina used for my experiments, after being by mechanical means freed, as far as possible, from all visible impurities, was exposed to a red heat for the purpose of expelling the mercury" (*9*).

Dr. Wollaston dissolved a portion of crude platinum in aqua regia, and neutralized the excess acid with caustic soda. He then added sal ammoniac to precipitate the platinum as ammonium chloroplatinate, and mercurous cyanide to precipitate the palladium as palladious cyanide. After filtering off the precipitate, he decomposed the excess mercurous cyanide in the filtrate by adding hydrochloric acid and evaporating to dryness. When he washed the residue with alcohol, everything dissolved except a beautiful dark red powder, which proved to be a double chloride of sodium and a new metal (*3*), which, because of the rose color of its salts, Dr. Wollaston named *rhodium* (*9*). He found that the sodium rhodium chloride could be easily reduced by heating it in a current of hydrogen, and that after the sodium chloride had been washed out, the rhodium remained as a metallic powder. He also obtained a rhodium button.

Thomas Thomson said that Dr. Wollaston had amazingly keen vision and remarkably steady hands. He could write on glass with a diamond in clear, well-formed letters which were so small that other persons could read them only with a microscope (*4*).

That Berzelius was well acquainted with Dr. Wollaston and held him in high esteem may be seen from his letter to Berthollet written in London in October, 1812:

My stay here [said Berzelius] has been most interesting and instructive in furnishing me a quantity of chemical resources of which I formerly had no idea. But what I value most of all is the personal acquaintance of the admirable Wollaston and the brilliant Davy. I am sure that among the chemists who are at present in the prime of life there is none that can be compared with Wollaston in mental depth and accuracy as well as in resourcefulness, and all this is combined in him with gentle manners and true modesty. I have profited more by an hour's conversation with him than frequently by the reading of large printed volumes. . . . Simplicity, clarity, and the greatest appearance of truth are always the accompaniments of his reasoning (5).

William Hyde Wollaston, 1766–1828. English chemist and physicist. Discoverer of palladium and rhodium. Inventor of a process for making platinum malleable. Famous for his researches on force of percussion, gout, diabetes, columbium (niobium), tantalum, and titanium, and his scale of chemical equivalents.

In the diary which he kept on this visit to England, Berzelius wrote,

Dr. Wollaston, Secretary of the Royal Society, known through his numerous discoveries in chemistry and physics, is a man between forty and fifty years old, of very pleasant appearance, very polished manners, plainness and clearness in his conversation, interest in his slightest gesture, and with such a spirit of justice and gifted with such moderation in his views that it has become a common proverb that whoever argues with Wollaston is wrong (30).

The letters of Dr. Alexandre Marcet to Berzelius give us a pleasing picture of Dr. Wollaston's friendly nature. On May 24, 1814, Dr. Marcet wrote:

Would you believe it, my dear friend, that while your kind and interesting letter of April 12th was on its way to London, I was occupied with friend Wollaston in enjoying all the dissipations of Paris. One fine morning, near the end of April, Wollaston came into my house and said to me: "I have curious news for you." "What!" I replied, "Has Bonaparte returned to Paris?" "No," he said, "it is even more curious than that. . . . I am going to Paris tomorrow, and you are one of the party." I rubbed my eyes, thinking I was dreaming; but he finally proved to me that it was not a dream; and as everything Wollaston says is gospel (Sir John Sebright has nick-named him "The Pope"), I immediately told my wife that fate was calling me to Paris for a fortnight, gave a good dose to each of my patients, and left . . . (10).

Sir Edward Thorpe gives quite a different picture of Wollaston, however, when he says,

He resembled Cavendish in temperament and mental habitudes, and, like him, was distinguished for the range and exactitude of his scientific knowledge, his habitual caution, and his cold and reserved disposition (11).

On another occasion Dr. Marcet wrote, "The excellent Wollaston has just lost his father, who leaves a large fortune, which I dare to reply, will not spoil our friend" (12). On January 23, 1816, he suggested in reply to a question asked by Berzelius,

If you wish to send Wollaston a present in the name of the prince, the only idea that comes to me is a fine hunting gun of your splendid Swedish steel. The dear Doctor, pope that he is, has taken seriously to hunting, and already acquits himself with much success. The fact is he does not know how to do anything poorly (10).

Dr. Wollaston was a man of very broad interests, as a list of his publications will show. His papers were on such diverse subjects as: force of percussion, fairy rings, gout, diabetes, seasickness, metallic titanium, the identity of columbium (niobium) and tantalum, a reflection goniometer, micrometers, barometers, a scale of chemical equivalents, and the finite extent of the atmosphere. He died in London on December 22, 1828 (13).

In 1824 A. M. del Río analyzed a gold-rhodium alloy from the parting-house in Mexico, but did not state the original source of the metal (119). In the introduction to his paper he stated: "In 1810 Mr. Cloud, refiner (now director) of the mint at Philadelphia, discovered that two ingots from Brazil were alloys of gold with palladium: we have here one of gold with rhodium, a discovery hitherto unknown in Europe, like numberless other remarkable things which, under the auspices of liberty, will be brought to light in a country so extensive and highly favoured by nature" (119).

From Figuier's "Vies des Savants Illustres"

Georges-Louis Leclerc, Comte de Buffon, 1707–1788.
French naturalist famous for his beautiful literary style.
Founder of the Jardin des Plantes. Author of a "Natural History" in forty-four volumes, in which he discussed insects, birds, quadrupeds, minerals, the theory
of the earth, and the epochs of Nature. One of the
first to investigate platinum.

Rhodium occurs associated with platinum ores, and also in the mineral rhodite in the gold-bearing sands of Brazil and Colombia.

OSMIUM AND IRIDIUM

Smithson Tennant, the discoverer of osmium and iridium, like Dr. Wollaston, was the son of a clergyman. He was born in Wensleydale, near Richmond, Yorkshire, on November 30, 1761. At the age of nine years he had the misfortune to lose his father, and not many years later he witnessed the tragic death of his mother, who, while riding with him, was thrown from her horse and instantly killed. Tennant's elementary education was fragmentary, but even when very young he was fond of reading chemical books and performing experiments. When he was only nine years old he made some gunpowder for fireworks (14).

In 1781 he went to Edinburgh to study under the famous chemist and physician Dr. Joseph Black, and in the following year he entered Christ's College, Cambridge, where he studied chemistry, botany, mathematics, and Newton's "Principia." His room at college was a scene of confusion: books, papers, and chemical apparatus littered the floor, and his indolent and unsystematic habits were indeed a serious handicap throughout his scientific career (15).

When he was twenty-three years old, he traveled through Denmark and Sweden, where he met the famous C. W. Scheele, and for the rest of his life he delighted in showing his English friends the minerals that the great Swedish chemist had given him on this occasion. Tennant also traveled through France and the Netherlands and met the most eminent chemists of those countries. Berzelius said that Tennant always carried in his pocket a map of Sweden which had become worn and soiled through years of use and that he spoke French "gladly and well" (30). He received his degree of Doctor of Medicine from Cambridge in 1796, but never practiced.

In the same year he proved by an ingenious experiment that the diamond consists solely of carbon. This he did by burning a weighed diamond by heating it with saltpeter in a gold tube. The carbon dioxide united with the potash in the saltpeter, and was later evolved. Most chemists would have felt deep concern over the outcome of such a costly and important experiment, but Tennant went horseback riding at his usual hour, leaving the results to the mercy of his assistant. However, since the assistant was the gifted William Hyde Wollaston, the outcome was successful (14, 16).

In 1803 Tennant found that when crude platinum is dissolved in dilute aqua regia, there remains a black powder with a metallic luster. This had been observed before and was thought to be graphite, but

Tennant investigated it carefully in an attempt to alloy lead with it, and concluded that it contained a new metal (*17*). In the autumn of the same year H.-V. Collet-Descotils, a friend and pupil of N.-L. Vauquelin, found that this powder contains a metal which gives a red color to the precipitate from an ammoniacal platinum solution (*18*). When Vauquelin treated the powder with alkali he obtained a volatile oxide which he believed to be that of the same metal with which Descotils was dealing (*19*).

In the meantime Tennant continued his researches, and the results which he communicated to the Royal Academy in the spring of 1804 showed that the powder contains two new metals, which may be separated by the alternate action of acid and alkali. One of these he named *iridium* because its salts are of varied colors, and the other he called *osmium* because of its odor (*20*).

These discoveries may best be described in his own words:

Upon making some experiments, last summer, on the black powder which remains after the solution of platina, I observed that it did not, as was generally believed, consist chiefly of plumbago, but contained some unknown metallic ingredients. Intending to repeat my experiments with more attention during the winter, I mentioned the result of them to Sir Joseph Banks, together with my intention of communicating to the Royal Society my examination of this substance, as soon as it should appear in any degree satisfactory.

Two memoirs were afterward published in France [continued Tennant] one of them by M. Descotils and the other by Messrs. Vauquelin and Fourcroy. M. Descotils chiefly directs his attention to the effects produced by this substance on the solution of platina. He remarks that a small portion of it is always taken up by nitromuriatic acid during its action on platina; and, principally from the observations he is thence enabled to make, he infers that it contains a new metal, which, among other properties, has that of giving a deep red colour to the precipitates of platina. M. Vauquelin attempted a more direct analysis of the substance, and obtained from it the same metal as that discovered by M. Descotils. But neither of these chemists have observed that it contains also another metal, different from any hitherto known. . . .

Tennant gave the name iridium to the metal which Descotils and Vauquelin had observed, and the name osmium to the new one (*20*). In speaking of iridium, osmium, palladium, and rhodium, W. T. Brande stated in his lectures in 1817, "Of these, the two former were discovered by the late Mr. Tennant and the two latter by Dr. Wollaston; and had we searched throughout chemistry for an illustrative instance of the delicacy of the modern art of analysis, it would be difficult to have found any one more notorious than the history of the discovery and separation of these bodies exhibits" (*46*). During the entire course of the researches which led to the discovery of these four metals, Dr. Wollaston and Tennant had friendly intercourse with each other, and each kept in close touch with the other's work.   As a brief relaxation from their scientific labors, they visited the Giants' Causeway together.

Smithson Tennant had a most kind and forgiving nature.   When a dishonest steward on his estate, who had become so heavily in debt that Tennant was obliged to examine the accounts, committed suicide, Tennant not only excused the unfortunate family from the payment of the debt, but assisted them financially in the kindest possible manner (14).

Tennant, like Wollaston, enjoyed the esteem and friendship of the great Swedish master, Berzelius, who paid him a visit in the summer of 1812.   Together they rode on horseback to inspect the 100-acre experimental oat field in which Tennant had mixed lime with the soil in decreasing ratio from one end to the other (31).   After he had shown Berzelius the tall, well-developed oats at the highly limed end and the sickly plants at the other end of the field, they visited the limekiln which Tennant himself had designed (30).

Berzelius may perhaps have envied the English chemist's horsemanship, for, after receiving the Cross of the Order of the Northern Star, he said in a letter to Dr. Marcet, "Here I am then a kind of cavalier, I whose manner of mounting a horse Tennant can describe to you"* (24).   In a letter to J. G. Gahn, Berzelius wrote: "Tennant is of about the same age as Wollaston, but is gray-haired and looks like an old man.   He is a charming man, gets off a lot of droll ideas which entertain any sort of society, scientific or otherwise.   He is a rather good, reliable chemist, but doesn't have either Wollaston's or Davy's head; and now he has lost much of his memory, so that one can tell him the same thing on two successive days with full assurance that it will be new to him.   He is badly dressed, is careless of his appearance, and makes a poor showing.   His chemicals are so helter skelter that he gets permission to pull out all the table drawers in the parlor to convince himself of the absence of what one would never expect to find except in a laboratory" (53).

In May, 1813, Dr. Marcet wrote to Berzelius, "Our friend Tennant has just been elected professor of chemistry at Cambridge after a very long struggle with a candidate who had many friends.   His position demands that he give twenty lectures a year, which will not be very difficult for him" (22).   Berzelius replied, "Congratulate Tennant for me on his new profession and tell him that we expect from his hands the life of Newton more correct than we have yet seen it" (23).

Tennant was destined to give his lecture course at Cambridge only once, for his life was cut short by a tragic accident, the following account of which was written by Dr. Marcet to Berzelius on March 29, 1815:

* "Me voilà donc une espèce de chevalier, moi, dont Tennant peut vous apprendre comment je monte à cheval."

You have doubtless learned of the tragic death of poor Tennant. I was often on the point of writing you, but the grief of being the first to tell you this story restrained me. He had spent six months in France and was returning loaded with curious observations in geology, chemistry, political economy, etc. He had, it is said, discovered in sea water the source and origin of iodine. He announced himself every week for a month or so, and nevertheless did not come. Quite like himself, he clung to all the objects along the way, and advanced only very slowly. He finally arrives at Calais, then at Boulogne, and after having spent about fifteen days between these two place while waiting for a perfectly favorable wind, he finally sets sail. But a calm arises and they are obliged to return to port. Our friend seeks to console himself for this disappointment by taking a horseback ride; he proposes to a Prussian officer who was on board with him that they go together to see a column erected to Bonaparte a few miles from Boulogne.

They had to pass over a little draw-bridge [continued Dr. Marcet]. The officer goes over first, but as soon as he is on the bridge he notices it pivoting on its center and that it is going to open into the ditch. He cries to Tennant, "Don't come any farther," and at the same time rushes on to re-establish equilibrium, but it was too late; he feels that another force is pressing on the bridge and forcing it to an inclined plane . . . he slides back with his horse and falls from twelve to fifteen feet into the ditch. Recovered from his shock, he looks around him and sees poor Tennant lying against the wall at the end of the ditch with his horse writhing on top of him. He pushes the horse away, lifts our friend, and finds him dying. . . . Who would have thought that our friend would die while visiting a work of war, of which you know he had the greatest horror. You well know, and I have no need to tell you, all that his friends, all that science, have lost. He was a unique man and one who will probably never be replaced. He loved you dearly, and I know you will mourn him sincerely (24).

Tennant had "an expressive, intelligent face . . . an intuitive and prompt perception of truth . . . a broad mind, deep moral feelings, and a zeal for the improvement of mankind" (15). He delighted in the artistic achievements of Virgil, Milton, Pascal, Gray, Handel, and Raphael. His never-failing sense of humor consisted in "fanciful trains of imagery, in natural, but ingenious and unexpected, turns of thought and expression, and in amusing anecdotes, slightly tinged with the ludicrous. The effect of these was heightened by a perfect gravity of countenance, a quiet, familiar manner, and a characteristic beauty and simplicity of language" (15).

According to W. T. Brande, Wollaston also discovered "a separate ore, consisting of iridium and osmium, among the grains of crude platinum. Its specific gravity is 19.5; it is hard, not malleable, and very brilliant" (120, 124). Osmium occurs in laurite and in osmiridium. A kind of iridosmium (osmiridium high in iridium) called irite was discovered prior to 1841 by Hans Rudolph Hermann in the gold mines of the Urals (*125*). K. K. Klaus stated that this mineral also contained 3 per cent of ruthenium (*126*).

In 1805 Dr. Wollaston published in the *Philosophical Transactions* an account of an ore of iridium intermixed with grains of crude platinum, which could be dissolved out with aqua regia. In the insoluble portion of the ore he found only iridium and osmium. Although Smithson Tennant was prevented by his fatal accident from analyzing the mineral specimen which Wollaston gave him, Thomas Thomson analyzed it in 1826 and found it to consist of iridium, osmium, and a small amount of iron (*127*).

RUTHENIUM

The element ruthenium is the little Benjamin of the platinum family. It did not see the light until more than a century after the discovery of platinum, but, to avoid separating it too far from its older brothers, its story will be told here.

In 1828 Berzelius and G. W. Osann (*25*), professor of chemistry at the University of Dorpat, examined the residues left after dissolving crude platinum from the Ural mountains in aqua regia. Berzelius did not find in them any unusual metals except palladium, rhodium, osmium, and iridium, which had already been found by Wollaston and Tennant in similar residues from American platinum. Professor Osann, on the other hand, thought that he had found three new metals, which he named pluranium, ruthenium, and polinium (*25, 36*). In 1844, however, Professor Klaus, another Russian chemist, showed that Osann's ruthenium oxide was very impure, but that it did contain a small amount of a new metal (*26, 33*).

Karl Karlovich Klaus* spent his infancy and boyhood in a harsh, unkind environment.† He was born in the Baltic-Russian city of Dorpat‡ on January 23, 1796. His father, a talented painter whose pictures later adorned Klaus's library, died in 1800. Soon after her husband's death the mother married another artist, and she, in turn, died when the boy was only five years old. Her second husband soon married again, and thus the little boy found himself a strange child in a strange home, left without affection and almost without care (*36*).

* The name is frequently written Carl Ernst Claus. It is a German name, not a Russian one.
† Most of the details regarding the life of Klaus would have been inaccessible without the kind assistance of Mr. M. K. Elias of the Kansas State Geological Survey, who translated B. N. Menshutkin's biographical sketch from the Russian. The author is sincerely grateful to him.
‡ This city is located in Estonia, and is now known as Tartu.

THE PLATINUM METALS 441

Klaus soon showed ability in design and sculpture, and his love for art, poetry, and drama helped him at times to forget the none-too-gentle home surroundings. He attended the grade school and gymnasium in Dorpat, but was unable, in spite of his excellent record, to complete the course at the latter institution. However, the praise given by his teachers stimulated him to further efforts which, even at this early age, revealed the fundamental features of his character: resoluteness, optimism, and a desire to reach at any cost a once-attempted goal. As a boy he enjoyed the few bright aspects of his cheerless life, and as an adult he never complained of the sufferings of his childhood.

Karl Karlovich Klaus, 1796–1864. Professor of pharmacy and chemistry at the Universities of Dorpat and Kazan. He was a great authority on the chemistry of the platinum metals.

Courtesy Mr. W. D. Trow

When forced to earn his own living at the age of fourteen years, he became an apprentice in a pharmacy in St. Petersburg. Here he spent his spare moments reading books on chemistry, pharmacy, and allied sciences. These attempts at self-education were so successful that Klaus was soon able to pass the examinations, first for assistant pharmacist and then for the position of provisor (36).

In 1815 he went back to Dorpat, passed the pharmacy examinations at the University, and returned to the St. Petersburg apothecary. His study of the natural sciences having awakened in him a desire to study Nature at first hand, he went to Saratov in 1817 as provisor of a pharmacy so that he might spend his leisure hours investigating the flora and fauna of the Volga steppes, or prairies, in eastern Russia. The results of this ten-year research were published in the Russian journals.

After his marriage in 1821 Klaus longed to have an apothecary shop of his own, and five years later he began business in Kazan, where he soon had the best pharmacy in the town.   Here, with more adequate financial resources, he continued his study of the flora and fauna.   He soon became recognized as an authority on that subject, and his advice was sought whenever a scientific expedition was to be sent into the steppes.   This brought him into contact with many famous scientists, who always carried away a pleasant recollection of his modesty and willingness to coöperate. His own expedition in 1827 through the region between the Urals and the Volga afforded material for his large book entitled "Volga Flora" (36).

When an assistantship in the chemistry department of the University of Dorpat was offered to him in 1831, Klaus sold his store at a loss, made the long trip back to Estonia, and accepted the modest position, in order to devote all his time to scientific research.   While completing the work for his master's degree in chemistry, he found time to explore with Fr. Göbel and A. Bergmann the Trans-Volga salt marshes and to prepare all the sketches for a large, two-volume record of the expedition, which was published at Dorpat in 1837 and 1838.   In recognition of this work they were awarded the Demidoff prize by the Academy of Science.

Wishing to return to Kazan, Klaus applied to the Secretary of Public Instruction for a position at the University.   The Secretary approved the application, but only after listening to a trial demonstration lecture "On the Shortest Methods for Making Chemicopharmaceutical Preparations," which Klaus was required to deliver at the Medico-Surgical Academy of St. Petersburg (36).   Although he had applied for a position in the department of pharmacy he was appointed adjunct in chemistry.

Upon returning to Kazan as adjunct in chemistry, he entered enthusiastically into the work of remodeling the old chemical museum into a chemical laboratory.   Klaus also succeeded in getting six additional rooms in a newly completed university building.   These were arranged like Liebig's laboratory at Giessen, and included a large lecture room, well equipped for demonstration experiments.   He was granted an appropriation of about 10,000 rubles ($5000) for the purchase of glassware, reagents, and apparatus.

In 1838 Klaus, with his student assistant Kabalerov, made an analysis of the water from the Sergievsky Mineral Springs, which provided the data for his dissertation for the doctorate in pharmacy.   Immediately after receiving this degree, he was made extraordinary professor at the University, and six years later he was promoted to the position of ordinary professor.

In 1840 Klaus became interested in platinum residues.   The reader will recall that in 1828 Professor G. W. Osann of Dorpat University had announced the presence in these residues of three new metals, the existence of which Berzelius had denied. Professor Klaus wished to settle this question, and the first step in his investigation was a careful repetition of Osann's work. He obtained two pounds of platinum residues from P. G. Sobolevskiï, a platinum refiner in St. Petersburg, and was surprised to find that they contained 10% of platinum, besides smaller amounts of osmium, iridium, palladium, and rhodium. In his report one may read,

The unexpected richness of the residues, great quantities of which lie unused at the laboratory of the Government Mint at St. Petersburg, appeared to me so important that I immediately reported the results of my investigation to the government mining authorities, and in 1842 I went to the capital (36).

In St. Petersburg he interviewed Count Egar F. Kankrin, the Secretary of the Treasury who introduced platinum coinage in Russia. Kankrin expressed complete approval of Professor Klaus's investigation, and Chevkin, the chief of the staff of mining engineers, presented him with eighteen pounds (half a pood) of the platinum residues.

The working of these residues did not prove as profitable as Professor Klaus had hoped, for, as he said in 1844:

These residues were poorer than the first, and thus my hope of adapting my method for profitable extraction of platinum from them was not fulfilled. There remained only an investigation interesting for science. Since I came to realize this two years ago, I have worked constantly on this hard, prolonged, and even unhealthful investigation; now I report to the scientific world the results obtained: (1) results of analysis of rich residues; (2) new methods for the separation of the metals of the platinum group; (3) methods for working up poor residues; (4) discovery of a new metal, ruthenium; (5) results of the analysis of poor residues and the simplest methods of decomposition of platinum ores and residues; (6) new properties and compounds of the previously known metals of the platinum group. All this may serve as a contribution to the chemical history of a precious product of our fatherland (36).

Klaus obtained six grams of the new metal from osmiridium, the portion of the crude platinum which is insoluble in aqua regia. He calcined a mixture of osmiridium, potash, and potassium nitrate in a silver crucible placed inside a Hessian crucible on a layer of magnesia (27). After heating it for an hour and a half at bright redness, he poured the molten contents into an iron capsule. He then took up the melt in a very large volume of water, and allowed it to stand four days in the dark in a completely filled bottle.

The orange-colored solution, containing, among other things, potassium ruthenate, was treated with nitric acid, whereupon a black precipitate of osmium dioxide containing from fifteen to twenty per cent of ruthenium oxide was thrown down as a velvety deposit. Klaus distilled this with aqua regia, taking care to condense the osmium tetroxide. The residue remaining after the distillation consisted mainly of the sesquichloride and tetrachloride of ruthenium. By adding ammonium chloride, Klaus prepared ammonium chlororuthenate, $(NH_4)_2RuCl_6$, a salt which upon calcination yields spongy ruthenium (27, 38).

This report, which was entitled "Chemical investigation of the residues of Ural platinum ore and of the metal ruthenium," occupied one hundred and eighty-eight pages in the *Scientific Annals of Kazan University* for 1844. In the following year it was published in book form. For patriotic reasons and also in recognition of the earlier work of Professor Osann, Klaus retained the name *ruthenium*, which means *Russia*. The white substance which Osann had taken for the oxide of this new metal consisted chiefly of silicic and titanic acids, iron peroxide, and zirconia (37). Klaus also found ruthenium in the osmiridium from American ores (36, 128). It constituted only from 1 to $1^1/_2$ per cent of these residues and did not occur in the portion which is soluble in aqua regia (126).

When Professor Klaus sent a sample of the new metal to Berzelius, the great Swedish master was skeptical. On January 21, 1845, he remarked in a letter to F. Wöhler:

Probably Klaus's experiments on the residues from platinum ores and on the new metal ruthenium have already been described in the German journals. He sent me his paper in manuscript. You see thereby that he has also prepared colorless salts of iridium with sulfurous acid. The early severe winter in November interrupted the postal communication between Ystad and Stralsund, so that I have not received the German journals for three months (28).

In the meantime Klaus continued his investigation of the compounds of ruthenium, specimens of which he sent to Stockholm, one after another, with detailed descriptions of their properties and the methods of preparation. This evidence was so convincing that in 1845 Berzelius announced in the *Jahresbericht* his acceptance of ruthenium as a new element (36, 37).

On March 9, 1846, he again mentioned Klaus's paper to Wöhler, saying:

Klaus in Kazan has sent me a résumé [*Nachernte*] concerning ruthenium, which I expect to read tomorrow at the Academy and which you shall then receive in the Öfversigten. It is strange that he does not publish his longer paper. A copy of it has been in my hands since November, 1844. Yet he surely cannot have intended that I should publish it. At least he has never said a word about it. . . .

Berzelius finally suggested to Klaus that he send the ruthenium paper to Wöhler for publication in the *Annalen,* and it may now be seen in Volume 63 of that journal (29, 38).

Alexander Mikhaïlovich Butlerov, 1828–1886. Russian organic chemist. He worked with K. K. Klaus on the preparation of antimony at the University of Kazan and later studied organic chemistry under N. N. Zinin. After working with some of the most famous chemists in Europe and serving as professor of chemistry at the University of Kazan he was appointed ordinary professor of chemistry at the University of St. Petersburg. See ref. (*94*).

All of Klaus's papers on the platinum metals were collected and published in 1854 in a Jubilee Volume issued in honor of the fiftieth anniversary of the founding of the University of Kazan.   He continued to teach inorganic, analytical, and organic chemistry, and was assisted for a time in the organic course by Nikolaï Nikolaevich Zinin, who later became the founder of the modern school of organic chemistry in Russia (*93*), and in the inorganic course by Alexander Mikhaïlovich Butlerov (*94*).

In 1852 Klaus was invited to occupy the chair of pharmacy at the University of Dorpat and to take charge of the Pharmaceutic Institute, at that time the only institution of its kind in all Russia.   He accepted the appointment, left his position at Kazan in charge of Butlerov, abandoned the long-cherished steppes of the Volga, and made the long trip back to Estonia.

J. Henri Debray, 1827–1888.   French chemist who collaborated with Henri Sainte-Claire Deville at the École Normale Supérieure in researches on gaseous dissociation.   He also investigated beryllium, molybdenum, tungsten, and the metals of the platinum group, and made contributions to synthetic mineralogy.   It was in Debray's laboratory that Moissan liberated fluorine.

At Dorpat he continued his investigation of the platinum metals and their alloys.   After devoting twenty years to research in this field, he wished to publish a monograph which should include not only his own researches but those of other scientists.   In 1863 the Russian government sent him to western Europe to visit the laboratories and platinum refineries and to study the history of the platinum metals in the libraries of the great scientific centers.   Klaus's achievements were so well known that he was honored wherever he went.   In Berlin he met Heinrich and Gustav Rose, J. C. Poggendorff, and Gustav Magnus, and in Paris he studied the electric furnaces of Henri Sainte-Claire Deville and H. Debray (*36*).

Professor Klaus returned to Dorpat in January, 1864, with a wealth of material for the monograph on the platinum group, but illness unfortunately overtook him, and the work was never completed. He passed away on March 24, 1864, loved and respected by his students and colleagues.* In his last public address before the Pharmaceutical Society of St. Petersburg, he emphasized the desirability of providing scholarships for needy students (36).

In 1866 Friedrich Wöhler discovered a ruthenium mineral. When he analyzed the shining black grains of what seemed to be an unusual platinum mineral which "Herr Waitz of Cassel" had brought back from Borneo, he found it to be a sulfide of ruthenium and osmium. Wöhler stated that this mineral, which he named *laurite*, presented the first example of the natural occurrence of sulfur compounds of the platinum metals (129).

LITERATURE CITED

(1)   PRIESTLEY, J., "Experiments and Observations on Different Kinds of Air," J. Johnson, London, 1774, p. xvii.

(2)   DIXON, JOSHUA, "Biographical account of William Brownrigg, M.D.," *Annals of Phil.*, 10, 321–38, 401–17 (Nov., Dec., 1817).

(3)   JAGNAUX, R., "Histoire de la Chimie," Vol. 2, Baudry et Cie., Paris, 1891, pp. 402–5.

(4)   THOMSON, THOMAS, "History of Chemistry," Vol. 2, Colburn and Bentley, London, 1831, pp. 246–50.

(5)   SÖDERBAUM, H. G., "Jac. Berzelius Bref," Vol. 1, part 3, Almqvist and Wiksells, Upsala, 1912–1914, pp. 40–2.

(6)   *Ibid.*, Vol. 1, part 3, p. 47.

(7)   WALLACH, O., "Briefwechsel zwischen J. Berzelius und F. Wöhler," Vol. 1, Verlag von Wilhelm Engelmann, Leipzig, 1901, p. 253.

(8)   "Reward of twenty pounds for the artificial production of palladium," *Nicholson's J.*, 7, 75 (Jan., 1804); R. CHENEVIX, "Enquiry concerning the nature of a metallic substance lately sold in London as a new metal, under the title of palladium," *ibid.*, 7, 85–101 (Feb., 1804); 176–82 (Mar., 1804); Letter from Wollaston to Nicholson concerning Pd, *ibid.*, 10, 204–5 (Mar., 1805); T. THOMSON, "History of Chemistry," ref. (4), Vol. 2, p. 217.

(9)   WOLLASTON, W. H., "On a new metal found in crude platina," *Nicholson's J.*, (2) 10, 34–42 (Jan., 1805).

(10) SÖDERBAUM, H. G., "Jac. Berzelius Bref," ref. (5), Vol. 1, part 3, p. 98.

(11) THORPE, T. E., "History of Chemistry," Vol. 1, G. P. Putnam's Sons, London, 1909–1910, p. 114.

(12) SÖDERBAUM, H. G., "Jac. Berzelius Bref," ref. (5), Vol. 1, part 3, pp. 128–9.

(13) POGGENDORFF, J. C., "Biographisch-Literarisches Handwörterbuch zur Geschichte der exakten Wissenschaften," 6 vols., Verlag Chemie, Leipzig and Berlin, 1863–1937. Articles on Wollaston, Claus, and Scaliger.

(14) THOMSON, T., "History of Chemistry," ref. (4), Vol. 2, pp. 232–40.

* According to the Russian (Julian) calendar Klaus was born on Jan. 11, 1796, and died on March 12, 1864.

(15) "Some account of the late Smithson Tennant, Esq.," *Annals of Phil.*, **6**, 1–11 (July, 1815); 81–100 (Aug., 1815); *Gentleman's Mag.*, **117**, 281 (Mar., 1815).

(16) TENNANT, S., "On the nature of the diamond," *Nicholson's J.*, **1**, 177–9 (July, 1797).

(17) "Discovery of two new metals in crude platina by Smithson Tennant, Esq., F.R.S.," *ibid.*, **8**, 220–1 (July, 1804).

(18) COLLET-DESCOTILS, H.-V., "On the cause of the different colours of the triple salts of platina, and on the existence of a new metallic substance in the metal," *Nicholson's J.*, **8**, 118–26 (June, 1804).

(19) VAUQUELIN, N.-L., "Mémoire sur l'iridium et l'osmium, métaux qui se trouvent dans le résidu insoluble de la mine de platine, traitée par l'acide nitromuriatique," *Ann. chim. phys.*, (1), **89**, 150–81 (Feb., 1814); 225–50 (Mar., 1814).

(20) TENNANT, S., "On two metals, found in the black powder remaining after the solution of platina," *Nicholson's J.*, **10**, 24–30 (Jan., 1805).

(21) WHITE, A. M. and H. B. FRIEDMAN, "On the discovery of palladium," *J. Chem. Educ.*, **9**, 236–45 (Feb., 1932).

(22) SÖDERBAUM, H. G., "Jac. Berzelius Bref," ref. (5), Vol. 1, part 3, p. 46.

(23) *Ibid.*, Vol. 1, part 3, p. 61.

(24) *Ibid.*, Vol. 1, part 3, pp. 117–9.

(25) "New metals in the Uralian platina," *Phil. Mag.*, **2**, 391 (Nov., 1827).

(26) BROWN, J. C., "History of Chemistry," P. Blakiston's Son, Philadelphia, **1913**, p. 523.

(27) JAGNAUX, R., "Histoire de la Chimie," ref. (3), Vol. 2, pp. 406–7.

(28) WALLACH, O., "Briefwechsel zwischen J. Berzelius und F. Wöhler," ref. (7), Vol. 2, p. 520.

(29) *Ibid.*, Vol. 2, p. 580.

(30) "Aus Berzelius's Tagebuch während seines Aufenthaltes in London im Sommer 1812," translated into German by Emilie Wöhler, *Z. angew. Chem.*, **18**, 1946–8 (Dec., 1905) and **19**, 187–90 (Feb., 1906).

(31) TENNANT, S., "On the different sorts of lime used in agriculture," *Nicholson's J.*, **3**, 440–6 (Jan., 1800).

(32) ST. JOHN, "The Lives of Celebrated Travellers," Vol. 2, J. & J. Harper, New York, **1832**, pp. 320–38. Chapter on de Ulloa.

(33) KLAUS, K. K., "Ruthenium, ein neues Metall der Platinerze," *Ann.*, **56**, 257–61 (Heft 3, 1846).

(34) DIMITRY, "A king's gift," *Mag. Am. History*, **16**, 308–16 (Oct., 1886).

(35) OGBURN, S. C., "The platinum metals," *J. Chem. Educ.*, **5**, 1371–84 (Nov., 1928).

(36) MENSCHUTKIN, B. N., "Karl Karlovich Klaus," *Ann. inst. platine* (Leningrad), No. 6, 1–10 (1928); "Discovery and early history of platinum in Russia," *J. Chem. Educ.*, **11**, 226–9 (Apr., 1934).

(37) "On the new metal ruthenium," *Phil. Mag.*, (3), **27**, 230–1 (Sept., 1845).

(38) KLAUS, K. K., "Mine de platine; osmium, ruthénium," *J. Pharm. Chim.*, (3), **8**, 381–5 (Nov., 1845); "Beiträge zur Chemie der Platinmetalle," *Ann.*, **63**, 337–60 (Heft 3, 1847).

(39) FARABEE, W. C., "A golden hoard from Ecuador," *Museum Journal*, University of Pennsylvania, Philadelphia, **12**, 43–52 (1921).

(40) BERGSØE, P., "The Metallurgy of Gold and Platinum among the pre-Columbian Indians," Ingeniørvidenskabelige Skrifter No. A44, Danmarks Naturvidenskabelige Samfund, Copenhagen, 1937, 48 pp.; *Nature*, 137, 29 (Jan. 4, 1936); *ibid.*, 139, 490 (March 20, 1937).

(41) KOPP, H., "Geschichte der Chemie," Vol. 4, Vieweg und Sohn, Braunschweig, 1847, pp. 220–6.

(42) SCHEFFER, H. T., "Das weisse Gold oder siebente Metall, in Spanien *Platina del Pinto*, Kleines Silber von Pinto genannt, seiner Natur nach beschrieben," *Crell's Neues chem. Archiv*, 5, 103–6 (1786); Chem. Abh. königl. schw. Akad., 1752, pp. 275–82.

(43) PELLETIER, BERTRAND, "Mémoires et observations de Chimie," Vol. 2, Paris, 1798 (an VI), pp. 120–133. "Rapport fait au Bureau de Consultation sur les Moyens proposés par M. Jeanety pour travailler le platine (Juillet, 1792), par MM. Berthollet et Pelletier."

(44) HUSSAK, EUGEN, "Über das Vorkommen von Palladium und Platin in Brasilien," *Sitzungsber. math.-naturwiss. Klasse, Akad. Wiss.* (Wien), 113, 379–466 (1904).

(45) BARUEL, "Process for procuring pure platinum, palladium, rhodium, iridium, and osmium from the ores of platinum," *Quarterly J. Sci.*, 12, 262 (1822); N.-L. VAUQUELIN, "Mémoire sur le palladium et le rhodium," *Ann. chim. phys.* (1), 88, 170–1 (Nov. 30, 1813).

(46) "Report of Mr. Brande's lectures on mineralogical chemistry," *Quarterly J. Sci.*, 5, 64–7 (1818).

(47) FONDA, J. S., "Historic set of weights," *Hexagon*, 15, 81–2 (Nov., 1924); *J. Chem. Educ.*, 2, 308 (Apr., 1925).

(48) DEL RÍO, A. M., "Analysis of a specimen of gold found to be alloyed with rhodium," *Am. J. Sci.*, 11, 298–304 (1826); *Ann. chim. phys.* (2), 29, 137–47 (1825).

(49) CLOUD, J., "On the discovery of palladium in a native alloy of gold," *Nicholson's J.* (2), 30, 137–40 (Oct., 1811); *Trans. Am. Philos. Soc.*, 6, 407 (1809).

(50) SMITH, E. F., "Chemistry in Old Philadelphia," J. B. Lippincott Co., Philadelphia, 1919, pp. 86–8.

(51) MATTHEY, G., "Obituary of Percival Norton Johnson," *J. Chem. Soc.*, 20, 395, (1867); *Proc. Roy. Soc.* (London), 16, xxiii–xxv (1867–68).

(52) JOHNSON, P. N. and W. A. LAMPADIUS, "Über brasilianisches Palladgold und dessen Ausbringung und Scheidung," *J. prakt. Chem.*, 11, 309–15 (1837).

(53) SÖDERBAUM, H. G., ref. (5), Vol. 9, p. 73. Letter of Berzelius to Gahn, Jan. 25, 1813.

(54) "Julii Cæsaris Scaligeri, Exotericarum exercitationum Liber XV de Subtilitate ad Hieronymum Cardanum," apud Claudium Marnium & hæredes Joannis Aubrii, Francofurti, MDCVII, pp. 323–4.

(55) DE ULLOA, A., "Relación Histórica del Viage á la América Meridional," Vol. 1, Antonio Marín, Madrid, 1748, book 6, chap. 10, p. 606.

(56) JUAN, JORGE and ANTONIO DE ULLOA, "A Voyage to South America," Vol. 1, Lockyer Davis, London, 1772, pp. 131–2, 452–3; Vol. 2, pp. 417–8.

(57) PINKERTON, JOHN, "A General Collection of the Best and Most Interesting Voyages and Travels," Vol. 14, Longman, Hurst, Rees, and Orme, London, 1812, p. 540. De Ulloa's "Voyage to South America."

(58) SEMPERE Y GUARINOS, J., "Ensayo de Una Biblioteca Española de los Mejores Escritores del Reynado de Carlos III," Vol. 6, Imprenta Real, Madrid, 1789, pp. 158–76.

(59)   DE VILLIERS DU TERRAGE, BON MARC "Les Dernières Années de la Louisiane française," E. Guilmoto, Paris, 1903, pp. 225–326, 398, 415.

(60)   PHELPS, ALBERT, "Louisiana, a Record of Expansion," Houghton, Mifflin and Co., Boston and New York, 1905, pp. 108–23.

(61)   PINKERTON, JOHN, ref. (57), Vol. 13, p. 786.   N. J. Thiery de Menonville's "Travels to Guaxaca."

(62)   TOWNSEND, JOSEPH, "A Journey through Spain in the Years 1786–7," 3rd ed., Vol. 2, James Moore, Dublin, 1792, pp. 152–3.

(63)   STEPHEN, LESLIE, "Dictionary of National Biography," Vol. 7, Smith, Elder and Co., London, 1886, pp. 85–6.   Article on Brownrigg by G. T. Bettany.

(64)   Obituary on Brownrigg, Gentleman's Mag., 70, 386–8 (1800).

(65)   WATSON, WILLIAM, "Several papers concerning a new semi-metal called platina," Phil. Trans. Abridgment, 10, 671–6 (1756); Phil. Trans., 46, 584–96 (Nov., 1750).

(66)   "Discurso del Ilmo. Sr. D. Juan Fages y Virgili," Establecimiento Tipográfico y Editorial, Madrid, 1909, pp. 41–3, 57–61.

(67)   LEWIS, WILLIAM, "Experimental examination of a white metallic substance said to be found in the gold mines of the Spanish West Indies . . . ," Phil. Trans., 48 (2), 313–38 (1754).

(68)   CRONSTEDT, A. F., "Åminnelse-tal öfver . . .Henric Theoph. Scheffer," Lars Salvius, Stockholm, 1760, 31 pp.

(69)   KOPP, H., "Geschichte der Chemie," Vol. 4, Fr. Vieweg und Sohn, Braunschweig, 1847, pp. 220–6.

(70)   VON CRELL, L., Review of Baron von Sickingen's "Versuche über die Platina," Crell's Neueste Entdeckungen, 6, 197–206 (1782).

(71)   HOWE, J. L., "Bibliography of the metals of the platinum group, 1748–1896," Smithsonian Miscellaneous Collections, 38, 1–318 (1897).

(72)   HOWE, J. L., "Chabaneau: an early worker on platinum," Pop. Sci. Mo., 84, 64–70 (Jan., 1914).

(73)   QUENNESSEN, LOUIS, "A propos de l'histoire du platine   Pierre François Chabaneau, 1754–1842," Rev. Sci., 52 (1), 553–7 (1914).

(74)   MAFFEI, E. and R. RUA FIGUEROA, "Apuntes para una Biblioteca Española . . . de las Riquezas Minerales . . . ," Vol. 2, J. M. Lapuente, Madrid, 1873, p. 625; Manuscript letter of J. C. Mutis dated June 15, 1774.

(75)   "El primer centenario de Fausto de Elhuyar," Anales Soc. Españ. de Física y Química, 31, 7–23 (1933).

(76)   DE GÁLVEZ-CAÑERO, A., "Apuntes Biográficas de D. Fausto de Elhuyar y de Zubice," Gráficas Reunidas, Madrid, 1933, pp. 62–70.

(77)   DIERGART, PAUL, "Beiträge aus der Geschichte der Chemie dem Gedächtnis von G. W. A. Kahlbaum," Franz Deuticke, Leipzig and Vienna, 1909, p. 412.

(78)   PELLETIER, CHARLES and SÉDILLOT, JEUNE, "Mémoires et Observations de Chimie de Bertrand Pelletier," Vol. 2, Croullebois, Fuchs, Barrois, and Huzard, Paris, 1798, pp. 120–33.

(79)   Crell's Ann., 14, 53–4 (1790).

(80)   LACROIX, ALFRED, "Figures de Savants," Vol. 2, Gauthier-Villars, Paris, 1932, pp. 144–6.

(81)   HARE, ROBERT, "Account of the fusion of strontites and volatilization of platinum," Trans. Am. Philos. Soc., 6 (1), 99 (1804).

(82)   SMITH, E. F., "Life of Robert Hare," J. B. Lippincott Co., Philadelphia and London, 1917, pp. 5–6, 204–5.

(83) SÖDERBAUM, H. G., ref. (5), Vol. 13, p. 132.   Letter of Berzelius to E. Mitscherlich, Feb. 24, 1829.

(84) "Laboratory of powder metallurgy established at Stevens Institute of Technology," *Ind. Eng. Chem., News Ed.*, **18**, 548 (June 25, 1940).

(85) "Russian coinage of platina," *Phil. Mag.* (2), **4**, 458 (Dec., 1828).

(86) KELLY, F. C., "Powder metallurgy," *Sci. Mo.*, **57**, 286–8 (Sept., 1943).

(87) WEEKS, M. E., "Don José Celestino Mutis, 1732–1808," *J. Chem. Educ*, **21**,
55 (Feb., 1944).

(88) FERGUSON, ELSIE G., "Bergman, Klaproth, Vauquelin, Wollaston," *J. Chem.
Educ.*, **18**, 3–7 (Jan., 1941).

(89) DELÉPINE, MARCEL, "Joseph Pelletier and Joseph Caventou," *J. Chem. Educ.*,
28, 454–61 (Sept., 1951).

(90) BROWNE, C. A., "The past and future of the History of Chemistry Division,"
J. Chem. Educ., **14**, 503–15 (Nov., 1937).

(91) MENSCHUTKIN, B. N., "Discovery and early history of platinum in Russia,"
J. Chem. Educ., **11**, 226–9 (Apr., 1934).

(92) PROF. KLENCKE, "Alexander von Humboldt.   A Biographical Monument,"
Ingram, Cooke, and Co., London, **1852**, pp. 119–21.

(93) LEICESTER, HENRY M., "N. N. Zinin, an early Russian chemist," *J. Chem.
Educ.*, **17**, 303–6 (July, 1940).

(94) LEICESTER, HENRY M., "Alexander Mikhaïlovich Butlerov," *ibid.*, **17**, 203–9
(May, 1940).

(95) BRONK, DETLEV W., "Joseph Priestley and the early history of the American
Philosophical Society," *Proc. Am. Philos. Soc.*, **86**, 103–7 (Sept. 25, 1942).

(96) CORTENOVIS, A. M., "Dissertation sur le platine, dans laquelle on démontre
que ce métal étoit connu des anciens," *Ann. chim. phys.*, (1), **12**, 59–60
(Jan., 1792); "Che la platina americana era un metallo conosciuto dagli
antichi, etc.," Bassano, **1790**.

(97) LIPPMANN, E. O. VON, "Entstehung und Ausbreitung der Alchemie," J.
Springer, Berlin, **1919**, p. 531, footnote 10.

(98) "Contributions towards the chemical knowledge of mineral substances, by the
late M. H. Klaproth," *Quarterly J. Sci.*, **11**, 272–3 (1821).

(99) BERTHELOT, M., "Sur les métaux égyptiens: Présence du platine parmi les
caractères d'une inscription hiéroglyphique," *Compt. rend.*, **132**, 729–32
(Mar. 25, 1901).

(100) LUCAS, A., "Ancient Egyptian Materials and Industries," 2nd ed., Edward
Arnold and Co., London, **1934**, p. 202.

(101) SCHWEIGGER, J. S. C., "Ueber Platina, Altes und Neues," *J. prakt. Chem.*, **34**,
385–420 (1845).

(102) MOROS, F. A., "Minerales y mineralogistas españoles," *Revista real acad.
ciencias*, **21**, 278–82 (1923–24).

(103) BOSTOCK and RILEY, "The Natural History of Pliny," Vol. 6, George Bell and
Sons, London, **1857**, pp. 212–5; PLINY, "Historia naturalis," book 34, chaps.
47–8; BAILEY, K. C., "The Elder Pliny's Chapters on Chemical Subjects,"
Vol. 2, Edward Arnold, London, **1932**, p. 65.

(104) CRELL, L. VON, "Ueber die Platina die den Alten schon bekannt war.   Von
P. Don Ant. Mar. Cortinovis [*sic*]," *Crell's Ann.*, **25**, 166–7 (1796).

(105) LEWIS, WILLIAM, "The Chemical Works of Caspar Neumann, M.D.," W.
Johnston, G. Keith, etc., London, **1759**, pp. 43–4.

(106) BERNAYS, JACOB, "Joseph Justus Scaliger," Wilhelm Hertz, Berlin, **1855**, pp.
31–104.

(107) NETTLESHIP, HENRY, "Essays by the Late Mark Pattison," Vol. 1, Clarendon Press, Oxford, **1889**, pp. 132–7, 154. Article on Joseph Scaliger, reprinted from *Quarterly Review*, **108**, 34 (July, 1860); same article in *Living Age*, **66**, 579.

(108) ROBINSON, GEORGE W., "Autobiography of Joseph Scaliger," Harvard University Press, **1927**, 128 pp.

(109) HUMBOLDT, A. VON, "Ensayo político sobre Nueva España," Vol. 3, Lecointe, Paris, **1836**, pp. 46–9, 275–6.

(110) LUMB, A. D., "The Platinum Metals," John Murray, London, **1920**, pp. 55–6.

(111) LACROIX, ALFRED, "Figures de savants," Vol. 2, Gauthier-Villars, Paris, **1932**, pp. 144–6.

(112) BEJARANO, D. M. M., "Diccionario de escritores, maestros, y oradores natural de Sevilla y su actual provincia," Vol. 3, Tipografia Girones, Seville, **1925**, pp. 33–9.

(113) BROWNRIGG, WILLIAM, "On the uses of a knowledge of mineral exhalations when applied to discover the principles and properties of mineral waters, the nature of burning fountains, and those poisonous lakes called averni," *Phil. Trans.*, **55**, 218–43 (1765); *ibid.*, **64**, 357–71 (1774).

(114) FRANKLIN, B., W. BROWNRIGG, and FARISH, "Of the stilling of waves by means of oil," *Phil. Trans.*, **64**, 445–60 (1774).

(115) GOODMAN, NATHAN G., "The Ingenious Dr. Franklin," University of Pennsylvania Press, Philadelphia, **1931**, pp. 188–95. Letter of Franklin to Brownrigg, Nov. 7, 1773.

(116) "Platina from the mines of Chaco [Chocó], in Terra Firma," *Medical Repository*, **6**, 213–14 (Aug., Sept., Oct., 1802).

(117) HEULAND, HENRY, "On a mass of platinum at Madrid," *Annals of Philos.*, **12**, 200–1 (Sept., 1818); *Ann. chim. phys.*, (2), **9**, 331 (1818).

(118) PADELFORD, F. M., "Select Translations from Scaliger's Poetics," Henry Holt and Co., New York City, **1905**, 96 pp.

(119) DEL RÍO, "Analysis of a specimen of gold found to be alloyed with rhodium," *El Sol*, Dec. 11, 1824; *Am. J. Sci.*, **11**, 298–304 (1826); *Ann. chim. phys.*, (2), **29**, 137–47 (1825); *Annals of Philos.*, (2), **10**, 251–6 (Oct., 1825).

(120) WOLLASTON, W. H., "On a new metal found in crude platina," *Phil. Trans.*, **94**, 419–30 (1804); *ibid.*, **95**, 316–30 (1805).

(121) BERZELIUS, J. J., "Analyse des 'Ouro podre' (faules Gold) von Südamerika," *Berzelius Jahresber.*, **15**, 205 (1836).

(122) WOLLASTON, W. H., "On platina and native palladium from Brazil," *Phil. Trans.*, **99**, 189–94 (1809).

(123) GEHLEN, A. F., "Platin und Palladium in Brasilien und St. Domingo gefunden," *Schweigger's J.*, (4), **1**, 362–73 (1811).

(124) "Report of Mr. Brande's lectures on mineralogical chemistry delivered in the theatre of the Royal Institution in the spring of 1817," *Quarterly J. of Sci.*, **5**, 64–7 (1818).

(125) HERMANN, R., "Ueber Ural-Orthit und Irit, zwei neue Mineralien," *J. prakt. Chem.*, (1), **23**, 276–8 (1841).

(126) KLAUS, K. K., "On the chemical properties of ruthenium and some of its compounds," *Chem. Gazette*, **4**, 437 (Nov. 16, 1846); *Ann.*, **59**, 234–60 (Aug., 1846).

(127) THOMSON, THOMAS, "Analysis of the ore of iridium," *Annals of Philosophy*, new series, **11**, 17–19 (Jan., 1826).

(128) KLAUS, K. K., "Ueber die chemischen Verhältnisse des Rutheniums," *Ann.*, **59**, 234 (1846).

(*129*) WÖHLER, F., "Ueber ein neues Mineral von Borneo," *Ann.*, **139**, 116–20 (1866).

(*130*) REILLY, DESMOND, "Richard Chenevix (1774–1839) and the discovery of palladium," *J. Chem. Educ.*, **32**, 37–9 (Jan., 1955).

From Li Ch'iao-p'ing's "Chemical Arts of Old China"

Drawing Up Sea Water for Making Salt. Salt was an important commodity to the ancient Chinese. They used several processes, one of which was the evaporation of sea water.

> *"How is it then that from the fern*
> *Both ash and clearest glass is made*
> *By those most learned in the trade:*
> *Can simple depurations turn*
> *The fern to glass? Glass is not fern*
> *Nor does the fern exist in glass"* (28).

17

Some old potassium and sodium compounds

Long before sodium and potassium metals were isolated, many of their compounds were in common use. Among the most important of these were potash (potassium carbonate), cream of tartar, saltpeter, alum, common salt, Glauber's salt, and soda (sodium carbonate). Both potash and soda have been used since ancient times in the manufacture of glass.

Potash from Vegetable Ash. Dioscorides Pedanios knew that a soluble substance can be leached out of wood ashes with water, but did not tell how to prepare it in solid form (*1*). Haudicquer de Blancourt, in his book on "The Art of Glass" (1697), described the preparation of potassium carbonate from the ash of the fern and other plants. "The daily Experience of Salt of Fern in the Glass-Houses," said he, "assures us of its usefullness in making Glass. It grows (in France) in great abundance in the woods and among the Mountains. . . . You will have from it very good ashes, from which . . . may be extracted a fine and good salt; which being afterward purified, with it and Tarso, or very fine Sand, a Fritt may be made which will yield a very fair Crystal, much better than the ordinary, and [it] will be strong and bend much more than one would conceive the nature of Crystal would permit . . ." (*2*).

Primitive peoples sometimes used the ashes of certain plants as a condiment in place of salt. Some of the American Indians in Virginia used the ash of the saltwort; the Delawares, Iroquois, Wyandots, Cherokees, Chickasaws, and Creeks seasoned and preserved their meats with clean wood ashes (*3, 4*). The *Medical Repository* for 1804 mentions a similar custom among the natives of Bengal: "In the seventh volume of the *Asiatic Researches* is a paper by Surgeon John Macrae on the manners and customs of the Cúcis, Kookies, or Lunctas, a race of people that live among the mountains to the northeast of the Chittagong province in India. Of this peculiar nation he relates a fact which corresponds with the practice described in *Medical Repository*, Hexade I, volume vi, p. 330, among American Indians, of using pure and fresh wood-ashes in lieu of sea-salt, as a condiment with animal food. . . . The hunter, . . . in his excursions through the forests, boils his food in a particular kind of bamboo. From the ashes of a different species of the same plant, he extracts a substitute for salt to eat with his victuals . . ." (*4*).

Origin of Potash in Plants.   Early chemists disagreed as to the origin of the vegetable alkali.   Louis-Claude de Bourdelin (1696–1777) and others maintained that it pre-existed as a salt in the living plant and that the combustion merely liberated it (5, 6).   Paracelsus, Andreas Libavius, Urban Hiärne, and other distinguished chemists also believed in the pre-existence of this alkali in the plant (5).   Others, including Robert Boyle, Nicolas Lémery, J. J. Becher, G. E. Stahl, Johann Kunckel, Etienne-François Geoffroy, and Herman Boerhaave, believed that the vegetable alkali was produced only during the combustion (5).

Boerhaave even stated in his "Elements of Chemistry" that "all the vegetables which have grown on the earth since the beginning of the world to the present, and which have putrefied without being reduced to ash by the action of fire, and have been consumed in the course of time, have never yielded a single grain of fixed alkaline salt.   On the contrary, they have been dispersed in volatile particles . . ." (7).

In 1755 Joseph Black explained why alkali freshly leached from vegetable ash is so caustic and why it becomes milder on exposure to air.   "It never appears," said he, "until the subject be converted into ashes, and is supposed to be formed by the fire, and to be the result of a particular combination of some of the principles of the vegetable; one of which principles is air, which is contained in large quantity in all vegetable matters whatever.   But, as soon as the smallest part of a vegetable is converted into ashes, and an alkali is thus formed, this salt necessarily suffers a calcination, during which it is kept in a spongy form by the ashes, and shows a very considerable degree of acrimony, if immediately applied to the body of an animal; but if the ashes are for any time exposed to the air, or if we separate the alkali from them by the addition of a large quantity of water and subsequent evaporation, the salt imbibes fixed air [carbon dioxide] from the atmosphere, and becomes nearly saturated with it; tho', even in this condition, it is generally more acrid than salt of tartar [pure potassium carbonate], when this is prepared with a gentle heat" (8).

In 1770 C. W. Scheele showed that the natural product cream of tartar is a salt with a vegetable alkaline base (potash) supersaturated with a vegetable acid (tartaric).   When he dissolved cream of tartar [potassium acid tartrate] in boiling water and added powdered chalk to the solution, the lime combined with part of the tartaric acid and gave a copious white precipitate.   On evaporating the supernatant liquid he obtained crystals of "soluble tartar" [normal potassium tartrate] (9, 10).

G.-F. Rouelle, A. S. Marggraf, and others showed experimentally that potash can be extracted from plants without the use of fire (11).   In 1764 Marggraf, for example, prepared saltpeter by treating tartar with nitric acid.   Since saltpeter was known to contain the vegetable alkali, the latter must have pre-existed in the plant (5).   Although J. H. Pott had stated definitely that the vegetable alkali is produced only by burning plants, an editorial note in *Crell's Neues chemisches Archiv* for 1785 stated that the incorrectness of this statement had been adequately demonstrated by Marggraf and Wiegleb (*12*).

P.-J. Macquer pointed out in his "Dictionary of Chemistry" (1778) that when plants are decomposed without combustion, acidic substances such as tartar and potassium acid oxalate are produced; that plants from which these acidic substances have been removed by extraction or distillation yield much less vegetable alkali than they otherwise would; that by ignition tartar can be converted almost completely to this alkali (potassium carbonate); that the alkali in vegetable ash is therefore produced by the combustion of this acidic substance; that decayed wood, in which the plant acids have been destroyed by fermentation, yields scarcely any alkali (as Boerhaave had observed); and that plants containing little or no acid yield on combustion little or no vegetable alkali (*5*).

Although Macquer's explanation is correct, A.-L. Lavoisier still held to the more conservative opinion.   In his "Elementary Treatise on Chemistry," which was first published in 1789, he explained the formation of potassium carbonate in vegetable ash as follows: "As the potash is not formed, or at least not liberated," said he, "except as the carbon of the plant is converted into carbonic acid by the addition of oxygen, either from the air or from the water, the result is that each molecule of potash, at the moment of its formation, finds itself in contact with a molecule of carbonic acid, and since there is great affinity between these two substances, combination must take place" (*13*).

Lavoisier realized that potash is present in the ash of all plants, but he was not convinced of its pre-existence in the living organism.   "There are no vegetables," said he, "which do not yield more or less potash on incineration. . . .   One can scarcely doubt that the ash, or in other words the earth which plants leave when one burns them, pre-existed in those vegetables before the combustion; this earth apparently forms the bony part, or skeleton of the plant.   But it is not the same with the potash. No one has yet succeeded in separating this substance from plants except by using methods or intermediates which can provide oxygen or nitrogen, such as combustion or combination with nitric acid; thus it has not been proved that this substance is not a product of these operations" (*13*).

In 1789 Dr. M. Wall of Oxford, recalling Scheele's experiments on tartar, added some "Glauber's spirit of nitre" to cream of tartar dissolved in boiling water.   By careful evaporation of the solution, he obtained well-formed crystals of niter (saltpeter).   He concluded that cream of tartar "is not, as has been commonly supposed, a peculiar acid, joined with impurities, but that it is really a compound salt, containing an alkali joined with an acid; and further, that the alkaline salt, obtained from tartar by incineration, is not generated in the fire, but was actually preexistent in the tartar" (9).

A.-F. de Fourcroy stated in 1806: "The exact nature of potash is not known: it was formerly believed to have been formed from lime and nitrogen, because it is often found mixed with this earth in vegetables, but this is still merely a hypothesis which, during the fifteen years since I proposed it, has not been proved by any positive fact" (14).

Potash prepared in Hungary by leaching wood ashes was shipped to the glassblowers and soapmakers in Austria, Bohemia, Poland, and Germany, but by the end of the eighteenth century the number of potash works in Hungary had decreased because of deforestation (69).

Potash in Alum.   In the seventeenth and eighteenth centuries, chemists believed that potash existed only in the vegetable kingdom. Although it had been shown repeatedly (by Michael Ettmüller, G. E. Stahl, Jean Hellot, Geoffroy the Younger, and J. H. Pott) that alum can be made simply by treating clay with sulfuric acid, chemists did not suspect that the *vegetable* alkali could be present in clay, and hence did not recognize potash as an essential constituent of common alum (12, 15, 16, 17).

In an undated letter to J. G. Gahn, which was probably written in 1774, Scheele stated that he had precipitated alum with lime water. "When I had the right proportion of the lime water to the acid in the alum," said he, "I got a precipitate of alumina and gypsum (calcium sulfate) in the solution . . . and I found neither lime or gypsum in the clear solution, but pure water" (18). Thus it is evident that Scheele was at that time unaware of the presence of potash in alum.

When A. S. Marggraf tried to prepare alum from alumina and vitriolic acid, he found that unless he added fixed alkali he obtained no crystals (19). In 1777 Lavoisier clearly stated that potash is an essential constituent of alum (18, 20). In analyzing a water containing aluminum sulfate, which the younger Cassini had sent him from Italy, Lavoisier added some potash. When he evaporated the solution, he obtained crystals of alum and realized that this was a verification of the results of Marggraf and of Macquer.

"The necessity for the addition of a portion of alkali in order to form alum is also confirmed," said Lavoisier, "by a very interesting observation of M. Monet [A.-G. Monnet (1734–1817)] on the earth extracted from the alum at Tolfa; the chemical examination which he made of specimens of this earth, brought from Italy by M. Guettard, showed him that it contains a portion of fixed vegetable alkali already formed. It is doubtless to this alkali that this earth owes its property of furnishing

alum without addition" (20).   Since Antoine-Grimoald Monnet's discovery of potassium in the alum from Tolfa attracted little notice, chemists still continued to regard that element as peculiar to the vegetable
realm.   A.-F. de Fourcroy, however, was aware at least as early as 1789 of
its occasional presence in minerals (14).

When M. H. Klaproth analyzed some native alum (alunite) from
Cape Miseno, near Naples, he computed that one thousand pounds of
it contained 470 pounds of "alum provided by Nature herself with the
requisite quantity of pot-ash" and 290 pounds of "alum whose crystallization is promoted by adding pot-ash" (21).   The presence of this alkali
raised in his mind the question: "As this grotto consists merely of volcanic
tufa, in which no vegetation takes place, whence does Nature procure
the vegetable alkali requisite to the generation of the crystallizable alum?"
(21).

When he analyzed some native saltpeter from the Pulo mine at
Molfetta in Apulia and found that "the alkaline base of prismatic nitre
constitutes nearly one-half of the whole of that compound," the same
question struck him even more forcibly.   "The conjecture that Nature
possesses means of producing that alkali beyond the limits of the vegetable
kingdom, nay, even without any immediate influence of vegetation,
acquires, by this singular phenomenon, a very high degree of probability"
(21).

Potash in Leucite.   In 1797 Klaproth analyzed some Vesuvian leucite,
a mineral which had been described by J. J. Ferber in 1773, and found
54.50 per cent of silica, 24.50 per cent of alumina, and nothing else! (22).
In order to account for the 21 per cent loss, he examined the mineral more
carefully, and was astonished to find potassium, which he recognized by
the crystalline form of its sulfate and also by precipitating it with tartaric
acid and igniting the resulting potassium acid tartrate to form potassium
carbonate, which "shot into prismatic nitre" when he treated it with nitric
acid.   He also analyzed specimens of leucite from Albano, Pompeii, and
Ronciglione, and concluded that "this constituent part of leucite, which
now appears in the character of an oryctognostic or mineral substance,
is no other than pot-ash, which hitherto has been thought exclusively to
belong to the vegetable kingdom . . ." (23).   When the American mineralogical chemist J. Lawrence Smith analyzed leucites from Vesuvius,
Andernach, Borghetta, and Frescati in 1870, he also found rubidium and
cesium in every specimen he tested (24).

Potash in Pumice.   In 1798 Dr. Robert Kennedy of Edinburgh demonstrated the presence of potash in pumice.   He noticed that the pumice
fused to a glassy enamel.   Although Klaproth had found only silica,
alumina, and iron, and had failed to detect potash, in the specimen he

analyzed, he mentioned that the pumice melted in the porcelain furnace in Berlin.   Dr. Kennedy therefore concluded that Klaproth's specimen, as well as his own, must have contained some alkali, for a compound of only silica, alumina, and a very little iron would not have melted at this temperature (25).

A.-F. de Fourcroy stated in 1806 that Klaproth and Vauquelin had found potash "in several rocks, especially in leucite, feldspar, and some volcanic products" (14).

In the latter half of the nineteenth century the United States was dependent on the vast Stassfurt deposits of Germany for the potassium compounds needed as fertilizers.   In 1911 Congress appropriated funds for a search for domestic minerals, salts, brines, and seaweeds suitable for potash production (67).   The complex brines of Searles Lake, California, a rich source of potassium chloride, have been worked up scientifically on the basis of phase-rule studies with outstanding success.   Oil drillers exploring the Permian Basin for oil became aware of the possibility of discovering potash deposits through chemical analysis of the cores of saline strata.   A rich bed of sylvinite, a natural mixture of sylvite (potassium chloride) and halite (sodium chloride), was found at Carlsbad, New Mexico.   At the potash plane near Wendover, Utah, the raw material, a brine, is worked up by solar evaporation (67).

Potassium in Animals.   Professor Abildgaard of Copenhagen discovered potassium in the blood of the horse.   After adding nitric acid to the blood, he prepared and purified crystals of saltpeter (26).   Potassium is essential to both plant and animal life, and the adult human body contains more potassium than sodium (27).

SOME SODIUM COMPOUNDS

> *"Hence with diffusive salt old Ocean steeps*
> *His emerald shallows, and his sapphire deeps.*
> *Oft in wide lakes, around their warmer brim*
> *In hollow pyramids the crystals swim;*
> *Or, fused by earth-born fires, in cubic blocks*
> *Shoot their white forms, and harden into rocks.*
> *Thus, cavern'd round in Cracow's mighty mines,*
> *With crystal walls a gorgeous city shines;*
> *Scoop'd in the briny rock long streets extend*
> *Their hoary course, and glittering domes ascend . . .*
> *Form'd in pellucid salt with chissel nice,*
> *The pale lamp glimmering through the sculptured ice,*
> *With wild reverted eyes fair Lotta* stands,*
> *And spreads to Heaven, in vain, her glassy hands . . ."* (29).

* This refers to a rock salt statue of Lot's wife.

Salt. The oldest Chinese treatise on pharmacology and pharma-cognosy, the "Peng-Tzao-Kan-Mu," which some authorities believe to date back to about 2700 B.C., describes both solar and rock salt. Shu-Sha (or Sou-Cha), a subject of the Emperor Huang, invented the art of extracting salt from sea water (*30, 75*). In about 300 B.C., Li-Ping, prefect of S-Tchuan province, discovered salt deposits in the earth; the inhabitants had obtained their salt hitherto from Chan-Si in exchange for tea. L. G. M. Baas-Becking stated that the early Chinese pictogram for salt was undoubtedly a diagram of the hopper-shaped crystal of sodium chloride and is probably the earliest picture of a crystal.

From Li Ch'iao-p'ing's "Chemical Arts of Old China"

Pumping Salt brine in ancient China, from a depth of 1200 feet or more. In addition the Chinese produced lake salt, sea salt, and rock salt.

An account of the salt industry at Tzu-Liu-Ching published by Li Jung (ca. 1820–1889) in 1890 was translated by Lien-che Tu Fang and published with handsome illustrations in *Isis* (*65*). Along the seacoast from Manchuria to Kwangtung, salt is produced by evaporation of sea water. In the northwest it is obtained by evaporation of the water of salt ponds and salt lakes. In the southwest the rock salt deposits are reached by wells. In Szechwan the rock salt is accompanied at some places, including Tzu-liu-ching, by natural gas, which is burned to accelerate the evaporation (65).

Two bricks or tiles bearing reliefs depicting the salt industry as practiced in the first or second century A.D. have been unearthed in Szechwan. Rubbings of these bricks, which were used in the construction of two tombs of the Later Han dynasty (A.D. 24–220), were published in *Isis* by Richard C. Rudolph (66).

The prescriptions in the Ebers papyrus (sixteenth century B.C.) mention both common salt and soda (*natron*) (31). Both the Old and New Testaments abound in literal and figurative allusions to salt: "Ye are the salt of the earth"; "Have salt in yourselves and have peace one with another" (32). Strabo described the mining of rock salt and its preparation from salt springs in 18 A.D. (1). Dioscorides of Anazarba said in 64 A.D. that the best salt came from Cyprus, Sicily, Africa, and Phrygia (1).

Aboriginal Indians in the southern part of what is now the United States used to purify salt by allowing water to percolate through it in leaching baskets (33) and boiling the strained leachings down over a fire. Hernando de Soto's party prepared salt by this old Indian method in 1541 for their expedition through Arkansas (34). The Aztecs concentrated the water from salt lakes by boiling it down in pottery vessels and also by allowing it to stand in shallow pools where the sun could evaporate it. They used it not only as a condiment but also for preserving meat (33).

Herman Boerhaave stated that the salt mines of Wieliczka, near Cracow, Poland, were discovered in the year 1251. He described them as "a subterraneous republic, which has its polity, laws, families, and even high-ways and common carriers. . . . When a traveller is arrived at the bottom of this strange abyss, . . . he is surpriz'd with a long series of lofty vaults . . . which . . . appear by the light of flambeaux . . . as so many crystals . . . casting a lustre which the eye can scarce bear" (35).

When the British fisheries lacked an adequate supply of pure salt, Dr. William Brownrigg published an important book "On the Art of Making Common Salt," which was condensed by Sir William Watson and published in 1848 in the *Philosophical Transactions* (36).

Per Kalm found in 1748–51 that the inhabitants of Quebec were entirely dependent on France for their salt. Because of a French monopoly, the salt industry could not flourish in Quebec (37).

The salt industry of Avranchin was mentioned by G. Dumoulin in 1631 and described by Jean-Etienne Guettard in 1758. In the calm bay, the sea water deposited its salt with the sand. By means of horse-drawn rakes, the salty sand was collected in spiral-shaped piles, which were then covered with twigs and clay. The leaching with sea water was done in wooden boxes, the brine filtering through the sand and passing through tubes into the boiling-house. The evaporating pans were of lead, and the output one hundred pounds of salt per day (38).

The *Medical Repository* for 1802 stated that "at Dennis, in the county of Barnstable [Massachusetts], common salt is crystallized from ocean water, without culinary heat or boiling, in considerable quantity. The amount is stated at 20,000 bushels a year of domestic sea salt. This is estimated at one-fifth of the quantity consumed in the Cape Cod fishery annually" (39).

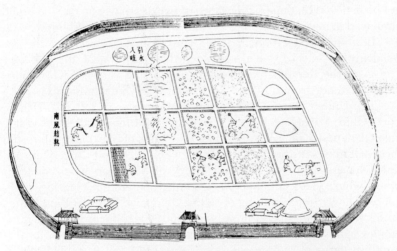

From Li Ch'iao-p'ing's "Chemical Arts of Old China"

Ancient China's Lake Salt was produced in plants such as this, usually built along the shores of salt lakes, in the Kansu and Shansi provinces.

In colonial times, some salt was made by evaporating sea water from large boilers, but much of it was imported from the West Indies. Timothy Dwight, president of Yale College, in his "Travels in New England and New York," described its manufacture by solar evaporation at Yarmouth and Dennis, Massachusetts, at the beginning of the nineteenth century. Four kinds of shallow, water-tight wooden vats were used. "The first class, or that next to the ocean, is called the water room; the second the pickle room; the third the lime room; and the fourth the salt room. Each of these rooms, except the first, is placed so much lower than the preceding that the water flows readily from it into another in the order specified. The water room is filled from the ocean by a pump, furnished with vans or sails, and turned by the wind. Here it continues until of the proper strength to be drawn into the pickle room, and thus successively into those which remain. The lime, with which the water of the ocean abounds, is deposited in the lime room. The salt is formed into small crystals in the salt room, very white and pure, and weighs from seventy to seventy-five pounds a bushel. The process is carried on through the warm season. After the salt has ceased to crystallize, the remaining water is suffered to freeze. In this manner a large quantity of Glauber's salt is obtained in crystals, which are clean and good. . . . The marine salt made here is sold for seventy-five cents a bushel; and the Glauber's salt, at from six to ten cents a pound. . . . The people of Dennis, the town immediately East of Yarmouth, began this business. . . . May it not be believed that many thousands of persons may, one day, be profitably employed in making salt along the immense extent of our shore . . ." (40).

In about 1865 Professor B. F. Mudge, first president of the Kansas Academy of Science, gave a geological description of the salt beds of Kansas in the Republican, Solomon, and Saline valleys. This enormous deposit extends from northern Kansas into Oklahoma and Texas (41).

The United States has inexhaustible supplies of salt (68, 70). New York, Ohio, Michigan, Kansas, Louisiana, and Texas all have vast commercial deposits of solid salt (halite). One of the most interesting of these salt mines is situated beneath the City of Detroit. The Ohio Valley-Kanawha area and the Saginaw Valley of Michigan have underground brines which yield salt, calcium chloride, magnesium chloride, and bromine. The hydraulic mining of salt in Ohio gave Herman Frasch the idea for his remarkable process of mining Louisiana sulfur by melting it underground with superheated water and pumping it out in molten form (68). Another source of sodium chloride is the Great Salt Lake in Utah.

Natural Soda. The proverb "As he that taketh away a garment in cold weather, and as vinegar upon nitre, so is he that singeth songs to an heavy heart" (Prov. 25, 20) is an allusion to the action of vinegar on sodium carbonate. The detergent property of this alkali is mentioned in Jeremiah 2, 22: "For though thou wash thee with nitre and take thee much sope, yet thine iniquity is marked before me."

In the eighteenth century some chemists believed that the word *natrum* referred to saltpeter (potassium nitrate). Geoffroy the Elder, however, distinguished clearly between the niter, or natrum, of the ancients (sodium carbonate) and modern niter (saltpeter). Even in his time, the inhabitants of Smyrna and Ephesus still washed their clothes with a lye leached from small alkaline hillocks in their fields. "The ancient nitre," said Geoffroy, "was likewise used to make Glass, being mixed with Sand; as they afterwards did with the salt of the Plant Kali, or Glass-Wort, as may be gathered from what Tacitus says . . . that

the Sands of Palestine and Syria, near Egypt, were made into Glass with
Nitre" (42). In Geoffroy's time sodium carbonate was rare in Europe,
and little used.

In 1799 Luigi Palcani published analyses of two authentic specimens
of natural Oriental natrum: one which Pietro Andrea Mattioli had
brought, more than two centuries before, from Constantinople for Ulisse
Aldrovandi's Museum of Natural History, and another which Edward
Wortley Montague had brought from Alexandria. Palcani found, as du
Hamel had stated, that the natrum was composed mainly of sodium
carbonate (43). It also contained varying amounts of sodium bicarbonate, sodium chloride, sodium sulfate, and water (44).

Another early description of the African trona is to be found in the
first volume of Crell's Neueste Entdeckungen in der Chemie. C. Bagge,
Swedish consul to Tripoli, said that a very thin crust of white, crystalline
trona covered the ground at a place two days' journey from Fezzan in
the Sahara. It was shipped to Egypt, Tripoli, and "the land of the
Negroes" to be used in bleaching and soap making (45). The Wadi
Natrûn, or Natron Valley, near Cairo and Alexandria, lies below the
level of the sea. Its lakes, formed by the flood waters of the Nile, become
almost dry in summer, and its great deposits of natron have been worked
for thousands of years (46).

Georg Adolph Suckow, in his "Introduction to Economic and Technical Chemistry," described in 1784 the preparation of soda by burning
certain marine plants such as Fucus vesiculosus, Chenopodium maritimum,
and Salsola kali, and leaching it from the half-vitrified ashes. This
industry flourished at Alicante, Spain, at Alexandria, Egypt, and along
the coasts of Italy and France (47).

When these natural sources of soda became depleted and inadequate
to meet the demand, various processes were devised for the manufacture
of it from the cheapest raw material, common salt. An account of the
most successful of these early processes and the tragic story of its discoverer, Nicolas Leblanc, has been told by Dr. Ralph E. Oesper in the
Journal of Chemical Education (71). The same journal also contains
other valuable articles on the alkali industry by Dr. Oesper (72), E. Berl
(73), and Desmond Reilly (74).

Glass. Pliny the Elder (in Book 36, Chapter 26 of his "Historia
Naturalis") described a pure sand found on the Phoenician coast at the
mouth of the river Belus, near the settlement of Ptolemais. "The shore,"
said Pliny, "does not exceed half a mile in extent, and yet, for long ages,
it was the only source of sand for making glass. The story is that merchants put in there with a cargo of crude soda (nitrum), and when,
scattered over the beach, they were preparing a meal and could find
no stones of the right height to prop up their pots, they supported them on

lumps of soda which they had fetched from the ship. When these were melted by the heat and mingled with the sand, transparent streams of a strange liquid were seen to flow, and thus glass was discovered" (48).

Cornelius Tacitus, a friend of Pliny the Younger, also mentioned the manufacture of glass by fusing native niter with sand from the beach at the mouth of the river Belus (49).

Although pure silica and pure sodium carbonate would yield only soluble "water glass," K. C. Bailey and A. Lucas believe that if the materials used by the Phoenicians contained lime as an impurity, true glass could possibly have been produced by the method described by Pliny (44). Many writers, however, regard Pliny's account as highly improbable.

The composition of the glass found in the tomb of Tut-ankh-Amen, according to Lucas, suggests that it may have been made by fusing together a mixture of natron and siliceous sand containing calcium carbonate as an impurity (50). The Egyptians, according to Albert Neuburger, manufactured glass long before the Phoenicians. The oldest known piece of glass is in the Berlin Museum. It is a green bead taken from a prehistoric Egyptian grave believed to be about fifty-four centuries old (51).

Herman Boerhaave once wrote with deep feeling: "If there is an art useful to mankind, it is certainly that of making glass. Glass, when ground, corrects the defects of our vision; without it, as soon as one had reached a certain age, he could no longer hope to read" (64).

Glauber's Salt. When Johann Rudolph Glauber (1604–1670) was visiting Austria in his youth, he was stricken with a serious stomach ailment which was finally relieved when he drank water from a spring near Wiener-Neustadt. When he evaporated some of this water, he found that the residue contained a salt "which Paracelsus called *enixum* and I call *mirabile*" (52, 53). Since Glauber succeeded in preparing it from common salt, made an extended study of its properties, and introduced its use into medicine, it came to be known as the *sal mirabile of Glauber* and finally as *Glauber's salt,* sodium sulfate (54, 55, 56). Although he made some extravagant claims for it, Glauber was nevertheless conservative enough not to regard it as the elixir of life. "But let no one imagine," said he, "that I would like to demonstrate immortality with it. Alas, no, because for death, no herb is grown" (52).

Glauber's salt of excellent quality was manufactured at Dennis, Massachusetts. At the beginning of the nineteenth century, about fifty tons per year was produced there (39).

Sodium in Basalt and Lava. *Nicholson's Journal* for October, 1798, contains an account of the first discovery of sodium in a stony mineral. Early in August of that year Dr. Robert Kennedy announced to the Royal

Society of Edinburgh that he had discovered soda in several varieties of Scottish whinstone and in lava from Mt. Aetna (25). He used the term "whinstone" to include basalt, trap, and certain kinds of porphyry, wacke, and other argillaceous stones. When he analyzed a specimen which had been broken from one of the famous basaltic columns of Staffa, he found that the sum of the earths, silica, and iron never amounted to more than 94 per cent. Suspecting the presence of an alkali, he heated the pulverized mineral with pure sulfuric acid and extracted a salt which he identified as sodium sulfate (25). He proved, moreover, that the sodium compounds had not been dissolved from his glass apparatus. Dr. Kennedy also found 4 per cent of soda in a specimen of lava brought to him by Sir James Hall and Dr. James Home from the famous current of Mt. Aetna which in 1669 had destroyed part of the town of Catania. He published these analyses in 1800 in *Nicholson's Journal* (25).

"The celebrated Mr. Klaproth of Berlin," said Dr. Kennedy, "has already shown that pot-ash enters into the composition of several stony substances; and by the experiments described in this paper, the other fixed alkali, soda, has also been proved to exist in mineral bodies, as it has been separated from nine different varieties . . ." (25).

Richard Kirwan mentioned "the ingenious, accurate, and skilfully conducted analyses of Dr. Kennedy, who bids fair to rival the excellence attained by the greatest masters of that sublime and difficult art" (57).

Klaproth showed in 1800 that cryolite, a mineral discovered a few years previously in Greenland, also contains sodium (58).

Sodium in Plants and Animals. By macerating certain plants in warm water acidified with different mineral acids, G.-F. Rouelle (1703–1770) prepared and identified the neutral sodium salts of the corresponding acids and thus demonstrated the presence of the mineral alkali (sodium carbonate) in these plants. He believed that the sodium carbonate was not merely absorbed from the soil but that it was a true product of vegetation (11).

Although sodium is not essential to plant life, plants grown under natural conditions do absorb sodium compounds from the soil. As early as 1874, G. Bunge pointed out that, in experimental attempts to raise plants entirely free from sodium, glass containers must be avoided because of the solubility of sodium compounds contained in the glass (59). In 1878 Pierre-Paul Déhérain raised beans and potatoes in an artificial culture medium entirely free from sodium (60, 61).

Hilaire-Marin Rouelle, a younger brother of Guillaume-François (Rouelle the Elder), observed in 1773 that the blood of man and animals contains free mineral alkali, common salt, and potassium chloride ("sylvisches Fiebersalz") (26, 62). Jean-Baptiste-Michel Bicquet made this discovery independently at about the same time (63). Sodium occurs in all animal organs, principally as sodium chloride, but also as secondary sodium orthophosphate, sodium sulfate, sodium carbonate, sodium hydrogen carbonate, and other compounds. Together with potassium, it is essential for animal life (27, 60).

LITERATURE CITED

(1) DARMSTAEDTER, LUDWIG, "Handbuch zur Geschichte der Naturwissenschaften und der Technik," 2nd ed., J. Springer, Berlin, 1908, pp. 29 and 31.

(2) BLANCOURT, H. DE, "The Art of Glass," Smith, Greenwood and Co., London, 1699, p. 49.

(3) BROWNE, C. A., "The chemical industries of the American aborigines," Isis, 23 (2), 411 (Sept., 1935).

(4) "A substitute for culinary salt contained in ashes," Med. Resspository, (1), 6, 330–1 (Nov., Dec., 1802, and Jan., 1803); ibid., (2), 2, 72 (May, June, July, 1804).

(5) KOPP, H., "Geschichte der Chemie," Vol. 3, Fr. Vieweg und Sohn, Braunschweig, 1847, pp. 42–51; Vol. 4, pp. 3–11.

(6) O'CONNOR, A. CONDORCET, "Oeuvres de Condorcet," Vol. 2, Firmin Didot Frères, Paris, 1847, pp. 270–82.

(7) BOERHAAVE, H., "Elemens de chymie," Vol. 5, Chardon, fils, Paris, 1754, pp. 263–4.

(8) BLACK, JOSEPH, "Experiments upon Magnesia Alba, Quicklime, and Other Alcaline Substances," Alembic Club Reprint No. 1, Wm. F. Clay, Edinburgh, 1893, p. 40.

(9) WALL, M., "Remarks on the origin of the vegetable fixed alkali, with some collateral observations on nitre," Memoirs Lit. and Philos. Soc. (Manchester), 2, 67–79 (1789), 2nd ed.

(10) NORDENSKIÖLD, A. E., "C. W. Scheele. Efterlemnade bref och anteckningar," P. A. Norstedt and Sons, Stockholm, 1892, p. 39.

(11) ROUELLE, "Beobachtungen über das völlig gebildete mineralische Laugensalz in den Pflanzen und über das Mittel, es unmittlebar ohne Verbrennen daraus zu erhalten," Crell's Beyträge zu den chem. Ann., 1, Stück 1, pp. 124–5 (1786).

(12) "Pott's Betrachtungen über das Alkali des Kochsalzes," Crell's Neues chem. Archiv, 3, 307 (1785); Abh. königl. Akad. Wiss. (Berlin), 1735–42, p. 285.

(13) LAVOISIER, A.-L., "Traité élémentaire de chimie," 2nd ed., Vol. 1, Cuchet, Paris, 1793, pp. 164–9.

(14) FOURCROY, A.-F. DE, "Elements of Natural History and Chemistry," Vol. 1, C. Elliot and T. Kay, London, 1790, pp. 329–33. (Translated from the Paris edition of 1789.)

(15) KOPP, HERMANN, Ref. (5), Vol. 3, pp. 260–2; Vol. 4, pp. 36–7, and 63.

(16) MARGGRAF, A. S., "Chymische Schriften," revised ed., Vol. 1, Arnold Wever, Berlin, 1768, p. 188.

(17) GEOFFROY THE YOUNGER, "Untersuchung verschiedener Vitriole, nebst einigen Versuchen über die künstliche Bildung des weissen Vitriols und des Alauns," Crell's Neues chem. Archiv, 3, 127 (1785); Mém. de l'acad. roy. des sciences, 1727, p. 425.

(18) NORDENSKIÖLD, A. E., Ref. (10), pp. 140, 143.

(19) MARGGRAF, A. S., Ref. (16), Vol. 1, pp. 193–4.

(20) "Oeuvres de Lavoisier," Vol. 2, Imprimerie Impériale, Paris, 1862, pp. 157–9.

(21) KLAPROTH, M. H., "Analytical Essays towards Promoting the Chemical Knowledge of Mineral Substances," T. Cadell and W. Davies, London, 1801, pp. 266–73.

(22) FERBER, J. J., "Briefe aus Wälschland . . . an J. von Born," Prague, **1773**, pp. 165 and 176.

(23) KLAPROTH, M. H., Ref. (*21*), pp. 238–47, 348–67, 471–5; "Beytrag zur chemischen Naturgeschichte des Pflanzenalkali," *Crell's Ann.*, **27**, 90–6 (1797). Articles on Leucite and Lepidolite.

(24) SMITH, J. LAWRENCE, "Mineralogy and Chemistry," John P. Morton and Co., Louisville, Kentucky, **1873**, pp. 188–9.

(25) KENNEDY, ROBERT, "On the analysis of pumice, which is found to contain potash, and of basaltes and lava containing soda," *Nicholson's J.*, **2**, 289 (Oct., 1798); *ibid.*, **4**, 407, 438 (1800–01).

(26) "Alkaligehalt des Bluts," *Scherer's Allg. J. der Chemie*, **2**, 231 (1798).

(27) SHOHL, A. T., "Mineral Metabolism," Reinhold Publishing Corporation, New York City, **1939**, pp. 121–5.

(28) WALKER, FREDERIC, "Jean de Meun and alchemy," *J. Chem. Educ.*, **7**, 2865 (Dec., 1930). Extract from the "Romance of the Rose," a 13th-century poem.

(29) DARWIN, ERASMUS, "The botanic garden," 2nd ed., part 1, J. Johnson, London, **1791**, pp. 70–2, 132–3, 206.

(30) BAAS-BECKING, L. G. M., "Historical notes on salt and salt-manufacture," *Sci. Monthly*, **32**, 434–46 (May, 1931).

(31) LIPPMANN, E. O. VON, "Abhandlungen und Vorträge zur Geschichte der Naturwissenschaften," Vol. 2, Veit and Co., Leipzig, **1913**, pp. 12–13.

(32) MATTHEW **5**, 13; Mark **9**, 50.

(33) BROWNE, C. A., "The chemical industries of the American aborigines," *Isis*, **23** (2), 411–12 (Sept., 1935).

(34) HALE, HARRISON and P. G. HORTON, "The history of chemistry in Arkansas," *J. Chem. Educ.*, **19**, 357 (Aug., 1942).

(35) BOERHAAVE, HERMAN, "A New Method of Chemistry," 2nd ed., Vol. 1, T. Longman, London, **1741**, p. 105.

(36) "An account of a treatise by Wm. Brownrigg, M.D., F.R.S., entitled [*sic*], 'The art of making common salt' . . . , abstracted by Mr. Watson," *Phil. Trans.*, Abridgment, **10**, 657–67 (1756); *Phil. Trans.*, No. **487**, p. 351 (Apr., 1748).

(37) PINKERTON, JOHN, "A General Collection of the Best and Most Interesting Voyages and Travels," Vol. 13, Longman, Hurst, Rees, and Orme, London, **1812**, pp. 473 and 675. Per Kalm's "Travels in North America."

(38) GUETTARD, J.-E., "Beschreibung der Salzsiedungen im Lande Avranchin," *Crell's Neues chem. Archiv*, **8**, 138–9 (1791); *Hist. de l'Acad. Roy. des Sciences* (*Paris,*) **1758**, p. 261.

(39) ANON., "Muriate and sulphate of soda manufactured in Massachusetts," *Med. Repository*, **6**, 219 (Aug., Sept., Oct., 1802).

(40) DWIGHT, TIMOTHY, "Travels in New England and New York," Vol. 3, T. Dwight, New Haven Conn., **1822**, pp. 79–82.

(41) HOWES, CECIL, "Kansas, now a leading producer, once offered a bounty for salt," *Kansas City Star*, May 3, 1940.

(42) GEOFFROY, E.-F., "A Treatise of the Fossil, Vegetable, and Animal Substances That Are Made Use of in Physick," W. Innys, R. Manby *et al.*, London, **1736**, pp. 92–6.

(43) PALCANI, LUIGI, "Del natro orientale,"*Memorie de matematica e fisica della soc. Italiana*, **8** (1), 77–84 (1799).

(44) LUCAS, ALFRED, "Ancient Egyptian Materials and Industries," 2nd ed., Edward Arnold & Co., London, **1934**, pp. 110 and 118.

(45) "Chr. Bagge's (Consuls in Tripoli) Beschreibung von Trona, oder einer Art Natron aus Tripoli," *Crell's Neueste Entdeckungen*, **1**, 95–6 (1781); K. *Svenska Vet. Acad. Handl.*, **35**, 131.

(46) MORTON, H. V., "Through Lands of the Bible," Dodd, Mead and Co., New York, **1938**, pp. 252 and 262.

(47) Suckow, G. A., "Anfangsgründe der ökonomischen und technischen Chymie," Weidmanns Erben und Reich, Leipzig, **1784**, p. 211.

(48) Bailey, K. C., "The Elder Pliny's Chapters on Chemical Subjects," Vol. 2, Edward Arnold and Co., London, **1932**, pp. 147–9; Pliny, *"Historia naturalis,"* Book 36, Chapter 26, paragraphs 190–1.

(49) Fyfe, W. H., "Tacitus, The Histories," Vol 2, Clarendon Press, Oxford, **1912**, p. 111; "Tacitus, history," Book 5, Chap. 7.

(50) Carter, Howard, "The Tomb of Tut-ankh-Amen," Vol. 2, George H. Doran Co., New York, **1927**, pp. 241–2. "The chemistry of the tomb," by A. Lucas.

(51) Neuburger, Albert, "The Technical Arts and Sciences of the Ancients," Methuen and Co., London, **1930**, pp. 152–3.

(52) Bauer, A., "Naturhistorisch-biographische Essays," Ferdinand Enke, Stuttgart, **1911**, pp. 76–84. "Der Alchemist R. Glauber in Wiener-Neustadt."

(53) Glauberi, Johannis Rudolphi, "Opera chymica," T. M. Götzen, Frankfort-on-the Main, **1658**, pp. 491–501. In German.

(54) Glauber, J. R., "A Description of New Philosophical Furnaces," Richard Coats, London, **1651–2**. Preface by J. F., the English translator, also pp. 10–13, 31, 76–8, 96–7.

(55) Bugge, G., "Das Buch der grossen Chemiker," Vol. 1, Verlag Chemie, Berlin, **1929**, pp. 151–72. Article on Glauber by P. Walden.

(56) Jorissen, W. P., "Iets over Glauber's Amsterdamschen Tijd," *Chem. Weekbl.,* **15**, 268–71 (1918).

(57) Kirwan, R., "Observations on the proof of the Huttonian theory of the earth," *Nicholson's J.,* **4**, 102 (June, 1800).

(58) Diergart, Paul, "Beiträge aus der Geschichte der Chemie dem Gedächtnis von G. W. A. Kahlbaum," Franz Deuticke, Leipzig and Vienna, **1909**, p. 501. Chapter by S. M. Jörgensen, "Zur Geschichte des Kryoliths und der Kryolith-Industrie."

(59) Bunge, G., "Ueber den Natrongehalt der Pflanzenaschen," *Ann.,* **172**, 16–27 (1874).

(60) "Gmelin's Handbuch der anorganischen Chemie," 8th ed., Vol. 20, Verlag Chemie, Berlin, **1927**, pp. 1–14; *ibid.,* Vol. 2, pp. 1–9; *ibid.,* Vol. 21, pp. 1–41.

(61) Déhérain, P.-P., *Ann. Sci. Natur.,* (6), **6**, 340 (1878).

(62) Rouelle, H.-M., "Versuche und Beobachtungen über das Salz, welches man im Blute der Menschen und Thiere, wie auch im Wasser der Wassersüchtigen findet," *Crell's Beyträge zu den chem. Annalen,* **1**, part 3, 92–6 (1785); *J. de Méd.,* **40**, 68 (1773).

(63) Desbois de Rochefort, "Beobachtungen über die Existenz des mineralischen Laugensalzes in der Milch und im Blute der Thiere," *Crell's Beyträge zu den chem. Ann.,* **1**, part 3, 108–9 (1785).

(64) Boerhaave, H., "Elemens de chymie," Vol. 1, Chardon, fils, Paris, **1754**, pp. 188, 197.

(65) Jung, Li, "An account of the salt industry at Tzu-liu-ching," *Isis,* **39**, 228–34 (Nov., 1948).

(66) Rudolph, R. C., "A second-century Chinese illustration of salt mining," *Isis,* **43**, 39–41 (Apr., 1952).

(67) Turrentine, J. W., "The American potash industry," *Sci. Mo.,* **70**, 41–7 (Jan., 1950).

(68) Wilcox, W. G., "Salt production," *Sci. Mo.,* **70**, 157–64 (Mar., 1950).

(69) Szathmáry, L., "Potash boilery in Hungary," Különlenyomat a Magyar Gyógyszerésztud., Társaság Értesitöje, **1935** évi 3. számából., 9 pp. In Hungarian with German summary.

(70) Hyler, J. E., "The production of salt," *J. Chem. Educ.,* **12**, 203–7 (May, 1935).

(71) Oesper, R. E., "Nicolas Leblanc (1742–1806)," *J. Chem. Educ.,* **19**, 567–72 (Dec., 1942); **20**, 11–20 (Jan., 1943).

(72) OESPER, R. E. and CLARA DEASY, "Ernest Solvay (1838–1922)," *J. Chem. Educ.*, **15**, 401, 424 (Sept., 1938).
(73) BERL, E., "Georg Lunge (1839–1923)," *J. Chem. Educ.*, **16**, 453–60 (Oct., 1939).
(74) REILLY, DESMOND, "The Muspratts and the Gambles. Pioneers in England's alkali industry," *J. Chem. Educ.*, **28**, 650–53 (Dec., 1951).
(75) CH'IAO-P'ING, LI, "The Chemical Arts of Old China," Journal of Chemical Education, Easton, Pa., **1948**, pp. 55–65.

Sir Humphry Davy, 1778–1829. English chemist and physicist. One of the founders of electrochemistry. Inventor of the safety lamp for miners. He was the first to isolate potassium, sodium, calcium, barium, strontium, and magnesium. Davy in England and Gay-Lussac and Thenard in France, working independently, were the first to isolate boron.

There is now before us a boundless prospect of novelty in science; a country unexplored, but noble and fertile in aspect; a land of promise in philosophy (1).

18

Three alkali metals

A number of the chemical elements, including some that play an important rôle in modern life, remained practically unknown outside the scientific world for many years after their discovery. Some, like tellurium, vanadium, and titanium, were forgotten for several decades even by chemists, and were later rediscovered. The reader will recall, however, that when phosphorus was discovered in the latter half of the seventeenth century the news spread rapidly throughout Europe. In a similar manner Davy's isolation of sodium and potassium immediately fired the imagination of the nineteenth-century public and aroused intense interest. These elements, like phosphorus, made their entrance upon the chemical stage in a manner nothing short of dramatic, and the accompanying phenomenon of light helped to focus all eyes upon them. Lithium, however, entered the chemical world in a more quiet manner and was introduced by a scientist of lesser prominence, J. A. Arfwedson, a student of Berzelius.

POTASSIUM AND SODIUM

*A*ncient writers did not distinguish between sodium carbonate (the mineral alkali) and potassium carbonate (the vegetable alkali) (*42*). When Johann Bohn prepared aqua regia in 1683 by distilling a mixture of salt and aqua fortis (nitric acid), he noticed that the cubic crystals which remained differed from those of saltpeter prepared in the ordinary manner from wood ashes. This clear distinction between "cubic saltpeter" (sodium nitrate) and ordinary saltpeter was an important step in the proof that soda and potash are two different alkalies. In the latter part of the eighteenth century, Torbern Bergman wrote: "There are to this day persons who insist that the vegetable alkali cannot be exhibited in the form of crystals, notwithstanding that Professor Bohnius (*Diss. Physico Chym., ann.* 1696, pa. 381) of Leipsic, so long ago as the end of the last century, had demonstrated the contrary; but his method had been so long unknown that it was lately offered to the public as a new discovery" (*42, 43, 44*).

473

In speaking of the loss to both chemistry and medicine by too narrow specialization in either science, Herman Boerhaave once wrote, "What praise then is not merited by Jean Bohn and Frederic Hoffmann, who excel in both and who thereby acquired such a great reputation" (45).

Potash was made on a small scale in New England in the seventeenth century, and for two centuries American potash and pearlash, made by burning wood and leaching the ashes, were shipped to European countries, with incalculable loss to American agriculture (50).

Georg Ernst Stahl distinguished between the "natural and artificial alkalies" (soda and potash) as early as 1702, and noted that certain

Henri-Louis du Hamel (or Duhamel) du Monceau, 1700–1782. French chemist and agriculturist who proved in 1736 that the mineral alkali (soda) is a constituent of common salt, of Glauber's salt, and of borax. With his brother, M. de Denainvilliers, he carried out important experiments in plant nutrition on their estate.

Gal. franç., 1823.
Drouais père pinx., H. Grevedon del.

sodium salts differ in crystalline form from those of potassium (42). Hermann Kopp quoted a passage from the "Specimen Becherianum" in which Stahl stated that the natural alkali (soda) in common salt appeared in the retort after distillation with concentrated oil of vitriol or spirit of niter (sulfuric or nitric acid) in the form of new salts differing from the corresponding salts of the artificial alkali (potash) in their crystalline form, solubility in water, and behavior toward heat.

Henri-Louis du Hamel du Monceau (or Dumonceau) proved conclusively in 1736 that the mineral alkali (soda) is a constituent of common salt, of Glauber's salt, and of borax. He was born in Paris in 1700 and educated at Harcourt College. Even before his election to membership, the Academy of Sciences selected him to study a disease which was threatening the saffron crop in Gâtinois. Du Hamel found the cause of it to be a parasitic plant, and decided to devote his life to scientific agriculture and the public welfare (50).

Although the acidic constituent of common salt was already known, the nature of its basic constituent was still a matter of conjecture. "Soda, *natrum*, and borax," wrote du Hamel in 1736, "give with vitriolic acid Glauber's salt; with acid of saltpeter, cubic saltpeter [sodium nitrate]; and with acid of salt, a kind of sea salt. Does this not permit one to decide as to the base of the sea salt?" (46).

He prepared soda from salt by two methods. In the first of these, he evaporated a mixture of salt and oil of vitriol, heated the resulting Glauber's salt with charcoal dust in a closed crucible, distilled the reduced mixture with wine vinegar, and calcined the hard, black residue of sodium acetate left in the broken retort. In his other method, he poured concentrated spirit of saltpeter (nitric acid) on the salt, and distilled off the resulting aqua regia. After repeating the distillation four times, he exploded the residue of cubic saltpeter (sodium nitrate) with charcoal dust in a red-hot crucible. On dissolving the residue, he obtained "the crystalline salt of an alkali, as in the foregoing process" (46). He concluded that "soda is certainly nothing other than the true base of sea salt; this is shown by the habitat of soda plants" (46).

In an attempt to find out whether the presence of soda or potash depended on a specific difference in the plants which produce them or on the composition of the soils, du Hamel devoted many years to agricultural experiments, at his estate at Denainvilliers, on the culture of the common saltwort (*Salsola kali*), a plant used for the manufacture of soda ash. The final analyses of the ash of this plant proved that in the first year the mineral alkali still predominated, but that in succeeding years the vegetable alkali rapidly increased until finally, after a few generations, the soda had almost disappeared (50). In these experiments, he had for many years the invaluable and enthusiastic help of his brother, M. de Denainvilliers. In his eulogy of du Hamel in the History of the Academy of Sciences, the Marquis de Condorcet gave the following characterizations of the two brothers:

While M. du Hamel wrote his books, consulted with scientists, kept up a correspondence with the most enlightened men in Europe, engaged in new scientific researches, and planned his experiments and observations, M. de Denainvilliers carried out, in his retreat, the observations and experiments which his brother had entrusted to him, always unknown and content to be so . . . . asking no other recompense than the pleasure of having done good. To judge M. du Hamel, one would have to see him at Denainvilliers, the fields covered with exotic productions which were enriching growers whose fathers had not known even the names of these useful and salutary plants, . . . forests filled with exotic trees brought from all countries of the globe, . . . all the instruments invented for observing nature and studying her laws, distributed in the mansions, in the gardens, in the parks; and in the midst of all these objects of instruction, two men united by the love of the good, different in character as in occupation . . . (50).

In his books, M. du Hamel reported his own experiments and their results, and also included much elementary information for the use of practical farmers. "At the age of fifty years," said Condorcet, "he was one of the best informed men in Europe in all the scientific branches with the applications of which he later occupied himself almost exclusively . . . and if he has often been justly cited to show what use scholars ought to make of their learning, one can also prove by his example that, in order rightfully to aspire to the honor of making the sciences useful, one must be very learned" (50). M. du Hamel "kept all his life the principles of religion he had received in his childhood; . . . to serve humankind, to penetrate nature's marvels, and to ascribe them to their Author, seemed to him, for a scientist and citizen, the most fitting exercise of piety" (50). He lived tranquilly with his nephews, one of whom shared his scientific labors. After the death of M. de Denainvilliers, these nephews and a niece relieved M. du Hamel of all domestic cares. He lived to be eighty-two years old.

Georg Brandt in 1746 prepared both crystalline and amorphous sodium carbonate and observed that the latter is not hygroscopic and that it crystallizes more readily than does potassium carbonate (47).

In 1758–59 A. S. Marggraf prepared very pure cubic saltpeter from common salt. "After cooling the vessel and breaking the retort," said he, "I found in it a saline substance which took fire on glowing charcoal, without the slightest crackling (just as ordinary saltpeter does when very pure) and, as the chemists say, detonated, but with the difference that the flame was yellow; for that with ordinary prismatic niter is usually whitish" (48). In his next paper, which was entitled "Proof that the alkaline part separated from common salt is a true alkaline salt and not an alkaline earth," he mentioned the yellow flash of gunpowder made with cubic saltpeter and the blue (violet) flash of that made with prismatic saltpeter (48).

Although chemists had long suspected that the alkaline earths are metallic oxides, the true nature of soda and potash was not surmised before the early nineteenth century (28). Lavoisier believed that they might contain nitrogen:

Up to the present [said he] the principal constituents of soda are no better known than those of potash. We are not even certain whether or not that substance is already formed in vegetables before combustion.   Analogy might lead us to believe that nitrogen is one of the principal constituents of alkalies in general, and we have the proof of it in the case of ammonia, as I shall explain; but as far as potash and soda are concerned, we have only slight presumptions, not yet confirmed by any decisive experiment (29).

From A. H. Norway's "Highways and Byways in Devon and Cornwall"

St. Michael's mount and Bay near Penzance, Cornwall, where Sir Humphry Davy was born.

In his list of elements Lavoisier mentioned thirty-three substances:

light	muriatic radical	copper	platinum
caloric	fluoric radical	tin	lead
oxygen	boric radical	iron	tungsten
nitrogen	antimony	manganese	zinc
hydrogen	silver	mercury	lime
sulfur	arsenic	molybdenum	magnesia
phosphorus	bismuth	nickel	baryta
carbon	cobalt	gold	alumina
			silica

In commenting on this list he said, "I have not included in this table the fixed alkalies, such as potash and soda, because these substances are evidently compound, although however the nature of the principles which enter into their composition is still unknown" (30).   The chemical nature

of these common alkalies remained unknown until the beginning of the
nineteenth century, when the brilliant young English chemist Humphry
Davy succeeded in decomposing both of them with his voltaic pile.

High above an azure bay on the rugged coast of Cornwall rises
lofty St. Michael's Mount, a gigantic rock surmounted by an ancient
turreted castle. The nearby town of Penzance in Mount's Bay may
suggest to lovers of light opera the adventurous pirates of Gilbert and
Sullivan, but chemists revere it as the birthplace of Sir Humphry Davy,
who once gave the following vivid picture of the scene so dear to him:

> The sober eve with purple bright
> Sheds o'er the hills her tranquil light
> In many a lingering ray;
> The radiance trembles on the deep,
> Where rises rough thy rugged steep,
> Old Michael, from the sea.
>
> Around thy base, in azure pride,
> Flows the silver-crested tide,
> In gently winding waves;
> The Zephyr creeps thy cliffs around,—
> Thy cliffs, with whispering ivy crown'd,—
> And murmurs in thy caves (2).

Humphry Davy was born on December 17, 1778. He was a healthy,
active, affectionate child, who made many friends by his knack of telling
stories and reciting original verses. His teacher, Dr. Cardew, said the
boy's best work was done in translating the classics into English verse (3).
Davy's schooling ended when he was only fifteen years old, but his education continued for the rest of his life. In 1795 he was apprenticed to
Bingham Borlase, a surgeon and apothecary in Penzance, and two years
later he began to study natural philosophy and chemistry (20). His
textbook was Lavoisier's "Elements of Chemistry," his reagents were
the mineral acids and the alkalies, and his apparatus consisted largely
of wine glasses and tobacco pipes. When he was twenty years old Davy
became superintendent of the Pneumatic Institution which Dr. Thomas
Beddoes had recently established at Clifton for studying the medicinal
value of gases. He was most happy in sharing the delightful home life
of Dr. Beddoes and the social contacts with such distinguished literary
men as Robert Southey and Samuel Taylor Coleridge (4).

In 1801 Count Rumford (Benjamin Thompson) obtained for Davy a
position as assistant lecturer on chemistry and director of the laboratory
at the Royal Institution. In the *Philosophical Magazine* one finds the
following description of Davy's first lecture, which was on galvanism:

Sir Joseph Banks, Count Rumford and other distinguished philosophers were present. The audience was highly gratified, and testified their satisfaction by general applause. Mr. Davy, who appears to be very young, acquitted himself admirably well. From the sparkling intelligence of his eye, his animated manner, and the tout ensemble, we have no doubt of his attaining distinguished excellence (5).

Literary persons and the members of fashionable society, as well as scientists, flocked to his lectures. Davy kept a careful record of all his experiments and showed it willingly to all who were interested. He remained with the Royal Institution for eleven years, and then retired at the time of his marriage.

Dr. Thomas Beddoes, 1760–1808. English physician and chemist. Founder of the Pneumatic Institution at Clifton for studying the therapeutic value of gases. Sir Humphry Davy became the superintendent of this institution at the age of twenty years.

Humphry Davy's greatest successes were in the field of electrochemistry. In his first attempts to decompose the caustic alkalies, he used saturated aqueous solutions, but succeeded in decomposing nothing but the water. On October 6, 1807, however, he changed his plan of attack. "The presence of water appearing thus to prevent any decomposition," said he, "I used potash in igneous fusion" (22, 23, 26).

To his great surprise he noticed intense light at the negative pole and a column of flame rising from the point of contact. When he reversed the current the flame came always from the negative pole. Since perfectly dry potash is a non-conductor, Davy gave it a brief exposure to the air:

A small piece of potash [said he], which had been exposed for a few seconds to the atmosphere so as to give conducting power to the surface, was placed upon an insulated disc of platina, connected with the negative side of the battery of the power of 250 of 6 and 4, in a state of intense activity; and a platina wire, communicating with the positive side, was brought in contact with the upper surface of the alkali. The whole apparatus was in the open atmosphere.

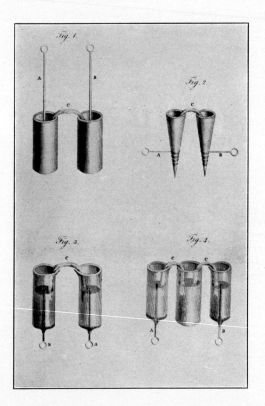

Electrochemical Apparatus of Sir Humphry Davy. Fig. 1. Agate cups. Fig. 2. Gold cones. Fig. 3. Glass tubes. Fig. 4. The two glass tubes with the intermediate vessel. In all the figures, *AB* denote the wires, one positive and one negative; and *C* the connecting pieces of moistened amianthus.

Under these circumstances [said Davy] a vivid action was soon observed to take place. The potash began to fuse at both its points of electrization. There was a violent effervescence at the upper surface; at the lower, or negative, surface, there was no liberation of elastic fluid; but small globules having a high metallic lustre, and being precisely similar in visible characters to quicksilver, appeared, some of which burnt with explosion and bright flame, as soon as they were formed, and others remained, and were merely tarnished, and finally covered by a white film which formed on their surfaces.

These globules, numerous experiments soon shewed to be the substance I was in search of, and a peculiar inflammable principle the basis of potash. I found that the platina was in no way connected with the result, except as the medium for exhibiting the electrical powers of decomposition; and a substance of the same kind was produced when pieces of copper, silver, gold, plumbago, or even charcoal were employed for compleating the circuit.

The little metallic globules always appeared at the cathode, and these had an astonishing way of bursting into flame when thrown into water. They skimmed about excitedly with a hissing sound, and soon burned with a lovely lavender light. Davy found that the new metal

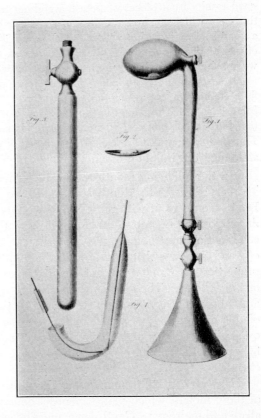

Apparatus of Sir Humphry Davy. Fig. 1. Retort of plate glass for heating potassium in gases. Fig. 2. Platinum tray for receiving the potassium. Fig. 3. Platinum tube for receiving the tray in distillation experiments. Fig. 4. Apparatus for taking the voltaic spark in sulfur and phosphorus

liberated hydrogen from the water and that the flame was caused by the burning of this gas (*6, 23*). Because he had obtained the metal from potash, he named it *potassium*. Dr. John Davy, who was present when potassium was isolated for the first time, said that his brother became greatly excited and almost delirious with joy (*7, 19*).

In 1811 the Irish-American chemist William James MacNeven published in the *American Philosophical and Medical Register* an article on the decomposition of potash in which he described the preparation of potassium metal by reduction of potash with iron turnings in a sealed gun barrel (71).

After his successful decomposition of caustic potash Humphry Davy attempted to decompose caustic soda by a similar method, and found that a larger current was required (6), or, as he himself expressed it, that "the decomposition demanded greater intensity of action in the batteries, or the alkali was required to be in much thinner and smaller pieces":

With the battery of 100 of 6 inches in full activity [he explained] I obtained good results from pieces of potash weighing from 40 to 70 grains, and of a thickness which made the distance of the electrified metallic surfaces nearly a quarter of an inch; but with a similar power it was impossible to produce the effects of decomposition on pieces of soda of more than 15 or 20 grains in weight, and that only when the distance between the wires was about one-eighth or one-tenth of an inch. The substance produced from potash remained fluid at the temperature of the atmosphere at the time of its production; that from soda, which was fluid in the degree of heat of the alkali during its formation, became solid on cooling, and appeared having the lustre of silver (23, 24). Thus only a few days after the discovery of potassium Davy was able to announce the isolation of another new metal, which he named sodium.

In the following month the Quaker chemist William Allen wrote in his diary: "Eleventh Month 16th.—Went to the Royal Institution to see Davy.—Pepys went with me. He showed us his new experiments on the decomposition of potash and soda. From the oxygen, or zinc end of a combination of troughs, pure potash was decomposed, oxygen driven off, and a new substance produced, in little globules, which has the properties of a metal, except that its specific gravity is only sixteen, or thereabouts. The globule explodes and ignites in contact with water, and, absorbing oxygen from it, returns to the state of alkali. One part of this new substance amalgamates with, and fixes, forty-eight parts of quicksilver. Pepys and I concluded we would cheerfully have walked fifty miles to see the experiment. Here is another grand discovery in chemistry" (72).

However, it still remained for Davy to prove the elementary nature of these metals, which many chemists believed to be compounds of the alkali and hydrogen. Gay-Lussac and Thenard argued, for example, that, since ammonium = ammonia + hydrogen, potassium = potash + hydrogen. It was finally proved, however, that no hydrogen can be evolved from potassium, and that Davy was correct in regarding sodium and potassium as elements (8).

Mr. A. Combes, one of Davy's admirers, communicated some interesting comments on this discovery to Nicholson's Journal (27):

I attended his course of lectures of 1807 [said Mr. Combes] and in referring to my notes I find that he stated it as a fact, that all bodies of known com-

Edgar Fahs Smith Memorial Collection, University of Pennsylvania

A Letter by Sir Humphry Davy in which he introduces Mme. Lavoisier de Rumford to Dr. Ure of Glasgow.

position attracted by the negative pole in the Voltaic circuit consisted principally of inflammable matter, and were naturally positive; and that it was probable therefore, that all bodies of unknown composition attracted by this pole, and which were naturally positive, might also contain inflammable matter.   In his lectures in 1801,* he stated, that, in looking for *inflammable matter* after those ideas in the fixed alkalies, he had *discovered* it, and that he had likewise found what he had not expected, that it was metallic in its nature.   In this instance sagacious conjecture and sound analogy were followed up by experimental research, and ended in a great discovery.

* This date as given in *Nicholson's Journal* is obviously incorrect.

Davy's isolation of the alkali metals was brilliant in every sense of the word. It soon led to the discovery of the alkaline earth metals by a similar electrochemical method; and the alkali metals themselves were destined to become powerful tools in the search for other elements.

LITHIUM*

At the close of the eighteenth century, the great Brazilian scientist and statesman Jozé Bonifácio de Andrada e Silva made a mineralogical journey through Scandinavia (*41*). He was born on June 13, 1763, at Vila de Santos near Rio de Janeiro, the eldest of three gifted brothers, all of whom were sent to the University of Coímbra, Portugal, to complete their education.

Jozé Bonifácio de Andrada E Silva, 1763–1838. Brazilian scientist, statesman and poet. Discoverer of petalite and spodumene, minerals in which Arfwedson discovered lithium. He worked tirelessly to improve the social conditions of the dispossessed Indians and enslaved Negroes and to bring about their gradual emancipation.

Sisson, Gal. dos Brazileiros Illus., 186
A. Sisson, lith.

On recommendation of the Duke of Lafões, Jozé Bonifácio was elected to the Academy of Sciences and in 1790 was sent on a journey through France, Germany, the Netherlands, Scandinavia, Bohemia, Hungary, Turkey, and Italy to study under A.-L Lavoisier, A.-F. de Fourcroy, Laurent Jussieu, the Abbé R.-J. Haüy, A. G. Werner, and Alessandro Volta. In 1800 he returned to Coímbra to teach metallurgy (*51, 52, 53*). In a letter to Mine Surveyor Beyer of Schneeberg, which

* See also Chapter 19, pp. 494–502.

was published in January, 1800 in *Scherer's Journal,* de Andrada described an infusible, laminated mineral from Utö, Sala, and the Finngruva near New Kopparberg, which he called petalite and which dissolved in nitric acid very slowly and without effervescence, and another new mineral which he called spodumene (*34*).

After returning to Brazil in 1819, de Andrada became Minister of State and was a signer of the Brazilian constitution. Like many a great scientist of today, he was obliged to live for several years in exile, but these were spent in quiet study in France. When he again returned to Brazil, the abdicating Emperor Dom Pedro I confided to him the care and education of the royal heirs. De Andrada spent the closing years of his life in retirement on an island in the Bay of Rio de Janeiro and died at Niterói (Nictheroy) on April 6, 1838 (*51, 52, 54*).

He was a versatile scientist and linguist, a gifted poet, and a great statesman and humanitarian sincerely devoted to the best interests of his fellow countrymen. He worked tirelessly to improve the social conditions of the dispossessed Indians and the slaves and bring about their gradual emancipation. He was a positivist, or disciple of Auguste Comte, and is known to Brazilians as "the father of independence" (*41*). A fine biography of him was published in 1938 by a Brazilian author, Venâncio de Figueiredo Neiva (*41*).

Mineralogists long remained in doubt as to the existence of petalite until E. T. Svedenstjerna rediscovered it in 1817 on Utö (an island in Sweden), thus confirming the original discovery by de Andrada (*36*).

N.-L. Vauquelin's analysis of spodumene, which the Abbé Haüy published in his "Traité de Minéralogie" in 1801, showed a loss of 9.5 per cent, which was never correctly interpreted until J. A. Arfwedson in 1818 discovered a new alkali metal, lithium, first in petalite, and soon after in spodumene and in lepidolite (*35*). Even before the discovery of lithium, Johann Nepomuk von Fuchs observed the red color which spodumene imparts to the flame; he afterward expressed chagrin because he had neglected to investigate the cause of this color (*36*). Vauquelin detected the presence of an alkali in a specimen of petalite obtained from the metallurgist E. T. Svedenstjerna, but mistook it for potash (*13, 37*). Wilhelm Hisinger also analyzed this mineral at least as early as January, 1818, and obtained preliminary results similar to those of Arfwedson (*38*). When the Reverend Edward Daniel Clarke of the University of Cambridge analyzed a specimen of it in the same year, his results showed a puzzling "loss" of 1.75 per cent, the reason for which became evident as soon as Arfwedson's analysis was published (*39, 40*).

Johan August Arfwedson, the discoverer of lithium, was born at Skagerholms-Bruk, Skaraborgs Län, on January 12, 1792 (*10*). He studied chemistry under Berzelius, and it was in the latter's famous

Stockholm laboratory that he made this great discovery at the age of twenty-five years. Berzelius described this chemical event in a letter to C.-L. Berthollet written on February 9, 1818:

The new alkali [said he] was discovered by Mr. Arfvedson, a very skillful young chemist who has been working in my laboratory for a year. He found this alkali in a rock previously discovered by Mr. d'Andrada in the mine at Utö and named by him petalite. This rock consists in round numbers, of 80% silica, 17% alumina, and 3% of the new alkali. To extract the latter from it one uses the ordinary method of heating the pulverized rock with barium carbonate and separating from it all the earths. . . .

This alkali [continued Berzelius] has a greater capacity for saturating acids than the other fixed alkalies, and even surpasses magnesia. It is by this cir-

Edward Daniel Clarke, 1769–1822. English mineralogist and traveler. One of the founders of the Cambridge Philosophical Society. One of the first chemists to analyze the lithium mineral petalite. His "Travels in Various Countries of Europe, Asia, and Africa" contains intimate glimpses of many contemporary scientists and their laboratories. See ref. (49).

Engraved by W. T. Fry from an original picture by J. Opie, R.A.

cumstance that it was discovered. For the salt with the [new] alkali as base, obtained by analysis, exceeds greatly in weight what it ought to have weighed if its base had been soda or potash. It was very natural to conclude that a salt with an alkali base which is not precipitated at all by tartaric acid ought to contain soda. So did Arfvedson at first, but, having repeated the analysis of the petalite three times with exactly the same results, he thought he ought to examine each constituent more thoroughly, and it is in consequence of such an examination that he noticed that the alkaline substance had properties different from other alkalies. We have given this alkali the name of lithion [lithia] to recall that it was discovered in the mineral kingdom, whereas the two others were [discovered] in the vegetable kingdom (11).

Arfwedson's own account of his analysis of petalite is to be found in the *Annales de Chimie et de Physique* for 1819. He found that it contained silica, alumina, and an alkali metal which he tried to determine by weighing it as the sulfate.

But [said he] it was still necessary to learn the base of the salt. Its solution could not be precipitated either by tartaric acid in excess or by platinum chloride. Consequently it could not be potassium. I mixed another portion of a solution of the same salt with a few drops of pure potash, but without its becoming cloudy. Therefore it contained no more magnesia: hence it must be a salt with soda for a base. I calculated the quantity of soda which would be necessary to form it; but it always resulted in an excess of about 5 parts in 100 of the mineral analyzed. Therefore, since it seemed probable to me that the different substances might not have been well washed, or that the analysis might not have been made with sufficient precision in other respects, I repeated it twice more with all the care possible, but always with results very little different. I obtained: Silica: 78.45, 79.85; Alumina: 17.20, 17.30; Sulfate: 19.50, 17.75. At last, having studied this sulfate more closely, I soon found that it contained a definite fixed alkali, whose nature had not previously been known (*21*).

Petalite is now known to be lithium aluminum silicate, $LiAl(Si_2O_5)_2$.

On April 22, 1818, Berzelius wrote to his London friend Dr. Marcet that Arfwedson had also found lithium in spodumene and lepidolite, and that the former contains about 8 per cent of this metal, whereas the latter contains about 4 per cent. In the spring of the memorable year (1824) that Friedrich Wöhler spent at Stockholm, he accompanied a distinguished group of Swedish chemists, including Berzelius, Wilhelm Hisinger, Arfwedson, and C. Retzius, on a holiday excursion to Utö Island, about two miles out from shore in the Baltic Sea. The island interested them greatly, not only because of its rich iron mines, but also because of its rare minerals, including petalite and spodumene, in which Arfwedson had found the new alkali metal (*9*). Lepidolite is also found on this island (*12*).

Arfwedson also studied the most important lithium salts, and his results were quickly confirmed by Vauquelin (*13*). Lithium differs from potassium in that it does not give a precipitate with tartaric acid, and from sodium in that its carbonate is only sparingly soluble. The beautiful red color which lithium salts impart to a flame was first observed in 1818 by C. G. Gmelin (*14, 25*).

Arfwedson and Gmelin tried in vain to isolate lithium metal. After failing to reduce the oxide by heating it with iron or carbon, they tried to electrolyze its salts, but their voltaic pile was not sufficiently powerful (*14*). W. T. Brande succeeded in decomposing lithia with a powerful battery and obtained a white, combustible metal, and Davy also obtained a small amount of lithium in the same manner (*14, 15, 31, 32, 33*).

Although these early investigators obtained only an extremely small quantity of the metal, R. Bunsen and A. Matthiessen succeeded in 1855 in preparing enough of it for a thorough study of its properties (16). They accomplished the reduction by heating pure lithium chloride in a small thick-walled porcelain crucible with a spirit lamp such as Berzelius used, while a current from four to six carbon-zinc elements (Bunsen cells) was passed through the molten mass. After a few seconds they saw a fused, silver-white regulus form at the cathode and build up in two or three minutes to the size of a pea. They carefully removed the globule with an iron spoon, placed it under petroleum, and repeated the operation every three minutes until they had reduced an ounce of lithium chloride (16). They also showed that lithium, although it was first found in the mineral kingdom, is widely distributed in all three of the natural realms.

That the famous mineralogist, the Abbé Haüy, held Arfwedson in high esteem is evident from his letter of June 13, 1820, in which he said to Berzelius, "Be so kind, Monsieur, as to offer to M. Arfvedson, of whom it suffices to say that he is your worthy pupil, the assurance of the profound esteem and distinguished respect which I bear him" (17).

In the same year Arfwedson bought an ironworks (forge de feu) and a large estate at Hedensö in the province of Södermanland, which caused Berzelius to fear lest this promising young chemist might abandon his scientific career (17). Perhaps his misgivings were well founded, for Thomas Thomson, after mentioning Arfwedson's experiments on the oxides of uranium* and on the action of hydrogen on metallic sulfates, said, "He has likewise analyzed a considerable number of minerals with great care; but of late years he seems to have lost his activity. His analysis of chrysoberyl does not possess the accuracy of the rest; by some inadvertence, he has taken a compound of glucina and alumina for silica" (18). Arfwedson died at his Hedensö estate on October 28, 1841 (10).

Gustaf Flink once said "Petalite can be said to be an almost exclusively Swedish mineral, for in foreign localities, Elba, and a few places in North America, it has occurred as a great rarity. In the Utö mines, however, it occurs in well-nigh inexhaustible amounts" (35). The first petalite found in America was described in 1824 by Gerard Troost, a native of the Netherlands, who studied mineralogy under the Abbé R.-J. Haüy and later became a naturalized citizen of the United States, a founder of the Academy of Natural Sciences in Philadelphia, and professor of chemistry at the Philadelphia College of Pharmacy (55). When Dr. Troost analyzed a Canadian mineral presented to him by Dr. Bigsby,

* See Chapter 9, p. 267 and Chapter 19, pp. 500–01.

he found that an alcoholic solution of it "burned with a red flame of a more dense colour than that of Strontian . . . Dr. Bigsby received a specimen of this mineral in 1820 from Dr. Lyons, now of Montreal, together with other rolled rock masses, and considered it a Tremolite. In 1823 he visited the locality . . . The Petalite occurs on the north shore of lake Ontario, on the beach in front of York, the capital of Upper Canada, a few yards to the right of the wharf used by the steamboat Frontinac [sic] . . ." (56).

In 1823 Thomas Nuttall discovered spodumene at Sterling, Massachusetts. The Journal of the Philadelphia Academy of Natural Sciences for 1824 stated that "Mr. Nuttall, in a letter to Dr. Hays, dated November 22, 1823, communicates his having discovered, whilst on a mineralogical excursion during the last summer, a mineral which he considers to be Spodumen [sic]. As this mineral had never been previously found in the United States, the following notice will probably be interesting. The Spodumen occurs on the farm of Mr. Putnam, in Sterling, Massachusetts, where it is found abundantly in a Granitic rock, composed principally of hyaline Quartz and Mica, the Spodumen supplying the place usually occupied by Feldspar. . . Mr. George Bowen, who examined this mineral, and ascertained that it contains lithia, lately discovered the same mineral in a collection of specimens from the vicinity of Deerfield, Massachusetts . . ." (57).

Mr. Bowen fused the pulverized mineral with caustic potash, dissolved the melt in hydrochloric acid, evaporated the solution to dryness, and digested the residue with warm alcohol. "That it was really the muriate of lithia," said Bowen, "was evident from its tingeing the flame of alcohol of a deep crimson colour; and from its affording, when added to a concentrated solution of carbonate of soda, an abundant precipitate of carbonate of lithia. The precise locality of the Spodumen from Deerfield, I am not able to point out . . ." (57).

Lithium in Natural Waters. In 1825–26 Berzelius determined the lithium content of several mineral waters from Bohemia and found as much as a centigram of lithium carbonate "in every bottle" of the water from the Kreuzbrunn Spring at Marienbad (58, 59, 60). One of the first spectroscopic analyses ever made resulted in the detection of lithium in sea water. In a letter to Sir Henry Roscoe written on November 15, 1859, Robert Bunsen mentioned that the spectroscope could be used to determine the chemical composition of the sun and fixed stars. "Substances on the earth," he added, "can be determined by this method just as easily as on the sun, so that, for example, I have been able to detect lithium in twenty grams of sea water" (61).

Lithium in Plants and Animals. Although Berzelius and Arfwedson named the new alkali *lithia* because it was first discovered in the mineral kingdom, it was found to exist in all three of the natural realms. In 1860 G. R. Kirchhoff and Robert Bunsen detected it in the ash of the grape, in farm products from the Palatinate, and in kelp from the Gulf Stream and the coast of Scotland (58, 62). They stated that "all the ashes we investigated of wood grown on granitic soil in the Odenwald, as well as Russian and other commercial potashes, contain lithium. Even in the ashes of tobacco, of the grape leaf, vine, and grapes, as well as in the ash of farm products which were raised on non-granitic soils in the Rhine Valley near Waghäusel, Deidesheim, and Heidelberg and in the milk of animals nourished on these products, lithium is not lacking" (62, 63). In the following year they demonstrated its presence spectroscopically in the ash of the milk and blood of animals which had been fed plants from the Palatinate (58, 64).

In 1867 H. Ritthausen discovered lithium in the marl and arable soil at Weitzdorf, East Prussia (58, 63, 65). Other investigators afterward detected it in many other soils, and in 1915 L. A. Steinkoenig and W. O. Robinson found it to be present in every American soil which they analyzed (58, 66, 65).

In 1918 these two chemists and C. F. Miller analyzed about fifty samples of legumes, grasses (including grains), vegetables, trees, and shrubs grown in nine different soils of known composition or from localities where certain rare elements were known to occur. Lithium was found in spectroscopic traces in all the plants they examined (67).

In 1880 C. Schiapparelli and G. Peroni showed that lithium also occurs in normal human urine (68). Alexandre Desgrez (1863–1940) and J. Meunier showed in 1927 that human bones and teeth contain lithium phosphate (69, 70).

LITERATURE CITED

(1) DAVY, DR. JOHN, "The Collected Works of Sir Humphry Davy, Bart., Vol. 1, Smith, Elder and Co., London, 1839, p. 117. Quotation from Sir H. D.

(2) PARIS, J. A., "Life of Sir Humphry Davy, Bart.," Vol. 1, Colburn and Bentley, London, 1831, pp. 33–4. Ode to St. Michael's Mount in Cornwall.

(3) DAVY, J., "The Collected works of Sir Humphry Davy, Bart.," ref. (1), Vol. 1, pp. 10–1.

(4) Ibid., p. 51.

(5) Ibid., p. 88.

(6) JAGNAUX, R., "Histoire de la Chimie," Vol. 2, Baudry et Cie., Paris, 1891, pp. 68–73.

(7) DAVY, J., "The Collected Works of Sir Humphry Davy, Bart.," ref. (1), Vol. 1, p. 109.

(8) FÄRBER, E., "Geschichtliche Entwicklung der Chemie," Springer, Berlin, 1921, pp. 116–9.

(9) WÖHLER, F., "Early recollections of a chemist," Am. Chemist, 6, 131 (Oct., 1875).

(10) POGGENDORFF, J. C., "Biographisch-Literarisches Handwörterbuch zur Geschichte der exakten Wissenschaften," 6 vols., Verlag Chemie, Leipzig and Berlin, 1863–1937. Article on Arfvedson [sic].

(11) SÖDERBAUM, H. G., "Jac. Berzelius Bref," Vol. 1, part 1, Almqvist and Wiksells, Upsala, 1912–1914, pp. 63–4; "Lettre de M. Berzelius à M. Berthollet sur deux Métaux nouveaux," Ann. chim. phys., (2), 7, 199–201 (1818).

(12) SÖDERBAUM, H. G., "Jac. Berzelius Bref," ref. (11), Vol. 1, part 3, pp. 171–2.

(13) VAUQUELIN, NICOLAS-LOUIS, "Note sur une nouvelle espèce d'Alcali minéral," Ann. chim. phys., (2), 7, 284–8 (1818).

(14) JAGNAUX, R., "Histoire de la Chimie," ref. (6), Vol. 2, pp. 124–9.

(15) GMELIN, L., "Handbuch der theoretischen Chemie," ersten Bandes zweite Abtheilung, dritte Auflage, F. Varrantrapp, Frankfurt am Main, 1826, pp. 597–8; W. T. BRANDE, "Manual of Chemistry," Vol. 2, John Murray, London, 1821, p. 57; Scherer's Allgem. Nordische Ann. der Chemie, 8, 120 (1822).

(16) BUNSEN, R., "Darstellung des Lithiums," Ann., 94, 107–10 (1855).

(17) SÖDERBAUM, H. G., "Jac. Berzelius Bref," ref. (11), Vol. 3, part 2, p. 165.

(18) THOMSON, THOMAS, "History of Chemistry," Vol. 2, Colburn and Bentley London, 1831, p. 229.

(19) GREGORY, J. C., "The Scientific Achievements of Sir Humphry Davy," Oxford University Press, London, 1930, pp. 37–57.

(20) Ibid., pp. iii–vii and 1–9.

(21) ARFWEDSON, J. A., "Analyses de quelques minéraux de la mine d'Utò en Suède, dans lesquels on a trouvé un nouvel alcali fixe," Ann. chim. phys., (2), 10, 82–107 (1819); Afhandlingar i Kemi, Fysik och Mineralogie, 6, (1818); Sci. News Letter, 18, No. 493, 186 (Sept. 20, 1930).

(22) DAVY, H., "The decomposition of the fixed alkalies and alkaline earths," Sci. News Letter, 14, No. 390, 201–2 (Sept. 29, 1928).

(23) DAVY, H., "The Decomposition of the Fixed Alkalies and Alkaline Earths," Alembic Club Reprint No. 6, Univ. of Chicago Press, Chicago, 1902, 51 pp.

(24) DAVY, H., "The Bakerian lecture, on some new phenomena of chemical changes produced by electricity, particularly the decomposition of the fixed alkalies, etc.," Sci. News Letter, 18, No. 493, 186–7 (Sept. 20, 1930).

(25) KOPP, H., "Geschichte der Chemie," Vol. 4, F. Vieweg und Sohn, Braunschweig, 1847, p. 41.

(26) BROCKMAN, C. J., "Fused electrolytes—an historical sketch," J. Chem. Educ., 4, 512–23 (April, 1927).

(27) COMBES, A., "Second letter on the subject of the new metals," Nicholson's J., 21, 365 (Suppl., 1808).

(28) DAVY, H., "Electro-chemical researches, on the decomposition of the earths; with observations on the metals obtained from the alkaline earths, and on the amalgam procured from ammonia," Nicholson's J., 21, 366–83 (Suppl., 1808).

(29) "Oeuvres de Lavoisier," Vol. 1, Imprimerie Impériale, Paris, 1864, pp. 119–20.

(30) Ibid., Vol. 1, pp. 135 and 137.

(31) THOMSON, T., "History of Chemistry," ref. (18), Vol. 2, pp. 264–5; Annals of Philos., (1), 12, 16 (July, 1818).

(32) WEEKS, M. E. and M. E. LARSON, "J. A. Arfwedson and his services to chemistry," J. Chem. Educ., 14, 403–7 (Sept., 1937).

(33) ARFWEDSON, J. A., "Undersökning af någre mineralier," K. Vet. Acad. Handl., 1822, pp. 87–94; Annals of Philos., 23, 343–8 (May, 1824).

(34) DE ANDRADA, J. B., "Kurze Angabe der Eigenschaften und Kennzeichen einiger neuen Fossilien aus Schweden und Norwegen, nebst einigen chemischen Bemerkungen über dieselben," Scherer's Allg. J. der Chemie, 4, 28–39 (Jan., 1800).

(35) FLINK, G., "Bidrag till Sveriges mineralogi," Arkiv för Kemi, Mineralogi och Geologi, 5, 21, 221–2 (1914).

(36) von Kobell, Franz, "Bibliography of Johann Nepomuk von Fuchs," *Am. J. Sci.*, (2), **23**, 99 (1857).

(37) Vauquelin, Nicolas-Louis, *Schw. J.*, **21**, 397–401 (1817).

(38) Söderbaum, H. G., ref. (*11*), Vol. 8, pp. 50–1. Letter of Berzelius to Hisinger, Jan. 12, 1818.

(39) Gmelin, C. G., "Analysis of petalite and examination of the chemical properties of lithia," *Annals of Philos.*, **15**, 341–51 (May, 1820).

(40) Clarke, E. D., "Description and analysis of a substance called petalite, from Sweden," *Annals of Philos.*, **11**, 196–8 (March, 1818); *Ibid.*, **11**, 365–6 (May, 1818).

(41) Neiva, Venâncio de Figueiredo, "Rezumo Biográfio de Jozé Bonifácio de Andrada e Silva, o Patriarca da Independência do Brazil," Irmãos Pongetti, Rio de Janeiro, **1938**, 305 pp.

(42) Kopp, H., ref. (*25*), Vol. 4, pp. 3–41.

(43) Cullen, Edmund, "Physical and Chemical Essays Translated from the Original Latin of Sir Torbern Bergman," Vol. 1, J. Murray, Balfour, Gordon, and Dickson, London, **1784**, p. 21; *ibid.*, Vol. 2, footnote to p. 438.

(44) Bohnius, D. Joh., "Dissertationes Chymico-Physicae," Thomas Fritsch, Leipzig, **1696**, pp. 381–2.

(45) Boerhaave, H., "Elemens de Chymie," Vol. 1, Chardon, fils, Paris, **1754**, pp. 188, 197.

(46) du Hamel du Monceau, H.-L., "Ueber die Basis des Seesalzes," *Crell's Neues chem. Archiv.*, **4**, 166–70 (1785); *Hist. de l'acad. roy. des sciences* (Paris), **1736**, p. 89.

(47) "Recueil des mémoires de chymie . . . dans les actes de l'acad. des sci. de Stokolm (sic) . . .," Vol. 2, pp. 515–7; G. Brandt, "Observations et expériences sur les différences qui se trouve entre la soude et la potasse," *Mém. de l'acad. roy. de Suède*, Vol. 8 (1746).

(48) Marggraf, A. S., "Chymische Schriften," revised ed., Vol. 1, Arnold Wever, Berlin, **1768**, pp. 134–78.

(49) Obituary of Edward Daniel Clarke, Annual Register, **1822**, pp. 274–6.

(50) Browne, C. A., "Historical notes upon the domestic potash industry in early Colonial and later times," *J. Chem. Educ.*, **3**, 749–56 (July, 1926).

(51) Fletcher, J. C. and D. P. Kidder, "Brazil and the Brazilians . . .," Little, Brown and Co., Boston, **1879**, pp. 72–5, 83, 215, 224, 373–6.

(52) Wilgus, A. C., "Modern Hispanic America," George Washington University Press, Washington, D. C., **1933**, pp. 71, 115–6.

(53) "Grande enciclopédia portuguesa e brasileira," Vol. 2, Editorial Enciclopédia, Ltd., Lisbon and Rio de Janeiro, not dated, pp. 525–6.

(54) "Nouvelle biographie générale," Vol. 2, Firmin Didot Frères, Paris, **1855**, columns 539–45. Article on de Andrada by Ferdinand Denis.

(55) Smith, Edgar F., "Chemistry in old Philadelphia," J. B. Lippincott Co., Philadelphia, **1919**, pp. 82–3.

(56) Troost, G., "Description of the American petalite from Lake Ontario," *J. Acad. Natural Sciences* (*Philadelphia*), **3**, (2), 234–7 (1824).

(57) "Notices of American spodumene," *ibid.*, **3**, (2), 284–6 (1824).

(58) "Gmelin's Handbuch der anorganischen Chemie," 8th ed., Vol. 20, Verlag Chemie, Berlin, **1927**, pp. 1–14; Vol. 2, pp. 1–9; Vol. 21, pp. 1–41.

(59) "Lithia in mineral water," *Quarterly J. Sci. and the Arts*, **21**, 176 (1826); *Annals of Philos.*, new series, **11**, 69, 145–6 (Jan., Feb., 1826).

(60) Söderbaum, H. G., Ref. (*11*), Vol. 2, p. 61. Letter of Berzelius to Dulong, July 5, 1825.

(61) Ostwald, Wilhelm, "Männer der Wissenschaft. R. W. Bunsen," Verlag von Wilhelm Weicher, Leipzig, **1905**, pp. 13–22.

(62) Kirchhoff, G. R. and R. Bunsen, "Chemische Analyse durch Spectralbeobachtungen," *Pogg. Ann.*, **110**, 171–2 (1860).

(63) RITTHAUSEN, H., "Lithionhaltiger Mergel und Boden in Ostpreussen," *J. prakt. Chem.*, **102**, 371–3 (1867).

(64) KIRCHHOFF, G. R. and R. BUNSEN, "Chemische Analyse durch Spectralbeobachtungen," *Ann.*, **118**, 355 (1861).

(65) ROBINSON, W. O., "The inorganic composition of some important American soils," *U. S. Dept. Agric., Bull.* **122.**

(66) STEINKOENIG, L. A., "Lithium in soils," *J. Ind. Eng. Chem.*, **7**, 425–6 (May, 1915).

(67) ROBINSON, W. O., L. A. STEINKOENIG, and C. F. MILLER, "The relation of some of the rarer elements in soils and plants," *U. S. Dept. Agric., Bull.* **600** (1917).

(68) SCHIAPPARELLI, C. and G. PERONI, "Di alcuni nuovi componenti dell'urina umana normale," *Gazz. chim. ital.*, **10**, 390–2 (1880).

(69) DESGREZ, A. and J. MEUNIER, "Sur la présence du lithium et du strontium dans les dents et dans les os humains et sur leur état chimique," *Compt. rend.*, **185**, 160–3 (July 18, 1927).

(70) PERRIER, G., "Notice sur M. Alexandre Desgrez," *Compt. rend.*, **210**, 153–6 (Jan. 29, 1940); MICHEL POLONOVSKI, "Alexandre Desgrez (1863–1940)," *Bull. Soc. Chimie Biologique*, **22**, 334–6 (May–June, 1940).

(71) REILLY, DESMOND, "An Irish-American chemist, William James MacNeven, 1763–1841," *Chymia*, **2**, 17–26 (1949).

(72) ANON., "Life of William Allen, with selections from his correspondence," Vol. 1, Henry Longstreth, Philadelphia, **1847**, p. 66.

Johan August Arfwedson, 1792–1841. This lithograph by Fehr and Müller of Stockholm was labeled by Berzelius "Reskamraten Arfvedson" (traveling companion Arfvedson). Berzelius placed it in the manuscript of his travel diary "Reseanteckningar."

19

J. A. Arfwedson and his service to chemistry

Although the histories of chemistry devote but little space to the work of J. A. Arfwedson, the discoverer of lithium, Berzelius' correspondence, travel-diary, and autobiography contain much interesting information about him. The superb biography of Berzelius which H. G. Söderbaum completed near the close of his life also throws much light on Arfwedson's chemical activity.

J ohan August Arfwedson was born in January, 1792,* (1, 2), on the family estate at Skagerholms-Bruk in Skaraborg County, Sweden. Until the age of fourteen, he was educated at home, and in 1806 he entered the college (högskolan) at Upsala. After completing the mining course at Upsala and the mining examination, he entered the Royal Bureau of Mines at Stockholm, where he served as secretary at the Bureau, and still found time to carry on research in chemical analysis in Berzelius' famous laboratory. When the twenty-five-year-old Arfwedson entered this laboratory early in 1817, he had among his classmates Count H. G. Trolle-Wachtmeister, ten years his senior, and Lieutenant C. A. Arrhenius, the discoverer of gadolinite, who was then sixty years of age.

Arfwedson immediately set to work analyzing meionite and leucite (3, 4, 5). He observed that although the leucite was very infusible, the meionite melted readily before the blowpipe, swelled, and formed an enamel. Since his analysis of meionite agreed closely with Klaproth's analysis of leucite, Arfwedson analyzed a specimen of leucite and found these two minerals to be very similar in composition, except that the leucite contained no lime. Suspecting, therefore, that the lime must be the cause of the meionite's fusibility, he mixed a little lime with the leucite, after which it, too, could be easily melted.

In the autumn of the same year, Arfwedson completed a beautiful research on the oxides of manganese. He determined the per cent of

This chapter was originally presented by Mary E. Larson and the author before the Divisions of History of Chemistry and Chemical Education at the Midwest Regional Meeting of the A. C. S., Omaha, Nebraska, April 30, 1937.
* Söderbaum (1) and Leijonhufvud (2) give the date of Arfwedson's birth as January 4th; the unsigned obituary (4) in the *Kongl. Vet. Acad. Handl.* gives it as January 12th.

manganese in the brown powder obtained by igniting manganous oxide and in the black powder, manganic oxide, obtained by evaporating this brown manganosic oxide with nitric acid and gently igniting the residue. Since he found it difficult to get the black powder of constant composition, he recommended that in analytical work the oxide should always be strongly ignited and weighed as manganosic (mangano-manganic) oxide, Mn_3O_4.

Arfwedson also observed that the ratio of the oxygen in manganous oxide to the oxygen in manganic oxide is as 1 to $1^1/_2$ a relation which the modern chemist expresses in the formulas MnO and Mn_2O_3. He realized that manganosic oxide must be a compound of these two oxides, and reasoned that "if this compound, like ferrous-ferric oxide, may be supposed to be of such composition that the oxide contains twice as much metal and three times as much oxygen as the protoxide, this compound consists of 72.82 per cent metal and 27.18 per cent oxygen. . . . I have called this oxide *oxidum manganoso-manganicum* because of its resemblance to ferroso-ferric oxide, the composition of which Herr Professor Berzelius described in his 'Attempt to lay the foundations of a purely scientific system for Mineralogy,' page 92."

Manganosic oxide is now known to contain only 72.03 per cent of manganese. Since Arfwedson obtained 1.0735 grams of manganosic oxide by igniting one gram of manganous oxide, which is in good agreement with the value now accepted (1.0752 grams), his experimental work must have been excellent. In computing the per cent of manganese in manganosic oxide, however, he made the mistake of accepting 21.88 per cent as the oxygen content of manganous oxide, a value which Professor Johann Friedrich John of Berlin had obtained by the analysis of manganous sulfate. Arfwedson determined the composition of manganous oxide by passing hydrogen chloride over a weighed portion of manganous carbonate, treating the resulting manganous chloride with an excess of silver nitrate, and weighing the silver chloride. Although his value of 22.14 per cent oxygen in manganous oxide was somewhat better than that of John (the value now accepted is 22.56 per cent), Arfwedson lacked confidence in it and stated, "I have reason to suspect a slight admixture of oxide in the muriate I investigated, and therefore the result of my analysis is probably less reliable." In September, 1817, Berzelius reported Arfwedson's research in letters to Dr. Marcet and Gay-Lussac (6), and in the following year Arfwedson published it in the *Afhandlingar i Fysik, Kemi och Mineralogi* (7), the editorial staff of which he had recently joined.

When he had completed the manganese research, Berzelius set him to work at analyzing a new mineral, petalite, from the iron mine on Utö, one of the many rocky islands or skerries which comprise Stockholm's superb archipelago. Arfwedson fused the petalite with potassium carbonate, determined the silica in the usual manner, and precipitated the alumina with ammonium carbonate. His analysis totaled only 96 per cent. Surprised to find such a large loss in such a simple analysis, he decomposed the petalite with barium carbonate. After removing the silica and alumina and the barium sulfate obtained by adding excess sulfuric acid, he evaporated the washings, volatilized the ammonium salts, and found a fused residue of a soluble, non-volatile sulfate. Since an aqueous solution of this salt gave no precipitate with tartaric acid, "platina solution," or caustic potash, the base could be neither potash nor magnesia. Arfwedson therefore assumed that the salt must be sodium sulfate, but when he calculated his results on that assumption, his analysis totaled about 105 per cent. Thinking that this excess weight must be due to improper washing of his precipitates, he repeated the analysis twice and obtained in duplicate determinations 19.500 and 17.75 per cent of the unknown sulfate.

In a letter to Wilhelm Hisinger, who was then analyzing the same mineral, Berzelius wrote on January 12, 1818, ". . . All these facts have led us to believe that petalite perhaps contains a new alkali . . . of such great saturating capacity that, when the salt is computed as a sodium salt, the excess in weight arises through the fact that the salt contains much less base than a sodium salt. If this be true, Arfwedson has had the good fortune to make in his second mineralogical analysis one of the most remarkable discoveries which can be made in this manner . . ." (3). Berzelius also announced Arfwedson's discovery of lithium to Dr. Marcet and Count Berthollet in the same letters in which he mentioned his own discovery of selenium (8). Arfwedson's announcement of the discovery was published in the *Afhandlingar* in the same year (9). According to Dr. Söderbaum (3), Berzelius himself deserves a great deal of credit for discovery of lithium as well as selenium, but was generous enough to let the lithium research be published under Arfwedson's name alone.

Arfwedson prepared lithium acetate, ignited it, and noted the insolubility of the resulting lithium carbonate in water and its action on platinum. He also prepared and studied the bicarbonate, sulfate, nitrate, chloride, tartrate, borate, hydroxide, and a double sulfate which he reported as lithium alum. He mentioned that lithium hydroxide is much less soluble than the other caustic alkalies and that it has a greater "saturation capacity" [lower equivalent weight] than they. Because of its ability to form deliquescent salts with nitric and hydrochloric acids, Arfwedson recognized the close relation between the new alkali and the alkaline earths, especially magnesia.

His attempt to decompose the new base with Berzelius' galvanic battery of fifty pairs of plates in an electrolyte of sodium chloride was unsuccessful.   As early as 1818, however, Sir Humphry Davy obtained a minute amount of lithium metal (10).   When he passed a current through fused lithium carbonate in a platinum capsule, "the alkali decomposed with bright scintillations, and the reduced metal being separated, afterward burnt.   The small particles which remained a few moments before they were reconverted into alkali . . . were . . . very similar to sodium.   A globule of quicksilver made negative and brought into contact with alkaline salt, soon became an amalgam of lithium, and had gained the power of acting on water. . . ."

Most standard works of reference also contain incomplete statements that lithium was isolated by Brande (or Brandes) and refer to Scher., 8, 120 or Schweigger's J., 8, 120.   The correct reference is Scherer's *Allgemeine Nordische Annalen der Chem.*, 8, 120 (1822), which merely states that W. T. Brande used a voltaic pile to prepare lithium as a shining, white, combustible metal and refers to the second London edition of his "Manual of Chemistry," Volume 2, page 57.   This edition was published by John Murray in 1821.   Brande's complete statement therein is as follows: "When lithia is submitted to the action of the Voltaic pile, it is decomposed with the same phenomena as potassa and soda; a brilliant white and highly combustible metallic substance is separated, which may be called *lithium,* the term *lithia* being applied to its oxide.   The properties of this metal have not hitherto been investigated, in consequence of the difficulty of procuring any quantity of its oxide."[*]

In 1821 Arfwedson published a supplementary note to his lithium research (11), in which he stated that the salt which he had previously reported as lithium acid sulfate must be the normal sulfate and that the double sulfate he had at first taken for lithium alum was really potassium alum resulting from a trace of potassium in his alumina.

In the summer of 1818 Arfwedson went to England, taking with him specimens of Berzelius' new element selenium to present to Dr. Marcet, Sir Humphry Davy, and Dr. W. H. Wollaston as gifts from the discoverer. Berzelius met him there later and accompanied him on visits to Dr. Wollaston, William Prout, Sir Joseph Banks, F. C. Accum, William Allen, and the geologist John Farey, Senior.   In company with Berzelius he studied at first hand the soda water, gas, and brewing industries of England.   In October of the same year the aged Abbé R.-J. Haüy of Paris entertained Berzelius and Arfwedson and gave them some inspiring lessons on mineralogy (12).

In June, 1819, Berzelius, Arfwedson, Alexandre and Adolphe Brongniart, and several other scientists made a geological tour of the Fontainebleau Forest and the country surrounding Clermont.   Part of the journey was made in a crowded diligence in which "Arfwedson's slender form became still more compressed."   At the inn in Clermont, Arfwedson,

[*] This may serve as a correction to "The Discovery of the Elements," 3rd ed., p. 125.

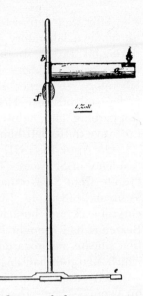

Berzelius' Blowpipe Lamp

From Berzelius' "Lehrbuch der Chemie"

N. V. Almroth, and Berzelius finally relinquished one of their two wax candles to the insistent maid servant, who needed it for another guest, and continued their studies by the light of Berzelius' famous blowpipe lamp.

The Mont-Dore region could be explored only on horseback. "I cannot mention," said Berzelius, " all the troubles I had (1) in getting my left foot up into its stirrup and (2) in throwing the right one so high up into the air that it arrived right over the little portmanteau which was tied back of the saddle. . . . However, after several attempts, and after Almroth and Arfwedson had laughed to their hearts' content at my awkwardness, I finally succeeded."

On their journey to le Puy, their fellow passengers were good natured, inquisitive peasants who thought the Swedish language was a kind of French patois. "Arfwedson," said Berzelius, "was, in their opinion, a prince, for he was wearing in the cabriolet the same suit he wore on the streets of Paris, whereas Almroth and I had adapted ourselves more to the dirty, careless traveling costume of the French."

In Lyons, Arfwedson and Berzelius observed the manufacture of silk and velvet in the homes of the workers. In Geneva they visited Dr. and Mrs. Alexandre Marcet. While they were in Zurich, Professor M. A. Pictet of Geneva announced to them that they had both been elected to honorary membership in the Helvetian Scientific Society.

To simplify their journey across Prussia and homeward through Sweden, Arfwedson bought a fine carriage in Dresden. Berzelius and he visited the porcelain works at Berlin, where Berzelius bought several porcelain stopcocks and was delighted to find them completely airtight.

After their return to Stockholm in the winter of 1819, Arfwedson set up his own laboratory and equipped it with apparatus he had bought during his travels. In the following year he purchased a handsome estate at Hedensö (Heden's Island), where he equipped another chemical laboratory. However, since he owned the Näshulta Works and mill in Södermanland near Hedensö and shares in the Gravendal Works in Kopparberg and industrial plants at Skagerholm and Brunnsberg, his executive duties left him little time for research.

On April 18, 1821, he was elected to membership in the Swedish Academy of Sciences. In the same year he published some analyses of cyanite from St. Gotthard and Röräs and nepheline and sodalite from Vesuvius (13). In 1822 he published analyses of cinnamon stone, chrysoberyl, and boracite (14). He found the cinnamon stone which Berzelius had brought back from Vermland to be a calcium aluminum iron silicate and regarded it as a true garnet like the one from Ceylon which Klaproth had analyzed.

Arfwedson's analysis of Brazilian chrysoberyl was severely criticized by Thomas Thomson, who said that "by some inadvertence, he has taken a compound of glucina and alumina for silica" (15). Glucina, or beryllia, had been discovered by N.-L. Vauquelin 24 years before (16).

Arfwedson fused the chrysoberyl three times with caustic potash in a silver crucible. Since a portion of the melt corresponding to about 18 per cent of the mineral failed to dissolve in hydrochloric acid, he reported this residue as silica. It is now known that beryllium hydroxide, when freshly precipitated, dissolves readily in hydrochloric acid, but becomes after a time almost completely insoluble in it (17). Therefore, it is probable that Arfwedson's "silica" was really the beryllium hydroxide. He then precipitated the alumina by adding ammonium hydroxide to the acid filtrate. To satisfy himself of the purity of his alumina, he saturated the alkaline solution with hydrochloric acid until the precipitate dissolved, and added a large excess of ammonium carbonate. "Had any glucina [beryllia] or yttria existed in the matter," said Arfwedson, "it would have been dissolved by this excess of carbonate of ammonia, and would have fallen when the filtered liquid was boiled till the excess of ammonia was driven off; but the liquid stood this test without any precipitate appearing." Arfwedson was evidently unable to detect beryllia here because he had already filtered it off and reported it as silica. When American chemist Henry Seybert analyzed the same mineral in 1824 he found it to contain 15 to 16 per cent of beryllia (22).

In 1822 Arfwedson published his paper on uranium (18). More than thirty years before, M. H. Klaproth had heated a paste made with uranic oxide and linseed oil, and obtained a brown powder with a metallic luster, which he regarded as metallic uranium. Although others had used carbon crucibles in their attempts to reduce uranium oxide to the metal, Arfwedson used hydrogen. He placed a weighed portion of ignited "uranous oxide" [uranosic, or uranous-uranic oxide] in a bulb blown out at the center of a piece of barometer tubing, drove off the moisture, and passed dry hydrogen over it. As soon as the air had been removed, he heated the bulb with an Argand spirit lamp. A vigorous reaction took place, and in a few minutes the green "uranous oxide" had been changed to "a powder of a liver-brown color," which Arfwedson believed to be uranium metal.

He also prepared the "potash muriate of uranium" [potassium uranyl chloride, $K_2(UO_2)Cl_4$], and attempted to analyze it by reduction with hydrogen just as Berzelius had analyzed potassium chloroplatinate (19). As Arfwedson passed hydrogen over the strongly heated salt, it continued to lose hydrochloric acid for more than two hours. After cooling the apparatus, he washed out the potassium chloride and the undecomposed salt and obtained a dark, crystalline powder with a metallic luster. When this was heated, it became converted into green "uranous oxide" [uranosic oxide]. During this change, 100 parts of the so-called "metal" [uranous oxide] gained 3.7 parts of oxygen. This was evidently the reaction: $3UO_2 + O_2 = U_3O_8$, in which 100 parts of uranous oxide actually gain 3.95 parts of oxygen; 100 parts of true uranium metal would have gained 17.9 parts of oxygen. Arfwedson, however, did not believe that his powder could be an oxide, for, according to Sir Humphry Davy's new theory regarding the composition of muriatic [hydrochloric] acid, the double chloride of uranium and potassium contained no oxygen.

Although Arfwedson, Klaproth, Berzelius, and many other eminent chemists long regarded this crystalline powder as the metal, E. M. Peligot in 1841 obtained the true metal. When he heated uranous oxide with carbon in a current of chlorine, he obtained carbon monoxide, carbon dioxide, and a green crystalline compound which is now known to be uranous chloride, UCl_4. Since the evolution of carbon dioxide and carbon monoxide showed that the so-called "uranium" must contain oxygen, Peligot heated the uranous chloride with potassium and succeeded for the first time in preparing and studying true metallic uranium. As early as 1824, however, Friedrich Stromeyer had doubted that Arfwedson's "uranium" was the metal (23).

When Arfwedson tried to analyze lead uranate by reducing it with hydrogen, it gained weight and became hot. When he placed the reduced mass on paper, he was astonished to see it burst into flame. He also prepared other pyrophoric alloys of uranium in the same way. "The uranium alloys," said he, "absorb oxygen again at ordinary temperatures, become ignited, and thus constitute a peculiar kind of pyrophors which are not inferior in flammability to those already known."

In 1822 Arfwedson published a paper on the decomposition of sulfates with dry hydrogen (20). In the following year the British Mineralogist H. J. Brooke (1771–1857) described a new mineral, *arfwedsonite* (21). "The benefits which mineralogy has derived from the labours of Mr. Arfwedson," said he, "have induced me to associate his name with this mineral, which is from Greenland, and is black and foliated, and has been hitherto called ferriferous hornblende. . . ."

In the autumn of 1824 Arfwedson helped Berzelius and Wilhelm Hisinger arrange the mineral collection of the Academy of Sciences according to Berzelius' chemical system. Two years later Berzelius visited Arfwedson at Hedensö. "This," said he, "is a most beautiful place, and Arfwedson and his wife have improved it since I was here last time. Inside there reigns extreme neatness and a degree of luxury which could be much less and still be sufficient" (3).* Berzelius' pleasure was marred, however, by an attack of gout which did not yield even when Arfwedson himself applied nine leeches to the affected knee.

Although Arfwedson's business interests more and more distracted his attention from chemical research, this was not caused by the love of money. When one of his uncles bequeathed him the magnificent Forssby estate with its precious collection of oil paintings, Arfwedson allowed this inheritance to be shared according to law with the other heirs.

In the last year of his life, the Swedish Academy of Sciences awarded him its large gold medal (2) in honor of his discovery of lithium. He died at Hedensö on October 28, 1841, and was survived by his wife and three sons. The *Vetenskapsacademiens Handlingar* for that year contained the following tribute to his memory: "His love of order gave an impress of neatness not only to his person but also to everything about him. He had a pleasant manner; when different points of view were exchanged, he expressed himself with a deliberateness which was not compliance and with a thoroughness which showed deep thought. One may venture to say that, because he was obliged to devote his time to the management of a considerable fortune, . . . the science to which he devoted himself in his youth lost much (4)."

In conclusion we wish to thank Mr. Carl Björkbom of the Royal Library at Stockholm and Miss Amy Wästfelt of Upsala for their kind assistance.

LITERATURE CITED

(1) BOETHIUS, B., "Svenskt biografiskt lexikon," A. Bonnier, Stockholm, 1918. Article on Arfwedson by H. G. Söderbaum.

(2) LEIJONHUFVUD, K. A. K:SON, "Ny svensk släktbok," P. A. Norstedt & Söner, Stockholm, 1906, pp. 94–5.

(3) SÖDERBAUM, H. G., "Berzelius levnadsteckning," 3 vols., Almqvist & Wiksells Boktryckeri A.-B., Upsala, 1929–31.

* Letter of Berzelius to Carl Palmstedt, July 26, 1826.

(4) ANON., "Biografi öfver Johan August Arfvedson, Brukspatron," *Kongl. Vet. Acad. Handl.*, **1841**, pp. 249–55.

(5) ARFWEDSON, J. A., "Analys af meïonit dioctaèdre och af leucit från Vesuvius," *Afh. i Fysik, Kemi och Mineralogi*, **6**, 255–62 (1818).

(6) SÖDERBAUM, H. G., "Jac. Berzelius Bref," Vol. 1, part 3, Almqvist & Wiksells, Upsala, **1912–1914**, pp. 158–9. Letter of Berzelius to Marcet, Sept. 23, 1817; *Ann. chim. phys.*, (2), **6**, 204–5 (1817). Letter of Berzelius to Gay-Lussac, Sept. 28, 1817.

(7) ARFWEDSON, J. A., "Undersökning af oxidum manganoso-manganicum, en hittills okänd kemisk förening af manganoxidul och oxid," *Afh. i Fysik, Kemi och Min.*, **6**, 222–36 (1818); *Annals of Philos.*, **23**, 267–75 (Apr., 1824).

(8) SÖDERBAUM, H. G., "Jac. Berzelius Bref," Vol. 1, part 1, Almqvist & Wiksells, Upsala, **1912–14**, pp. 63–4. Letter of Berzelius to Berthollet, Feb. 9, 1818; *ibid.*, Vol. 1, part 3, p. 160. Letter of Berzelius to Dr. Marcet, Feb. 6, 1818.

(9) ARFWEDSON, J. A., "Undersökning af några vid Utö Jernmalmsbrott förekommande Fossilier, och af ett deri funnet eget Eldfast Alkali," *Afh. i Fysik, Kemi och Min.*, **6**, 145–72 (1818); "Tillägg af Berzelius," *ibid.*, **6**, 173–6 (1818).

(10) ANON., "Additional observations on lithium and selenium by Professor Berzelius," *Annals of Philos.*, (1), **11**, 374 (May, 1818); THOMAS THOMSON, "History of Physical science from the commencement of the year 1817," *ibid.*, (1), **12**, 16 (July, 1818); ANON., "An account of the new alkali lately discovered in Sweden," *Quarterly J. of Sci. and the Arts*, **5**, 337–40 (1818); "Von Petalit und dem schwedischen rothen dichten Feldspath vom Dr. Clarke, Prof. der Mineralogie zu Cambridge," *Gilbert's Ann. der Physik*, **59**, 241–7 (1818).

(11) ARFWEDSON, J. A., "Tillägg och rättelser vid afhandlingen om lithion i Kongl. Vet. Acad. Handl. för År 1818," *Kongl. Vet. Acad. Handl.*, **1821**, pp. 156–9.

(12) BERZELIUS, J. J., "Reseanteckningar," P. A. Norstedt & Söner, Stockholm, **1903**, 430 pp.

(13) ARFWEDSON, J. A., "Undersökning af några mineralier," *Kongl. Vet. Acad. Handl.*, **1821**, pp. 147–55.

(14) ARFWEDSON, J. A., "Undersökning af några mineralier," *ibid.*, **1822**, pp. 87–94; *Annals of Philos.*, **23**, 343–8 (May, 1824).

(15) THOMSON, THOMAS, "History of Chemistry," Vol. 2, Colburn and Bentley, London, **1831**, p. 229.

(16) VAUQUELIN, N.-L., "Analyse de l'aigue marine, ou béril, et découverte d'une terre nouvelle dans cette pierre," *Ann. chim. phys.*, [1], **26**, 155–77 (May (30 Floréal), 1798).

(17) HABER, F. and G. VAN OORDT, "Über Berylliumverbindungen," *Z. anorg. Chem.*, **38**, 380–1, 397 (Feb. 17, 1904).

(18) ARFWEDSON, J. A., "Bidrag till en närmare kännedom om uranium," *Kongl. Vet. Acad. Handl.*, **1822**, pp. 404–26; *Annals of Philos.*, **23**, 253–67 (April, 1824).

(19) BERZELIUS, J. J., "Note sur la composition des oxides du platine et de l'or," *Ann. chim. phys.*, (2), **18**, 149–50 (1821).

(20) ARFWEDSON, J. A., "Om svafvelsyrade metallsalters sönderdelning med vätgas," *Kongl. Vet. Acad. Handl.*, **1822**, pp. 427–49; *Annals of Philos.*, **23**, 329–43 (May, 1824).

(21) BROOKE, H. J., "A description of the crystalline form of some new minerals," *Annals of Philos.*, **21**, 381–4 (May, 1823).

(22) SMITH, E. F., "Chemistry in America," D. Appleton and Co., New York and London, **1914**, p. 151; HENRY SEYBERT, "Analyses of the chrysoberyls from Haddam and Brazil," *Trans. Am. Philos. Soc.* (N. S.), **2**, 116–23 (1825). Read March 5, 1824.

(23) WALLACH, O., "Briefwechsel zwischen J. Berzelius und F. Wöhler," Vol. 1, Wilhelm Engelmann, Leipzig, **1901**, p. 19. Letter of Wöhler to Berzelius, Nov. 11, 1824.

Courtesy Sir James C. Irvine

Thomas Charles Hope, 1766–1844. Scottish chemist and physician. Successor to Dr. Joseph Black at Edinburgh. The first chemist in Great Britain to teach Lavoisier's views on combustion. Hope and Dr. Adair Crawford were the first to distinguish between baryta and strontia.

If matter cannot be destroy'd,
  The living mind can never die;

If e'en creative when alloy'd,
  How sure its immortality!

Then think that intellectual light,
  Thou loved'st on earth is burning still,
Its lustre purer and more bright,
  Obscured no more by mortal will (1).

20

Alkaline earth metals, magnesium, cadmium

The isolation of the alkaline earth metals required the combined genius of Davy and Berzelius. After the latter had succeeded in decomposing lime and baryta by electrolyzing a mixture of the alkaline earth and mercury, Davy was able in 1808 to prepare the amalgams in larger quantity and, by distilling off the mercury, to isolate the metals, strontium, barium, calcium, and magnesium. In the year 1817 a number of preparations of zinc oxide sold by German apothecaries were confiscated by the inspectors, who found that zinc carbonate had been substituted for the oxide, that the carbonate became yellow upon heating, and that, when hydrogen sulfide was passed into an acid solution of the carbonate, a yellow precipitate resembling arsenious sulfide was thrown down. The researches of Dr. Stromeyer, Dr. Roloff, and Mr. Hermann proved, however, that this yellow precipitate was not arsenious sulfide, but the sulfide of an unknown metal. Thus the good name of the manufacturing pharmacies was restored, and the chemical world was enriched by the discovery of the new element, cadmium.

CALCIUM

*A*lthough the ancients had many uses for lime, they knew nothing of its chemical nature. The "De Re Rustica" of Marcus Porcius Cato the Censor (234–149 B.C.), the "De Architectura" of Marcus Vitruvius Pollio (who lived in the reign of Augustus), and the "Historia Naturalis" of Pliny the Elder all discuss the preparation, properties, and uses of lime (44, 45, 46). Vitruvius noticed that lime from the kiln, though it was as bulky as the original limestone, had "lost about one third of its weight owing (he said) to the boiling out of the water" (47). In 1755 Dr. Joseph Black proved that this loss in weight is actually due to the escape of "fixed air" (carbon dioxide gas). These experiments were described in his paper entitled, "Experiments upon magnesia alba, quick-lime, and some other alkaline substances" (67).

Although the word alabaster is sometimes applied to a kind of translucent gypsum (calcium sulfate), Egyptian alabaster was a form of calcite (calcium carbonate). Howard Carter's great work describing the tomb of Tut-ankh-Amen contains a picture of a lovely calcite lamp found in the tomb (71).

Ancient Egyptian and Grecian mortars and plasters were made by heating crude gypsum (calcium sulfate dihydrate) until it became partially dehydrated (72). Roman mortars, however, were prepared by burning limestone, for the lime mortar withstood better the moist climate of Italy (73). A. Lucas states that the mortar used in the pyramids at Gizeh and in the temples of Karnak was made from gypsum, and that all the plaster in Tut-ankh-Amen's tomb is crude gypsum similar to that still made near Cairo and Alexandria (71).

Theophrastus of Eresus used the word gypsum to include both the crude mineral and the product (plaster of Paris) obtained by partially dehydrating it. "The Stone," said he, "from which Gypsum is made, by burning, is like Alabaster; it is not dug, however, in such large Masses, but in separate Lumps. Its Viscidity and Heat, when moistened, are very wonderful. They use this in Buildings, casing them with it, or putting it on any particular Place they would strengthen. They prepare it for Use by reducing it to Powder and then pouring Water on it, and stirring and mixing the Matter well together with wooden Instruments. For they cannot do this with the Hand because of the Heat. They prepare it in this Manner immediately before the Time of using it; for in a very little While after moistening, it dries and becomes hard, and not in a Condition to be used. This Cement is very strong, and often remains good even after the Walls it is laid on crack and decay. . . . It is also excellent, and superior to all other Things, for making Images; for which it is greatly used, and especially in Greece, because of its Pliableness and Smoothness" (74).

Dioscorides Pedanios said that calx viva (quicklime) was made by heating shells of "sea fishes called Buccinoe" (whelks), pebble stones, or marble (75).

In about 975 A.D. the Persian pharmacist Abu Mansur Muwaffaq wrote his "Book of Pharmacological Principles," in which he described for the first time the use of the plaster of Paris bandage for bone fractures (76).

Soon after the United States purchased the vast region known as "Louisiana" in Thomas Jefferson's administration, the following article on "Gypsum from Upper Louisiana" appeared in S. L. Mitchill's *Medical Repository:* "Among the productions of this newly-acquired country is to be reckoned plaster of Paris. Specimens of a very pure gypsum have been brought from about 150 leagues up the Missouri. It is said to exist there in abundance. This, in process of time, will amply supply that inland country with the sulphate of lime for all the purposes of agriculture, architecture, and the other arts. It is remarkable how scantily gypsum is scattered through Fredonia.* Except some small parcels which have been brought from St. Mary's, between the Patuxent and Potowmac [*sic*] in Maryland, some other samples from the town of Marcellus, in Onondaga County, New York, and some other pieces obtained from the bed of the river below the Falls of Niagara, we have hitherto seen but few traces of this valuable stone in the United States. It is owing to the scarcity of plaster of Paris within our territories that we are obliged to import the

Sir Humphry Davy, 1778–1829. Professor of chemistry and lecturer at the Royal Institution, London. Scientist, poet, and humanitarian. Donor of the Davy Medal.

From Muspratt's "Chemistry, Theoretical, Practical and Analytical"

greater part of what we consume. And the principal portion of the great quantity employed in constructing houses and manuring lands is brought from the British dominions bordering on the Bay of Fundy" (*77*).

George Ernst Stahl (1660–1734) thought that in the slaking of lime the earthy element combined with the watery element to form a salt. He admitted that there are distinct earths that might be converted into metals by combining with phlogiston. Though most eighteenth-century chemists thought that lime and baryta were elements, Lavoisier believed them to be oxides (*2, 12*). "It is probable," said he, "that we know only part of the metallic substances which exist in Nature; all those, for example, that

---

* Since it is impossible to make an adjective from the name *United States of America*, the *Medical Repository* proposed and used the words *Fredonia* and *Fredonian*.

have more affinity for oxygen than for carbon are not capable of being reduced or brought to the metallic state, and they must not present themselves to our eyes except in the form of oxides, which we do not distinguish from the earths. It is very probable that baryta, which we have just classified with the earths, is one of these; it presents experimentally properties which closely ally it with metallic substances. It is possible, strictly speaking, that all the substances which we call earths may be simply metallic oxides irreducible by the methods we employ" (12).

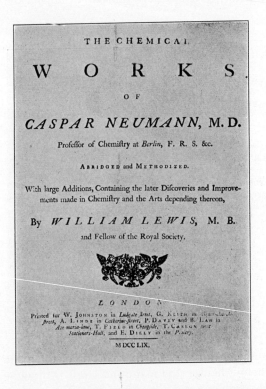

THE CHEMICAL

W O R K S.

O F

CASPAR NEUMANN, M.D.

Profeſſor of Chemiſtry at *Berlin*, F. R. S. &c.

ABRIDGED and METHODIZED.

With large Additions, Containing the later Diſcoveries and Improvements made in Chemiſtry and the Arts depending thereon,

By *WILLIAM LEWIS*, M. B.

and Fellow of the Royal Society.

LONDON

Printed for W. JOHNSTON in *Ludgate-ſtreet*, G. KEITH in *Gracechurch-ſtreet*, A. LINDE in *Catherine-ſtreet*, P. DAVEY and B. LAW in *Ave-maria-lane*, T. FIELD in *Cheapſide*, T. CASLON near Stationers-Hall, and E. DILLY in the *Poultry*.

M DCC LIX.

Title Page of the "Chemical Works of Caspar Neumann" (1683–1737).   Apothecary and professor of chemistry at Berlin.   His writings were carefully studied by Scheele and Davy.

Caspar Neumann made some elaborate but unsuccessful attempts to obtain a metal from quicklime (3), but for this difficult reduction new methods, new apparatus, and the genius of a Davy were required.

Sir Humphry's ardent nature could not rest content with his recent triumphs over sodium and potassium. With a conqueror's enthusiasm he pushed ahead toward the still more difficult task of decomposing the alkaline earths. In his first attempts he passed a current through the moist alkaline earth, which was protected from the air by a layer of naphtha. There was slight decomposition, but any metal that may have been formed combined immediately with the iron cathode (3).

Davy then tried to use potassium directly as a reducing agent. "I heated potassium," said he, "in contact with dry, pure lime, barytes, strontites, and magnesia, in tubes of plate glass; but as I was obliged to use very small quantities, and as I could not raise the heat to ignition without fusing the glass, I obtained in this way no good results." Although the potassium attacked the earth and the glass, no distinct metallic globules were obtained (3).

One method he finally adopted was to mix the non-conducting, dry earth (lime, strontia, or baryta) with excess potash and fuse it. When he covered the alkaline mixture with naphtha and passed an electric current through it, he soon saw metallic globules rising and bursting into flame, but when the flame died out, there remained nothing except potash and the alkaline earth with which he had started (2, 3).

Although greatly disappointed over this failure, Sir Humphry soon thought out another plan of attack. This time he mixed lime with mercuric oxide and obtained a small amount of calcium amalgam. He also made similar alloys of the other alkaline earths with mercury, silver, tin, and lead, but never obtained enough of the alloy to permit the isolation of the alkaline earth metal. In May, 1808, however, Berzelius wrote Davy that he and Dr. M. M. af Pontin, the king's physician, had decomposed lime by mixing it with mercury and electrolyzing the mixture, and that they had been equally successful in decomposing baryta and preparing barium amalgam (2, 13).

With the help of this suggestion, Davy finally worked out a method of obtaining the alkaline earth metals themselves. He mixed the moist earth with one-third its weight of mercuric oxide, and placed it on a platinum plate connected to the positive pole of a powerful battery. He then hollowed out a little cavity in the center of the mixture, and poured a globule of mercury into it in order to make possible the use of a heavy current from "a battery of five hundred." A platinum wire dipping into the mercury was connected to the negative pole. By this means Sir Humphry obtained enough of the calcium amalgam so that he could distil off the mercury and see for the first time the silvery-white metal, calcium (2, 3, 7).

In his letter of July 10, 1808, Davy acknowledged his indebtedness to Berzelius and Dr. Pontin. After describing his early failures he said:

Since I have been favoured with your papers, I have, however, made new and more successful attempts, and by combining your ingenious mode of operating with those that I before employed, I have succeeded in obtaining sufficient quantities of amalgams for distillation. At the red heat the quicksilver rises from the amalgams and the bases remain free. The metals of strontites, barytes, and magnesia are all that I have experimented upon in this way; but I doubt not the other earths will afford similar results. . . . I consider this letter as addressed in common to you and your worthy fellow labourer, Dr. Pontin, to whom I must beg you to present my compliments" (*14*).

Pure calcium cannot be prepared by the method of Davy and Berzelius, and a successful commercial process was not perfected until nearly a century later (*32*).

Calcium in Plant and Animal Nutrition.   Calcium is essential to plant and animal life and is present in adequate amounts in many soils (*78*). The outer green leaves of cabbages and certain other leafy vegetables contain much more calicum than the inner white ones (*79, 80, 81*).   Large amounts of it are present in the human body.   The composition of bone suggests that it must be closely related to the apatite series of minerals, which have the formula $nCa_3(PO_4)_2 \cdot CaCO_3$, in which n has a value

Dr. Pontin (M. M. af Pontin), 1781–1858. Physician to the King of Sweden. He collaborated with Berzelius in preparing amalgams of calcium and barium by electrolyzing lime or baryta in presence of mercury. Author of a biography of Berzelius.

between 2 and 3, and fluorine, hydroxyl, etc. may replace the carbonate radical. X-ray analyses by H. H. Roseberry, A. B. Hastings, and J. K. Morse show that bone salts most closely resemble the rare mineral dahlite (*82, 83*). Although most of the calcium in the body is located in the skeleton and teeth, that present in the blood and tissues is of great physiological importance (*82*).

BARIUM

Early in the seventeenth century Vincenzo Casciarolo, a shoemaker and alchemist in Bologna, noticed that when heavy spar is mixed with a combustible substance and heated to redness, the resulting mixture, which became known as the "Bologna stone," emits a phosphorescent glow.

Casciarolo communicated his discovery to Giovanni Antonio Magini, a
mathematician in Bologna (56). In a scholarly article on the history of
this substance, A. Bernardi quoted from the volume "Phosphorus, or the
Bolognian stone prepared to shine again in the dark," which Marco
Antonio Celli had published in 1680 (56). According to Celli, Casciarolo
carried home some shining pebbles he had found on a sterile slope of
Mount Paterno, experimented with them (perhaps to see whether they
had any occult virtues), and noticed that after they had been heated in a
certain way and exposed to the sun, they became luminous even in the
dark. Celli suggested that Casciarolo may have been deceived both by
the high specific gravity and by the sulfur content of the mineral into
considering it a suitable substance for transmutation into gold (56). Some
of the earliest descriptions of this "Bologna stone" and the "Bolognian
phosphorus" prepared from it were written by J. C. La Galla (1612),
P. Poterius (Potier) (1622), Ovidio Montalbanus (1634), A. Kircher
(1641), Nicolas Lémery (1697), and L. F. Marsigli (1698) (84). The
Aristotelian philosopher Fortunio Liceto (Licetus) maintained in 1640
that the phosphorescence of the Bologna stone could be compared to the
secondary light of the moon, a hypothesis which the aged Galileo effect-
ively contested in the last of his many scientific contributions (85).

W. Derham in 1726 gave the following account of the "Bolognian
phosphorus": "The stone is found in three Places near the City of
Bologna; the first is called Pradalbino; the second is a small Brook near the
Village Roncaria; the third is called Monte Paterno, and is most noted for
these Stones; . . .. It's known by a Glittering . . . which surprizes the eye.
It was first found out by . . . Vincenzo Casciarolo, a Cobler, but
ingenious, and a Lover of Chymistry; who, trying several Experiments
with these Stones, by Chance happened on this Way of preparing them,
so as to make them shine in the Dark, after they had been some Time
exposed to the Sun. . . . It's usually no bigger than an Orange; and
tho' Licetus affirms, there never was any greater than that in Androvandus'
[Ulisse Aldrovandi's] Museum, weighing about two Pound and a half;
yet the Author hath had of five Pound. It's very heavy, considering the
Bulk, as being probably compounded of several mineral Substances. . . .
When It's well prepared, it leaves a Lustre in the Superficies, and is
enlightened, not only by the Sun, but the Moon, and a Fire; but by these
not so strongly, as the Sun. The Light, tho' it appear like a Coal, yet is
not sufficient to read with, unless applied close to the Word. It will not
retain the Light very long, at one Time, nor its Vertue above five or six
Years . . ." (37). Derham also described in great detail the method of
preparing the "Bolognian phosphorus" from the mineral.

Ulisse Aldrovandi had a large specimen of this mineral in his museum.
He was born in Bologna in 1522 of noble parentage. To satisfy his boyish

curiosity, he made long secret journeys, often on foot. In his studies at
Bologna and Padua he showed intense interest in every branch of science
and in Roman antiquities. He received his doctorate in natural history
in Bologna in 1553 and later became a professor of pharmacognosy there.
Aldrovandi founded a great botanical garden and museum where he
exhibited rare and valuable natural productions from all parts of the world.
In this costly undertaking he was aided by the Senate and philanthropic
Italian princes. The museum with its rich library was located in his own
home. His descriptions of the specimens were published during his lifetime in four folio volumes. Other volumes for which he had collected

Ulisse Aldrovandi (or Aldrovandus),
1522–1605 (?). Italian scholar and collector, well versed in all branches of natural science. Professor of pharmacognosy
at Bologna. Founder of a great botanical garden, museum, and library, which
he bequeathed to the state. Volume 4 of
the superbly illustrated 1642 folio edition
of his complete works contains an account
of the "Bologna stone," barite (De
lapide illvminabili.)

Naturalist's Library, vol. 7

the data were published after his death by other scholars. After forty-
eight years of teaching, Aldrovandi was pensioned. He died in 1605 at
the age of eighty-three years and bequeathed his great collections and
library to the state (86). The superbly illustrated 1642 edition of his
complete works contains an account of the Bologna stone (de lapide
illvminabili) (87).

Father Athanasius Kircher said that the "phosphorus" was made by
pulverizing the Bologna stone, mixing it with white of egg or linseed oil,
and calcining it in a special furnace. He found specimens in the alum
mines at Tolfa (59). Biographical sketches of Father Kircher were published in The Hormone in 1934 (109) and in the Journal of Chemical
Education in 1955 (139).

Nicolas Lémery stated in his "Cours de Chymie" that "this Stone is
bituminous, and full of Sulphur, which is the thing that gives it this dis-

position to shine in the dark. . . . When it has not been calcined enough, it yields no light at all, because the sulphureous parts have not been put into sufficient motion, and when it is calcined too much, these sulphureous parts are thereby lost" (88).

A seventeenth-century item in the *Philosophical Transactions* states that "Though several Persons have pretended to know the Art of Preparing and Calcining the Bononian Stone, for keeping a while the Light once Imbibed, yet there hath been indeed but One who had the true Secret of performing it. This was an Ecclesiastick, who is now dead, without having left that Skill of his to any one. . . . S. [Marcello] Malpighi takes notice, That one S. Zagonius had a way of making out of the Bononian Stone Calcin'd, Statues and Pictures variously Shining in the Dark. But he adds (to our sorrow) that that Person lately Dy'd, without discovering to any Body his Method of Preparing it" (58). In his "History . . . of Vision, Light, and Colours," Joseph Priestley stated that "the best method of preparing the Bolognian stone had been kept a secret in the Zagonian family, all of whom had died without revealing it" (59).

Wilhelm Homberg observed that Balduin's phosphorus (anhydrous calcium nitrate) was similiar to the Bolognian but shone with a somewhat feebler light. B.-B. de Fontenelle's eulogy states that Homberg "worked at Bologna on the stone which bears the name of that city, and restored to it all its light, for the secret of it had almost been lost" (55). When he repeated the experiment in Paris, he was unsuccessful. Homberg himself finally found that when he ground the materials in an iron mortar, the experiment failed, but when he used a bronze mortar and pestle, he obtained a luminous product (56). Some impurities serve as activators for producing a high degree of fluorescence, whereas others have an inhibiting effect. Hence in the most modern plants for the manufacture of fluorescent lamps, dust must be completely excluded (57).

Homberg performed some of these experiments in the presence of his friend Nicolas Lémery. According to Lémery, the Bologna stone was found "in several places in Italy, as near the City of Roncaria, at Pradalbino, at the foot of Mt. Paterno, which is part of the Alps and about one French league from the City of Bologna. Father Kirker [Kircher], in his book "de Magnete," said that he found them near the rock alum pit at Tolfa, but the greatest quantity and the best ones come from Mt. Paterno" (88).

The Abbé Jean-Antoine Nollet, in his "Leçons de physique expérimentale," mentioned the cold light of the Bologna stone and the sulphurous odor which the flame imparted to it. "The odor that the Bologna stone acquires on passing through the flame," said he, "gives sufficient evidence that these natural sulphurs have been liberated from the terrestrial part and from the other principles so that they are able to pass easily from the interior to the outside: these refined sulphurs, like all the rest, contain particles of fire, but with this difference: that being strongly disposed to obey the expansive force of that element, the merest trifle inflames them; even the faintest daylight gives sufficient fire to illumine them. It is perhaps also by a slow dissipation of these inflammable parts from its surface that the stone gradually loses its quality; one can at least suppose so, since it can be kept longer when wrapped in cotton . . . and is restored by a new calcination, as if the action of the fire brought new sulphurs to the surface" (89).

Priestley mentioned that Jacopo Bartolomeo Beccari and other scientists of Bologna in 1711 "took a great deal of pains with the chymical analysis of this fossil, by which they thought they discovered in it some sulphur and also an *alkaline salt*" (59). Before testing his phosphors, Beccari used to remain for some time in a dark, portable booth, or cell. When the pupils of his eyes had become sufficiently dilated, he was able to observe the dim, cold light which the phosphorescent substances emitted (89).

Beccari was born in Bologna in 1682. After teaching medicine at the University of Bologna for nearly a quarter of a century, he became in 1737 its first professor of chemistry—the first, in fact, in all Italy. After forty years of service to the University, he was pensioned, but nevertheless continued his work there for several years more. He died in Bologna in 1766 at the age of eighty-three years (90, 138).

J. G. Wallerius regarded heavy spar as a kind of gypsum (91), but Cronstedt classified it as a special species. In 1750 A. S. Marggraf proved it to be a sulfate, and he too believed the base of it to be lime (92, 93).

J. W. von Goethe collected specimens of the Bologna stone at Paterno in 1786, took them back to Weimar, made many experiments with them, and in 1792 discovered that only the violet end of the spectrum caused the phosphorescence. Goethe said that in Bologna the little phosphorescent cakes prepared from the Bologna stone were called "fosfori" (94). The modern name of the Bologna stone is barite, barium sulfate.

In his famous investigation of pyrolusite, which was published in 1774, C. W. Scheele discovered a new base, baryta, which gave a white, nearly insoluble precipitate with sulfuric acid and with vitriols (15, 18). Although he first encountered the new alkali merely as an accidental or nonessential constituent of pyrolusite, he soon received from Torbern Bergman a specimen of this mineral to which some peculiar crystals were attached. On February 28, 1774, Scheele wrote to J. G. Gahn, "Haven't you seen, Sir, on Braunstein, especially on some of it, a few white sparry crystals? You undoubtedly have. One might take it for gypsum or calcite, but incorrectly. It is the new earth itself, combined with sulfuric acid. I'm curious to know with what kind of a name Herr Professor Bergman will christen this earth. He thinks that there must be rocks which contain a great deal of this earth" (60). A month later, Scheele sent some of these crystals to Gahn, who found that they had the same composition as massive heavy spar, or Bologna stone.

Although baryta was at first a great rarity, Gahn's discovery of the composition of Bologna stone opened up to chemists an abundant source of it. In his letter of May 16, 1774, Scheele congratulated Gahn as follows: "I am delighted that you have discovered the presence in heavy spar of the earth I mentioned. It must therefore be named *Schwerspatherde* (earth of heavy spar). Scarcely had I investigated the crystals you sent me until I hurried to Herr Professor Bergman and received from him a piece of this spar, on which I immediately began to experiment" (60).

Baryta was first distinguished from lime in 1779 by Scheele, who prepared it from heavy spar, a naturally occurring barium sulfate. He reduced the sulfate to the sulfide by heating a sticky, pasty mixture of heavy spar, powdered charcoal, and honey. After decomposing the barium sulfide with hydrochloric acid, he added excess potassium carbonate to precipitate the barium as the carbonate (15).

Witherite. Torbern Bergman predicted that baryta would also be found in nature combined with fixed air (carbon dioxide), and in 1784 Dr. William Withering discovered in the collection of Matthew Boulton the natural barium carbonate which is now known as witherite (84). Dr. Withering (1741–1799) was a British physician, botanist, and mineralogist. He was a member of the Society for Promoting the Abolition of the Slave Trade and of the famous Lunar Society, in which he was closely associated with Joseph Priestley, Matthew Boulton, and James Watt. At one of their meetings Dr. Withering read an original humorous poem entitled "The Life and Death of Phlogiston" (95).

In 1783 he published an annotated translation of Torbern Bergman's "Sciagraphia regni mineralis," and in the following year he communicated to the *Philosophical Transactions* his "Experiments and observations on terra ponderosa" (barium carbonate, or witherite) (96). He stated that the specimen he examined came from a lead mine at Alston Moor, on the Pennines of Cumberland. Although he at first mistook it for heavy spar (barite) he soon found it to be a compound of heavy earth (barium oxide) and fixed air (carbon dioxide) (97).

Commenting on this discovery, A.-F. de Fourcroy said that "Barytes is less copious than either of the other two salino-terreous substances (lime or magnesia), but it is probably more copious than it is thought to be. Formerly it was not known to exist in any body but barytic sulfate or ponderous spar" (98).

In 1790 James Watt published a map of a lead mine at Anglezark, Lancashire, in which the "aerated barytes" (witherite) is found. Since Watt believed that Dr. Withering must have been mistaken as to the source of his first specimen of this mineral, many mineralogists regard Anglezark rather than Alston Moor as the place of its discovery (99).

In 1785 Dr. Withering introduced the use of digitalis (foxglove) as a specific remedy for dropsy (100). During the Birmingham riots of July, 1791, in which Joseph Priestley's house was sacked, Dr. Withering too was forced to take flight, carrying his books and specimens in wagons loaded with hay. Dr. Withering's house, however, was not destroyed (101). Priestley wrote him in 1792, "One of the things that I regret most in being expelled from Birmingham is the loss of your company and that of the rest of the Lunar Society" (95).

Flame Tests. In 1821 Nils Nordenskiöld wrote to Berzelius, "I have sometimes thought that I noticed that fossils containing lithia, when strongly heated alone, give the flame a crimson color; could that observation be something other than my imagination? Döbereiner in Jena said that some chemist from Prague found that baryta gives the flame a green color; this I have not yet tried" (102). Thomas Charles Hope had already observed this green color in 1793 (48). The red color of lithium, as we have seen, was first observed by C. G. Gmelin in 1818 (103).

Metallic Barium. Because of the high specific gravity of baryta and its salts, Torbern Bergman believed that it must be a metallic oxide (98). A.-L. Lavoisier also expressed the same view (12). Bertrand Pelletier's attempts to isolate the metal were cut short by his fatal illness. Bidding farewell to his friend D.-G.-S.-T. Gratet de Dolomieu, he said, "I am already convinced that this earth is of a metallic nature, although my experiments have not yet led to the complete reduction of it; but, if my illness had not made me aware that I can never resume my research, I would certainly have succeeded; if I cannot accomplish it, make known what I am now confiding to you, and challenge chemists to undertake this reduction; it requires special means, but is no longer subject to doubt" (104). Pelletier died in 1797, and the "special means" with which barium was finally isolated was the voltaic pile which Alessandro Volta invented only three years later. Sir Humphry Davy first prepared this metal in 1808 (2, 3, 4).

Although the mineral (barite) in which this element was first recognized has a high specific gravity, the metal itself is very light. Edward Daniel Clarke objected therefore to the inappropriate name *barium* (meaning heavy) for this metal (105). The name persists nevertheless.

Barium in Plants and Animals. As early as 1771–72 Scheele discovered the presence of barium in plants. In his laboratory notes for his first years in Upsala (1771–72), he wrote: "The special earth which comes from *magn. nigra et acidis per praecipitationem cum oleo vitrioli* must be present in plants, for vegetable ash, well extracted with water so that all *tartarus vitriolatus* is removed, when dissolved in *acido nitri et salis*, gives with *acido vitrioli* such a precipitate" (*60*). A. E. Nordenskiöld, the editor of Scheele's notes, regarded this as strong indication that Scheele's investigation of pyrolusite must have been carried out in the years 1771–72. In a letter to J. G. Gahn, Scheele wrote: "I have also discovered some of this earth [baryta] as well as a little *Braunstein* [manganese dioxide] in vegetable ash" (*60*). In 1776 Scheele introduced the use of barium nitrate as a precipitant for oxalic acid and as an indispensable reagent in analytical chemistry (*60*). Barium chloride however has been found preferable to the nitrate.

J. G. Forchhammer found in 1865 that "Baryta occurs both in sea-weeds and in sea animals, but the ashes of seaweeds contain more of it than the corals and shells. It can even be determined directly in sea water and in the deposits of the boilers of the Transatlantic steamers" (*106*).

In 1909–10 Professor E. H. S. Bailey and Dean L. E. Sayre of the University of Kansas detected barium in the ash and extract of elder, ragweed, agrimony, and certain other Kansas weeds (*107, 108*). It is also present in minute amounts in many edible plants (*107*).

STRONTIUM

In about 1787 a rare mineral, which had long been exhibited in one or two collections, was brought to Edinburgh in considerable quantity by a dealer in minerals. Although some mineralogists mistook it for fluorite, most of them regarded it as a kind of "aerated barytes" (witherite, or barium carbonate). It was found in the lead mine at Strontian, Argyleshire, intermingled with the lead ore and with "calcareous and ponderous spars" (calcite and witherite) (*48*).

In 1790 Dr. Adair Crawford (1748–1795) published a paper on "The medicinal properties of the muriated barytes" (barium chloride) (*18*). "The muriated barytes exhibited in St. Thomas's Hospital since the month of May, 1789," said he, "was obtained by the decomposition of the heavy spar. Having procured some specimens of a mineral which is sold at Strontean [*sic*], in Scotland under the denomination of aerated barytes, I was in hopes that the salt might be formed with less difficulty by immediately dissolving that substance in the muriatic acid. It appears, however, from the following facts, which have been verified by the experiments of my assistant, Mr. Cruikshank, as well as by my own, that this mineral really possesses different properties from the terra ponderosa [baryta] of Scheele and Bergman" (*49*).

Dr. Crawford showed in this paper that the salt (strontium chloride) obtained by dissolving the new mineral in hydrochloric acid differs in several respects from barium chloride. It is much more soluble in hot water than in cold, the strontium salt is much the more soluble in water and produces a greater cooling effect, and these two chlorides have different crystalline forms. He concluded therefore that "the mineral which is sold at Strontean [sic] for aerated terra ponderosa possesses different qualities from that earth, although at the same time it must be admitted that in many particulars they have a very near resemblance to each other." He also stated that "it is probable that the Scotch mineral is a new species of earth which has not hitherto been sufficiently examined" and that "Mr. Babington . . . has for some time entertained a suspicion that the Scotch mineral is not the true aerated terra ponderosa." In 1790 Dr. Crawford sent a specimen of the new mineral (strontianite, strontium carbonate) to Richard Kirwan for analysis (50, 66).

Adair Crawford was born at Antrim, Ireland, and received his degree of doctor of medicine at Glasgow in 1780. After settling in London he became a physician at St. Thomas's Hospital, a member of the Royal College of Physicians, and professor of chemistry at Woolwich. He died in 1795 at the estate of the Marquis of Lansdowne, near Lymington, Hants (51).

According to Robert Hunt, Dr. Crawford "was distinguished by his desire to be accurate in all his investigations. All his pieces of apparatus were graduated with delicate minuteness which has never been surpassed" (52). In his epitaph for Dr. Crawford, Mr. Gilbert Wakefield described him as follows: "In the practice of his profession intelligent, liberal, and humane; in his manner gentle, diffident, and unassuming; his unaffected deference to the wants of others, his modest estimate of himself, the infant simplicity of his demeanor, the pure emanation of kind affection, and a blameless heart rendered him universally beloved. To these virtues of the man his contemporaries alone can testify. As a votary of science and author of a treatise on Animal Heat, posterity will repeat his praise" (51).

Near the close of 1791, Thomas Charles Hope of Edinburgh began an elaborate investigation of the Strontian spar, the results of which he presented to the College Literary Society of Edinburgh in March, 1792, and to the Royal Society of Edinburgh on November 4, 1793. In these experiments he made a clear distinction between witherite and strontian spar (strontianite) and proved conclusively that the latter contains a new earth "strontites," or strontia (26, 30, 48). He noticed that strontia slakes even more avidly with water than does lime; that, like baryta, it is much more soluble in hot water than in cold; that its solubility in water is extremely great; and that all its compounds, especially the chloride, tinge the flame of a candle red. "This flame color," said Hope, "was first mentioned to me in the year 1787 by an ingenious gentleman, Mr. Ash, who was then studying physic at Edinburgh." Dr. Hope also noticed the green flame color of barium and the red of calcium, which he was able to distinguish from the more brilliant red of strontium.

Although many of the properties of strontia are intermediate between those of lime and baryta, he proved that it is not a combination of the two and that it "bears repeated solutions, crystallizations, and precipitations without showing the smallest disposition to a separation of principles" (48). Thus it is evident that Dr. Hope foreshadowed in 1793 one of the triads which J. W. Döbereiner pointed out in 1829.

Benjamin Silliman the Elder, 1778-1864. American chemist, geologist, mineralogist, and pharmacist. This miniature by Rogers was made in 1818, the year in which Silliman founded the *American Journal of Science* (thirteen years after he had studied in Edinburgh under T. C. Hope).

Benjamin Silliman the Elder studied at Edinburgh in 1805. "My earliest introduction," said he, "among men of science was to Dr. Thomas Hope, Professor of Chemistry &c. in the University of Edinburgh. I found him at his house in New Town and received a very kind and courteous welcome. Dr. Hope was a polished gentleman, but a little stately and formal withal. . . . He proved himself a model professor and fully entitled to act as a mentor. The professorship of chemistry was, at the time of my Edinburgh residence, very lucrative. The chair was so ably filled and the science so fully illustrated by experiments that the course drew a large audience which, at three guineas a ticket, probably gave him an income of four thousand dollars or more—some said, five thousand. He with his brother kept bachelors' hall in a handsome house on Princes Street, in the New Town. . . .

"Dr. Hope's lectures . . . were not only learned, posting up the history of the discovery, and giving the facts clearly and fully, but the experiments were prepared on a liberal scale. They were apposite and beautiful, and so neatly and skilfully performed that rarely was even a drop spilled upon the table. . . . Dr. Hope lectured in full dress, without any protection for his clothes; he held a white handkerchief in his hand, and performed all his experiments upon a high table, himself standing on an elevated platform, and surrounded on all sides and behind by his pupils. . . ." (53).

Richard Kirwan, 1733–1812. Irish chemist. Author of a treatise on water analyses, which is one of the first books on quantitative analysis. Famous for his early researches on strontia.

In his "Story of the University of Edinburgh," Sir Alexander Grant said that "Hope was fully alive to the importance of the quantitative age in Chemistry . . . he had learnt Lavoisier's views from himself, and in personal communication with Dalton had imbibed his ideas of atomic constitution." Professor Hope's two greatest contributions to science were his research on strontia and his observation of the curious and beneficent property that water has of attaining its maximum density at a certain temperature (now fixed accurately at 4°C.). He abandoned research, however, in order to devote all his time to the improvement of his lectures.

Since he sometimes had more than five hundred students, it was necessary for him to perform the lecture experiments on a very large scale (54).

Among the first to investigate strontia were F. G. Sulzer, J. F. Blumenbach, J. G. Schmeisser (18), Court-Apothecary J. K. F. Meyer of Stettin, R. Kirwan (28, 29, 50), M. H. Klaproth (19), Bertrand Pelletier (16), Tobias Lowitz (64), and Fourcroy and Vauquelin (17). In 1799 George Smith Gibbes of Bath analyzed a crystalline stone from the neighborhood of Sodbury, Gloucestershire, where it was used for making gravel walks, and found it to be strontium sulfate (celestite) (110).

Sir Humphry Davy isolated the metal in 1808 by the method he had used for calcium and barium (5, 3). In 1924 P. S. Danner of the University of California allowed the oxides of barium and strontium to react with magnesium or aluminum and, upon distilling, obtained both barium and strontium in a high state of purity. His method was a refinement of the one previously used by A. Guntz (33, 34).

Strontium in Plants and Animals. In 1812 Professor Giuseppe Moretti of Milan stated that strontium sulfate (celestite) is found in lavas and volcanic conglomerates, in conchiferous rock, and in certain madreporites (111). In 1865 J. G. Forchhammer detected strontium in the boiler scale of Transatlantic steamers and in fucoid plants, especially in *Fucus vesiculosus* (106). In 1927 A. Desgrez and J. Meunier detected strontium carbonate in human bones and teeth (112, 113, 114). Since radiostrontium, like radiocalcium, has a tendency to deposit in bone tissue, it has been used experimentally in the treatment of bone cancers (115).

MAGNESIUM

During a drought in the summer of 1618 Henry Wicker (or Wickes) discovered on the common at Epsom, Surrey, a small hole filled with water. To his astonishment, not one of his thirsty cattle would drink there. This bitter water was found to have a healing effect on external sores and to be useful also as an internal medicament. By the middle of the seventeenth century, Epsom had become a fashionable spa, attracting famous visitors from the continent (40, 62).

In 1695 Dr. Nehemiah Grew published a dissertation on the medicinal value of salt from these wells (41). Dr. Grew prepared solid Epsom salt from this well water and recognized it as a unique substance: "The Purging bitter Salt . . . does differ in its Nature and Species from all other Salts" (62, 69). Nehemiah Grew in England and Marcello Malpighi in Italy laid the foundations for the science of plant anatomy (70).

In 1726 John Toland said of the Epsom spring: "these aluminous waters are experienc'd to be very beneficial . . .; the salt that is chymically made of 'em being famous over all Europe" (40).

Since the supply of the natural salt was insufficient to meet the demand for it, it was soon superseded by an artificial product. Gilles-Egide-François Boulduc stated in 1731 that if all this salt on the market came from the Epsom well, the latter must consist entirely of salt without any water (116).

Dr. Mendez, a physician in England, found after long searching that the artificial Epsom salt came from two salt springs, one at Limington, Hampshire, and the other at Portsea Island near Portsmouth. Since the liquor from the salt piles there was very bitter, it was necessary to remove the bitter salt from the sodium chloride. After these salts had crystallized out together in canals dug in the earth, the mass was boiled in large vessels until completely dissolved. The earthy impurities and the heavy concentrated solution of sodium chloride sank to the bottom. As long as the upper layer continued to be bitter, it was skimmed off, concentrated, and allowed to crystallize to form the artificial Epsom salt (117). Boulduc found that this artificial product could be prepared not only from the mother liquor of sea salt but also from rock salt (116).

According to Torbern Bergman, crystals of artificial Epsom salt from sea water "are sometimes so large that they are sold for Glauber's salt; and on the other hand, in France, Glauber's salt, being reduced to small speculae, by agitating it during the crystallization, is sold for Epsom salt. "These frauds," said he, "are indeed of little consequence, yet they throw a veil over the truth, and are not easily discovered" (42).

Caspar Neumann (1683-1737) stated that the artificial Epsom salt was prepared at Portsmouth by adding sulfuric acid to the mother liquors left in the purification of sea salt imported from Spain and Portugal (43). He distinguished clearly between Epsom salt and the "sal mirabile of Glauber" (sodium sulfate), and stated that "The earth of the bitter purging salt is called *Magnesia alba*. . . . I have nowhere met with this earth in the mineral kingdom. . . ." He did not distinguish between magnesia alba and lime, however (43).

An excellent account of the early history of magnesia is to be found in Torbern Bergman's "Physical and Chemical Essays" (42). At the beginning of the eighteenth century, a certain canon regular sold at Rome a secret panacea called *magnesia alba,* or *Count Palma's powder.* In 1707 Michael Bernhard Valentini of Giessen revealed the method of preparing it by calcination from "the last lixivium of nitre." Two years later, Johann Adrian Slevogt of Jena gave an easier way of preparing it by precipitation. Since this powder effervesced with acids, chemists long confused it with "calcareous earth," or calcium carbonate, which they used to prepare from crabs' eyes, oyster shells, and egg shells. Friedrich Hoffmann (1660-1742) observed, however, that when calcareous earth was treated with vitriolic (sulfuric) acid, it yielded an insipid salt, whereas magnesia was converted by similar treatment into an intensely bitter one (*42*).

At this time is was believed that when carbonates were calcined they combined with an acrid principle from the fire to form caustic alkalies. In 1755, however, Dr. Joseph Black (*26*) of Edinburgh published a famous treatise entitled, "Experiments upon Magnesia Alba, Quicklime, and some other Alkaline Substances," in which he proved that carbonates *lose* weight during calcination and that the substance

Johann Rudolph Glauber, 1604–1670. German chemist who detected sodium sulfate (Glauber's salt, the *enixum* of Paracelsus) in water from a spring near Vienna and introduced its use into medicine. His "Description of New Philosophical Furnaces" contains methods for the preparation of pyroligneous acid and the mineral acids. See ref. (*63*).

expelled is carbon dioxide, "fixed air." In this treatise he showed that magnesia is entirely different from lime, and four years later A. S. Marggraf in Berlin made the same discovery independently (*6, 18, 20, 21, 38*).

Other Magnesian Minerals. In 1760 A. S. Marggraf analyzed some Saxon serpentine, which, because of its property of becoming hard when burned, was then supposed to be a clay, or mineral containing calcium or aluminum. "This so-called serpentine-stone," said he, "which I have used in the following experiments, is that which is found so abundantly in the Saxon mountains, in the great quarry near Zöplitz, that a brisk trade is carried on, near and far, in vessels made from it. It is of various colors, black, gray, greenish, whitish, pale yellow, with red veins (or) spots, intermingled with amianthus (silky asbestos); of varying hardness, to be sure, but always so soft that all kinds of vessels can be turned from it, such as mortars, boxes, tea- and coffee-pots, cups, bowls, dishes, warming-stones, etc. Although it is for this reason well known to everyone, the true composition and base of this stone are nevertheless unknown" (118).

Since the serpentine did not cling to the tongue nor gradually disintegrate in water, as clays do even after moderate heating, Marggraf believed that it must contain a soluble earth entirely distinct from alumina. When he decomposed the mineral with sulfuric acid, he noticed that a residue of silicic acid remained and that the solution contained a peculiar alkaline earth which was neither lime nor alumina. When he evaporated the solution, it formed no alum but displayed crystals identical with those from natural Epsom salt and easily distinguishable from those of selenite (calcium sulfate dihydrate). He noticed that magnesium nitrate is deliquescent; that the chloride is identical with that obtained from the mother liquor of common salt and that heat decomposes it with loss of hydrogen chloride; that the acetate, unlike calcium acetate, does not crystallize; and that ignited magnesia does not become hot when treated with water (118, 119, 120).

Joseph Black, in his "Lectures on the Elements of Chemistry," described some of the minerals which even in the eighteenth century were known to contain magnesia. "There is a set of earthy or stony substances," said he, "concerning the classing of which fossilists were a long time undecided and disagreed. Most ranked them among the clays, and Cronstedt among the rest. They have been known by the names steatites [soapstone], lapis serpentinus [serpentine], lapis nephriticus [a kind of jade], and lapis ollaris [potstone]. . . . In general they are soft like soap or suet; so soft as to be cut or turned. . . . It hardens in the fire without melting. Hence some species are turned into vessels. This is the lapis ollaris. Inverary House is built of an impure species of it. Mr. Margraaf [sic!] first shewed that all these contain more or less of magnesia, closely combined with some other earthy substances, and often with much iron, by which they are tinged with the green colour, more or less deep, that appears in many of them" (118, 121).

At the beginning of the eighteenth century, J.-P. de Tournefort recognized the most important properties of amianthus, or silky asbestos. "'Tis a vulgar Error," said he, "to think the feather'd Alum to be the same with the *Lapis Amianthus*, or incombustible Stone. Whenever I ask'd for feather'd Alum, either in France, Italy, England, or Holland, they always shew'd me a base sort of *Amianthus* brought from Carysto in the

Negropont: it is easy to break and divide, and of all the kinds of *Amianthus* is certainly the most despicable; but it does not melt or consume either in Fire or Water, any more than the Amianthus of Smyrna, Genoa, and the Pyrenees. To make short, the *Amianthus* is a stony insipid Substance which softens in Oil and thereby acquires Suppleness enough to be spun into Threads: it makes Purses and Handkerchiefs, which not only resist the Fire, but are whiten'd and cleansed in it. The plumous Alum, contrariwise, is a true Salt, not differing from the common Alum otherwise than as it is divided into small Strings. . ." (*122*). Marg-

Side View of the École Supérieure de Pharmacie, showing the laboratories for practical pharmacy.

graf later determined the magnesia in amianthus, a fine, silky asbestos named for Amiandus on the Island of Cyprus. The mines there have been worked since ancient times (*123*).

The Indians and colonists of New England found many uses for serpentine, soapstone, and asbestos. Per Kalm, in describing his journey to North America in 1748–51, wrote as follows: "Mr. [Benjamin] Franklin gave me a piece of stone which, on account of its indestructibility in the fire, is made use of in New England for making melting furnaces and forges. It consists of a mixture of lapis ollaris, or serpentine stone, and of asbest. . . . Another stone is called soapstone by many of the Swedes, being as smooth as soap on the outside. They make use of it for rubbing spots out of their cloaths. . . . If the people can get a sufficient quantity of this stone, they lay the steps before the houses with it, instead of bricks . . . ; and in several public buildings, such as the house of assembly for the province, the whole lower wall is built of it. . . .

"The mountain flax," said Kalm, "or the amiant with soft fibres, which can easily be separated, is found abundantly in Pensylvania [sic]. . . . Mr. Franklin told me that, twenty and some odd years ago, when he made a voyage to England, he had a little purse with him, made of the mountain flax of this country, which he presented to Sir Hans Sloane. I have likewise seen paper made of this stone. . . .

"The old boilers or kettles of the Indians," continued Kalm, "were either made of clay or of different kinds of potstone [lapis ollaris]. . . . A few of the oldest Swedes could yet remember seeing the Indians boil their meat in these pots. . . . The Indians, notwithstanding their being unacquainted with iron, steel, and other metals, have learnt to hollow out very ingeniously these pots or kettles of potstone. The old tobacco-pipes of the Indians are likewise made of clay or potstone or serpentine-stone" (124).

Thomas Henry mentioned in 1789 another magnesium mineral, "the Spuma Maris, an earthy substance, from which the Turkey tobacco-pipes are made" (125). This was the hydrated magnesium silicate known as meerschaum. For the use of artists and potters, Henry published a list of the principal compounds, minerals, and rocks containing magnesium, and gave the chemical composition of each. "Magnesia as prepared for the shops," said he, "would be too expensive for the purposes of manufactures, which may perhaps often be equally answered by using it in these combined forms" (125).

When Sir Humphry Davy isolated a little magnesium metal in the famous experiments already described, he called it magnium because, as he said, the word magnesium is easily confused with manganese. Nevertheless, the name magnesium has persisted, and the metal is no longer known by the one which Davy gave it.

In 1792 Anton Rupprecht prepared impure magnesium (contaminated with iron) by reduction of magnesium oxide with carbon and called the metal "austrium" in honor of Austria (68).

The quantity of metal which Davy prepared was very small, and it was not until 1831 that it was first prepared in a coherent form. This was done by the French chemist, Antoine-Alexandre-Brutus Bussy, who was born at Marseilles on May 29, 1794. He studied at the École Polytechnique for a time, but his interest in chemistry soon led him to abandon his military career and to become apprenticed to a pharmacist. After studying pharmacy at Lyons and at Paris he became a pupil of P.-J. Robiquet, who was then a préparateur in chemistry at the École de

Pharmacie. Bussy graduated in pharmacy in 1823 and received his medical degree in 1832.

Although most of his researches were of a pharmaceutical nature, he published in 1831 a paper entitled "Sur le Radical métallique de la Magnésie," in which he described a new method of isolating magnesium, which consisted in heating a mixture of magnesium chloride and potassium in a glass tube. When he washed out the potassium chloride, small, shining globules of metallic magnesium remained (8, 20, 27).

Antoine-Alexandre-Brutus Bussy, 1794–1882. French chemist, pharmacist, and physician. Professor of chemistry at the École de Pharmacie in Paris. He was connected with this school for more than fifty years, and for nearly thirty years he served as its director. In 1831 he obtained magnesium in coherent form.

For several years Bussy taught pharmacology in the medical school at the École de Pharmacie, and in 1856 he served as president of the Academy of Medicine. For fifty-six years he served on the editorial staff of the *Journal de Pharmacie et de Chimie.* He died at Paris on February 1, 1882, at the age of eighty-seven years (22).

Magnesium in Plants and Animals. Even in the eighteenth century, chemists realized that plants contain magnesia. William Lewis, in his notes to "The Chemical Works of Caspar Neumann, M.D.," said in 1759 that "the ashes of vegetables freed from their saline parts dissolve readily and plentifully in all acids, and appear to be similar to the mineral earth called Magnesia, or the earthy basis of the bitter purging Salts of mineral waters. . . . It forms the same compounds with acids; and like that earth also, it acquires no acrimony nor any change of its quality from fire . ." (43).

"The late Dr. Lewis," said Thomas Henry, "has considered the earth which is obtained from vegetables, after incineration and washing, as of the same nature with Magnesia; and if we endeavour to trace the origin of magnesian earth, it may appear not improbable that, as all calcareous earth is the result of the destruction of testaceous animals, so the magnesium arises from vegetables, which have perished and undergone some process in the great laboratory of nature whereby they are reduced to this state. By putrefaction they are altered to a fine black Mold. And it may be that Nature, who often operates by slow and secret steps, may make such further changes as to convert this Mold into magnesian earth" (125).

L. von Crell mentioned in 1791, in a footnote to J. G. Wallerius's paper on the earths derived from plants, that the presence of magnesia in plants had been established through the researches of Rückert (126). This was probably G. C. A. Rückert, court apothecary at Ingelfingen, who published a book on agricultural chemistry in 1789.

Richard Willstätter prepared in 1906 some very pure chlorophyll which yielded on incineration 1.84 per cent of ash, 1.67 per cent of which was magnesia. The ash was free from calcium and iron. When he prepared chlorophyllin from phanerogams, mono- and dicotyledons, and gymnosperms, from *Fucus,* from the stinging nettle, from grass, and from pine needles, he found that the ash always contained magnesium and no other metal. He concluded that plants, like animals, live by the catalytic action of metals which they contain in the form of complex organic compounds. He stated that assimilation of carbonic acid is a reaction of the basic metal magnesium, which, even in complex organic molecules, exhibits great reactivity. He compared this absorption of carbon dioxide to the Grignard synthesis. Whereas animals live by the decomposition of organic compounds by the oxygen in their blood, plants, according to Willstätter, live synthetically by means of their magnesium (127). In most animals the oxygen carrier is iron.

Since magnesium is a constituent of the chlorophyll molecule, it is essential to the growth of all green plants (78). It occurs in all the cells and fluids of the human body, especially in bones and muscles (82). E. V. McCollum and his collaborators have proved that it is essential to animal life. The principal sources of magnesium in human diets are milk, vegetables, and green plants (128, 129).

Magnesium from Sea Water. Even in the eighteenth century, Torbern Bergman knew that sea water derives its bitter taste from magnesium chloride (130, 125). On January 21, 1941, the Dow Chemical Company produced at Freeport, Texas, an ingot of magnesium which was the first commercial ingot of any metal ever to be taken from sea water (131).

CADMIUM

Cadmium was discovered in 1817 by Dr. Friedrich Stromeyer, a professor of chemistry and pharmacy at Göttingen University. He was born on August 2, 1776, at a time when the phlogiston theory was drawing its last breath (8). After studying chemistry, botany, and pharmacy in his native city of Göttingen, he worked in Paris under the great master of analytical chemistry N.-L. Vauquelin. Following the example of this

Science Service

Friedrich Stromeyer, 1776–1835. German physician, botanist, chemist, and pharmacist. Inspector-general of all the Hanoverian apothecary shops. Discoverer of the element cadmium. His collection of thirty mineral analyses is a classic of analytical chemistry.

famous teacher, he devoted himself almost entirely to the analysis of minerals (9).

In 1802 he became a *Privatdozent* in the faculty of medicine at Göttingen, and was rapidly promoted until in 1810 he became a full professor (*Professor ordinarius*). In the German universities, as in certain American ones, professors frequently hold government offices. Dr. Stromeyer was the inspector-general of all the apothecaries of Hanover. On an inspection trip to Hildesheim in the autumn of 1817 he noticed that a certain preparation which, according to the Hanoverian Pharmacopœia, ought to have contained zinc oxide, contained zinc carbonate instead. The events which followed were described by Dr. Stromeyer in his letter to Dr. J. S. C. Schweigger written on April 26, 1818:

As I was last harvest inspecting the apothecaries' shops in the principality of Hildesheim, in consequence of the general inspection of the apothecaries of the kingdom having been entrusted to me by our most gracious Regency, I observed in several of them, instead of the proper oxide of zinc, carbonate of zinc, which had been almost entirely procured from the chemical manufactory at Salzgitter. This carbonate of zinc had a dazzling white colour; but when heated to redness, it assumed a yellow colour, inclining to orange, though no sensible portion of iron or lead could be detected in it.

In an attempt to determine why this substitution had been made, Dr. Stromeyer visited the pharmaceutical firm at Salzgitter:

When I afterwards visited Salzgitter, during the course of this journey [said he] and went to the chemical manufactory from which the carbonate of zinc had been procured; and when I expressed my surprise that carbonate of zinc should be sold instead of oxide of zinc, Mr. Jost, who has the charge of the pharmaceutical department of the manufactory, informed me that the reason was, that their carbonate of zinc, when exposed to a red heat, always assumed a yellow colour, and was on that account supposed to contain iron, though the greatest care had been taken beforehand to free the zinc from iron, and though it was impossible to detect any iron in the oxide of zinc itself.

The fact that the zinc carbonate could not be converted into the oxide without discoloration interested Dr. Stromeyer greatly:

This information [said he] induced me to examine the oxide of zinc more carefully, and I found, to my great surprise, that the colour which is assumed was owing to the presence of a peculiar metallic oxide, the existence of which had not hitherto been suspected. I succeeded by a peculiar process in freeing it from oxide of zinc, and in reducing it to the metallic state . . . (10).

His method of obtaining the metal was as follows. He dissolved the impure zinc oxide in sulfuric acid and passed in hydrogen sulfide. After filtering and washing the precipitate of mixed sulfides, he dissolved it in concentrated hydrochloric acid and evaporated to dryness to drive off excess acid. After dissolving the residue in water, he added a sufficient excess of ammonium carbonate solution to redissolve any zinc and copper that may have been precipitated. Since the carbonate of the new element was not soluble in excess ammonium carbonate, Dr. Stromeyer filtered it off, washed it, and ignited it to the oxide. After mixing the brown oxide with lampblack in a glass or earthen retort, he heated the mixture to moderate redness. Upon opening the retort he found a bluish gray metal with a bright luster (*10*).

Exhibit of Drugs and Medicinals at the École Supérieure de Pharmacie.
Vauquelin was the director of this school from the time of its reorganization
in 1803 until his death in 1829.

However, since he had only three grams of the new metal, he was unable at first to make a thorough study of its properties. Fortunately, he soon received more of it from an unexpected source, for in the same letter to Dr. Schweigger he wrote:

I am happy, therefore, to be able to inform you, that within these few days, through Mr. Hermann, of Schönebeck, and Dr. Roloff, of Magdeburg, who took an interest in this metal, I have been placed in a situation which will enable me to carry my experiments further. During the apothecary's visitation in the state of Magdeburg some years ago, there was found in the possession of several apothecaries, a preparation of zinc from Silesia, made in Hermann's manufactory at Schönebeck, which was confiscated on the supposition that it contained arsenic, because, when dissolved in acids, and mixed with sulphuretted hydrogen, it let fall a yellow precipitate, which, from the chemical experiments made on it, was considered as orpiment.

This fact [continued Stromeyer] could not be indifferent to Mr. Hermann, as it affected the credit of his manufactory, and the more especially as the Medicinal Counsellor Roloff, who had assisted at the Apothecaries' visitation, had drawn up a statement of the whole, and sent it to Hufeland, who published it in the February number of his *Medical Journal*. He, therefore, subjected the suspected oxide of zinc to a careful examination; but he could not succeed in detecting any arsenic in it (24).

He then requested the Medical Counsellor Roloff (23) to repeat his experiments on the oxide once more. This he did very readily and he now perceived that the precipitate which had at first been taken by him for orpiment, was not so in reality; but owed its existence to the presence of another metal, having considerable resemblance to arsenic, but probably new. To obtain full certainty on the subject, both the gentlemen* had recourse to me, and have sent me, within these few days, both a portion of the Silesian oxide of zinc and specimens of the orpiment-like precipitate and of the metal extracted from it, with the request that I would subject these bodies to a new examination, and in particular that I should endeavour to ascertain whether they contained any arsenic (10).

Dr. Stromeyer soon surmised that the metal which Mr. K. S. L. Hermann and Dr. J. C. H. Roloff had extracted from the Silesian zinc oxide was the same as the one he had obtained from the Salzgitter product (31, 35, 39).

From the particulars already stated [said he] I considered it as probable that this Silesian oxide of zinc contained likewise the metal which I had discovered; and as it gives with sulphuretted hydrogen a precipitate similar in colour to orpiment, I considered this to be the reason why the oxide was supposed to contain arsenic. Some experiments made upon it fully confirmed this opinion. I have, therefore, informed Mr. Hermann of the circumstance by the post; and I shall not fail to give the same information to Medicinal Counsellor Roloff, whose letter I received only the day before yesterday

This discovery gave great satisfaction and relief to Mr. Hermann because it again brought his pharmaceutical establishment into good standing, and it also gave Dr. Stromeyer the opportunity to make a more thorough study of the new metal and its compounds. Because this metal is so frequently found associated with zinc, he named it *cadmium*, meaning *cadmium fornacum or furnace calamine*. In the researches which led to this discovery, he was assisted by two of his students, Mr. Mahner of Brunswick and Mr. Siemens of Hamburg.

W. Meissner (36) of Halle and C. Karsten (25) of Berlin, without

---

* Dr. Roloff (31) explained that this was not done to settle a dispute.

any knowledge of the work done by Stromeyer, Roloff, and Hermann, also discovered cadmium independently (*11*). Meissner analyzed two products from the Schönebeck plant sent him by Superintendent of Mines von Veltheim, one of which proved to be the carbonate and the other the sulfide of the new metal. By dissolving the carbonate in nitric acid and placing a rod of pure zinc in the solution, he obtained a voluminous, light gray deposit. When he washed and dried it and ground the resulting powder in an agate mortar, it exhibited a metallic luster. Meissner made a careful study of the metal and its compounds.

In 1817, perhaps as a result of his great discovery, Dr. Stromeyer received the honorary title of *Hofrath*, or court counselor. After pub-

Old Filter Stand

lishing many papers on mineralogy and chemistry, and serving his university for many years as an inspiring teacher, he died on August 18, 1835, in the city where he was born and where he had spent most of his life (*8, 65*).

In 1821 Nils Nordenskiöld wrote to Berzelius, "Stromeijer [*sic*] has the finest and neatest laboratory I have yet seen in Germany, and is certainly one of the few whose analyses are somewhat reliable. Nevertheless his procedures differ from yours in many important respects. I shall take the liberty of mentioning a few of the differences I have noticed. One sees no filter stand. All filtrations are made in glass cylinders such as come with our brandy gauges, one foot high and from 3 to 1 inch in diameter; as the funnels are wider, they are simply placed over the edge of the glass the liquid spatters around, but the filter takes up that which spatters out. The filter is folded like the French ones and always extends over the rim of the funnel. The filter is not burned. The solutions are also precipitated in the above-mentioned glass cylinders, and the digestions are made in retorts or small flasks with long necks and thin bottoms. The sandbath is not used; the heating is done over the free flame or on hot plates. In regard to reagents, I have noticed that he prefers to use the fixed alkalies as precipitating agents instead of ammonium hydroxide which I believe involves difficulty in washing the filter, especially such as they use here. The balance Stromeyer uses is very good, but one has to walk through a hall to reach the room where it is kept" (*61*).

Cadmium from Zinc Ores. In an editorial note in volume 59 of his *Annalen der Physik*, L. W. Gilbert gave the following quotation from a "Report of a metallurgical trip through Silesia in Professor Kastner's German *Gewerbsfreunde,* 1818, Number 24: In Silesia and in the nearby parts of Poland, zinc is obtained only from calamine. . . . In the zinc smelters one sees the metal burning with a bright flame from all the condensers, and in the receptacles where the separated metal collects, piles of zinc oxide are always found." Gilbert then added that the zinc oxide in which Hermann discovered cadmium probably came from these piles (*132*).

Dr. Stromeyer detected cadmium in tutty and other kinds of zinc oxide, in metallic zinc, in Silesian zinc ores, and in several blendes, especially one from Przibram, Bohemia, which contained 2 or 3 per cent of it (*10, 24*). Thus it is evident that cadmium was first discovered in substances of which it is merely a non-essential constituent.

In a letter to the *Annals of Philosophy*, dated Cambridge, February 18, 1820, Edward Daniel Clarke wrote as follows: "Some varieties of *radiated blende* from Przibram in Bohemia are described by Stromeyer as containing two or three per cent of cadmium. At a sale . . . in London, I procured specimens of the particular mineral thus alluded to, which were sold under the name of *splendent fibrous blende from Przibram, pronounced Pritzbram.* I found afterwards that they had been brought to England by Mr. J. Sowerby of Lisle-street, a dealer in minerals. . . . Upon my return to Cambridge, I endeavoured to obtain cadmium from this ore, and succeeded . . ." (*133*). Clarke also found this element in the zinc silicate from Derbyshire, England, and his results were soon confirmed by W. H. Wollaston and J. G. Children. In 1822 Clarke published a paper on the presence of cadmium in commercial sheet zinc (*134*).

In the same year, William Herapath analyzed some sublimate from a zinc smelter, and found from 12 to 20 per cent of cadmium in it. Since cadmium is even more volatile than zinc, much of it was lost. Herapath suggested a modification of the zinc distillation process which would make it possible to recover the cadmium (*135*).

Greenockite the First Cadmium Mineral. In 1841 Charles Murray Cathcart (Lord Greenock) discovered a rare mineral of which cadmium is an essential constituent. Greenockite, or cadmium sulfide, "was found in the course of excavating the Bishopton Tunnel, near Port Glasgow." Lord Greenock (second Earl Cathcart) was born in 1783, entered the army at a very early age, and devoted most of his life to military affairs in Spain, Holland, Scotland, and Canada. He served as Commander-in-chief of the British forces in North America and in 1846–47 as Governor-general of Canada (*136*).

The Royal Staff Corps which he commanded was a scientific one, which maintained a museum of objects collected by its members. After Lord Greenock's death in 1859, Lord Neaves said before the Royal Society of Edinburgh, "If it be considered how total a revolution of habits and employments was involved in the transition from his military to his civil life, it is remarkable what success and energy attended his scientific career during the years he spent among us. He was distinguished by persevering and acute observation in what regarded geological and mineralogical research, which he carried on in a minute, laborious, and systematic manner. He detected many interesting phenomena in the very neighbourhood of Edinburgh, which had escaped those who had lived there always. His conversation on these subjects was pre-eminently instructive; and it is believed that he never took an ordinary walk without bringing home some specimen, or at least some remembered fact, which served him for subsequent meditation. He was fond of the society of men of science, and his continued interest in the Royal Society formed an essential element in its prosperity" (*137*).

Fluorescent Lighting. An important application of the cold light from certain compounds of zinc, cadmium, and other elements of Group II of the periodic system is the modern fluorescent lamp. A long tube, containing an inert gas at low pressure and a few droplets of mercury, is constructed with an electrode at each end. This tube has an inside coating of some stable, fluorescent substance which will absorb the resonance line of a low-pressure mercury discharge in the ultraviolet at 2537 Ångström units and reradiate this energy in a desirable part of the visible spectrum (*57*). The basic part of the fluorescent compound used always contains a lower atomic weight metal from Group II. Zinc silicate, for example, gives a green fluorescence; cadmium silicate and the borates of cadmium and zinc give pink; magnesium tungstate and zinc beryllium silicate give white light, and calcium tungstate gives blue. Although the sulfides of zinc and cadmium are sometimes used in fluorescent paints, they are not stable enough for use inside fluorescent lamps (*57*).

LITERATURE CITED

(1) DAVY, DR. J., "The Collected Works of Sir Humphry Davy, Bart.," Vol. 1, Smith, Elder and Co., London, 1839, p. 235. Poem by Sir H. D.

(2) JAGNAUX, R., "Histoire de la Chimie," Vol. 2, Baudry et Cie., Paris, 1891, pp. 140–4.

(3) DAVY, H., "Electro-chemical researches, on the decomposition of the earths; with observations on the metals obtained from the alkaline earths, and on the amalgam procured from ammonia," *Nicholson's J.*, 21, 366–83 (Suppl., 1808); 22, 54–68 (Jan., 1809).

(4) JAGNAUX, R., "Histoire de la Chimie," ref. (2), Vol. 2, pp. 130–7.

(5) *Ibid.*, vol. 2, pp. 138–40.

(6) *Ibid.*, Vol. 2, pp. 153–5.

(7) DAVY, DR. J., "Memoirs of the Life of Sir Humphry Davy, Bart.," Vol. 1, Longman, Rees, etc., London, 1836, pp. 395–6.

(8) POGGENDORFF, J. C., "Biographisch-Literarisches Handwörterbuch zur Geschichte der exakten Wissenschaften," 6 vols., Verlag Chemie, Leipzig and Berlin, 1863–1937. Articles on Stromeyer and Bussy.

(9) THOMSON, THOMAS, "History of Chemistry," Vol. 2, Colburn and Bentley, 1831, pp. 217–21.

(10) Letter from Dr. Stromeyer to Dr. Schweigger, *Annals of Phil.*, 13, 108–11 (Feb., 1819); translated from *Schweigger's J.*, 21, 297 (May 28, 1818); F. STROMEYER, "New details respecting cadmium," *Annals of Phil.*, 14, 269 (Oct., 1819); *Ann. der Physik*, 60, 193; *Sci. News Letter*, 19, 75–6 (Jan. 31, 1931).

(11) BUDGEN, "Cadmium: Its Metallurgy, Properties and Uses," Chas. Griffin and Co., London, 1924, p. xiii.

(12) "Oeuvres de Lavoisier," Vol. 1, Imprimerie Impériale. Paris, 1864, p. 122.

(13) BROCKMAN, C. J., "Fused electrolytes—an historical sketch," *J. Chem. Educ.*, 4, 512–23 (Apr., 1927).

(14) SÖDERBAUM, H. G., "Jac. Berzelius Bref," Vol. 1, part 2, Almqvist and Wiksells, Upsala, 1912–1914, pp. 7–8.

(15) SCHEELE, C. W., "Sämmtliche physische und chemische Werke," Vol. 2, 2nd edition translated by Hermbstädt, Rottmann, Berlin, 1793, pp. 179–82.

(16) PELLETIER, B., "Extrait d'Observations sur la Strontiane," *Ann. chim. phys.* (1), 21, 113–43 (Feb. 28. 1797).

(17) FOURCROY, A.-F. and N.-L. VAUQUELIN, "Extrait de deux Mémoires sur un nouveau moyen d'obtenir la Baryte pure, et sur les propriétés de cette terre comparées à celles de la Strontiane," *Ann. chim. phys.*, (1), 21, 276–83 (Mar., 1797).

(18) KOPP, H., "*Geschichte der Chemie*," Vol. 4, F. Vieweg und Sohn, Braunschweig, 1847, pp. 42–55; J. G. SCHMEISSER, "Account of a mineral substance called strontionite [*sic*]," *Phil. Trans.*, 84, 419 (1794).

(19) KLAPROTH, M. H., "Analytical Essays towards Promoting the Chemical Knowledge of Mineral Substances," Cadell and Davies, London, 1801, pp. 223–37 and 387–98.

(20) WOOTTON, A. C., "Chronicles of Pharmacy," Vol. 1, Macmillan and Co., London, 1910, pp. 354–8.

(21) BUGGE, G., "Das Buch der grossen Chemiker," Vol. 1, Verlag Chemie, Berlin, 1930, pp. 240–52. Biographical sketch of Black by Max Speter.

(22) BOURQUELOT, "Le Centenaire du Journal de Pharmacie et de Chimie, 1809–1909," Octave Doin et Fils, Paris, 1910, pp. 53–4.

(23) ROLOFF, C. H., *Gilb. Ann.*, 61, 205 (1819); 70, 194 (1822).

(24) HERMANN, K. S. L., "Ueber das schlesische Zinkoxyd und über ein darin gefundenes sehr wahrscheinlich noch unbekanntes Metall," *Gilb. Ann.* 59, 95–6 (1818); *ibid.*, 59, 113–16 (1818). Stromeyer's letter of Apr. 19, 1818, on cadmium, *ibid.*, 66, 276, (1820).

(25) KARSTEN, C., *Archiv Berg. Hütt.*, i, p. 209; "Aus einem Schreiben des Prof, [J. F. W.] Brandes in Breslau an den Prof. Gilbert," *Gilbert s Ann. der Physik*, 59, 104–7 (1818). Letter of May 13, 1818 regarding Karsten's work on cadmium.

(26) IRVINE, SIR J., "Scotland's contribution to chemistry," *J. Chem. Educ.*, 7, 2810–4 (Dec., 1930).

(27) BUSSY, A.-A.-B., "Mémoire sur le radical métallique de la magnésie," *Ann. chim. phys.*, (2), 46, 434–6 (1831).

(28) SMITH, E. F., "Forgotten chemists," *J. Chem. Educ.*, 3, 35 (Jan., 1926).

(29) BROCKMAN, C. J., "Richard Kirwan—chemist, 1733–1812," *J. Chem. Educ.*, 4, 1275–82 (Oct., 1927); REILLY and O'FLYNN, "Richard Kirwan, an Irish chemist of the eighteenth century," *Isis*, 13 (2), 298–319 (Feb., 1930).

(30) DAINS, F. B., "John Griscom and his impressions of foreign chemists in 1818–19," *J. Chem. Educ.*, 8, 1307–8 (July, 1931).

(31) ROLOFF, J. C. H., "Zur Geschichte des Kadmiums von dem Medicinalrath und Kreisphysikus Dr. Roloff in Magdeburg," *Gilbert's Ann. d. Physik*, 61, 205–10 (1819).

(32) BRACE, "Notes on the metallurgy of calcium," *Chem. Met. Eng.*, 25, 105–9 (July 20, 1921).

(33) GUNTZ, A., "Sur la préparation du baryum," *Compt. rend.*, 133, 872–4 (Nov. 25, 1901); "Sur le strontium métallique et son hydrure," *ibid.*, 133, 1209–10 (Dec. 23, 1901).

(34) DANNER, P. S., "The preparation of very pure barium and strontium," *J. Am. Chem. Soc.*, 46, 2382–5 (Nov., 1924).

(35) "Aus einem Schreiben des Herrn Ober.-Berg.-Hauptmann Gerhardt an den Prof. Gilbert," *Gilbert's Ann. der Physik*, 59, 97–9 (1818). Letter of May 1, 1818.

(36) "Ueber ein neues Metall in den schlesischen Zinkoxyde, vom Dr. W. Meissner, Besitzer der Löwenapotheke in Halle," *ibid.*, 59, 99–104 (1818). Letter of May 4, 1818.

(37) DERHAM, W., "Philosophical experiments and observations of the late eminent Dr. Robert Hooke, F.R.S. . . . and other eminent Virtuoso's in his time," W. and J. Innys, London, 1726, pp. 174–83.

(38) SPETER, MAX, "Joseph Black," *Chem.-Ztg.*, 52, 913 (Nov., 1928).

(39) "Sur un nouveau métal (le cadmium)," *Ann. chim. phys.* (2), 8, 100–1 (1818).

(40) HOME, GORDON, "Epsom. Its History and Its Surroundings," The Homeland Assoc., Epsom and London, 1901, pp. 43–63.

(41) GREW, NEHEMIAH, "Tractatus de Salis Cathartici Amari in Aquis Ebeshamensibus . . . Natura et Usu," London, 1695.

(42) CULLEN, EDMUND, "Physical and chemical Essays Translated from the Original Latin of Sir Torbern Bergman," Vol. 1, J. Murray, Balfour, Gordon, and Dickson, London, 1784, pp. 423–40, 460–3.

(43) LEWIS, WM., "The Chemical Works of Caspar Neumann, M.D.," W. Johnston, G. Keith, A. Linde, etc., London, 1759, 586 pp.

(44) BAILEY, K. C., "The Elder Pliny's Chapters on Chemical Subjects," Vol. 2, Edward Arnold, London, 1932, p. 139; PLINY THE ELDER, "Historia Naturalis," Book 36, chaps. 23–4.

(45) BLANK, E. W., "Lime and lime kilns," *J. Chem. Educ.*, 17, 505–8 (Nov., 1940).

(46) BREHAUT, E., "Cato the Censor on Farming," Columbia University Press, 1933, pp. 33–5, 64–6.

(47) MORGAN, M. H., "Vitruvius. The Ten Books on Architecture," Harvard University Press, Cambridge, 1914, pp. 45–6.

(48) HOPE, T. C., "Account of a mineral from Strontian and of a peculiar species of earth which it contains," *Trans. Roy. Soc. (Edinburgh)*, 4 (2), 3–39 (1798). Read Nov. 4, 1793.

(49) CRAWFORD, ADAIR, "On the medicinal properties of the muriated barytes." *Medical Communications* (*London*) **2**, 301–59 (1790). Read Nov. 10, 1789.

(50) KIRWAN, R., "Versuch über eine neuere Erde, die in der Nähe von Stronthian in Schottland gefunden ist," *Crell's Ann.*, **24**, 119–25 (1795).

(51) MUNK, WM., "The Roll of the Royal College of Physicians of London," Vol. 2, published by the College, London, **1878**, pp. 339–40.

(52) STEPHEN, L. and S. LEE, "Dictionary of National Biography," Vol. 5, Oxford University Press, London, **1921–2**, pp. 49–50. Article on Adair Crawford by Robert Hunt.

(53) FISHER, G. P., "Life of Benjamin Silliman," Vol. 1, Charles Scribner and Co., New York, **1866**, pp. 159–69.

(54) GRANT, SIR A., "The Story of the University of Edinburgh," Vol. 2, Longmans, Green and Co., London, **1884**, pp. 397–8.

(55) "Eloge de M. Guillaume Homberg," Hist. de l'Acad. Roy. des Sciences (Paris), **1715**, pp. 82 ff.

(56) BERNARDI, A., "La storia del fosforo di Bologna nel XVII e XVIII secolo," *La Chimica nell' Industria, nell' Agricoltura, nella Biologia*, **16**, 69–74 (Feb., 1940).

(57) MARDEN, J. W., "Chemicals in fluorescent lamps," *Chem. Met. Eng.*, **48**, 80–4 (Aug., 1941); Editorial, "Operations begin at Fairmont Fluorescent Lamp Plant," *ibid.*, **48**, 82–4 (Aug., 1941).

(58) "The Philosophical Transactions and Collections to the End of the Year 1700 abridg'd . . . John Lowthorp," Vol. 3, Bennet, Knaplock, and Wilkin, London, **1705**, p. 346; *Phil. Trans.*, **1**, n. 21, p. 375 (1665); *ibid.*, **12**, n. 134, p. 842.

(59) PRIESTLEY, J., "The History and Present State of Discoveries Relating to Vision, Light, and Colours," Vol. 1, J. Johnson, London, **1772**, pp. 361–6.

(60) NORDENSKIÖLD, A. E., "C. W. Scheele. Nachgelassene Briefe und Aufzeichnungen," P. A. Norstedt and Sons, Stockholm, **1892**, pp. 115, 118, 121, 243–4, 253, 457.

(61) SÖDERBAUM, H. G., ref. (*14*), Vol. 11, p. 40. Letter of Nils Nordenskiöld to Berzelius, Aug. 3, 1821.

(62) NEAVE, E. W. J., "The Epsom spring," *Isis*, **34**, 210–11 (Winter, 1943).

(63) ARMSTRONG, Eva V. and C. K. DEISCHER, "Johann Rudolf Glauber (1604–70). His chemical and human philosophy," *J. Chem. Educ.*, **19**, 3–8 (Jan., 1942).

(64) LEICESTER, HENRY M., "Tobias Lowitz. Discoverer of basic laboratory methods," *J. Chem. Educ.*, **22**, 149–51 (Mar., 1945); "The history of chemistry in Russia prior to 1900," *ibid.*, **24**, 440–1 (Sept., 1947).

(65) LOCKEMANN, GEORG and R. E. OESPER, "Friedrich Stromeyer and the history of chemical laboratory instruction," *J. Chem. Educ.*, **30**, 202–4 (Apr., 1953).

(66) BROCKMAN, C. J., "Richard Kirwan Chemist 1733–1812," *J. Chem. Educ.*, **4**, 1275–82 (Oct., 1927).

(67) LOWRY, T. M., "Historical Introduction to Chemistry," Macmillan & Co., London, **1936**, pp. 48– 63.

(68) *Crell's Chem. Annalen*, **1792**, p. 195.

(69) GREW, NEHEMIAH, "A Treatise of the Nature and Use of the Bitter Purging Salt contain'd in Epsom and Such Other Waters," London, **1697**.

(70) ARBER, AGNES, "Nehemiah Grew (1641–1712) and Marcello Malpighi (1628–1694): An essay in comparison," *Isis*, **34**, 7–16 (Summer, 1942).

(71) CARTER, HOWARD, "The tomb of Tut-ankh-Amen," Vol. 2, George H. Doran Co., New York City, **1927**, pp. 233–5, 239–40. "The chemistry of the tomb," by A. Lucas.

(72) FELSING, W. A. and A. D. POTTER, "Gypsum and gypsum products," *J. Chem. Educ.*, **7**, 2788–2807 (Dec., 1930).

(73) NEWELL, L. C., "Chemistry in the service of Egyptology," *J. Chem. Educ.*, 10, 259–66 (May, 1933).

(74) HILL, JOHN, "Theophrastus's History of Stones," 2nd ed., printed for the translator, London, 1774, pp. 249–65.

(75) GUNTHER, R. T., "The Greek Herbal of Dioscorides," Oxford University Press, Oxford, 1934, pp. 623–6, 638, 648.

(76) DARMSTAEDTER, LUDWIG, "Handbuch zur Geschichte der Naturwissenschaften und der Technik," 2nd ed., J. Springer, Berlin, 1908, pp. 46–7.

(77) "Disclosures in mineralogy from specimens brought to Dr. [S.L.] Mitchill, "*Medical Repository*, (2), 2, 81 (May, June, July, 1804).

(78) THATCHER, R. W., "The Chemistry of Plant Life," McGraw-Hill Book Co., New York, 1921, pp. 2–11.

(79) WILLIS, L. G. "Bibliography of References to the Literature on the Minor Elements and Their Relation to Plant and Animal Nutrition," Chilean Nitrate Educational Bureau, New York, 1939, columns 148 and 169.

(80) COWELL, S. J., "A note on the calcium content of cabbage," *Biochem. J.*, 26, 1422–3 (1932).

(81) HSU, PENG-CHENG and W. H. ADOLPH, "The distribution of calcium in leafy vegetables," *Chinese Med. J.*, 49, 325–7 (1935).

(82) SHOHL, A. T., "Mineral Metabolism," Reinhold Publishing Corporation, New York, 1939, pp. 32–3, 96, 141, 145, 162–8, 246–7.

(83) ROSEBERRY, H. H., A. B. HASTINGS, and J. K. MORSE, "X-ray analysis of bone and teeth," *J. Biol. Chem.*, 90, 395–406 (Feb., 1931).

(84) "Gmelin's Handbuch der anorganischen Chemie," Verlag Chemie, Berlin, No. 30, pp. 1–3. History and occurrence of barium.

(85) "The Private Life of Galileo," John E. Potter and Co., Philadelphia, 1869, pp. 283–5.

(86) TIRABOSCHI, GIROLAMO, "Storia della letteratura italiana," Vol. VII, Società Tipografica de' Classici Italiani, Milan, 1824, pp. 901–07.

(87) ALDROVANDI, ULISSE, "Opera omnia," Vol. 4, Bononiae, Feronii, 1642, p. 688. "De lapide illvminabili."

(88) LÉMERY, N., "A Course of Chymistry," 2nd English ed. from the 5th French, Walter Kettilby, London, 1686, pp. 525–6; 11th French ed., Theodore Haak, Leyden, 1716, pp. 823–7.

(89) NOLLET, ABBÉ J.-A., "Leçons de physique expérimentale," 5th ed., Vol. 5, Durand, Neveu, Paris, 1771, pp. 23–38.

(90) BETTI, MARIO, "Nel secondo centenario della istituzione della prima cattedra di chimica in Italia, 1737–1937," *Soc. Ital. per il Progresso delle Scienze, Atti della XXVII Riunione*, 6, 501–10 (Sept., 1939).

(91) MELLOR, J. W., "Comprehensive treatise on inorganic and theoretical chemistry," Vol. 3, Longmans, Green and Co., London, 1923, pp. 619–22.

(92) MARGGRAF, A. S., "Von den Bestandtheilen der Steine, die durch die Kalcination auf Kohlen das Vermögen erhalten, das Licht an sich zu ziehen, und von der künstlichen verfertigung dieser Steine," *Crell's Neues chem. Archiv*, 4, pp. 351–6 (1785); *Abh. Königl. Akad. Wiss. (Berlin)*, 1750, p. 144.

(93) MARGGRAF, A. S., "Chymische Schriften," part 2, Arnold Wever, Berlin, 1768, pp. 113–63.

(94) WINDERLICH, R., "Goethe und die Leuchtsteine," *Chem.-Ztg.*, 60, 188 (Feb. 29, 1936).

(95) THORPE, T. E., "Joseph Priestley," J. M. Dent and Co., London, and E. P. Dutton and Co., New York, 1906, pp. 101 and 148.

(96) WITHERING, W., "Experiments and observations on terra ponderosa," *Phil. Trans.*, 74, 293 (1784).

(97) FOWLES, G., "The history of witherite," *Chem. News*, 135, 309–10 (Nov. 11, 1927).

(98) FOURCROY, A.-F. DE, "Elements of natural history and chemistry," Vol. 1, C. Elliot and T. Kay, London, 1790, p. 319. (Translated from the Paris ed. of 1789.)

(99) WATT, JAMES, "Some account of a mine in which the aerated barytes is found," *Memoirs Lit. and Philos. Soc. (Manchester)*, **3**, 598–609 (1790).

(100) *Medical Classics*, **2**, 295–302 (Dec., 1937).

(101) STEPHEN, LESLIE and SIDNEY LEE, Ref. (*52*), Vol. 21, pp. 739–41.

(102) SÖDERBAUM, H. G., Ref. (*14*), Vol. 11, p. 42. Letter of Nils Nordenskiöld to Berzelius, Aug. 3, 1821.

(103) KOPP, H., Ref. (*18*), part 4, p. 41.

(104) "Letzte Aeusserung des für die Chemie zu früh verstorbenen Pelletier's," *Scherer's J. der Chemie*, **2**, 229–30 (1798).

(105) KOPP, H., Ref. (*18*), part 4, p. 44.

(106) FORCHHAMMER, J. G., "On the composition of sea water in the different parts of the ocean," *Phil. Trans.*, **155**, 203–62 (1865).

(107) WILLIS, L. G., Ref. (*79*), columns 45–50.

(108) BAILEY, E. H. S., and L. E. SAYRE, "On the presence of barium in the ash and extract of certain Kansas weeds," *Trans. Kansas Acad. Sci.*, **23–4**, 194–8 (1909–10).

(109) MARTUS, J. A., "The life and work of Father Athanasius Kircher, S.J.," *The Hormone*, **7**, 105–11, 120 (Nov., 1934).

(110) GIBBES, G. S., "Discovery of sulphate of strontian near Sodbury in Gloucestershire," *Nicholson's J.*, **2**, 535–6 (March, 1799).

(111) MORETTI, G., "Sur le sulfate de strontiane trouvé dans les corps marins pétrifiés . . .," *Ann. chim. phys.*, (1), **86**, 262–3 (June 30, 1813).

(112) "Gmelin's Handbuch . . .," Ref. (*84*), Vol. 26, pp. 1–35; Vol. 29, pp. 1–16. History and occurrence of beryllium and strontium.

(113) DESGREZ, A. and J. MEUNIER, "Sur la présence du lithium et du strontium dans les dents et dans les os humains et sur leur état chimique," *Compt. rend.*, **185**, 160–3 (July 18, 1927).

(114) PERRIER, G., "Notice sur M. Alexandre Desgrez," *Compt. rend.*, **210**, 153–6 (Jan. 29, 1940); Polonovski, Michel, "Alexandre Desgrez (1863–1940)," *Bull. Soc. Chimie Biologique*, **22**, 334–6 (May–June, 1940).

(115) "Radio-strontium tested as treatment for bone cancer," *Sci. News Letter*, **40**, 243 (Oct. 18, 1941).

(116) BOULDUC, G.-E.-F., "Untersuchung des Epsomsalzes," *Crell's Neues chem. Archiv*, **3**, 195–6 (1785); *Mém. de l'acad. roy. des sciences (Paris)*, **1731**, p. 488.

(117) "Ueber das Epsomsalz." *Crell's Neues chem. Archiv*, **1**, 203–6 (1784); *Hist. de l'acad. roy. des sciences (Paris)*, **1718**, p. 47.

(118) MARGGRAF, A. S., Ref. (*93*), part 2, pp. 1–49.

(119) LIPPMANN, E. O. VON, "Abhandlungen und Vorträge zur Geschichte der Naturwissenschaften," Veit and Co., Leipzig, **1906**, pp. 282–3. Article on Marggraf.

(120) MARGGRAF, A. S., "Chemische Versuche über die Erdart, welche in der zuletzt zurückbleibenden Salzmuttersole enthalten ist, und die Basis des Serpentinsteins ausmacht," *Crell's Neues chem. Archiv*, **7**, 281–5 (1788); *Abh. königl. Akad. Wiss. (Berlin)*, **1760**.

(121) BLACK, JOSEPH, "Lectures on the Elements of Chemistry," Vol. 2, Mundell and Son, Edinburgh, **1803**, pp. 68–9.

(122) TOURNEFORT, J.-P. DE, "A Voyage into the Levant," Vol. 1, D. Midwinter, R. Ware, C. Rivington *et al.*, London, **1741**, p. 176.

(123) HILL, SIR GEORGE, "A History of Cyprus," Vol. 1, University Press, Cambridge, **1940**, p. 10.

(124) PINKERTON, JOHN, "A General Collection of the Best and Most Interesting Voyages and Travels," Vol. 13, Longman, Hurst, Rees, and Orme, London, **1812**, pp. 472–3, 516. Per Kalm's "Travels in North America."

(125) HENRY, THOMAS, "On the natural history and origin of magnesian earth," *Memoirs Lit. and Philos. Soc. (Manchester)*, **1**, 448–73 (1789).

(126) WALLERIUS, J. G., "Untersuchung von der Beschaffenheit der Erde, die man aus Wasser, Pflanzen und Thieren erhält, zweytes Stuck: von der Erde aus Pflanzen," *Crell's Neues chem. Archiv*, **8**, 283–5 (1791).

(127) WILLSTÄTTER, RICHARD, "Zur Kenntniss der Zusammensetzung des Chlorophylls," *Ann.*, **350**, 48–82 (1906).

(128) SHOHL, A. T., Ref. (*82*), pp. 162–74.

(129) KRUSE, H. D., E. R. ORENT, and E. V. McCOLLUM, "Symptomatology resulting from magnesium deprivation," *J. Biol. Chem.*, **96**, 519–39 (1932).

(130) CULLEN, EDMUND, Ref. (*42*), Vol. 1, pp. 99, 423–5, 436, 439–40, 460–3.

(131) KIRKPATRICK, S. D., "Magnesium from the sea," *Chem. Met. Eng.*, **48**, 76 (Nov., 1941); Killeffer, D. H., *Ind. Eng. Chem.*, *News Ed.*, **19**, 1189–93 (Nov. 10, 1941).

(132) GILBERT, L. W., *Ann. der Physik*, **59**, 104–7 (1818).

(133) CLARKE, E. D., "Observations upon the ores which contain cadmium and upon the discovery of this metal in the Derbyshire silicates and other ores of zinc," *Annals of Philos.*, **15**, 272–6 (Apr., 1820); **19**, 123–8 (Feb., 1822).

(134) CLARKE, E. D., "On the presence and proportion of cadmium in the metallic sheet zinc of commerce," *ibid.*, **19**, 195–9 (Mar., 1822).

(135) HERAPATH, WILLIAM, "On cadmium and the sources of procuring it in quantity," *Annals of Philos.*, **19**, 435–7 (June, 1822).

(136) WALLACE, W. STEWART, "The Encyclopedia of Canada," Vol. 2, University Associates of Canada, Toronto, **1935**, p. 14.

(137) LORD NEAVES, *Proc. Roy. Soc.* (Edinburgh), **4**, 222–4 (Dec. 5, 1859). Obituary of Lord Greenock.

(138) PROVENZAL, GIULIO, "Profili Bio-Bibliografici di Chimici Italiani. Sec. XV–Sec. XIX." Istituto Nazionale Medico Farmacologico "Serone," Rome, **1937**, pp. 27–9.

(139) REILLY, CONOR, "Athanasius Kircher, S. J.," *J. Chem. Educ.*, **32**, 253–8 (May, 1955).

Martin Heinrich Klaproth, 1743–1817. German analytical chemist. First professor of chemistry at the University of Berlin. In 1810 he published, with F. Wolff, a chemical dictionary containing references to the researches cited therein. Klaproth's six-volume "Beiträge zur chemischen Kenntniss der Mineralkörper" is a collection of his remarkable mineral analyses. He rediscovered Gregor's "menachanite," made a thorough study of its properties, and rechristened it *titanium*.

Es hat wohl nie eine Wissenschaft, in einem kleinern Zeitraume, raschere Fortschritte gemacht, als die chemische Naturkenntniss (1)—No science has ever made more rapid progress in a shorter time than chemistry.

21

Elements isolated with the aid of potassium and sodium

The earths of the titanium group had a cosmopolitan origin. The German chemist Klaproth discovered zirconia in 1789 while analyzing a zircon from Ceylon. Two years later the English clergyman William Gregor found titania, or "menachanite," in a black sand from his own parish in Cornwall, but announced his discovery in such a modest manner that it made little impression on the scientific world. Klaproth rediscovered this earth four years later in a Hungarian red schorl, and named it "Titanerde," or titania. Hisinger and Berzelius discovered ceria in 1803 while investigating the Swedish mineral "heavy stone of Bastnäs," now known as cerite. Berzelius found thoria, the last of these earths, in 1829 in a specimen of thorite that had been sent to him from an island off the coast of Norway. The difficult isolation of the metals titanium, cerium, zirconium, and thorium was accomplished by various methods involving the powerful reducing action of sodium and potassium.

ZIRCONIUM

Zirconium minerals are widely distributed in Nature, and have been used for centuries. In his enraptured description of the four-square city, Saint John the Divine mentioned the jacinth (or hyacinth) as one of the twelve precious stones that garnished the foundations of the city wall (*14*).

Although zircon was frequently used by the ancients for intagli, and although hyacinth and jargon were well known in the Middle Ages, the presence in these minerals of an unknown metal was not suspected until near the end of the eighteenth century. The earth zirconia was overlooked because of its great similarity to alumina, and it took the analytical skill of a Klaproth to detect it.

In 1787 Johann Christian Wiegleb analyzed a zircon from Ceylon and reported only silica, with small amounts of magnesia, lime, and iron (*54*). Only two years later, Klaproth discovered the earth zirconia in a jargon, one of "the rough or uncut precious stones coming from Ceylon. . . . Romé de l'Isle," said he, "was the first, to my knowledge, who mentions these gems as a particular species of stones; giving them the name *Jargon of Ceylon* and stating their weight, according to Brisson's experiments, at 4.416. Other mineralogists and writers who notice this stone class it— some with the sapphire, others with the topaz, others with the ruby, others with the diamond, and some with the hyacinth. But Werner has assigned to it a peculiar place in the mineralogic system, immediately under the diamond and the chrysoberyl, and called it *Zircon (Silex*

Baron Louis-Bernard Guyton de Morveau, 1737–1816. French attorney and chemist. Professor of chemistry at the École Polytechnique from 1794 to 1815. With Lavoisier, Fourcroy, and Berthollet he brought chemical nomenclature into accord with modern views on combustion. He made the first serious researches on the structure of steel.

circonius)" (*55*). Klaproth named the earth *Zirconerde*, or, as one says in English, zirconia (*9, 31, 32*). All analyses of zirconium minerals made before the discovery of this earth were incorrect. The celebrated Torbern Bergman, for example, had reported the following composition for a certain hyacinth from Ceylon:

Silica	Alumina	Iron Oxide	Lime
25%	40%	13%	20%

When Klaproth analyzed the same specimen he found:

Silica	Iron Oxide	Zirconia (Jargonia)
25%	0.5%	70%

His results were soon confirmed by Guyton de Morveau,* who extracted the same earth from a hyacinth from Expailly, France, and by N.-L. Vauquelin (*9, 33, 34, 35*). In 1795 Klaproth detected zirconia in a

---

* During the Revolution, the scientific papers of Morveau were signed "Cit[oyen] Guyton."

hyacinth from Ceylon (56). Jargon and hyacinth are both forms of the mineral now known as zircon, zirconium silicate, $ZrSiO_4$. An important commercial source of zirconium is the native zirconia, or baddeleyite, of Brazil (37).

In 1808 Sir Humphry Davy tried in vain to decompose zirconia with the electric current, but Berzelius (36) finally obtained the metal in 1824 by heating a dry mixture of potassium and potassium zirconium fluoride in a very small closed iron tube placed inside a platinum crucible. After the quiet reaction had taken place, he cooled the tube and placed it in distilled water, whereupon, to use his own words, "There fell from the tube a black powder as fast as the salt dissolved, and at the same time there was evolved a small quantity of hydrogen. . . . The zirconium obtained in this manner is easily deposited. It can be washed with water without oxidizing. Washed and dried, it forms a black powder resembling charcoal, which cannot be compressed nor polished like a metal" (15).

Although Berzelius' method yielded impure zirconium, highly contaminated with zirconia, he had chosen his materials with great scientific acumen (37). Through the attempts of many research workers, including Ludwig Weiss and Eugen Naumann (38), Edgar Wedekind (39), and Henri Moissan (40), zirconium of higher and higher purity was obtained. Finally, in 1914, D. Lely, Jr., and L. Hamburger (41) of the research staff of the Philips Metal-Incandescent Lamp Works in Eindhoven, Holland, obtained the metal 100 per cent pure. Their method consisted in heating a mixture of the tetrachloride and sodium in a bomb, using the electric current as the source of heat. The metal consisted of laminae which could be pressed into rods, drawn into wire, or burnished to a bright, mirror-like surface.

The element is still best known, however, in the form of its oxide. Zirconia linings for metallurgical furnaces are very permanent, and, because of their low heat conductivity, may be made very thin. Zirconia refractories, such as crucibles, are very resistant to the action of heat, slags, and most acids, and may safely be plunged into water while red-hot (42).

TITANIUM

Joseph Priestley was not the only English clergyman to discover a new element. The Reverend William Gregor met with similar good fortune. He was born in 1761 at Trewarthenick in the parish of Cornelly, Cornwall, on Christmas Day, 1761. He graduated in 1784 from St. John's College, Cambridge, where he excelled in mathematics and the classics and was awarded a prize for excellence in Latin prose. After receiving his master's degree three years later, he took charge of the rectory at

Deptford, near Totnes, which his father had purchased for him, and later served for a time at Bratton Clovelly, Devonshire (2). Most of his life, however, was spent at the rectory of Creed, in Cornwall. He displayed great talent for landscape painting, etching, and music. Through attendance at some lectures at Bristol, he became interested in chemistry and analytical mineralogy (47).

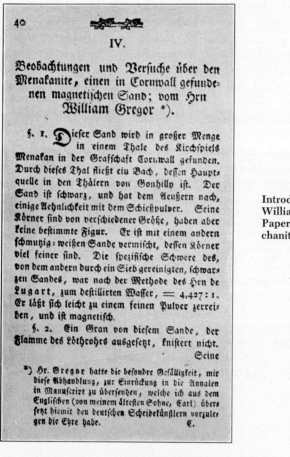

Introduction to the Reverend William Gregor's Original Paper on Titanium, or "Menachanite," *Crell's Annalen*, 1791.

He was fascinated by the minerals of England, and acquired such great skill in analyzing them that Berzelius and other competent judges referred to him as "a famous mineralogist" (3). He was a founder and honorary member of the Royal Geological Society of Cornwall, and his analyses of such substances as bismuth carbonate, topaz, wavellite, uranium mica (Uranglimmer) (*16*), and native lead arsenate (*17*) were of high excellence (*4*).

The most interesting mineral that Mr. Gregor ever analyzed, however, was a black, magnetic sand from the Menachan valley in his own parish. His account of this analysis, as it appeared in *Crell's Annalen* in 1791, was introduced by the following editorial note:

Mr. Gregor did me the special favor of sending the manuscript of this paper for insertion in the *Annalen*, the translation of which from the English by my eldest son Carl, I have the honor to present to German analytical chemists.

D. Lorentz von Crell, 1744–1816. Editor of *Chemische Annalen für die Freunde der Naturlehre, Arzneigelahrtheit, Haushaltungskunst und Manufakturen* and of *Crell's Neues Chemisches Archiv*. Professor of chemistry and counselor of mines at Helmstädt.

The Edgar Fahs Smith Memorial Collection, University of Pennsylvania

The paper begins with a minute description of the sand:

This sand [said Mr. Gregor] is found in large quantity in a valley of the Menachan parish in the county of Cornwall. Through this valley there flows a stream whose principal source is in the valleys of Gonhilly. The sand is black, and in external appearance resembles gunpowder. Its grains are of various sizes, but have no definite shape. It is mixed with another dirty-white sand, the grains of which are much finer. . . .

Gregor found that the black portion of this sand had the following composition:

Magnetite	*Silica*	*Reddish Brown Calx*	*Loss*
$46^9/_{16}\%$	$3^1/_2\%$	45%	$4^{15}/_{16}\%$

The "reddish brown calx" dissolved in sulfuric acid to give a yellow solution which became purple when reduced with zinc, tin, or iron, and when the pulverized mineral was fused with powdered charcoal, a purple slag was formed.

Mr. Gregor modestly stated that his paper was not a complete investigation, but merely a record of disconnected facts, the interpretation of which he would leave to more skilful workers and keener philosophers than himself. His friend, John Hawkins, to whom he showed the black sand, agreed that it must be a new mineral.

The opinion of a man so distinguished in mineralogy [said Mr. Gregor], together with the extraordinary properties of the sand, led me to believe that it must contain a new metallic substance. In order to distinguish it from others, I have ventured to give it a name derived from the region where it was found—namely, the Menachan parish—and therefore the metal might be called menachanite.

He cautiously added that perhaps the researches of other chemists might some day explain the unusual properties of the mineral and "rob it of its novelty." His many duties unfortunately prevented him from continuing the investigation (5) of this black magnetic sand now known as ilmenite, $FeTiO_3$. Strangely enough, his announcement did not attract much attention, and thus titanium, like tellurium, was quickly forgotten.

William Gregor died at Creed in the summer of 1817, after prolonged suffering with tuberculosis (47). Thomas Thomson once said of him:

Mr. Gregor of Cornwall was an accurate man, and attended only to analytical chemistry; his analyses were not numerous, but they were in general excellent. Unfortunately the science was deprived of his services by a premature death (6).

Mr. Gregor's intimate friend, the Reverend J. Trist of Veryan, mentioned the exemplary manner in which he had fulfilled all the duties of his Christian pastorate, "dispensing to his neighbors both spiritual and temporal benefits, and enlivening the society of his friends by his cheerful and instructive conversation" (2).

The reader will recall how the honored chemist Martin Heinrich Klaproth resurrected tellurium, giving full credit to the original discoverer, Müller von Reichenstein. After Mr. Gregor's discovery had likewise fallen into oblivion, Klaproth again came to the rescue. In 1795 he separated what seemed to be a new oxide from a specimen of red schorl, or rutile, found in Boinik, Hungary, and presented to him by Count Würben of Vienna (7, 8). However, since this oxide bore such a close resemblance to the one previously described by Mr. Gregor, Klaproth analyzed a specimen of menachanite, or "iron-shot titanite from Cornwall," as he preferred to call it, for comparison (21):

Within a few years [said he] a fossil has been brought into notice by the name of *Menachanite*, which has been found in the parish of *Menachan*, in *Cornwall*, and consists of grey-black, sand-like grains, obeying the magnet. Mr. M'Gregor, of Menachan, who dedicates his study to mineralogical chemistry, has given not only the first information of this fossil, but also a full narrative of his chemical researches concerning it. The chief result of these is, that menachanite has for its constituent parts iron, and a peculiar *metallic oxyd of an unknown nature*. By the following examination it will appear that this substance, which, besides iron, forms the second chief component principle of menachanite, is precisely the very same which constitutes the Hungarian red schörl; namely, *oxyd of titanium*. With this opinion also, most of the phenomena noted down by M'Gregor, in his operations with menachanite, agree.

Klaproth gave the following curious reason for preferring to call the new element titanium:

Whenever [said he] no name can be found for a new fossil which indicates its peculiar and characteristic properties (in which situation I find myself at present), I think it best to choose such a denomination as means nothing of itself, and thus can give no rise to any erroneous ideas. In consequence of this, as I did in the case of uranium, I shall borrow the name for this metallic substance from mythology, and in particular from the Titans, the first sons of the earth. I therefore call this new metallic genus TITANIUM (8, 9).

Other Sources of Titanium. Berzelius once said that the poet Goethe "had a love for the minerals containing titanium and had a collection of them, in so far as possible, from all known localities where they occur. When I showed him how easily titanium is demonstrated by a beautiful reaction, he lamented feelingly that his years now prevented him from perfecting himself in the use of the blowpipe" (53).

Klaproth found that the mineral which Professor Hunger discovered in 1794, and which crystallized in small quadrangular rhombic columns, was a calcium titanium silicate, *titanite*. It is also known as sphene and has the composition $CaTiSiO_5$. Although titanium was once incorrectly thought of as a rare element, it is widely distributed in nature. Of 800 igneous rocks analyzed by the United States Geological Survey, 784 contained titanium. While serving as chemist on the Virginia Geological Survey, W. M. Thornton, Jr., obtained a positive test for it in every silicate he analyzed (23).

Titanium in Plants and Animals. In 1896 C. E. Wait found large amounts of titanium in the ashes of bituminous and anthracite coals, oak wood, and apple and pear wood (23, 57). L. G. Willis, in his bibliography on the minor elements in plant and animal nutrition, gave several references to the presence of small amounts of titanium in soils, in plants, and in the human body (58).

Klaproth, Vauquelin, Heinrich Rose (22), and others tried in vain to isolate the metal. In 1822 Dr. W. H. Wollaston thought he had found it in the form of minute cubic crystals in the slag of the iron works at

Merthyr Tydvil, but F. Wöhler (*18*) showed in 1849 that these were not the metal itself but a mixture of the nitride and cyanide. In 1825 Berzelius (*20*) prepared some very impure amorphous titanium by reducing potassium fluotitanate, K_2TiF_6, with potassium. Although the resulting black powder gave a metallic streak, it was insoluble in hydrofluoric acid and therefore could not have contained much titanium metal (*23*).

In 1849 Wöhler and H. Sainte-Claire Deville attempted to prepare pure titanium by Berzelius' method, but used a closed crucible in order to exclude air. When they found that the product thus obtained still contained titanium nitride, they heated boats containing potassium and potassium fluotitanate in an atmosphere of hydrogen and obtained a gray powder which showed a metallic luster when examined with a microscope (*7, 10, 18*). Wöhler and Deville thought they had the metal, but, in the opinion of W. M. Thornton, Jr. (*23*), they were still dealing with the nitride.

Sven Otto Pettersson, 1848–1941. Professor of chemistry at the University of Stockholm from 1881–1908. Hydrographer and oceanographer. He collaborated with Lars Fredrik Nilson in researches on metallic titanium and the physical constants of titanium and germanium. He was one of the first chemists to support Svante Arrhenius in his views on electrolytic dissociation. For a discussion of his hydrographic work see ref. (*69*).

In 1887 Lars Fredrik Nilson and Otto Pettersson finally prepared the metal 95 per cent pure by reducing the tetrachloride with sodium in an airtight steel cylinder (*24, 48*). The titanium that Henri Moissan obtained from his electric furnace was free from nitrogen and silicon and contained only 2 per cent of carbon (*25*).

In 1910 M. A. Hunter (*26*) obtained the metal 99.9 per cent pure by a modification of Nilson and Pettersson's method in which pure titanic chloride and sodium were heated in a 1000-cc. machine steel bomb capable of bearing 40,000 kilograms of pressure. The lid, which rested on an intervening gasket of soft copper, was securely held in place by six braces. After the temperature had been raised to low redness, the reaction took place quickly and violently. The sodium chloride was then leached out with water, leaving the pure titanium.

The oxide titania, TiO_2, because of its high refractive index, is used in high-grade white pigments of great opacity and covering power. The

M. A. Hunter's Bomb for preparing metallic titanium.

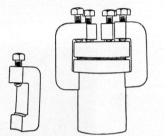

Rensselaer Polytechnic Institute, Eng. Sci. Series, No. 1, p. 6 (1911)

metal unites with iron to form the useful alloy, ferrotitanium, which is added to molten steel to prevent formation of air bubbles, which would form holes in the finished castings. Thus the element that lay hidden for centuries in the sand of Mr. Gregor's parish is now of direct benefit to mankind.

CERIUM

In 1751 A. F. Cronstedt described a heavy mineral found among the copper and bismuth ores in the Bastnäs Mine at Riddarhyttan, Vestmanland (62). Because of its high specific gravity, this mineral, which Cronstedt regarded as a difficultly reducible iron ore, came to be known as "tungsten (heavy stone) of Bastnäs." In 1782 Wilhelm Hisinger, then a mere lad of fifteen years, sent a specimen of it to Scheele for analysis. In the same year one of the de Elhuyar brothers from Spain also analyzed it for practice when he was studying under Torbern Bergman. Although Bergman did not state which of the two brothers studied under him, P. J. Hjelm and L. von Crell both stated that it was the one who afterward became director of all the smelters of New Granada (63, 64). If this be true, the analysis of the "heavy stone of Bastnäs" (cerite) must have been made by Juan José de Elhuyar.

Scheele and de Elhuyar proved independently that this so-called "reddish tungsten" contains no tungsten (wolfram), but neither of them was able to discover anything new in it.

Wilhelm Hising, or Hisinger, as he was called after being raised to the nobility, belonged to a wealthy Swedish family that owned the famous Riddarhyttan* property in Vestmanland and the Bastnäs mine, in which the mineral cerite was discovered. He was born in December, 1766, and soon learned to love the beautiful minerals of Sweden. Although Scheele was unable to discover any new metal in the cerite, this mistake, as A. E. Nordenskiöld said, is very excusable, for the mineral is difficult to handle even with modern methods of analysis (11).

Statue of Carl Wilhelm Scheele at Köping, Sweden.

Berzelius described cerite as follows:

In the iron mine at Bastnäs, now abandoned, in the vicinity of Vestmanland, one finds a mineral of exceedingly high specific gravity, called "heavy stone of Bastnäs"; that is why Scheele searched there, but in vain, for tungsten. This mineral remained in oblivion until 1803, when it was simultaneously examined by Klaproth (44), by Hisinger and by myself (29). We found in it a new substance; Klaproth called it terre ochroite. Hisinger and I called it cerous oxide, because there is a higher oxide, and the two oxides give salts of different colors and properties. The root of the name cerium was deduced from that of Ceres,† which Klaproth changed to cererium, but this name was soon abandoned. The mineral is composed mainly of cerous silicate, and for this reason receives the name of cerite. Cerium was afterward discovered in minerals from other localities; for example, in gadolinite, orthite, allanite, yttrocerite, cerous fluoride, etc." (12).

* The reader will recall that Riddarhyttan was also the birthplace of Georg Brandt, the discoverer of cobalt.
† The element was named for the planet Ceres, which had been recently discovered by Piazzi.

The main object of Berzelius and Hisinger's analysis of cerite was to search for yttria, which might easily have escaped the attention of Scheele and de Elhuyar since it was unknown at the time their investigation was made (29). Although they failed to find yttria, Berzelius and Hisinger discovered instead the new earth ceria.*

Axel Fredrik Cronstedt,† **1722–1765.** Swedish chemist and mineralogist. Discoverer of nickel. Author of a "System of Mineralogy" which was translated into several languages. He called the heavy mineral now known as *cerite* "*tungsten of Bastnäs.*" Hence Scheele thought it might contain tungsten. See also ref. (52).

Medallion by Kjellberg

In his "Early Recollections of a Chemist," Wöhler gave a charming picture of Hisinger's home:

After a five days' stay at Fahlun [he wrote] we drove to Skinnskatteberg, Hisinger's estate, where, after a drive of twenty-four hours, we arrived one afternoon, finding Berzelius there. The venerable, genial, and most original Hisinger, so well known through his contributions to the geognostic mineralogy and botany of Sweden, and through the liberality with which he had supported Berzelius during the commencement of his studies, lived here a very rich man (Brukspatron) on a princely estate, surrounded by magnificent forests, gardens, and iron mines. We spent a week here most delightfully, partly occupied in examining his collections, with making blowpipe tests of unknown minerals, and with the reading aloud of my translation of Hisinger's "Mineral Geography." In company with Berzelius and Hisinger, we made an excursion a few miles distant to the mines of Riddarhyttan, among which the Bastnäshaft is known

* In volumes 9 and 10 of *Nicholson's Journal* this paper was accredited to W. D'Hesinger and J. B. Bergelius [*sic*!].
† See Chapter 5, pp. 161–5, for biographical sketch.

as the only locality for the occurrence of cerite.   At the mouth of this mine, which at that time had already been abandoned, we collected in the scorching sun hundreds of the most characteristic specimens of cerite and cerin [allanite] (*13*).

Hisinger was indeed one of Sweden's most eminent mineralogists and geologists. He died on June 28, 1852, at the venerable age of eighty-five years.

Skinnskatteberg, Vestmanland, Sweden, where Wilhelm Hisinger once lived.
The mineral cerite was first found in one of the mines on his estate.

When Thomas Thomson visited the Bastnäs Mine in 1812, he wrote: "One of the most remarkable tracts in the province of Westmanland is Riddarhyttan, a copper mine which lies in the parish of Skinskatteberg, about eighteen miles west and a little south from Sala. . . .   The most remarkable mineral which is found in this mine is the cerite, a mineral first noticed by Bergman and conceived by him to belong to that called tungsten, and composed of tungstic acid and lime. Eluyart [*sic*] analysed it, and showed that it was not tungsten. No attention was paid to it for many years, till at last it was analysed by Klaproth and by Hisinger and Berzelius nearly about the same time. Klaproth discovered in it a new substance which he considered as an earth and to which he gave

Wilhelm Hisinger, 1766–1852. Swedish mineralogist and geologist. Owner of the famous Riddarhytta mining property in Vestmanland, where cerite was discovered. He was one of the first to analyze the lithium mineral petalite.

From Söderbaum's Jac. Berzelius Brev

William Francis Hillebrand,* 1853–1925. Chemist with the U. S. Geological Survey, later Chief Chemist at the Bureau of Standards. President of the American Chemical Society in 1906. Author of "The Analysis of Silicate and Carbonate Rocks." He was the first to suggest the possibility of recovering potash from the fumes from cement kilns.

* See ALLEN, "Pen Portrait of William Francis Hillebrand, 1853–1925," *J. Chem. Educ.*, **9**, 72–83 (Jan., 1932).

the name *ochroita*. Hisinger and Berzelius discovered in it a new substance which they conceived to be a metallic oxide, to which they gave
the name of *cerium*. Their results were confirmed by Vauquelin and
have been adopted by chemists. . . . Since the original discovery of
cerium in this mineral, it has been found in various other parts of the
world. A mineral from Greenland, to which the name of allanite has been
given, contains about the third of its weight of it . . ." (*65*).

On one of Berzelius' busy summer vacations at the hospitable home
of Assessor J. G. Gahn, they discovered still another cerium mineral. "For
two and a half months," said Berzelius in a letter to Dr. A. Marcet on
October 7, 1814, "we occupied ourselves with nothing whatever except

Thomas H. Norton,* **1851–1941.** Professor of chemistry at the University of
Cincinnati. American consul at Harput,
Turkey, at Smyrna, and at Chemnitz,
Saxony. Author of books on dyes, the
cottonseed industry, potash production,
and the utilization of atmospheric nitrogen. Collaborator with W. F. Hillebrand in researches on cerium (*46, 49*).

mineralogy, and I am sure that few mineralogists have been more fortunate in their efforts than we. We set out to analyze everything we found,
not merely to learn their composition but also, by means of these analyses,
to verify the ideas on which my investigation of mineralogy is based. . . .
Behold our first attempt: a new mineral composed of acid of fluorspar
[hydrofluoric acid], lime, yttria, and cerium oxide [yttrocerite] . . ." (*45*).

J. G. Gahn in Sweden and N.-L. Vauquelin in France tried in vain to
obtain metallic cerium. C. G. Mosander prepared anhydrous cerous chloride and subjected it for a long time to the action of potassium vapor. After
washing the residue with cold alcohol, he obtained a brown powder which,

* See *Ind. Eng. Chem., News Ed.,* **13**, 318–19 (Aug. 10, 1935).

when burnished, exhibited a dark metallic luster.   This cerium was far
from pure, however, for it was badly contaminated with the oxychloride.
Impure cerium was also prepared by Wöhler.   W. F. Hillebrand and T.
H. Norton (27) succeeded in 1875 in preparing the metal in a coherent
form by electrolyzing fused cerous chloride.   In 1911 Dr. Alcan Hirsch

From "Industry in Sweden," Federation of Swedish Industries

Mine Head-Frame at Riddarhyttan.   The mineral cerite
was discovered there in 1751 by A. F. Cronstedt.   Georg
Brandt, the discoverer of cobalt, was born at Riddarhyttan.

(30) made some electrolytic cerium containing only two per cent of
impurities (iron, cerium oxide, and cerium carbide).   The metal was
purified by amalgamating it and distilling off the mercury in an evacuated
quartz tube lined with magnesia.   This elaborate investigation required
more than three years of work at the University of Wisconsin.

Cerium forms with iron a peculiar pyrophoric alloy which, when struck, emits showers of sparks, and which is used somewhat in the manufacture of automatic gas-lighters (28).

Cerium in Plants and Animals. Professor Alfonso Cossa, finding the rare earths of the ceria series to be present in many apatites, and realizing the close association in nature between these earths and calcium and phosphorus, tested for them and detected their presence in bone (66). He also detected them in the ash of barley, beech wood, and tobacco. With the aid of C. Schiapparelli and G. Peroni of the University of Turin, he demonstrated their presence in human urine (66, 67, 68).

THORIUM

While analyzing one of the rare minerals from the Falun district, Berzelius found in 1815 a substance that he believed to be the oxide of a new metal which he named thorium in honor of the ancient Scandinavian god, Thor. Ten years later he himself found that this substance was not a new earth, but simply yttrium phosphate. He evidently liked the name thorium, however, for when in 1829 he really did discover a new element, he christened it with the same name (45).

In his account of the discovery, Berzelius wrote:

The mineral on which I made the following experiments is found in the syenite on the island of Lövö near Brevig, Norway. It was discovered by the pastor Esmarck, son of Jens Esmarck, famous professor at the University of Christiania. It is the latter who sent me a specimen, asking me to examine it, because, on account of its high specific gravity, he believed it to be the earth of tantalum. This mineral is black, with no indication of crystalline form or texture, and looks exactly like gadolinite from Ytterby; the exterior presents sometimes a thin rust-colored surface layer (12).

After a visit to Professor Jens Esmark, Edward Daniel Clarke once wrote, "There is a Public seminary at Kongsberg, in which Lectures on Mineralogy are delivered by Professor Esmark, who is also one of the Assessors, and the most scientific mineralogist, perhaps, in all Europe. This gentleman is well known in all Foreign Academies for the works which he has published. He has done more towards the overthrow of the wild systems of the Plutonists than even Werner himself. . . . Professor Esmark conducted us to the grand chamber of the Kongsberg Academy, where we saw a collection of minerals, in beautiful order, and most scientifically arranged. . . . From him we learned that the School of this Academy is a Royal Institution for the instruction of the children of the miners, in mineralogy, chemistry, physic, mathematics, and other branches of science. There are three Professors, among whom Professor

Esmark holds the mineralogical and geological department. Any of the miners or children of the miners may attend this institution. Two days in every week and two hours in each day are dedicated to the instruction of the miners and all other persons who choose to attend. *For these lectures, no payment whatsoever* is required" (59).

The discoverer of the black mineral sent to Berzelius was Professor Esmark's son, the Reverend Hans Morten Thrane Esmark (1801–1882), who had acquired a lifelong interest in mineralogy, geology, and chemistry under his father's inspiring guidance. During his long pastorate in Brevik he studied the minerals of Langesund Fjord and Bamle and near Kragerø, corresponded with scientists in other countries, and sent them specimens of minerals for their researches. He also communicated his enthusiasm for science to his children Axel Thrane Esmark, a mineral collector like his father and grandfather, and Birgitte Elise Esmark, who became a great philanthropist and an authority on mollusks (50).

Although the mineral which H. M. T. Esmark discovered looked a great deal like gadolinite, his father believed it to be new, possibly a kind of tantalite. Berzelius' analysis of it proved it to be a silicate of a new metal, which he named thorium (50, 60). Although Pastor Esmark wished to name the mineral *berzelite*, Berzelius preferred the shorter name *thorite* (45).

Paulin Louyet, in his eulogy of Berzelius, quoted the Scottish agricultural chemist James Finlay Weir Johnston, who visited Stockholm in 1829 (the year in which thorium was discovered) and afterward wrote a description of Berzelius and his laboratory. "The visitor," said Johnston, "will recognize from various utensils in the first room that it is part of a chemical laboratory. If he be neither a chemist nor even an amateur, and be his sense of smell ever so delicate, he need not fear those emanations which, in most laboratories, affect so painfully the organs of respiration. Here a system of ventilation, planned with the greatest care, makes them disappear immediately. At his right he will see, near the window, a carefully adjusted trough of mercury, gleaming in the sun. . . . After having glanced at the blowpipe, the large lamp, and all the objects near it, he will come to the sandbath. He will look in vain for furnaces of brick or stone . . . they are useless in the delicate operations of analysis. . . .

"In the second room," continued Johnston, "the first object one notices is a glass case standing on a table. It is the balance. How much light this fragile, simple instrument has shed on the natural sciences! How many phenomena it has explained! How many hidden truths it has revealed! Who could enumerate the discussions it has ended, the hypotheses it has destroyed! Who, in former times, would have believed that the determination of abstract truths and the development of the laws of nature would depend on the oscillations of this moving beam! But consider this balance attentively, for it has rendered great services to science, and its modifications have contributed in no slight degree. This manner of raising the beam and the pans and keeping them at rest is due to the late Assessor Gahn, whose skill at this kind of work was well known. Not far from there are the little lead weights which are the exact counterpoises, or tares, of all the crucibles and small platinum utensils in the laboratory, so that each of them can be balanced in an instant. . . .

"Berzelius is always busy," said Johnston. "He works twelve to fourteen hours every day. But in spite of all he has done for experimental chemistry, one must not think that he works without respite in his laboratory. Often, when he is composing, he stops for months at a time. If, during his writing, he comes across some passage which seems obscure to him, he lays down his pen, goes into his laboratory, and carries out new researches. . . .

"Everything in Berzelius's laboratory," said Johnston, "is conspicuously clean and in admirable order; everything is in its place, ready for immediate use. . . . He also uses many ingenious machines which facilitate or shorten his operations, the invention of which he attributes to Assessor Gahn. But many of them have been made by himself, for he turns or constructs those which are of wood" (61).

Thorium, like the other metals of this group, is isolated with great difficulty. Berzelius prepared the impure metal by heating a mixture of potassium and potassium thorium fluoride in a glass tube. D. Lely, Jr., and L. Hamburger prepared it 99 per cent pure by distilling sodium and thorium chloride into an exhausted steel cylinder and also succeeded in obtaining it as a coherent metal (9, 41). It is interesting to note that all four of the elements of this group, titanium, cerium, zirconium, and thorium, were isolated with the aid of the alkali metals discovered by Sir Humphry Davy.

In 1898 Mme. Curie in Paris and Professor G. C. Schmidt at the University of Münster, working independently, found that thorium, like uranium, is radioactive (43). This discovery opened up a vast new field of research as a result of which thorium is now known to be the parent substance of an entire series of radioactive elements. The story of their discovery will be reserved, however, for a later chapter.

LITERATURE CITED

(1) KLAPROTH, M. H., "Ueber die vorgegebene Reduction der einfachen Erden," Crell's Ann., 15, 119 (1791).

(2) "Biographical notice of the Rev. William Gregor," Annals of Phil., [1], 11, 112–4 (Feb., 1818).

(3) SÖDERBAUM, H. G., "Jac. Berzelius Brev," Vol. 3, part 6, Almqvist and Wiksells, Upsala, 1912–1914, p. 47. Letter of Berzelius to Thomson, Autumn, 1816.

(4) POGGENDORFF, J. C., "Biographisch-Literarisches Handwörterbuch zur Geschichte der exakten Wissenschaften," 6 vols., Verlag Chemie, Leipzig and Berlin, 1863–1937. Article on Gregor.

(5) GREGOR, W., "Beobachtungen und Versuche über den Menakanite, einen in Cornwall gefundenen magnetischen Sand," Crell's Ann., 15, 40–54, 103–19 (1791).

(6) THOMSON, THOMAS, "History of Chemistry," Vol. 2, Colburn and Bentley, London, 1831, p. 231.

(7) JAGNAUX, R., "Histoire de la Chimie," Vol. 2, Baudry et Cie., Paris, 1891, pp. 339–40.

(8) KLAPROTH, M. H., "Analytical Essays towards Promoting the Chemical Knowledge of Mineral Substances," Cadell and Davies, London, 1801, pp. 200–10.

(9) MELLOR, J. W., "Comprehensive Treatise on Inorganic and Theoretical Chemistry," Vol. 7, Longmans, Green and Co., London, 1927, pp. 1–2, 98–9,174–8. Articles on Titanium, Zirconium, and Thorium.

(10) WÖHLER, F., "Sur le titane," letter to Pelouze, Compt. rend., 29, 505 (Nov. 5, 1849); F. WÖHLER and H. STE.-CLAIRE DEVILLE, "Mémoire sur l'affinité spéciale de l'azote pour le titane," Compt. rend., 45, 480–3 (Oct. 5, 1857); "Recherches sur le titane et son affinité spéciale pour l'azote," Ann. chim. phys., [3], 52, 92–7 (Jan., 1858).

(11) NORDENSKIÖLD, A. E., "Scheeles nachgelassene Briefe und Aufzeichnungen," Norstedt & Söner, Stockholm, 1892, p. 351.

(12) JAGNAUX, R., "Histoire de la Chimie," ref. (7), Vol. 2, pp. 195–9.

(13) WÖHLER, F., "Early recollections of a chemist," translated by Laura R. Joy, Am. Chemist, 6, 131 (Oct., 1875); "Jugend-Erinnerungen eines Chemikers," Ber., 8, 838–52 (1875).

(14) Revelation 21: 20.

(15) JAGNAUX, R., "Histoire de la Chimie," ref. (7), Vol. 2, p. 176.

(16) GREGOR, W., "Experiments on a mineral substance formerly supposed to be zeolite, with some remarks on two species of uran-glimmer," Proc. Roy. Soc. London, 1, 209–10 (July 4, 1805).

(17) GREGOR, W., "On a native arseniate of lead," ibid., 1, 331 (Apr. 13, 1809). Communicated by Chas. Hatchett.

(18) WÖHLER, F., "Note sur le titane," Ann. chim. phys., [3], 28, 382–3 (Mar., 1850); [3], 29, 166–87 (June, 1850); Phil Mag., [3], 36, 67–8 (Jan., 1850); "Ueber die Natur des metallischen Titans," Ann., 73, 34–49 (1850).

(19) WOLLASTON, W. H., "On metallic titanium," Annals of Phil., [1], 21, 67–8 (Jan., 1823).

(20) BERZELIUS, J. J., Pogg. Ann., 4, 3(1825).

(21) KLAPROTH, M. H., "Analytical Essays towards Promoting the Chemical Knowledge of Mineral Substances," ref (8), pp. 499–509.

(22) ROSE, H., Pogg. Ann., 16, 57 (1829).

(23) THORNTON, W. M., JR., "Titanium," Chem. Catalog Co., New York City, 1927, 262 pp.

(24) NILSON, L. F. and S. O. PETTERSSON, "Über einige physikalische Konstanten des Germaniums und Titans," Z. physik. Chem., 1, 27–8 (Feb., 1887).

(25) MOISSAN, H., "Préparation et propriétés du titane," Compt. rend., 120, 290–6 (Feb 11, 1895).

(26) HUNTER, M. A., "Metallic titanium," J. Am. Chem. Soc., 32, 330–6 (Mar., 1910).

(27) HILLEBRAND, W. F. and T. H. NORTON, Pogg. Ann., 155, 631 (1875); 156, 466 (1875).

(28) LEVY, "The Rare Earths," Longmans, Green and Co., London, 1915, pp. 314–7.

(29) HISINGER, W. and J. J. BERZELIUS, "Account of cerium, a new metal found in a

mineral substance from Bastnäs, in Sweden," *Nicholson's J.*, **9**, 290–300 (Dec., 1804); **10**, 10–2 (Jan., 1805); J. J. BERZELIUS, "Analyse de la gadolinite," *Ann. chim. phys.*, [2], **3**, 26–34 (Sept., 1816).

(30) HIRSCH, A., "The preparation and properties of metallic cerium," *Met. Chem. Eng.*, **9**, 540–4 (Oct., 1911).

(31) KLAPROTH, M. H., "Kleine mineralogische Beiträge." *Crell's Ann.*, **11**, 7 (1789); *Ann. chim. phys.*, [1], **1**, 6 (1789).

(32) KLAPROTH, M. H., "Analytical Essays towards Promoting the Chemical Knowledge of Mineral Substances," ref. (8), pp. 175–94.

(33) *Ibid.*, pp. 195–9.

(34) DE MORVEAU, G., "Sur l'Hyacinte de France, congénère à celle de Ceylan, et sur la nouvelle terre qui entre dans sa composition," *Ann. chim. phys.*, [1], **21**, 72–95 (Jan., 1797).

(35) "Extrait d'un mémoire du Cit. Vauquelin, contenant l'analyse comparative des Hyacinthes de Ceylan et d'Expailly, et l'exposé de quelques-unes des propriétés de la terre qu'elles contiennent," *ibid.*, [1], **22**, 179–210 (May, 1797).

(36) "Extrait d'une lettre de M. Berzelius à M. Dulong," *ibid.*, [2], **26**, 43 (1824).

(37) VENEABLE, F. P., "Zirconium and Its Compounds," Chem. Catalog Co., New York City, **1922**, 173 pp.

(38) WEISS, L. and E. NAUMANN, "Darstellung und Untersuchung regulinischen, Zirkoniums," *Z. anorg. Chem.*, **65**, 248–78 (Jan. 8, 1910).

(39) WEDEKIND, E. and LEWIS, "Studien über das elementare Zirkonium," *Ann.*, **371**, 366–87 (Heft 3, 1910); E. WEDEKIND, *Ann.*, **395**, 149–94 (Heft 2, 1912).

(40) MOISSAN, H., "Sur la volatilisation de la silice et de la zircone et sur la réduction de ces composés par le charbon," *Compt. rend.*, **116**, 1222–4 (May 29, 1893).

(41) LELY, D. and L. HAMBURGER, "Herstellung der Elemente Thorium, Uran, Zirkon, und Titan," *Z. anorg. Chem.*, **87**, 209–28 (May 26, 1914).

(42) VENABLE, F. P., "Zirconium and Its Compounds," ref. (37), pp. 126–32.

(43) "Classic of science: Radioactive substances by Mme. Curie," *Sci. News Letter* **14**, 137–8 (Sept. 1, 1928).

(44) "Classic of science: Account of experiments made on a mineral called cerite, and on the particular substance which it contains, and which has been considered as a new metal, by M. Vauquelin," *ibid.*, **20**, 138 (Aug. 29, 1931).

(45) SÖDERBAUM, H. G., "Jac. Berzelius levnadsteckning," Vol. 2, Almqvist & Wiksells Boktryckeri A.-B., Upsala, **1929–31**, pp. 66–8, 501–7, 524–6.

(46) ANON., "Thomas H. Norton receives Lavoisier medal," *Ind. Eng. Chem., News Ed.*, **15**, 542 (Dec. 20, 1937).

(47) "Dictionary of National Biography," Vol. 23, Smith, Elder & Co., London, **1890–91**, pp. 89–90. Article on Gregor by G. C. Boase.

(48) VON EULER, HANS, "Sven Otto Pettersson. In memoriam," *Svensk Kemisk Tidskrift*, **53**, 28–32 (Jan., 1941).

(49) "Necrology. Thomas H. Norton," *Ind. Eng. Chem., News Ed.*, **19**, 1474 (Dec. 25, 1941).

(50) BULL, E. and E. JANSEN, "Norsk Biografisk Leksikon," Vol. 3. H. Aschenhoug and Co., Oslo, **1926**, pp. 595–6. Articles on the Esmark family.

(51) BARTOW, VIRGINIA, "W. F. Hillebrand and some early letters," *J. Chem. Educ.*, **26**, 367–72 (July, 1949).

(52) BARTOW, VIRGINIA, "Axel Fredrik Cronstedt," *ibid.*, **30**, 247–52 (May, 1953).

(53) SÖDERBAUM, H. G., "Jac. Berzelius Själfbiografiska Anteckningar," Kongl. Svenska Vetenskapsakademien, P. A. Norstedt and Sons, Stockholm, **1901**, p. 84; LARSELL, OLOF, "Jöns Jacob Berzelius. Autobiographical Notes," Williams & Wilkins Co., Baltimore, Md., **1934**, p. 114.

(54) WIEGLEB, J. C., "Chemische Untersuchung der Zirkonen aus Zeilon," *Crell's Ann.*, **8**, 139–43 (1787).

(55) KLAPROTH, M. H., Ref. (8), pp. 175–217.

(56) KLAPROTH, M. H. and F. WOLFF, "Dictionnaire de chimie," Vol. 4, Klostermann Fils, Paris, **1811**, p. 547.

(57) WAIT, C. E., "The occurrence of titanium," *J. Am. Chem. Soc.*, **18**, 402–4 (Apr., 1896).

(58) WILLIS, L. G. "Bibliography of References to the Literature on the Minor Elements and Their Relation to Plant and Animal Nutrition," 3rd ed., Chilean Nitrate Educational Bureau, New York, **1939**, columns 883–6.

(59) CLARKE, E. D., "Travels in Various Countries of Europe, Asia, and Africa," Vol. 10, T. Cadell, London, **1824**, pp. 441–3.

(60) WALLACH, O., "Briefwechsel zwischen J. Berzelius und F. Wöhler," Vol. 1, Wilhelm Engelmann, Leipzig, **1901**, p. 252.   Letter of Berzelius to Wöhler, May 1, 1829.

(61) LOUYET, PAULIN, "Notice sur la vie et les travaux de J.-J. Berzelius," *Annuaire de l'Acad. Roy. des Sciences, des Lettres, et des Beaux-Arts de Belgique*, **15**, 134–63 (1849).

(62) CRONSTEDT, A. F., "Rön och försök gjorde med trenne järnmalms arter," *K. Vet. Acad. Handl.*, **12**, 226–32 (July, Aug., Sept., 1751).

(63) HJELM, P. J., "Åminnelse-tal öfver . . . Torbern Bergman," J. G. Lange, Stockholm, **1786**, p, 86.

(64) CRELL, L. VON, "Zum Andenken Torbern Bergmans," *Crell's Ann.*, **7**, 74–96 (1787).

(65) THOMSON, THOMAS, "Travels through Sweden in the Autumn of 1812," Robert Baldwin, London, **1813**, pp. 193–4, 228–9, 241–4.

(66) COSSA, ALFONSO, "Sulla diffusione del cerio, del lantano e del didymio," *Gazz. chim. ital.*, **9**, 118–40 (1879); **10**, 465–6 (1880).

(67) SCHIAPPARELLI, C. and G. PERONI, "Di alcuni nuovi componenti dell'urina umana normale," *Gazz. chim. ital.*, **10**, 390–2 (1880).

(68) PROVENZAL, GIULIO, "Profili Bio-Bibliografici di Chimici Italiani.   Sec. XV–Sec. XIX," Istituto Nazionale Medico Farmacologico "Serono," Rome, **1937**, pp. 221–9.

(69) CARSON, RACHEL L., "The Sea Around Us," Mentor Book published by the New American Library, New York, **1954**, pp. 136–41.

René-Just Haüy, 1743–1822. French mineralogist. He deduced the fundamental laws of crystallography, and explained cleavage by postulating that a crystal is built up of small similar parallelepipeds. He was the first to recognize that beryl and the emerald are geometrically identical. Vauquelin's proof of their chemical identity, made at the suggestion of Haüy, led to the discovery of the element beryllium. See also ref. (*164*).

Aber neue Phaenomena zu erklären, dieses macht meine Sorgen aus, und wie froh ist der Forscher, wenn er das so fleissig Gesuchte findet, eine Ergötzung wobei das Herz lacht (1).—"To explain new phenomena, that is my task; and how happy is the scientist when he finds what he so diligently sought, a pleasure that gladdens the heart."

22

Other elements isolated with the aid of potassium and sodium

When the Abbé Haüy pointed out the close similarity and probable identity of beryl and the emerald, Vauquelin analyzed them carefully, and found in 1798 that they are indeed identical, and that they contain a new earth, which he named glucina, but which is now known as beryllia. The metal was isolated thirty years later by Wöhler and Bussy independently. Boron was isolated in 1808 by Gay-Lussac and Thenard in France and by Davy in England by reduction of boric acid with potassium. Although amorphous silicon was prepared by Berzelius in 1824, the crystalline form of it was not obtained until about thirty years later, when Henri Sainte-Clarie Deville prepared it by an electrolytic method. Aluminum was isolated in 1825 by the Danish physicist, Oersted, and two years later Wöhler prepared it by a better method. Successful commercial processes for the manufacture of this important metal were perfected by Henri Sainte-Claire Deville, by Charles Martin Hall, and by Dr. Paul L. T. Héroult.

BERYLLIUM

*B*eryl was probably not used in Egypt before Ptolemaic times (87). A. Lucas stated that the mines in the Red Sea hills, which were mentioned by Strabo and Pliny the Elder, were probably the only source of beryl in ancient times (87). In 1817 F. Cailliaud discovered the emerald mines near Mt. Zabara "nearly in the same state in which they had been left by the engineers of the Ptolemies. He penetrated into a vast number of excavations and subterraneous canals, some of which are so deep that four hundred men may work in them at once. . . . M. C. himself set about working the mines, and he has presented six pounds of emeralds to Mahommed Ali Pashaw" (88).

Pliny the Elder realized that beryl and the emerald are closely related (56). "Beryls, it is thought, are of the same nature as the smaragdus, or at least closely analogous. India produces them, and they are rarely to be found elsewhere" (56). William Ridgeway stated in the "Encyclopaedia Biblica" that the Greeks and Romans executed some of their finest gem engraving in beryl. The Stockholm papyrus, which dates from the third or fourth century A.D., gives several recipes for the preparation of artificial beryl and emerald (89).

In 1590 Father José de Acosta described the Peruvian emeralds. "They have been found in diverse partes of the Indies," said he. "The Kings of Mexico didde much esteeme them; some did vse to pierce their nosthrils, and hang therein an excellent emerald; and they hung them on the visages of their idolles. The greatest store is found in the New Kingdome of Grenada and in Peru, neere vnto Manta and Puerto Viejo. There is towardes that place a soile which they call the Land of Emeraldas, for the knowledge they have of aboundance to be there; and yet vnto this day they have not conquered that land. . . . In the fleete, the yeare one thousand five hundred eighty and seven, in the which I came from the Indies, they brought two chests of emeralds, every one weighing at least four *arrobas* [1 arroba = 25 lbs.], whereby we may see the aboundaunce they have. The holy Scripture commends these emeralds as pretious iewels, they number them amongst the pretious stones which the hie Priest carried on his Ephod or breastplate, as those which did beautifie the walles of the heavenly Ierusalem" (90). The term *smaragdus* as used in the Bible, however, may have included other green gems as well as the emerald.

The correct composition of beryl and the emerald was not known until the close of the eighteenth century, when the Abbé R.-J. Haüy pointed out the remarkable similarity in crystalline structure, hardness, and density of a beryl from Limoges and an emerald from Peru, and N.-L. Vauquelin discovered that they both contain as an essential constituent glucinum, or beryllium, and that the emerald, except for the presence in it of a little chromium, has the same composition as the beryl (25, 27, 91).

The latter wrote in 1798: "Klaproth had no sooner discovered the different substances with which he has enriched the science, but they were found in various other bodies; and if I may refer to my own processes, it will be seen that after I had determined the characters of chrome, first found in the native red lead, I easily recognized it in the emerald and the ruby. The same has happened with regard to the earth of the beryl. I have likewise detected it in the emerald; in which, nevertheless, it was overlooked by Klaproth and myself in our first analysis; so difficult it is to be aware of the presence of a new substance, particularly when it possesses some properties resembling those already known . . ." (23).

At the close of his paper Vauquelin added: "I present to the Institute a certain quantity of this earth, and shall produce at one of its future sittings a series of combinations formed with this earth . . ." (23).

In speaking of the discovery of beryllium A.-F. de Fourcroy once said, "It is to geometry that we owe in some sort the source of this discovery; it is that [science] that furnished the first idea of it, and we may say that without it the knowledge of this new earth would not have been acquired for a long time, since according to the analysis of the emerald by M. Klaproth and that of beryl by M. Bindheim one would not have thought it possible to recommence this work without the strong analogies or even almost perfect identity that Citizen Haüy found for the geometrical properties between these two stony fossils" (5).

As a result of his analysis of a Peruvian emerald, Klaproth had stated that this gem has the following composition:

Silica "Silex"	Alumina, "Alumine or Argil"	Iron Oxide
66.25%	31.25%	0.50%

To explain his extravagance he said, "For the specimen of emerald sacrificed to this analytical process, I am indebted to the liberal kindness of Prince Dimitri Gallitzin, whose zeal for the study of mineralogy is most honourably known" (22).

Beryl had also been analyzed by T. Bergman, F. K. Achard, J. J. Bindheim, and N.-L. Vauquelin, and was supposed to be a calcium aluminum silicate (23). The identity of beryl and the emerald was not suspected until the famous French mineralogist the Abbé R.-J. Haüy made a careful study of their crystal forms and physical properties and was so struck by the similarity of the two minerals that he asked Vauquelin to analyze them chemically.

Although the latter had previously overlooked the new earth because of its similarity to alumina, he found in 1798 that the hydroxide that precipitates when caustic potash is added to an acid solution of the beryl does not dissolve in an excess of the alkali. It also differs from alumina in other respects, for it forms no alum, it dissolves in ammonium carbonate, and its salts have a sweet taste. Vauquelin's paper read before the French Academy on "le 26 pluviose an VI" of the Revolutionary Calendar, or the fifteenth of February, 1798 (6, 23), proved that, except for a little chromium in the emerald, the two gems have the same composition and that they contain a new earth, a sample of which he presented to the Academy. At the suggestion of the editors* of the Annales de Chimie et de Physique, he called the new earth glucina, meaning sweet. The specimen of beryl that Vauquelin analyzed was presented to him by

* Guyton de Morveau, G. Monge, C.-L. Berthollet, A.-F. de Fourcroy, A. Seguin, J.-A.-C. Chaptal, and N.-L. Vauquelin.

"Citizen Patrin, whose zeal for the advancement of the sciences is well known to every one of their cultivators" (23).

Vauquelin believed that Torbern Bergman's incorrect conclusions as to the chemical nature of the beryl had been caused by the unwillingness of his "active mind to submit to the details of experiment." Thus Bergman, and Bindheim as well, had entrusted their analyses to young pupils who were incapable of distinguishing a new substance when they saw it. According to Bindheim's analysis, the beryl consisted of 64 per cent of silica, 27 per cent of alumina, 8 per cent of lime, and 2 per cent of iron (total 101 per cent) (23).

Johann Friedrich Gmelin, 1748–1804. Father of Leopold Gmelin. Professor of chemistry at Tübingen and Göttingen. Famous chemical historian. His remarkable "Geschichte der Chemie" was published in 1797–99.

When Vauquelin analyzed a Peruvian emerald (25) after his discovery of chromium and glucina, the results differed greatly from his previous ones and from those of Klaproth. He found:

Silica	64.60
Alumina	14.00
Glucina	13.00
Lime	2.56
Chromium oxide	3.50
Moisture, or other volatile matter	2.00
	99.66

J. F. Gmelin's analysis of a Siberian beryl soon confirmed Vauquelin's conclusions as to the essential constituents of that gem, for he found no lime, but only silica, alumina, glucina, and a small amount of iron oxide (26).

Since yttria, as well as glucina, forms sweet salts, Klaproth preferred to call the latter earth beryllia, and it is still known by that name. Beryl and the emerald are now known to be a beryllium aluminum silicate [$Be_3Al_2(SiO_3)_6$].

Metallic beryllium was first prepared in August, 1828, by F. Wöhler and A.-A.-B. Bussy independently by the action of potassium on beryllium chloride (7, 8). Wöhler placed alternate layers of the chloride and flattened pieces of potassium in a platinum crucible, wired the cover on strongly, and heated the mixture with an alcohol lamp. The reaction began immediately and took place with such intensity that the crucible became white-hot. After cooling it thoroughly, he opened it and placed

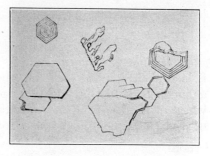

Hexagonal Crystals of Pure Beryllium
prepared by P. Lebeau.

it in a large volume of water, whereupon the beryllium separated out as a gray-black powder. After washing this insoluble material, Wöhler saw that it consisted of fine metallic particles which could be burnished to show a dark metallic luster. He did not succeed in melting the beryllium (8).

The first person to prepare pure beryllium by an electrolytic process was the French chemist, P. Lebeau (27, 29). After adding potassium or sodium fluoride to pure beryllium fluoride to make it conduct the current, he placed the mixture in a nickel crucible. After melting the double salt with a Bunsen burner, he placed the positive (graphite) electrode in the fluoride mixture and connected the nickel crucible to the negative side of a battery of twenty amperes under eighty volts. In less than an hour crystals of beryllium were deposited on the sides of the crucible. After washing them, first with water and then with absolute alcohol, and drying them in a vacuum desiccator containing phosphorus pentoxide, Lebeau found that they contained from 99.5 to 99.8 per cent of beryllium.   This research provided the data for his thesis for the doctorate in June, 1898.

Nearly a century after Wöhler and Bussy liberated beryllium, Alfred Stock and Hans Goldschmidt devised the first commercial process, in which a mixture of the fluorides of beryllium and barium is electrolyzed. The molten beryllium separates out at the water-cooled iron cathode (*24*).

A MON AMI

GAY-LUSSAC,

MEMBRE DE L'ACADÉMIE ROYALE DES SCIENCES
DE L'INSTITUT DE FRANCE,

PROFESSEUR DE CHIMIE A L'ÉCOLE ROYALE
POLYTECHNIQUE,

PROFESSEUR DE PHYSIQUE A LA FACULTÉ DES SCIENCES
DE L'ACADÉMIE DE PARIS, etc., etc., etc

Dedication Page of Thenard's "Traité de Chimie," a five-volume work.

Beryllium in Plants and Animals.   In 1888 F. Sestini found beryllium in land plants grown in soils containing it (*92, 93*).   He found later that, although beryllium may take the place of magnesium as a nutrient for wheat, it is not a complete substitute for magnesium in the production of seed (*93*).   Beryllium is occasionally present in bone (*94*).

BORON

Tincal (Borax).   Even in the eighteenth century, borax was believed to be an artificial production (*59, 60*).   Caspar Neumann (1683–1737) said that "Borax is a saline substance, of which neither the origin nor the component parts are as yet known.   It comes from the East-Indies in little crystalline masses. . . .   The refining of Borax was formerly practised only at Venice, and hence the refined Borax was called Venetian; but the Dutch are now the only masters of this manufacture.   Serapio calls the rough Borax as it comes from the Indies *Tincar;* and the dealers in this commodity still distinguish it by the name *Tincar* or *Tincal,* never calling it Borax till it is refined" (*95*).

P.-J. Macquer (1718–1784) said that "Though Borax is of great use in many chymical operations, especially in the fusion of metals, . . . yet till of late years Chymists were quite ignorant of its nature, as they still are of its origin; concerning which we know nothing with certainty, but that it comes rough from the East Indies and is purified by the Dutch" (*96*).

Macquer stated that borax contains "an Alkali like the basis of Sea-salt. This Alkali is not perfectly neutralized by the sedative salt [boric acid], which is also contained in Borax; for its alkaline properties are so perceptible as to have led some Chymists to think that Borax was only an Alkali of a particular kind" (96).

In 1772, however, the Swedish merchant Johan Abraham Grill (Abrahamsson) described in volume thirty-four of *Vetenskapsacademiens Handlingar* a natural borax called *pounxa* sent him from Thibet by Jos. Vit. Kuo, a native Chinese Catholic missionary. "From the report of my correspondent Vit. Kuo," said he, "it can be inferred that the *pounxa* is found in Thibet, that to obtain it one digs into the ground to the depth of two yards; . . . it positively cannot be made artificially by heating the earth; it is found already prepared by nature" (61).

In the same year Gustaf von Engeström analyzed the different kinds of *pounxa* and also two kinds of *tincal,* one from the Netherlands and another which the Councilor of Mines Georg Brandt ("Bergrath Brand") had received from East India (97). Through their connections with the Swedish East India Company, von Engeström, Johan Abraham Grill, and Peter Johan Bladh were able to obtain and analyze several minerals from the Orient, especially from China (98). The results of these analyses were published in *Vetenskapsacademiens Handlingar* from 1772 to 1776.

Analyses by R. Nasini and R. Grassini indicated that boric acid entered into the composition of the brilliant coral red glazes on the Aretine vases (first century B.C. to first century A.D.) excavated at Arezzo (57, 76). Because of the seal, or impression, on the bottom, these vases were known as "terra sigillata ware." Paul Diergart of the research staff of the Royal Porcelain Works in Berlin questioned these analyses, however (58).

Boric acid was first prepared in 1702 by Wilhelm Homberg. He was born on January 8, 1652, at Batavia on the island of Java. When his father left the service of the Dutch East India Company, the family settled in Amsterdam, where young Wilhelm (or Willem) had a much better opportunity to study than in the torrid climate of the East Indies. After studying law at Jena and Leipzig, he was admitted to the bar in Magdeburg in 1674. Soon becoming more interested in the laws of nature than in those devised by man, he began to devote much time to botany, astronomy, and mechanics.

The Burgomaster of the city, Otto von Guericke, was then performing "the Magdeburg miracles" with the evacuated hemispheres which sixteen horses could not separate and with his curious barometer, "the little man who remained hidden in a tube when the weather was to be rainy and came out when it was to be fair" (62). These wonders still further diverted Homberg's attention from his practice of law.

At Padua and Rome, he studied medicine, optics, art, and music. After further study in France, he went to England to work with Robert Boyle, thence to the Netherlands, where he studied anatomy, and finally to Württemberg, where he received the degree of doctor of medicine. Homberg then visited the mines of Saxony, Hungary, and Bohemia, and

Raffaello Nasini, 1854–1931. Italian chemist who reported the presence of boric acid in the glazes of ancient Aretine vases, and studied the rare gases of the boric acid soffioni, or hot springs, of Tuscany. In his youth he assisted Stanislao Cannizzaro and in later life he collaborated with Giacomo Ciamician.

went to Sweden to see the great copper mine at Falun. Although it has often been stated, on the basis of Fontenelle's eulogy, that Homberg worked for a time with Urban Hiärne at the newly established chemical laboratory at Stockholm, Sten Lindroth found no record of this and believes that Homberg may possibly have worked in Hiärne's private laboratory before the new laboratory at Stockholm was established in 1683 (85). When Homberg returned to Paris, the Duke of Orleans studied under him, caught his enthusiasm, and equipped for him "the most superb and best furnished laboratory Chemistry had ever seen" (62).

In 1702 Homberg stated in the Memoirs of the Academy of Sciences at Paris that he had heated borax with a solution of iron vitriol (ferrous sulfate) and sublimed off with the water vapor a substance which he called *sel volatil narcotique du vitriol* ("volatile sedative salt from the vitriol"). Thus it is evident that he must have prepared boric acid and that he believed that it came from the ferrous sulfate (*63*). He used hot water to extract the colcothar or residue which remained in the retort after distillation of Nordhausen sulfuric acid, filtered the solution, and mixed with it a hot solution of borax. After evaporating the mixture to incipient crystallization, he heated it on a sandbath, using a cucurbit and alembic. When the liquid products of distillation ceased to drip into the receiver, snow-white platelets with a mother-of-pearl luster sublimed in the still-head. By redistilling the aqueous distillate eight or ten times, Homberg obtained a good yield of the "sedative salt" (*63*).

F. M. Jaeger found in the correspondence of Elisabeth Charlotte of Orleans (1652–1721) a firsthand character sketch of the discoverer of boric acid. "One cannot know Homberg," said she, "without admiring him for his clear mind,—not at all confused as the highly educated usually are, and not solemn, but always jolly; everything he knows, even the most difficult arts, seem with him to be a jest, as though he were playing tricks. . . . He has a soft voice, and speaks very slowly but clearly" (*64*).

During his last illness, Homberg's patience "was that of a hero or a saint. A few days before his death," said B. Le Bovier de Fontenelle in his eulogy, "he took the liberty of writing to His Royal Highness the Duke of Orleans . . . to recommend to him all that he had most loved, the widow whom he was about to leave and the Academy of Sciences. His prayer for the Academy had more success than he would have dared to hope; the prince has reserved for himself alone the direct management of this Company. He treats our sciences like his own domain, of which he is jealous" (*62*).

Wilhelm Homberg died on the twenty-fourth of September, 1715. "Although he had a weak constitution, he was most industrious; although he lacked strength, he had courage to compensate for it. Besides a prodigious quantity of curious facts of natural philosophy collected in his mind and retained in his memory, he had the qualifications of an ordinary scholar in history and languages. He even knew Hebrew. His quality of mind is evident in all his work: above all, an ingenious attentiveness which caused him to make observations where others saw nothing. . . .

"We have already mentioned his complete freedom from ostentation," said Fontenelle. "He was equally free from mystery, so common among chemists, which is merely another kind of ostentation in which one conceals instead of displaying. . . . Although French was always a foreign language for him and he naturally was not rich in vocabulary and

had continually to search for the right word, he always found it. No
one ever had more gentle manners nor more sociable habits. . . . A
wholesome, peaceful philosophy made him receive calmly the different
events of life, immune to those agitations for which one has, if one
wishes, so many occasions" (62). Further information concerning Homberg may be found in Professor Heinrich Rheinboldt's book on the
balance and weights in the preclassical epoch of chemistry (82).

Louis-Jacques Thenard, 1777–1857. Professor of chemistry at the École Polytechnique. Discoverer of hydrogen
peroxide. Collaborator with Gay-Lussac
in his researches on potassium, boron,
iodine, and chlorine. He also investigated many fatty acids, esters and ethers.

G. E. Stahl showed in 1723 that the "sedative salt" could be prepared
by treating borax not only with sulfuric acid but also with other acids
(99, 100). Louis Lémery, son of Homberg's friend Nicolas Lémery,
made the same discovery five years later but thought that the acid merely
combined with the borax to form the sedative salt. In 1732 Geoffroy
the Younger observed the green color which an alcoholic solution of
this substance imparts to the flame (101). Although Louis-Claude
Bourdelin thought this green flame color must be caused by the presence
of copper in the sedative salt, he was unable to detect that metal (102).

In 1747–48 Théodore Baron de Hénouville (1715–1768) proved
that borax is composed of "sedative salt" and soda (65). After A. S.
Marggraf had investigated alumina ("the earth from alum"), Baron de
Hénouville in 1760 published a paper on the basis of alum. Although
some of his observations were erroneous, he pointed out the close rela-

tion between this earth and "sedative salt," that is to say, between the compounds of aluminum and boron (*103*).

In his "Elective Attractions," Torbern Bergman stated emphatically that the so-called "sedative salt" is not a salt but an acid. "The substance commonly called sedative salt," said he, "is more nearly allied to acids than any other class of bodies. It reddens turnsole and saturates alkalis and soluble earths. It also dissolves various metals, and has other properties which shew its acid nature; and it seems better entitled to the name of acid of borax than to that of sedative salt" (*66*).

Louis-Joseph Gay-Lussac, 1778–1850. Professor of chemistry at the École Polytechnique and at the Jardin des Plantes. With Thenard, he prepared potassium without the use of a battery, and isolated boron. In 1809 Gay-Lussac enunciated his famous law of combining volumes of gases.

After the chemical revolution, "sedative salt" came to be regarded as an acidic oxide, boric (or boracic) acid. Even at the close of the eighteenth century, its chemical nature was not understood. In a letter to the *Annales de Chimie et de Physique*, A. N. Scherer wrote in 1799: "I have just been assured that Crell has recognized carbon as the radical of boracic acid" (*67*).

Lavoisier believed that it contained oxygen, and had mentioned its radical in his list of elements* (*20*). The first proof of the composition of boric acid was given in 1808 when Gay-Lussac and Thenard in France and Davy in England succeeded in decomposing it by reduction with

* See Chapter 18, p. 477.

potassium, and in liberating a new element which the French chemists called *bore* and Sir Humphry called *boracium*.

Louis-Joseph Gay-Lussac was born at St. Léonard, near Limoges, on December 6, 1778, and was therefore just eleven days older than Davy. After receiving his elementary education in St. Léonard he went to Paris, and when he was nineteen years old, he enrolled at the École Polytechnique, where he soon became acquainted with his lifelong friend and collaborator, Thenard.

Somewhat later he won the friendship of C.-L. Berthollet at the École des Ponts et Chaussées, who said to him, "Young man, your destiny is to make discoveries" (3). For a time he worked with Berthollet's son in a factory in Arcueil where chlorine was used to bleach linen. On New Year's day in the year 1802 Gay-Lussac became a répétiteur at the École Polytechnique, where he often substituted for Fourcroy in his lectures on chemistry.

Two years later Gay-Lussac and J.-B. Biot made a daring balloon ascension to study the behavior of a magnetic needle and the chemical composition of the atmosphere at high altitudes. On another occasion, when Gay-Lussac alone had reached an elevation of 7016 meters and wished to ascend still higher, he threw overboard some small objects to lighten the balloon. A shepherdess in the field was astonished to see a white wooden chair fall from the sky into some bushes, and the peasants who heard her story were at a loss to explain why, if the chair had come direct from Heaven, the workmanship on it should be so crude (3).

After a period of extended travel and study in Italy with Alexander von Humboldt, Gay-Lussac returned to the École Polytechnique and began a long series of researches with Thenard. Louis-Jacques Thenard,* a carpenter's son, was born at La Louptière near Nogent-sur-Seine on May 4, 1777. After receiving private instruction from the village priest, he went to Paris to study chemistry, where, after three years of hard study and severe privations, he finally succeeded in winning the recognition of Vauquelin and Fourcroy. The latter scientist had befriended the poor peasant boy Vauquelin in his early struggles, and now Vauquelin in turn helped Thenard to obtain a teaching position in a Parisian pension. In 1798 Gay-Lussac and Thenard met at the École Polytechnique, where both later became professors.

When the news of Davy's isolation of the alkali metals reached Paris in 1808, Napoleon provided Gay-Lussac and Thenard with a powerful voltaic pile. Before it could be set up, however, they showed that these metals can be obtained without a battery simply by reducing the caustic alkali with metallic iron at a high temperature, a method which

* He always spelled his name thus, without the acute accent over the *e*.

From Appleton's "Beginners' Hand-Book of Chemistry"

Gay-Lussac and Biot Making Their Balloon Ascension.   Gay-Lussac was then
twenty-five years old.

Davy soon adopted in preference to his own. The potassium which the
French chemists prepared in this manner was soon put to good use
when they attempted to decompose boric acid.

On June 21, 1808, a note from Gay-Lussac and Thenard was read
before the Institute. It announced that the results they had obtained by
treating boric acid with potassium could be explained only by admitting
that that acid is composed of a combustible substance and oxygen (*21*).

At the time this notice was read, Gay-Lussac was seriously ill as the result of an explosion in which he had almost lost his sight (30).

Before regarding their proof as complete, Gay-Lussac and Thenard wished not only to decompose boric acid, but to recompose it. On November 30 of the same year they were able to state in the *Annales de Chimie et de Physique* that "the composition of boracic acid is no longer problematical. In fact," said they, "we decompose and we recompose this acid at will." Their method was as follows:

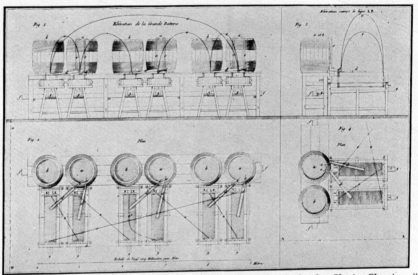

From Gay-Lussac and Thenard's "Recherches Physico-Chymiques"

The Great Battery That Napoleon Presented to the École Polytechnique. The scale is 25 mm. for 1 meter. Figs. 1 and 2. Elevation and plan of the great battery. Figs. 3 and 4. Elevation and plan of two cells. *a,a,a.* Barrels containing liquid for filling the troughs. *b,b,b.* Barrels containing water for washing the troughs. *c,c,c.* Lead siphons for the flow of liquid from the barrels. *d,d,d.* Conduits for receiving liquid from the barrels by means of the siphons, and conducting it into the troughs. *e,e,e.* Wires connecting the different cells of the battery. *f,f,f.* Trough for receiving liquid from all the cells by means of the individual troughs, *g,g.*

To decompose it, place equal parts of metal [potassium] and very pure, vitreous boracic acid in a copper tube to which a tube of bent glass is attached. Place the copper tube in a small furnace, with the end of the glass tube in a flask of mercury. When the apparatus is ready, heat the copper tube gradually until it becomes faintly red; keep it in this condition for several minutes; then, the operation being ended, allow it to cool and take out the material.

Gay-Lussac and Thenard then gave a detailed description of the experiment, saying:

When the temperature is about 150 degrees, the mixture suddenly glows strongly, which appears in a striking manner if a glass tube is used. So much heat is produced that the glass tube melts slightly and sometimes breaks, and the air is almost always driven out of the vessel with force. From the

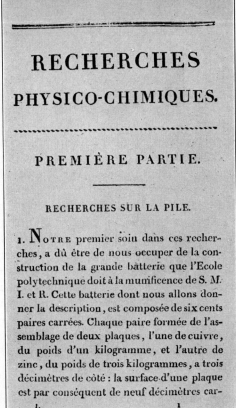

On the First Page of Their "Recherches Physico-Chimiques" Gay-Lussac and Thenard thank Napoleon for the large battery that he had presented to the École Polytechnique.

beginning to the end of the experiment, only atmospheric air is released, with a few bubbles of hydrogen gas, which do not amount to the fiftieth part of that given off when the metal combines with water. The metal [potassium] is used up decomposing part of the boracic acid; and these two substances are converted by their mutual reaction into an olive gray material which is a mixture of potassium, potassium borate, and the radical of boracic acid. Extract this mixture in a tube by pouring water into it and heating slowly, and separate the boracic radical by washing with cold or hot water. That which does not dissolve is the radical itself. . . .

By burning the new "radical" in oxygen, or, better still, by oxidizing it vigorously with potassium chlorate, potassium nitrate, or nitric acid, Gay-Lussac and Thenard were able to make some synthetic boric acid, a sample of which they presented to the Institute. As a result of their experiments they concluded "that this body, which we now propose to call *bore,* is of a definite nature, and can be placed beside carbon, phosphorus, and sulfur; and we are led to think that to pass into the state of boracic acid it requires a great quantity of oxygen, but that before arriving at that state it first passes through that of the oxide" (*21, 38*).

In the following year Gay-Lussac gave an even greater contribution to chemistry, his statement of the famous law of combining volumes. In later life he taught chemistry both at the École Polytechnique and at the Jardin des Plantes. After Bernard Courtois discovered iodine in 1811, Gay-Lussac and Thenard made a thorough study of its properties, and published their results in a memoir now treasured by chemists as a great scientific classic. Gay-Lussac died in Paris on May 9, 1850 (*3*). Davy once said of him, "Gay-Lussac was quick, lively, ingenious, and profound, with great activity of mind, and great facility of manipulation. I should place him at the head of all the living chemists of France" (*4*).

Besides carrying out many inorganic researches with Gay-Lussac, Thenard made important contributions to organic chemistry. He outlived his famous collaborator by seven years, and when he died on June 21, 1857, at the age of eighty years, his native village honored him by changing its name to La Louptière-Thenard (*3*).

Davy's method of isolating boron was very similar to that of the French chemists. While engrossed in the study of the alkalies, he had passed a current through boric acid and had noticed a dark, combustible substance at the negative pole, but had not at that time thoroughly investigated it (*36*). In the following year, however, he placed a mixture of boric acid and potassium in a copper tube and heated it to dull redness for fifteen minutes. When he examined the contents, he found that the potassium had disappeared and that in its place there was an olive-gray powder which did not effervesce when treated with water or with acids. Davy's paper announcing the discovery of metallic boron was read before the Royal Society on June 30, 1808 (*28, 30*).

In 1909, Dr. E. Weintraub of the General Electric Company ran high-potential alternating current arcs between cooled copper electrodes in a mixture of boron chloride with a large excess of hydrogen (*51*), obtaining pure fused boron which differed greatly in properties from the impure amorphous product of earlier workers.

Natural Boric Acid (Sassolite).   In describing an experiment on the preparation of borax from sedative salt and natron, Robert Dossie stated in 1759: "Natron not being to be obtained as a native substance, except in very few places, and the sal sedativus in none hitherto known, when they are required for this experiment, they must be previously separated from sea-salt and borax" (*104*).   Natural boric acid was first discovered in a boiling hot spring in Tuscany in 1778 (*105*).   Hubert Franz Höfer, a German from Cologne in charge of the apothecaries of Pietro Leopoldo, Grand Duke of Tuscany, analyzed the water from the hot springs, or *lagoni,* called Cerchiajo and Castelnuovo.   The Cerchiajo, or "hoop" spring at Monte Rotondo had received this name from its property of rendering wood soaked in it so pliable that it could be bent into a hoop.   Höfer found that the water contained from 36 to 72 grains of "sedative salt" per pound, depending on the season of the year (*108*). The editor of the "Taschen-Buch für Scheidekünstler und Apotheker" for 1782 regarded the presence of "sedative salt" in hot springs as good evidence that the borax from Holland and Venice must likewise be a natural product (*106*).

Because of the practical importance of Höfer's discovery, the Academy of Sciences at Paris offered a prize for the best paper (*a*) on a chemical investigation of borax and sedative salt and the earth of crude East Indian borax; (*b*) on the artificial preparation of borax or sedative salt or on a satisfactory substitute for borax, especially for soldering; and (*c*) on the discovery of natural "sedative salt" (boric acid) elsewhere than in the marsh of Monte Rotondo (*107*).

In February, 1779, Dr. Paolo Mascagni (1755–1815), professor of anatomy at Siena and Pisa, discovered solid boric acid (sassolite) at the basins, or *lagoni,* of Montecerboli and Castelnuovo, and published a paper on it.   In another very thorough historical paper, published twenty years later, he explained that the term *lagone* is not an augmentative of *lago,* a lake, but is a corrupted form of the Latin *lacuna,* a pond. He described the *lagoni* as white, denuded areas with many clefts and fissures "from whence one can see rising, here and there, to greater or lesser heights, varying amounts of white vapors, like clouds which disperse in the air and vanish, sending forth to considerable distances a strong odor of liver of sulfur; and now are seen various springs of hot mineral water, which in some places emerge quietly and are limpid, and in others are more or less turbid because of continual agitation by the vapors and exhalations released through the vents at the bottom with different amounts of force . . . and which produce more or less boiling, together with a rumbling sound of varying intensity. . . .   If the *lagoni* are visited long after a rain, the ground is seen to be entirely covered with varying amounts of inflorescences and saline masses . . ." (*108*).

These masses contained boric acid, ammonium borate, sulfates of iron and calcium, and (occasionally) magnesium sulfate.

In shallow places where the water had evaporated, Mascagni found solid boric acid (sassolite) covering the sediment. On examining the mud with a lens, he saw clusters of small, shining crystals. He found this solid boric acid in the hot springs at Castelnuovo, Montecerboli, Monte Rotondo, Edifizio, Benifei, Sasso, Lustignano, and Serazzano (108).

At least twenty years passed before this discovery was utilized. In 1799 Dr. Mascagni (who had previously been too occupied with his professional duties) published a plan for the exploitation of the *lagoni* by increasing the surface of the drier areas by piling up the sediment into mounds exposed to the vapors, and allowing the natural heat of the springs to concentrate the boric acid by evaporation. The last stage of the evaporation was to be carried out in leaden kettles. He suggested that the boric acid be shipped to the saltpits at Portoferrajo, where it could be converted into borax, with hydrochloric acid as a by-product (108, 109). Mascagni taught anatomy, physiology, and chemistry for a time at the Santa Maria Nuova Hospital in Florence, and was a friend of Felice Fontana (110, 111).

In 1818 Francesco Giacomo de Larderel (1789–1858) founded the Tuscan boric acid industry, and nine years later he succeeded in using the natural steam as a source of heat, thus making an unprofitable industry one of the most successful in Italy. P. Le Neve Foster, Jr. wrote in 1875: "At the present time there are no less than seven separate establishments belonging to Count Larderel, all situated within a few miles of the little town of Castelnuovo. . . . The works at Larderello are the most important of all. . . . This little colony, which was founded by the late Count, is situated at a short distance from the village of Monte Cerboli, on the torrent Possera, and shows what might be done in other parts of Italy for improving the social condition of the working classes. There is a neat square, 'La Piazza dell' Industria,' surrounded by blocks of buildings, which on one side include the offices, church, museum of mineralogy, and schools, and on the other, the model lodging-houses for the workmen, stores, workshops for various tradesmen, such as tailors, shoemakers, etc., and a weaving establishment for giving employment to the wives and daughters of the workmen" (112). The native boric acid is found in a region of about one hundred square miles, between Pisa and Siena. Unlike geysers, the soffioni, or vents, eject more steam than water (113, 114, 115).

Prince Piero Ginori Conti, Senator of the Kingdom of Italy, devoted his life to the scientific and practical development of a great modern boric acid and borax industry.   He was born in Florence on June 3, 1865.   After receiving his doctorate in social science at the Cesare Alfieri Institute, he became interested in the boric acid works of his father-in-law, Count Florestano de Larderel, a grandson of Francesco de Larderel.   Count Florestano de Larderel was a patron of music and of Pietro Mascagni, composer of *Cavalleria Rusticana* (*110*).

Had it not been for the many improvements and economies made by Prince Ginori Conti and his sons, the Italian boric acid industry might have been unable to survive after the discovery of the great borax deposits in the salt crust marshes of Death Valley, California (*130*).   To obtain larger amounts of volcanic steam for power and for the large-scale production of boric acid, borax, liquid and solid carbon dioxide, and ammonium carbonate, Prince Ginori Conti drilled wells, often at considerable risk, and solved many difficult engineering problems (*116*). Among the by-products of this industry are helium and other inert gases. He also developed the manufacture of a borosilicate optical glass.   Felice Sorgès observed on his visit to Larderello not merely a great center of industry but also many manifestations of the kindness and liberality of the Prince and his consort (*117*).

In 1926 Prince Ginori Conti attended the International Union of Pure and Applied Science at Washington, D. C., and gave an inspiring lecture on the use of geothermal power in Tuscany, which was later published in the *Journal of Chemical Education* (*115*).   His death on December 3, 1939, was an irreparable loss to chemical engineering.

Boracite.   The first stony mineral of which boric acid was recognized to be a constituent was one which G. S. O. Lasius described as a "cubic quartz" from Lüneburg, Hanover (*118*).   It is now known as boracite. When Johann Friedrich Westrumb, an apothecary in Hamelin, analyzed it in 1788, he found lime, magnesia, alumina, silica, iron, and, to his complete surprise, about 60 per cent of "sedative salt."   At the close of his paper he conscientiously stated, "I regret that I cannot get enough of the mineral in order to experiment with several hundred grains and carry out the decomposition very accurately; for I cannot, like many assayers, state the proportions in very small quantities precisely" (*119*). The composition of boracite is expressed by the formula $6MgO \cdot MgCl_2 \cdot 8B_2O_3$ (*120*).

Borax in California.   The great deposits of borax and other soluble salts in San Bernardino County, California, were discovered by Dennis Searle and E. M. Skillings on February 14, 1873.   In the following year Arthur Robottom of London explored the borax regions of Nevada and California, "travelled with a mule team over a very rough country at the rate of from 12 to 14 miles per day, and arrived at length . . . at the shanty kept by Jim Bridger, some 42 miles from the Slate Range, and which is situated on the main road to Cerre Gorda, a wild looking spot. . . ." A pioneer prospector who had been to Death Valley told him of the plentiful supply of borax there but stated that "no one knows what it's good for." After a short stay at Jim Bridger's shanty, Mr. Robottom "again proceeded, steering for the Foot Hills, some 22 miles from the shanty, then onward through a great cañon, or divide, partly covered with salt, on emerging from which I found myself on the border of the most important borax lake yet discovered in the world. I was met by John and Dennis Searle, two men belonging to the California discovery army that sprang into existence in the year 1849. . . . These men, masters of almost every kind of handicraft," said he, "had made their way to this great lake with a view to exploration. Consequently, though I can claim to be the first Englishman who visited the borax lake, the honour of its discovery does not rest with me. I stayed some time in the hut of these men, and together we examined the ground. I very soon discovered natural borax of the finest quality in a pure state, and though Messrs. John and Dennis Searle had begun prior to my arrival to develop the ground, the first shipment was made by me to England. The borax I found was crystallized borax, in the same form as the regular borax of commerce, and is the only known deposit of natural borax yet discovered in the world. In the centre of the lake is a bed of salt about five miles long; on the outside of this salt is a deposit of carbonate of soda, and some thousands of acres of land covered with crude borax, from three inches to two feet thick. The crude borax is collected and put into cowhide baskets, carried to a large boiling-pan, and boiled for 36 hours; the solution is then run into vats, and the crystals form on the sides of the vats. After drying it is put into bags, about 70 lbs. in each bag, and sent to San Francisco, a distance of about 420 miles, and conveyed at that time by mule teams" (*121*).

The *American Journal of Science* for 1889 contains a description by Henry G. Hanks of the early process of recovering the borax. "The plant," said he, ". . . consists of a large steam flue boiler, and a multitude of boiling and crystallizing tanks. . . . Fifty men and thirty-five animals are employed in these works. The product is hauled in wagons to Mojave station, a distance of about seventy miles, over a sandy desert, so dry and sterile that a supply of water must be hauled in other wagons for the use of men and animals. The fuel used has been generally the sagebrush, which is gathered at heavy cost and thrown under the boilers with pitchforks, like hay into a barn; but recently, California crude petroleum has been substituted" (*122*).

Boric Acid in Sea Water. In 1865 J. G. Forchhammer detected boric acid in sea water (*123*). "I have long tried," said he, "to find boracic acid in sea water, but for a long time all my endeavours were vain. Notwithstanding, I felt convinced it must be there, since both boracic acid and borates are not very rare, and a great part of its salts with lime and magnesia are more or less soluble in water. Thus I thought that water from the land must have carried boracic acid into the sea, where it still must be accumulating, since we do not know any combination by which it could be separated again from the water. An additional proof of the correctness of this idea I found in the occurrence of stassfurthite (mostly consisting of borate of magnesia), together with all other salts that occur in sea water, in the beds of rock salt at Stassfurth in Germany" (123).

Forchhammer evaporated six pounds of sea water from the Sound near Copenhagen and heated the residue to white heat in a perfectly clean platinum crucible. After further purification of the remaining hemiprismatic crystals, he treated them with alcohol and detected boron by the green color it imparted to the alcohol flame and the brown color it gave to curcuma paper. In 1877 L. Dieulafait found boric acid to be a normal constituent of sea water (124). Its presence in many mineral waters has also been demonstrated.

Boron in Plants and Animals. "When I had convinced myself," said Forchhammer, "that boracic acid occurred in sea water, it appeared to me in the highest degree probable that the organisms of the sea would collect it, and that it might be found in their ashes. I was so fortunate as to begin my experiments with a plant that contained it in a rather large quantity, viz. the *Zostera marina*. . . . Even *Fucus vesiculosus* contains the same acid, but in a much smaller quantity" (123).

Johan Georg Forchhammer was a Danish geologist and chemist. He was born at Husum, Schleswig, in 1794, studied at Kiel, and started his career as a pharmaceutical chemist. While still in his early twenties, he began to collaborate with H. C. Oersted and Jens Esmark. In his doctor's dissertation in 1820 he distinguished between manganic and permanganic acids. He published about two hundred papers on geological and chemical subjects, and made many contributions to soil analysis and hydrography. His famous paper on the composition of sea water was first published in Danish in 1859. In completed form, it appeared in English in the *Philosophical Transactions* in 1865, the year of his death (125, 126).

In 1887 C. A. Crampton of the United States Department of Agriculture examined 36 samples of wine from different parts of the country and found boric acid in all but two of them. Hesitating to believe that adulteration could be such a universal practice, he analyzed many specimens of natural grape juice and found that boric acid is a natural constituent of California grapes. Other experimenters found it to be almost universally present in foreign grapes and wines. Hence mere qualitative detection of its presence in a food does not necessarily prove that boric acid has been fraudulently added as a preservative (127).

The bibliography on the minor elements and their relation to plant and animal nutrition by L. G. Willis of the North Carolina Experiment Station at Raleigh lists sixty pages of abstracts of researches proving that small amounts of boron are essential for the normal growth of many food plants (128, 163). Its presence in organic nature has been thoroughly investigated by Professor Gabriel Bertrand and H. Agulhon, who found that it is a normal constituent of the animal organism and that marine animals contain more of it than do the land forms (129).

SILICON

Quartz and Glass. Rock crystal was used in Egypt for the manufacture of beads, small vases, and the corneas of the eyes of statues even in predynastic times (131). When the Book of Job was written, glass (crystal) must have been very costly. Speaking of wisdom, Job said, "The gold and the crystal cannot equal it" (Job 28, 17). The Phoenicians, like the Egyptians before them, were skilled glassworkers. The oldest known glass vessel is in the British Museum. Since it bears the name Tutmosis (Thothmes III), it is believed to date back to 1500 B.C. (132). From the excavation of an Egyptian glassworks of the year 1370 B.C. in Tel-el-Amarna, Flinders Petrie found that the ancient Egyptians made their glass by fusing together quartz and an alkaline salt in clay crucibles (132). Pliny the Elder was familiar with quartz and its use in glassmaking, and gave a good description of rock crystal.

Although Sir Humphry Davy felt certain that silica is not an element, he was unable to decompose it with his powerful voltaic pile, and was also unsuccessful in his attempts to isolate silicon by passing potassium vapor over red-hot silica. Gay-Lussac and Thenard observed that silicon tetrafluoride and potassium react violently when the metal is heated, and that a reddish brown, combustible solid is obtained. This was probably very impure amorphous silicon (37, 39).

Berzelius heated a mixture of silica, iron, and carbon to a very high temperature, and obtained iron silicide. When he decomposed this with hydrochloric acid, silica was precipitated, and the amount of hydrogen evolved was in excess of the iron, indicating that some other metal must have been present (9). Berzelius finally showed in 1824 that this other seemingly metallic substance was derived from the silica, and succeeded in preparing the amorphous form of it by two methods. In the first of these he heated potassium in an atmosphere of silicon tetrafluoride gas, as Cay Lussac and Thenard had done, and obtained a brown mass. When this was thrown into water, hydrogen was freely evolved, and the new element silicon was precipitated as a dark brown, insoluble powder containing potassium fluosilicate, which is difficultly soluble. Although Davy, Thenard, and Gay-Lussac had all handled the brown powder before, only Berzelius had the patience for the prolonged washing required to remove the fluosilicate (9, 32).

In his other method Berzelius heated the potassium fluosilicate with excess potassium. The resulting potassium silicide was easily decomposed with water, the amorphous silicon settling to the bottom.

Nothing is easier [said he] than to procure this substance; the following is the method I have adopted: The double fluate of silica and potash, or soda, heated nearly to redness to drive off the hygrometric water, is put into a glass tube, closed at one end. Bits of potassium are added and mixed with the powder by fusing the metal and gently rapping the tube. It is then heated by the spirit-lamp, and before it is red-hot, a feeble detonation ensues and the silicium is reduced. The mass is suffered to cool, and then treated with water as long as it dissolves anything. Hydrogen gas is at first evolved, in consequence of siliciuret of potassium having been formed, which cannot exist in water.

The washed substance [continued Berzelius] is a hydruret of silicium, which, at a red heat, burns vividly in oxygen gas, although the silicium is not thereby completely oxidated; it is then heated in a covered platina crucible, the heat being slowly raised to redness. The hydrogen alone is oxidated, and the silicium is now no longer combustible in oxygen, but chlorine attacks it readily. The small portion of silica that is formed may be dissolved by fluoric [hydrofluoric] acid. If silicium has not been exposed to a strong red heat, the acid dissolves it, with a slow disengagement of hydrogen. According to my synthetical experiments, silica contains 0.52 of its weight of oxygen.

Berzelius' product was impure amorphous silicon. Zirconium may be obtained by an analogous process (32).

The first crystalline silicon was prepared by Henri Sainte-Claire Deville in 1854 (9, 31). In the course of his researches on aluminum, he decomposed an impure sodium aluminum chloride with the voltaic pile, and obtained a gray, brittle, granular melt containing 10.3 per cent of silicon. When he dissolved away the aluminum, some shining platelets remained.

Sainte-Claire Deville explained his results by saying that an alloy often behaves like a true solution of one metal in another. "Thus it is," said he, "that carbon, boron, and silicon, dissolving like metals in iron and in aluminum, separate from them in cooling, and can be obtained in the crystalline state by the use of reagents which act on the

aluminum and the iron without attacking the carbon, the boron, and
the silicon.   This is the principle of the method which has served for
the preparation of the last two metalloids in the adamantine state." In
spite of the metallic luster of his crystalline silicon, he realized that the
element was not a true metal.   "On the contrary," said he, "I think this
new form of silicon bears the same relation to ordinary silicon that
graphite does to carbon" (33, 34, 35).

Silica in Plants and Animals.   Diatoms flourishing in both fresh
and salt water have for untold ages been extracting silica from the water
to build up their exquisitely designed cell walls, which, as these unicel-
lular algae die, are constantly sinking to the bottom and forming deep
deposits of diatomaceous earth or kieselguhr.   J. G. Wallerius found in
1760 that the ash of the straw from rye, barley, wheat, and oats easily
fuses to form a green glass (133, 134).   This early observation of the
presence of silica in grains was soon confirmed by L. von Crell, P. C.
Abildgaard, J. F. Westrumb, and others.   Sir Humphry Davy concluded
from similar experiments that the siliceous parts of plants are similar
in function to the skeletons of animals (133, 135, 136, 137).   Silica is
always present in the ash of plants (138), and in 1811 A.-F. de Fourcroy
and N.-L. Vauquelin detected it in human bones (139).

ALUMINUM

Aluminum is the most abundant metal on the earth's surface and
one of the most useful ones, yet it remained unknown for many centuries.

Alum (Alunite).   Although the ancient Greeks and Romans used
alum in medicine and as a mordant in dyeing, they did not distinguish
it clearly from other natural astringents such as copperas (ferrous sulfate)
(68, 69, 140, 141).   The question as to whether or not the ancients were
acquainted with true alum is debatable.   Johann Beckmann, author of
the famous "History of Inventions," answers it in the negative (140).
Herbert Hoover however gave strong evidence that their alum was a
rather impure product ranging in composition from alum to vitriol, and
that since they were thoroughly acquainted with soda (niter), they may
possibly have been able to manufacture alum artificially (73).

Early alum works in Phocis near Ionia and in Lesbos sold their
product to the Turks for the manufacture of brilliant Turkey red (68,
69).   The manufacture was also carried on in Syria, at Foya Nova near
Smyrna, and at Constantinople.   In 1254 A.D., Friar William De Rubruquis (Ruysbroek) wrote in his journal, "I found many Frankes at Iconium
[Konia], and a certaine Januensian Marchant, called Nicholas de Sancto
Syrio.   Who with a certaine companion of his a Venetian, called Boniface

de Molendino, carried all the Allum out of Turkie, so that the Soldan could not sell any, but to those two, and they made it so deare, that what was wont to be sold for fifteene Bizantians, is now sold for fifty" (70).

In about 1459 Bartholomew Perdix (Bartolomeo Perdice, or Pernice), a Genoese merchant who had been in Syria, found a rock suitable for alum on the island of Ischia; he has been regarded as the first to introduce this industry into Europe (68). Gino Testi gave evidence, however, that alum was manufactured in Italy long before this. He quoted a passage from Diodorus Siculus (first century B.C.) which shows that the Romans profitably exported alum from Lipari for use in Phoenician dyeing. According to Testi, the alum mines on the island of Ischia have been known since the twelfth century A.D., and Perdice, already aware of their richness, brought skilled workmen from Genoa who had learned the trade in Rocca (Orfa) but had fled from Asia because of the Turkish conquests (71).

Before 1454 Giovanni de Castro learned the process at Constantinople. On returning to Italy after that city had fallen into the hands of the Turks, he happened to find, in about 1462, in the barren hills near Tolfa, some holly plants like those he had seen growing near the alum mines in Syria. On searching, he found some white stones similar to the Syrian ore from which alum was prepared (71). Unemployed alum workers, brought from Genoa, "thanked God for having restored to them their means of subsistence." For this discovery Pius II granted Giovanni de Castro a generous annuity and had a statue erected in his honor (71). In the alum works at Tolfa, Genoese workmen dissolved the calcined rock in a large volume of water, boiled the lye in leaden caldrons, and allowed it to evaporate spontaneously in wooden vats (69, 72). The so-called "Roman alum" produced there was the double basic potassium alum, which crystallizes in cubes rather than octahedra (71, 73).

As early as 1554 an alum works was established at Oberkaufungen, Hesse-Cassel, Germany (142). At the beginning of the seventeenth century Sir Thomas Chaloner noticed the sickly green color of the vegetation on his estate at Guisborough, Yorkshire, found alum there, and founded an industry (143). In 1702 E.-F. Geoffroy described the manufacture of alum at Civita Vecchia and Solfatara, Italy, in Yorkshire and Lancashire, England, and in Sweden. He stated that "the same mine which affords it does also, or may at least, afford sulphur, nitre, and vitriol. Perhaps these different minerals," said he, "are at the bottom only one principle, disguised under these four salts, according as it has been mixed by nature with certain substances or according as it has been managed by men" (144). Geoffroy concluded from his analysis of alum that it "consists of an acid Salt of the Vitriolick Kind, and an astringent Earth like Bole, or Chalk, very closely united together" (145).

J. P. de Tournefort, who journeyed through the Levant in 1700, said that "the Island of Milo [Melos, Greece] . . . certainly abounds with all the Materials necessary to the production of Alum and Sulphur. As for Nitre, there's none at all, whatever the Inhabitants say, who confound it with alum" (146). He had the erroneous idea that the alum was a chloride produced by "spirit of salt."

In the eighteenth century, according to Caspar Neumann, alum "was used in large quantity in some mechanic businesses; particularly by the dyers, paper makers, goldsmiths, bookbinders, for preserving watery liquors from corruption, for preserving anatomical preparations, and in the embalming of animal bodies: It is far more powerfully antiseptic than the Vitriols" (147).

Although G. E. Stahl and Caspar Neumann both believed that alum contained lime, J. H. Pott was unable to prepare it from lime and vitriolic acid, but always obtained merely selenite (calcium sulfate) (74). When Stahl leached with water a broken clay tube he had used for distilling spirit of vitriol (sulfuric acid), he obtained crystals of alum (74). Pott, too, prepared alum from clay and sulfuric acid (74).

Antoine Baumé stated that the purest alum came from Civita Vecchia near Rome and that a good grade of it was also made at Solfatara. He based his account on the Abbé J.-A. Nollet's description, read before the Académie des Sciences in 1750, of his visit to the Solfatara alum works and on the Abbé Mazéas's memoir on the alunite mines of Tolfa, Italy, and Polinier, Brittany, which was published in volume five of the "Savants étrangers" (148).

After the Abbé Lazaro Spallanzani (1729–1799) found an unworked deposit of native alum (alunite) in a grotto at Cape Miseno, near Naples, M. H. Klaproth analyzed some specimens of it which John Hawkins collected there. The Abbé Scipione Breislak described the extensive alunite deposits at Solfatara in 1792–93 and afterward became the director of an alum works there. In his "Travels in the Two Sicilies and Some Parts of the Apennines," Spallanzani wrote: It is well known that for a long time alum and sal ammoniac have been extracted from this half-extinguished volcano (Solfatara)." The methods employed were as follows: "In the process for the alum, certain square places were cleared out in the plain of Solfatara, in which it effloresced, and the efflorescences were swept together, and from them, by methods well known, the salt was collected purified." The sal ammoniac fumes were allowed to condense on pieces of tile near the apertures from which that salt issued.

After stating that there had been some criticism of these inefficient methods, Spallanzani added, "But we may now hope that both these manufactures may become objects of importance under the direction of the Abbé Breislak and the liberal patronage of Baron Don Giuseppe Brentano, who has taken this celebrated Phlegrean field at a constant rent. The Abbé . . . has greatly extended the spaces alloted . . . and surrounded them with small ditches" (*149*). The ditches were to prevent rain water from diluting the alum.

The United States has great deposits of alunite in Utah, Arizona, Colorado, California, Nevada, and Washington. By means of the Kalunite process, alumina can be made from alunite at a cost which permits of competition with alumina from bauxite (*161*).

In an attempt to determine the composition of alum, A. S. Marggraf in 1754 added pure alkali to several pounds of it and precipitated what he called the "earth of alum" (Alaunerde). After he had thoroughly washed and dried this alumina, he tried in vain to regenerate the alum by adding sulfuric acid.

Marggraf then collected clays from various places in Germany, Silesia, and Poland, and distilled them with sulfuric acid, but obtained no satisfactory crystals of alum. When he added fixed alkali in the proper amount, however, he obtained beautiful, large crystals of it (*74*).

Marggraf noticed that, when he dissolved the earth from alum in nitric acid, evaporated the solution, and calcined the residue, he merely regenerated the "earth" but obtained no "Balduin's phosphorus" (calcium nitrate). He realized, therefore, that the earth in alum must be different from that in chalk or limestone. He also demonstrated the presence of alumina in clay and in roofing slate (*74*).

Andreas Sigismund Marggraf was born in Berlin on March 3, 1709, studied chemistry and pharmacy first under his father and then under Caspar Neumann, took the medical course at Halle, and received further chemical and metallurgical training in Freiberg from the famous director of mines, J. Fr. Henckel. He devoted fifty years of his life to scientific research, and was a pioneer in analytical chemistry. He proved that potash and soda are different, that calamine contains a peculiar metal, zinc, and that alumina, magnesia, and lime are three distinct earths, and was one of the first persons to prepare phosphorus. In 1747 he made the important discovery that sucrose exists in plants endemic to Europe, especially in the beet species *Beta alba* and *Beta rubra*. Although the sweetness had been noticed long before, Marggraf actually recovered this sugar from the juice by crystallization (*40, 86, 162*). Marggraf died in his native city on August 7, 1782, at the age of seventy-three years. D. Lorenz Crell called him the second father of European analytical chemistry (*10*), and he must also have been a great teacher. One of his most famous pupils was Franz Karl Achard (*40*).

M.-J.-A.-N. de Caritat Condorcet once said of Marggraf, "Perhaps no physicist ever so completely excluded every system and hypothesis . . . if, for example, he admits Stahl's doctrine on phlogiston, one would think, from the reserve with which he speaks of it, that he had a presentiment that this doctrine, then so widely accepted, would soon, at least, be overthrown. His memoirs confine themselves to the statements of the facts . . . his results have a precision which was not known before him . . ." (75).

Hans Christian Oersted, 1777–1851. Danish physicist, chemist, physician, and pharmacist. Discoverer of the magnetic action of the electric current. The first person to isolate the metal aluminum.

From Oersted's "The Soul in Nature"

In his eulogy, Condorcet said that "M. Marggraf had a kind, good-natured, happy temperament; his only distraction and his greatest pleasure except study was a small circle of friends and enlightened men who could understand him and to whom he could say what he believed" (75).

The attempts of Berzelius and Davy to use the voltaic current for

Courtesy Ralph E. Oesper

Heinrich Rheinboldt, 1891–1955.   German-Brazilian chemist.
Head of the chemistry department at the University of São Paulo.
Grandson of the great German dye chemist Heinrich Caro. He
has investigated the mechanism of the Grignard reaction, the
organic compounds of sulfur and its congeners, and the chemo-
therapy of leprosy, and has published a fine collection of lecture
experiments and many articles and books on all fields of the
history of chemistry. See also refs. (*54*) and (*165*)

isolating the metal present in alumina were unsuccessful. Although most chemical historians credit F. Wöhler with the first isolation of aluminum, the claims of Oersted cannot be lightly dismissed (11, 42).

Hans Christian Oersted (41) was born on Langeland Island in southern Denmark in 1777, the year in which Lavoisier overthrew the phlogiston theory. His father was a rather unsuccessful apothecary, who had very little money for the education of his children. Hans Christian learned arithmetic alone out of an old schoolbook and sometimes received a little instruction from private tutors. When he was twelve years old he became his father's assistant in the pharmacy, where he soon learned to enjoy his chemical duties. As he was very eager to attend the University of Copenhagen, he studied conscientiously until, at the age of seventeen years, he had earned the coveted certificate (Reifezeugnis) entitling him to matriculation. His studies at Copenhagen included science, philosophy, and medicine, and at the age of twenty-two years he received the degree of Doctor of Medicine.

At this time he began to lecture on chemistry and metaphysics, and took over the management of a pharmacy. After Volta's discovery became known, Oersted immediately became interested in physics and electricity. When he visited the famous universities in Germany, the scientists he met were charmed by his active mind, his youthful enthusiasm, and his almost childlike appearance and bearing. In 1806 he became a professor of physics at the University of Copenhagen. His fame rests chiefly on his epoch-making discovery of the magnetic action of the electric current and the close relation between electricity and magnetism.

In 1825, however, he studied the chemical action of the voltaic current, and tried to isolate chemically the metal believed to be present in alumina. He first prepared liquid aluminum chloride by passing a current of chlorine gas over a mixture of charcoal and alumina heated to redness. By allowing potassium amalgam to react with the aluminum chloride, he prepared an aluminum amalgam, and by distilling off the mercury out of contact with the air, he obtained a metal that looked like tin (11).

Oersted gave the following description of his method:

The compound of chlorine with the combustible element of the clay (aluminum chloride) is volatile at a temperature which is not much above that of boiling water; it is somewhat yellowish, perhaps however from admixed carbon; it is soft, but still has crystalline form; it absorbs water with avidity and dissolves therein with great ease and with evolution of heat. Rapidly heated with potassium amalgam, it is decomposed, potassium chloride and aluminum amalgam being formed. This amalgam is very quickly decomposed in contact with the atmosphere. By distillation without contact with the atmosphere, it forms a lump of metal which in color and luster somewhat resembles tin. Moreover, the author has found, both in the amalgam and the aluminum, remarkable properties which do not permit him to regard the experiments as complete, but show promising prospects of important results (*42, 43*).

Oersted's product must have been impure, metallic aluminum containing mercury, but when Wöhler repeated the experiment he found that the gray molten mass formed by the action of the potassium amalgam on the aluminum chloride volatilized completely when heated (*12, 46*). Kirstine Meyer's careful study of Oersted's unpublished notes and I. Fogh's and M. Tosterud and J. D. Edwards' repetitions of his experiment show that the great Danish physicist allowed a dilute amalgam containing about 1.5 per cent of potassium to react with excess aluminum chloride, and that it is possible to prepare the metal in this manner (*42, 44, 45, 53*).

Since Oersted's results were published in an obscure Danish journal,

Friedrich Wöhler, 1800–1882. German chemist. Student of Leopold Gmelin and Berzelius. He was the first person to synthesize urea and to describe the properties of metallic aluminum. He isolated aluminum, beryllium, and yttrium by the action of potassium on the respective chlorides.

From Muspratt's "Chemistry, Theoretical, Practical, and Analytical"

they made little impression on the scientific world. Nevertheless, his discovery of electromagnetism brought him the prizes, honors, and influence he so richly deserved. He lived to be seventy-four years old (*41*).

Friedrich Wöhler, one of the most versatile chemists Germany ever produced, was born in the little village of Eschersheim near Franfort-on-the Main on July 31, 1800. His father, who himself had a keen appreciation of Nature and a liking for experimentation, delighted to see the same tastes and talents develop in the young child. At the age of fourteen years Wöhler entered the gymnasium at Frankfort, where he was regarded as an average student. As he was passionately absorbed in collecting minerals and making chemical experiments, he frequently neglected his assigned lessons, but these hobbies led him to make the acquaintance of some famous mineral collectors, among them Johann Wolfgang von Goethe (13).

Wöhler was always greatly interested in new elements. Soon after Berzelius discovered selenium in Swedish sulfuric acid, Wöhler found that the Bohemian acid also contained it. Soon after Professor F. Stromeyer discovered cadmium, young Wöhler sent him some that he had prepared from zinc. Wöhler's great ambition was to make potassium, but since his voltaic pile made of alternate layers of Russian copper coins and zinc

This Wöhler Plaque, cast in aluminum, was presented to Dr. F. B. Dains by Dr. Howard M. Elsey, Westinghouse Research Laboratory, East Pittsburgh, Pennsylvania. For the history of it, see ref. (50).

plates was not powerful enough for this, he devised a purely chemical method, somewhat similar to that of Gay-Lussac and Thenard, in which he heated a mixture of potash and charcoal to white heat in a graphite crucible. Since his sister shared the exhausting labor of blowing the bellows, she rejoiced as much as he did when the shining globules of metallic potassium appeared (13).

The youthful Wöhler also had many other interests. He won prizes in mathematics, made oil paintings and etchings, collected coins and other small objects from Roman ruins, and read with enjoyment the best German poetry. At the age of nineteen years he began his medical course at the University of Marburg, but in the following year he transferred to Heidelberg in order to study under Leopold Gmelin (47). He was deeply interested in medicine, and intended to become a practicing physician specializing in obstetrics. On September 2, 1823, he received the degree of Doctor of Medicine, Surgery, and Obstetrics, *insigni cum laude* (*13*).

He had continued his chemical experiments all through his medical course, and Professor Gmelin, who had not failed to notice his surprising skill, advised him to relinquish medicine for chemistry. Wöhler therefore wrote to Berzelius for permission to enter his laboratory in Stockholm. On August 1 the great Swedish master gave his famous reply: "One who has studied under the direction of Herr Leopold Gmelin will certainly find little to learn with me. . . . You may come when you wish."

Leopold Gmelin, 1788–1853. Professor of chemistry and medicine at Heidelberg. First author of the "Handbuch der anorganischen Chemie." Discoverer of potassium ferricyanide. Son of Johann Friedrich Gmelin, the author of the "Geschichte der Chemie." Leopold's nephew, Christian Gottlob Gmelin, was the first to observe the red color imparted to a flame by lithium salts.

From Muspratt's "Chemistry, Theoretical, Practical, and Analytical"

Berzelius must have realized at once that he had a remarkable student, for he started out by assigning Wöhler the difficult analysis of a zeolite. If Berzelius had a remarkable student, however, Wöhler also had a most unusual teacher, for Berzelius first went through the entire analysis himself, showing his student the details of every operation. Whenever Wöhler worked too hastily, Berzelius remarked, "Doctor, that was quick, but poor"* (*13*). Although Wöhler spent less than a year in Stockholm, the teaching of Berzelius influenced the whole course of his life and, like his great master, he made important contributions both to organic and to inorganic chemistry. Minds such as these cannot be encompassed within narrow boundaries. As long as Berzelius lived, he carried on a lively correspondence with Wöhler, and these letters are a rich source of pleasure and profit to all chemists interested in the history of their

* *"Doctor, das war schnell, aber schlecht."*

science. Wöhler became a teacher of chemistry and mineralogy at the newly founded "Städtische Gewerbeschule" (Municipal Technical School) in Berlin in 1825 and three years later was appointed as professor (83). It was here that he made the two great discoveries for which his name will always be honored: the isolation of aluminum and the synthesis of urea.

As previously stated, Wöhler was unable to obtain metallic aluminum by Oersted's method. However, since the latter encouraged him to continue his attempts, he prepared some anhydrous aluminum chloride by Oersted's method, and devised a new plan for isolating the metal. After adding an excess of hot potassium carbonate solution to a boiling hot solution of alum, he washed and dried the precipitated aluminum hy-

Wöhler's Residence at Göttingen

droxide, and mixed it with powdered charcoal, sugar, and oil to form a thick paste. Upon heating this paste in a closed crucible, he secured a very intimate mixture of alumina and charcoal, and upon passing a current of dry chlorine gas over this red-hot black mixture, he obtained anhydrous aluminum chloride (12, 46).

Wöhler once said that the method by which he isolated aluminum in 1827 was based on the decomposition of anhydrous aluminum chloride by potassium and on the stability of aluminum in presence of water. Since the reaction is too violent to be carried out in glass, he used a platinum crucible with the cover wired on. Although only gentle heat was applied to start the reaction, the crucible soon became white hot. It

Justus von Liebig, 1803–1873. German organic and agricultural chemist. Professor of chemistry at Giessen. Friend and collaborator of Wöhler. Discoverer of the isomerism of silver fulminate and silver cyanate. Editor of the *Annalen*. He devised a new combustion train for determining the ultimate constituents of organic compounds and proved that animal heat and energy are produced by the combustion of food in the body. See also ref. (79).

was not badly attacked, but in order to prepare aluminum free from platinum he repeated the experiment, using porcelain and Hessian crucibles. When he cooled the crucible completely and plunged it into water, metallic aluminum always separated as a gray powder. Wöhler obtained only a small quantity of the metal, and it was not pure, but contaminated with potassium, platinum, or aluminum chloride (12). However, he was the first to describe the properties of aluminum, and in 1845 he finally succeeded in melting the powder to a coherent metallic mass (49, 54). He also prepared beryllium and yttrium in the same manner (8).

Wöhler's life was a long and eventful one. In spite of his unceasing labors for science, he found time for many social contacts, and had a deep capacity for friendship. The lifelong intimacy between Wöhler and Liebig caused the latter to write in one of his last letters:

Even after we are dead and our bodies long returned to dust, the ties which united us in life will keep our memory green, as an instance—not very frequent—of two men who wrought and strove in the same field without envy or ill feeling, and who continued in the closest friendship throughout (14).

In 1835 Wöhler became Friedrich Stromeyer's successor as professor of chemistry at Göttingen, where he taught for the rest of his life. Wöhler spent his old age in the midst of his happy family. He had a son and four daughters, and when they all visited their parents in the summer, some of them stayed with the neighbors, for the family home was not large enough to hold all the grandchildren. He received high scientific honors of all kinds, but none were dearer to him than the celebrations planned by his students on the occasions of his sixtieth, seventieth, and eightieth birthdays, and on the fiftieth anniversary of the synthesis of urea (13, 48).

Some of the most eminent chemists in the United States, including several who later became presidents of the American Chemical Society, studied under Wöhler (84). Dr. Edgar Fahs Smith, America's great chemical historian, once gave the following picture of the aged Wöhler:

Two or three days before Christmas the chemical laboratories in the University of Göttingen were nearly deserted. Only a few students remained. Late in the afternoon, some one began singing, "Stille Nacht, Heilige Nacht." One by one the other students in the laboratory gathered about the singer and solemnly joined in the song. Soon we noticed that the door of the laboratory opened and in walked the old Master. Immediately he took from his head the black skull cap he was accustomed to wear in the laboratories, placed it under his arm, folded his hands, and with bowed head stood just inside the door while the song continued. When the singing was over the old Master came forward and said, "Thank you, gentlemen," and withdrew (15).

Photo loaned by Frau Hückel, Göttingen, Germany
Wöhler in Later Life.* Professor of chemistry at Göttingen. Famous for his researches on cyanogen, cyanuric acid, and the radical of benzoic acid, and on the metals titanium, aluminum, yttrium, beryllium, and vanadium. German translator of Berzelius' "Textbook of Chemistry" and Hisinger's "Mineral Geography."

* The author acknowledges her gratitude to Dr. L. C. Newell for the use of this portrait.

Wöhler's room was filled with portraits of his two best friends, Liebig and Berzelius. Not long before his death, he hesitatingly held out to a friend at parting a little box wrapped in paper, saying to him, "Keep it in remembrance of me. Do not open it until you are on the train." The box was found to contain a spoon and the words, "A present from Berzelius; he used this platinum spoon many years in his researches." Wöhler died on September 23, 1882. In accordance with his wish, there is no bronze or marble monument to mark his resting place, but only a stone with the name Friedrich Wöhler (13).

Charles Sainte-Claire Deville, 1814–1876. French geologist who explored the Antilles, the Azores, and the Canary Islands and studied the allotropic forms of sulfur.

Henri Sainte-Claire Deville, 1818–1881. Professor of chemistry and dean at the University of Besançon, afterward professor of chemistry at the École Normale Supérieure. He discovered toluene in balsam of Tolu, prepared anhydrous nitrogen pentoxide, and made sodium and aluminum on a commercial scale.

From Gay's "Henri Sainte-Claire Deville, sa Vie et ses Travaux"

The first pure aluminum was prepared by the great French chemist Henri Sainte-Claire Deville, who was born on the Island of St. Thomas in the Antilles on March 11, 1818. Both Henri and his elder brother Charles were educated at the Institution Sainte-Barbe in Paris, where Charles studied geology under Élie de Beaumont at the School of Mines, while Henri took the medical course and studied chemistry under Thenard. Both brothers were crowned by the Institute, and both were in the same section. Throughout their lives they had the deepest affection for one another, and when one of Henri's sons married Charles's daughter, one of the fathers remarked, "My brother and I do not know how to tell which of the two belongs to each of us, whether it is my son who has married his daughter, or my daughter who has married his son" (*16*).

Henri's first paper, published in 1839, was a research on turpentine, and two years later he discovered toluene in balsam of Tolu. His most important work, however, was in inorganic and physical chemistry. In 1844 conservative university officials were horrified to learn of the appointment by Thenard of the twenty-six-year-old Henri Sainte-Claire Deville as dean to reorganize the faculty at Besançon. Nevertheless, Thenard's

Louis-Léonce Elie de Beaumont, 1798–1874. French geologist and mining engineer. Perpetual secretary of the Académie des Sciences. He described the course of great rivers and the effects of their mechanical work, and investigated the materials ejected by volcanoes. With O.-P.-A. Petit-Dufrénoy he made the first accurate and complete geological map of France.

mature judgment proved correct, and Sainte-Claire Deville's career proved to be even more brilliant than he had predicted. While at Besançon, Sainte-Claire Deville devised new analytical methods for testing the city water supply, and succeeded in preparing anhydrous nitrogen pentoxide (*17*).

When A.-J. Balard, the discoverer of bromine, went to the Collège de France, Deville was called to fill the vacancy at the École Normale Supérieure, and it was there that the first beautiful aluminum ingots were made. Sainte-Claire Deville was attempting in 1854 to prepare a protochloride of aluminum by allowing aluminum to react with the chloride, $AlCl_3$, and in preparing his aluminum he used Wöhler's method, but substituted sodium for the potassium. He noticed some large globules of shining metallic aluminum, and immediately set to work to make the process commercially profitable (35).

Although the first experiments were made at the École Normale Supérieure, the generosity of Napoleon III made it possible for him to continue them on a larger scale at the Javel works. Since Sainte-Claire

Frank Fanning Jewett, 1844–1926. Research assistant at Harvard University under Wolcott Gibbs. Professor of chemistry at the Imperial University of Japan. Professor of chemistry and mineralogy at Oberlin College. His account of Wöhler's researches on aluminum inspired Charles M. Hall to search for a commercial process for preparing the metal.

Courtesy H. N. Holmes

Deville's commercial process required large amounts of sodium, it was necessary for him to perfect at the same time a cheaper process for preparing that metal. When he began his experiments, the price of sodium was even higher than that of potassium, but he knew that sodium compounds are more abundant in Nature than those of potassium, and that sodium, because of its smaller equivalent weight, would be the more economical metal to use.

After perfecting a process for the manufacture of sodium which caused a rapid fall in its price, Deville attempted the large-scale production of aluminum. There is found in southern France and elsewhere an ore, bauxite, named for the village of Baux, near Arles in Provence. In the Sainte-Claire Deville process, alumina obtained from this ore was intimately mixed with charcoal, heated, and treated with chlorine to form the chloride. An excess of aluminum chloride vapor was then passed over molten sodium in an iron tube, after which the reaction mass was transferred to iron or clay crucibles and heated to complete the reaction. It was found later, however, that the reaction proceeds more quietly with double sodium aluminum chloride, which acts as a flux and allows the aluminum globules to coalesce, and that the fluidity of the charge can be increased by addition of cryolite (*18, 78*).

Certain trouble makers who were poor judges of character tried to create ill-will between Wöhler and Sainte-Claire Deville, advising the

The Aluminum "Crown Jewels." In this chest, carefully preserved by the Aluminum Company of America at Pittsburgh, are the original buttons of the metal made by Charles M. Hall in Oberlin, February 23, 1886 (left), the larger ones made by Hall in December, 1886 (center), and the first button or ingot (right) produced by the Aluminum Company of America.

Courtesy Fisher Scientific Co.

latter that, since Wöhler's aluminum was of such doubtful purity, he ought to claim for himself the honor of discovering the metal. The French chemist's reaction to this counsel throws an interesting sidelight on his character. As soon as he had obtained a sufficient quantity of malleable aluminum, he had a medal cast, bearing simply the name Wöhler and the date 1827, and sent it to the great German master. Deville and Wöhler always remained fast friends, and collaborated in a number of important researches. In his book entitled "L'Aluminium, ses Propriétés, sa Fabrication et ses Applications," the former wrote, "I will say with pleasure that I consider it an unexpected good fortune to have been able to take a few more steps in a path opened by Berzelius' eminent successor in Germany" (*18*).

In 1854 R. W. Bunsen in Heidelberg and H. Sainte-Claire Deville in Paris, working independently of each other, obtained metallic aluminum by electrolysis of fused sodium aluminum chloride (*54, 80, 81*).

Henri Sainte Claire Deville also made important investigations of boron, silicon, magnesium, and the metals of the platinum family. The platinum researches were dangerous, and he often suffered severely from poisoning by the vapors of osmic acid. His fame, however, rests even more on his enunciation of the laws of gaseous dissociation. Sainte-Claire Deville was described as ardent, vivacious, charming, sympathetic, gay, and generous. At the École Normale he used to eat at the students' table, jesting familiarly with them but never for a moment losing their profound respect (19). His married life was a most happy one, and his five sons were a credit to their parents. He died in 1881, mourned by his family and by his scientific colleagues throughout the world (18), and the funeral oration was delivered by Louis Pasteur.

The next scene of the aluminum drama is laid in the United States. Henri Sainte-Claire Deville's process had made the metal a commercial product, but it was still expensive. Charles Martin Hall, a student at Oberlin College, inspired by the accounts which Professor F. F. Jewett had given of his studies under Wöhler, decided that his supreme aim in life would be to devise a cheap method for making aluminum. In an improvised laboratory in the woodshed, and with homemade batteries, he struggled with this problem. On February 23, 1886, this boy of twenty-one years rushed into his professor's office and held out to him a handful of aluminum buttons. Since these buttons led to a highly successful electrolytic process for manufacturing aluminum, it is small wonder that the Aluminum Company of America now treasures them and refers to them affectionately as the "crown jewels." A beautiful statue of the youthful Charles M. Hall, cast in aluminum, may now be seen at Oberlin College (11, 55).

At about the same time that Hall perfected his process, Dr. Paul-Louis-Toussaint Héroult, a young French chemist of the same age, made the same discovery independently. Dr. Héroult was born in 1863 at Thury-Harcourt in the department of Calvados.* When the war of 1870 broke out, he was sent to live with his grandfather in London, and thus he acquired a good command of the English language. Three years later he returned to France to continue his education.

At the Institution Sainte-Barbe he learned of Sainte-Claire Deville's researches on aluminum, and at the age of fifteen years he read the latter's famous treatise. Using the steam engine and dynamo of a small tannery which he had inherited in 1885, Héroult attempted to electrolyze various aluminum compounds. In the following year, when he was attempting to electrolyze cryolite, his iron cathode melted. Since the temperature was not high enough to account for this, Héroult realized that

---

* Vauquelin, the discoverer of chromium and beryllium, was also a native of Calvados.

CHARLES MARTIN HALL

Charles Martin Hall, 1863–1914. American chemist, inventor, metallurgist, and philanthropist who developed a highly successful electrolytic process for manufacturing aluminum. This cheap method of obtaining the metal from its ores made possible the present widespread use of aluminum for domestic, industrial, and transportation purposes.

an alloy had been formed. A few days later, when he tried to lower the temperature of the electrolytic bath by adding some sodium aluminum chloride, he noticed that the carbon anode was being attacked. He concluded that he must be dealing with an oxide of aluminum, which was being reduced at the expense of the anode. This was indeed the case, for the sodium aluminum chloride he had bought had been previously

Paul-Louis-Toussaint Héroult.* 1863–1914. French metallurgist. Independent discoverer of the electrolytic method of preparing aluminum now known as the Hall-Héroult process. He designed electric furnaces, and made many important contributions to the electrometallurgy of iron and steel.

Courtesy Hobbs, Bruce Publishing Co.

exposed to moist air and converted into hydrated alumina. The first Héroult patent for this process was announced shortly before the Hall patents (77).

M. Héroult also made many important contributions to the electrometallurgy of iron and steel. He made frequent trips to the United States, and when the Perkin Medal was awarded to Charles M. Hall in 1911, M. Héroult crossed the ocean in order to be present at the ceremony and congratulate him. By this gracious act, he proved himself to be a worthy successor of his great, generous countryman, Henri Sainte-Claire Deville (11, 52). Dr. Héroult and C. M. Hall both died in 1914.

Cryolite. In 1795 Heinrich Christian Friedrich Schumacher, Danish scientist and court physician, published a description of an unknown white, sparry mineral which had been sent to Copenhagen from Green-

* The author is most grateful to *Aluminum*, Hobbs, Bruce Publishing Co., for the portrait of Héroult.

Frank Burnett Dains, 1869–1948. Lecture assistant to Dr. W. O. Atwater at Wesleyan University, Middletown, Connecticut, and later assistant professor at Northwestern University and professor at Washburn College in Topeka, Kansas. From 1911 until the time of his retirement in 1942 he was in charge of the department of organic chemistry at the University of Kansas, where he made notable contributions to the chemistry of the aldehydes, urea ethers, substituted ureas, thiazoles, imidazoles, and pyrazoles, and was an enthusiastic collector of books, portraits, and other memorabilia connected with the history of chemistry. He was a charter member of the Chicago Section of the American Chemical Society and served as Councilor of the Society, as Chairman of the Divisions of Organic Chemistry and History of Chemistry, and as contributing editor and abstractor for the *Journal of Chemical Education.* See also ref. (*166*).

land (*150*). Three years later Professor Peder Christian Abildgaard analyzed it and found it to contain alumina and "acid of fluorspar" (hydrofluoric acid). He stated that nothing like it had yet been found in the mineral kingdom and that it melted before the blowpipe "like frozen brine." From this property it received the name *cryolite* (*152*).

When he heated the pulverized mineral with concentrated sulfuric acid, it dissolved with evolution of hydrofluoric acid. When he evaporated the solution without adding any alkali, he obtained octahedral crystals. Since sodium alum was not yet known to exist, he concluded that the cryolite must contain potassium (*150*). When the Brazilian scientist J. B. de Andrada e Sylva described this mineral in 1800, he too stated that it contained potassium (*151*). Klaproth's analysis in the same you showed, however, that the alkali metal in the cryolite was not potassium but sodium (150).

The locality from which the cryolite had been obtained remained unknown until 1822, when Karl Ludwig Giesecke, mineral dealer and author of the libretto for the *Magic Flute,* found that it came from Ivigtut on the Arsuk Fjord in South Greenland and that the deposit was much more extensive than had been believed. In the middle of the nineteenth century Julius Thomsen developed a great cryolite industry for the production of soda, aluminum sulfate, and alumina (150). In 1866 nearly 20,000 tons of cryolite were shipped from Greenland. The Greenland Cryolite Mining Company exhibited a mass of it, three feet long by two feet thick, from Ivigtut at the Paris Exposition of 1867 (153). In 1886 the Hall-Héroult process of manufacturing aluminum by the electrolysis of alumina dissolved in molten cryolite made this metal available in large quantities.

Aluminum in Plants and Animals. Lorenz von Crell stated in 1791 that the presence of alumina in plants had been established through the researches of Rückert (154). In 1811 A.-F. de Fourcroy and N.-L. Vauquelin found aluminum phosphate to be present in human bones "in very small quantity, yet enough for its presence to be fully recognized and established" (139). Since aluminum in small amounts is widely distributed in the plant kingdom, all animals consume some of it with their food. Thus minute amounts of it are often found in animal tissues (155). The presence of aluminum in many plants was verified by M. Gabriel Bertrand, Professor Louis Kahlenberg, E. Kratzmann, Mlle. Georgette Levy, and many others (156, 157, 158, 159). The color of hydrangeas can be changed from pink to blue by addition of a dilute solution of aluminum sulfate to the soil in which they are grown (156, 160).

LITERATURE CITED

(1) NORDENSKIÖLD, A. E., "Scheeles nachgelassene Briefe und Aufzeichnungen," Norstedt & Söner, Stockholm, **1892,** p. 151. Letter of Scheele to Gahn, Dec. 26, 1774.

(2) JAGNAUX, R., "Histoire de la Chimie," Vol. 1, Baudry et Cie., Paris, **1891,** pp. 695–703.

(3) BUGGE, G., "Das Buch der grossen Chemiker," Vol. 1, Verlag Chemie, Berlin, **1929,** pp. 386–404.

(4) DAVY, J., "Memoirs of the Life of Sir Humphry Davy, Bart.," Vol. 1, Longman, Rees, Orme, Brown, Green, and Longman, London, **1836,** p. 469.

(5) MELLOR, J. W., "Comprehensive Treatise on Inorganic and Theoretical Chemistry," Vol. 4, Longmans, Green and Co., London, **1923,** pp. 204–7. Article on beryllium.

(6) JAGNAUX, R., "Histoire de la Chimie," ref (2), Vol. 2, pp. 169–72.

(7) BUSSY, A.-A.-B., "Préparation du glucinium," *J. chim. médicale,* **4,** 453 (1828); *Dingl. poly. J.,* **29,** 466 (1828).

(8) WÖHLER, F., "Sur le Glucinium et l'Yttrium," *Ann. chim. phys.*, [2], **39**, 77 81 (1828).

(9) JAGNAUX, R., "Histoire de la Chimie," ref. (2), Vol. 1, pp. 707–10.

(10) CRELL, L., "Lebensgeschichte A. S. Marggraf's," *Crell's Ann.*, **5**, 181–92 (1786).

(11) HOLMES, H. N., "The story of aluminum," *J. Chem. Educ.*, **7**, 233–44 (Feb., 1930).

(12) JAGNAUX, R., "Histoire de la Chimie," ref. (2), Vol. 2, pp. 158–64.

(13) VON HOFMANN, A. W., "Zur Erinnerung an Friedrich Wöhler," *Ber.*, **15**, 3127–290 (1882).

(14) VON HOFMANN, A. W. and EMILIE WÖHLER, "Aus Justus Liebig's und Friedrich Wöhler's Briefwechsel," Vol. 2, F. Vieweg und Sohn, Braunschweig, **1888**, p. 324. Letter of Liebig to Wöhler, Dec. 31, 1871.

(15) "Some experiences of Dr. Edgar F. Smith as a student under Wöhler," *J. Chem. Educ.*, **5**, 1555 (Dec., 1928).

(16) GAY, JULES, "Henri Sainte-Claire Deville; Sa Vie et ses Travaux," Gauthier-Villars et Fils, Paris, **1889**, p. 5.

(17) *Ibid.*, p. 9.

(18) *Ibid.*, p. 33.

(19) VALLERY-RADOT, R., "The Life of Pasteur," Doubleday, Page and Co., New York City, **1926**, p. 146.

(20) "OEUVRES DE LAVOISIER," Vol. 1, Imprimerie Impériale, Paris, **1864**, pp. 135–7.

(21) GAY-LUSSAC, L.-J. and L.-J. THENARD, "Sur la décomposition et la recomposition de l'acide boracique," *Ann. chim. phys.*, [1], **68**, 169–74 (Nov. 30, 1808); *Sci. News Letter*, **19**, 171–2 (Mar. 14, 1931).

(22) KLAPROTH, M. H., "Analytical Essays towards Promoting the Chemical Knowledge of Mineral Substances," Cadell and Davies, London, **1801**, pp. 325–8.

(23) VAUQUELIN, N.-L., "Analyse de l'aigue marine, ou béril; et découverte d'une terre nouvelle dans cette pierre," *Ann. chim. phys.*, [1], **26**, 155–77 (May (30 Floréal), 1798); "Discovering the sweet element: A classic of science," *Sci. News Letter*, **18**, 346–7 (Nov. 29, 1930); *Nicholson's J.*, **2**, 358–63 (Nov., 1798); 393–6 (Dec. 1798).

(24) STOCK, A. E., "Beryllium," *Trans. Electrochem. Soc.*, **61**, 255–74 (1932).

(25) VAUQUELIN, N.-L., "Analyse de l'Émeraude du Pérou," *Ann. chim. phys.*, [1], **26**, 259– 65 (June (30 Prairial), 1798).

(26) GMELIN, J. F., "Analyse du béril de Nertschinsk en Sibérie, et examen de quelques caractères qui distinguent la glucine qu'il contient," *Ann. chim. phys.*, [1], **44**, 27–9 (Oct. (30 Vendémiaire), 1803); *Crell's Ann.*, **35**, 87–102 (Zweytes Stück, 1801).

(27) MARCHAL, G., "La découverte, la préparation, les propriétés et les applications du glucinium," *Chimie et Industrie*, **22**, 1084–92 (Dec., 1929); **23**, 30–3 (Jan., 1930).

(28) DAVY, H., "Electro-chemical researches on the decomposition of the earths; with observations on the metals obtained from the alkaline earths, and on the amalgam procured from ammonia," *Phil. Trans.*, **98**, 343 (1808). Read June 30, 1808; "An account of some new analytical researches on the nature of certain bodies, particularly the alkalies, phosphorus, sulphur, carbonaceous matter, and the acids hitherto undecompounded, etc.," *ibid.*, **99**, 75–85 (1809). Read Dec. 15, 1808.

(29) LEBEAU, P., "Recherches sur le glucinium et ses composés," *Ann. chim. phys.*, [7], **16**, 457–503 (Apr., 1899).

(30) BIOT, J.-B., "Mélanges Scientifiques et Littéraires," Vol. 3, Michel Levy Frères, Paris, **1858**, pp. 125–42.

(31)   Sainte-Claire Deville, H., "Note sur deux procédés de préparation de l'aluminium et sur une nouvelle forme du silicium," *Compt. rend.*, **39**, 321–6 (Aug. 14, 1854); *J. pharm. chim.*, [3], **26**, 285–9 (Oct., 1854); *J. prakt. Chem.*, **63**, 113–20 (Zweites Heft, 1854); "Du silicium et du titane," *Compt. rend.*, **40**, 1034–6 (Apr. 30, 1855).

(32)   Berzelius, J. J., "On the results of some chemical analyses, and the decomposition of silica," *Annals of Phil.*, [1], **24**, 121–3 (Aug., 1824). Extract from letter to Dulong.

(33)   Gay, J., "Henri Sainte-Claire Deville, Sa Vie et ses Travaux," ref. (16), pp. 37–9.

(34)   Sainte-Claire Deville, H. and Caron, "Du silicium et des siliciures métalliques," *Ann. chim. phys.*, [3], **67**, 435–43 (Apr., 1863).

(35)   Sainte-Claire Deville, H., "Recherches sur les métaux et en particulier sur l'aluminium et sur une nouvelle forme du silicium," *ibid.*, [3], **43**, 7–33 (Jan., 1855).

(36)   Davy, H., "Some new phenomena of chemical changes produced by electricity, particularly the decomposition of the fixed alkalies, and the exhibition of the new substances which constitute their bases, etc.," *Phil. Trans.*, **98**, 43 (1808). Read Nov. 19, 1807.

(37)   Friend, J. N., "A Textbook of Inorganic Chemistry," Vol. 5, Chas. Griffin and Co., London, **1917**, pp. 176–81.

(38)   Gay-Lussac, L.-J. and L.-J. Thenard, "Recherches Physico-Chimiques," Vol. 1, Imprimerie de Crapelet, Paris, **1811**, pp. 276–308.

(39)   *Ibid.*, Vol. 1, pp. 313–4; Vol. 2, pp. 54–65.

(40)   Bugge, G., "Das Buch der grossen Chemiker," ref. (3), Vol. 1, pp. 228–39. Article on Marggraf by Max Speter.

(41)   Lenard, Philipp, "Grosse Naturforscher," J. F. Lehmanns Verlag, Munich, **1929**, pp. 183–8.

(42)   Edwards, J. D., F. C. Frary, and Jeffries, "The Aluminum Industry," Vol. 1, McGraw-Hill Book Co., Inc., New York, **1930**, pp. 1–43.

(43)   Oersted, H. C., "Oversigt over det Kongelige Danske Videnskabernes Selskabs Forhandlinger," **1824–25**, 15–6.

(44)   Meyer, Kirstine, "H. C. Oersted," *Naturvidenskabelige Skrifter, Copenhagen,* **2**, 465 (1920).

(45)   Fogh, I., *Det Kgl. Danske Videnskabernes Selskab Mathematiskfysiske Meddelelser*, **3**, 3–17 (1921). (In German.)

(46)   Wöhler, F., "Sur l'aluminium," *Ann. chim. phys.*, [2], **37**, 66–80 (1828); *Pogg. Ann.*, **11**, 146–61 (1827).

(47)   Editor's Outlook, "Friedrich Wöhler," *J. Chem. Educ.*, **5**, 1537–8 (Dec., 1928).

(48)   Warren, W. H., "Contemporary reception of Wöhler's discovery of the synthesis of urea," *J. Chem. Educ.*, **5**, 1539–53 (Dec., 1928).

(49)   Bugge, G., "Das Buch der grossen Chemiker," ref. (3), Vol. 2, p. 37; A. W. von Hofmann and Emile Wöhler, "Aus Justus Liebig's und Friedrich Wöhler's Briefwechsel" ref. (14), Vol. 1, p. 251.

(50)   Warren, W. H., "The Wöhler plaque," *J. Chem. Educ.*, **6**, 559 (Mar., 1929).

(51)   Weintraub, E., "Preparation and properties of pure boron," *Trans. Am. Electrochem. Soc.*, **16**, 165–84 (1909).

(52)   "Award of the Perkin medal to C. M. Hall," *J. Ind. Eng. Chem.*, **3**, 144–9 (March, 1911); Reprinted by L. A. Goldblatt, "Collateral Readings in Inorganic Chemistry," D. Appleton-Century Co., New York and London, **1937**, pp. 187–92.

(53)   Tosterud, M. and J. D. Edwards, "The 'discovery' of aluminum," *Trans. Am. Electrochem. Soc.*, **51**, 125–8 (1927).

(54) RHEINBOLDT, H., "Hundert Jahre Aluminium," Sitzungsber. der Niederrhein. Gesellschaft für Natur- und Heilkunde, Bonn, 1928, 20 pp.; *Metallwirtschaft*, 6, 2 (1927).

(55) HOLMES, H. N., "Fifty years of industrial aluminum, 1886–1936," *Bulletin of Oberlin College*, N. S., No. 346, 1–30 (Aug. 30, 1937); *Sci. Mo.*, 42, 236–9 (March, 1936).

(56) CHEYNE, T. K. and J. S. BLACK, "Encyclopaedia Biblica," Vol. 1, The Macmillan Company, New York, 1899, columns 545–6; PLINY THE ELDER, "Historia Naturalis," Book 37, chaps. 16–20.

(57) NASINI, R., "Discovery of boric acid in the glazes of Aretine vases," *Compt. rend.*, 191, 903–5 (Nov. 10, 1930); *Nature*, 126, 877–8 (Dec. 6, 1930).

(58) DIERGART, PAUL, "Bemerkung zum neuerlichen Borbefund in der Terrasigillata-Glasur," *Chem. Ztg.*, 60, 997 (Dec. 5, 1936).

(59) KOPP, H., "Geschichte der Chemie," Vol. 3, Fr. Vieweg und Sohn, Braunschweig, 1847, pp. 339–44.

(60) "Pott's Auszug aus einem Briefe des H. Sam. Ben. Cnoll über das indianische natürliche Alkali und den Borax," *Crell's Neues chem. Archiv*, 3, 317–20 (1785); *Abh. königl. Akad. Wiss (Berlin)*, 1735–42, p. 318.

(61) GRILL, JOHAN ABRAHAM (ABRAHAMSSON), "Vom Pounxa, oder natürlichen Borax," *Crell's Neueste Entdeckungen in der Chemie*, 1, 84–5 (1781); *K. Vet. Acad. Handl.*, 34, 317 (1772).

(62) "Eloge de M. Guillaume Homberg," Hist. de l'Acad. Roy. (Paris), 1715, pp. 82 ff.

(63) PETERS, HERMANN, "Wilhelm Homberg. Mitteilungen aus Briefen der königlichen Bibliothek zu Hannover," *Chem. Ztg.*, 27, 1249–52 (Dec. 23, 1903).

(64) JAEGER, F. M., "Naschrift: Willem Homberg," *Chem. Weekbl.*, 15, 602–5 (1918).

(65) "Ueber das Sedativsalz vom Herrn Bourdelin," *Crell's Neues chem. Archiv*, 7, 89–111 (1788); *Abh. königl. Akad. Wiss. (Paris)*, 1753; Mém. de math. et de phys., p. 305.

(66) BERGMAN, T., "A dissertation on Elective Attractions," J. Murray, London, 1785, p. 127.

(67) SCHERER, A. N., "Sur le radical boracique," *Ann. chim. phys.* (1), 31, 17 (1799). (30 Messidor, an VIIᵉ.)

(68) HUNT, ROBERT, "Ure's Dictionary of Arts, Manufactures, and Mines," 6th ed., Vol. 1, Longmans, Green and Co., London, 1867, pp. 100–3.

(69) MUSPRATT, SHERIDAN, "Chemistry, Theoretical, Practical, and Analytical," Vol. 1, Wm. Mackenzie, London, Glasgow and Edinburgh, 1803, pp. 149–76.

(70) PURCHAS, SAMUEL, "Hakluytus Posthumus, or Purchas His Pilgrimes," Vol. 11, James MacLehose and Sons, Glasgow, 1906, p. 146. *Journal of Friar William de Rubruquis.*

(71) TESTI, GINO, "Le antiche miniere de allume e l'arte tintoria in Italia," *Archeion*, 13, 440–8 (1931).

(72) KLAPROTH, M. H., "Chemische Untersuchung des Alaunsteins von Tolfa und des erdigen Alaunschiefers von Freienwalde," *Gehlen's J.* (2), 6, 35–54 (1806); L.-J. GAY-LUSSAC, "Nachtrag zu vorstehender Analyse des Alaunsteins von Tolfa," *ibid.* (2), 6, 55–62 (1806).

(73) HOOVER, H. C. and L. H. HOOVER, "Georgius Agricola. De re metallica," *Mining Mag.*, London, 1912, pp. 564–70.

(74) MARGGRAF, A. S., "Von den Bestandtheilen des Alauns," *Crell's Neues chem. Archiv*, 6, 216–24 (1787); *Abh. königl. Akad. Wiss. (Berlin)*, 1754, "Chymische Schriften," revised ed., Vol. 1, Arnold Wever, Berlin, 1768, pp. 187–233.

(75) O'Connor, A. C., "Oeuvres de Condorcet," Vol. 2, Firmin Didot Frères, Paris, 1847, pp. 598–610. Eulogy of Marggraf.

(76) Testi, Gino, "Sulla presenza dell'acido borico nelle ceramiche aretine," Archeion, 15, 247–8 (1933).

(77) "Gmelin's Handb. der anorg. Chem.," 8th ed., No. 35 A–1, Verlag Chemie, G. m. b. H., Berlin, 1934, p. 125.

(78) Oesper, R. E. and Pierre Lemay, "Henri Sainte-Claire Deville, 1818–1881," Chymia, 3, 205–21 (1950).

(79) Oesper, R. E., "Justus von Liebig. Student and teacher," J. Chem. Educ., 4, 1461–76 (Dec., 1927).

(80) Bunsen, R. W., Poggendorff's Ann. der Physik und Chemie, 92, 648 (July 9, 1854).

(81) Deville, H. Sainte-Claire, Compt. rend., 39, 325 (Aug. 14, 1854).

(82) Rheinboldt, Heinrich, "Balança e pesagens na epoca preclassica da química," Boletim da Associacão dos Ex-alunos de Química da Faculdade de Filosofia, Ciências, e Letras da Universidade de São Paulo, 1945, pp. 137–8.

(83) Ber., 15, 3146–8 (1882).

(84) Van Klooster, H. S., "Friedrich Wöhler and his American pupils," J. Chem. Educ., 21, 158–70 (Apr., 1944).

(85) Lindroth, Sten, "Urban Hiärne och Laboratorium Chymicum," Lychnos, 1946–1947, pp. 51–116.

(86) Coons, George H., "The sugar beet. Product of science," Sci. Monthly, 68, 149–64 (Mar., 1949).

(87) Lucas, A., "Ancient Egyptian materials and industries," 2nd ed., Edward Arnold and Co., London, 1934, pp. 338–9.

(88) "Emerald mines," Am. J. Sci., (1), 2, 354 (1820).

(89) Caley, E. R., "The Stockholm papyrus. An English translation with brief notes," J. Chem. Educ., 4, 979–1002 (Aug., 1927).

(90) Acosta, Father Joseph de, "Natural and moral history of the Indies," Vol. 1, The Hakluyt Society, London, 1880, pp. 224–6.

(91) Howard, Joseph W., "Emeralds," J. Chem. Educ., 11, 323–7 (June, 1934).

(92) "Gmelin's Handbuch . . . ," Ref. (77), Vol. 26, pp. 1–35; Vol. 29, pp. 1–16. History and occurrence of beryllium and strontium.

(93) Sestini, F., "Experiments with wheat on the substitution of beryllium for magnesium," Staz. sperim. agrar. Ital., 15, 290–8 (1888); 20, 256–8 (1893).

(94) Shohl, A. T., "Mineral Metabolism," Reinhold Publishing Corporation, New York, 1939, pp. 32–3, 96, 141, 145, 162–8, 246–7.

(95) Lewis, William, "The Chemical Works of Caspar Neumann, M.D.," W. Johnston, G. Keith et al., London, 1759, pp. 226–9.

(96) Macquer, P.-J., "Elements of the Theory and Practice of Chymistry," 2nd ed., Vol. 1, A. Millar and J. Nourse, London, 1764, p. 289; Vol. 2, p. 285.

(97) Engeström, Gustav von, "Versuche mit der Pounxa," Crell's Neueste Entdeckungen, 1, 85–8 (1781); K. Vet. Acad. Handl., 34, 319 (1772).

(98) Zenzén, Nils, "Om den s. k. Swedenborgsstammen och det Swedenborgska marmorbordet," Svenska Linné-Sällskapets Årsskrift, 14, 98–9 (1931).

(99) Lémery, L., "Versuche und Betrachtungen über den Borax," Crell's Neues chem. Archiv, 3, 124–5 (1785); Abh. königl. Akad. Wiss (Paris), 1727.

(100) Macquer, P.-J., Ref. (96), Vol. 1, pp. 36–7.

(101) Geoffroy the Younger, "Neue Erfahrungen über den Borax," Crell's Neues Chem. Archiv, 3, 217 (1785); Mém. de l'acad. roy. des sciences (Paris), 1732, p. 549.

(102) Bourdelin, L.-C., "Zweite Abhandlung über das Sedativsalz," Crell's Neues chem. Archiv, 8, 46–54 (1791); Mém. de math. et de physique, Acad. Roy. des Sciences (Paris), 1755, p. 591.

(103) Baron de Hénouville, Théodore, "Ueber die Grundlage des Alauns," Crell's Neues chem. Archiv, 8, 178–84 (1791); Mém. de physique, Acad. Roy. des Sciences (Paris), 2, 295 (1760).

(104) Dossie, Robert, "Institutes of Experimental Chemistry," Vol. 1, J. Nourse, London, 1759, pp. 294 5.

(105) Schiff, Ugo, "Il Museo di Storia Naturale . . . di Firenze," Archeion, 9, 295–6 (1928).

(106) "Taschen-Buch für Scheidekünstler und Apotheker," Hoffmann Buchhandlung, Weimar, 1782, pp. 56–8.

(107) Höfer, H. F., "Nachricht von dem in Toskana entdeckten natürlichen Seda-tivsalze, und von dem Borax, welcher daraus bereitet wird," Crell's Neueste Entdeckungen in der Chemie, 7, 253–5, 269–70 (1782).

(108) Mascagni, Paolo, "Sopra il sal sedativo d'Hombergio o sia acido boracico . . .," Memorie di matematica e di fisica, Società italiana delle scienze (Rome), 8, (1), 487–515 (1799).

(109) Mascagni, Paolo, "Erste Abhandhing über die Boraxsäure und die ver-schiedenen boraxsauren Salze, die man in den Lagoni von Volterrano und in der Nachbarschaft von Siena findet," Crell's Neueste Entdeckungen in der Chemie, (2), 6, 181–93 (1806).

(110) "Enciclopedia italiana di scienze, lettere, ed arti," Vol. 20, Istituto della Enciclopedia Italiana, Rome, 1933, p. 538; ibid., 1934, Vol. 22, p. 479.

(111) Fedeli, Carlo, "Paolo Mascagni e la Università di Pisa, 1799–1815," Arche-ion, 3, 97–123 (1922).

(112) Foster, P. Le Neve, Jr., "The manufacture of boracic acid in Tuscany," Am. Chemist, 5, 455–7 (June, 1875).

(113) Conti, Prince P. Ginori, "The manufacture of boric acid in Tuscany," J. Soc. Chem. Ind., 44, 343–5T (July 17, 1925).

(114) Cass, W. G., "The geothermic resources of Italy," Ind. Eng. Chem., News Ed., 17, 680 (Nov. 10, 1939).

(115) Conti, Prince Piero Ginori, "The utilization of geothermal power in Tus-cany," J. Chem. Educ., 4, 281–97 (March, 1927).

(116) "Obituary of Prince Ginori Conti," Ind. Eng. Chem., News Ed., 18, 108 (Feb. 10, 1940).

(117) Sorges, Felice, "Le visite agli stabilimenti e regioni industriali," La Chimica nell 'Industria, nell' Agricoltura e nella Biologia, 5, 274 (Aug. 31, 1929).

(118) "Vom Hrn. Ingenieur-Lieut. Lasius in Hannover," Crell's Ann., 8, 333–6 (1787).

(119) Westrumb, J. F., "Neuentdecktes Sedativsalz im Lüneburgischen sogenann-ten cubischen Quartz," Crell's Ann. 9, 483–5 (1788).

(120) Kobell, Franz von, "Geschichte der Mineralogie von 1650–1860," Baierische Akad. Wiss., Munich, 1864, pp. 424–5.

(121) Robottom, Arthur, "The history of Californian borax," Chem News, 54, 244–6 (Nov. 12, 1886).

(122) Hanks, H. G., "On the occurrence of hanksite in California," Am. J. Sci., 137, 63–6 (Jan., 1889).

(123) Forchhammer, Georg, "On the composition of sea water in the different parts of the ocean," Phil. Trans., 155, 203–62 (1865).

(124) Dieulafait, L., "L'acide borique . . .," Compt. rend., 85, 605–7 (Oct. 1, 1877).

(125) Meisen, V., "Prominent Danish Scientists through the ages," Levin and Munksgaard, Copenhagen, 1932, pp. 107–9. Chapter on Forchhammer by Axel Garboe.

(126) Hansen, P., "Illustreret Dansk Litteratur Historie," 2nd ed., Vol. 3, Det Nordiske Forlag, Copenhagen, 1902, pp. 1003–4, 1109–10, 1116–8.

(127) Crampton, C. A., "Boracic acid as a plant constituent," Am. Chem. J., 11, 227–32 (Apr., 1889).

(128) Willis, L. G., "Bibliography of References to the Literature on the Minor Elements," 3rd ed., Chilean Nitrate Educational Bureau, 1939, columns 53–128; ibid., 1st suppl. to the 3rd ed., columns 7–30; ibid., 2nd suppl., columns 9–34.

(129) BERTRAND, G. and H. AGULHON, "Sur la présence normale du bore chez les animaux," *Compt. rend.*, **155**, 248–51 (July 16, 1912); **156**, 732–5 (March 3, 1913); "Sur la présence du bore dans le lait et dans les oeufs," **156**, 2027–9 (June 30, 1913); "Dosage rapide de l'acide borique normal ou introduit dans les substances alimentaires," **158**, 201–4 (Jan. 19, 1914).

(130) DINGLEY, W. F., "The borax industry in Southern California," *J. Chem. Educ.*, **8**, 2113–25 (Nov., 1931).

(131) LUCAS, A., Ref. (87), pp. 209–11, 214, 352.

(132) NEUBURGER, ALBERT, "The Technical Arts and Sciences of the Ancients," Methuen and Co., London, **1930**, pp. 152–3.

(133) "Kieselerde auch ein Bestandtheil der Vegetabilien," *Scherer's Allgemeines J. der Chemie*, **3**, 74–5 (1799).

(134) WALLERIUS, J. G., "Untersuchung von der Beschaffenheit der Erde die man aus Wasser, Pflanzen, und Thieren bekömmt," *Crell's Neues chem. Archiv*, **8**, 283–6 (1791); *K. Vet. Acad. Handl.*, **22**, 36, 141, 188 (1760).

(135) "Humphry Davy's Versuche über den Kieselgehalt der Pflanzen," *Scherer's Allgemeines J. der Chemie*, **3**, 75–80 (1799).

(136) GUYTON DE MORVEAU, "Sur la silice dans l'épiderme de quelques végétaux," *Ann. chim. phys.*, (1), **31**, 279–83 (1799).

(137) SCHERER, A. N., "Sur l'existence de la silice dans les roseaux et les gramens," *Ann. chim. phys.*, (1), **32**, 169–70 (1799).

(138) THATCHER, R. W., "The Chemistry of Plant Life," McGraw-Hill Book Co., New York, **1921**, p. 5.

(139) FOURCROY, A. F. DE, and N.-L. VAUQUELIN, "Experiments on human bones, as a supplement to the paper on the bones of the ox," *Nicholson's J.*, (2), **30**, 256–60 (Dec., 1811).

(140) BECKMANN, JOHANN, "A History of Inventions, Discoveries, and Origins," 4th ed., Vol. 1, Henry G. Bohn, London, **1846**, pp. 180–98.

(141) BAILEY, K. C., "The Elder Pliny's Chapters on Chemical Subjects," Vol. 2, Edward Arnold and Co., London, **1932**, pp. 103–5, 233–7; PLINY, "Historia naturalis," Book 35, paragraphs 183–7.

(142) CREIGHTON, M., "A History of the Papacy," Vol. 3, Longmans, Green and Co., New York and Bombay, **1897**, pp. 314–15.

(143) CULLEN, EDMUND, "Physical and Chemical Essays Translated from the Original Latin of Sir Torbern Bergman," Vol. 1, J. Murray, Balfour, Gordon, and Dickson, London, **1784**, pp. 338–43.

(144) MARTYN, J., and E. CHAMBERS, "The Philosophical History and Memoirs of the Royal Academy of Sciences at Paris," Vol. 1, John and Paul Knapton *et al.*, *London*, **1742**, pp. 326–8; E.-F. GEOFFROY, Hist. Roy. Acad. Sci. (Paris), **1702**.

(145) GEOFFROY, E.-F., "A Treatise of the Fossil, Vegetable, and Animal Substances That Are Made Use of in Physik," W. Innys, R. Manby *et al.*, London, **1736**, pp. 117–8.

(146) TOURNEFORT, J.-P. DE, "A Voyage into the Levant," Vol. 1, D. Midwinter, R. Ware, C. Rivington *et al.*, London, **1741**, pp. 168, 175–9.

(147) LEWIS, WILLIAM, Ref. (95), p. 189.

(148) BAUMÉ, ANTOINE, "Chymie expérimentale et raisonnée," Vol. 3, P. F. Didot le jeune, Paris, **1773**, pp. 462–73.

(149) PINKERTON, JOHN, "A General Collection of the Best and Most Interesting Voyages and Travels in All Parts of the World," Vol. 5, Longman, Hurst, Rees, and Orme, London, **1809**, pp. 32 and 45. Spallanzani's "Travels in the two Sicilies."

(150) DIERGART, PAUL, "Beiträge aus der Geschichte der Chemie dem Gedächtnis von G. W. A. Kahlbaum," Franz Deuticke, Leipzig and Vienna, **1909**, pp. 500–08. Chapter by S. M. Jörgensen, "Zur Geschichte des Kryoliths und der Kryolith-Industrie."

(151) ANDRADA, J. B. DE, "Kurze Angabe der Eigenschaften und Kennzeichen einiger neuen Fossilien aus Schweden und Norwegen . . .," *Scherer's Allg. J. der Chemie,* **4,** 28–39 (Jan., 1800).

(152) *Scherer's J.,* **2,** 502 (1798).

(153) BLAKE, W. P., "Notes upon some of the mineralogical curiosities of the Paris Exposition of 1867," *Am. J. Sci.,* (2), **45,** 197 (March, 1868).

(154) WALLERIUS, J. G., Ref. (*134*), Footnote to p. 285.

(155) SHOHL, A. T., Ref. (*94*), pp. 235–6.

(156) WILLIS, L. G., Ref. (*128*), 3rd ed., columns 1–13.

(157) BERTRAND, G. and G. LEVY, "The content of plants, notably food plants, in aluminum," *Compt. rend.,* **192,** 525–9 (1931).

(158) KAHLENBERG, L. and J. O. CLOSS, "On the presence of aluminum in plant and animal matter," *J. Biol. Chem.,* **83,** 261–4 (1929).

(159) KRATZMANN, E., "The microchemical detection and distribution of aluminum in the plant kingdom," *Sitzungsber. K. Akad. Wiss. (Vienna), Math.-Naturw. Kl.,* **122,** 311–36 (1913).

(160) CHENERY, E. M., "The problem of the blue hydrangea," *J. Roy. Hort. Soc.,* **62,** 304–20 (1937); R. C. ALLEN, *Proc. Am. Soc. Hort. Sci.,* **32,** 632–4 (1934).

(161) ANON., "New process purifies aluminum from alunite," *Science News Letter,* **40,** 3 (July 5, 1941).

(162) BROWNE, C. A., "A source book of agricultural chemistry," *Chronica Botanica,* **1944,** pp. 116–17.

(163) WOODBRIDGE, C. G., "The role of boron in the agricultural regions of the Pacific Northwest," *Sci. Mo.,* **70,** 97–104 (Feb., 1950).

(164) ADAMS, F. D., "The Birth and Development of the Geological Sciences," Dover Publications, Inc., New York, **1954,** pp. 205–7.

(165) OESPER, R. E., "Heinrich Rheinboldt," *J. Chem. Educ.,* **27,** 296 (June, 1950).

(166) WEEKS, M. E., "Frank Burnett Dains," *Ind. Eng. Chem., News Ed.,* **13,** 118 (March 20, 1935); ANON., *Chem. Eng. News,* **26,** 264 (Jan. 26, 1948).

Robert Wilhelm Bunsen, 1811–1899. German chemist who investigated the cacodyl radical, the geysers of Iceland, and the chemical action of light. Inventor of the Bunsen battery, the grease-spot photometer, ice and vapor calorimeters, the thermoregulator, the constant-level water-bath, and the filter pump.

*Nur immer zu! wir wollen es ergründen,
In deinem Nichts hoff' ich das All zu finden (1).*

*But go on! We want to fathom it.
In thy nothing I hope to find the universe.*

Thus there was for him nothing small or great in Nature. Every phenomenon embraced for him an endless diversity of factors, and in the yellow flame of an ordinary alcohol lamp whose wick was sprinkled with salt, he saw the possibility of accomplishing the chemical analysis of the most distant stars (2).

So gab es für ihn nichts Kleines oder Grosses in der Natur. Jede Erscheinung umfasste ihm eine unbegrenzte Mannigfaltigkeit von Faktoren, und in der gelben Flamme einer gewöhnlichen Weingeistlampe, deren Docht mit Salz bestreut war, sah er die Möglichkeit, die chemische Analyse der fernsten Gestirne auszuführen.

23

Some spectroscopic discoveries

Many elements are present in the earth's crust in such minute amounts that they could never have been discovered by ordinary methods of mineral analysis. In 1859, however, Kirchhoff and Bunsen invented the spectroscope, an optical instrument consisting of a collimator, or metal tube fitted at one end with a lens and closed at the other except for a slit, at the focus of the lens, to admit light from the incandescent substance to be examined; a turntable containing a prism mounted to receive and separate the parallel rays from the lens; and a telescope to observe the spectrum produced by the prism. With this instrument they soon discovered two new metals, cesium and rubidium, which they classified with sodium and potassium, which had been previously discovered by Davy, and lithium, which was added to the list of elements by Arfwedson. The spectroscopic discovery of thallium by Sir William Crookes and its prompt confirmation by C.-A. Lamy soon followed. In 1863 F. Reich and H. T. Richter of the Freiberg School of Mines discovered a very rare element in zinc blende, and named it indium because of its brilliant line in the indigo region of the spectrum.

*T*he Swiss-German alchemist Leonhard Thurneysser (1531–1596) recognized several substances by their behavior when heated and by the colors they impart to the flame, and described his method of analysis in a poem that begins:

> *"Des Schlichs Gehalt du im Glühen kennst*
> *An der Farbe der Flamme, wenn du ihn brennst"*
> (91, 92)

> *What the slime contains, the glowing reveals*
> *By the flame's bright hue when you ignite it.*

Sir Henry E. Roscoe stated in his "Spectrum Analysis": "So long ago as 1752, Thomas Melvill [or Melville], while experimenting on certain coloured flames, observed the yellow soda flame, although he was unacquainted with its cause" (63, 64).

In 1758 A. S. Marggraf noticed the yellow color imparted to a flame

From a painting by Karla Fischer, 1909.
Courtesy Bausch & Lomb Optical Co.

In 1818 Josef Fraunhofer (1787–1826) exhibited his newest spectroscope before Counselor Utzschneider and Mr. Reichenbach, his partners in the glassworks and optical establishment at Benedictbeuern. He discussed with them his latest researches on the diffraction of light which had led him to the discovery of grating spectra, the exact measurement of wave lengths, and a brilliant confirmation of the undulatory theory of light.

by sodium salts and the lavender color imparted by potassium salts (*3*). In 1802 Dr. Wollaston examined the spectrum of a candle flame through a prism, and saw the discontinuous band spectrum (*4, 22*). He said (*33*):

When a very narrow line of the blue light at the lower part of the flame is examined alone, in the same manner, through a prism, the spectrum, instead of appearing a series of lights of different hues contiguous, may be seen divided into five images, at a distance from each other. The 1st is broad red, terminated by a bright line of yellow; the 2nd and 3rd are both green; the 4th and 5th are blue, the last of which appears to correspond with the division of blue and violet in the solar spectrum. . . .

In 1814 Josef Fraunhofer, a young German physicist who had had thorough training in the art of glassmaking, made an unusually fine prism, saw for the first time the dark lines in the sun's spectrum, and

William Henry Fox Talbot, 1800–1877. English antiquarian, physicist, and pioneer in optics and photography. One of the first to decipher the Assyrian inscriptions at Nineveh. In 1839 he made negative prints on silver chloride paper, and two years later he invented the calotype process for making positives.

Sir David Brewster 1781–1868. Scottish physicist famous for his researches on the absorption, reflection, refraction, and polarization of light, and on doubly refracting crystals. One of the founders of the British Association for the Advancement of Science. He invented the kaleidoscope and improved the stereoscope. His optical researches led to great improvement in the construction of lighthouses.

designated eight of the most prominent ones by letters (3, 23). Ten years later Sir John Herschel showed that a small amount of an alkali can be detected by its flame spectrum. Later, however, the presence of the orange-yellow lines of sodium in almost every source he investigated prevented him, as it did many another scientist, from realizing that each element has its own characteristic spectrum (53). Henry

Fox Talbot (24), an English scientist, found in 1834 that, with the aid of a prism, he could distinguish lithium from strontium,* even though the salts of both give red flames (4, 26, 32). He stated that the dark lines previously observed by Sir David Brewster (33) in the spectrum of light which had passed through vapors of nitrous acid were caused by absorption of light (5, 25).

Dr. David Alter, 1807–1881. American physician, physicist, and inventor. He observed the spark spectra of various metals and gases and predicted that "the prism may also detect the elements in shooting stars, or luminous meteors." See also ref. (63).

Courtesy W. A. Hamor

In 1854 David Alter of Freeport, Pennsylvania, showed that each element studied had its own spectrum (53, 54, 56). At an early age he read books on electricity and "natural philosophy" (physics), and later, while he was practicing medicine, he found time to design and invent several electrical devices, to construct lenses, prisms, telescopes, and spectroscopes, and to make an excellent daguerreotype of the dark lines of the solar spectrum. From a mass of brilliant glass found in the pot of a glass factory destroyed in the great Pittsburgh fire of 1845 he constructed a fine prism for his spectroscope. In 1854, in his paper "On certain physical properties of light produced by the combustion of different metals in the electric spark, refracted by a prism," he pointed out that an alloy of two metals shows the lines of both, and clearly stated that each element has a characteristic spectrum (53, 54). He

* Strontium salts were very rare at that time, and Talbot was indebted to Michael Faraday for the specimen he used.

Bunsen's Old Laboratory at Heidelberg, now torn down

was not confused by the universal presence of the sodium lines. In 1855, in his paper "On certain physical properties of the light of the electric spark, within certain gases, as seen through a prism," Dr. Alter predicted that "the prism may also detect the elements in shooting stars, or luminous meteors" (53, 54). A few years later G. R. Kirchhoff and Robert Bunsen firmly established the science of spectroscopic analysis.

Robert Bunsen was the son of a professor of modern languages at Göttingen, and was born in that city on March 31, 1811. After attending the academy at Holzminden he entered the University of Göttingen, and studied chemistry under Professor Friedrich Stromeyer. At the age of twenty years he received his degree of doctor of philosophy. This does not mean that Bunsen was precocious, for, as Wilhelm Ostwald explains, students graduated at a much earlier age then than they do now.

Aided by a grant from the Hanoverian government, the youthful Bunsen broadened his scientific education by traveling, mostly on foot, through Germany, France, Austria, and Switzerland, and meeting the scientists of those countries. For three years he went about studying geological formations, visiting factories and mines, and meeting technical men and professors (2). In 1836 he succeeded Friedrich Wöhler at the higher technical school at Cassel. After serving in similar positions at Marburg and at Breslau, he finally became Leopold Gmelin's successor at Heidelberg, where he taught for thirty-eight years, finally retiring at the venerable age of seventy-eight years (2, 50).

Bunsen's very first paper contained a discovery of great benefit to humanity, for he showed that freshly precipitated ferric hydroxide is an antidote for arsenic poisoning.   His important and dangerous research on cacodyl was carried out at Cassel and Marburg.   Since his laboratory at Cassel was not equipped with hoods, he wore a mask with a long tube leading to the fresh air.   While he was investigating cacodyl cyanide, an explosion occurred which shattered the mask, destroyed the sight of his right eye, and nearly ended his life; yet, after he recovered from the resulting critical illness, he carried the research to a successful conclusion.

Heinrich Debus, 1824–1915.   German chemist who taught for many years at Guy's Hospital, London, and at the Royal Naval College, Greenwich.   He prepared pure purpurin, discovered glyoxylic acid, glyoxal, and glyoxaline, and reduced hydrocyanic acid to methylamine.   He wrote a delightful biography of his professor, Robert Bunsen.

This serious accident made him very cautious.   When one of his students, Heinrich Debus, once wished to use some mercuric fulminate in a research, Bunsen objected and said (6),

When I came to Marburg, I found in the collection of preparations a glass-stoppered bottle containing an ounce or more of mercuric fulminate. I took the flask and carried it to a nearby deep stone-quarry, and threw it in.

Bunsen made a thorough study of the gases of the blast furnace, and it was in this connection that he developed his famous methods of gas analysis.   He invented the carbon-zinc battery, the grease-spot photometer, and the ice and vapor calorimeters, and perfected the Bunsen burner (61).   After the famous eruption of Mount Hekla in 1845, he went with a Danish expedition to study the active hot springs and geysers of Iceland, and by careful thermometric measurements, made at great risk, explained their action before any scientific description of the American geysers had been given (7, 27, 57).

CESIUM

Bunsen afterward carried out an elaborate series of photochemical researches with his lifelong friend, Sir Henry Roscoe, but suddenly discontinued this work. The reason for this may best be told in his own words as quoted from his letter to Roscoe written on November 15, 1859 (7):

At present [said he] Kirchhoff and I are engaged in a common work which doesn't let us sleep. . . . Kirchhoff has made a wonderful, entirely unexpected discovery in finding the cause of the dark lines in the solar spectrum, and increasing them artificially in the sun's spectrum, and in producing them in spectra which do not have lines, and in exactly the same position as the corresponding Fraunhofer lines. Thus a means has been found to determine the composition of the sun and fixed stars with the same accuracy as we determine sulfuric acid, chlorine, etc., with our chemical reagents. Substances on the earth can be determined by this method just as easily as on the sun, so that, for example, I have been able to detect lithium in twenty grams of sea water.

Gustav Robert Kirchhoff, a young professor from Königsberg, Prussia, who had recently followed Bunsen from Breslau to Heidelberg, is generally regarded as Bunsen's greatest discovery of the Breslau period. Kirchhoff was born in Königsberg on March 12, 1824, the third son of a counselor of justice. When he was twenty-four years old, he became a member of the teaching staff at the University of Berlin. After serving for a time as professor extraordinary at Breslau, he went to Heidelberg in 1854, and collaborated with Bunsen for many years. In 1875, however, he left the scene of his brilliant achievements, and went back to Berlin to serve as professor of physics and to work with Helmholtz. He died on October 17, 1887, at the age of sixty-three years.

Kirchhoff's mind was more speculative than Bunsen's, he had greater fondness for pure mathematics, and he was thoroughly familiar with the researches of Sir Isaac Newton, Josef Fraunhofer, and Rudolf Clausius (8, 46). He showed Bunsen that, instead of looking through colored glass to distinguish between similarly colored flames, he ought to use a prism to separate the light into its constituent rays (9). On this principle they developed the Kirchhoff-Bunsen spectroscope, an instrument which proved to be of supreme importance not only in chemical analysis, but also in the discovery of new elements (28).

They noticed that when ordinary salt was sprinkled into the flame of a Bunsen burner, a yellow line was seen through the spectroscope in exactly the position formerly occupied by the dark double line of the sun's spectrum known as the D-line. Attempting then to observe the dark D-line and the bright sodium line simultaneously, by allowing

Gustav Robert Kirchhoff, 1824–1887.
German physicist and physical chemist. Professor of physics at Heidelberg
and Berlin. Independent discoverer of
the Kirchhoff-Stewart law of radiation
and absorption. He explained the
Fraunhofer lines of the solar spectrum,
and, with Bunsen, founded the science
of spectroscopic analysis and discovered
the elements cesium and rubidium.

sunlight and yellow sodium light to shine on the slit of the spectroscope
at the same time, they were astonished to find that the dark line did not
become yellow, but became darker than before. Kirchhoff was so
puzzled by this that he spent the entire day and night trying to account
for it, and finally succeeded in producing the dark D-line artificially.
He did this by using, instead of sunlight, a luminous flame, which gives
a continuous spectrum containing no dark lines, and then bringing the
yellow sodium flame in front of the slit as before. Kirchhoff gave as
his explanation the analogy of sympathetic vibrations. The white light
from the luminous flame, upon passing through the sodium flame, lost
those vibrations which correspond to the yellow lines; and therefore the
spectrum contained a dark line at that place (*9, 34*).

On April 11, 1860, Bunsen wrote, "Don't be angry with me, dear
Roscoe, if I have still done nothing more on our photochemical work,"
and explained that he was searching for a new alkali metal (*9*). On
November 6 of the same year he wrote again to Roscoe:

I have been very fortunate with my new metal. I have fifty grams of
the almost pure chlorplatinate, which I can easily make absolutely pure. To
be sure these fifty grams were obtained from 600 hundred weights (quintals)
of mineral water, whereby $2^1/_2$ pounds of lithium chloride were obtained as
a by-product. Since I have a simple method of separating it, I find it widely
distributed. I shall name it *cesium* because of its beautiful blue spectral line.
Next Sunday I expect to find time to make the first determination of its
atomic weight.

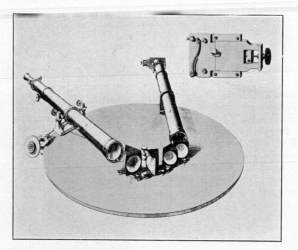

The Kirchhoff-Bunsen Spectroscope

Bunsen had announced this discovery to the Berlin Academy of Sciences on May 10, 1860 (8).

In one of their papers Bunsen and Kirchhoff told just how they traced down the new element:

If one brings into the flame of the spectroscope a drop of mother liquor from the Dürkheim mineral water, one recognizes only the characteristic rays of sodium, potassium, lithium, calcium, and strontium. If then, after having precipitated by known methods the lime, strontia, and magnesia, one takes up the residue with alcohol previously treated with nitric acid to fix the bases, one obtains, after having removed the lithia by means of ammonium carbonate, a mother liquor which in the spectroscope gives the lines of sodium, potassium, and lithium, and, in addition, two remarkable blue lines, very close together, one of which coincides almost exactly with the line Sr δ.

Now there is no simple substance known which gives two such rays in this part of the spectrum; one may therefore conclude the certain existence of a simple unknown substance, belonging to the group of alkali metals. We propose to give this new metal the name *cesium* (symbol Cs) from *caesius*, which the ancients used to designate the blue of the upper part of the firmament. This name seems to us to be justified by the facility with which one may confirm, by the beautiful blue color of the incandescent vapor of this new element, the presence of a few millionths of a milligram of this simple substance mixed with soda, lithia, and strontia (*4, 29, 30*).

Other chemists had examined cesium minerals before but had failed to recognize the presence of the new metal. August Breithaupt (1791–1873), in his examination of some corroded quartzes from Elba in 1846,

(*Left to right*) **G. Kirchhoff, R. W. Bunsen, and H. E. Roscoe, in 1862.**
Kirchhoff and Bunsen invented the spectroscope and founded the science of
spectroscopic analysis.   Roscoe collaborated with Bunsen in photochemical
researches, and was the first to prepare metallic vanadium.

distinguished two closely related minerals which he named *castor* (which was afterward shown to be a kind of petalite) and *pollux,* which was later found to contain cesium (*66, 67*). In the same year C. F. Plattner analyzed the latter mineral very carefully, but his results added up to only 92.75 per cent (*10, 36*). Although he made special tests for chlorine, fluorine, and other substances which might be present in a silicate, his results were negative, and because of the smallness of his specimen he was unable to repeat the quantitative analysis. He was impressed by the fact that pollux (pollucite) had a higher alkali content than any silicate previously known (*36*).

Carl Friedrich Plattner,[*] 1800–1858. Professor of metallurgy at the Freiberg School of Mines. Author of books on blowpipe analysis and the roasting of ores. He was an expert analyst, trained under Heinrich Rose. When his careful analysis of pollux was made in 1846, the spectroscope had not yet been invented, and he was unable to recognize the presence of the new element cesium.

Carl Friedrich Plattner was born in 1800 at Klein-Waltersdorf near Freiberg, was educated at the Freiberg School of Mines, and became a professor of metallurgy and blowpipe analysis there. He was a great master of the art and science of analytical chemistry, and applied the blowpipe even to quantitative analysis. He made many promising experiments on the oxidation of sulfur dioxide to the trioxide by means of catalysts. Before the work was completed, however, he was stricken with apoplexy, which terminated fatally in 1858 (*68*). When Félix Pisani (1831–1920) examined pollucite four years after the discovery of cesium, he found that Plattner had mistaken his cesium sulfate for a mixture of the sulfates of sodium and potassium (*8, 37, 58*).

[*] The portrait of Plattner has been reproduced from F. G. Corning's "A Student Reverie" by kind permission of the author.

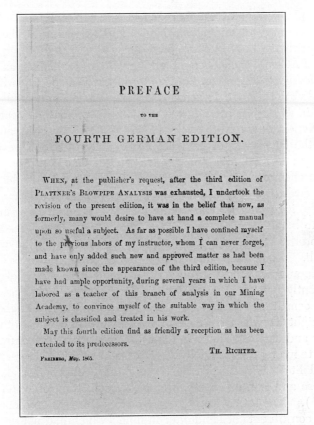

PREFACE

TO THE

FOURTH GERMAN EDITION.

WHEN, at the publisher's request, after the third edition of PLATTNER'S BLOWPIPE ANALYSIS was exhausted, I undertook the revision of the present edition, it was in the belief that now, as formerly, many would desire to have at hand a complete manual upon so useful a subject. As far as possible I have confined myself to the previous labors of my instructor, whom I can never forget, and have only added such new and approved matter as had been made known since the appearance of the third edition, because I have had ample opportunity, during several years in which I have labored as a teacher of this branch of analysis in our Mining Academy, to convince myself of the suitable way in which the subject is classified and treated in his work.

May this fourth edition find as friendly a reception as has been extended to its predecessors.

TH. RICHTER.

FREIBERG, *May*, 1865.

Plattner's "Blowpipe Analysis" was revised by his former student, Hieronymus Theodor Richter, who, with Ferdinand Reich, discovered the element indium.

Félix Pisani was a well known French-Italian analytical chemist and mineral dealer who taught chemistry and did consulting analytical work in a private school in Paris which C. F. Gerhardt had formerly conducted. He lived to be almost ninety years old, and continued his researches almost to the time of his death (58).

RUBIDIUM

On February 23, 1861, only a few months after the discovery of cesium, Bunsen and Kirchhoff announced to the Berlin Academy the existence of another new alkali metal in lepidolite.

Klaproth said that lepidolite, the first source of rubidium, was discovered by the Abbé Nicolaus Poda of Neuhaus (1723?–1798), a Jesuit scholar and member of the hereditary Austrian nobility. For several years he lectured on mining mechanics and surveying at the School of Mines of Schemnitz (69).

The first published account of lepidolite (or lilalite, as the Abbé Poda called it) is Baron von Born's description of a specimen from Count Mittrowsky's estate at Rozena, Moravia, which appeared in *Crell's Annalen* in 1791, just after Baron von Born's premature death. Count Johann Nepomuk von Mittrowsky (1757–1799) of Bystrzitz and Rožinka devoted the later years of his brief life entirely to science, especially to the botany and mineralogy of Moravia (69). One of Baron von Born's last researches was his investigation of lepidolite. When he ignited it between coals, it frothed, and fused to a porous slag. When he heated it strongly, it formed a dense white glass. He found its principal constituent to be silica (70).

Klaproth's first analysis of lepidolite did not show the presence of any alkali. When he examined it a second time, however, he wrote: "Since the analysis of leucite, described in the earlier part of this work, has evidently proved that it contains the *vegetable alkali* as one of its essential constituent parts, it was to be expected that this alkaline substance might likewise be found in the mixture of various other species of stones and earths. The first confirmation of this conjecture has been afforded to me by the Lepidolite." His final analysis of "the amethystine red lepidolite" yielded silica 54.50, alumina 38.25, potash 4, oxides of manganese and iron 0.75, and "loss, partly consisting of water" 2.50 per cent (71). Klaproth's analysis failed to show the presence of two essential constituents of lepidolite: lithium (which had not yet been discovered) and fluorine.

In 1861 Robert Bunsen and G. R. Kirchhoff separated the alkalies from some lepidolite from Saxony and precipitated the potassium with platinic chloride. After they had washed this precipitate, they examined it with the spectroscope and observed two new lines which proved to be those of an unknown element, which they named rubidium. The report runs as follows:

If one treats lepidolite from Saxony by one of the known methods which yield a solution of the alkalies separated from the other elements, and if one pours some platinic chloride into the liquid, one obtains an abundant precipitate which, tested in a spectroscope, shows only the lines of potassium.

If one washes this precipitate several times with boiling water, and tests it at intervals in the apparatus, one notices two new lines of a magnificent violet located between the lines Sr δ and the Ka β* line of potassium. As the washing is continued, these lines stand out more and more against the con-

---

* Bunsen and Kirchhoff used the symbol *Ka* for potassium (*kalium*), instead of K.

tinuous spectrum of potassium, which fades away.   Soon one sees a certain number of new rays in the red, the yellow, and the green.   None of these lines belong to elements hitherto discovered.   Among them we may mention especially two remarkable red lines just beyond the brilliant Fraunhofer line A, or, if one prefers, the brilliant K^a line which corresponds to it, which ray is located at the extreme red end of the solar spectrum.   The magnificent dark red color of these rays of the new alkali metal led us to give this element the name rubidium and the symbol Rb from *rubidus,* which, with the ancients, served to designate the deepest red (*4, 30, 31, 35*).

The colorless flame of the burner which Bunsen perfected in 1854–55 made this research possible.

Although Bunsen succeeded in isolating rubidium (*42*), he observed cesium only by means of its spectral lines (*41*).   Twenty years later Dr. Carl Setterberg succeeded in isolating cesium by electrolysis of the cyanide in presence of barium cyanide.   The electrolytic part of the research was performed in Bunsen's laboratory.

When the five-hundredth anniversary of Heidelberg University was celebrated in 1886, an elaborate breakfast was served which lasted more than three hours.   Bunsen fell asleep during one of the tiresome speeches, but at one place in the address the speaker's loud oratory caused the aged chemist to awake with a start.   Rubbing his eyes, he whispered to his neighbor, "I thought I had let a test-tube full of rubidium fall to the floor"* (*11*).

On another occasion an Englishwoman, to whom he had just been introduced, mistook him for Josias Bunsen, the ambassador, and asked him if he had finished his book entitled "Gott in der Geschichte."   "Alas," replied Bunsen, "My untimely death prevented me"† (*11*).

Robert Bunsen was one of the most modest of men.   When he found it necessary to mention his own discoveries in his lectures, he never said, "I have discovered," but always "Man hat gefunden."   However, when the lecture dealt with spectral analysis, his students showed by prolonged applause that they understood and were proud of his great achievements.   Bunsen won many honors and medals, but of these he once said sadly, "Such things had value for me only because they pleased my mother; she is now dead"‡ (*12, 49*).

Like N.-L. Vauquelin and Henry Cavendish, Bunsen never married, and, when asked for the reason, he used to say, "I never could find the time."   Perhaps this lack of family ties made his students even more dear

---

* *Mir war als hätte ich ein Probierröhrchen mit Rubidium auf den Boden fallen lassen.*
† *Ach daran hat mich ja mein frühzeitiger Tod verhindert.*
‡ *Solche Dinge hatten nur Werth für mich, weil sie meine Mutter erfreuten; sie ist nun todt.*

Hermann (Ludwig Ferdinand) von Helmholtz, 1821–1894. Professor of physiology at Bonn and at Heidelberg. Professor of physics at Berlin. Inventor of the ophthalmoscope, an instrument for examining the retina of the eye. He expressed the principle of the conservation of energy in mathematical form.

to him, for he used to work all day in the laboratory, patiently showing them the fine details of chemical manipulation. When he was seventy years old, he wrote to Roscoe, "In the years which I am rapidly approaching, one lives more in the recollection of past happy days than in the present; and to the most pleasure-giving of them belong those which for many years we spent in true friendship together." After his long day's work, his favorite recreation was to go walking over the chestnut-wooded hills near Heidelberg in company with a friend like Kirchhoff or Hermann von Helmholtz (13).

Bunsen was blessed with a brilliant mind, a happy disposition, a strong, healthy body, and a long life (48). He was seventy-six years old when he invented the vapor calorimeter, and after he retired from his Heidelberg professorship at the age of seventy-eight, he still had ten years to live. These last days were brightened by the honor and respect paid him by his former students and colleagues. Sir Henry Roscoe said that during the peaceful sleep in which Bunsen lay for three days preceding his death on August 16, 1899, his face retained "the fine intellectual expression of his best and brightest days" (13).

After the brilliant researches of Bunsen and Kirchhoff had paved the way, other new elements were soon revealed by the spectroscope. Among these may be mentioned thallium, indium, gallium, helium, ytterbium, holmium, thulium, samarium, neodymium, praseodymium, and lutetium.

Bunsen Memorial in Heidelberg

THALLIUM

The first indication of the existence of thallium was noted by Sir William Crookes. Sir William was born on June 17, 1832, and was educated in the grammar school at Chippenham. At the age of sixteen years he entered the Royal College of Chemistry, where A. W. von Hofmann was serving as the first professor; yet in spite of the latter's inspiring influence, he never cared for organic chemistry. His first paper entitled "On the Selenocyanides" was published when he was nineteen years of age. In 1859 he started the publication of *Chemical News,* and until 1906 he was the sole editor of that important journal (*14*).

One day, very soon after Bunsen and Kirchhoff had announced their discovery of rubidium, Crookes happened to examine some residues from a sulfuric acid plant at Tilkerode in the Harz. Hofmann had given him these residues some years before, because they contained selenium compounds which could be converted into selenocyanides; and, after removing the selenium, Crookes had saved them because he thought they also contained tellurium.

When he examined the residues with the spectroscope, however, he found no lines of tellurium, and the lines of selenium soon faded out. Soon there appeared a beautiful green line that he had never seen before. He concluded that the material must contain a new element, and because of the green line in the spectrum he named it *thallium*, or *green branch*. In his first announcement, which appeared in the *Chemical News* on March 30, 1861 (*38*), Sir William Crookes stated: "In the year 1850 Professor Hofmann placed at my disposal upwards of ten pounds of the seleniferous deposit from the sulfuric acid manufactory at Tilkerode, in the Harz Mountains, for the purpose of extracting from it the selenium, which was afterwards employed in an investigation upon the seleno-cyanides. Some residues which were left in the purification of the crude selenium, and which, from their reactions, appeared to contain tellurium, were collected together and placed aside for examination at a more convenient opportunity. . . .

From Muspratt's "Chemistry, Theoretical,
Practical, and Analytical"

August Wilhelm von Hofmann, 1818–1892. German chemist who served for many years as the first professor at the Royal College of Chemistry in London. Founder of the aniline dye industry. He devised the simple process of preparing aniline by nitrating benzene and reducing the nitrobenzene. He was one of the founders of the Deutsche Chemische Gesellschaft, and was elected president fourteen times. See also ref (*65*).

"It was not until I had in vain tried numerous chemical methods for isolating the tellurium which I believed to be present, that the method of spectrum analysis was used. A portion of the residue introduced into a gas-flame gave abundant evidence of selenium; but as the alternate light and dark bands due to this element became fainter, and I was expecting the appearance of the somewhat similar but closer bands of tellurium, suddenly a *bright-green line* flashed into view and quickly disappeared" (*38*). Although he at first believed thallium to be a nonmetal similar to sulfur, he soon changed his mind, and in 1862 he was awarded a prize for some specimens labeled "Thallium, a new metallic element," which he exhibited at the International Exhibition (*14*).

Sir William Crookes will probably be longest remembered for his study of rarefied gases and for his discoveries in radioactivity and molecular physics. After Sir William Ramsay discovered helium in 1895, it was Crookes who established its identity with the helium that Sir Norman Lockyer had observed spectroscopically in the sun's atmosphere. Crookes also invented the radiometer and the spinthariscope. As early as 1886- 88 he recognized the existence of atomic species of identical

Sir William Crookes, 1832– 1919. English physicist and chemist. Professor at the Royal College of Chemistry. Inventor of the radiometer and the spinthariscope. Founder and editor of *Chemical News*. He was the first to observe the green line of thallium and the first to prove the identity of solar and terrestrial helium. The discoverer of uranium X_1.

Courtesy Lyman C. Newell

chemical properties but different atomic weights, which he called "meta-elements," and thus came close to the modern concept of isotopes (*59, 60*). While serving on the Glass Workers' Cataract Committee of the Royal Society, he carried out practical research of great humanitarian value. He prepared a kind of glass which, although nearly colorless, cut off the injurious rays from the white-hot molten glass, and protected the eyes of the workers (*14*). On two occasions Sir William visited the famous diamond mines at Kimberley, and in 1909 he wrote a little book on diamonds, which he dedicated to his wife.

Charles Baskerville once wrote a biographical sketch of Crookes, in which he gave the following pleasing description of his home (15):

> Sunday evenings Sir William is at home. Within his study walls, be-booked to the ceiling, one may find then the finest minds of science in England or in other lands, grappling in discussion with the unsolved problems, which oftentimes become no clearer than the increasing denseness of the tobacco smoke. Promptly at eleven o'clock there comes a bright rift in the clouds as Lady Crookes enters and charmingly leads all to the dining-room below. Punctilious in the performance of every duty, courteous but vigorous in argument, modestly assertive, learning from the youngest, Sir William draws out the humblest until he would become almost bold, yet, in return, he gives generously from his rich store of wide knowledge and large experience.

After Lady Crookes died in 1916 Sir William never recovered from his loss. He died on April 4, 1919, at the age of eighty-six years (14).

Although there seems to be no doubt that Sir William Crookes was the first to observe the green line of thallium, many chemical historians, especially the French ones, attribute the isolation of the metal itself to Claude-Auguste Lamy. He was born on July 15, 1820, at Néry in the Jura department of France, attended the École Normale Supérieure in Paris, and at the age of thirty-one years received his doctorate from Lille, He taught physics, first at Limoges and later at Lille (16).

C.-A. Lamy first observed the green line of thallium in March, 1862, in a sample of selenium which his brother-in-law M. Frédéric Kuhlmann had extracted from the slime in the lead chambers of a plant where sulfuric acid was made by burning pyrite. On June 23, 1862, he presented a 14-gram ingot of thallium metal to the Académie des Sciences. He stated that thallium exists in several kinds of pyrite used for the manufacture of sulfuric acid, including the Belgian pyrites of Theux, Namur, and Philippeville and some mineralogical specimens from Nantes and Bolivia. He found it much easier to extract the thallium from the slime in the lead chambers than from the pyrite. Lamy's method of isolating thallium may best be described in his own words:

> When burned in suitable pits, pyrite yields, among other products, sulfur dioxide, arsenious and selenious acids, and the oxide of thallium, which are carried over into the first lead chamber, with the ferruginous dust. In this first chamber, especially if it has no other communication with the following ones than the gas pipe, the oxide of thallium deposits and accumulates, and finally thallium sulfate, with sulfates of lead, iron, and other foreign substances coming from the pyrite.

The thallium [continued Lamy] is extracted from these deposits in the first chamber. When these deposits are heated almost dry, with approximately an equal volume of aqua regia, until the acid almost disappears, and the mass is then taken up with twice its weight of boiling water, one sees formed in the liquid as it cools an abundance of yellow crystalline plates which, when purified by several successive recrystallizations, give a magnificent compound of thallium sesquichloride. When this chloride is submitted to the decomposing action of the electric current from four or five Bunsen cells, for example, there appears at the negative pole pure thallium. This is the experiment by which we have, for the first time, isolated the new metal (*17, 39*).

Claude-Auguste Lamy, 1820–1878. President of the *Société Chimique de France* in 1873. The first person to prepare an ingot of metallic thallium. He made a thorough study of its compounds and proved that they are poisonous. Author of many papers on optics, electricity, pyrometry, organic and inorganic chemistry, and sugar technology.

From "*Cinquantenaire de la Société Chimique de France*"

Although Lamy claimed that Sir William Crookes's thallium was really a sulfide, the latter replied that he had prepared metallic thallium as early as May 1, 1862, but that because of its volatility he had not dared to melt the black powder to form an ingot (*18*). However, a committee from the French Academy, including Henri Sainte-Claire Deville, Théophile-Jules Pelouze, and J.-B.-A. Dumas, credited Lamy, rather than Crookes, with the isolation of thallium metal (*17, 40*).

After a careful study of the chemical compounds of the new metal, Professor Lamy concluded that it forms two series of salts, the thallous and the thallic, in which the metal is respectively mono- and trivalent. Since the thallous compounds resemble those of the alkali metals, whereas the thallic salts are similar to those of aluminum, Dumas once said, "It is no exaggeration to say that from the point of view of the classification generally accepted for the metals, thallium offers a combination of contradictory properties which would entitle one to call it the paradoxical metal, the ornithorhynchus of the metals"* (*40, 47*).

In 1865 Lamy became a professor of chemistry at the Central School of Arts and Manufactures at Paris. He published papers on magnetism, the progress of physics, the toxic effect of thallium, and the solubility of lime in water. He died at Paris on March 20, 1878 (*16*).

Jean Baptiste-André Dumas, 1800–1884. Professor of chemistry at the Athenaeum and at the Sorbonne. He devised a method of determining vapor density, and developed the theory of types in organic chemistry, which he defended against Berzelius' dualistic electrochemical theory. From a study of the aliphatic alcohols, Dumas and Peligot developed the conception of homologous series. See also ref. (*62*).

Courtesy Lyman C. Newell

In 1863 R. C. Böttger of Frankfort-on-the Main found that thallium occurs in some spring waters. A certain salt mixture from Nauheim contained, in addition to the chlorides of sodium, potassium, and magnesium, those of cesium, rubidium, and thallium. Since he was able to prepare a thallium ferric alum exactly analogous to potassium ferric alum, he regarded thallium as an alkali metal (*72, 73*). Although it is sometimes univalent like sodium and potassium, it is now classified in Group III of the periodic system.

* "*Il n'y a pas d'exagération à dire qu'au point de vue de la classification généralement acceptée pour les métaux, le thallium offre une réunion de propriétés contradictoires qui autoriserait à l'appeler le métal paradoxal, l'ornithorynche des métaux.*"

Crookesite, a Thallium Mineral. When Baron Nils Adolf Erik Nordenskiöld analyzed specimens of the selenium minerals euoairite and beizellanite from Skrikerum, Sweden, in 1866, he detected thallium in both of them. On examining the specimens in the Royal Museum, he found a new mineral which C. G. Mosander had regarded as copper selenide but which, on analysis, proved to be a rare selenide of silver, copper, and thallium. Baron Nordenskiöld named it crookesite in honor of the discoverer of thallium, and for many years it was the only known mineral containing thallium as an essential constituent. Nordenskiöld described it as a mineral forming compact, lead-gray masses with a metallic luster; resembling chalcocite in hardness; and having a specific gravity of 6.9. It melts easily before the blowpipe to form a dark green pellet; colors the flame an intense green; and is insoluble in hydrochloric acid but readily soluble in nitric acid (74, 75).

Thallium in Pyrite. In 1867 Dr. E. Carstanjen found that the flue dust from the pyrite-roasting kilns of L. Röhr's sulfuric acid plant at Oranienburg was unusually rich in thallium. It yielded on analysis 3.5 per cent of metallic thallium. By working up a large quantity of flue dust from several kilns, he prepared twenty or thirty pounds of the metal.

In an attempt to trace out the source of the thallium in nature, Carstanjen found that the pyrite had come from rich deposits near the village of Meggen in Siegerland, Germany. On examining the pyrite in this locality with a lens, he saw some small black specks with a dull luster. Specimens of pyrite which contained these specks gave a distinct reaction for thallium (76). In the 1866 edition of his "Mineralogische Studien," August Breithaupt mentioned a pyrite from Grosskamsdorf near Saalfeld, Thuringia, which H. T. Richter had found to be unusually rich in thallium (77).

Effect of Thallium on Plants and Animals. On January 29, 1863, R. C. Böttger announced that he had detected spectroscopic traces of thallium in wine, chicory, tobacco, sugar beet, and beech wood, and had concluded that it must be widely diffused in the vegetable kingdom (47, 73). Because of the toxicity of thallium compounds, they are sometimes added in small concentrations to the soil of rodent-infested fields. Too high a concentration of thallium inhibits germination, growth rate, and chlorophyll formation in the crops, especially in rainy weather (78).

INDIUM

In 1863 Ferdinand Reich, a professor of physics at the famous School of Mines at Freiberg, and his assistant, Hieronymus Theodor Richter,

Ferdinand Reich, 1799–1882. Professor of physics and inspector at the Freiberg School of Mines. Discoverer of indium. He studied the deviations in the declination of the magnetic needle, the rainfall and snowfall in Freiberg, and the temperature of the rocks at different depths.

discovered the element indium. The former was born at Bernburg on February 19, 1799, and was educated at Leipzig, Freiberg, Göttingen, and Paris.

In 1822 he went on foot to Göttingen to study chemistry under Friedrich Stromeyer, whom he admired "because of his clarity and his appropriate choice of material" (51), and at the request of the Freiberg authorities he selected apparatus, minerals, and rare books for the Mining Academy. In the following year he was sent to Paris on a similar mission, and returned with platinum ware, certified weights, apparatus, and minerals for the Freiberg Academy and for Stromeyer in Göttingen. While in Paris he studied at the Sorbonne, the School of Mines, and the Collège de France, and met Alexandre Brongniart, D.-F. Arago, L.-J. Gay-Lussac, L.-J. Thenard, Justus von Liebig, Élie de Beaumont, and Alexander von Humboldt. He especially admired Gay-Lussac "because of his modest simplicity, his thoroughness, and the wealth of his knowledge" (51).

From 1824 until his retirement in 1866 Reich served as inspector of the academy, and had charge of the mineral collections, purchase of supplies, keeping of records, cataloging of the library, and the editing of a mining and metallurgical calendar. He made an extended study of the deviations in the declination of the magnetic needle, and for many years kept an accurate record of the rainfall and snowfall in Freiberg. Soon after his return from Paris he began to lecture on the French system of weights and measures, and the metric system was first introduced into Saxony by Reich, S. A. W. Herder, and Brendel.

Chemical Laboratory at the Freiberg School of Mines

Reich's observations of the temperatures of the rocks at different depths were of great scientific interest, and his results for the mean density of the earth were in good agreement with those of Henry Cavendish.

In the winter of 1830–31 Reich gave a continuation course of private lectures before about sixty educated citizens of Freiberg, most of whom were connected with the mines and smelters. Although these lectures added to his income, he discontinued them because they necessarily had to be less scientific than those designed for his regular students. For twelve years he also lectured on mineralogy, and for many years he had charge of the course in general chemistry.

Since Reich was always deeply concerned about the welfare of his students and set apart a special evening for entertaining them, they regarded him as a true friend. He occasionally gave private lectures in French for foreign students who had difficulty with the German language.

Smelter fumes which damaged crops, fodder, and stock were a serious problem. While Professor Carl Friedrich Plattner was studying means of removing sulfur dioxide, Reich devised a simple apparatus for determining the sulfur dioxide content of vapors and gases. Even the erection at Hilbersdorf of the tallest smokestack in Europe failed

Hieronymus Theodor Richter, 1824–1898. Director of the Freiberg School of Mines. The first to observe the characteristic blue spectral lines of indium. Metallurgist, assayer, and authority on blowpipe analysis.

to overcome the difficulty, for the damage to fruits and trees then extended over a wider area than before.   Although Professor Reich studied the fumes in forty smelters and chemical plants in Germany, Belgium, and England, the problem was not settled until after his death, when in 1890 a tall smokestack was erected at Halsbrücke (51).

In 1863 Reich began a search for thallium in some Freiberg zinc ores from the Himmelsfürst mine consisting mainly of arsenical pyrites, blende, lead glance, silica, manganese, copper, and small amounts of tin and cadmium (19, 43).   After roasting the blende to remove most of the sulfur and arsenic, he decomposed it with hydrochloric acid (47).   When Clemens Winkler, who was then a metallurgist in the Saxon smalt works, visited Professor Reich in 1863, the latter showed him a straw-yellow precipitate and said, "This is the sulfide of a new element" (52).   Because of his colorblindness, however, Reich entrusted the spectroscopic examination to his assistant, Richter.

Hieronymus Theodor Richter was born at Dresden on November 21, 1824.   He became a metallurgical chemist at the Freiberg School of Mines.   When he placed some of the zinc blende in the loop of a platinum wire and heated it in the flame of a Bunsen burner, he observed a brilliant indigo line which did not coincide with either of the blue lines of cesium (20, 52).   Because of this characteristic spectral line the new element was christened *indium*.   The publication of this contribution under joint authorship was a mistake which Professor Reich afterward regretted, for Richter tried to make it appear that he was the sole discoverer (2, 51, 52).

Group of Rocks at the Freiberg School of Mines.

Reich and Richter found later that there are two indium lines, the brighter one being slightly more refrangible than the blue line of strontium, and the weaker one still more refrangible and located near the blue line of calcium. Indium compounds impart such a brilliant indigo-violet color to the Bunsen flame that they can be recognized even without a spectroscope.

They separated the chloride and hydrated oxide of indium in small amounts, and, by cautiously heating a mixture of indium oxide and sodium carbonate on charcoal by means of a blowpipe, they also obtained some impure metal (*21, 43*). Metallic indium is a white, ductile, easily fusible metal like tin, and it leaves a mark when drawn across paper.

Reich and Richter found that it is easier to isolate it from the zinc than from the original blende. They reduced indium oxide in a current of hydrogen or illuminating gas and melted the metal under potassium cyanide (*44, 45*). At the suggestion of Ferdinand Reich, Clemens Winkler made a thorough study of the metal and its compounds (*20*).

In Wells's "Annual of Scientific Discovery" one finds an interesting description of the first metallic indium:

Two specimens of indium were exhibited at the Académie des Sciences in April, 1867, by Richter. They were prisms, each about four inches long, the section being that of a trapezium with a height of one-half inch and with bases respectively $1/2$ inch and $3/4$ inch in breadth. The metal was very

pure and resembled cadmium; and Richter valued these two specimens at
£ 800 (21).

Professor Reich took no part in political life, and his excellent
library contained no books on that subject. For a few years, however,
he served as commissioner of the poor, and always acted for the best
interests of those in need. Although he had no children of his own,
Reich helped to support and educate the eleven children of his unfortunate brother Ludwig, who had lost both wife and fortune. Some of
the nieces lived for years at the home of Professor and Mrs. Reich, and
one nephew received his gymnasium and university education through
their generosity (51).

Reich loved to travel, and even in his boyhood days he kept a
detailed diary of all his trips. After his retirement at the close of 1865
he bought a little house, where he lived for more than twenty years,
spending much time with his scientific journals and books. After the
death of his wife in 1876, a grandniece kept house for him until his
death on April 27, 1882.

In 1875 Richter became director of the Freiberg School of Mines.
His American student, LeRoy Wiley McCay, describes him as "a
nervous, high-strung, mobile little man." He was expert in metallurgy
and assaying, and revised some of the later editions of Plattner's "Blowpipe Analysis." One of his papers was on the extraction of gold from
gold ores with chlorine water. He was most exacting with his students,
who, nevertheless, enjoyed his unfailing good humor and bright flashes
of wit (20). Richter died at Freiberg on September 25, 1898 (16).

Rudolph Christian Böttger (1806–1881) found in 1866 that the
flue dust which condensed in the chimneys of the zincworks near Goslar
contained about one part of indium oxide in one thousand (79). He
perfected methods of preparing the rare metals indium, thallium, and
cesium (80).

Indium, like cadmium, was first discovered in substances of which
it is only a non-essential constituent. Clemens Winkler said in 1867,
"True indium minerals have not yet been discovered. So far as I
know, indium has been detected up to the present only in a few zinc
blendes: in those of Freiberg, the spectral-analytical investigation of
which led to the discovery of the new metal, and in the black
blende, or christophite, of Breitenbrunn in Saxony, which I analyzed
at the request of Mining Superintendent Breithaupt and found to
contain 0.0062 per cent of indium. However, I could not detect indium
in black blende of Turcz, Hungary, which is closely related to christophite, nor in Silesian calamine and the zinc and cadmium obtained
from it. Böttger finally found indium in the flue dust of the zinc

roasting kilns at the Julius Smelter near Goslar, in which zinc ores from the Rammelsberg are worked

"While the blendes contain indium as the sulfide," continued Winkler, "Hoppe-Seyler found it in another form, which could not be definitely determined, in a tungsten ore from an unknown locality, and later in the wolframite from Zinnwald. The latter contains 0.0228 per cent of indium. In the meantime, I have placed many minerals (without previous concentration, to be sure) before the slit of the spectroscope, but have never found one which gave the desired reaction. It therefore seems as if the occurrence of indium in nature is exceedingly scarce or it must in most cases play the role of a difficultly discoverable satellite" (81).

In 1873 H. B. Cornwall detected indium in zinc blendes from West Ossipee and Eaton, New Hampshire, and from Roxbury, Connecticut. The last-mentioned blende was so rich that the indium line showed distinctly when the spectroscopic test was applied to the raw powdered blende, without use of acids. In 1876 he found that certain zinc blendes from Nevada County, Colorado, also were rich in indium (82, 55). In the following year A. and G. de Negri of the University of Genoa found that the calamine from the Oneta mine in the province of Bergamo, Italy, was rich in this element (83). W. N. Hartley and H. Ramage found that the pumice from the Krakatoa eruption of 1883 contained small amounts of it (84, 85). Although this metal is usually associated with zinc blende, H. Romeyn, Jr. found an indium content of from 1.0 to 2.8 per cent in cross sections of a pegmatite dike in western Utah, which contained, among other minerals, iolite (cordierite, magnesium ferrous aluminum silicate) in which part of the aluminum had probably been replaced by indium (84, 86).

Indium, unlike germanium, is found in zinc blendes which are geologically old. Whereas cadmium occurs mainly in the well-formed crystals of pure zinc blende, indium is found in the fine-grained mixtures in thin ramifying cracks (84). Professor Georges Urbain found that blendes rich in germanium are usually rich also in gallium put poor in indium (84, 87).

Commercial Development of Indium. William S. Murray and his colleagues searched many years for an ore containing paying quantities of indium. After examining in vain hundreds of specimens of zinc, lead, silver, and gold ores, they finally found one that gave an unusually intense and unwavering blue line in the spectroscope. The source of this specimen was finally traced, and a deposit of 35,000 tons of the ore was found to average 1.93 ounces of indium per ton. In 1932 Mr. Murray displayed before the Rotary Club in Utica, New York, an indium ingot weighing more than three thousand grams (55).

Daniel Gray perfected a stable bath from which indium can be plated simultaneously with other elements (90). Alloyed with precious metals, indium has been made into jewelry; alloyed with silver, it is sometimes used to plate silverware with a surface resistant to tarnish; in the form of an amalgam, it can be used for dental fillings (88, 89, 93).

The portraits of Reich and Richter and much of the information about indium have been obtained through the kind assistance of Professor L. W. McCay of Princeton University and Professor O. Brunck, Rector of the Freiberg Academy.

LITERATURE CITED

(1)   von GOETHE, J. W., "Faust," Part 2, lines 6255–6.
(2)   OSTWALD, WILHELM, "Männer der Wissenschaft—R. W. Bunsen," Verlag von Wilhelm Weicher, Leipzig, 1905, pp. 4–7.
(3)   FÄRBER, E., "Geschichtliche Entwicklung der Chemie," Springer, Berlin, 1921, p. 210.
(4)   JAGNAUX, R., "Histoire de la Chimie," Vol. 2, Baudry et Cie., Paris, 1891, pp. 182–6.
(5)   DEBUS, H., "Erinnerungen an Robert Wilhelm Bunsen," Th. G. Fischer and Co., Cassel, 1901, p. 126.
(6)   Ibid., p. 23.
(7)   OSTWALD, WILHELM, "Männer der Wissenschaft—R. W. Bunsen," Ref. (2), pp. 13–22.
(8)   "Chemical Society Memorial Lectures, 1893–1900," Gurney and Jackson, London, 1901, pp. 530–2. Bunsen Memorial Lecture by SIR HENRY ROSCOE.
(9)   OSTWALD, WILHELM, "Männer der Wissenschaft—R. W. Bunsen," Ref. (2), pp. 25–30.
(10) von MEYER, ERNST, "History of Chemistry," 3rd English edition from 3rd German, Macmillan, London, 1906, p. 426.
(11) OSTWALD, WILHELM, "Männer der Wissenschaft—R. W. Bunsen," Ref. (2), pp. 35–6.
(12) Ibid., p. 40.
(13) "Chemical Society Memorial Lectures, 1893–1900," Ref. (8), p. 553.
(14) TILDEN, W. A., "Sir William Crookes," Trans. Chem. Soc., 117, 444 (1920).
(15) BASKERVILLE, C., "Sir William Crookes," Science [N. S.], 31, 100–3 (Jan. 21, 1910).
(16) POGGENDORFF, J. C., "Biographisch-Literarisches Handwörterbuch zur Geschichte der exakten Wissenschaften," 6 vols., Verlag Chemie, Leipzig, 1863–1937. Articles on Lamy, Reich, and Richter.
(17) JAGNAUX, R., "HISTOIRE de la Chimie," Ref. (4), Vol. 2, pp. 186–9.
(18) "Thallium und Verbindungen desselben," Jahresber. Chem., 1862, 176–89.
(19) REICH, F. and H. T. RICHTER, "Preliminary notice of a new metal," Chem. News, 8, 123 (Sept. 12, 1863).
(20) McCAY, L. W., "My student days in Germany," J. Chem. Educ., 7, 1085–6 (May, 1930).
(21) "The new metals," Wells's Annual of Scientific Discovery, 1864, 174–7. Indium, rubidium, cesium, and thallium are discussed.
(22) WOLLASTON, W. H., "A method of examining refractive and dispersive powers by prismatic reflection," Nicholson's J., 4, 100 (Feb., 1803).
(23) LENARD, P., "Grosse Naturforscher," J. F. Lehmanns Verlag, Munich, 1929, pp. 169–76.

(24) SHEPPARD, S. E., "The chemistry of photography. I. Historical considerations," *J. Chem. Educ.*, **4**, 306–12 (Mar., 1927),

(25) TALBOT, W. H. F., "On the nature of light," *Phil. Mag.*, [3], **7**, 117 (Aug., 1835).

(26) TALBOT, W. H. F., *Pogg. Ann.*, **31**, 592 (1834).

(27) "Bunsen and the geysers in Iceland: A classic of science," *Sci. News Letter*, **18**, 262–71 (Oct. 25, 1930); R. W. BUNSEN, "Ueber den innern Zusammenhang der pseudo-vulkanischen Erscheinungen Islands," *Ann.*, **62**, 1–59 (Heft 1, 1847).

(28) "Classics of science: Spectrum analysis," *Sci. News Letter*, **13**, 121–2 (Feb. 25, 1928); G. KIRCHHOFF and R. W. BUNSEN, *Pogg. Ann.*, **110**, 161 (1860).

(29) "On a new alkali metal, by MM. Bunsen and Kirchhoff," *Chem. News*, **2**, 281 (Nov. 24, 1860).

(30) "Discovering the alkali metals: A classic of science," *Sci. News Letter*, **18**, 186–8 (Sept. 20, 1930).

(31) "On a fifth element belonging to the alkali group, by Professor Bunsen," *Chem. News*, **3**, 357 (June 15, 1861).

(32) TALBOT, W. H. F., "Facts relating to optical science. No. 1," *Phil. Mag.*, [3], **4**, 114 (Feb., 1834).

(33) BREWSTER, D., "Observations on the lines of the solar spectrum, and on those produced by the earth's atmosphere, and by the action of nitrous acid gas," *Phil. Mag.*, [3], **8**, 384–92 (May, 1836).

(34) KIRCHHOFF, G. R. and R. BUNSEN. "Chemische Analyse durch Spectralbeobachtungen," *Ann.*, **118**, 349–61 (Heft 3, 1861).

(35) BUNSEN, R. W., "Ueber Cäsium and Rubidium," *Ann.*, **119**, 107–14 (Heft 1, 1861).

(36) PLATTNER, C. F., *Pogg. Ann.*, **69**, 443 (1846).

(37) "Analysis of the mineral pollux of the Island of Elba," *Chem. News*, **10**, 49 (July 30, 1864); *Bull. soc. chim.*, [2], **1**, 456–7 (1864); F. PISANI, "Étude chimique et analyse du pollux de l'île d'Elbe," *Compt. rend.*, **58**, 714–6 (Apr. 18, 1864).

(38) CROOKES, W., "On the existence of a new element, probably of the sulphur group," *Chem. News*, **3**, 193–5 (Mar. 30, 1861).

(39) LAMY, C.-A., "De l'existence d'un noveau métal, le thallium," *Compt. rend.*, **54**, 1255–8 (June 16, 1862); *Ann. chim. phys.*, [3], **67**, 385–417 (Apr., 1863); "Nouvelles observations sur le thallium," *Compt. rend.*, **55**, 836–8 (Dec. 1, 1862).

(40) PELOUZE, T.-J., H. SAINTE-CLAIRE DEVILLE, and J.-B.-A. DUMAS, "Rapport sur un Mémoire de M. Lamy, relatif au thallium," *Compt. rend.*, **55**, 866–72 (Dec. 8, 1862); *Ann. chim. phys.*, [3], **67**, 418–27 (Apr., 1863).

(41) SETTERBERG, C., "Ueber die Darstellung von Rubidium- und Cäsiumverbindungen und über die Gewinnung der Metalle selbst," *Ann.*, **211**, 100–16 (Heft 1, 1882).

(42) BUNSEN, R. W., "Ueber die Darstellung und die Eigenschaften des Rubidiums." *Ann.*, **125**, 367–8 (Heft 1863).

(43) REICH, F. and H. T. RICHTER, "Vorläufige Notiz über ein neues Metall, *J. prakt. Chem.*, **89**, 441–2 (Heft 7, 1863).

(44) REICH, F. and H. T. RICHTER, "Ueber das Indium," *ibid.*, **90**, 172–6 (Heft 3, 1863); **92**, 480–5 (Heft 8, 1864).

(45) RICHTER, H. T., "Sur l'indium," *Compt. rend.*, **64**, 827–8 (Apr. 22, 1867).

(46) LENARD, P., "Grosse Naturforscher," Ref. (23), pp. 269–80.

(47) MELLOR, J. W., "Comprehensive Treatise on Inorganic and Theoretical Chemistry," Vol. 5, Longmans, Green and Co., London **1924**, pp. 406–20 (article on thallium); pp. 386–90 (article on indium).

(48) McCAY, L. W., "My student days in Germany," *J. Chem. Educ.*, **7**, 1094–9 (May, 1930).

(49) OESPER, R. E., "Robert Wilhelm Bunsen," *J. Chem. Educ.*, **4**, 431–9 (Apr., 1927).

(50) FREUDENBERG, K., "The study of chemistry at Heidelberg: A glimpse of an historic home of research," *J. Chem. Educ.*, **4**, 441–6 (Apr., 1927).

(51) TÄSCHNER, "Ferdinand Reich," Mitteilungen des Freiberger Altertumsvereines, Heft 51, pp. 1–39.

(52) BRUNCK, O., "Ein Beitrag zur Geschichte der Chemie. Freiberg und die Chemie," *Technische Blätter* (*Wochenschrift zur deutschen Bergwerks-Zeitung*), No. 5 (Feb. 1, 1931) and No. 8 (Feb. 22, 1931), pp. 1–8.

(53) HAMOR, W. A., "David Alter and the discovery of spectroscopic analysis," *Isis*, **22**, 507–10 (Feb., 1935).

(54) ALTER, DAVID, "On certain physical properties of light produced by the combustion of different metals in the electric spark, refracted by a prism," *Am. J. Sci.*, [2], **18**, 55–7 (July, 1854); "On certain physical properties of the light of the electric spark, within certain gases, as seen through a prism," *ibid.*, [2], **19**, 213–4 (March, 1855); *Am. Chemist*, **5**, 410–2 (May, 1875).

(55) FRENCH, S. J., "A story of indium," *J. Chem. Educ.*, **11**, 270–2 (May, 1934); H. A. POTRATZ and J. B. EKELEY, "A bibliography of indium, 1863–1933," *University of Colorado Studies*, **21**, 151–87 (June, 1934).

(56) JOHNSON, ALLEN, "Dictionary of American Biography," Vol. 1, Charles Scribner's Sons, New York, **1928**, p. 230. Article on David Alter by Dinsmore Alter.

(57) OESPER, R. E. and KARL FREUDENBERG, "Bunsen's trip to Iceland," *J. Chem. Educ.*, **18**, 253–60 (June, 1941); R. E. OESPER, "Robert Wilhelm Bunsen," *ibid.*, **4**, 431–9 (Apr., 1927).

(58) SPENCER, L. J., "Biographical sketches of mineralogists recently deceased . . . Félix Pisani," *Mineralogical Mag.*, **19**, 254 (1920–22).

(59) PRZIBRAM, KARL, in G. Bugge's "Das Buch der grossen Chemiker," Vol. 2, Verlag Chemie, Berlin, **1930**, pp. 288–97.

(60) PARTINGTON, J. R., "The concepts of substance and chemical element," *Chymia*, **1**, 109–21 (1948).

(61) KOHN, MORITZ, "Remarks on the history of laboratory burners," *J. Chem. Educ.*, **27**, 514–16 (Sept., 1950).

(62) ALSOBROOK, JANE W., "Jean-Baptiste-André Dumas," *J. Chem. Educ.*, **28**, 630–3 (Dec., 1951).

(63) PEARSON, T. H., and A. J. IHDE, "Chemistry and the spectrum before Bunsen and Kirchhoff," *J. Chem. Educ.*, **28**, 267–71 (May, 1951).

(64) ROSCOE, H. E., "Spectrum Analysis," 2nd ed., London, **1870**, p. 96; THOMAS MELVILLE, "Edinburgh Physical and Literary Essays, Edinburgh, **1752**, Vol. 2, p. 12.

(65) WINDERLICH, RUDOLF, "August Wilhelm von Hofmann," *Aus der Heimat*, **55**, 49–53 (Apr.–May, 1942).

(66) GROTH, P. H., "Entwicklungsgeschichte der mineralogischen Wissenschaften," Julius Springer, Berlin, **1926**, p. 251.

(67) BREITHAUPT, AUGUST, "Neue Minerale: Mangano-Calcit . . . Kastor und Pollux," *Pogg. Ann.*, **69** (1846).

(68) WESTERMANN, ILJA, "Aus Plattners Leben und Werken," *Metall und Erz*, **30**, 101–3 (March 2, 1933).

(69) WURZBACH, C. VON, "Biographisches Lexikon des Kaiserthums Oesterreich," Vol. 22, K. K. Hof- und Staatsdruckerei, Vienna, **1856–91**, pp. 452–3 (article on Poda von Neuhaus); Vol. 18, pp. 394–6 (article on Mittrowsky, Baron Johann Nepomuk); Vol. 2, pp. 71–4 (article on Born, Ignaz Edler von).

(70) BORN, I. E. VON, "Einige mineralogische Nachrichten," *Crell's Ann.*, **16**, 195–6 (1791).

(71) KLAPROTH, M. H., "Analytical Essays towards Promoting the Chemical Knowl-
      edge of Mineral Substances," T. Cadell and W. Davies, London, 1801, pp.
      238–47, 348–67, 471–5; "Beytrag zur chemischen Naturgeschichte des
      Pflanzenalkali," *Crell's Ann.*, **27**, 90–6 (1797).   Articles on leucite and
      lepidolite.
(72) BÖTTGER, R. C., "Ueber das Vorkommen von Cäsium, Rubidium, und Thallium
      in der Nauheimer Soole," *Ann.*, **127**, 368–70 (1863); **128**, 240–7 (1863).
(73) BÖTTGER, R. C., "Vorkommen des Thalliums," *J. prakt. Chem.*, **90**, 478–9
      (1863).
(74) Obituaries of Crookes and of Nordenskiöld, *Mineralogical Mag.*, **18**, 394
      (1916–19); **13**, 191–2 (1901–3).
(75) NORDENSKIÖLD, A. E., "Die Selenmineralien von Skrikerum," *J. prakt. Chem.*,
      102, 456–8 (1867); *Oefvers. af Akad. Forhandl.* **1866**, p. 361.
(76) CARSTANJEN, E., "Ueber das Thallium und seine Verbindungen," *J. prakt.
      Chem.*, **102**, 65–8 (1867).
(77) BREITHAUPT, AUGUST, "Mineralogische Studien," Arthur Felix, Leipzig, 1866,
      p. 93.
(78) WILLIS, L. G., "Bibliography of References to the Literature on the Minor
      Elements and Their Relation to Plant and Animal Nutrition," Chilean Nitrate
      Educational Bureau, New York, 1939, columns 877–80.
(79) BÖTTGER, R. C., "Extraction of indium from the products of the roasting of
      blende," *Chem. News*, **15**, 228 (May 3, 1867); *J. prakt. Chem.*, **98**, 26
      (1866).
(80) PETERSEN, "Rudolph Christian Boettger," *Ber.*, **14**, 2913–9 (1881).
(81) WINKLER, CLEMENS, "Beiträge zur Kenntniss des Indiums," *J. prakt. Chem.*,
      102, 273–4 (1867).
(82) CORNWALL, H. B., "Indium in American blendes," *Am. Chemist*, **3**, 242 (Jan.,
      1873); **7**, 339 (March, 1877).
(83) NEGRI, A. DE and G. DE NEGRI, "Calamina ricca d'indio," *Gazz. chim. ital.*, **8**,
      120 (1878).
(84) "Gmelin's Handbuch der anorganischen Chemie," 8th ed., Vol. 36, Verlag
      Chemie, Berlin, 1936, pp. 1–8; Vol. 37, pp. 1–6.   History and occurrence of
      gallium and indium.
(85) HARTLEY, W. N., and H. RAMAGE, *Proc. Roy. Soc. (London)*, **68**, 99 (1901).
(86) ROMEYN, H., "Indium and scandium in pegmatite," *J. Am. Chem. Soc.*, **55**,
      3899–3900 (Sept., 1933).
(87) URBAIN, G., "Analyse spectrographique des blendes," *Compt. rend.*, **149**, 602–
      3 (Oct. 11, 1909).
(88) LINFORD, H. B., "Indium," *Ind. Eng. Chem., News Ed.*, **18**, 624 (July 25,
      1940).
(89) LAWRENCE, R. E., and L. R. WESTBROOK, "Indium. Occurrence, recovery, and
      uses," *Ind. Eng. Chem.*, **30**, 611–4 (June, 1938).
(90) MURRAY, W. S., "Indium available in commercial quantities," *Ind. Eng. Chem.*,
      24, 686 (June, 1932).
(91) BUGGE, G., "Der Alchimist. Die Geschichte Leonhard Thurneyssers—des Gold-
      machers von Berlin," Wilhelm Limpert Verlag, Berlin, 1939, pp. 117–8.
(92) VOGEL, OTTO, "Thurneyssers Flammenfarben zur Unterscheidung der Metalle,"
      Chem.-Ztg., **38**, 180 (1914).
(93) MURRAY, W. S., "Production and deposition of indium," *Ind. Eng. Chem.,
      News Ed.*, **11**, 300 (Oct. 20, 1933).

TABLE II.

The Atomic Weights of the Elements

Distribution of the Elements in Periods

Groups	Higher Salt-forming Oxides	Typical or 1st small Period	Large Periods				
			1st	2nd	3rd	4th	5th
I.	R_2O	Li = 7	K 39	Rb 85	Cs 133	—	—
II.	RO	Be = 9	Ca 40	S 87	Ba 137	—	—
III.	R_2O_3	B = 11	Sc 44	Y 89	La 138	Yb 173	—
IV.	RO_2	C = 12	Ti 48	Zr 90	Ce 140	—	Th 232
V.	R_2O_5	N = 14	V 51	Nb 94	—	Ta 182	—
VI.	RO_3	O = 16	Cr 52	Mo 96	—	W 184	Ur 240
VII.	R_2O_7	F = 19	Mn 55	—	—	—	—
VIII. {			Fe 56	Ru 103	—	Os 191	—
			Co 58·5	Rh 104	—	Ir 193	—
			Ni 59	Pd 106	—	Pt 196	—
I.	R_2O	H = 1. Na = 23	Cu 63	Ag 108	—	Au 198	—
II.	RO	Mg = 24	Zn 65	Cd 112	—	Hg 200	—
III.	R_2O_3	Al = 27	Ga 70	In 113	—	Tl 204	—
IV.	RO_2	Si = 28	Ge 72	Sn 118	—	Pb 206	—
V.	R_2O_5	P = 31	As 75	Sb 120	—	Bi 208	—
VI.	RO_3	S = 32	Se 79	Te 125	—	—	—
VII.	R_2O_7	Cl = 35·5	Br 80	I 127	—	—	—
		2nd small Period	1st	2nd	3rd	4th	5th
					Large Periods		

From Mendeleev's "Principles of Chemistry," Vol. 1

Mendeleev's Periodic Table of the Elements. The groups are arranged horizontally instead of vertically.

Refrain from illusions, insist on work and not words, patiently search divine and scientific truth (1, 15).

Wer ruft das Einzelne zur allgemeinen Weihe, Wo es in herrlichen Accorden schlägt? (2)*

* Who calls the individual to the universal consecration, where it vibrates in glorious harmony?

24

Periodic system of the elements

Before continuing the story of the discovery of the chemical elements, it will be necessary to outline the early attempts at classification made by Döbereiner, Beguyer de Chancourtois, and Newlands, and to discuss briefly the periodic system of the elements which was developed independently by Lothar Meyer and Mendeleev. This classification enabled Mendeleev to predict the properties of a number of undiscovered elements and of their compounds with surprising accuracy, and proved to be of great assistance in all subsequent discoveries of new elements.

*A*lthough the alkali metals and the spectroscope aided greatly in revealing hidden elements, each new discovery was an unexpected event. Before the periodic law was discovered independently by Lothar Meyer and by D. I. Mendeleev in 1869, there was no way to predict what elements lay undiscovered nor to foretell their physical and chemical properties.

One of the important steps leading up to this great generalization was the discovery by Professor Johann Wolfgang Döbereiner of Jena of his famous triads (*10, 11*). He was born in December, 1780, the son of a coachman at Hof, near Bayreuth. On a foundation of only meager elementary instruction, practical training in various pharmacies, and attendance at a few lectures on philosophy, chemistry, botany, mineralogy, and languages, he developed such great ability for original research in chemistry that in 1810 A. F. Gehlen, the editor, and Duke Carl August made him professor extraordinary of chemistry at Jena (*22*). His personal and intellectual qualities soon won the high esteem of the Duke and the poet Goethe (*23, 24, 27, 44*).

Döbereiner noticed in 1829 that there are several *triads* in which the middle element, that is, the one whose atomic weight lies midway between those of the other two, has properties which likewise are a mean of those of the other elements of the triad (*29, 31*).

Professor Döbereiner also made a thorough investigation of the

Johann Wolfgang Döbereiner, 1780–1849. Professor of chemistry at Jena. His discovery of the *triads* was an important step toward the systematic classification of the chemical elements. He wrote many books and papers on general and pharmaceutical chemistry, mineral waters, the manufacture of vinegar, and the use of platinum as a catalyst. The original of this portrait is in the City Museum at Jena.

From Chemnitius' "Die Chemie in Jena von Rolfinck bis Knorr"*

catalytic action of platinum,† and wrote books on general and pharmaceutical chemistry, on the manufacture of vinegar, and on mineral waters for therapeutic purposes. Even before the time of Liebig, he gave practical laboratory instruction in analytical chemistry. He died on March 24, 1849.

Alexandre E. Beguyer de Chancourtois (1820–1886), a professor of geology in the School of Mines in Paris, made in 1862 a "telluric screw," or helix, on a vertical cylinder, on which he placed the symbols of the elements at heights proportional to their atomic weights. He plotted the atomic weights as ordinates on the generatrix of a cylinder the circumference of which, since the atomic weight of oxygen is 16, he divided into sixteen equal parts. He then traced on the surface of the cylinder a helix making a 45° angle with the axis. The spiral therefore crossed a given generatrix at distances from the base which were a multiple of 16. Thus lithium, sodium, and potassium, with atomic weights of 7, 23, and 39, respectively, fell on one perpendicular, whereas oxygen, sulfur, selenium, and tellurium fell on another.

Beguyer de Chancourtois observed the great similarity existing between elements appearing on the same generatrix, mentioned the periodic recurrence of properties, and stated that "the properties of substances are the properties of numbers." He presented to the French

---

* Reproduced by courtesy of Dr. Fritz Chemnitius.
† Döbereiner was assisted for a time by Gottfried Wilhelm Osann, whose researches on platinum led to the discovery of ruthenium by Klaus.

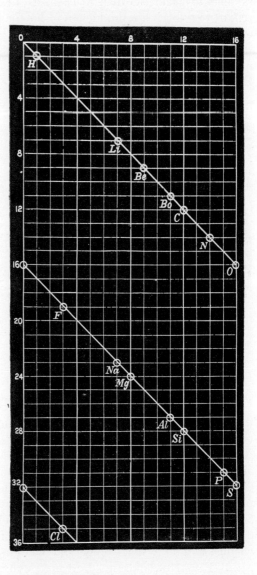

A Portion of the
Telluric Screw of
Beguyer de Chancourtois

Academy a lithograph and a model of his "telluric screw" (*12, 13, 14*). Unfortunately, his heavy, obscure literary style, his use of terms more familiar to geologists than to chemists, and the failure of the *Comptes rendus* to publish a reproduction of his diagram all contributed to a lack of appreciation of his contribution* (*19*).

Another important advance in the classification of the elements was made by John Alexander Reina Newlands. He was born in Southwark, England, in 1837, and was educated privately by his father, a minister of

Alexandre-Emile Beguyer de Chancourtois, 1820–1886. Inspector-general of mines and professor of geology at the École Supérieure des Mines in Paris. He made geological explorations in France, Asia Minor, Iceland, and Greenland. As a humanitarian reform to prevent accidents from firedamp, he compelled mine owners to sink two shafts for each coal mine. His most important contribution to chemistry was his spiral periodic arrangement of the elements. Courtesy Mme. Jean Presne and the École Supérieure des Mines, Paris.

the Established Church of Scotland. When J. A. R. Newlands was nineteen years old he entered the Royal College of Chemistry to study under A. W. von Hofmann. His sympathy for Italy, the land of his maternal ancestors, led him to volunteer in 1860 for military service under Giuseppe Garibaldi. When Italian freedom had been won he returned to London, practiced for a time as an analytical chemist, and taught at the Grammar School of St. Saviour's, Southwark, at the School of Medicine for Women, and at the City of London College. For many years he was the chief chemist in a large sugar refinery at Victoria Docks, and with his brother, Mr. B. E. R. Newlands, he afterward published a treatise on sugar.

In 1864 he arranged the elements in the order of increasing atomic weights, and noticed that after each interval of eight elements, similar

* The *Comptes rendus* finally published it, however, nearly thirty years later. See ref. (*35*).

physical and chemical properties reappeared (*16*). Thus he divided them into natural families and periods, but for this law of octaves he gained nothing but public ridicule from the English Chemical Society. So little was the importance of atomic weights realized that a certain wag once asked him if he could not get the same result by arranging the elements according to the initials of their names (*3, 18*). The Chemical Society refused to publish his paper, but in 1887 the Royal Society awarded him the Davy Medal for it (*9, 17, 42*).

John Alexander Reina Newlands,[*] **1837–1898.** Professor of chemistry at the School of Medicine for Women and at the City of London College. Discoverer of the law of octaves. He was an authority on the chemistry of sugar refining.

In a biographical sketch in *Nature*, W. A. T. (Tilden?) stated that this tardy recognition, which came five years after the same honor had been conferred on Mendeleev and Lothar Meyer, did not do Newlands full justice. "If Newlands had been a Frenchman," said he, "the Academy of Sciences and the Chemical Society, even if they had at first fallen into error, would have taken care that in the distribution of honours their own countryman should not come in last" (*36*). Nevertheless, Newlands kept up his regular attendance at the meetings of the Chemical Society and won many friends by his kindness and courtesy. He died of influenza on July 29, 1898.

The periodic system of the elements was developed independently and almost simultaneously by Lothar Meyer in Germany and D. I. Mendeleev in Russia. Julius Lothar Meyer was born on August 19, 1830, at Varel on

[*] This portrait was obtained through the courtesy of Mr. R. B. Pilcher, Registrar and Secretary of the Institute of Chemistry of Great Britain and Ireland.

the Jade in the Grand Duchy of Oldenburg. His father was a physician, and his mother used to assist at operations. Both of the sons received a medical education, but Lothar became a chemist and Oskar Emil a physicist. Since Lothar was not a robust child, he was given an out-of-door education under the guidance of the chief gardener at the Grand Duke of Oldenburg's summer palace at Rastede. By this means he developed not only a sturdy body, but also an abiding interest in Nature. He received his degree of doctor of medicine from Würzburg University in 1854 (33).

Meyer knew by this time that he was more interested in research than in the practice of medicine. Therefore, he went to Heidelberg to

(Julius) Lothar Meyer, 1830–1895. German chemist and physician. Professor of chemistry at Breslau and at Tübingen. Co-discoverer with Mendeleev of the periodic system of the elements. Some of his researches were on the gases of the blood, the molecular volumes of chemical compounds, atomic weights, a sensitive thermo-regulator, the paraffins, and the constitution of fuchsin.

study under Robert Bunsen and G. R. Kirchhoff, where the latter soon aroused in him an intense interest in applied mathematics. In 1858 Lothar Meyer became a privatdocent in physics and chemistry at Breslau, and six years later his brother Oskar Emil joined him there as professor of mathematics and mathematical physics. Lothar Meyer's book, "Moderne Theorien der Chemie," which was published in the same year and which contained his first incomplete periodic table, made his name well known throughout the scientific world (4).

In 1868 he went to the *Carlsruhe Polytechnicum*, which, during the war between France and Germany, was used as an army hospital. Here he made good use of his medical training, and rendered such valuable

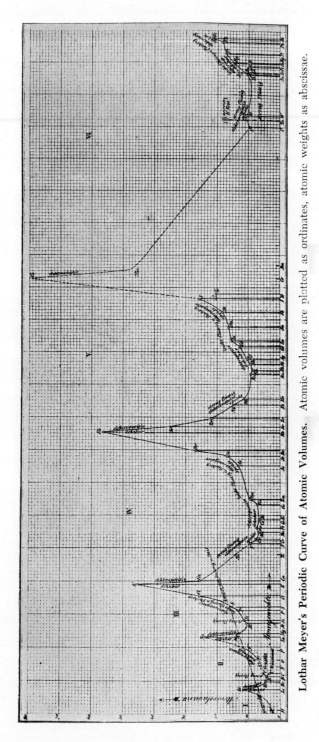

Lothar Meyer's Periodic Curve of Atomic Volumes. Atomic volumes are plotted as ordinates, atomic weights as abscissae.

service as army surgeon that, at the close of the war, he was awarded a medal (4).

In December, 1869, he arranged fifty-six elements in a table consisting of groups and sub-groups (26, 30). He also drew a curve showing the relation between the atomic weights and the atomic volumes of the elements, and found that this is divided by maxima into six sections. In

J. Heyrovský, Collection Czechoslov. Chem. Communications
Dmitri Mendeleev and Bohuslav Brauner in Prague, 1900.
The latter was a professor of chemistry at the Bohemian University of Prague. He wrote a charming biographical sketch of his friend, Mendeleev, who once had the portraits of Lecoq de Boisbaudran, Nilson, Winkler, and Brauner framed together because they had contributed most toward the development of his periodic system (40).

the second and third sections the atomic weight increases by increments of sixteen units, but in the fourth and fifth sections the atomic weight increments are much larger—about forty-six units each. He then prepared other curves which showed that fusibility, volatility, malleability, brittleness, and electrochemical behavior are also periodic properties. The volatile and easily fusible elements lie on the ascending portions of the curves, whereas the refractory elements are on the descending portions or at the minima.

In 1876 Lothar Meyer became a professor of chemistry at the University of Tübingen. He served the university devotedly in this capacity and as rector, and his fame and ability attracted students from all parts of the world (4). He died on April 11, 1895.

Dmitri Ivanovich Mendeleev was born in Tobolsk in western Siberia on February 8, 1834. He was of Russian and Mongolian descent, and was the youngest child in a very large family. Some biographers mention seventeen children, but Mendeleev's personal friend Dr. Bohuslav Brauner stated that there were fourteen (37).

Maria Kornileva Mendeleeva was especially fond of her youngest child, Dmitri, and called him by the affectionate name, Mitjenka (15). While Mitjenka was still very young, his father, who was the director of the Tobolsk gymnasium, lost his sight because of cataracts in both eyes. Although the government granted him a pension of one thousand roubles (about $500), this would not begin to feed and clothe his large family. It therefore fell to the lot of Maria Mendeleeva not only to care for her poor, blind husband and her eight children who were still dependent, but also to undertake a business career. The Kornilev family had founded the first glassworks and paper mill in Tobolsk, and Maria Mendeleeva now established in the neighboring village of Axemziansk her own glassworks, which she directed as an efficient and successful executive while carrying her heavy household burdens (9, 21, 37).

As a child, Dmitri excelled in mathematics, physics, and history, but he never liked Latin. His first science teacher was his brother-in-law, Bassargin, a well-educated Russian who had been exiled for attempting to start a revolution (9, 25). Bassargin was one of the "Decembrists" who in December, 1825, made an unsuccessful attempt to overthrow the Emperor Nicholas I.

Dmitri completed the gymnasium course at the age of sixteen years, but shortly before his graduation a profound double tragedy had occurred. His helpless father had died of tuberculosis, and the glassworks had burned to the ground. Maria Mendeleeva, then fifty-seven years old, secured horses and started out with her two youngest children for Moscow, hundreds of miles away. Unable to enroll Dmitri in the university because of insufficient political influence, she went to Petrograd to interview Pletnov, the director of the Central Pedagogic Institute and friend of her late husband, who succeeded in obtaining financial aid from the government and in making it possible for Dmitri to begin his work in the department of physics and mathematics (34).

A few months later Maria Mendeleeva laid down her heavy burdens, consoled in her last hours by the thought that her Dmitri was, after all to have an education. Some years later he wrote in the preface to his famous book on solutions:

This investigation is dedicated to the memory of a mother by her youngest offspring. Conducting a factory, she could educate him only by her own work. She instructed by example, corrected with love, and in order to devote him to science she left Siberia with him, spending thus her last resources and strength. When dying, she said, "Refrain from illusions, insist on work, and not on words. Patiently search divine and scientific truth." She understood how often dialectical methods deceive, how much there is still to be learned, and how, with the aid of science without violence, with love but firmness, all superstition, untruth, and error are removed, bringing in their stead the safety of discovered truth, freedom for further development, general welfare, and inward happiness. Dmitri Mendeleev regards as sacred a mother's dying words. October, 1887 (1).

Henri-Victor Regnault, 1810–1878. French chemist and physicist. He made precise measurements of specific heats and heats of fusion and vaporization, and of the velocity of sound, and contributed to the theory of organic radicals. Among his students may be mentioned Cannizzaro, Kekulé, and Mendeleev.

When Mendeleev graduated from the Pedagogical Institute, he received a gold medal for excellence in scholarship. Between 1859 and 1861 he worked with H.-V. Regnault in Paris and with Robert Bunsen in Heidelberg. Upon returning to Petrograd in 1861, he was granted his doctorate and was appointed professor of chemistry at the Technological Institute. Eight years later he became the professor of general chemistry at the University of Petrograd.

In March of the same year he presented to the Russian Chemical Society his famous paper on "The relation of the properties to the atomic weights of the elements." Mendeleev's great merit as a discoverer lay in the boldness with which he asserted that the atomic weights of certain elements which did not fit into his system had been incorrectly determined, and that new elements would some day be discovered to fit into the vacant spaces in the periodic table (30, 32). He even predicted the properties of a number of these undiscovered elements, and three of them, which he called ekasilicon, ekaboron, and ekaaluminum, were discovered during his lifetime, and are now known, respectively, as germanium, scandium, and gallium.* Thus he was able to say in his Faraday lecture in 1889: "The law of periodicity first enabled us to perceive undiscovered elements at a distance which formerly was inaccessible to chemical vision; and long ere they were discovered, new elements appeared before our eyes possessed of a number of well-defined properties" (5, 20, 28). Mendeleev's periodic table (6) was more complete than any of the preceding ones, and more thoroughly founded on experiment.

He willingly recognized Lothar Meyer's claim to independent discovery. He was asked to speak before the British Association in Manchester in 1887, but, feeling unable to address the assembly in English, he simply rose and bowed. Lothar Meyer then rose to thank the English scientists for their hospitality and, fearing lest a wrong impression be made, began with the modest words, "I am not Mendeleev. I am Lothar Meyer." He also was greeted with generous applause. In 1882 the Davy Medal had been awarded jointly to Mendeleev and Meyer (7).

Professor William McPherson, president of the American Chemical Society in 1930, said in his presidential address that he once asked a former student who had distinguished himself in the field of literature whether he had derived any benefit from his course in chemistry. The young gentleman replied that the idea that had helped most to frame his philosophy of life was the periodic law. "He had been much confused by what seemed to him an entire absence of order in the universe; . . . and he recognized for the first time in his study of the periodic law unmistakable evidence of order in the universe, for in no other kind of universe could one predict not only the existence of unknown elements but the properties of these unknown elements as well . . ." (45).

Mendeleev and his students contributed to all branches of chemistry, and his literary work was also of great value. His textbook "Principles of Chemistry" was the best chemistry text in the Russian language, and for this reason the Petrograd Academy awarded him the Demidoff prize (46). It is written in a peculiar style, with the footnotes occupying more space

* See Chapter 25, pp. 671–93.

than the portion of the text in large type; yet, in spite of its strange appearance, it is a great chemical classic. He also investigated the Baku
oil fields, the naphtha springs in the Caucasus, and the Pennsylvania oil
fields (8, 38).

Courtesy of the College of Charleston
Lewis Reeve Gibbes, 1810–1894. Professor of chemistry
and other sciences at the College of Charleston. He
published many scholarly papers on chemistry, astronomy,
zoölogy, and geology.

Mendeleev had a keen appreciation of art and literature. He sometimes wrote articles on art, and his study was furnished with pencil
sketches of Lavoisier, Newton, Descartes, Galileo, Copernicus, Graham,
Mitscherlich, Rose, Chevreul, Faraday, Dumas, and Berthelot drawn by
his wife. His favorite author was Jules Verne, and his chief consolation

during his last illness was the reading of "The Journey to the North Pole" (9, 25). He died of pneumonia on Saturday, February 2, 1907, and in a telegram to the widow, Czar Nicholas said, "In the person of Professor Mendeleev, Russia has lost one of her best sons, who will ever remain in our memory" (5).

In 1934, in honor of the centenary of Mendeleev's birth, the U.S.S.R. issued a set of four denominations of commemorative postage stamps bearing a handsome portrait against a background of the periodic table. Reproductions of two of these stamps appeared in the *Journal of Chemical Education* in July of that year.

TABLE OF CHEMICAL ELEMENTS.

a	A	B	C	D	E	F	G	H, I	K	GROUPS.
−4		C=12	Si=28	Ti=50			Sn=118			Silicon Gr.
−3		N=14	P=31	V=51.3	As=75	Cb=94	Sb=122	Ta=182	Au=196.6	Phosphorus Gr.
−2		O=16	S=32	Cr=52.5	Se=79	Mo=96	Te=128	W=184	Os=199	Sulphur Gr.
−1		F=19	Cl=35.5		Br=80		I=127			Chlorine Gr.
0										
+1	Li=7	Na=23	K=39		Rb=85	Ag=108	Cs=133		Tl=204	Kalium Gr.
+2	Gl=9.3	Mg=24	Ca=40	Zn=65	Sr=87.5	Cd=112	Ba=137		Pb=207	Calcium Gr.
+3	−B=11								Bi=210	

Al=27.5——Cr=52.5 ; Mn=55 ; Fe=56 ; Co=59 ; Ni=59 ; Cu=63.5——U=120   Iron Gr.

Y=61.7   Zr=89.5;Ce=92 ; La=92 ; D=96   Er=112 ; Th=115.7

In=74   Ru=104;Ro=104;Pd=106——Pt=197 ; Ir=197   Platinum Gr.

H=1   Hg=200

Courtesy Wendell H. Taylor

Gibbes's Synoptical Table (1875)

Another very early classification of the elements was made by Lewis Reeve Gibbes, professor of chemistry at the College of Charleston, South Carolina, who worked out the first version of his "Synoptical Table of the Chemical Elements" between 1870 and 1874, and in 1875 discussed an improved form of it before the Elliott Society of Charleston. The hardships of the reconstruction period, however, made prompt publication impossible. When the paper was finally published in 1886, it attracted little attention because the periodic tables of Lothar Meyer and Mendeleev were already well known (39).

Instead of arranging all the elements in the order of increasing atomic weights, as the European scientists had attempted to do, Gibbes (probably without knowledge of their work) conceived the idea of assembling the well-known families on horizontal lines numbered from minus four to plus three to correspond with the principal valence of the elements in each family. In each of these horizontal rows, however, he placed the elements in the order of increasing atomic weights. He then found that throughout this table, which he had based on stepwise change of valence, most of the elements in the vertical rows also followed one another in the order of increasing atomic weights. Thus his approach to the problem of classifying the elements was the reverse of that used by Lothar Meyer and Mendeleev.

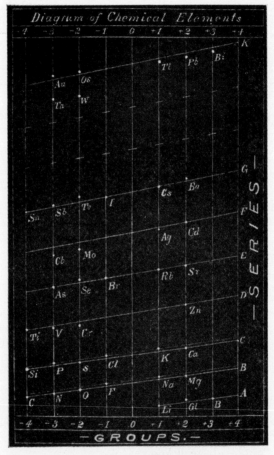

Courtesy Wendell H. Taylor
Gibbes's Diagram (1875)

Gibbes observed certain blank spaces in his table and recognized the possibility that these might some day be filled by newly discovered elements. He differentiated the two subgroups of each family of elements and recognized the peculiarities of the "typical elements" or "group introducers," carbon, nitrogen, oxygen, and fluorine. He also constructed a spiral chart based on his "Synoptical Table." Although it resembled somewhat the earlier table of Beguyer de Chancourtois, it was doubtless an independent discovery. A much more detailed account of the life and work of Professor Gibbes is to be found in an article by Wendell H. Taylor in the *Journal of Chemical Education* for September, 1941 (*39*).

LITERATURE CITED

(*1*) HARROW, B., "Eminent Chemists of Our Time," D. Van Nostrand Co., New York City, **1920**, p. 22; P. WALDEN, "Dmitri Iwanowitsch Mendelejeff," *Ber.,* **41**, 4723 (1908). Last words of Maria Mendeleeva to her son, Dmitri.

(*2*) VON GOETHE, J. W., "Faust," part 1, lines 148–9.

(*3*) VON MEYER, ERNST, "History of Chemistry," 3rd English edition from 3rd German edition, The Macmillan Co., London, **1906**, pp. 387–8.

(*4*) "Chemical Society Memorial Lectures, 1893–1900," Gurney and Jackson, London, **1901**, pp. 1427–9. Lothar Meyer Memorial Lecture by BEDSON.

(*5*) GRIFFITHS, A. B., "Biographies of Scientific Men," Robert Sutton, London, **1912**, pp. 126–36.

(*6*) MENDELEEV, D., "Principles of Chemistry," Vol. 2, English translation from 5th Russian edition by Kamensky and Greenaway, Longmans, Green and Co., London, **1891**, p. 487.

(*7*) "Chemical Society Memorial Lectures, 1893–1900," ref. (*4*), p. 1420.

(*8*) THORPE, T. E., "Essays in Historical Chemistry," The Macmillan Co., London, **1894**, p. 364.

(*9*) HARROW, B., "Eminent Chemists of Our Time," ref. (*1*), pp. 19–40.

(*10*) VENABLE, F. P., "The Development of the Periodic Law," Chem. Publishing Co., Easton, Pa., **1896**, pp. 11–12; 28–36.

(*11*) WURZER, "Report on Döbereiner's triads," *Gilbert's Ann.,* **56**, 332 (1816); J. W. DÖBEREINER, *ibid.,* **57**, 436 (1817); "Versuch zu einer Gruppierung der elementaren Stoffe nach ihrer Analogie," *Pogg. Ann.,* **15**, 301 (1829).

(*12*) BEGUYER DE CHANCOURTOIS, A.-E., "Mémoire sur un classement naturel des corps simples ou radicaux appelé vis tellurique," *Compt. rend.,* **54**, 757–61 (Apr. 7, 1862); 840–3 (Apr. 21, 1862); 967–71 (May 5, 1862).

(*13*) VENABLE, F. P., "The Development of the Periodic Law," ref. (*10*), pp. 73–6; 82–5.

(*14*) BEGUYER DE CHANCOURTOIS, A.-E., "Tableau du classement naturel des corps simples, dit vis tellurique," *Compt. rend.,* **55**, 600–1 (Oct. 13, 1862).

(*15*) WALDEN, P., "Dmitri Iwanowitsch Mendelejeff," *Ber.,* **41**, 4719–4800 (1908).

(*16*) NEWLANDS, J. A. R., "On relations among the equivalents," *Chem. News,* **7**, 70–2 (Feb. 7, 1863); **10**, 59–60 (July 30, 1864); 94–5 (Aug. 20, 1864); "On the law of octaves," *ibid.,* **12**, 83 (Aug. 18, 1865); "On the discovery of the periodic law, and on relations among the atomic weights," *ibid.,* **49**, 198–200 (May 2, 1884).

(*17*) Presentation of Medals, *Proc. Roy. Soc. (London),* **43**, 195 (Nov. 30, 1887).

(*18*) VENABLE, F. P., "The Development of the Periodic Law," ref. (*10*), pp. 74–85.

(*19*) HARTOG, P. J., "A first foreshadowing of the periodic law," *Nature,* **41**, 186–8 (Dec. 26, 1889).

(*20*) MENDELEEV, D., "The periodic law of the chemical elements," *J. Chem. Soc.,* **55**, 634–56 (1889).

(21) "Chemical Society Memorial Lectures, 1901–1913," Gurney and Jackson, 1914, pp. 125–53. Mendeleev Memorial Lecture by W. A. TILDEN.

(22) CHEMNITIUS, F., "Die Chemie in Jena von Rolfinck bis Knorr (1629–1921)," Verlag der Frommannschen Buchhandlung, Walter Biedermann, Jena, 1929, pp. 28–31.

(23) SCHIFF, J., "Briefwechsel zwischen Goethe und Johann Wolfgang Döbereiner (1810–1830)," Hermann Böhlaus Nachfolger, Weimar, 1914, 144 pp.

(24) DÖBLING, H., "Die Chemie in Jena zur Goethezeit," Verlag von Gustav Fischer, Jena, 1928, 220 pp.

(25) TILDEN, W. A., "Famous Chemists. The Men and Their Work," George Routledge and Sons, London, 1921, pp. 241–58.

(26) MEYER, LOTHAR, "Die Natur der chemischen Elemente als Function ihrer Atomgewichte," Ann., Supplementband VII, 1870, 354–64 (Heft 3).

(27) LEWES, G. H., "The Life and Works of Goethe," E. P. Dutton & Co., New York City, 1916, pp. 546–7.

(28) "Classics of science: Periodic law of the elements," Sci. News Letter, 14, 41–2 (July 21, 1928). Mendeleev's Faraday Lecture.

(29) MEYER, LOTHAR, "Die Anfänge des natürlichen Systemes der chemischen Elemente. Abhandlungen von J. W. Döbereiner und Max Pettenkofer," Ostwalds Klassiker. Verlag von Wilhelm Engelmann, Leipzig, 1895, pp. 3–8; 27–34.

(30) SEUBERT, "Das Natürliche System der Chemischen Elemente. Abhandlungen von Lothar Meyer und D. Mendeléeff," Ostwalds Klassiker. Verlag von Wilhelm Engelmann, Leipzig, 1895, 134 pp.

(31) MONTGOMERY, J. P., "Döbereiner's triads and atomic numbers," J. Chem. Educ., 8, 162 (Jan., 1931).

(32) REINMUTH, O., "The structure of matter. II. The periodic classification of the elements," J. Chem. Educ., 5, 1312–20 (Oct., 1928).

(33) BUGGE, G., "Das Buch der grossen Chemiker," Vol. 2, Verlag Chemie, Berlin, 1930, pp. 230–41. Article on Lothar Meyer by P. WALDEN.

(34) Ibid., pp. 241–50. Article on Mendeleev by P. WALDEN.

(35) DE BOISBAUDRAN, P. E. L. and DE LAPPARENT, "Sur une réclamation de priorité en faveur de M. de Chancourtois, relativement aux relations numériques des poids atomiques," Compt. rend., 112, 80 (Jan. 12, 1891).

(36) W. A. T., "John A. R. Newlands," Nature, 58, 395–6 (Aug. 25, 1898).

(37) BRAUNER, B., "D. I. Mendeleev as reflected in his friendship to Prof Bohuslav Brauner," Collection Czechoslov. Chem. Communications, 2, 219–43 (1930).

(38) SWIATLOWSKY, E., "Mendeléeff centenary," Chem. Met. Eng., 41, 468–9 (Sept., 1934).

(39) TAYLOR, W. H., "Lewis Reeve Gibbes and the classification of the elements," J. Chem. Educ., 18, 403–7 (Sept., 1941).

(40) PANETH, F. A., "Radioactivity and the completion of the periodic system," Nature, 149, 565 (May 23, 1942).

(41) LEICESTER, H. M., "Mendeleev and the Russian Academy of Sciences," J. Chem. Educ., 25, 439–41 (Aug., 1948).

(42) TAYLOR, W. H., "J. A. R. Newlands: A pioneer in atomic numbers." J. Chem. Educ., 26, 491–6 (Sept., 1949).

(43) WINDERLICH, RUDOLF, "Lothar Meyer," J. Chem. Educ., 27, 365–8 (July, 1950).

(44) PRANDTL, W., "Johann Wolfgang Döbereiner, Goethe's chemical adviser," J. Chem. Educ., 27, 176–81 (Apr., 1950); CLUSKEY, J. E., "Goethe and chemistry, ibid., 28, 536–8 (Oct., 1951).

(45) McPHERSON, WILLIAM, "Chemistry and Education," *Science*, **72**, 485–93 (1930); see also *Ind. Eng. Chem.*, **22**, 1028 (1930).

(46) LEICESTER, HENRY M., "Factors which led Mendeleev to the periodic law," CHYMIA, **1**, 67–74 (1948).

Dmitri Ivanovich Mendeleev, 1834–1907. Professor of chemistry at the University of Petrograd. Author of the "Principles of Chemistry," a remarkable textbook. He studied the important oil fields of Russia and the United States. The periodic system of the elements was discovered independently by Mendeleev in Russia and Lothar Meyer in Germany.

Die wirklich erfolgreiche Durchführung anorganisch-chemischer Arbeiten ist nur demjenigen möglich, der nicht allein theoretischer Chemiker, sondern auch vollendeter Analytiker ist, und zwar nicht nur ein praktisch angelernter mechanischer Arbeiter, sondern ein denkender, gestaltender Künstler (1).*

*The truly successful performance of researches in inorganic chemistry is possible only to one who is not only a theoretical chemist but also an accomplished analyst and, moreover, not merely a practically trained, mechanical worker, but a thinking, creative artist.

Reinheit der Substanzen ist die Feinheit des Ganzen (6).

On the purity of substances depends the perfection of the whole.

25

Some elements predicted by Mendeleev

Three of the undiscovered elements whose properties Mendeleev foretold in great detail, ekaaluminum, ekaboron, and ekasilicon, were discovered within fifteen years from the time of their prediction. The first was found by Lecoq de Boisbaudran in France, the second by Lars Fredrik Nilson in Sweden, and the third by Clemens Winkler in Germany. These elements were named gallium, scandium, and germanium in honor of these countries.

*W*hen Mendeleev predicted that occupants would be found for the vacant spaces in the periodic system, he little dreamed that three of them would be discovered during his lifetime.

GALLIUM

One of these elements, which he called ekaaluminum, was soon revealed by Lecoq de Boisbaudran in a mineral which Georgius Agricola used to call *galena inanis,* or useless lead ore, and which Georg Brandt in his dissertation on the half-metals proved to be a zinc mineral (37, 38). It is now known as sphalerite, zinc sulfide, or blende, and often contains both indium and gallium (ekaaluminum). Paul-Émile (dit François) Lecoq de Boisbaudran was born in Cognac on April 18, 1838, a descendant of the Protestant nobility. His father and brothers were distillers, and Paul-Émile also in time became a member of the firm. His mother, a gifted, well-educated woman, taught him foreign languages, the classics, and history. By studying the syllabi of the École Polytechnique, he acquired a splendid scientific foundation, especially in his favorite branches, physics and chemistry. Throughout his life he was encouraged by the sympathy and intelligent aid of his entire family, for, according to Sir William Ramsay, their watchwords were "justice, kindness, and the sense of personal responsibility." An uncle helped him to finance a small private laboratory, and it was there that ekaaluminum, or gallium, was discovered (2).

The finding of this element was by no means accidental. Boisbaudran had been studying spectra for fifteen years, and had found that in those emitted by several metals of the same family, the lines are repeated according to the same general arrangement. Anxious to verify this law for the aluminum family, and to find the missing member between aluminum and indium, he reasoned that, since most minerals had already been carefully analyzed, there was little hope of finding new elements among the essential constituents of these minerals. The difficulty of recognizing an unknown element present only as a trace did not escape him, for he said, "The uncertainty which inevitably reigns over the exact chemical reactions of a hypothetical substance, defined only by its position in a natural series, renders quite problematical a success founded solely on the direct application of these reactions *calculated in advance;* for the least error in predicting one of these can throw the substance being sought out of the analytical position which theory assigns to it" (*3, 11*).

Lecoq de Boisbaudran, 1838–1912. French chemist who discovered gallium, samarium, and dysprosium, and perfected methods of separating the rare earths. He ranks with Bunsen, Kirchhoff, and Crookes as one of the founders of the science of spectroscopy.

In February, 1874, Boisbaudran began to investigate "fifty-two kilograms of blende of Pierrefitte obtained for that purpose in the autumn of 1868." The Pierrefitte mine was situated in the Argeles Valley in the department of Hautes Pyrénées (*11, 13*). This blende was given to Lecoq de Boisbaudran by M. Malgor, an engineer at that mine. When Lecoq de Boisbaudran dissolved the ore and placed metallic zinc in the solution, a deposit formed on the zinc. When he heated this deposit with the oxyhydrogen flame and examined it with the spectroscope, he saw two lines that had never been seen before. These, however, did not appear when he heated the deposit simply with the Bunsen burner.

The following account of the discovery was written by Boisbaudran himself for *Chemical News:*

Between three and four in the evening of August 27, 1875, I found indications of the probable existence of a new elementary body in the products of the chemical examination of a blende from Pierrefitte. The oxide, or perhaps a sub-salt, is thrown down by metallic zinc in a solution containing chlorides and sulfates. It does not appear to be the metal itself which is reduced by the zinc. . . .

The extremely small quantity of the substance at my disposal did not permit me to isolate the new body from the excess of zinc accompanying. The few drops of zinc chloride in which I concentrated the new substance gave under the action of the electric spark a spectrum composed chiefly of a violet ray, narrow, readily visible, and situate at about 417 on the scale of wave lengths. I perceived also a very faint ray at 404 (*4, 16*).

Adolph Wurtz, 1817–1884. Professor of chemistry at the École de Médecine in Paris. Discoverer of methyl and ethyl amines and the synthesis of hydrocarbons from alkyl iodides and sodium. He studied the oxidation products of the glycols and the homologs of lactic acid. The proof of the elementary nature of gallium was demonstrated in his laboratory by Lecoq de Boisbaudran.

From Hofmann's "Zur Erinnerung an vorangegangene Freunde"

A month later Boisbaudran performed in Wurtz's laboratory in Paris, in the presence of the chemistry section of the Institute, a series of experiments to prove that gallium, the metal he had discovered and named in honor of France, is a true element. In order that he might attempt to isolate the metal, the technical zinc-mining societies known as "La Vieille Montagne" and "La Nouvelle Montagne" presented him with a quantity of gallium-containing zinc minerals.

Boisbaudran decomposed several hundred kilograms of the crude zinc blende in aqua regia containing excess hydrochloric acid. He also used a slight excess of blende in order that all the nitric acid might be consumed. After filtering off the insoluble matter, he placed sheets of zinc in the acid filtrate in order that the copper, arsenic, lead, cadmium, indium, thallium, mercury, selenium, silver, bismuth, tin, antimony, and gold might be deposited. Before the acid had been entirely consumed by the zinc, Boisbaudran filtered off this spongy deposit. By adding a large excess of zinc to the filtrate, and heating the mixture for several hours on the water bath, he was able to precipitate the basic salts of zinc and the hydroxides of aluminum, iron, gallium, cobalt, and chromium.

Emile-Clément Jungfleisch,* 1839–1916. French chemist and pharmacist. Professor of organic chemistry at the École Supérieure de Pharmacie and at the Collège de France. Although most of his ninety-nine papers were organic or pharmaceutical in nature, he also made valuable contributions to the chemistry of gallium and indium.

Although gallium sulfide does not precipitate from a solution of the pure salt, it is readily carried down with zinc sulfide. Boisbaudran therefore added ammonium acetate and acetic acid to the hydrochloric acid solution of the above precipitate, and passed in hydrogen sulfide. As long as the line Ga α (417.0) continued to show in the spectrum of the precipitate, he kept on adding zinc to the filtrate until finally all the gallium had been precipitated.

By dissolving gallium hydroxide in caustic potash, and electrolyzing the solution with a current from five or six Bunsen cells, Boisbaudran prepared more than a gram of gallium metal. This was first prepared in November, 1875. On December 6th he presented 3.4 milligrams of solid gallium (14) to the Academy of Sciences, and three months later he

* The portrait of Jungfleisch was obtained through the kindness of Dr. Tenney L. Davis, Massachusetts Institute of Technology.

presented a specimen of the liquid metal.   Since gallium, when free from
the solid phase, has a great tendency to remain in the superfused state,
this specimen may have remained liquid even at a temperature below
30° Centigrade (17). Boisbaudran and Jungfleisch afterward worked up
four thousand kilograms of the blende at the Javel works, and obtained
seventy-five grams of the metal (18).

PROPERTIES PREDICTED FOR EKAALUMINUM (Ea) BY MENDELEEV	PROPERTIES FOUND FOR BOISBAUDRAN'S GALLIUM (Ga)
Atomic weight about 68.	Atomic weight 69.9.*
Metal of specific gravity 5.9; melting point low; non-volatile; unaffected by air; should decompose steam at red heat; should dissolve slowly in acids and alkalies.	Metal of specific gravity 5.94; melting point 30.15; non-volatile at moderate temperature; not changed in air; action of steam unknown; dissolves slowly in acids and alkalies.
Oxide: formula Ea_2O_3; specific gravity 5.5; should dissolve in acids to form salts of the type EaX_3. The hydroxide should dissolve in acids and alkalies.	Oxide: Ga_2O_3; specific gravity unknown; dissolves in acids, forming salts of the type GaX_3. The hydroxide dissolves in acids and alkalies.
Salts should have tendency to form basic salts; the sulfate should form alums; the sulfide should be precipitated by H_2S or $(NH_4)_2S$. The anhydrous chloride should be more volatile than zinc chloride.	Salts readily hydrolyze and form basic salts; alums are known; the sulfide is precipitated by H_2S and by $(NH_4)_2S$ under special conditions. The anhydrous chloride is more volatile than zinc chloride.
The element will probably be discovered by spectroscopic analysis.	Gallium was discovered with the aid of the spectroscope.

In discovering this element Lecoq de Boisbaudran was guided, not
by the periodic table and the predictions of Mendeleev but by his own
law of spectra (31). On November 22, 1875, however, the great Russian
chemist stated in the Comptes rendus (15) that he believed gallium to
be identical with ekaaluminum (20). Further study of the properties of
the new element and its compounds fully confirmed this view (19), as
is evident from the foregoing table. Lecoq de Boisbaudran also found
gallium in a transparent blende from Santander given to him by M.
Friedel (14). After testing a large number of blendes and products
of zinc works, Boisbaudran succeeded "in finding only two richer than
Pierrefitte blende; these were the yellow transparent blende from Asturias
and the black blende from Bensberg. All the other substances I examined
were much too poor" (11). He proved that the gallium had come from
the blendes themselves and not from the Vieille Montagne metallic zinc
used in the precipitations (14). Georges Urbain and his collaborators
found gallium in 59 of the 64 blendes which they examined (39).

* The 1954 atomic weight of gallium is 69.72.

Boisbaudran's researches on the rare earths also yielded a rich harvest of results, for he discovered samarium and dysprosium (2). His investigations in the field of spectroscopy were also of high merit.

Boisbaudran spoke English fluently, but without regard for fine distinctions, and he sometimes made the mistake of translating his French thoughts too literally. According to Sir William Ramsey, he once startled his dinner partner, a dignified, elderly English lady, with the remark, "The soup is devilish hot." Like Berzelius, he married late in life. His contributions to science were cut short by the pain and disability resulting from severe anchylosis of the joints, but he stoically bore this misfortune for many years until death relieved him on May 28, 1912, at the age of seventy-four years (2, 12).

Although gallium is one of the rarest of elements, it has an interesting use. Since it melts at about 30° Centigrade and boils at about 1700°, a gallium-in-quartz thermometer can be used for measuring high temperatures far above the range of the ordinary mercury-in-glass thermometer. Unfortunately, it differs from mercury in that it wets glass and quartz surfaces (40, 41).

Gallium often occurs closely associated with aluminum. Sir Walter N. Hartley and H. Ramage detected it, in 1897, in all the specimens of bauxite, kaolin, and aluminous iron ores which they analyzed (42). They found that the blast-furnace iron smelted at Middlesbrough on Tees from the Yorkshire clay-ironstone contained even more gallium than the Bensberg blende from the Franzisca adit of the Lüderich mine near Cologne, which had previously been the richest known source of that metal (43). They also detected gallium in feldspar, mica, basalt, pumice from Krakatoa, volcanic dust from New Zealand, and meteoric iron and dust (42, 43).

In about 1915 F. G. McCutcheon, chemist of the Bartlesville Zinc Company of Oklahoma, presented some gallium of American production to W. F. Hillebrand and J. A. Scherrer for analysis. According to Mr. Kurt Stock, superintendent of this company, Mr. McCutcheon had observed "peculiar beads and drops, in appearance like mercury, which seemed to sweat out of zinc-lead dross plates after these had been exposed to the weather for a time." Mr. McCutcheon and his assistants proved that this was an alloy of gallium and indium with small amounts of zinc. The great demand at that time for high-grade spelter (metallic zinc) "had led zinc smelters to the practice of redistillation, and it is the final leady residue from such continued redistillation that carries gallium in noticeable quantities . . ." (40). This gallium was known to come from domestic ores, probably from the Joplin area (40, 44, 45).

W. Feit, in his unsuccessful search for ekamanganese (element 43) in 1933, unexpectedly found gallium in several of the intermediate products from the working of cupriferous slate from Mansfeld, and developed its commercial production (*41, 44*).

According to J. Papish and C. B. Stilson, the zinc minerals sphalerite, gahnite, hopeite, parahopeite, and adamite all contain gallium (*44, 46*). It has also been detected spectroscopically in certain French, Spanish, and Japanese mineral waters (*47, 48*). Germanite from Tsumeb, German Southwest Africa, contains from 0.57 to 1.85 per cent of gallium and is thus a rich source of this rare metal (*44, 49*).

SCANDIUM

Mendeleev had predicted that another element, which he called ekaboron and which he said would have an atomic weight between 40 (calcium) and 48 (titanium), would some day be revealed (*20*). It was discovered in 1879 by Lars Fredrik Nilson.

Euxenite, the original source of scandium (ekaboron), was dis-

Lars Fredrik Nilson, 1840–1899. Professor of analytical chemistry at the University of Upsala and at the Agricultural Academy at Stockholm. Discoverer of scandium. His researches on soils and fertilizers transformed the barren plains of his native island into an agricultural region. With Otto Pettersson he investigated the rare earths and prepared metallic titanium.

From À. G. Ekstrand's Minnesteckning

covered by C. J. A. Theodor Scheerer (1813–1875). He was educated at the University of Berlin and the Freiberg School of Mines, and for several years taught metallurgy and assaying at the University of Christiania. In 1840 he published in Poggendorff's *Annalen* the first description of euxenite, a new mineral found, first near Jölster in northern Bergenhuus-Amt and later at Tvedestrand near Arendal, Norway (*50, 51*).

The specimen Scheerer analyzed was given to him by Professor B. M. Keilhau (*51*). Using a very small sample, Scheerer made an approximate quantitative analysis, from which he reported the presence of tantalic and titanic acids, yttria, uranous, cerous, and lanthanum oxides, lime, magnesia, and water. He named the mineral *euxenite* because of

Berzelius* at the Age of Forty-Four Years. This represents him as he appeared in 1823 when the youthful Friedrich Wöhler came to Stockholm to study chemistry.

its many rare constituents. He believed it to be closely related to yttro-tantalite, yet different from it in specific gravity, in water content, and in the presence of titanic acid, cerium, and lanthanum among its constituents (*51*).

L. F. Nilson was born on May 27, 1840, in Östergötland, was educated at Visby and at the Linköping Gymnasium, and at the age of nineteen years went to Upsala to study biology, chemistry, and geology. Just as he was ready to take his examinations for the doctorate in 1865, he received word that his father had been seriously injured. Although Lars Nilson himself was then in very poor health, and suffering from frequent hemorrhages from the lungs, he immediately returned to Gothland Island, took charge of the farm, purchased an engine and a threshing

* Reproduced from H. G. Söderbaum's "Jac. Berzelius-Levnadsteckning" by kind permission of the author.

machine, harvested the crops, and cheered and encouraged his sick father. After a few months, both father and son were in good health. Life in the open air had quickly cured Nilson's lung trouble, and he enjoyed good health for the rest of his life (5).

He returned to Upsala, passed his examinations successfully, and was placed in charge of the laboratory. Here, among Berzelius' balances, blowpipes, and preparations, he became a true disciple of that great master. After completing some researches on the compounds of selenium, Nilson and Pettersson began to study the mineral euxenite, hoping to measure the chemical and physical constants of the rare earth elements

Inside the City Wall of Visby.* Lars Fredrik Nilson, the discoverer of scandium, received his early education in this beautiful old city on Gothland Island.

and their compounds and thus to verify the periodic law. Although they never succeeded in this, Nilson extracted sixty-three grams of the rare earth erbia from gadolinite and euxenite, and converted it into the nitrate. Upon decomposing this salt by heat, as Marignac had done, he obtained some very pure ytterbia and, to his great surprise, a feebly basic earth that was unknown to him (21).

Upon thoroughly investigating this new earth, he found that it contained an element whose properties coincided almost exactly with those Mendeleev had predicted for ekaboron. P. T. Cleve had also encountered

* Photo by Miss Mary Larson, Dept. of Zoölogy, The University of Kansas.

the same substance in his researches on the rare earths. Since this element was first discovered in the minerals euxenite and gadolinite which had not yet been found anywhere except in Scandinavia, Nilson called it *scandium* (22) in honor of his fatherland, and it was indeed appropriate that it should be named for the little country where so many new elements had been discovered (6).

By working up ten kilograms of euxenite, some of Cleve's ytterbia from gadolinite, and some ytterbia residues from keilhauite, Nilson prepared about two grams of scandium oxide of high purity (34). "When I began this work," said he, "I had at my disposal 63 g. of erbia of molecular weight 129.25 which had been extracted partly from gadolinite and partly from euxenite" (21, 22). Although Nilson was at first inclined to believe that scandium was present only in the euxenite, T. R. Thalén observed one of the spectral lines of scandium in a mixture of erbium and yttrium prepared from gadolinite by Höglund and Cleve (21, 22). The identity of scandium and Mendeleev's hypothetical ekaboron was pointed out by Per Theodor Cleve (20, 25). The table below shows the predicted and observed properties of this element (19).

PROPERTIES PREDICTED FOR EKABORON (Eb) BY MENDELEEV	PROPERTIES FOUND FOR NILSON'S SCANDIUM (Sc)
Atomic weight 44.	Atomic weight.*
It will form one oxide Eb_2O_3 of specific gravity 3.5; more basic than alumina, less basic than yttria or magnesia; not soluble in alkalies; it is doubtful if it will decompose ammonium chloride.	Scandium oxide, Sc_2O_3, has a specific gravity of 3.86; is more basic than alumina, less basic than yttria or magnesia. It is not soluble in alkalies and does not decompose ammonium chloride.
The salts will be colorless and give gelatinous precipitates with potassium hydroxide and sodium carbonate. The salts will not crystallize well.	Scandium salts are colorless, and give gelatinous precipitates with potassium hydroxide and sodium carbonate. The sulfate crystallizes with difficulty.
The carbonate will be insoluble in water; and probably be precipitated as a basic salt.	Scandium carbonate is insoluble in water. and readily loses carbon dioxide.
The double alkali sulfates will probably not be alums.	The double alkali sulfates are not alums.
The anhydrous chloride, $EbCl_3$ should be less volatile than aluminum chloride, and its aqueous solution should hydrolyze more readily than that of magnesium chloride.	Scandium chloride, $ScCl_3$, begins to sublime at 850°. Aluminum chloride begins to sublime above 100°. In aqueous solution the salt is hydrolyzed.
Ekaboron will probably not be discovered spectroscopically.	Scandium was not recognized by spectrum analysis.

The spectra of scandium and ytterbium were first studied by Tobias Robert Thalén (22, 32). Although scandium salts possess no visible

* The 1954 atomic weight of scandium is 44.96.

absorption spectrum, the element may be detected by means of spark and arc spectra (*24, 33*). The atomic weights of both these elements were soon determined by Nilson (*23*).

From 1878 to 1883 Nilson served as professor of analytical chemistry at the University of Upsala, but in his later years he taught at the Agricultural Academy at Stockholm. He found that the sterility of the calcareous moors of his native island was caused by lack of potash. After liberal use of kainite fertilizer, recommended by Nilson, Gothland Island began to yield good crops of sugar beets (*6*).

Tobias Robert Thalén, 1827–1905. Swedish physicist, astronomer, and spectroscopist. He mapped the spectra of yttrium, erbium, didymium, lanthanum, scandium, thulium, and ytterbium, and in 1866 wrote a historical review of spectrum analysis. He also studied the magnetic properties of iron and iron ores.

From Hasselberg's, "Biografier. T. R. Thalén"

Å. G. Ekstrand, in his biography of Nilson written for the Swedish Academy of Sciences, expressed admiration that "A person can work with chemicals and chemical apparatus in such a neat and truly elegant manner as he does. In the laboratory at Upsala, where I worked beside him for many years, I cannot recall ever having seen him in a laboratory coat" (*34*). Ekstrand described Nilson as a practical chemist, not much given to theorizing.

Nilson's long hours in the laboratory left him little time for recreation, but his brief periods of relaxation were free from worry. Otto Pettersson, professor of chemistry at the University of Stockholm, once said of him:

Whilst it was customary, in the private laboratory where Nilson presided, to enliven the hours of work with conversation, anecdotes, puns, occasionally by a song, etc., it was considered unfitting to introduce scientific matters into the conversation of leisure hours. Nilson positively did not admit it, and woe to him who dared to speak of political or philosophical matters when Nilson intended to be merry. And he was always merry when he was with his friends, the merriest of them all. He had a thousand devices for putting a stop to a conversation which threatened to take a tiresome turn. He would, for example, sit listening for a while with a grave face, and then interpose with a short nonsensical observation, delivered with great solemnity in the accents of some political or scientific worthy of pedantic fame, while a gleam of fun shot forth from under his heavy, dusky eyebrows. The effect was irresistibly comic, so much the more as it came unforeseen. His hearers were at first puzzled, then one chuckled, another laughed, and in a minute the impending political or philosophical discourse was drowned in a chorus of laughter in which Nilson's voice at last joined in accents swelling like big waves and rollers of an ocean of mirth (5).

Visby.Gamla Apoteket.

Old Apothecary Shop at Visby*

* Photo loaned by Miss Mary Larson, Dept. of Zoölogy, The University of Kansas.

Like all successful analysts, Nilson had a passion for neatness and order, and his motto, *"On the purity of substances depends the perfection of the whole,"* is well worth remembering (6). He died on May 14, 1899, at the age of fifty-nine years (34).

Until the end of the nineteenth century, scandium was believed to be one of the rarest of elements, but in 1908 Sir William Crookes and G. Eberhard found small amounts of it to be widely distributed on the earth, the sun, and other heavenly bodies (34).

GERMANIUM

A third element that Mendeleev had predicted was to be a member of the silicon family (20). This "ekasilicon" was discovered in 1886 by Clemens Winkler, who named it *germanium* in honor of his fatherland. Thus the three "nationalist" elements—gallium in France, scandium in

Clemens Alexander Winkler [*] **1838–1904.** Professor of chemistry at the Freiberg School of Mines. Pioneer in the analysis of gases. Manufacturer of nickel and cobalt. He discovered the element germanium and made pioneer researches on indium.

Sweden, and germanium in Germany—were all discovered within fifteen years after their prediction by the great Russian chemist. Although Mendeleev was the first person to describe the properties of ekasilicon, the gap in the periodic table had been observed about seven years before by the English chemist J. A. R. Newlands, who had noticed that silicon and tin form the extremities of a triad, the middle member of which was missing (29).

[*] This photograph of Winkler was made by Dr. O. Brunck, Rector of the Freiberg School of Mines, who graciously sent Dr. Dains a copy.

Nils Gabriel Sefström, 1787–1845. Swedish physician, chemist, and metallurgist. Head teacher at the School of Mines at Falun from 1822 to 1838, later adviser to the Mining Society in Stockholm, director of the Mineral Cabinet, Chemical Laboratory, and Library of the Royal Mining College, and editor of the Annals of the Corporation of Ironmasters. See ref. (*59*).

Clemens Alexander Winkler was born at Freiberg on December 26, 1838, but grew up in Zschopenthal, a village in the Saxon Erzgebirge where his father, Kurt Alexander Winkler, operated a smalt works. Kurt Winkler was himself a well-known chemist and metallurgist, who had studied under Berzelius and N. G. Sefström, and had fitted up an excellent metallurgical laboratory in the smalt works (*7, 30*).

Since the son soon learned to love Nature, his father taught him to identify and classify plants, animals, and minerals. The boy, however, never acquired a passion for collecting. He wanted to learn as much as

possible about each specimen, but had no desire to own it. At the age
of twelve years he entered the Freiberg gymnasium, where he studied
mineralogy under August Breithaupt. Winkler did not like foreign
languages, but nevertheless acquired such a thorough mastery of his
mother tongue that his scientific papers are valued not only for their
genuine scientific merit but also for their beautiful, faultless German (7).

He continued his education at the Realschule, or scientific school, at
Dresden and at the Gewerbeschule, or technical school, in Chemnitz,
spending the vacations in his father's laboratory. When he entered the
Freiberg School of Mines in 1857, he already knew more analytical chemistry than was taught there, and because of this thorough preparation
and his sound constitution, he was able to make remarkable progress in
research without missing any of the dances and gay parties so dear to
a student's heart (7).

Portrait Medallion of Berzelius by David
d'Angers, 1835.*

His paper on the reactions that take place in the Gay-Lussac towers
of sulfuric acid plants resulted from his successful experiments on the
absorption of obnoxious sulfur dioxide fumes from an ultramarine plant.
In order to analyze the gases, he invented the Winkler gas buret with a
three-way stopcock, and perfected his own methods. In the meantime
he made his living by producing nickel and cobalt on a commercial scale.

In 1873 he accepted a position as professor of chemical technology
and analytical chemistry at Freiberg. G. D. Hinrichs once said, "The
perfection of the analytical work of Winkler astonished me till I found
the name of his father, Kurt Winkler, in the list of special students of
Berzelius" (8). Winkler, who had learned neatness from his father,

* Reproduced from H. G. Söderbaum's "Jac. Berzelius-Levnadsteckning" by kind permission of the author.

soon transformed the slovenly laboratories, and trained his students to work so carefully that rubber aprons were not needed. One day, when a new student appeared, wearing a large apron, Winkler exclaimed, "And so you're going to mix lime" (7).

In the fall of 1885 there was found, at the approach of a vein in the Himmelsfürst mine near Freiberg, a new ore which the discoverer, Albin Weisbach, a professor of mineralogy at the Freiberg School of Mines, named argyrodite (28). Hieronymus Theodor Richter, the chemist who with Ferdinand Reich had discovered indium, made a

Albin Weisbach 1833–1901. German mineralogist, crystallographer, and physicist. Discoverer of argyrodite, the mineral in which Clemens Winkler afterward discovered germanium. He was a son of Julius Weisbach, the distinguished mining engineer, and a student of Ferdinand Reich, the discoverer of indium.

From Goldschmidt's "Erinnerungsblätter an Albin Weisbach"

qualitative blowpipe analysis of the argyrodite, and found that it contained silver, sulfur, and a trace of mercury (27). Professor Weisbach then asked Winkler to make a thorough quantitative analysis in order to establish the composition of the mineral.

"In the middle of last September [1885]," said Weisbach, "in the famous old Himmelsfürst Mine at St. Michaelis near Freiberg, in passage number $10^{1}/_{2}$, four hundred and sixty meters under ground, at an intersection of the shaft of the silver mine with an unknown spar, there occurred a break which yielded, among other things, an ore which attracted the attention of Mine Manager and Director Neubert, who therefore sent a specimen of it to Herr Wappler, director of the mineral depot at the Mining Academy, with the notation that the ore in question indeed bore some resemblance to silver glance [Silberkies], yet seemed to differ from it. Foreman Wappler," continued Weisbach, "also became convinced of these differences and therefore gave Superintendent Th. Richter a specimen of it for analysis. The latter established silver and sulfur as the main constituents. . . ."

"Herr Wappler," said Weisbach, "kindly sent word to me in Eisenerz, Steicrmark and, on my return to Freiberg, gave me a larger number of specimens from the Himmelsfürst break. At the meeting of our mining society on October first, I was therefore able to give a short description of the new mineral, which I called argyrodite, a few specimens of which were already in circulation; on October 15th I showed the members of the society a wooden model representing the crystal form of the argyrodite. . . .

'Th. Richter," said Weisbach. "had already determined the silver content in two concordant blowpipe analyses as $73^1/_2$ per cent. My colleague Cl. Winkler then obtained as the mean of several experiments 75 per cent of silver and 18 of sulfur, hence a loss of 7 per cent. This loss, after long remaining inexplicable, finally led, in the course of further investigations, to the discovery of a new element similar in properties to arsenic or antimony, which Winkler, the discoverer, on February 1st named germanium" (28).

The argyrodite consisted of fine, steel-gray crystals resembling silver pyrite, and formed a thin layer over the impure ore, which consisted mainly of siderite, pyrite, red silver ore, and argentine (52). Even in his first researches on germanium, Winkler was hampered by lack of sufficient argyrodite, and the supply of this mineral at Freiberg soon became exhausted.

Winkler's results were consistent, but, since they invariably came out 7 per cent too low, he concluded that the ore must contain an unknown element[*] (26). Believing that the mineral must be a sulfo salt of silver and that the new element must belong in the same analytical group with arsenic, antimony, and tin, he fused a pulverized portion with sodium carbonate and sulfur, took up the melt with water, and filtered off the residue. By making the filtrate *slightly* acidic with hydrochloric acid, he precipitated and removed the sulfides of arsenic and antimony. Now, since the new element had not been removed with any of the precipitates, it would *have* to be present in the filtrate as a sodium sulfo salt. Yet when Winkler added a little more hydrochloric acid, a precipitate containing free sulfur, but no sulfide, was thrown down. Even upon evaporating the filtrate to dryness, he obtained nothing but sodium chloride.

[*] The reader will recall that similar results obtained in the analysis of petalite led Arfwedson to the discovery of lithium in 1818. See pp. 484–90, 496–7.

Unwilling to submit to this failure, Winkler toiled incessantly for four months, thinking constantly of the elusive element. On February 6, 1886, he filtered off the precipitated sulfur as he had done so many times before and, reckless with discouragement, poured into the clear filtrate a *large quantity* of hydrochloric acid. To his great delight a heavy. flaky, white precipitate immediately appeared (9). This substance, the sulfide of the new element, dissolved readily in ammonium hydroxide, and precipitated again upon addition of a large excess of hydrochloric acid, for it has a most surprising property: it is quite insoluble in concentrated acids, yet readily soluble in water and dilute acids (7).

The new element, which he called *germanium*, was isolated by heating the dry sulfide in a current of hydrogen. The gray, metallic powder was found to be less volatile than antimony, but the volatility of the chloride explains why Winkler obtained nothing but sodium chloride when he evaporated the filtrate from the precipitated sulfur. The germanium chloride had all been lost as vapor. The ore argyrodite is now known to be a double sulfide of silver and germanium, $GeS_2 \cdot 4Ag_2S$.

Winkler thought at first that germanium was a metalloid like antimony and arsenic, and that it would be found to be identical with Mendeleev's predicted ekastibium, an element which ought to lie between antimony and bismuth. The scientific world immediately became interested in the new element. On February 26th Mendeleev contributed to the *Berichte der deutschen chemischen Gesellschaft* a list of properties which the new element would have to have in order to fit into the space between antimony and bismuth. He thought it more likely, however, because of the solubility of the chloride in water and because of the white color of the sulfide, that germanium was ekacadmium, an element between cadmium and mercury. At the same time Victor von Richter of Breslau wrote to Winkler saying he believed germanium to be ekasilicon, the lowest homolog of tin, an undiscovered element between gallium and arsenic. Two days later Lothar Meyer said in the *Berichte* that he, too, believed germanium to be the longed-for ekasilicon, and that he had already expressed that opinion to his advanced students (7).

Winkler's months of discouragement were ended, and he worked joyously, stimulated by the interest and encouragement of these eminent chemists. A vast amount of work remained to be done, and the obtaining of sufficient quantities of germanium compounds became increasingly difficult. Pure argyrodite contains only 7 per cent of germanium, the rich ore had been exhausted, and Winkler was obliged to work up large quantities of the low-grade ore. He had at first hoped to strike richer deposits of argyrodite, and had therefore been too generous with his valuable germanium compounds. Nevertheless, he finally obtained convincing proof that germanium is the ekasilicon predicted by Mendeleev in 1871. In the following table the predicted properties of ekasilicon are compared with the actual properties of germanium:

	Ekasilicon (Es)	Germanium (Ge)
Atomic weight	72	72.32*
Specific gravity	5.5	5.47
Atomic volume	13	13.22
Valence	4	4
Specific heat	0.073	0.076
Specific gravity of dioxide	4.7	4.703
Molecular volume of dioxide	22	22.16
Boiling point of tetrachloride	under 100°	86°
Specific volume of tetrachloride	1.9	1.887
Molecular volume of tetrachloride	113	113.35

Mendeleev had made only one mistake in his prophecy. He had thought that ekasilicon, like titanium, would be difficult to liquefy and volatilize. Lothar Meyer, who had disagreed with him on this point, proved to be correct. Winkler afterward said that germanium contradicted all expectations in its occurrence in nature. He said that he might have expected to find it combined with oxygen and accompanied by titanium and zirconium in rare Scandinavian minerals, but would never have thought to look for it in silver mines among the related compounds of arsenic and antimony (10).

Clemens Winkler made brilliant contributions both to pure and applied chemistry, and had many interests beyond the chemical field. Like H. Davy and A. G. Ekeberg, he had poetic ability, and many of his songs are preserved in the songbook of the Freiberg Academy. O. Brunck said that these were written in good form and with well-chosen words (7). For the entertainment of his guests, Winkler often used to write humorous chemical verses for them to sing while he played a gay accompaniment on almost any instrument they might prefer. He resigned his professorship in 1902, and died of carcinoma on October 8, 1904. His name will always be honored wherever true scientific greatness is appreciated.

In 1893 the great American mineralogist and analytical chemist Samuel Lewis Penfield analyzed a mineral from Bolivia, which he found to be identical in composition with argyrodite, Ag_8GeS_6. Since it crystallized in the regular system whereas argyrodite was then believed to be monoclinic, the Bolivian mineral was at first regarded as a new species, canfieldite. A. Weisbach soon showed, however, that argyrodite, too, crystallizes in the regular form. The name canfieldite was therefore transferred to another kind of argyrodite in which some of the germanium is replaced by tin (52, 53, 54).

* The 1954 atomic weight of germanium is 72.60.

In 1920 H. Schneiderhöhn discovered a red complex copper germanium sulfide of uncertain composition in the Tsumeb Mine, Otavi, Southwest Africa (52, 56). This mineral, now known as germanite, is an important source of germanium (52). Many zinc blendes, including those of the Joplin (Missouri) and Wisconsin areas, contain this metal, which can be enriched during the smelting process (39, 52, 55, 57). L. M. Dennis and A. W. Laubengayer of Cornell University showed in 1926 that satisfactory optical glass can be made by replacing any part of the silica in ordinary glass with germanium dioxide (58).

Although traces of germanium have been found in many parts of the world, no mineral has been discovered in which it is the main constituent. Most of the ores which contain it (argyrodite, canfieldite, germanite, lepidolite, sphalerite, and tourmaline) are rare. In England, coal flue dust is utilized as a source of the metal. In 1935 the flue dusts of a zinc smelter at Henryetta, Oklahoma, were found to contain germanium in rather concentrated form (35). No great demands for it arose until 1942, when the National Defense Research Council of the United States had need of a very pure semi-conducting metal for use in electronic equipment. When it was found that germanium has remarkable versatility in this field, it acquired great commercial importance and soon became five times as valuable as gold (35). Most of the world production of germanium comes from the zinc ores of the tri-state district (Oklahoma, Kansas, and Missouri), which contain from 0.01 to 0.10 per cent of it (35).

The remarkable electrical property of germanium that caused the unprecedented demand for it is its ability to permit the flow of electricity in one direction and resist the flow in the other direction. Although vacuum tubes are used in the construction of rectifiers to convert alternating current to direct current, many of them are bulky, fragile, and not sufficiently durable. A germanium rectifier only a few millimeters in diameter dissipates no heat, reacts instantly, and has about ten times the average life of a vacuum tube.

In 1948, scientists of the Bell Telephone Laboratories perfected an improved form of the germanium rectifier known as a transistor (35, 36). In certain applications these transistors can compete successfully with vacuum tubes. They are already being used in hearing aids. The semiconductors of chief interest in transistor physics are germanium and silicon (36).

LITERATURE CITED

(1) WINKLER, CLEMENS, "Ueber die vermeintliche Umwandelung des Phosphore in Arsen," *Ber.*, **33**, 1697 (Band 2, 1900).

(2) RAMSAY, W., "Paul Émile (dit François) Lecoq de Boisbaudran," *J. Chem. Soc. Trans.*, **103**, 742–6 (Part 1, 1913).

(3) JAGNAUX, R., "Histoire de la Chimie," Vol. 2, Baudry et Cie., Paris, **1891**, pp. 189–94.

(4) DE BOISBAUDRAN, P.-E. L., "Chemical and spectroscopic character of a new metal, gallium, discovered in the blende of the mine of Pierrefitte, in the Valley of Argeles, Pyrenees," *Am. Chemist*, **6**, 146 (Oct., 1875).

(5) "Chemical Society Memorial Lectures, 1893–1900," Gurney and Jackson, London, **1901**, pp. 1277–94. Nilson Memorial Lecture by S. O. PETTERSSON, *J. Chem. Soc. Trans.*, **77**, 1277–94 (Part 2, 1900).

(6) KLASON, "Lars Fredrik Nilson," *Ber.*, **32**, 1643–6 (Band 2, 1899).

(7) BRUNCK, O., "Clemens Winkler," *Ber.*, **39**, 4491–548 (Band 4, 1906).

(8) HINRICHS, G. D., "The Proximate Constituents of the Chemical Elements Mechanically Determined from Their Physical and Chemical Properties," C. G. Hinrichs, St. Louis, Mo., **1904**, introduction.

(9) McCAY, L. W., "My student days in Germany," *J. Chem. Educ.*, **7**, 1081–99 (May, 1930).

(10) WINKLER, C., "Ueber die Entdeckung neuer Elemente im Verlaufe der letzten fünfundzwanzig Jahre, und damit zusammenhängende Fragen," *Ber.*, **30**, 15–6 (Band 1, 1897).

(11) DE BOISBAUDRAN, P.-E. L., "Sur un nouveau métal, le gallium," *Ann. chim. phys.*, [5], **10**, 100–41 (Jan., 1877); *Chem. News*, **35**, 148–50 (Apr. 13, 1877); 157–60 (Apr. 20, 1877); 167–70 (Apr. 27, 1877).

(12) GARDINER, J. H., "M. Lecoq de Boisbaudran," *Nature*, **90**, 255–6 (Oct. 31, 1912).

(13) DE BOISBAUDRAN, P.-E. L., "Caractères chimiques et spectroscopiques d'un nouveau métal, le Gallium, découvert dans une blende de la mine de Pierrefitte, vallée d'Argeles (Pyrénées)," *Compt. rend.*, **81**, 493–5 (Sept. 20, 1875).

(14) DE BOISBAUDRAN, P.-E. L., "Sur quelques propriétés du gallium," *Compt. rend.*, **81**, 1100–5 (Dec. 6, 1875).

(15) MENDELEEV, D., "Remarques à propos de la découverte du gallium," *Compt. rend.*, **81**, 969–72 (Nov. 22, 1875).

(16) DE BOISBAUDRAN, P.-E. L., "Sur le spectre du gallium," *Compt. rend.*, **82**, 168 (Jan. 10, 1876).

(17) DE BOISBAUDRAN, P.-E. L., "Nouvelles recherches sur le gallium," *ibid.*, **82**, 1036–9 (May 1, 1876).

(18) DE BOISBAUDRAN, P.-E. L. and E.-C. JUNGFLEISCH, "Extraction du gallium," *Compt. rend.*, **86**, 475–8 (Feb. 18, 1878); *Bull. soc. chim. (Paris)*, [2], **31**, 50 (1879).

(19) MELLOR, J. W., "Comprehensive Treatise on Inorganic and Theoretical Chemistry," Vol. 5, Longmans, Green and Co., London, **1924**, pp. 373–7 (article on gallium); pp. 480–4 (article on scandium); Vol. 7, **1927**, pp. 254–7 (article on germanium).

(20) MENDELEEV, D., "Die periodische Gesetzmässigkeit der chemischen Elemente," *Ann.*, Supplementband VIII, **1871**, 196–206 (Heft 2).

(21) NILSON, L. F., 'Sur l'ytterbine, terre nouvelle de M. Marignac," *Compt. rend.*, **88**, 642–5 (Mar. 24, 1879); "Ueber die ytterbinerde," *Ber.*, **12**, 550–3 (Mar. 24, 1879).

(22) NILSON, L. F., "Sur le scandium, élément nouveau," *Compt. rend.*, **88**, 645–8 (Mar. 24, 1879); "Ueber Scandium, ein neues Erdmetall," *Ber.*, **12**, 554–7 (Mar. 24, 1879).

(23) NILSON, L. F., "Sur le poids atomique et sur quelques sels caractéristiques de l'ytterbium," *Compt. rend.*, **91**, 56–9 (July 5, 1880); "Sur le poids atomique et sur quelques sels caractéristiques du scandium," **91**, 118–21 (July 12, 1880); *Ber.*, **13**, 1430–50 (July 12, 1880).

(24) FRIEND, J. N., "A Textbook of Inorganic Chemistry," Vol. 4, Chas. Griffin and Co., London, **1917**, pp. 205–6 and 215.

(25) CLEVE, P. T., "Sur le scandium," *Compt. rend.*, **89**, 419–22 (Aug. 18, 1879); *Chem. News*, **40**, 159–60 (Oct. 3, 1879).

(26) WINKLER, C., "Germanium, Ge, ein neues, nichtmetallisches Element," *Ber.*, **19**, 210–1 (Feb. 8, 1886).

(27) WINKLER, C., "Mittheilungen über das Germanium," *J. prakt. Chem.*, [2], **34**, 177–229 (Heft 4, 1886); [2], **36**, 177–209 (Heft 4, 1887).

(28) WEISBACH, A., "Argyrodit, ein neues Silbererz," *Neues Jahrb. Mineralogie*, 67– 71, **1886** (Band 2).

(29) NEWLANDS, J. A. R., "Relations between equivalents," *Chem. News*, **10**, 59 (July 30, 1864).

(30) BUGGE, G., "Das Buch der grossen Chemiker," Vol. 2, Verlag Chemie, Berlin, **1930**, pp. 336–50. Article on Winkler by O. BRUNCK.

(31) URBAIN, G., "Lecoq de Boisbaudran," *Chem.-Ztg.*, **36**, 929–33 (Aug. 15, 1912).

(32) HASSELBERG, "Biografier. Tobias Robert Thalén," Kungl. Svenska Vetenskapsakademiens Årsbok, **1906**, pp. 219–40.

(33) SPENCER, L. F., "The Metals of the Rare Earths," Longmans, Green and Co., London, **1919**, p. 133; LEVY, "The Rare Earths," Edward Arnold, London, **1915**, p. 218.

(34) EKSTRAND, Å. G., "Lars Fredrik Nilson. Minnesteckning," Almqvist and Wiksells Boktryckeri, Stockholm, **1921**, 101 pp.

(35) FITE, ROBERT C., "Germanium, a secondary metal of primary importance," *Scientific Monthly*, **78**, 15–18 (Jan., 1954).

(36) SHOCKLEY, W., "Transistor physics," *Am. Scientist*, **42**, 41–72 (Jan., 1954).

(37) KOPP, H., "Geschichte der Chemie," Vol. 4, Vieweg und Sohn, Braunschweig, **1847**, p. 123.

(38) Recueil des mémoires . . . de chymie . . . contenus dans les Actes de l'Acad. d'Upsal et dans les mémoires de l'Acad. Royale des Sciences de Stockolm [*sic*] . . . 1720–1760," Vol. 1, P.-F. Didot le Jeune, Paris, **1764**, pp. 16–25. Georg Brandt's dissertation on the half metals. *Actes Acad. d'Upsal*, **4**, (1735).

(39) URBAIN, G., "Analyse spectrographique des blendes," *Compt. rend.*, **149**, 602– 3 (Oct. 11, 1909).

(40) HILLEBRAND, W. F. and J. A. SCHERRER, "Recovery of gallium from spelter in the United States," *J. Ind. Eng. Chem.*, **8**, 225 (March, 1916).

(41) FEIT, W., "Die technische Gewinnung des Rheniums und Galliums," *Angew. Chem.*, **46**, 216–8 (Apr. 15, 1933).

(42) RAMAGE, H., "Gallium. Its wide distribution," *Chem. News*, **108**, 280 (Dec. 5, 1913); HARTLEY and RAMAGE, *Sci. Trans. Roy. Dublin Soc.*, (2), **7**, 1 (1898).

(43) HARTLEY, W. N. and H. RAMAGE, "On the occurrence of the element gallium in the clay-ironstone of the Cleveland District of Yorkshire," *Proc. Roy. Soc. (London)*, **60**, 35–7 (May 7, 1896); **60**, 393–407 (Dec. 17, 1896).

(44) "Gmelin's Handbuch der anorganischen Chemie," 8th ed., Vol. 36, Verlag Chemie, Berlin, **1936**, pp. 1–8; Vol. 37, pp. 1–6. History and occurrence of gallium and indium.

(45) BROWNING, P. E. and H. S. UHLER, "On a gallium-indium alloy," *Am. J. Sci.*, (4), **41**, 351–4 (1916).

(46) PAPISH, J. and C. B. STILSON, "Occurrences of gallium in zinc minerals," *Am. Mineralogist*, **15**, 521–7 (1930).

(47) KURODA, KAZUO, "The occurrence of gallium in the hot springs of Japan," *Bull. Chem. Soc. (Japan)*, **15**, 234–6 (June, 1940).

(48) BARDET, J., "Etude spectrographique des eaux minérales françaises," *Compt. rend.*, **157**, 224–6 (1913).

(49) MORITZ, H., "The sulfide ores of the Tsumeb mine," *Neues Jahrb. Mineral. Geol., Beilagebd.* (Suppl.), **67A**, 118–53 (1933).

(50) WINKLER, CLEMENS, "Carl Johann August Theodor Scheerer," *J. prakt. Chem.*, **120**, 459–63 (1875).

(51) SCHEERER, C. J. A. T., "Ueber den Euxenit, eine neue Mineralspecies," *Pogg. Ann.*, **50**, 149–53 (1840).

(52) "Gmelin's Handbuch," Ref. (*44*), Vol. 45, pp. 1–10.   History and occurrence of germanium.

(53) PENFIELD, S. L., "On canfieldite, a new germanium mineral and on the chemical composition of argyrodite," *Am. J. Sci.*, (3), **46**, 107–13 (1893); "On argyrodite and a new sulphostannate of silver (canfieldite) from Bolivia," *ibid.*, (3), **47**, 451–4 (1894).

(54) "Biographical memoirs," Vol. 6, National Acad. of Sciences, Washington, D. C., **1909**, pp. 119–46.   Memoir on S. L. Penfield by HORACE L. WELLS.

(55) BUCHANAN, G. H., "The occurrence of germanium in zinc materials," *J. Ind. Eng. Chem.*, **8**, 585–6 (1916); "The occurrence of germanium in Missouri and Wisconsin blendes," *ibid.*, **9**, 661–3 (1917).

(56) SCHNEIDERHÖHN, H., *Metall und Erz*, **17**, 364 (1920); *Mineralog. Abstr.*, **1**, 1589.

(57) DENNIS L. M. and J. PAPISH, "Germanium. I. Extraction from germanium-bearing zinc oxide," *J. Am. Chem. Soc.*, **43**, 2142 (Oct., 1921); *Z. anorg. Chem.*, **120**, 21 (Dec. 14, 1921).

(58) DENNIS, L. M., and A. W. LAUBENGAYER, "Germanium. XVII. Fused germanium dioxide and some germanium glasses," *J. Phys. Chem.*, **30**, 1510–26 (1926).

(59) SJÖBERG, S. G., "Nils Gabriel Sefström and the discovery of vanadium," *J. Chem. Educ.*, **28**, 294–6 (June, 1951).

Courtesy E. R. Schierz

The Gadolin Medal. The Gadolin Fund was established in 1935 by the Society of Finnish Chemists. The first award for this handsome medal was made in 1937 to Ossian Aschan and Gust. Komppa. The obverse bears a portrait of Johan Gadolin, investigator of gadolinite; the reverse side shows a group of chemists studying the rare earths from this mineral. *See* ref. *(64)*. This picture of the plaster cast of the medal, taken in the studio of the designer, Emil Wikström, was sent to Dr. Schierz by Dr. E. S. Tomula of Helsinki.

The rare earths perplex us in our researches, baffle us in our speculations, and haunt us in our very dreams. They stretch like an unknown sea before us, mocking, mystifying, and murmuring strange revelations and possibilities (1).

26

The rare earth elements

*The rare earths are so very much alike and occur closely associ-
ated in such complex minerals that it is extremely difficult to
separate them. They have all been obtained, however, by
elaborate and laborious fractionation of two mixtures, the "yttria"
of Gadolin and the "ceria" of Klaproth, Berzelius, and Hisinger,
originally believed by their discoverers to be pure oxides. The
patient researches of Mosander, Delafontaine, Marignac, Cleve,
Boisbaudran, Urbain, Charles James, and many others finally
resulted in the decomposition of the so-called "yttria" into the
oxides now known as yttria, terbia, erbia, ytterbia, lutetia, holmia,
thulia, and dysprosia. Through the persistent skilful work of
Mosander, Marignac, Boisbaudran, Brauner, Auer von Welsbach,
Demarçay, Hopkins, McCoy, and others, the old "ceria" was
finally broken down into the oxides ceria, lanthana, neodymia,
praseodymia, samaria, gadolinia, europia, and promethium.**
Most of the rare earth elements are extremely rare and costly
even in the form of their compounds.*

Rich stores of the rare earth minerals lay hidden for centuries
in the Scandinavian peninsula until, one day in 1787, Lieutenant Carl Axel
Arrhenius found, near the Ytterby feldspar quarry in Roslagen, an unusual
black rock which he at first called ytterite, but which was later named
gadolinite for the famous Finnish scientist Johan Gadolin who detected in
it yttria, scandia, and all the rare earths of the yttria group.

In the laboratory of the Royal Mint, Bengt Reinhold Geijer and
P. J. Hjelm had taught Arrhenius how to test gunpowder and had aroused
his interest in the minerals at the School of Mines (*22*). On returning
from a visit to Paris, where he had heard A.-L. Lavoisier, C.-L. Berthollet,
A.-F. de Fourcroy, and Guyton de Morveau discuss the new antiphlogistic
doctrine, Arrhenius explained it clearly to his Swedish confreres, who had
hitherto heard only vague and distorted accounts of it (*69*).

---

* The discovery of promethium will be discussed in Chapter 31.

The interruptions of army life were never able to stifle Arrhenius's love of science, and he always regretted "that he had been snatched away so early from his studies and thrust into the occupations of practical life" (69). In the school year 1816–17, when he was about sixty years old, he studied chemistry in Berzelius' laboratory. Almost to the close of his life he continued to attend Berzelius' lectures. Even the disconnected words which Arrhenius uttered during the delirium of his last illness showed that his mind was still occupied with mineralogical chemistry (69).

The first description of gadolinite was published by Bengt Reinhold Geijer (1758–1815) in *Crell's Annalen* in 1788. "I am now sending you," said he, "a specimen of a heavy stone which one of my friends, Hr. Lieut. Arrhenius, found. It was discovered at Ytterby, three miles from Stock-

Johan Gadolin, 1760–1852. Professor of chemistry at the University of Åbo, Finland. Discoverer of the complex earth "yttria," which afterward yielded an entire series of simple oxides. He made a thorough study of the rare earth minerals from Ytterby, Sweden.

holm, in the neighborhood where one gets quartz for the glassworks. . . . It resembles asphalt or coal" (22, 74). Because of its high specific gravity it was believed to contain tungsten (wolfram).

In 1812 Thomas Thomson visited the Ytterby quarry. "It would be improper," said he, "while giving an account of the minerals of Upland, to pass by the quarry of Ytterby, become famous from the curious substances that have been found in it. It lies rather less than two English miles north from the fortress of Vaxholm, and consists of a rock obviously connected with gneiss, that constitutes the basis of the country; though it consists chiefly of beautiful white felspar, and felspar of a flesh red

Carl Axel Arrhenius, 1757–1824. Swedish chemist and mineralogist. In 1787 he discovered in the Ytterby quarry a new black rock which he named *ytterbite*. In 1794 Gadolin discovered the complex earth "yttria" in this mineral, which has since been renamed *gadolinite*.

Courtesy of M. Elizabeth Farson

colour. . . . It was in the flesh-red felspar that Arrhenius discovered the black conchoidal mineral, afterwards distinguished by the name of gadolinite. Its specific gravity is above 4. It was analyzed by Gadolin and found by him to contain a new earth, to which the name of *Yttria* was given, from the appellation of the quarry where the gadolinite is found. Probably the most accurate analysis of gadolinite is the last one which was made by Ekeberg and which I shall here state. It was as follows: yttria, 55.5; silica, 23.0; glucina [beryllia], 4.5; oxide of iron, 16.5; volatile matter, 0.5" (75).

Thomson also visited a quarry at Finbo, about three miles from Falun, where "specimens of gadolinite have been found, several of which I procured by the goodness of Assessor Gahn. This mineral," said Thomson, "is very scarce, having been hitherto found only in two places of Sweden: Ytterby and Finbo and in both places in a rock belonging to the species of granite. If the same kind of rock were properly examined in other countries, there can be little doubt that it would be found. A peculiar earth confined to a peculiar spot, and in very minute quantities, can hardly be conceived. Yet that is the predicament in which three of the earths stand at present, namely, zirconia, yttria, and glucina [beryllia];

Åbo, Finland, in 1823. Johan Gadolin, the discoverer of the first rare earths, was born in Åbo, and served there for twenty-five years as professor of chemistry.

while the other six are scattered in great profusion through the rocks constituting the surface of the earth" (75).

In 1890 Walfr. Petersson published a complete history of gadolinite and a thorough investigation of its chemical and mineralogical properties. His analyses, like those of F. A. Genth and C. W. Blomstrand, led to the formula:

$$\overset{\text{II}}{R_3}\ \overset{\text{III}}{R_2}\ Si_2O_{10} = Be_2FeY_2Si_2O_{10} \quad (76).$$

G. Flink stated that gadolinite "perhaps played a greater role in the history of inorganic chemistry than any other mineral" and that it "is mainly found only at two Scandinavian localities, namely Ytterby near Vaxholm and Hitterö near Flekkefjord in Norway. Other Scandinavian localities for it are of little importance, and in other countries it is found only as a rarity" (77).

Johan Gadolin was born at Åbo near Helsingfors (Helsinki) on June 5, 1760. His father, Jacob Gadolin, a well-known astronomer and physicist, taught him to love and understand Nature. After completing his course at the University of Åbo, he studied under Torbern Bergman at Upsala, and acquired a broad education through travel in Denmark, Germany, Holland, and England (43). In 1794 Gadolin investigated the mineral Lieutenant Arrhenius had discovered at Ytterby, and found that it contained about 38 per cent of a new earth. A. G. Ekeberg soon confirmed the analysis (40, 41), and mineralogists afterward named the mineral *gadolinite* in honor of the Finnish chemist (64).

Gadolin served the University of Åbo as a professor of chemistry for twenty-five years (1797–1822), and during this time he made a thorough study of the wonderful Ytterby minerals. He also studied fluxes for decomposing iron ores for analytical purposes, made contributions to thermo-chemistry, helped solve the questions of chemical proportions and chemical affinity, and published the first Swedish textbook that embraced Lavoisier's views (43).

He lived for thitry years after his retirement, and died at Wirmo, Finland, on August 15, 1852, at the age of ninety-two years (65). In 1827 the city of Åbo and the University buildings were destroyed by fire, and Gadolin's valuable mineral collections were lost. The University was then transferred to Helsingfors (2).

YTTRIA AND CERIA

Ekeberg (40, 41), M. H. Klaproth, and N.-L. Vauquelin all investigated Gadolin's new oxide, and it came to be called *yttria*, a name derived from Ytterby. In 1803 Klaproth discovered in the mineral cerite another earth which he called *"terre ochroite,"* but which is now known as *ceria.*[*] Berzelius and Wilhelm Hisinger also discovered ceria independently, but upon further investigation neither their yttria nor their ceria proved to be a pure oxide (3).

LANTHANA AND DIDYMIA

The proof of the complexity of ceria and yttria was given by Carl Gustav Mosander, one of Berzelius' assistants. He was born at Kalmar on September 10, 1797, was educated as a pharmacist and physician, and served for some time as an army surgeon (4). For many years he lived in the same house with Berzelius, and his wife, who was of Dutch ancestry, helped Berzelius to acquire a reading knowledge of that language (5). When the Stockholm Academy of Sciences moved into its magnificent new "palace," as Berzelius called it, Mosander became curator of the mineral collections, and was given an apartment adjoining them.

[*] See Chapter 21, pp. 551–8.

He also had charge of the chemical laboratory for medical students at the Caroline Institute, where he served as professor of chemistry and mineralogy for many years.

He and Friedrich Wöhler often used to go on long tramps together during the latter's memorable months at Stockholm, and Mosander helped his German friend prepare a valuable mineral collection to take back to

Carl Gustav Mosander,* 1797–1858. Swedish army surgeon, chemist, and mineralogist. Curator of the mineral collections at the Stockholm Academy of Sciences. Professor of chemistry and mineralogy at the Caroline Institute. Discoverer of lanthana and didymia. The latter earth was afterward split by Auer von Welsbach into praseodymia and neodymia.

his fatherland. Berzelius' letters to Wöhler contain frequent references to Mosander under the affectionate nickname "Pater Moses." On October 12, 1824, for example, Berzelius wrote:

Now here I am alone, chemically deserted. Pater Moses is now working for his examination, Hisinger has not yet returned, and Arfvedson, who was recently engaged, is moored near his fiancée. . . . However, my time is spent as usual in a certain pleasant monotony and in moving back and forth between the writing desk and the laboratory, where I am still busy with trifles, for example with the completion of the works begun on the preparation of lithia, yttria, and zirconia. . . .

In November of the same year he wrote again:

A thousand, thousand thanks for the interesting letter and for the beautiful minerals, which I arranged in their proper places several days ago. Father Moses thanks you no less than do I. I cannot accustom myself to the thought of no longer finding Wöhler at his desk in the laboratory, and even though I

* Reproduced from H. G. Söderbaum's "Jac. Berzelius. Levnadsteckning" by kind permission of Dr. Söderbaum.

prefer to see Moses' face there rather than none at all, yet the loss by the deception is too great. . . .

It may be assumed that Mosander passed his examinations successfully, for on July 15, 1825, Wöhler wrote to his Swedish master, "Moses heisst wohl jetzt Hr. Doctor Pater Moses, wozu ich gratulire"* (6).

In 1839 Mosander heated some cerium nitrate and treated the partly decomposed salt with dilute nitric acid. In the extract he found a new earth, which he named *lanthana,* meaning *hidden,* meanwhile retaining the old name, *ceria,* for the oxide which is insoluble in dilute nitric acid (7, 28, 45). In the same year, Axel Erdmann, one of Sefström's students, discovered lanthana in a new Norwegian mineral, which he named *mosandrite* in honor of Mosander.

Johan August Arfwedson,† **1792–1841.** Metallurgist, chemist, and mineralogist. The discoverer of lithium. He studied the action of hydrogen on metallic sulfates, and in 1823, by heating the green oxide of uranium in a current of hydrogen, he prepared uranous oxide, UO_2, which he believed to be the metal. He studied under Berzelius. (The spelling *Arfvedson* appears frequently in the literature.) See pp. 496–7.

On February 1st Berzelius wrote to Wöhler:

It is completely confirmed. When I showed Erdmann's little specimen to Mosander, he announced that he, too, had found something new in cerite. Although we see each other every day, he had never breathed a word of it to me. . . . I do not think that during the month when I was ill, Mosander did any work on his earth. I almost surmise that he thought, "Let Berzelius worry about it; I shall then be free from a lot of drudgery." A few days ago he began again. At first he let it be understood that what Hisinger and I had called cerium was a mixture of two oxides, neither of which possessed the properties

* "Moses may now be called Herr Doctor Father Moses, wherefore I offer congratulations."

† Reproduced from H. G. Söderbaum's "Jac. Berzelius. Levnadsteckning" by kind permission of Dr. Söderbaum.

of the mixture. . . . I have now studied pure ceric oxide and found that addition of the earth does not change any of its properties. If this were not the case, the discovery of the earth would have occurred before Mosander. : . . Mosander would not tell me what he expects to name his new earth. The communications I am now making are for you alone. You must not publish anything about them. . . .

Edgar Fahs Smith Memorial Collection,
University of Pennsylvania

Autograph Letter of C. G. Mosander. His script is almost illegible, but the following is an approximate translation:* "Stockholm, Nov. 5, 1841. Dear Brother: Especially great thanks to you for all your trouble with my specimens. The expense I have the honor to include is . . . (amount illegible), as nearly as I can estimate it. The account is enclosed. Would you please receipt it? Once again many thanks to you for all your trouble. Many greetings to Westring. Respectfully and cordially, C. G. Mosander. P. S. Coarse filter paper costs. . ."

* The writer is deeply grateful to Miss Mary Larson of the Zoölogy Department at The University of Kansas and to Mr. Einar Bourman for the translation of this letter from the Swedish and for assistance in securing Swedish illustrations.

On February 12 he wrote, "Mosander seems willing to take my suggestion to name it (the element) *lanthanum* (*lanthan*) and the oxide, *lanthanum oxide* or *lanthana* (*lanthanerde*)" (8).

Months passed by, and on June 18th Berzelius wrote again to Wöhler:

> I can give you no news from Mosander. For a long time he has not worked at the continuation of his experiments, and he no longer makes any mention of what he is finding, not so much from reserve as because he is not doing anything; but he has his mineral-water establishment to manage, so that he really has very little time. . . . If you write to Mosander yourself, you will probably receive something from him for the *Annalen*.

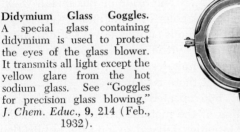

Didymium Glass Goggles. A special glass containing didymium is used to protect the eyes of the glass blower. It transmits all light except the yellow glare from the hot sodium glass. See "Goggles for precision glass blowing," *J. Chem. Educ.*, **9**, 214 (Feb., 1932).

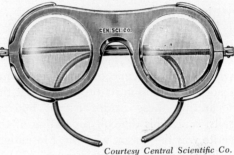

Courtesy Central Scientific Co.

Wöhler waited patiently for several months, and then wrote on February 25, 1840, "The chemical world cannot understand why Mosander has not yet published anything on lanthanum." Two years later Berzelius wrote, "Mosander still keeps working at his lanthanum, but says very little about it. Meanwhile I have learned enough to know that more depends on it than had been supposed."

On May 13, 1842, Berzelius again broached the subject to Mosander. To use his own words:

> I suggested to Father Moses that we soon have a paper on cerium for the *Annalen*. He laughed rather scornfully, went down into his laboratory, for he lives in the house of the Academy, and brought up a mortar half full of a white, slightly yellowish powder, and asked, "What is that?" I admitted my ignorance. "That, Sir," he said, "is the way ceric oxide looks when one has it pure

It has cost me a year's work to get that far." He added that he was not going to publish any of his results until he had them completely finished. Although he comes up nearly every morning to chat with me a while, and usually complains about the difficulties which keep him from getting pure preparations, he tells me nothing about his real results, and I am satisfied, for it will be all the more interesting when one gets them all at once (9).

In 1841 Mosander had treated lanthana with dilute nitric acid, and had extracted from it a new rose-colored oxide, which he believed contained a new element. He named the new metal *didymium* because, as he said, it seemed to be "an inseparable twin brother of lanthanum" (27, 29, 46).

On August 30–Sept. 2, 1842, Berzelius wrote Théophile-Jules Pelouze concerning a meeting of Scandinavian naturalists which had been held in Stockholm: "Mr. Mosander announced a new metal, found with lanthanum in cerite, a metal which seems to accompany the cerium and yttrium wherever one finds them. . . . The oxide of this metal, which is brown, gives pink salts; the pale pink color of yttric and cerous salts is due to its presence. When the ceric oxide is entirely devoid of didymium oxide it has a pale lemon yellow color; yttria and lanthanum oxide are white. The didymic oxide therefore imitates the cerous and lanthanic oxides so closely in its properties that there is scarcely any other way of separating these oxides except by repeated crystallizations of their salts. . . . This difficult separation of the metallic oxides present in the cerite was the reason why Mr. Mosander delayed so long the publication of his experiments on lanthanum" (73). Pelouze replied on October 19, 1842: "Mr. Mosander is a very skillful analyst. . . . I appreciate all the more the difficulties he overcame, since I spent three whole months on cerite without even suspecting that it had anything except cerium and lanthanum. I would be greatly obliged to you if you would send me in a letter a few traces of didymium oxide" (73).

Wöhler objected to this name because *Didym,* the German form of it, sounds rather childish and silly, "etwas Kindisches, etwas Läppisches." Berzelius replied in Mosander's defense:

No, my dear friend, I have no liking for this name, and yet I do not want to, and cannot, ask Mosander to change it, since he has announced it publicly. You surely do not understand our friend Father Moses. He takes suggestions from no one. The proposal to change a name given by him would be an offense which he would not easily pardon, and still he would not change it. He intentionally looked for a name beginning with *D* in order to have a symbol unlike those for other metals. To be sure, it is quite true, as you say, that the repetition of the same consonants, and of almost the same vowel sounds, has an unpleasant sound; but one soon gets accustomed to it, and finds it endurable, and you must do the same.

Berzelius then mentioned a number of accepted organic names which sound much worse than "Didym" (*10*). Didymia was regarded as a pure earth until 1885, when Auer von Welsbach decomposed it.

YTTRIA, ERBIA, AND TERBIA

Having shown that the earth originally called *ceria* was composed of an insoluble portion, *ceria,* and a soluble portion, *lanthana,* Mosander investigated yttria in a similar manner (*7*). In 1843 he showed that yttria from which all the ceria, lanthana, and didymia have been removed contains at least three other earths. These are: a colorless oxide, for

Marc Delafontaine, 1837–1911.   Swiss chemist who studied under J.-C.-G. de Marignac and taught for a time at the University of Geneva. Arriving in New York in 1870, he followed the advice of Louis Agassiz and went to teach in the High Schools of Chicago. He also served as analytical chemist and expert for the Chicago Police Department in famous criminal cases, and carried on research in spectrum analysis.

Courtesy Miss Elizabeth Farson and Mr. Jules Delafontaine

which he kept the name *yttria;* a yellow earth, *erbia;* and a rose-colored one, *terbia.* He separated them by fractional precipitation with ammonium hydroxide. Erbia, the least basic of the three, separated in the first fractions, while yttria, the most basic one, was found in the last fractions (*23*).

Mosander's work was confirmed by Marc Delafontaine, J.-C. G. de Marignac, J. Lawrence Smith, P. T. Cleve, and Lecoq de Boisbaudran, but, for some reason, a confusing shift of names occurred. The names *erbia* and *terbia* were interchanged, so that the former now applies to the rose-colored oxide (3). The names of the four elements, *yttrium*, *ytterbium*, *erbium*, and *terbium*, have all been derived, by the way, from that of the little Swedish town, Ytterby, where the rare earth minerals were first found.

Before closing this brief account of Mosander's work, it seems fitting to reflect for a moment over his sincere tribute to his honored teacher. On April 18, 1848, he wrote regarding a translation of Berzelius' textbook:

My dear Wöhler: In this case as always, I follow the irresistible impulse of my heart to say openly what I believe to be right; you may once more test it, and then judge, and I am convinced that you will appreciate the truth of what I have to say. The great master will perhaps soon pass into another world, but by us and our successors his name will long be honored and loved, and what he

J. Lawrence Smith, 1818–1883. American mineralogical and analytical chemist. His method of decomposing ores which are to be analyzed for sodium and potassium is still the standard procedure. He investigated the rare earths in samarskite and verified Mosander's conclusions regarding the complex nature of yttria.

Edgar Fahs Smith Memorial Collection,
University of Pennsylvania

has accomplished here—that you know as well as I do—was not done for the sake of vainglory, but out of pure zeal for truth and enlightenment, and the motive for his researches has always sprung from a pure source; then shall the right of defending Science and himself, ere his life is extinguished, be denied him in the last moment when he could devote his undiminished mental powers to the service of Science? Impossible. . . . Literal translation or none (11).

Berzelius died at Stockholm on August 7, 1848. His mind remained clear until the end, but during the last six days he lay half asleep, and spoke no more. Mosander died ten years later, on October 15, 1858, at Ångsholm near Drottningholm (4).

Portrait of Berzelius from a daguerreo-type taken in Berlin in 1845, three years before his death[*]

Betty Berzelius née Poppius (Baroness Berzelius),[†] 1811–1884. Daughter of state councilor, G. Poppius. When she married Berzelius in 1835 he was already a man of great renown, and the baronetcy was conferred on him at the wedding. See Chapter XI, p. 315.

[*] Reproduced from H. G. Söderbaum's "Jac. Berzelius. Levnadsteckning" by kind permission of Dr. Söderbaum.

[†] Reproduced from H. G. Söderbaum's "Jac. Berzelius. Levnadsteckning" by kind permission of Dr. Söderbaum.

ERBIA, YTTERBIA, AND SCANDIA

In 1878 the Swiss chemist Marignac discovered that erbia contained a new earth which he called *ytterbia* (*21*). Jean-Charles Galissard de Marignac, a descendant of a Huguenot family that had fled from Languedoc early in the eighteenth century, was born in Geneva on April 24, 1817. When he was sixteen years old, he entered the École Polytechnique at Paris. He also spent two profitable years at the School of Mines, and then rounded off his education by traveling through Scandinavia and Germany. In 1840 he went to Giessen to study under Justus von Liebig, but, in spite of the latter's influence, he preferred inorganic chemistry to organic.

Jean-Charles Galissard de Marignac, 1817–1894. Swiss chemist who discovered ytterbia and gadolinia and made many important contributions to the chemistry of the rare earths. Professor of chemistry at the University of Geneva. He made precise determinations of the atomic weights of many elements, and by separating tantalic and columbic (niobic) acids, proved that tantalum and columbium (niobium) are not identical.

Marignac's life work, which, like that of Stas, consisted in making many precise determinations of atomic weights in order to test William Prout's hypothesis (*71*), won Berzelius' sincerest praise, for he wrote:

I place the highest value on your experiments concerning atomic weights. The patience with which you repeat each experiment a large number of times, the sagacity with which you vary your methods, making use only of those which can give reliable results, and the conscientious manner in which you give the numbers dictated by the balance ought to assure for you the complete confidence of chemists (*44*).

After working for a time at the Sèvres porcelain works, Marignac returned to Switzerland to accept a modest position as professor of chemistry at the Geneva Academy. From 1845 to 1878 he taught both chemistry and mineralogy, and carried on his researches in a damp, dark cellar. During the last ten years of his life, he lay prostrate, suffering intensely from a disease of the heart, from which death finally brought release on April 15, 1894 (*12*).

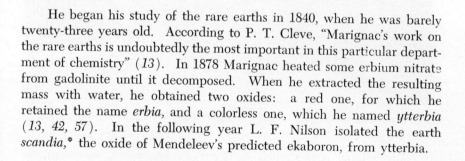

P. T. Cleve, 1840–1905. Swedish chemist, geologist, botanist, and hydrographer. Professor of chemistry at Upsala. Discoverer of thulium and independent discoverer of holmium.

He began his study of the rare earths in 1840, when he was barely twenty-three years old. According to P. T. Cleve, "Marignac's work on the rare earths is undoubtedly the most important in this particular department of chemistry" (*13*). In 1878 Marignac heated some erbium nitrate from gadolinite until it decomposed. When he extracted the resulting mass with water, he obtained two oxides: a red one, for which he retained the name *erbia*, and a colorless one, which he named *ytterbia* (*13, 42, 57*). In the following year L. F. Nilson isolated the earth *scandia*,* the oxide of Mendeleev's predicted ekaboron, from ytterbia.

ERBIA, HOLMIA, AND THULIA

The erbia left after the removal of ytterbia and scandia was still further resolved by Per Theodor Cleve,† who was born on February 10,

---

* See Chapter 25, pp. 677–83.

† For additional biographical notes on Cleve, see *J. Chem. Educ.*, **7**, 2698 (Nov., 1930).

1840. He was the thirteenth child of a Stockholm merchant. After graduating from the University of Upsala in 1863, he studied for a time in C.-A. Wurtz's laboratory in Paris, and in 1874 he became a professor at Upsala. True lover of Nature that he was, he could never confine his activities closely to one branch of science, but was interested alike in chemistry, geology, botany, and hydrography. He wrote his scientific papers in a lucid, pleasing style, and also produced literature of esthetic value (*14*).

Interior Court of a German Baker's House.° Berzelius' laboratory at the right.

Cleve's fame rests chiefly, however, on his discoveries among the rare earths. After obtaining some erbia from which all the ytterbia and scandia had been removed, and after noticing that the atomic weight of the erbium was not constant, he succeeded in resolving the earth into three constituents: *erbia, holmia,* and *thulia* (*21*). The absorption bands of holmium had already been noticed by the Swiss chemists M. Delafontaine

° Reproduced from H. G. Söderbaum's "Jac. Berzelius. Levnadsteckning" by kind permission of Dr. Söderbaum.

and J.-L. Soret (1827–1890), who had announced the existence of an "element X," later found to be identical with Cleve's holmium (35).

Louis Soret was a professor of physics at the University of Geneva. He studied the laws of electrolysis; defined the conditions for the production of ozone and determined its density and chemical constitution; devised ingenious optical instruments; and was the first scientist to make actinometric measurements on the summit of Mont Blanc (67). In 1878 he recognized the presence of a new "earth X" in erbia and characterized it by its absorption spectrum, but later accepted the name *holmia* which Cleve gave it (67). He died in Geneva in 1890 at the age of sixty-three

Jöns Jacob Berzelius,[°] 1779–1848. (From a painting by J. Way.) Berzelius was an independent discoverer of the earth "ceria" and much of the early research on the rare earths was done in his laboratory.

years. Since Cleve was an independent discoverer of the element holmium, his name for it has been accepted by chemists (14, 36, 67). Holmium was named for Cleve's native city, and the word *thulium* is derived from *Thule*, an old name for Scandinavia.

In spite of his devotion to organic and inorganic chemistry, Cleve never lost interest in biology. During his later years he made an extended study of the plankton of Skagerak and the North Sea, especially of the freshwater algae and diatoms, in order to locate the ocean currents.

Although he found little time to mingle with his colleagues, he enjoyed an occasional happy, social evening with his family and friends. Hans and Astrid Euler said of him, "His merry irony played upon all those for

[°] Reproduced from H. G. Söderbaum's "Jac. Berzelius. Levnadstecking" by kind permission of Dr. Söderbaum.

whom unyielding principles and passionateness caused unnecessary trouble, and upon scientific pedantry no less than upon religious and social prejudice; he himself was liberal in the broadest sense of the word, and unyielding only in his rectitude." He retired from teaching at the age of sixty-five years, hoping to devote the rest of his life to the study of plankton. He died a few months later, however, on June 18, 1905, after severe suffering with pleuritis (*14*).

SAMARIA AND GADOLINIA

Marignac believed as early as 1853 that Mosander's didymia was not a pure substance, and later spectroscopic work of Marc Delafontaine and of Lecoq de Boisbaudran indicated that the spectrum of didymia varied according to its source. Boisbaudran in 1879 added ammonium hydroxide to a solution of it, and noticed that another earth precipitated before the didymia. Since the spectrum of this new oxide was found to be different

A Reconstruction of Berzelius' Birthplace at Wäfversunda (Väversunda), Sweden, showing the buildings as they appeared in his time.*

from that of didymia, Boisbaudran concluded that it must be a new earth, which he named *samaria* (*26, 27*). In 1886 he obtained from it still another earth, which, however, proved to be identical with the sub-

* Reproduced from H. G. Söderbaum's "Jac. Berzelius. Levnadsteckning" by kind permission of Dr. Söderbaum.

stance which Marignac had separated from samarskite in 1880, and to which he had given the provisional name Yα (3). With Marignac's assent, Boisbaudran named this oxide *gadolinia* (34, 57). Both these earths were named for minerals in which they occur, samarskite and gadolinite.

NEODYMIA AND PRASEODYMIA

Marignac, Lecoq de Boisbaudran, Cleve, and Bohuslav Brauner all believed didymium to be a mixture of elements, but none of them were able to make the difficult separation (49). In 1882 Professor Brauner of the University of Prague examined some of his didymia fractions with the spectroscope and found a group of absorption bands in the blue region ($\lambda=449$–443) and another in the yellow ($\lambda=590$–568) (53, 66).* These two groups of bands are now known to belong to two earths, *praseodymia* and *neodymia*, respectively, which Baron Auer von Welsbach obtained in 1885 by splitting didymia (3, 30, 32, 58).

The Caroline Institute of Medicine and Surgery at Stockholm. Both Berzelius and Mosander taught chemistry at this School of Medicine.

Carl Auer, Baron von Welsbach, was born on September 1, 1858, at Vienna (4). After completing the courses at the gymnasium and Polytechnicum of his native city, he went to Heidelberg to study under Robert Bunsen. The quiet, industrious, unsociable boy from Austria soon became a favorite of the great German master. Auer was deeply interested in inorganic chemistry, and especially in minerals. The rare earth minerals of the north attracted him so much that he began to search for specimens.

* See p. 717.

Although the first little collection that he showed to Bunsen would not have filled a child's hand, Bunsen laughingly told him to begin his investigation (*16*). Carl Auer's researches on the rare earths, which were begun in this modest manner at Heidelberg, were continued for the rest of his life.

On June 18, 1885, he announced to the Vienna Academy of Sciences that by repeated fractionation of ammonium didymium nitrate he had succeeded in splitting didymia into two earths, for which he proposed the names *praseodymia* and *neodymia, green didymia* and *new didymia.* Many chemists were skeptical, and he afterward said, "Only Bunsen, to

Herbert Newby McCoy, 1870–1945. American chemist who made outstanding contributions to radioactivity and the chemistry of the rare earths. In 1904 he showed that radium is produced by spontaneous transmutation of uranium. Three years later, in collaboration with W. H. Ross, he pointed out the identical chemical behavior of the compounds of certain elements which F. Soddy later called *isotopes.* Dr. McCoy also gave the first quantitative proof that the α-ray activity of uranium compounds is directly proportional to their uranium content (*78*).

Courtesy Dr. Ethel M. Terry
(Mrs. H. N. McCoy)

whom I first showed the discovery, recognized immediately that a splitting of didymium had actually been accomplished. This acknowledgment from Bunsen, who had, as is known, published very beautiful and comprehensive researches on didymium, showed how unselfishly this great investigator used to judge the researches of younger men" (*16*). Neodymia and praseodymia have never been decomposed into simpler oxides.

Baron Auer is best remembered for his invention of the incandescent gas mantle, a truly great advance in the history of illumination (*55*). Instead of attempting to produce a gas which would burn with a luminous flame, he decided to use a non-luminous flame to heat a refractory mantle to incandescence. The problem, as he said, "was not to find a process by which an infusible compound could be given a definite shape. This invention is founded, above all, on the fact, proved by numerous experiments, that molecular mixtures of certain oxides are possessed of properties which cannot be deduced from those of their constituents." One of the engineers to whom he explained his plans said, "In my works we only take notice of serious ideas."

After many discouragements Baron von Welsbach finally impregnated the fabric for the mantles in a mixture containing one thousand grams of thorium nitrate, ten grams of cerium nitrate, five grams of beryllium nitrate, 1.5 grams of magnesium nitrate, and two thousand grams of water (*15*). His first patent for the incandescent lamp, known in Germany as the "Auerlicht" and in America as the *Welsbach mantle*, was dated September 23, 1885.

Baron Auer von Welsbach, 1858–1929. Austrian chemist and chemical technologist. Discoverer of praseodymium and neodymium. Inventor of the Welsbach gas mantle, the osmium filament electric lamp, and the automatic gas lighter.

Baron Auer chose as his motto the appropriate words *"more light,"* but preferred to write it *"plus lucis"* as a reminder of his early struggles with Latin (*49*). In 1901 Kaiser Franz Josef elevated him to the hereditary nobility with the title of Freiherr von Welsbach. When the Kaiser remarked, "You have had, so I hear, considerable success with your discoveries," Baron von Welsbach quickly replied, "Yes, Your Majesty, up to the present more than 40,000 people throughout the entire world have found employment through my discoveries." This reply left Franz Josef speechless (*16*).

Auer von Welsbach also invented the automatic gas lighter based on a pyrophoric alloy of iron and cerium, and the osmium-filament electric lamp (54), the first successful electric-light bulb with a metallic filament, which, however, was soon superseded by the tungsten and tantalum lamps.

His home, Welsbach Castle, commanded a glorious view of the Carinthian Alps, and his chief recreations were hunting, fishing, and gardening. In the park were many exotic plants, including cedars from Lebanon, that he had carefully nurtured until they could withstand the severe climatic conditions at the high altitude of 800 meters. On the ground floor of the castle there was a well-equipped laboratory containing a valuable

Bohuslav Brauner, 1855–1935. Professor of chemistry at the Bohemian University of Prague. He made brilliant contributions to analytical chemistry, the determination of atomic weights, and the chemistry of the rare earths. In 1902 he predicted the existence of element 61, now known as promethium.

J. Heyrovsky, Czechoslov. Chem. Communications

spectroscope which his aunt had provided for his early researches, a library of valuable books with uncut pages, which had belonged to Bunsen, and an unsurpassed collection of rare earths. These treasures were carefully guarded by the ever-faithful "Buzi," a terrier who allowed no one but his master to touch even a piece of paper. On August 2, 1929, Baron Auer was seized with severe abdominal pain. After a painful examination by physicians, who realized the serious nature of the illness, "he got up, went into the garden, looked around, closed up his study, burned a few papers, stood for a long time before his father's portrait, then went into the laboratory, covered his spectroscope, stroked it tenderly with his hand, glanced at the other things, took leave of his last unfinished thulium series with a motion of the hand, closed the rooms again, and quietly lay down" (49). Twelve hours later he entered into eternal rest.

The following literal translation of a postcard from Professor Bohuslav Brauner to Dr. Max Speter is published by kind permission of Dr. Speter. It was written in reply to a question as to whether or not Brauner and Auer von Welsbach were students under Mendeleev. Dr. Brauner was about seventy-eight years old when he wrote this card.

Prague, Weinberge, Polska 14,
May 18, 1933

ESTEEMED COLLEAGUE:

It pleased me that you welcomed my reprints. I am a genuine Praguer. I was with Master Mendelejew in 1882, but did not hear that *he* [Auer von Welsbach] had been with him. M. wished to work with me, on H_2:O in fact, yet I could not remain! M. visited me in Prague, and I later went to see him in Petersburg. I remember well that you once visited me in Prague. It is interesting that A. W. [Auer von Welsbach] often did the same as I. I learned from Bunsen in 1878–9 how to work with the rare earths; he did the same in 1883, but when I was visiting the same place, he [A. v. W.?] did not present himself. I found in 1882, through study of the decomposition products of the old didymium, that it can be split into two earths (absorption spectra) and published a note on it in the Wiener Anzeiger. He published his work on praseodymium and neodymium in 1885.

Cordially yours,
PROF. BRAUNER

HOLMIA AND DYSPROSIA

In the year 1886 Lecoq de Boisbaudran separated pure holmia into two earths, which he called *holmia* and *dysprosia*. He accomplished this by fractional precipitation, first with ammonium hydroxide and then with a saturated solution of potassium sulfate, and found that the constituents of impure holmium solutions precipitate in the following order: terbium, dysprosium, holmium, and erbium (3, 37, 48). Lecoq de Boisbaudran never had an abundant supply of raw materials for his remarkable researches on the rare earths, and he once confided to Professor Urbain that most of his fractionations had been carried out on the marble slab of his fireplace (56).

SAMARIA AND EUROPIA

Eugène-Anatole Demarçay, the discoverer of europium, was born in Paris on New Year's Day, 1852. He studied at the Lycée Condorcet, spent a year in England, and at the age of eighteen years entered the

École Polytechnique (4). He was interested not only in chemistry, but also in geology, natural history, and languages. His good humor, intellectual integrity, and ability to think independently soon won the respect and friendship of his professors, A.-A.-T. Cahours, C.-A. Wurtz, H. Sainte-Claire Deville, J.-B.-A. Dumas, Charles Friedel, M.-A. Cornu, Paul Schützenberger, and Lecoq de Boisbaudran, and his love of pure science brought him into contact with many younger investigators, including Henri Moissan, A.-H. Becquerel, and the Curies. After serving for some time as Cahours' assistant at the École Polytechnique, he gave up his position in order to travel through Algeria, Egypt, and India (50). When he returned to Paris, he devoted all his time to research in pure science.

Eugène-Anatole Demarçay, 1852–1904. French chemist who discovered the element europium and gave spectroscopic proof of the discovery of radium by M. and Mme. Curie. He investigated many terpenes and ethers, and studied the volatility of metals at low temperatures and pressures.

His first investigations, begun in 1876, were in organic chemistry. His study of the C_5 terpenes and the ethers of the unsaturated acids proved to be of practical value in the perfume industry. While studying the sulfides of nitrogen he suffered a serious accident. The explosion of a cast-iron vessel completely destroyed one of his eyes, yet, after recovering from the injury and shock, he continued his dangerous researches on compressed gases. In his famous laboratory on the Boulevard Berthier he had the finest apparatus for producing vacua to be found in Paris. This was used for studying the volatility of zinc, cadmium, and gold at low temperatures and pressures (50).

Berzelius' Grave* in the Solna Churchyard

In order to study the effect of very high temperatures on spark spectra, Demarçay constructed an induction coil with a short secondary wire of large diameter, which gave intensely hot, luminous, globular sparks. By using electrodes of very pure platinum, he was able to eliminate from the spectrum of the substance he wished to examine all foreign spectra except the well-known lines of platinum. This was the apparatus with which he studied the spectra of the rare earths.

In 1901 Demarçay made an elaborate series of fractionations of samarium magnesium nitrate which resulted in the discovery of a new earth, *europia* (3, 31, 59). Since he could read a complex spectrum "like an open book," he was frequently called upon to pass judgment on supposedly new elements, and was the first to observe the new lines of radium in some barium salts brought by Pierre Curie.

Had he been granted a longer life, Demarçay might have made a more thorough study of the compounds of europium, but in 1904 death

* Reproduced from H. G. Söderbaum's "Jac. Berzelius. Levnadsteckning" by courtesy of Dr. Söderbaum.

brought an end to his researches. Although he had realized for some time that his life would soon be cut short, he nevertheless felt "grateful for the years he had lived" and "asked for no further reward than that felt by a keen intelligence when it gives rise to a flash of thought that will be remembered throughout the world" (50).

YTTERBIA AND LUTETIA

In 1907 Georges Urbain separated ytterbia into two constituents. By repeated fractional crystallization of ytterbium nitrate from nitric acid solution, he obtained two oxides with different properties. One of these he named *neoytterbia* in order, as he said, "to leave to the illustrious

Georges Urbain, 1872–1938. French chemist, painter, sculptor, and musician. President of the Société de Chimie and of the International Committee on Atomic Weights. His enthusiasm for research was acquired from Pierre Curie and Charles Friedel. *See* ref. (70)

Courtesy Dr. R. E. Oesper

Marignac, in the future, the credit of his fundamental discovery" (52). The other oxide he called *lutecia* from an old name for his native city, Paris (3, 38, 39, 51). The spelling has been changed to *lutetia*. The element he named *neoytterbium* is now known simply as *ytterbium*. Although these elements were found to be identical with the "alde-baranium" and "cassiopeium" discovered independently by Auer von Welsbach at about the same time, Urbain's names for them have been widely accepted.*

* In German periodicals, however, lutetium is called cassiopeium.

P. SCHUTZENBERGER

URBAIN

1829-1929

CHIMIE MINÉRALE

MATIÈRES COLORANTES

INDUSTRIES CHIMIQUES

ALBUMINOÏDES

Courtesy Tenney L. Davis

Memorial Plaque Designed by Georges Urbain in Honor of the Schützen-berger Centennial. This is a fine example of Professor Urbain's artistic ability.

Georges Urbain was born on April 12, 1872, received his doctorate from the University of Paris in 1899, and afterward became a professor there (4). He received inspiration and encouragement in his researches from Pierre Curie and Lecoq de Boisbaudran (53). Until his death on November 5, 1938, he was a professor at the Sorbonne and chief of the chemical division of the French Institute of Physico-Chemical Biology founded by Baron Edmond de Rothschild (17). Professor Urbain was a member of the Institute of France and of the International Commission on Atomic Weights. He is famous not only for his work on the rare earths (52), spectroscopy, magnetism, cathode phosphorescence, and atomic weights, but also for his beautiful artistic productions, among which may be mentioned the plaque which he designed in honor of the Schützenberger centennial (18, 70).

Before the news of Urbain's discovery reached America, Professor Charles James of the University of New Hampshire had prepared a large amount of very pure lutetia. Although deeply disappointed because his caution and delay in publishing his results had caused him to lose priority in this discovery, he accepted Urbain's results without question and never pushed his own claim (19, 60).

Charles James was born at Earls Barton, near Northampton, England, on April 27, 1880. At the age of nineteen years he entered University

College, London, where Sir William Ramsay and his colleagues had recently discovered the inert gases. From 1906 until his untimely death in 1928, Professor James served as an inspiring teacher of chemistry at the University of New Hampshire. He published in the *Journal of the American Chemical Society* about sixty papers on the rare earth elements, worked out processes for extracting them from their minerals and separating them one from another, made accurate determinations of their atomic weights, and discovered new rare earth compounds. He often prepared these substances in unusually large amounts and generously shared them with other investigators (60).

Professor James displayed remarkable ingenuity in devising new, economical, efficient methods of separating the rare earths and in observing the progress of these separations by photographing the spectra of his products. After thorough study of the solubilities of the rare earth bromates, he worked out a bromate method of fractionating the members of the cerium group. The James method of fractional crystallization of the double magnesium rare earth nitrates is probably the most widely used means of separating this group into fractions (60).

Although it is extremely difficult to prepare rare earth salts pure enough for atomic weight determinations, the James values for thulium, samarium, and yttrium agree almost exactly with the atomic weights accepted by the International Committee. Professor James also made outstanding contributions to the chemistry of other rare elements such as scandium, gallium, germanium, beryllium, and uranium (60).

This remarkable work was all accomplished during a very short span of life. Professor James died in Boston on December 10, 1928, at the age of forty-eight years. In the following year, a fine, new, four-story chemistry building at the University of New Hampshire was named in his honor (19).

The following diagrams which Professor James prepared for the Fourteenth Edition of the Encyclopedia Britannica show very clearly the separations by which the original complex earths "ceria" and "yttria" were resolved into the simple oxides of the rare earth metals.

$$
\text{Ce}\begin{cases}\text{Ce}\\\text{La}\end{cases}\begin{cases}\text{La}\\\text{Di}\end{cases}\begin{cases}\text{Di}\\\text{Sa}\end{cases}\begin{cases}\begin{cases}\text{Nd}\\\text{Pr}\end{cases}\begin{cases}\text{Nd}\\\text{Il}^*\end{cases}\\\begin{cases}\text{Sa}\\\text{Gd}\end{cases}\begin{cases}\text{Sa}\\\text{Eu}\end{cases}\end{cases}
\qquad
\text{Y}\begin{cases}\text{Y}\\\text{Er}\ldots\text{Tb}\\\text{Tb}\ldots\text{Er}\end{cases}\begin{cases}\text{Yb}\begin{cases}\text{Yb}\\\text{Lu}\end{cases}\\\text{Er}\begin{cases}\text{Er}\\\text{Ho}\\\text{Tm}\end{cases}\begin{cases}\text{Ho}\\\text{Dy}\end{cases}\end{cases}
$$

* Element 61, then known as illinium (Il), is now called promethium (Pm).

Courtesy of University of New Hampshire

Charles James, 1880–1928. Director of the chemistry department at the University of New Hampshire. Author of many papers on the rare earths. Independent discoverer of lutetium. He was born in England and studied under Sir William Ramsay.

B. Smith Hopkins, Professor of Chemistry at the University of Illinois. He carried out many researches in the fields of rare earths and atomic weights.

The metals of the rare earths comprise the largest of all the natural groups (*25, 47*). Most of them have been prepared in the metallic state (*20, 24, 33, 61, 62, 63, 68*).

LITERATURE CITED

(*1*)   BASKERVILLE, C., "The elements: Verified and unverified," *Science* [N. S.] **19,** 93 (Jan. 15, 1904). Quotation from Sir William Crookes.

(*2*)   T. E. T., "Johan Gadolin," *Nature,* **86,** 48–9 (Mar. 9, 1911).

(*3*)   SPENCER, J. F., "The Metals of the Rare Earths," Longmans, Green and Co., London, **1919,** pp. 2–10.

(*4*)   POGGENDORFF, J. C., "Biographisch-Literarisches Handwörterbuch zur Geschichte der exakten Wissenschaften," 6 vols., Verlag Chemie, Leipzig and Berlin, **1863–1937.** Articles on Mosander, Auer (von Welsbach), Demarçay, Urbain, and Gadolin.

(*5*)   SÖDERBAUM, H. G., "Jac. Berzelius Bref," Vol. 2, part 5, Almqvist and Wiksells. Upsala, **1912–1914,** p. 43. Letter of Berzelius to Mulder, Sept. 24, 1837.

(*6*)   WALLACH, O., "Briefwechsel zwischen J. Berzelius und F. Wöhler," Vol. 1, Verlag von Wilhelm Engelmann, Leipzig, **1901,** p. 57.

(*7*)   "Latanium, a new metal," *Phil Mag.,* **14,** 390–1 (May, 1839); *Pogg. Ann.,* **46,** 648 (1839).

(*8*)   WALLACH, O., "Briefwechsel zwischen J. Berzelius und F. Wöhler," Ref. (*6*), Vol. 2, p. 94.

(9) *Ibid.*, Vol. 2, pp. 295–6.

(10) *Ibid.*, Vol. 2, pp. 320–1.

(11) *Ibid.*, Vol. 2, p. 718.

(12) ADOR, E., "Jean-Charles Galissard de Marignac, Sein Leben und seine Werke," *Ber.*, **27**, 979–1021 (Part 4, 1894).

(13) "Chemical Society Memorial Lectures, 1893–1900," Gurney and Jackson, London, **1901**, pp. 468–89. Marignac Memorial Lecture by Cleve.

(14) EULER, H. and A. EULER, "Per Theodor Cleve," *Ber.*, **38**, 4221–38 (Part 4, 1905); Kungl. Svenska Vetenskapsakademiens Årsbok, **1906**, pp. 187–217.

(15) AUER VON WELSBACH, CARL, "History of the invention of incandescent gas-lighting," *Chem. News*, **85**, 254–6 (May 30, 1902).

(16) FELDHAUS, "Zum 70. Geburtstage von Auer von Welsbach," *Chem.-Ztg.*, **52**, 689–90 (Sept. 1, 1928).

(17) KHOUVINE, Y., "The New French Institute of Physico-Chemical Biology," *J. Chem. Educ.*, **7**, 1053–4 (May, 1930).

(18) DAVIS, T. L., "Paul Schützenberger," *J. Chem. Educ.*, **6**, 1413 (Sept., 1929).

(19) IDDLES, H. A., "The Charles James Hall of Chemistry of the University of New Hampshire," *J. Chem. Educ.*, **7**, 812–20 (Apr., 1930).

(20) SPENCER, J. F., "The Metals of the Rare Earths," Ref. (*3*), pp. 71–158.

(21) "Some elements yielded by yttrium. A classic of science," *Sci. News Letter*, **20**, 22–3 (July 11, 1931).

(22) "Vom Hrn. Bergm. Geijer in Stockholm," *Crell's Ann.*, **9**, 229–30 (Part 1, 1788).

(23) MOSANDER, C. G., *Berzelius Jahresber.*, **23**, 145; **24**, 105.

(24) HILLEBRAND, W. F. and T. H. NORTON, *Pogg. Ann.*, **155**, 631 (1875); **156**, 466 (1876); W. MUTHMANN, HOFER, and L. WEISS, "Ueber die Darstellung der Metalle der Cergruppe durch Schmelzelektrolyse," *Ann.*, **320**, 231–69 (Heft 2, 1902); W. MUTHMANN and L. WEISS, "Untersuchungen über die Metalle der Cergruppe," *ibid.*, **331**, 1–46 (Heft 1, 1904); ALCAN HIRSCH, "Metallic cerium," *Met. Chem. Eng.*, **9**, 540–4 (Oct., 1911); WINKLER, K. A., "Ueber die Reduction von Sauerstoffverbindungen durch Magnesium," *Ber.*, **23**, 772–92 (Part 1, 1890); CLEVE, P. T., "Recherches sur l'erbium et sur l'yttrium," *Bull. soc. chim.* (Paris) [2], **21**, 344–8 (1874); CLEVE, P. T. and HÖGLUND, "Sur les combinaisons de l'yttrium et de l'erbium," *ibid.*, [2], **18**, 193–201 (1872).

(25) LEVY, "The Rare Earths. Their Occurrence, Chemistry, and Technology," Longmans, Green and Co., New York City, **1915**, pp. 135–41.

(26) DE BOISBAUDRAN, LECOQ, "Nouvelles raies spectrales observées dans des substances extraites de la samarskite," *Compt. rend.*, **88**, 322–4 (Feb. 17, 1879).

(27) "Cerium group of rare earths. A classic of science," *Sci. News Letter*, **20**, 138–40 (Aug. 29, 1931). Reprints and reviews of papers by Vauquelin, Mosander, Boisbaudran, Auer von Welsbach, Demarçay, and Harris, Yntema, and Hopkins.

(28) MOSANDER, C. G., "Lanthan, ein neues Metall," *Pogg. Ann.*, **46**, 648 (1839).

(29) MOSANDER, C. G., "Ueber ein neues Metall, Didym," *ibid.*, **56**, 503 (1842).

(30) AUER VON WELSBACH, CARL, "Die Zerlegung des Didyms in seine Elemente," *Ber.*, **18**, 605 (Part 3, 1885).

(31) DEMARÇAY, E.-A., "Sur le samarium," *Compt. rend.*, **130**, 1185–8 (Apr. 30, 1900); "Sur un nouvel élément, l'europium," *ibid.*, **132**, 1484–6 (June 17, 1901).

(32) AUER VON WELSBACH, CARL, "Die Zerlegung des Didyms in seine Elemente," *Monatsh.*, **6**, 477–91 (1885).

(33) LEVY, "The Rare Earths," Ref. (*25*), pp. 114–6.

(34) MARIGNAC, J.-C. G., "Sur les terres de la samarskite," *Compt. rend.*, **90**, 899–903 (Apr. 19, 1880).

(35) Soret, J.-L., "Sur les spectres d'absorption ultra-violets des terres de la gadolinite," *Compt. rend.*, **86**, 1062–4 (Apr. 29, 1878); *ibid.*, **89**, 521–3 (Sept. 15, 1879).

(36) Cleve, P. T., "Sur deux nouveaux éléments dans l'erbine," *Compt. rend.*, **89**, 478–81 (Sept. 1, 1879); "Sur l'erbine," *ibid.*, **89**, 708–9 (Oct. 27, 1879).

(37) de Boisbaudran, Lecoq, "L'holmine (ou terre X de M. Soret) contient au moins deux radicaux métalliques," *Compt. rend.*, **102**, 1003–5 (May 3, 1886).

(38) Auer von Welsbach, Carl, "Ueber die Elemente der Yttergruppe," *Monatsh.*, **27**, 935–45 (Heft 8, 1906); "Die Zerlegung des Ytterbiums in seine Elemente," *ibid.*, **29**, 181–225 (Heft 2, 1908).

(39) Urbain, G., "Un nouvel élément, le lutécium résultant du dédoublement de l'ytterbium de Marignac," *Compt. rend.*, **145**, 759–62 (Nov. 4, 1907).

(40) "The first of the rare earths. A classic of science," *Sci. News Letter*, **19**, 314–5 (May 16, 1931).

(41) Ekeberg, A. G., "Fernere Untersuchungen der schwarzen Steinart von Ytterby, und der in derselben gefundenen eigenthümlichen Erde," *Crell's Ann.*, **32**, 63–73 (Part 2, 1799).

(42) Marignac, J.-C. G., "Sur l'ytterbine, nouvelle terre contenue dans la gadolinite," *Compt. rend.*, **87**, 578–81 (Oct. 22, 1878).

(43) Komppa, G., "Über ältere finnische Chemiker," *Z. angew. Chem.*, **40**, 1431–4 (Dec. 1, 1927).

(44) Söderbaum, H. G., "Jac. Berzelius Bref," Ref. (5), Vol. 3, part 7, p. 210. Letter of Berzelius to Marignac, May 31, 1844.

(45) "Notice respecting lantanium, extracted from a letter of Berzelius to Professor Kersten of Freiberg," *Phil. Mag.* [3], **15**, 286–7 (Oct., 1839).

(46) Mosander, C. G., "On the new metals lanthanium and didymium, which are associated with cerium; and on erbium and terbium, new metals associated with yttria," *Phil. Mag.*, [3], **23**, 241–54 (Oct., 1843).

(47) Friend, J. N., "The periodic sphere and the position of the rare earth metals." *Chem. News*, **130**, 196–7 (Mar., 1925); *J. Chem. Educ.*, **2**, 409–11 (May, 1925).

(48) de Boisbaudran, Lecoq, "Sur le dysprosium," *Compt. rend.*, **102**, 1005–6 (May 3, 1886).

(49) D'Ans, J., "Carl Freiherr Auer von Welsbach," *Ber.*, **64**, 59–92 (May 6, 1931).

(50) Etard, M. A., "The life and work of Eugène Demarçay," *Chem. News*, **89**, 137–9 (Mar. 18, 1904); *Bull. soc. chim.* (Paris) [3], **32**, 1 (1904).

(51) Urbain, G., "A new element, lutecium, obtained by splitting up Marignac's ytterbium," *Chem. News*, **96**, 271–2 (Dec. 6, 1907); "Lutecium and neoytterbium," *ibid.*, **97**, 157 (Apr. 3, 1908); "Europium, gadolinium, terbium, neoytterbium, and lutecium," *ibid.*, **100**, 73–5 (Aug. 13, 1909).

(52) Urbain, G., "Twenty-five years of research on the yttrium earths," *Chem. Reviews*, **1**, 143–85 (July, 1924).

(53) Urbain, G., "Discours sur les Éléments Chimiques et les Atomes. Hommage au Professor Bohuslav Brauner," *Rec. trav. chim. Pays-Bas*, **44**, 281–304 (1925).

(54) "Karl Auer, Ritter von Welsbach," *J. Chem. Educ.*, **6**, 2051–2 (Nov., 1929).

(55) Wolfe, J. H., "Important facts in the development of the manufactured gas industry with particular regard to the influence of chemical research," *J. Chem. Educ.*, **6**, 739–40 (Apr., 1929).

(56) Urbain, G., "Lecoq de Boisbaudran," *Chem-Ztg.*, **36**, 929–33 (Aug. 15, 1912).

(57) Ador, E., "Oeuvres complètes de J.-C. G. de Marignac," Vol. 2, Masson et Cie., Paris, pp. 683–711.

(58) Sedlacek, F., "Auer von Welsbach," Julius Springer, Vienna, **1934**, 85 pp.

(59) McCoy, H. N., "Europium, a rae earth element," *Chem. Bull.*, **24**, 251–9 (Sept., 1937).

(60) SMITH, MELVIN M., L. A. PRATT, and B. S. HOPKINS, "The Life and Work of Charles James," Northeastern section of the American Chemical Society, Cambridge, Mass., 1932, 26 pp.

(61) TROMBE, F., "Metallic europium," Compt. rend., 206, 1380–7 (1938).

(62) KLEM, W. and H. BOMMER, "The rare earth metals," Z. anorg. allgem. Chem., 231, 138–71 (1937).

(63) BERTRAND, L., "Metallic europium," La Nature, 66, 92 (Aug. 1, 1938).

(64) SCHIERZ, E. R., "The Gadolin Medal," Ind. Eng. Chem., News Ed., 16, 585 (Nov. 10, 1938); "Finnish chemists," J. Chem. Educ., 14, 161–5 (Apr., 1937).

(65) HJELT, E. and R. TIGERSTEDT, "Johan Gadolin, 1760–1852. In memoriam. Wissenschaftliche Abhandlungen Johan Gadolins in Auswahl," Helsingfors, 1910. Finnish Society of Sciences.

(66) Private communication of Dr. Brauner to Dr. Speter, May 18, 1933.

(67) ANON., "L. Soret," Chem. News, 61, 288–9 (June 13, 1890).

(68) McCOY, H. N., "The electrolysis of rare earth acetates and the separation of europium as amalgam from other rare earths," J. Am. Chem. Soc., 63, 3432–3 (Dec., 1941); H. N. McCOY and R. P. HAMMOND, "The separation of ytterbium from accompanying rare earths by means of its amalgam," ibid., 64, 1009 (1942).

(69) "Biographie öfver Carl Axel Arrhenius," K. Vet. Acad. Handl., 1824, pp. 495–9.

(70) CHAMPETIER, G. and C. H. BOATNER, "Georges Urbain," J. Chem. Educ., 17, 103–9 (March, 1940).

(71) GLASSTONE, SAMUEL, "William Prout (1785–1850)," J. Chem. Educ., 24, 478–81 (Oct., 1947); BENFEY, O. T., "Prout's hypothesis," ibid., 29, 78–81 (Feb., 1952).

(72) SAMPEY, J. R., "J. Lawrence Smith," J. Chem. Educ., 5, 123–8 (Feb., 1928).

(73) SÖDERBAUM, H. G., "Jac. Berzelius Brev," Suppl. 2 (edited by Arne Holmberg), Royal Swedish Academy of Sciences, Stockholm, 1941, pp. 106–7, 110.

(74) ANON., "Öfver-Directeuren Bengt Reinh. Geyers [sic] Biographie," K. Vet. Acad. Handl., 1816, pp. 296–9.

(75) THOMSON, THOMAS, "Travels through Sweden in the Autumn of 1812," Robert Baldwin, London, 1813, pp. 193–4, 228–9, 241–4.

(76) PETERSSON, WALFR., "Studier öfver gadolinit," Geol. Fören. i Stockholm Förh., 12, 275–347 (1890).

(77) FLINK, G., "Bidrag till Sveriges Mineralogi," Arkiv Kemi, Mineralogi och Geologi, 6, 82–3 (1917).

(78) McCOY. H. N., "Retrospect." Address on the Occasion of the Award of the Willard Gibbs Medal, Chem. Bull., 24, 207–24 (June, 1937).

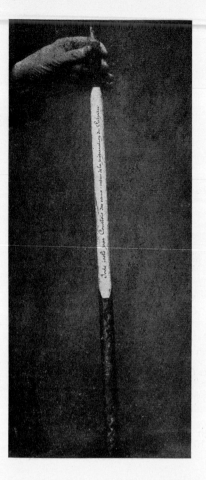

Sealed Tube Containing Iodine isolated by Courtois from the mother liquors from the preparation of saltpeter. This tube, belonging to the Solvay Company of Belgium, was presented at the iodine centenary (Nov. 9, 1913) through the courtesy of M. C. Crinon.

From Toraude's "Bernard Courtois et la Découverte de l'Iode"

La recherche d'un corps simple est toujours très captivante (1, 17).

The search for an element is always captivating.

La science ne paraît pas seulement avoir pour mission de satisfaire chez l'homme ce besoin de tout connaître, de tout apprendre, qui caractérise la plus noble de nos facultés; elle en a aussi une autre, moins brillante sans doute, mais peut-être plus morale, je dirai presque plus sainte, qui consiste à coördonner les forces de la nature pour augmenter la production et rapprocher les hommes de l'égalité par l'universalité du bien-être (2).

Science appears to have as its mission not merely the satisfaction of man's need of learning and understanding everything, which characterizes the noblest of our faculties; it has another aim, doubtless less brilliant but perhaps more moral, I would almost say more sacred, which consists in coördinating the forces of nature to increase production and make men more nearly equal by the universality of comfort.

27

The halogen family

The discovery of the four halogens required a little more than a century. Although Scheele prepared chlorine in 1774 by the action of manganese dioxide on hydrochloric acid, it was believed to be a compound until after 1810, when Sir Humphry Davy gave convincing proof of its elementary nature. In 1811 Bernard Courtois isolated iodine from the mother liquor obtained by leaching the ashes of marine algae. Balard's discovery of bromine fifteen years later was an especially important event in the history of science, for chemists were just beginning to realize that there are family groups among the elements and Döbereiner soon observed that chlorine, bromine, and iodine form a closely related triad. The long, dangerous search for fluorine, which brought suffering and death to several promising chemists, culminated successfully in 1886 through the brilliant efforts of Moissan.

CHLORINE

*I*n his famous research on pyrolusite, C. W. Scheele allowed hydrochloric acid, or *spiritus salis* as he called it, to stand in contact with finely ground pyrolusite (crude manganese dioxide), and noticed that the acid acquired thereby a suffocating odor like that of warm aqua regia, and "most oppressive to the lungs." He thought that the manganese dioxide had taken the combustible principle, phlogiston, from the hydrochloric acid, and therefore called the gas "*dephlogisticated marine acid*," or "*dephlogisticated muriatic acid*." He noticed that it dissolved slightly in water, imparting to it an acid taste, that it bleached colored flowers and green leaves, and that it attacked all metals (3).

A.-L. Lavoisier thought that all acids contain oxygen. Dr. William Henry, who obtained hydrogen by passing an electric discharge through gaseous "marine acid," concluded that it came from the water, and that water must be an essential constituent of hydrochloric acid (37, 38). C.-L. Berthollet, who was a partisan of Lavoisier and not a phlogistonist, noticed that calcined pyrolusite, which had lost some of the oxygen from its manganese dioxide, yielded less of the suffocating gas, "dephlogisticated marine acid," than could be obtained from an equal weight of fresh pyrolusite. He concluded that:

It is therefore to the vital air [oxygen] of the manganese [pyrolusite], which combines with the marine acid, that the formation of the dephlogisticated marine acid is due. I ought to state that this theory was presented and announced some time ago by M. Lavoisier, and that M. de Fourcroy made use of it in his "Elements of Chemistry and Natural History" to explain the properties of dephlogisticated marine acid such as they were then known.

Count Claude-Louis Berthollet, 1748–1822. French chemist and physician. Professor at the École Normale. He collaborated with Lavoisier in his researches and in reforming chemical nomenclature. Berthollet's "Essai de statique chimique" emphasized the importance of the relative masses of the reacting substances in chemical reactions.

Berthollet thought that the gas now known as chlorine was a loose compound of hydrochloric acid and oxygen (*112*), or, to use his own words, that:

[Dephlogisticated marine acid] is manifestly formed by the combination of vital air with marine acids but in it the vital air is deprived of a part of the principle of elasticity, and adheres so feebly to the marine acids that the action of light suffices to disengage it promptly, light having more affinity for its base than marine acid has (*4*).

In the year 1807 Sir Humphry Davy obtained hydrogen by the action of potassium on "muriatic acid," and concluded that it must have come from the water in the acid, and that the oxygen in the water must have converted the potassium to potassium oxide (*5*). Gay-Lussac and Thenard, however, did not accept the explanation. They argued that the hydrogen came neither from the acid nor from the water, but from

William Henry, 1775–1836. British chemist and manufacturer, and author of books on chemistry. He discovered that when a gas is absorbed in a liquid, the weight dissolved is proportional to the pressure of the gas (Henry's law). He thought that water was an essential constituent of hydrochloric acid.

Title Page of William Henry's "Epitome of Chemistry." In the original, Benjamin Silliman's autograph can be seen just above the words "Professor of Chemistry."

EPITOME

OF

CHEMISTRY,

IN

THREE PARTS.

PART I.
INTENDED TO FACILITATE THE ACQUISITION OF CHEMICAL KNOWLEDGE, BY MINUTE INSTRUCTIONS FOR THE PERFORMANCE OF EXPERIMENTS.

PART II.
DIRECTIONS FOR THE ANALYSIS OF MINERAL WATERS ; OF EARTHS AND STONES ; OF ORES OF METALS ; AND OF MINERAL BODIES IN GENERAL. AND,

PART III.
INSTRUCTIONS FOR APPLYING CHEMICAL TESTS AND REAGENTS TO VARIOUS USEFUL PURPOSES.

By WILLIAM HENRY.

FROM THE FOURTH ENGLISH EDITION :
MUCH ENLARGED AND ILLUSTRATED WITH PLATES.

To which are added NOTES by a Professor of Chemistry in this Country.

NEW-YORK :
PRINTED AND SOLD BY COLLINS AND PERKINS,
NO. 189, PEARL-STREET
1808.

the potassium, which was thereupon changed back into caustic potash, which then reacted with the acid. They tested the "oxidized marine acid" (chlorine) with glowing charcoal, but, since they could detect no oxygen they concluded that oxygen was formed only in the presence of water. All their attempts to decompose the chlorine by heating it with dry charcoal proved fruitless (6).

L.-J. Gay-Lussac and L.-J. Thenard believed (1) that muriatic gas contains one-fourth of its weight of water, (2) that oxymuriatic gas is a compound of oxygen and some other substance, and (3) that the substance obtained by heating calomel with phosphorus is a triple compound

Sir Humphry Davy, 1778-1829. British chemist who isolated the alkali and alkaline earth metals and boron, and proved that chlorine is an element. Gay-Lussac and Thenard isolated boron independently at about the same time.

consisting of dry muriatic acid, oxygen, and phosphorus. Davy's final views on these three points were as follows: (1) muriatic acid is composed of oxymuriatic acid (*chlorine*) and hydrogen, (2) chlorine is an element, and (3) the substance obtained by heating calomel with phosphorus is a compound of the elements chlorine and phosphorus.

Since Berthollet, Gay-Lussac, Thenard, A.-F. de Fourcroy, and J.-A.-C. Chaptal all belonged to the French school founded by the illustrious Lavoisier, it was difficult for them to admit the existence of an acid that contained no oxygen, but nevertheless they soon had to yield to the convincing evidence presented by Sir Humphry (8, 41). Dr. John Murray in Edinburgh and Berzelius in Stockholm continued, however, for some time to regard chlorine as a compound.

After iodine was discovered in 1811, the evidence for the elementary nature of chlorine became still more convincing, and by 1820 even Berzelius had yielded (9). When Anna, his cook, remarked one day that the flask she was washing smelled of "oxidized muriatic acid," Berzelius replied, "Anna, you mustn't speak of oxidized muriatic acid any more; from now on you must say chlorine" (10).

The discovery of bromine by A.-J. Balard and the preparation of prussic (hydrocyanic) acid, an oxygen-free acid, by Gay-Lussac made the evidence conclusive. Davy's formal announcement of the elementary

Jöns Jacob Berzelius,° 1779–1848. He was one of the last chemical authorities to be convinced of the elementary nature of chlorine.

nature of chlorine was made in a memoir which he read before the Royal Society on November 15, 1810 (8).

Sir Humphry Davy's life was a short one, and his last years were marred by continued illness. In a letter written in Rome in February, 1829, he said, "If I die, I hope that I have done my duty and that my life has not been vain and useless" (50). Three weeks later he was stricken with palsy, from which he never recovered. Even the devotion and medical skill of his younger brother, Dr. John Davy, were in vain.

° Reproduced from H. G. Söderbaum's "Jac. Berzelius Levnadsteckning" by kind permission of Dr. Söderbaum.

When spring came, Dr. Davy thought it best to take his brother from Rome to Geneva in order to avoid the hot Italian summer. The long journey by horse and carriage was most exhausting, and Sir Humphry died at Geneva on May 29, 1829. His desire that his life might be useful was so richly fulfilled that his name will always be honored as that of a supremely great scientist and humanitarian.

Bleaching with Chlorine. In 1785 Count C.-L. Berthollet noticed that an aqueous solution of chlorine destroys vegetable colors just as the gas itself does (*119*). In the following year he used it successfully in bleaching, and communicated his results to scientists and technical men,

Anna Sundström,[*] **Berzelius' House-keeper.** She kept house for him for many years before he was married and prepared the meals in the kitchen-laboratory, where his sand bath on the stove was never allowed to cool. Berzelius once said that he could not have thus entrusted the management of his home to any other person of the servant class.

including James Watt. "Mr. Watt of Birmingham," said William Henry, ". . . was the first person in this country [England] to carry the discovery into effect, by bleaching several hundred pieces of linen by the new process, at the works of a relative near Glasgow" (*120*). After Watt had tried out the process on 1500 yards of linen in the bleach-fields of his father-in-law near Glasgow, Professor Copeland introduced it to the bleachers of Aberdeen, and Dr. Thomas Henry, father of William Henry, began bleaching operations at Manchester (*120, 121, 122*).

In the early processes developed in England, France, Germany, and Austria, the bleaching agent was chlorine gas or chlorine water. To prevent its injurious effects on the respiratory system, workmen used to

[*] Reproduced from H. G. Söderbaum's "Jac. Berzelius. Levnadsteckning" by kind permission of Dr. Söderbaum.

protect their faces with handkerchiefs moistened with dilute alkali (*123*). Berthollet found, however, that the addition of alkali to the bleaching liquor deprived it of its disagreeable, suffocating odor without impairing its bleaching power. A solution of chlorine in potash was sold under the name of *Javelle water* (*123*). Hypochlorite solutions, however, do not keep well (*124*).

As early as 1788, Thomas Henry prepared a bleaching liquor from lime and chlorine, and it became a common practice among bleachers to economize by substituting lime for the more expensive pearlash from wood ashes (*123*). In 1795 the Hungarian botanist and chemist Paul Kitaibel distilled a mixture of salt, pyrolusite, and sulfuric acid, and passed the liberated chlorine ("oxygenated acid of salt") into limewater. He made many experiments with solid bleaching powder, and used it to bleach textiles and wax (*125*).

Charles Tennant of Glasgow, who was then engaged in bleaching at Darnley, prepared solid bleaching powder in 1798 and was granted a patent for it early in the following year. He originally prepared it by heating a mixture of salt, pyrolusite, and sulfuric acid in a leaden still and absorbing the liberated chlorine in sifted slaked lime in a leaden receiver (*124*). J. Lawrence Smith regarded this as "the greatest advancement since the discovery of chlorine towards rendering it available in the arts, for it can now be transported readily to all parts of the world, and, moreover, we are indebted to this form (so to speak) of chlorine for the discovery and manufacture of that great boon to suffering humanity, viz., chloroform" (*121*). The discovery of bleaching powder also stimulated the growth of cotton and saved for agricultural purposes thousands of acres of arable land which had formerly been used as greenswards for the slow bleaching of textiles by the oxygen of the air. Chlorine," said J. Lawrence Smith, "has revolutionized this, and a few hours accomplishes that which formerly required days; and a few hundred square feet containing properly constructed vats takes the place of thousands of acres of land" (*121*).

Disinfecting with Chlorine. A reviewer in the *Medical Repository* wrote in 1802 concerning Guyton de Morveau's "Treatise on the means of purifying infected air, of preventing contagion, and arresting its progress" that "The most powerful and efficacious anti-contagious agent which he knows is *the oxygenated muriatic acid gas* [chlorine]. The process for preparing this differs from the ordinary muriatic [hydrochloric] acid gas already mentioned, only by the addition of a small quantity of black oxyd of manganese . . . in powder" (*126*). This anonymous reviewer (possibly Samuel Latham Mitchill, editor of the *Medical Repository*) questioned the conclusions of Guyton de Morveau and believed that aqueous solutions of potash, soda, soap, and lime were more efficacious (*126*).

Chlorine in the Human Body. Chlorine enters into the composition of all secretions and excretions of the human body, and gastric digestion takes place in a medium containing hydrochloric acid (*127*).

IODINE*

Iodine, one of the most beautiful of all the elements, was first observed in 1811 by Bernard Courtois, who was born on February 8, 1777,

B   C E
From Toraude's "Bernard Courtois et la Découverte de l'Iode"
The Old Dijon Academy (B) and the Birthplace (E) of Bernard Courtois (present condition of the buildings). In the middle of the nineteenth century the latter building was enlarged and made higher. The street at C is the Rue Monge (formerly *Rue du Pont Arnauld*). When it was widened, the quarters in the Academy Building formerly occupied by Bernard's father, Jean-Baptiste Courtois, assistant to Guyton de Morveau, were torn down.

in a house just across the street from the famous old Dijon Academy. His father, Jean-Baptiste Courtois, was a saltpeter manufacturer who used

* The pictures of the Dijon Academy, the sealed tube containing the first iodine, and the Courtois autograph letter have been reproduced by courtesy of Dr. L.-G. Toraude from his book, "Bernard Courtois et la Découverte de l'Iode." The autograph letter belongs to the departmental archives of the Côte d'Or. The photograph of the sealed tube was taken at Dijon on Nov. 9, 1913, the day of the ceremony in honor of the one hundredth anniversary of the discovery of iodine.

From Toraude's "Bernard Courtois et la Découverte de l'Iode"

Autograph of Bernard Courtois (1794). Translation: "I have received from D'orgeu township 50 casks of saltpeter solution which they have drawn from their property and which they have asked me to take because they have no one sufficiently trained to extract the saltpeter from it.   Dijon the 11th of Messidor, the 2nd year of the Republic, one and indivisible.   B. Courtois, son. . . ."   He was seventeen years old when he wrote this receipt.

to assist Guyton de Morveau, the lawyer, in his brilliant lectures on chemistry.   Thus the son lived constantly in a chemical environment, dividing his time between the paternal saltpeter works and the laboratories of the Academy.

After Citizen Guyton was called to the Legislative Assembly in 1791, J.-B. Courtois gave up his position at the Academy in order to devote all his time to the manufacture of niter.   After assisting his father for a time, Bernard was apprenticed for three years to a pharmacist at Auxerre, M. Fremy, the grandfather of Edmond Fremy, the famous chemist.   In the meantime Guyton de Morveau had become the director of the École Polytechnique, and through his intervention Bernard Courtois was admitted to the laboratories of this school to study under Fourcroy.   Here Courtois entered into his research and courses in pure chemistry with pleasure and enthusiasm.   In 1799, however, he was called to serve his country as a pharmacist in the military hospitals.   In 1804, while serving as *préparateur* under Armand Seguin, he made an important investigation of opium (*51*).

Although J.-B. Courtois failed in business, he was an honest man, and both father and son struggled hard to pay their creditors. In 1808 Bernard Courtois married Madeleine Eulalie Morand, a young girl of humble parentage who could barely read and write.

Along the coasts of Normandy and Brittany many plants live at shallow depth in the ocean, and some of them are cast ashore by the waves and tides. For plants such as these the French writers of the early nineteenth century used the term *varech*,* from which the English words *wrack* and *wreck* have been derived (*13*). By burning *Fucus, Laminaria,* and other brown algae gathered at low tide, and by extracting the ash with water, Courtois obtained some mother liquors known as *salin de varech*, or *soude de varech*.

The algae that Courtois used yield an ash containing chlorides, bromide, iodides, carbonates, and sulfates of sodium, potassium, magnesium, and calcium. In his day, however, they were valued merely for their sodium and potassium compounds, which were recovered by burning the dried algae in longitudinal ditches along the seashore and leaching the ashes at the works.

As evaporation proceeded, sodium chloride began to precipitate and later potassium chloride and potassium sulfate. The mother liquor then contained the iodides of sodium and postassium, part of the sodium chloride, sodium sulfate, sodium carbonate, cyanides, polysulfides, and some sulfites and hyposulfites resulting from the reduction of sulfates during calcination.

To destroy these sulfur compounds Courtois added sulfuric acid, and on one eventful day in 1811 he must have added it in excess (*54*). To his astonishment lovely clouds of violet vapor arose, and an irritating odor like that of chlorine permeated the room. When the vapors condensed on cold objects, no liquid was formed, but there appeared instead a quantity of dark crystals with a luster surprisingly like that of a metal (*45*).

Courtois noticed that the new substance did not readily form compounds with oxygen or with carbon, that it was not decomposed at red heat, and that it combined with hydrogen and with phosphorus. He observed that it combined directly with certain metals without effervescence and that it formed an explosive compound with ammonia. Although these striking properties made him suspect the presence of a new element, he was too lacking in self-confidence to attempt a thorough investigation in his poorly equipped laboratory and too poor to take the time from his business (*11*). He therefore asked two of his Dijon friends, Charles-Bernard Desormes and Nicolas Clément, Desormes' future son-

---

* The word *varech* is at present applied only to certain marine phanerogams used for packing and upholstering.

in-law, to continue his researches in their laboratory at the *Conservatoire des arts et des métiers,* and allowed them to announce the discovery to the scientific world (*45, 55*).

In order that chemists might have an opportunity to study the new substance, Courtois generously presented some of it to the pharmaceutical firm of Vallée and Baget (*13*). He was unable to prepare it fast enough to supply the demand, however and could sell only small amounts of it, at a price of 600 francs per kilogram. In 1824 M. Tissier the elder perfected an industrial process which in a few months brought the price of iodine down to 200 francs per kilogram.

Dr. Alexandre Marcet stated that Smithson Tennant discovered the presence of iodine in sea water just before his fatal accident in 1815 (*128*). In his famous research on the composition of sea water, J. G. Forchhammer stated that iodine was "the first element in sea water dis-

Jean-Antoine-Claude Chaptal, Comte de Chanteloup, 1756–1832. French physician, chemist, and manufacturer of saltpeter, soda, and beet sugar. Minister of the Interior under Napoleon. Author of books on chemical industry.

covered not directly but by the analysis of the ashes of fucoidal plants, which by organic power had collected and concentrated it from sea water" (*98*). In 1825 Christian Heinrich Pfaff of Kiel proved that the water of the Baltic contains iodine, as Apothecary Krüger of Rostock had suspected in 1821 (*129, 130*).

Courtois was engaged for some years in the manufacture of iodine compounds and other chemical reagents, but in 1835 he was obliged to give up his business and go about the city taking orders. According to Fremy, he prepared very pure iodine, gave speciments of it to his chemical friends, and noted its action on organic substances. Fremy also said:

> They have been unjust to Courtois in treating him as a simple saltpeter-maker; he was a very skilful chemist (un chimiste très habile); he ought to have been rewarded for his discovery of iodine, and not left to die in proverty (*12, 13*).

Courtois died in Paris on September 27, 1838. The Montyon prize of six thousand francs which the Royal Academy had awarded him in 1831 "for having improved the art of healing" had all been spent, and the widow, poor and uneducated, struggled against approaching deafness and blindness in a vain attempt to earn her living by lacemaking. It is indeed sad to know that her last months were spent in a charitable institution.

In the auditorium of the Dijon Academy, harmoniously decorated in the style of Louis XIV, there occurred on November 9, 1913,* a solemn civic ceremony in honor of the one hundredth anniversary of the discovery of iodine. At that time a commemorative plaque was placed on the birthplace of Courtois, and in the following year a street was named for him.

While Desormes devoted most of his time to applied chemistry, Clément (1779–1841) carried out a classical research in which he prepared the new substance and made a thorough study of its properties. In his report in 1813 he wrote:

> The mother liquor from seaweed ash contains quite a large quantity of a very peculiar and curious substance; it is easily extracted; one merely pours sulfuric acid on the mother liquor and heats the mixture in a retort the mouth of which is connected to a delivery-tube leading to a bulb. The substance which is precipitated in the form of a black, shining powder immediately after the addition of sulfuric acid, rises, when heated, in vapor of a superb violet color. This vapor condenses in the delivery-tube and receiver in the form of very brilliant crystalline plates having a luster equal to that of crystalline lead sulfide. Upon washing these plates with a little distilled water, one obtains the substance in the pure state (*45, 13*).

Clément believed iodine to be an element similar to chlorine (*12*), and showed it, first to J.-A.-C. Chaptal and A.-M. Ampère, and later to Sir Humphry Davy. The proof of its elementary nature was given independently by Davy in England and by Gay-Lussac in France. Davy showed that iodine vapor is not decomposed by a carbon filament heated red-hot by a voltaic current (*12, 46*). In his classical research, the results of which were published in 1814, Gay-Lussac prepared hydrogen

---

* Although Courtois discovered iodine in 1811, the announcement by Clément and Desormes was not made until two years later. Therefore, the centenary was observed in 1913.

iodide and showed that it reacts with mercury, zinc, and potassium to give the corresponding metallic iodides, hydrogen, and no other product (5, 39).

In 1814 Thomas Charles Hope of Edinburgh wrote in a letter to the British Quaker chemist William Allen: "I should be very glad to know what doctrine you teach now with regard to oxymuriatic acid. Are you yet a convert to chlorine? I am impatient to see Lussac's paper on iodine, in particular to learn how far the facts respecting that substance go to confirm the new views of chlorine. Lussac appears to be a convert to Davy's sentiments, and certainly the acquisition of one who so strenuously opposed them must be accounted a *very* flattering occurrence" (*117*).

André-Marie Ampère, 1775–1836. French physicist, mathematician, and chemist. Professor at the École Polytechnique, Paris. One of the founders of electrodynamics. Inventor of the astatic needle. The practical unit of current strength was named for him.

Early in the nineteenth century the use of potassium iodide as a remedy for goiter was introduced by several physicians. William Prout mentioned in 1834, in his "Chemistry, Meteorology, and the Function of Digestion Considered with Reference to Natural Theology" (*168*), that "Iodine has lately been much celebrated for its medicinal properties," and added in a footnote:

"It may not be amiss also to notice, that the author of the present volume first employed the hydriodate of potash, as a remedy for goitre, in the year 1816; after having previously ascertained, by experiments upon himself, that it was not poisonous in small doses, as had been represented. Some time before the period stated, this substance had been found in certain marine productions; and it struck the author, that burnt sponge (a well-known remedy for goitre) might owe its properties to the presence of Iodine, and this was his motive for making the trial. He lost sight of the case in which the remedy was employed, before any visible alteration was made in the state of disease; but not before some of the most striking effects of the remedy were observed. The above employment of the compounds of Iodine in medicine was, at the time, made no secret; and so early as 1819, the remedy was adopted in St. Thomas' Hospital, by Dr. Elliotson, at the author's suggestion."

Jean-François Coindet, 1774–1834. Swiss physician who introduced the scientific use of iodine for treatment of goiter. Calcined sponge and other substances now known to contain iodine had long been used empirically for the same purpose. See ref. (110).

Aesculape, 1913

The Dr. Elliotson to whom Dr. Prout was referring was probably John Elliotson (1791–1868).

In 1820 Dr. J.-F. Coindet of Geneva introduced the use of iodine in the treatment of goiter (13, 56). Jean-François Coindet was born at Geneva, Switzerland, in July, 1774. After completing his medical course at Edinburgh in 1797, he returned to Geneva, where he practiced for the rest of his life. In 1809 he became chief physician at the civil and military hospital. Although his large practice made heavy demands on his time and strength, Dr. Coindet never lost his active interest in scientific research.

One day in 1819*, when nineteen-year-old J.-B. Dumas had charge of

---

* This is the date given by Van Tieghem, ref. (99); A. W. von Hofmann, ref. (103), gave the date as 1818 (when Dumas was only eighteen years old).

the laboratory at the Le Royer pharmacy in Geneva, Dr. Coindet asked him to test some calcined sponge for iodine. When the boy obtained clear proof of its presence, Dr. Coindet asked him to suggest different forms in which iodine could be conveniently administered. Even before any iodide was commercially available, Dumas proposed the tincture of iodine, potassium iodide, and a solution of iodine in potassium iodide. Two memoirs on this subject signed "A. Le Royer, pharmacist, and J.-B. Dumas, his pupil" were published in 1819 and 1820 in *Meisner's Journal* in Berne (*99, 100*).

In 1820 Dr. Coindet published in the *Annales de Chimie et de Physique* a paper entitled "Discovery of a new remedy for goiter" (*101, 102*). "A year ago," said he, "while looking for a formula in Cadet de Gassicourt's work, I found that Russel advised for goiter the use of kelp, *fucus vesiculosus,* under the name of *vegetable ethiops.* Not knowing then what relation might exist between this plant and the sponge, I suspected by analogy that iodine must be the active principle common to these two marine productions. . . . Up to the present, calcined sponge has formed the basis of all the remedies for goiter which have met with any success. It is Arnaud de Villeneuve who made it known" (*101*).

The earliest official recommendation of this remedy which Alexander Tschirch was able to find was in the eighth edition of the Augustana Pharmacopoeia of 1623 (*104*). The Chinese scholar Li Shi Chen, author of a famous pharmacopoeia (the Pen Ts'ao Kang Mu, sixteenth century A.D.), prescribed as a remedy for goiter a wine made from sea plants (*105*). In 1769 Dr. Russel recommended "vegetable ethiops" (charcoal made by burning fucoid seaweeds) for the same purpose (*13*).

As early as December, 1819, Dr. Johann Castor Straub, Professor of Chemistry at the Agricultural Institute at Hofwyl, Switzerland, noticed that calcined sponge (*spongia usta off.*) had an odor like that of iodine. He was soon able to demonstrate the presence in the sponge of this element, which had previously been detected only in marine plants. He therefore ascribed the medicinal value of the calcined sponge to its iodine content, and recommended the use of artificial substances containing iodine as specific for goiter (*104, 106, 107*).

At about the same time, Dr. Andrew Fyfe (1792–1861) of Edinburgh detected iodine in several species of *Fucus,* in a species of conferva, and in "the common sponge of the shops," and published a paper on it in the *Edinburgh New Philosophical Journal* (*108*). After serving as assistant to Professor Hope, he gave private lectures on chemistry and pharmacy at Edinburgh. From 1844 until his death in 1861 he occupied the chair of chemistry at the University of Aberdeen (*109*).

Although calcined sponge often caused cramps of the stomach, Coindet found that sodium or potassium iodide made the goiters disappear much more quickly and without this deleterious effect. "What is the substance in the sponge which acts as a specific against goiter? It seemed probable to me," he continued, "that it was iodine; I was confirmed in that opinion when I learned that, near the end of 1819, M. Fife [Fyfe] of Edinburgh found iodine in the sponge; as early as six months ago I had confirmed its surprising effects in this malady" (*101*).

Dr. Coindet was one of the founders of the Medical Society of the Canton of Geneva, and was for many years its president. He was also elected and re-elected to the representative council of this canton. He died at Nice in 1934 (*102, 110*). His son Dr. Charles W. Coindet, also published researches on the therapeutic uses of iodine (*105, 111*).

In 1814 Jean-Jacques Colin and Henri-François Gaultier de Claubry, professor of toxicology at the School of Pharmacy in Paris, described the blue substance produced when free iodine acts on starch, and studied the effects of temperature and of sulfurous acid, hydrogen sulfide, and other reagents on this reaction (*131*). In the same year Friedrich Stromeyer first applied this starch reaction to analytical chemistry and was able to detect as little as one part of iodine in 350,000 to 450,000 parts (*132*).

In 1825 A.-J. Balard detected iodine in "various marine mollusks, bare or testacean, such as the *doris,* the *venus,* oysters, etc.; several corals and marine plants, the *gorgonia,* the *zostera marina,* etc., and especially in the mother liquor of the salt works supplied by the Mediterranean" (*133*). This was his first research, which was soon followed by his discovery of bromine.

The *Quarterly Journal of Science and the Arts* for 1823 described the first discovery of iodine in a spring water: "The waters of Sales spring in considerable quantities from an argilo-calcareous ground at the foot of a hillock, on the left-hand side of the torrent Staffora, near the road to Godiaso, not far from Sales, in the province of Voghera. They are turbid and of a faint yellow colour. They have a strong odour approaching to that of urine, or a muriatic residuum; their taste is brackish and sharp; bubbles of air constantly rise from the bottom of the reservoir containing them. . . .

"In 1788 the Canon Volta analyzed them and found a twelfth of muriate of soda. In 1820, M. Romano repeated the analysis and found muriate of soda, several earthy muriates [chlorides], and a little oxide of iron. M. Laur. Angelina [Laurent Angelini], of Voghera, on using starch as a reagent, found a blue colour produced in the water, indicating the presence of iodine, and using the process generally adopted with the mother waters in the manufacture of soda, he succeeded in procuring a certain quantity of iodine from the water. It is remarkable that for a long time the water of Sales has been administered successfully in scrofulous cases and in cases of the goitre" (134).

Angelini's experiments were made in 1822 and were believed by Hermann Kopp to constitute the first discovery of iodine in a mineral water (129, 135). Apothecary Krüger found it soon afterward in the mother liquor of the saline springs of Sülzer in Mecklenburgh-Schwerin (134). J. N. Fuchs detected it in 1823 in the rock salt of Hall in the Tyrol, which had been used medicinally since the ninth century A.D. (105, 129, 134).

J. W. von Goethe never lost interest in chemistry. In the "Conversations of Goethe with [Johann Peter] Eckermann and Soret," Soret states that "Iodine and chlorine occupied him particularly; he spoke about these substances as if the new discoveries in chemistry had quite taken him by surprise. He had some iodine brought in, and volatilized, before our eyes, in the flame of a taper; by which means he did not fail to make us admire the violet vapour as a pleasing confirmation of a law in his theory of colours. . . . The investigations which are now being made touching the discovery of salt springs evidently interested him" (136). At that time (1822), Goethe was seventy-three years old.

In July, 1824, Lanzarote Island was shaken by violent earthquakes and volcanic eruptions. When R. Brandes analyzed some of the volcanic sal ammoniac which formed a thin yellow, orange, or brown crust over the lava, he found it to contain both selenium and iodine (137). When he opened the small chest in which E. Walte of Bremen had shipped specimens of these volcanic minerals to him, Brandes noticed a faint odor of iodine, which was easily identified after gentle warming of the sal ammoniac (137, 138).

An Iodide Mineral. As late as 1822 Christian Heinrich Pfaff of Kiel, in his "Handbuch der analytischen Chemie," classified the iodides with the "salts which up to the present have not been found in the mineral realm, but may occur there" (139). Berzelius too suggested, in his "New Mineral System" in 1825, that iodine might some day be discovered to be a mineral production. A. M. del Río, in his Spanish translation of this work two years later, made the following comment: "This has already been verified in this America. M. Vauquelin has found $18^{1}/_{2}$ per cent of iodine in a Mexican fossil which is embedded in the serpentine and was labeled *native silver*. With such a meager description and in such a vast republic, it was not easy to locate the vein. Fortunately I remembered the native and horn silver in serpentine which C(itizen) J. M. Herrera, my pupil and friend so esteemed for his learning and integrity, brought me from Albarradon, near Mazapil in the state of Zacatecas; and knowing that artificial silver iodide looks like horn silver, or silver chloride. I subjected it to the blowpipe, and as soon as the heat was applied, it melted and became reddish, giving off vapor which tinged the flame with a handsome violet, and spread little globules of silver into the charcoal. Even the specimen which by its color and luster appeared to be native and was rather translucent gave traces of iodine; the label *native silver* was not then so absurd. Therefore at least that from Albarradon is silver iodide, which does not dissolve in ammonia either. My dear friend Citizen Bustamante has just observed the violet flame with a brownish white lead from the mine at Catorce" (*140*).

The "native silver in serpentine" in which Vauquelin discovered iodine had been obtained from Joseph Tabary, a dealer in Mexican and South American minerals (*137*). In an attempt to ascertain the exact locality from which this mineral had been obtained, D.-F. Arago questioned some young Mexican army officers who had been sent by their government to study in Paris. To his surprise, one of them, Captain Yniestra, was able to give the following clear and definite reply:

"At the time when Vauquelin discovered iodine in a silver mineral from Mexico, M. del Río, professor of mineralogy in our school of mines, confirmed the presence of the same substance in the horn silver of Albarradon. This latter name is that of a district near that of Mazapil, in the department of Zacatecas. The name of the mountain of Albarradon where the silver mine is located is Temeroso.

"Our famous Bustamante also found iodine in a white lead from the mine at Catorce, situated in the department of Guanajuato. In 1834, I myself, together with M. Herrera, made the quantitative analysis of the latter mineral. . . .

"I do not know whether you have heard that iodine has been discovered in Mexico in the *sabila* and in the *romeritos*. The *sabila* is a plant similar to the magueys (agaves) which grow on the plains and at the top of the mountains. The *romeritos* are a kind of barilla which grow in the floating gardens on the fresh-water lakes near the capital. Everyone eats them during Lent." The preceding letter was published in the *Annales de Chimie et de Physique* in 1836 (*141*).

Diffusion of Iodine in Nature. The presence of iodine in the Chile saltpeter deposits was first noted by A. A. Hayes, who found it to be present as iodate (*142, 143*).

The occurrence of iodine in igneous rocks was first conclusively demonstrated by Armand Gautier in 1901 (*144*). Since it had previously been detected in volcanic emanations and lavas and in the sludges from mud volcanos, and since it is often associated with boric acid, Gautier concluded that it must come from great depths and that therefore it ought to be possible to detect it in the most ancient rocks. His results showed that "iodine, which exists in all the granites we have examined, seems not to form a constituent part of either their micas or of the apatites which are often abundantly mingled in these rocks. This element is evidently very variable, as any substance must be which is entrained in the form of a mere impurity" (*144*).

The detailed researches of A. Chatin and subsequent studies of T. von Fellenberg showed that iodine in small amounts occurs everywhere —in rocks, in the sea, and in all organisms (*145*). According to V. M. Goldschmidt's theory of the geochemical distribution of the elements, concentric shells or phases were formed as the earth solidified. The siderophile elements were concentrated in the iron kernel, the chalcophile elements in the sulfide shell, the lithophile elements in the silicate mass, and the atmophile elements in the steam phase. Gulbrand Lunde stated that "iodine is an element, as far as we hitherto know the only one, which on the earth's division into phases did not show remarkable affinity to any of the phases. It became part of them all, but showed, however, more conspicuous atmophile and lithophile than chalcophile and siderophile characteristics" (*144*). Iodine is also present in the biosphere, usually in greater concentration than in the rocks (*144*). It is probably not essential in plant nutrition (*146*).

BROMINE

Centuries before the element bromine was discovered, one of its organic compounds, Tyrian purple, was used as a rich costly dye prepared from a white juice secreted by the Mediterranean mollusk, the straight-spined Murex (*M. brandaris Linné*) (*91, 166*). Strabo described the Tyrian dyeworks in his *Geography*, and the product was mentioned frequently in the Bible (Ezek. **27**, 7, 16) (*92*). In 1909 H. Friedländer of Vienna discovered that this royal dye from *Murex brandaris* is identical with the 6:6′ dibrom indigo which F. Sachs of Berlin and his collaborators had prepared only five years previously from *p*-bromo-*o*-nitrobenzaldehyde (*93, 94, 95*).

In 1825 Carl Löwig, a new student who had just entered the chemical laboratory at Heidelberg, won the immediate interest of Leopold Gmelin, his professor. Löwig had brought with him from his home at Kreuznach a red liquid which he had prepared by passing chlorine into the mother liquor from a salt spring and shaking it out with ether. The red liquid had remained after he had distilled off the ether. Professor Gmelin asked him to prepare more of it in order to study its properties, but in the meantime there appeared in 1826 in the *Annales de chimie et de physique* a paper by A.-J. Balard announcing the discovery of bromine (*28, 36, 57*). The properties which Balard ascribed to bromine were identical with those Löwig had observed for the substance from Kreuznach. This explains why Balard, instead of Löwig, is regarded as the discoverer of bromine.

Carl Löwig was born at Kreuznach on March 17, 1803. In his youth he studied pharmacy, but his later study was confined entirely to chemistry. He continued his investigation of the compounds of bromine for several years, and in 1829 published a monograph on "Bromine and Its Chemical Relations."

In 1833 he was called to the newly founded University of Zurich, where, in spite of the very meager equipment, he analyzed many Swiss mineral waters and published monographs on them. His "Chemie der organischen Verbindungen," based on the radical theory, "was the Beilstein of that time, and was to be found in the hands of every chemist" (57, 66).

Carl Löwig,* 1803–1890. Professor of chemistry at Heidelberg, Zurich, and Breslau. He prepared bromine in 1825, but before his investigation was completed Balard had announced the discovery. Löwig discovered bromine hydrate, bromal hydrate, and bromoform, and was the founder of the Silesian chemical industry and of the Goldschmieden alumina works at Deutsch-Lissa.

In 1853 Löwig became Robert Bunsen's successor at Breslau. He was given offices of great responsibility, and served as Rector both at Zurich and at Breslau. He taught six semesters at Heidelberg, forty at Zurich, and seventy-two at Breslau, and hoped to teach two more in order to make the total one hundred and twenty. This hope was not to be realized, however, for, while walking in the zoölogical garden, he failed

* The author is indebted to Dr. Max Speter of Berlin and Dr. Julius Meyer of Breslau for their assistance in obtaining this portrait, the original of which hangs in the Chemical Institute at Breslau. Some valuable information about Löwig's scientific activities was also graciously contributed by Professor Meyer.

Antoine-Jérôme Balard, 1802–1876. French chemist and pharmacist who discovered bromine. Professor of chemistry at the Sorbonne and at the Collège de France. He discovered hypochlorous acid, worked out the constitution of Javelle water, and perfected industrial methods for extracting various salts from sea water.

One of the Laboratories of Mineralogical Chemistry at the Sorbonne.
Balard, the discoverer of bromine, Moissan, the discoverer of fluorine, Lamy
who isolated thallium, and M. and Mme. Curie, the discoverers of radium,
all taught at the Sorbonne.

to notice some steps, fell, and received a fracture of the hip from which he
never recovered. He died on March 27, 1890, ten days after his eighty-
seventh birthday (*57*).

Antoine-Jérôme Balard (*14*), was born at Montpellier on September
30, 1802. Since his parents were poor, he was adopted and educated by
his godmother. He studied at the College of Montpellier for a time, and
at the age of seventeen years he became a *préparateur* at the École de
Pharmacie, where he graduated in 1826 (*47, 66, 68*).

In 1824, while studying the flora of a salt marsh, he noticed a deposit
of sodium sulfate which had crystallized out in a pan containing mother
liquor from common salt. In an attempt to find a use for these waste
liquors he performed a number of experiments, and noticed that when
certain reagents were added, the mother liquor became brown. His
investigation of this phenomenon, made when he was only twenty-three
years old led to the remarkable discovery which P.-L. Dulong described
in the following letter to Berzelius written on July 1, 1826:

. . . But here is another piece of recent news. . . . It is a new simple
body which will find its place between chlorine and iodine. The author of this
discovery is M. Ballard of Montpellier. This new body, which he calls *muride*,
is found in sea water. He has extracted it from the mother liquor of Montpellier brines by saturating them with chlorine and distilling. He obtains a
dark red liquid substance boiling at 47°. The vapor resembles that of nitrous
acid. Its specific gravity is 3. One preserves it under concentrated sulfuric

acid. It combines with metals and gives compounds sensibly neutral, of which several are volatile, notably the muride of potassium . . . (15).

Since the name *muride* did not find favor with the French Academy's committee, consisting of Vauquelin, Thenard, and Gay-Lussac, the element is now known as *bromine*, meaning *bad odor* (12, 26).

When Balard made this eventful discovery, he was merely an obscure young assistant in the chemistry department of his college. He had noticed that when the lye from the ash of *Fucus* was treated with chlorine water and starch, two layers appeared in the solution. The lower layer was blue because of the action of the starch on the iodine, and the upper one was intensely orange. When he treated the mother liquor from the salt works in the same manner, he again observed this orange zone above the blue one. To separate the new substance, he passed a current of chlorine gas into the mother liquor from the saltworks, and shook the mixture until the new orange-colored substance passed into the ether layer. After removal of the aqueous layer, he added caustic potash to the orange-colored ethereal layer. By evaporation, he obtained cubic crystals of the soluble salt now known as potassium bromide.

The young assistant concluded that there were only two possible explanations: The yellow substance must either be a compound of chlorine with some constituent of the lye, or it must be a new element just liberated from one of its compounds by the chlorine, which had replaced it. Balard at first favored the first hypothesis and thought that he had an iodide of chlorine, but, when all attempts to decompose the new substance failed, he concluded that his second explanation must be the correct one and that the new element must be similar to iodine and chlorine (28).

Balard found that bromine can be shaken out of solution, first with ether and then with caustic potash. Upon heating the resulting potassium bromide with sulfuric acid and manganese dioxide, one can distil the bromine off and condense it as a red liquid or collect it in water (12). Just as mercury is the only common metal whose liquid phase is stable at room temperature, bromine is the only liquid non-metal.

In his first research on bromine, published in the *Annales de Chimie et de Physique* in 1826, Balard prepared and characterized many of its compounds and described some of its most important natural sources. This astonishingly rapid progress was possible only because of the close resemblance of bromine to chlorine and iodine, which were already well known.

"Bromine," said he, "is found in very minute amounts in sea water. The mother liquor of the salt works itself, although it has been singularly diminished in volume by the evaporation which has permitted the salt to deposit, and although the latter has not carried down appreciable amounts of it, contains only a little of it. The nature of the methods by which one can extract it seems to indicate that it is present in the form of hydro-bromic acid, and some considerations lead me to believe that this acid is combined with magnesia.

"As a matter of fact," continued Balard, "when one strongly calcines the residue from the evaporation of the water from the salt works it loses its ability to liberate bromine in contact with chlorine. If one recalls that the hydro-bromates [bromides] I have examined, with the exception of that of magnesia, are not at all decomposed by heat, one will be tempted to suppose that the water of the salt works actually contained this compound.

"The plants and animals living in the ocean also contain bromine. The ashes of plants growing in the Mediterranean all give a yellow tinge when one treats the product of their lixiviation with chlorine. I have also seen the same color produced on treating with this reagent the solution of the ash of *Ianthina violacea,* a testacean mollusk which I owe to the kindness of M. Auguste Bérard, and which that distinguished officer collected at the Island of St. Helena on his second voyage around the world.

"I have been able to extract considerable quantities of bromine from the mother liquors of the soda kelp which serves for the extraction of the iodine. Finally, it has seemed to me that the product of the evapora-tion of a mineral water from the eastern Pyrenees, which was strongly saline, became yellow in contact with chlorine. If the bromine actually existed in a water of this kind, one might hope to encounter it in the salt springs properly so called, and especially in the mother liquor of the rock salt. I have lacked material to verify it. All this makes it very likely that bromine will be found in a large number of marine productions or those of submarine origin" (28).

The French Academy's report of the meeting of Monday, August 14, 1826, signed by Vauquelin, Thenard, and Gay-Lussac, reads as follows:

If the few experiments which we have been able to perform have not afforded us that certainty of the existence of bromine as a very simple body which in the present day is properly required, we consider it at least very probable that it is so. The memoir of M. Balard is extremely well drawn up, and the numerous results which he relates would not fail to excite great interest, even if it should be proved that bromine is not a simple body. The discovery of bromine is a very important acquisition to chemistry, and gives M. Balard honorable rank in the career of the sciences. We are of the opinion that this young chemist is every way worthy of the encouragement of the Academy, and we have the honor to propose that his memoir shall be printed in the *Recueil des Savants Étrangers* (16, 29).

In the same report Gay-Lussac, Thenard, and Vauquelin stated "We have also obtained bromine, by the process described by M. Balard, by treating the mother liquors of the salt gardens (*marais salans*) of the plain of Aren which had been sent to us by our colleague M. d'Arcet" (*29*).

In 1842 Balard succeeded Thenard at the Sorbonne, and in 1851 he accepted a professorship at the Collège de France (*36*). He discovered hypochlorous acid, worked out the constitution of Javelle water (*44*), and perfected industrial methods for the extraction of various salts from sea water. He worked for twenty years at these technical researches, and extracted sodium sulfate, the basis of the soda industry, directly from sea water. He also extracted potassium salts from the sea water, and his artificial potash, entering into competition with that from the ashes of plants, soon lowered the price. Before the discovery of the Stassfurt deposits in 1858, all the bromine used by photographers was prepared by Balard's method.

The memory of his early poverty made Balard economical in his researches and ascetic in his manner of living. Although he survived his three children and his wife, his stepchildren were a great consolation to him in his old age. He died in 1876, honored because of his achievements and loved because of his generosity, modesty, and warmth of heart (*47*). In his eulogy, J.-B. Dumas mentioned Balard's love for the sea: "His thinking always drew him to the sea; he would have liked to live near it, he said, in order to fathom its chemical history; and, as soon as a free moment permitted, he took the train to become elated by the effluvia of the Mediterranean" (*96*).

The glory due to Balard for his discovery of bromine is enhanced when one knows that the great Justus von Liebig just missed it. Several years before, a German firm had asked Liebig to examine the contents of a certain bottle, and he had concluded, without thorough study, that the substance was iodine chloride. When he heard of the discovery of bromine, he immediately recognized his error and placed the bottle in a special case which he called his "cupboard of mistakes" (*11*). Hence, when his dear friend Friedrich Wöhler a few years later just missed discovering vanadium,* Liebig knew how to sympathize with him.

As soon as he had read Balard's paper on bromine, Liebig examined the brine from Theodorshalle near Kreuznach and prepared nearly twenty grams of bromine. His experiments led him to conclude, as Balard had done, that it must be a simple substance (*27*). "I know a chemist," said he, years later (referring to himself), "who during a visit to Kreuznach occupied himself with the investigation of the saline mother liquors there; he found iodine in them and observed that the iodine-starch, when left

* See also Chapter 13. pp. 353–5.

over night, acquired a fire-yellow color. . . . A few months later, he received Herr Balard's beautiful research and was in a position that very day to make known a series of experiments on the relation of bromine to iron, platinum, and carbon; for Balard's bromine stood in his laboratory labeled *liquid iodine chloride*. Since then he makes no more theories unless they can be directed and supported by unambiguous experiments" (97). Liebig's first paper on bromine was published in the *Annales de chimie et de physique* in 1826 (27).

Another chemist who just missed discovering bromine was J. R. Joss, who in 1824, and again in January, 1826, had recorded in his laboratory notes the appearance of a red color in some hydrochloric acid prepared from gray Hungarian rock salt and Bohemian fuming sulfuric acid. At the time, he attributed this color to the possible presence of selenium from the sulfuric acid. After Balard's discovery, however, he made further experiments with the same materials and became convinced that the red color must be due to bromine. His attempts to obtain more of the bromine-containing rock salt were unsuccessful (147).

After the publication of Balard's original paper, W. Meissner of Halle recalled that he, too, had observed an orange color when he had added sulfuric acid and starch to the water of the salt spring at Halle (154). Professor Geiger of Heidelberg soon detected bromine in the spring at Rappenau. When Dr. C. Fromherz of Freiburg investigated some brines sent to him by Althaus of Dürrheim, inspector of the salt-works, he isolated bromine from the mother liquors from Dürrheim and Schweningen and believed that it was originally present in the form of magnesium bromide. He also detected bromine in the salt springs of Rappenau, Wimpfen, Offenau, and Jaxfeld (148).

Bromine from Sea Water. Balard recognized in 1826 that bromine is present in low concentration in sea water. Professor Gmelin of Tübingen detected it in water from the Dead Sea, a discovery which was promptly confirmed by S. F. Hermbstädt of Berlin (149). In 1934 the Dow Chemical Company successfully extracted bromine commercially from raw ocean water at Kure Beach, North Carolina (150).

A Bromide Mineral. In 1841 Pierre Berthier of Nemours (1772–1862) discovered the first mineral known to contain bromine. "The district of Plateros," said he, "which is situated 17 leagues from Zacatecas and $1^{1}/_{2}$ leagues north of Fresnillo, differs from the other mining districts in the nature of the ore it contains. The silver in this ore is found in two different states: first, native and disseminated in very small particles in a gray, compact, highly plumbiferous mass; the Mexicans then call it *plata azul* (blue silver); secondly and principally, in the form of a compound occurring in little olive-green or yellowish crystals called *plata verde* (green silver), which was believed to be silver chloride but which I have recognized as perfectly pure bromide . . ." (*151*).

When Berthier treated a specimen of this ore from the San Onofe Mine with an excess of hot ammonium hydroxide, he observed, mixed with the metallic silver, a green powder which had been only incompletely attacked. "This was the circumstance," said he, "which drew my attention to the ore from Plateros and which led me to realize that the substance which had been taken for silver chloride is pure bromide, without admixture of chloride or iodide, a substance which had not yet been met within the mineral realm and which therefore constitutes a new species" (*151*). Berthier learned that this mineral is not rare in Mexico but is often found in beautiful cubic and octahedral crystals. He also found the same mineral at Huelgoeth, Department of Finistère, France, and discovered some of it among the Chilean silver minerals which Ignaz Domeyko, professor of chemistry at the College of Coquimbo, had sent to the School of Mines at Paris (*151, 152*). The mineral which Berthier analyzed was evidently bromyrite (silver bromide).

Bromine in Animals. In 1920 A. Damiens detected bromine in the blood, lungs, kidneys, and other organs of normal dogs, oxen, partridges, chickens, and human beings. He did not observe any tendency of this halogen to accumulate as iodine does in the thyroid gland (*153*).

FLUORINE

In his "Bermannus", Georgius Agricola in 1529 described the use of fluorspar as a flux: "*Bermannus.*—These stones are similar to gems, but less hard. . . . Our miners call them *fluores,* not inappropriately to my mind, for by the heat of fire, like ice in the sun, they liquefy and flow away. They are of varied and bright colors. . . . *Anton.*—What is the use of *fluores? Bermannus.*—They are wont to be made use of when metals are smelted, as they cause the material in the fire to be much more fluid . . ." (*70*).

In 1676 Johann Sigismund Elsholtz (or Elsholz) informed the members of the Imperial Society for Investigating Nature (Societati Imperiali Naturae Curiosorum) "that he was acquainted with a phosphorus which had its light neither from the sun nor from fire, but which, when heated on a metal plate over glowing coals, shone with a bluish-white lustre; so that by strewing the powder of it over paper, one might form luminous writing" (*71, 72, 113*).

In his history of the discovery of phosphorus, G. W. Leibniz stated in 1710: "I also showed this inquisitive prince [Duke Johann Friedrich] another kind [of phosphorus] which one might call *thermophosphorus.*

One draws letters and figures, for example, on an iron plate with a certain flux in the mines; lays the plate on glowing coals; whereupon they shine, even though the plate is not heated to redness" (73). An editorial footnote to this article in *Crell's Neues chemisches Archiv* in 1784 stated that this flux was undoubtedly fluorspar.

As early as 1670 Heinrich Schwanhard of Nuremberg, a member of a famous family of glass cutters, found that when he treated this mineral with strong acids, the lenses of his spectacles became etched (71, 74). This led him to discover and perfect a new means of etching glass without a diamond or any abrasive. In his "History of Inventions," Johann Beckmann described the process as follows: "At present," said he, "the glass is covered with a varnish, and those figures which one intends to etch are traced out through it; but Schwanhard, when the figures were formed, covered them with varnish, and then by his liquid corroded the glass around them; so that the figures, which remained smooth and clear, appeared when the varnish was removed, raised from a dim or dark ground" (71). Schwanhard raised this art to a high degree of perfection, and depicted people, animals, flowers, and herbs in relief on the glass (75). He did this work only for Emperor Charles II.

The formula for Matthäus Pauli's glass-etching fluid was made public in 1725 (76). Beckmann then quoted the following recipe from page 107 of the *Breslauer Sammlung zur Natur- und Medicin-Geschichte* for January, 1725: "When *spiritus nitri per distillationem* has passed into the recipient, ply it with a strong fire, and when well dephlegmated, pour it, as it corrodes ordinary glass, into a Waldenburg flask; then throw into it a pulverized green Bohemian emerald, otherwise called *hesphorus* (which, when reduced to powder and heated, emits in the dark a green light), and place it in warm sand for twenty-four hours . . ." (71, 74). The "Bohemian emerald" was undoubtedly green fluorspar. Fredrick Accum published an article in *Nicholson's Journal* for 1800 on the antiquity of the art of etching by means of hydrofluoric acid (74).

In 1768 A. S. Marggraf made the first chemical investigation of fluorite, distinguished it from heavy spar and selenitic spar (sulfates of barium and calcium), and showed that it is not a sulfate (77, 78). When he distilled pulverized fluorspar with sulfuric acid from a glass retort, the glass was badly attacked and even perforated. He noticed that an "earth" [silica] appeared in the receiver, and therefore concluded that the sulfuric acid had liberated a volatile earth from the fluorspar (77).

In 1771 C. W. Scheele investigated a green variety of fluorspar from Garpenberg and a white one from Gislöf in Scania. He found that the green specimen contained a trace of iron but that the white one did not. When he heated the pulverized mineral with oil of vitriol [sulfuric acid], he noticed that the inner surface of the glass retort became corroded,

JOH: SIGISM. ELSHOLTZ
MED. D. SERENISS. ELECT. BR.
FRID. WILHELM. MED. AULICUS.

Courtesy Wilhelm Prandtl

Johann Sigismund Elsholtz, 1623–1688. Scientific authority at the court of the Elector of Brandenburg. A pamphlet which he had printed at Berlin in 1676 is the earliest publication concerning elementary phosphorus and also contains descriptions of the previously known phosphors: Bologna stone, Baldwin's phosphor, and emerald phosphor (green fluorspar). See also ref. (*113*).

that the white solid mass left at the bottom consisted mainly of selenite [calcium sulfate], and that an acid passed over into the receiver. He concluded that fluorspar "consists principally of calcareous earth saturated with a specific acid" (79). By adding lime water to a dilute solution of this acid, he synthesized an artificial fluorspar which, like the natural mineral, phosphoresced when warmed in the dark.

Scheele stated that the acid of fluorspar [hydrofluoric acid] can dissolve siliceous earth and that therefore it is almost impossible to prepare the pure acid. He believed that the earthy deposit in the receiver (Marggraf's "volatile earth") was siliceous earth produced by a reaction

Johann Christian Wiegleb, 1732–1800. Pharmacist and chemist of Langensalza, Germany. Author of excellent books on pharmacy, chemistry, and the history of chemistry and alchemy. In his "Chemical Experiments on Alkaline Salts" (1774), he showed that all of the alkali obtained by the burning of plants is pre-existent in them.

Courtesy Edgar Fahs Smith

between the "acid of fluorspar" and water. In 1778 his friend Friedrich Ehrhart, a botanist at Hanover who had studied under Carl von Linné and T. Bergman, wrote Scheele that this deposit had merely been dissolved from the glass retort. When J. K. F. Meyer of Stettin repeated the experiment, using a lead retort instead of a glass one, he found no such deposit in the receiver (80). Carl Friedrich Wenzel (114) with a lead retort and Giovanni Antonio Scopoli with a gold-plated silver one obtained similar results (76). In 1781 Johann Christian Wiegleb proved quantitatively that the silica came from the glass retort, and in the same year Scheele became convinced of his error (77, 81, 82). These results

Courtesy the Deutsches Museum in Munich

Carl Friedrich Wenzel, 1740–1793. German physician and chemist. Chief assessor of the Freiberg mines and later chemist at the Meissen porcelain works. Author of "The Doctrine of the Affinity of Substances," a work that deals primarily with chemical proportions. He determined quantitatively the amounts of various acids necessary to neutralize given quantities of plant alkali (KOH) and mineral alkali (NaOH).

were also confirmed by Wilhelm Heinrich Sebastian Bucholtz (83). In 1780 and again in 1786 (the last year of his life), Scheele published papers defending his claim that fluorspar contains a peculiar acid (79).

The new acid immediately aroused widespread interest. John Hill, in the notes to his translation of Theophrastus' "History of Stones," stated in 1774: "There exists in the Mineral World a native acid; and probably only one; tho' it exhibits itself under different Forms. Of the existence of this we are certain; altho' we never have seen it pure; nor can. It never becoming an Object of our Senses, but in Mixture with other Bodies.

It has been called the Vague Acid and the Universal Acid. We have been accustomed to meet with it under two distinct Forms; and to know it under the Names of two Species: These are the Vitriolic and the Muriatic Acid: and to these we are lately taught to add a third, which, from the Place where it has been discovered, Authors have called the Swedish Acid; and to which some, tho' very improperly, have given the Name of the Sparry Acid. Perhaps, in distinction from the other two, it may be better named the Stony Acid" (*84, 85, 118*).

In 1786 M. H. Klaproth published in *Crell's Annalen* a method devised by Count von Gesler for etching letters and drawings on glass with hydrofluoric acid (*76, 86*), and in 1788 Jean-Pierre-Casimir de Marcassus,

Paulin Louyet, 1818–1850. Belgian chemist who investigated the compounds of fluorine. For his attempts to liberate fluorine, the Knox brothers placed at his disposal their costly fluorspar and platinum equipment. His premature death was caused by continued exposure for about a decade to the toxic compounds of this element (*69*). Engraving by Danse, Brussels, 1851.

Baron de Puymaurin (1757–1841) published a similar process in the *Mémoires de Toulouse* (*87, 88, 89*). The German translation of Macquer's chemical dictionary, published in 1790, contains the following detailed account of it (*88*).

"The acid of fluorspar has recently been used for etching pictures on glass coated with an etching ground through which the picture is etched. This art is to a certain extent in the process of development. Klaproth and Lichtenberg among the Germans and Graf von G. and M. de Puymaurin among the foreigners (*Crell's Beyträge* III, 467 ff) have proposed it and given instructions. The latter advises as the result of his experience that, first of all, one must know accurately the nature of the glass to be used. He observed that the Bohemian, since it is not homogeneous and not thoroughly fused, is not acted on uniformly by the acid; and that the English, since it contains too much lead, on which the acid works very fast, shows an unpleasant spot wherever there is the slightest break in the varnish which serves as the etching ground. The most suitable is white mirror-glass, especially that for small mirrors. . . .

"His best results were obtained with a varnish consisting of equal parts of mastix [mastic] and a drying oil which he had prepared by heating linseed oil with red mercury calx in the air apparatus; but this varnish could not easily be applied as a uniform layer, and in winter it could not be dried well without considerable heat. One applies it to the carefully cleaned glass, heated so hot that one cannot hold one's hand on it, by means of little taffeta balls stuffed with cotton, and then exposes it, as the copper etchers do, to the smoke of little resin candles. During the etching the coated glass should be laid on glass set into a table-leaf which can be raised toward the light, so that one can frequently observe the etched lines. One etches the glass either in demi-relief, with removal of the varnish between the pictures, or in high-relief, by letting it remain in the places where no line of the picture is to appear.

"M. de Puymaurin," continued Macquer, "advises that the acid to be used for etching be distilled from a leaden retort, at the temperature of boiling water, from a mixture of fluorspar with four times as much vitriolic acid. . . . On the demi-relief glass, one distributes the acid as uniformly as possible with the brush, removes the white crust when it appears, pours on fresh acid, and repeats this process until the picture is etched deeply enough. In high-relief pictures, one proceeds as in the etching of copper plates with the nitric acid used for parting. Here, too, the white dust covering the etched lines gives evidence of the etching. When it is deep enough, one lets the acid flow off and be kept for future use.

"In this entire process," said Macquer, "one must carefully consider the temperature of the atmosphere. At 16° in the shade on Réaumur's thermometer, one can etch the picture on the glass plate, which has been coated and treated with the acid in bright sunlight, within four or five hours; in winter, however, one needs as many days, and unless one heats the varnish from above with an oven, the work cannot be done at all. When the picture is sufficiently etched, and the acid poured off, one washes the glass a few times, removes the varnish with coarse linen and alcohol, and finally rubs it with fine chalk dust. This etching of glass with acid of fluorspar can also be used for the graduation of glass physical apparatus such as eudiometers, perhaps also for the plates for copying maps and other drawings" (88).

Baron de Puymaurin also tested the action of hydrofluoric acid on various kinds of stones placed in tin receptacles. Stephen Weston men-

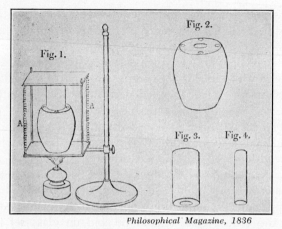

Philosophical Magazine, 1836

Apparatus Used by the Knox Brothers in Their Attempts to Liberate Fluorine. Upon treating dry "fluoride of mercury" with dry chlorine they obtained crystals of mercuric chloride. A piece of gold foil which had been acted on by the gas in the receiver was placed on glass and treated with sulfuric acid. Since the glass was attacked, they concluded that fluorine had been liberated and had formed gold fluoride. No hydrogen was detected. Fig. 1. Fluorspar vessel in the stand which holds down the receiver by means of spiral springs. Fig. 2. Vessel with cover off, showing the orifice and the small depressions containing gold leaf. Fig. 3. Receiver. Fig. 4. Stopper.

tioned the hydrofluoric acid etchings of Puymann [Puymaurin?] and stated in 1805 that "the best work of this kind is that which represents Chemistry weeping over the tomb of Scheele, the discoverer of the fluoric [hydrofluoric] acid" (*90*).

The history of fluorine gas is a tragic record. Lavoisier, it will be recalled, thought that all acids contain oxygen, but Sir Humphry Davy showed that "fluoric" [hydrofluoric] acid does not. A.-M. Ampère suggested to Davy that it must be a compound of hydrogen and an unknown element (*31, 32*). Paul Schützenberger expressed the belief that this unknown substance, fluorine, would be found to be the most active of all the elements, and correctly predicted some of its properties (*18, 19*). It is this extreme activity of the element that made its liberation such a difficult and dangerous task and brought agony and death to some of the pioneer investigators.

Davy, Gay-Lussac, and Thenard all suffered intensely from the effects of inhaling small quantities of hydrogen fluoride. Davy found that his silver and platinum containers were attacked, but believed that fluorine could be liberated if a fluorspar vessel were used (*23, 30, 62*). Two members of the Royal Irish Academy, George Knox and his brother, the Reverend Thomas Knox, of Toomavara, Tipperary, made an ingenious apparatus of fluorspar. They were unable, however, to collect and study the gas. Both suffered the frightful torture of hydrofluoric acid poisoning (*20*). The Reverend Thomas Knox nearly lost his life, and George Knox had to rest in Naples for three years in order to regain his health (*40*). P. Louyet of Brussels, although fully aware of the Knox brothers' misfortune, continued his dangerous researches too long, and died a martyr to science (*17, 18, 40, 42*). Professor Jérôme Nicklès of Nancy met a similar fate (*35, 43, 60, 67*).

Edmond Fremy, 1814-1894. Professor of chemistry at the École Polytechnique and director of the Muséum d'Histoire Naturelle. He electrolyzed anhydrous calcium fluoride but could not collect the fluorine. He was present, however, when his former pupil, Henri Moissan, exhibited the new gas before a committee from the Academy of Sciences. Fremy wrote a monograph on the synthesis of rubies. See *J. Chem. Educ.,* **8,** 1017–19 (June, 1931) for illustrations of his artificial rubies.

Edmond Fremy, who had watched Louyet perform some of his experiments (*33*), tried to decompose anhydrous calcium fluoride electrolytically, and did obtain calcium at the cathode, while a gas, which must have been fluorine, escaped at the anode (*34*). However, because of its tendency to add on to other substances and form ternary and quaternary compounds, Fremy failed in all his attempts to collect and identify the gas. When he allowed chlorine to act on a fluoride, he obtained no fluorine, but only a fluochloride; when he used oxygen in place of chlorine, he obtained an oxyfluoride.

This seemingly hopeless field of experimentation was soon abandoned, but in 1869 the English chemist George Gore liberated a little fluorine, which immediately combined explosively with hydrogen (*18,*

35). When he tried to electrolyze anhydrous hydrofluoric acid "with anodes of gas-carbon, carbon of lignum-vitae, and of many other kinds of wood, of palladium, platinum, and gold, . . . the gas-carbon disintegrated rapidly, all the kinds of charcoal flew to pieces quickly, and the anodes of palladium, platinum, and gold were corroded without evolution of gas" (35). Moissan mentioned the "remarkable exactitude" of Gore's memoir (23).

The apparently impossible task was finally accomplished by Moissan in 1886. Ferdinand-Frédéric-Henri Moissan was born at 5 Rue Montholon in Paris on September 28, 1852. When he was twelve years old, the family moved to the little town of Meau in the department of Seine-et-Marne, where he attended the municipal college. His first lessons in chemistry were received from his father, a railroad official (22, 58).

Obliged to leave school at the age of eighteen years, he became an apprentice in the Bandry apothecary shop located at the intersection of Rue Pernelle and Rue Saint Denis in Paris. Here his ready knowledge of chemistry enabled him to save the life of a man who had swallowed arsenic in an attempt at suicide (21, 22). In 1872 Moissan decided to give up his position at the pharmacy in order to study under Edmond Fremy at the Musée d'Histoire Naturelle. Here he not only made rapid progress in chemistry and pharmacy, but also became a connoisseur of art and litera-

Dr. George Gore,* 1826–1908. English electrochemist. Head of the Institute of Scientific Research, Easy Row, Birmingham. He improved the art of electroplating and wrote treatises on "The Art of Electrometallurgy" and "The Electrolytic Separation and Refining of Metals." His estate was bequeathed to the Royal Society of London and the Royal Institution of Great Britain.

* This portrait was obtained through the courtesy of Mr. R. B. Pilcher, Registrar and Secretary of the Institute of Chemistry of Great Britain and Ireland.

Professor Moissan Preparing Fluorine in His Laboratory at the École de Pharmacie in Paris

ture, and even wrote a rhymed play which was almost accepted for the audiences at the Odéon. He was afterward able to laugh at this early disappointment and to say, "I believe I did better to study chemistry"† (*22*).

In 1879 he passed his examination for first-class pharmacist and accepted a position at the École Supérieure de Pharmacie (*21, 58*).

Three years later there occurred in Moissan's life a most fortunate event—his marriage to Léonie Lugan. She proved to be a devoted wife and comrade, a hospitable, charming hostess, and a great help to him in his scientific work. M. Lugan was also an ideal father-in-law, in full sympathy with Moissan's scientific researches. He gladly provided material support for his daughter's family, and urged Moissan to devote all his time to science, unhampered by financial worries. Since the latter had no laboratory at the School of Pharmacy, he did his first experimental work in a building situated on the Rue Lancry, but J.-H. Debray afterward allowed him to use the more powerful battery in a temporary barracks on the Rue Michelet (*22*).

* The picture of Moissan preparing fluorine has been reproduced from an article by Gaston Tissandier, *La Nature*, **18**, [1], 177 (Feb. 22, 1890), by permission of Masson et Cie., Éditeurs, Paris.

† "Je crois que j'ai mieux fait de faire de la chimie."

Fremy had concluded from his experiments that fluorine had probably been liberated in the electrolysis of the fluorides of calcium, potassium, and silver, but that, because the temperature had been too high, it had immediately attacked the container. He prepared anhydrous hydrogen fluoride, but found himself caught in the horns of the following dilemma: when *moist* hydrogen fluoride was electrolyzed, he obtained only hydrogen, oxygen, and ozone; and dry hydrogen fluoride would not conduct the current (22).

Moissan reasoned that if he were trying to liberate chlorine he would not choose a stable solid like sodium chloride, but a volatile compound like hydrochloric acid or phosphorus pentachloride. His preliminary experiments with silicon fluoride convinced him that this was a very stable compound, and that, if he should ever succeed in isolating fluorine, it would unite with silicon with incandescence, and that therefore he might use silicon in testing for the new halogen. After many unsuccessful attempts to electrolyze phosphorus trifluoride and arsenic trifluoride, and after four interruptions caused by serious poisoning, he finally obtained powdered arsenic at the cathode and some gas bubbles at the anode. However, before these fluorine bubbles could reach the surface, they were absorbed by the arsenic trifluoride to form pentafluoride (18, 23).

Moissan finally used as electrolyte a solution of dry potassium acid fluoride in anhydrous hydrofluoric acid. His apparatus consisted of two platinum-iridium electrodes sealed into a platinum U-tube closed with fluorspar screw caps covered with a layer of gum lac (42, 49, 59). The U-tube was chilled with methyl chloride, the gas now used in many modern refrigerators, to a temperature of $-23°$.

Success finally came. On June 26, 1886, a gas appeared at the anode, and when he tested it with silicon, it immediately burst into flame. Two days later he made the following conservative announcement to the Academy:

One can indeed make various hypotheses on the nature of the liberated gas; the simplest would be that we are in the presence of fluorine, but it would be possible, of course, that it might be a perfluoride of hydrogen or even a mixture of hydrofluoric acid and ozone sufficiently active to explain such vigorous action as this gas exerts on crystalline silicon (42).

This announcement was read to the Academy by Debray, for Moissan was not then a member, and the president appointed a committee consisting of MM. J.-H. Debray, Marcelin Berthelot, and Edmond Fremy to investigate the discovery. In the presence of these distinguished guests, the apparatus acted like a spoiled child. Moissan could not obtain as much as a bubble of fluorine. However, on the following day he used fresh materials and demonstrated his discovery to the entire satisfaction of

Pierre-Eugène-Marcelin Berthelot, 1827–1907.   French chemist and historian of chemistry.   His researches were in the diverse fields of organic synthesis, chemical statics and dynamics, thermochemistry, explosives, nitrifying bacteria in the soil, and the oriental sources of alchemy. In his early days he assisted Balard at the Collège de France and many years later he served on a committee with Debray and Fremy to investigate Moissan's discovery of fluorine.   See also refs. (*115*) and (*116*).

the committee (22). Thus Fremy, who had come so near to making this discovery himself, was able to say with all sincerity, "A professor is always happy when he sees one of his students proceed farther and higher than himself" (60).

The successful isolation of fluorine made Moissan's name known throughout the scientific world, and in 1893 another achievement won for him more popular publicity than he desired. On February sixth of that year he apparently succeeded in preparing small artificial diamonds by subjecting sugar charcoal to enormous pressure (52, 53, 63). Most of his diamonds were black like carbonado, but the largest one, 0.7 of a

Alfred E. Stock. Former director of the Chemical Institute of the Technische Hochschule of Karlsruhe. Former student of Henri Moissan and author of an excellent biographical sketch of him. Visiting lecturer at Cornell University in 1932. He is an authority on the high-vacuum method for studying volatile substances, the chemistry of boron, the preparation and properties of beryllium, and chronic mercurial poisoning.

millimeter long, was colorless. His colleagues affectionately named this little diamond "The Regent," for to them it was as precious as the 137-carat specimen in the Louvre (22). Recent experimenters, however, have expressed doubt that Moissan's products were genuine diamonds (169).

Moissan's electric furnace was a valuable incentive to research. With its aid he prepared many uncommon metals such as uranium, tungsten, (wolfram), vanadium, chromium, manganese, titanium, molybdenum, columbium (niobium), tantalum, and thorium, much of this work being done at the Edison Works on Avenue Trudaine (24, 61). As a practical result of her husband's researches, Mme. Moissan was one of the first women in the world to use aluminum cooking utensils (*22*).

Moissan always insisted on extreme neatness in his laboratory, and the wooden floors were waxed every Saturday. Alfred Stock (*64*) relates that one day Professor Moissan looked critically at the floor and said reproachfully, "Who did that?" Upon careful examination, Dr. Stock noticed that a few drops of water from the tip of his wash-bottle had fallen to the waxed floor (*22*).

Henri Moissan, 1852–1907. Professor of chemistry at the École Supérieure de Pharmacie. The discoverer of the element fluorine. With his electric furnace he prepared many uncommon metals such as uranium, tungsten (wolfram), and vanadium.

Moissan was one of the most polished scientific lecturers in Paris. His ease of delivery, his well-modulated voice, his carefully chosen experiments, and his gentle humor attracted great crowds to his lectures at the Sorbonne. At exactly five o'clock the two large doors of the lecture room used to be opened simultaneously by two servants, and at a quarter past five the lecture began. Then for an hour and a quarter Moissan held the eager attention of his audience. Sir William Ramsay said of him,

His command of language was admirable; it was French at its best. The charm of his personality and his evident joy in exposition gave keen pleasure to his auditors. He will live long in the memories of all who were privileged to know him, as a man full of human kindness, of tact, and of true love for the subject which he adorned by his life and work (*22, 48*).

Moissan had an artistic, hospitable home in the quiet Rue Vauquelin, and was proud of his Corot landscape and his fine collection of autographs.   M. and Mme. Moissan and their son Louis usually spent their vacations traveling in Italy, Spain, Greece, the Alps, or the Pyrenees, and in 1904 Moissan came to America to visit the St. Louis World's Fair (*22*).

His life was undoubtedly shortened by his continued work with the toxic gases, fluorine and carbon monoxide.   He died on February 20, 1907.   His only child, Louis, an assistant at the École de Pharmacie, who was killed on a battlefield of World War I, left 200,000 francs to the school for the establishment of two prizes: the Moissan chemistry prize in memory of his father and the Lugan pharmacy prize in honor of his mother (*25, 65*).

Other Sources of Fluorine.   M. H. Klaproth discovered that cryolite, the mineral which later came to be used as a flux in the industrial electrolytic production of aluminum, is a fluoride of sodium and aluminum (*76*). In 1878 S. L. Penfield, in a research consisting of eight analyses of amblygonite, proved that, contrary to the views of Carl Friedrich Rammelsberg, fluorine and hydroxyl can replace each other in the same mineral (*155*).   Traces of fluorine are found in all types of natural water: in oceans, lakes, rivers, and springs (*156*).

Fluorine in Plants and Animals.   In 1802 Domenico Pini Morichini discovered the presence of fluorine in fossil ivory (*157*).   He later detected it in the enamel of the teeth, and Berzelius soon confirmed the discovery and showed that fluorine is also a normal constituent of bone (*158, 159, 165*).   The presence of excessive amounts of fluoride in drinking water causes the well-known mottling of the enamel of children's teeth (*160*), but small amounts of fluoride protect the teeth from dental caries (*161*).

J. D. Dana showed that fluorine occurs in the lime of corals (*162*). Dr. G. Wilson of Edinburgh and J. G. Forchhammer both detected it directly in sea water from the Sound near Copenhagen, and the latter demonstrated it still more easily in the boiler scale from Transatlantic steamers (*98*).

In 1857 Jérôme Nicklès demonstrated the presence of fluorine in the blood of many mammals and birds.   In disagreement with Berzelius, he regarded the fluorine in bones as an essential ingredient.   "Fluorine," said Nicklès, "exists in the bile, in the albumen of the egg, in gelatine, in urine, in saliva, in hair; in a word, the animal organism is penetrated by fluorine, and it may be expected to be found in all the liquids which impregnate it" (*163*).

Armand Gautier and Paul Clausmann found fluorine to be a universal accompaniment of phosphorus in plant tissues (*164*).   Although the unconditional necessity for fluorine for the plant has not been proved, it does occur in all plants and all plant parts (*167*).

LITERATURE CITED

(1) Moissan, H., "Le Fluor et ses Composés," Steinheil, Paris, 1900, preface, p. viii.

(2) Oswald, M., "L'Évolution de la chimie au XIXe Siècle," Bibliothèque Larousse, Paris, 1913, p. 26. Quotation from Balard.

(3) Alembic Reprint No. 13, "The Early History of Chlorine," University of Chicago Press, Chicago, 1902, pp. 8–9; C. W. Scheele, "On manganese and its properties."

(4) Ibid., p. 20. C.-L. Berthollet, "Memoir on Dephologisticated Marine Acid," Mémoires de l'Académie Royale, 1785, Paris, 1788, pp. 276–95.

(5) Färber, E. "Geschichtliche Entwicklung der Chemie," Springer, Berlin, 1921, pp. 119–22.

(6) Alembic Reprint No. 13, Ref. (3), pp. 37–48. L.-J. Gay-Lussac and L.-J. Thenard, "On the nature and properties of muriatic acid and of oxygenated, muriatic acid."

(7) Ibid., p. 49. L.-J. Gay-Lussac and L.-J. Thenard, "Extract from 'Recherches Physico-Chimiques,'" Vol. 2, Imprimerie de Crapelet, Paris, 1811, p. 262.

(8) Jagnaux, R., "Histoire de la Chimie," Vol. 1, Baudry et Cie., Paris, 1891, pp. 505–13.

(9) Thomson, Thomas, "History of Chemistry," Vol. 2, Colburn and Bentley, London, 1831, p. 268; J. Davy, "The Collected works of Sir Humphry Davy, Bart.," Vol. 1, Smith, Elder and Co., London, 1839, p. 123.

(10) A. W. H., "Zur Erinnerung an Friedrich Wöhler," Ber., 15, 3127–290 (Part 2, 1882).

(11) Oswald, M., "L'Évolution de la Chimie au XIXe Siècle," Ref. (2), pp. 22–6.

(12) Jagnaux, R., "Histoire de la Chimie," Ref. (8), Vol. 1, pp. 521–8.

(13) Toraude, L.-G., "Bernard Courtois et la Découverte de l'Iode," Vigot Frères, Paris, 1921, 164 pp.

(14) Hoefer, F., "Nouvelle Biographie Générale," Didot Frères, Paris, 1866. Article on Ballard (sic).

(15) Söderbaum, H. G., "Jac. Berzelius Bref," Vol. 2, part 4, Almqvist and Wiksells, Upsala, 1912–1914, p. 67.

(16) Balard, A.-J., "Memoir on a peculiar substance contained in sea water," Annals of Phil., [1], 28, 381–7 (Nov., 1826); 411–24 (Dec., 1826)

(17) Oswald, M., "L'Évolution de la Chimie au XIXe Siècle," Ref. (2), pp. 28–30.

(18) Jagnaux, R., "Histoire de la Chimie," Ref. (8), Vol. 1, pp. 528–49.

(19) Moissan, H., "Le Fluor et ses Composés," Ref. (1), pp. 8–9.

(20) Knox, G. J. and the Rev. Thomas Knox. "On fluorine," Phil Mag., [3]. 9, 107–9 (Aug., 1836); [3], 12, 105–6 (Jan., 1838); G. J. Knox, "Researches on fluorine," ibid., [3], 16, 192–4 (Mar., 1840).

(21) Harrow, B., "Eminent Chemists of Our Time," D. Van Nostrand Co., New York City, 1920, p. 138.

(22) Stock, A., "Henri Moissan," Ber., 40, 5099–130 (Band 4, 1907).

(23) Moissan, H., "Le Fluor et ses Composés," Ref. (1), pp. 1–36.

(24) Harrow, B., "Eminent Chemists of Our Time," Ref. (21), p. 148.

(25) Ibid., p. 153.

(26) Anglada, Letter to the editors, Ann. chim. phys., [2], 33, 222–3 (1826).

(27) Liebig, J., "Sur le brôme," Ann. chim. phys., [2], 33, 330–3 (1826).

(28) Balard, A.-J., "Mémoire sur une substance particulière contenue dans l'eau de la mer," Ann. chim. phys., [2], 32, 337–81 (1826).

(29) Vauquelin, N.-L., L.-J. Thenard, and L.-J. Gay-Lussac, "Rapport sur le mémoire de M. Balard relatif à une nouvelle substance," Ann. chim. phys., [2], 32, 382–4 (1826); Annals of Phil., [1], 28, 425–6 (Dec., 1826).

(30) Davy, H., "An account of some new experiments on the fluoric compounds; with some observations on other objects of chemical inquiry," Phil. Trans., 104, 62–73 (1814) .

(31)   DAVY, H., "Some experiments and observations on the substances produced in different chemical processes on fluor spar," *Phil. Trans.*, **103**, 263–79 (1813).

(32)   AMPÈRE, A.-M., "Suite d'une classification naturelle pour les corps simples," *Ann. chim. phys.*, [2], **2**, 19–25 (May, 1816).

(33)   FREMY, E., "Recherches sur les fluorures," *Compt. rend.*, **38**, 393–7 (Feb. 27, 1854).

(34)   FREMY, E., Décomposition des fluorures au moyen de la pile," *Compt. rend.*, **40**, 966–8 (Apr. 23, 1855).

(35)   GORE, G., "On hydrofluoric acid," *Chem. News*, **19**, 74–5 (Feb. 12, 1869); *J. Chem. Soc., Trans.*, **22**, 368–406 (1869); *Phil. Trans.*, **159**, 173 (1869).

(36)   SMITH, E. F., "Bromine and its discoverers, 1826–1926," *J. Chem. Educ.*, **3**, 382–4 (Apr., 1926).

(37)   WEHRLE, "Geschichte der Salzsäure," Carl Gerold, Vienna, **1819**, pp. 83–4.

(38)   HENRY, W., "Account of a series of experiments, undertaken with the view of decomposing the muriatic acid," *Phil. Trans.*, **90**, 188–203 (1800).

(39)   GAY-LUSSAC, L.-J., "Untersuchungen über das Jod," Ostwald's Klassiker, No. 4. Wilhelm Engelmann, Leipzig, **1889**, 52 pp.; *Ann. chim. phys.*, [1], **91**, 5–160 (1813).

(40)   LOUYET, P., "Nouvelles recherches sur l'isolement du fluor, la composition des fluorures, et le poids atomique du fluor," *Compt. rend.*, **23**, 960–8 (Nov. 23, 1846); *Ann.*, **64**, 239–40 (Heft 2, 1848); "De la véritable nature de l'acide fluorhydrique anhydre," *Compt. rend.*, 24, 434–6 (Mar. 15, 1847).

(41)   BALDWIN, R. T., "History of the chlorine industry," *J. Chem. Educ.*, **4**, 313–9 (Mar., 1927).

(42)   MOISSAN, H., "Action d'un courant électrique sur l'acide fluorhydrique." *Compt. rend.*, **102**, 1543–4 (June 28, 1886); **103**, 202–5 (July 19, 1886); 256–8 (July 26, 1886); *Ann. chim. phys.*, [6], **12**, 472–537 (Dec., 1887); *Chem. News*, **54**, 51 (July 30, 1886); 80 (Aug. 13, 1886).

(43)   NICKLÈS, J., "Recherche du fluor. Action des acides sur le verre," *Compt. rend.*, **44**, 679–81 (Mar. 30, 1857).

(44)   BALARD, A.-J., "Recherches sur la nature des combinaisons décolorantes du chlore," *Ann. chim. phys.*, [2], **57**, 225–304 (1834).

(45)   CLÉMENT, N. and C.-B. DESORMES, "Découverte d'une substance nouvelle dans le Vareck par M. B. Courtois," *Ann. chim. phys.*, [1], **88**, 304–10 (1813).

(46)   "Lettre de M. Humphry Davy sur la nouvelle substance découverte par M. Courtois dans le sel de Vareck," *Ann. chim. phys.*, [1], **88**, 322–9 (1813).

(47)   Obituary of Balard, *J. Chem. Soc., Abstr.*, **31**, 512–14 (1877).

(48)   RAMSAY, W., "Moissan memorial lecture," *J. Chem. Soc., Trans.*, **101**, 477–88 (Part 1, 1912); "Chemical Society Memorial Lectures, 1901–1913," Vol. 2, Gurney and Jackson, London, **1914**, pp. 189–98.

(49)   TISSANDIER, G., "Le fluor," *La Nature*, **18**, [1], 177–9 (Feb. 22, 1890).

(50)   DAVY, DR. JOHN, "The Collected Works of Sir Humphry Davy, Bart.," Vol. 1, Smith, Elder and Co., London, **1839**, p. 400.

(51)   TORAUDE, L.-G., "Bernard Courtois et la Découverte de l'Iode," Ref. (*13*), pp. 41–2.

(52)   "Classics of science: Moissan's artificial diamonds," *Sci. News Letter*, **14**, 99–100 (Aug. 18, 1928).

(53)   MOISSAN, H., "The Electric Furnace," English translation by Lenher, Chemical Publishing Co., Easton, Pa., **1904**, 305 pp.

(54)   TORAUDE, L.-G., "Bernard Courtois," Ref. (*13*), p. 59.

(55)   *Ibid.*, pp. 64–5.

(56)   STIEGLITZ, J., "Chemistry in Medicine," The Chemical Foundation Inc., New York City, **1928**, pp. 272–96. Article by Dr. David Marine on "Iodine in the prevention and treatment of goiter."

(57)   LANDOLT, H., "Carl Löwig," *Ber.*, **23**, 1013 (Part 1, 1890); 905–9 (Part 3, 1890).

(58)   GUTBIER, A., "Zur Erinnerung an Henri Moissan," Kommissionsverlag von Max Mencke, Erlangen, **1908**, pp. 2–3.

(59)   TISSANDIER, G., "Le fluor," *La Nature*, **14**, [2], 363–6 (Nov. 6, 1886).

(60)   MEUNIER, "Le fluor," *La Nature*, **14**, [2], 383–4 (Nov. 20, 1886).

(61)   GAUTIER, A., "Henri Moissan," *La Nature*, **35**, [1], 222–4 (Mar. 2, 1907).

(62)   GUTBIER, A., "Zur Erinnerung an Henri Moissan," Ref. (*58*), pp. 25–34.

(63)   "Editor's outlook," *J. Chem. Educ.*, **6**, 1509–10 (Oct., 1929) .

(64)   "Stock to be non-resident lecturer at Cornell," *Ind. Eng. Chem., News Ed.*, **10**, 20 (Jan. 10, 1932); *cf. J. Chem. Educ.*, **9**, 586 (Mar., 1932).

(65)   "A monument to Henri Moissan," *J. Chem. Educ.*, **9**, 393–4 (Feb., 1932).

(66)   COUPIN, HENRI, "Les vieux savants quand ils étaient jeunes," *La Nature*, No. 2885, pp. 82–3 (July 15, 1932).

(67)   BOUDET, "Obituary of J. Nicklès," *J. Pharm. Chim.*, **9**, 445–7 (June, 1869); *Chem. News*, **19**, 202 (Apr. 23, 1869).

(68)   WURTZ, C.-A., "A. J. Balard," *La Nature*, **4**, (1), 355–8 (May 6, 1876).

(69)   DE KONINCK, M., "Notice sur Paulin-L.-C.-E. Louyet," *Annuaire de l'Acad. Roy. de Belgique*, **17**, 120–45 (1851).

(70)   HOOVER, H. C. and L. H. HOOVER, "Agricola's de re metallica," *Mining Mag.*, London, **1912**, pp. 115 and 380–1.

(71)   BECKMANN, JOHANN, "A History of Inventions, Discoveries, and Origins," 4th ed., Vol. 2, Henry G. Bohn, London, **1846**, pp. 87–92.

(72)   "Vitae Joh. Sigismundi Elsholtz," *Acta Medicorum Berolinensium, Decad. II*, **6**, 1–5 (1726).

(73)   LEIBNIZ, G. W., "Geschichte der Erfindung des Phosphors," *Crell's Neues chem. Archiv*, **1**, 217 (1784); *Chem. Abh. k. Akad. Wiss.* (Berlin), **1700–1710**, p. 91.

(74)   ACCUM, F., "On the antiquity of the art of etching on glass," *Nicholson's J.*, **4**, 1–4 (Apr., 1800).

(75)   "Allgemeine deutsche Biographie," Vol. 33, Duncker and Humblot, Leipzig, **1891**, pp. 186–7. Article on Heinrich Schwanhard.

(76)   KLAPROTH, M. H. and F. WOLFF, "Dictionnaire de Chimie," Vol. 1, Klostermann, fils, Paris, **1810**, pp. 66–70.

(77)   WIEGLEB, J. C., "Chemische Untersuchung der Flussspatsäure, in Absicht der dabey befindlichen Erde," *Crell's Neueste Entdeckungen*, **1**, 3–15 (1781); A. S. MARGGRAF, *Mém. de l'Acad. R. de Berlin*, **24** (1768).

(78)   "Encyclopédie méthodique," Vol. 1, Panckoucke, Paris, **1786**, pp. 55–60. Article on Acide fluorique.

(79)   DOBBIN, L., "The Collected Papers of C. W. Scheele," G. Bell and Sons, London, **1931**, pp. 3–16, 46–7, 209–14, 295–304.

(80)   MEYER, J. K. F., "Flussspathsäure," *Crell's Ann.*, **4**, 520 (1785).

(81)   NORDENSKIÖLD, A. E., "C. W. Scheele. Nachgelassene Briefe und Aufzeichnungen," P. A. Norstedt and Sons, Stockholm, **1892**, pp. 118, 324–5, 399. Letters of Scheele to Gahn, Bergman, and Hjelm.

(82)   "Taschen-Buch für Scheidekünstler und Apotheker," Hoffmann Buchhandlung, Weimar, **1782**, pp. 62–4.

(83)   VON SCHERER, A. N., "Nekrolog. Wilhelm Heinrich Sebastian Bucholtz," *Scherer's Allg. J. der Chemie*, **2**, 591–615 (1798).

(84)   HILL, JOHN, "Theophrastus's History of Stones," 2nd ed., printed for the translator, London, **1774**, pp. 267–78.

(85)   BERLINER, J. F. T., "A neglected note by a neglected man," *Science*, **66**, 192–3 (Aug. 26, 1927). John Hill on Hydrofluoric Acid.

(86)   KLAPROTH, M. H., "Ueber das Verfahren, Zeichnungen in Glas zu ätzen," *Crell's Ann.*, **6**, 494 (1786).

(87)   VON CRELL, L., "Chemische Neuigkeiten," *Crell's Ann.*, **9**, 567 (1788); *Mém. de Toulouse*, **3** (1788).

(88)   MACQUER, P.-J., "Chymisches Wörterbuch oder allgemeine Begriffe der Chymie," Vol. 6, Weidmann, Leipzig, 1790, pp. 189–217. Article on Spathsäure.

(89)   "Biographie Universelle," Vol. 78, L. G. Michaud, Paris, 1846, pp. 180–1. Article on Puymaurin.

(90)   WESTON, STEPHEN, "Wernería, or Short Characters of the Earths," C. and R. Baldwin and W. Miller, London, 1805, pp. 17–18.

(91)   WEEKS, M. E., "An exhibit of chemical substances mentioned in the Bible," J. Chem. Educ., 20, 63–76 (Feb., 1943).

(92)   JONES, H. L., "The Geography of Strabo," Vol. 7, G. P. Putnam's Sons, New York, 1930, pp. 215–17, 269–71, 293–7; STRABO, Geography, 16, 1, 15; 16, 2, 23–5, 42–5.

(93)   THORPE, J. F. and R. P. LINSTEAD, "The Synthetic Dyestuffs," Charles Griffin and Co., London, 1933, pp. 198–9.

(94)   FRIEDLÄNDER, H., "Uber den Farbstoff des antiken Purpurs aus Murex brandaris," Ber., 42, 765–70 (1909).

(95)   SACHS, F. and R. KEMPF, "Ueber p-Halogen-o-Nitrobenzaldehyde," Ber., 36, 3303 (1903); F. SACHS and E. SICHEL, Ber., 37, 1868 (1904).

(96)   DUMAS, J.-B., "Discours et Éloges Académiques," Gauthier-Villars, Paris, 1885, pp. 83–114.

(97)   VON LIEBIG, J., "Ueber Laurent's Theorie der organischen Verbindungen," Ann., 25, 29–30 (1838).

(98)   FORCHHAMMER, GEORG, "On the composition of sea water in different parts of the ocean," Phil. Trans., 155, 203–62 (1865).

(99)   VAN TIEGHEM, PH., "Notice sur la Vie et les Travaux de J.-B. Dumas," Gauthier-Villars, Paris, 1912, pp. 10–11.

(100) MATIGNON, CAMILLE, "Le centenaire de l'iode. Les conséquences de sa découverte," Rev. gén. chimie, 16, 391–9 (1913).

(101) COINDET, J.-F., "Découverte d'un nouveau remède contre le goître," Ann. chim. phys. (2), 15, 49–59 (1820).

(102) "Nouvelle biographie générale," Ref. (14), Vol. 11, columns 83–4. Biographical sketch of Dr. Coindet.

(103) VON HOFMANN, A. W., "Zur Erinnerung an vorangegangene Freunde. J.-B.-A. Dumas," Vol. 2, F. Vieweg und Sohn, Braunschweig, 1888, p. 221; Ber., 17 (3), 637–8 (1884).

(104) TSCHIRCH, A., "Das Iod und die Schwammkohle," Schweiz. Apotheker-Ztg., 77, 85–6 (Feb. 18, 1939).

(105) VEIL, W. H. and R. STURM, "Geschichte der Jodtherapie," Deutsches Archiv klin. Med., 154, 327–57 (1927).

(106) "On iodine in the sponge," Quarterly J. Sci., 10, 456–7 (1821); Bibl. Univ., xiv, p. 301.

(107) "Discovery of iodine in the sponge," Schweigger's J., 31, 113 (1821); Bibl. Univ. (July, Aug., 1820).

(108) THOMSON, THOMAS, "Historical sketch of improvements in physical science during the year 1819," Annals of Philos., 16, 12 (July, 1820); ANDREW FYFE, "On the plants which yield iodine," Edinb. New Philos. J., 1 (1819).

(109) STEPHEN, L. and S. LEE, "Dictionary of National Biography," Vol. 7, Oxford University Press, 1921–2, pp. 780–1.

(110) REBER, BURKHARD, "Le docteur Coindet. L'Emploi de l'iode contre le goître Les crétins du Valais," Aesculape, 3, 93–6 (1913).

(111) "Biographisches Lexikon der Hervorragenden Ärzte aller Zeiten und Völker," 2nd ed., Vol. 2, Urban and Schwarzenberg, Berlin and Vienna, 1930, pp. 67–8. Article on J.-F. and Charles W. Coindet.

(112) LEMAY, PIERRE and R. E. OESPER, "Claude-Louis Berthollet (1748–1822)," J. Chem. Educ., 23, 158–65 (Apr., 1946); 23, 230–6 (May, 1946).

(113) PRANDTL, WILHELM, "Some early publications on phosphorus," J. Chem. Educ., 25, 414–19 (Aug., 1948).

(114) WINDERLICH, RUDOLF, "Carl Friedrich Wenzel, 1740–1793," *J. Chem. Educ.*, **27**, 56–9 (Feb., 1950).

(115) SABATIER, PAUL, "La chimie moderne et Marcelin Berthelot," *J. Chem. Educ.*, **3**, 1099–1102 (Oct., 1926).

(116) ASHDOWN, A. A., "Marcellin Berthelot," *J. Chem. Educ.*, **4**, 1217–32 (Oct., 1927).

(117) ANON., "Life of William Allen," Vol. 1, Henry Longstreth, Philadelphia, **1847**, pp. 161–2.

(118) EMERY, CLARK, " 'Sir' John Hill versus the Royal Society," *Isis*, **34**, 16–20 (Summer, 1942).

(119) BERTHOLLET, C.-L. and A.-B. BERTHOLLET, "Éléments de l'art de la teinture," 2nd ed., Firmin Didot, Paris, 1804 (an XIII), pp. 211–95.

(120) HENRY, WILLIAM, "A tribute to the memory of the late president of the Literary and Philosophical Society of Manchester [Thomas Henry]," *Memoirs Lit. and Philos. Soc. (Manchester)*, (2), **3**, 227–9 (1819).

(121) SMITH, J. LAWRENCE, "The century's progress in industrial chemistry," *Am. Chemist*, **5**, 62–3 (Aug., Sept., 1874).

(122) RUPP, G. L., "Ueber das Bleichen vermittelst der Salzsäure, nebst der Beschreibung eines Bleichapparats mit dieser in Wasser ohne Zusatz des Kali aufgelösten Säure," *Scherer's Allg. J. der Chemie*, **2**, 40–9 (1798).

(123) HIGGINS, S. H., "A history of bleaching," Longmans, Green and Co., London, **1924**, 176 pp.

(124) MACTEAR, JAMES, "On the growth of the alkali and bleaching-powder manufacture of the Glasgow district," *Chem. News*, **35**, 23 (Jan. 19, 1877).

(125) SZATHMÁRY, L. VON, "Paul Kitaibel entdeckt den Chlorkalk," *Chem.-Ztg.*, **55**, 645 (Aug. 22, 1931).

(126) "Guyton's rejection of nitrous fumigation to destroy the infection of air and contagion; and his recommendation of oxygenated muriatic acid gas instead of it," *Medical Repository*, **6**, 221–5 (Aug., Sept., Oct., 1802).

(127) SHOHL, A. T., "Mineral metabolism," Reinhold Publishing Corporation, New York, **1939**, pp. 19, 126.

(128) SÖDERBAUM, H. G., Ref. (*15*), Vol. 1, part 3, pp. 117–19. Letter of Dr. Marcet to Berzelius, March 29, 1815.

(129) KOPP, HERMANN, "Geschichte der Chemie," Vol. 3, Fr. Vieweg und Sohn, Braunschweig, **1845**, p. 372.

(130) PFAFF, C. H., "Ueber die Kalisalze, den Salmiak- und Iod-Gehalt des Ostseewassers," *Schweigger's J.*, (4), **45**, 378–82 (1825).

(131) COLIN, J.-J. and H.-F. GAULTIER DE CLAUBRY, "Mémoire sur les combinaisons de l'iode avec les substances végétales et animales," *Ann. chim. phys.*, (1), **90**, 87–100 (1814).

(132) SCHOLZ, "Ueber Iodine- und Platinaverarbeitung," *Schweigger's J.*, (4), **12**, 348–9 (1814). Letter of Scholz to Gehlen, Feb. 19, 1815; also footnote by the editor.

(133) BALARD, A.-J., "Note pour servir à l'histoire naturelle de l'iode," *Ann. chim. phys.*, (2), **28**, 178–81 (1825).

(134) "Iodine in spring water," *Quarterly J. Sci.*, **16**, 168 (1823); **17**, 180 (1824); *J. des Mines*, **8**, 293.

(135) "Vorkommen des Iodins im Mineralwasser zu Sales in Piemont, nach Angelini," *Schweigger's J.*, (4), **12**, 319–20 (1822).

(136) "Conversations of Goethe with Eckermann and Soret," new ed., George Bell and Sons, London, **1882**, pp. 1–3.

(137) VAUQUELIN, N.-L., "Ueber das Vorkommen des Iodins in dem Mineralreiche," *Schweigger's J.*, (4), **45**, 26–32 (1825); *Ann. chim. phys.*, (2), **29**, 99–104 (1825).

(138) BRANDES, R., "Ueber den vulkanischen Salmiak der Insel Lanzerote," *Schweigger's J.*, (4), **45**, 225–31 (1825).

(*139*)   PFAFF, C. H., "Handbuch der analytischen Chemie," Vol. 2, J. F. Hammrich, Altona, **1822**, pp. 142–5.

(*140*)   DEL RÍO, A. M., Nuevo sistema mineral del Señor Bercelio del año de 1825 . . .," Imprenta del Aguila, Mexico, **1827**, p. 8.

(*141*)   "Présence de l'iode dans différens minerais et dans des plantes croissant loin de la mer," *Ann. chim. phys.*, (2), **62**, 110–11 (1836).

(*142*)   DONALD, M. B., "History of the Chile nitrate industry," *Annals of Sci.*, **1**, 29–47, 193–216 (1936).

(*143*)   HAYES, A. A., "Peruvian nitrate of soda," *Am. J. Sci.*, **39**, 375 (1840).

(*144*)   GAUTIER, A., "Sur l'existence d'azotures, argonures, arséniures, et iodures dans les roches crystalliniennes," *Compt. rend.*, **132**, 934–5 (Apr. 22, 1901).

(*145*)   FELLENBERG, TH. VON, "Vorkommen und Bedeutung des Iods in der Natur," *Chem. Weekblad*, **30**, 250–8 (1933).

(*146*)   NICHOL, HUGH, "What the plant does with its materials," *Nature*, **150**, 13 (July 4, 1942).

(*147*)   JOSS, J. R., "Zur Geschichte des Broms," *J. prakt. Chem.*, **1**, 129–33 (1834).

(*148*)   FROMHERZ, C., "Ueber das Brom," *Schweigger's J.*, (4), **48**, 252–6 (1826).

(*149*)   HERMBSTÄDT, S. F., "Ueber das Brom im Wasser des todten Meeres," *Schweigger's J.*, (4), **48**, 256 (1826). Letter of Hermbstädt to Schweigger, Jan. 6, 1827.

(*150*)   KIRKPATRICK, S. D., "Magnesium from the sea," *Chem. Met. Eng.*, **48**, 76 (Nov., 1941).

(*151*)   BERTHIER, P., "Mémoire sur l'existence du bromure d'argent natif au Mexique, et au Huelgoeth, en France," *Ann. chim. phys.*, (3), **2**, 417–25 (1841); (3), **4**, 164–77 (1842).

(*152*)   NICKLÈS, J., "Obituary of Pierre Berthier," *Am. J. Sci.*, (2), **33**, 108 (May, 1862).

(*153*)   WILLIS, L. G., "Bibliography of references to the literature on the minor elements in their relation to plant and animal nutrition," 3rd ed., Chilean Nitrate Educational Bureau, New York, **1939**, column 239; DAMIENS, A., "The normal existence of chlorine and bromine in animal tissues," *Compt. rend.*, **171**, 930–3 (Nov. 8, 1920).

(*154*)   MEISSNER, W., "Ueber die Einwirkung des Clors auf die Mutterlauge der Salzsoole aus dem deutschen Brunnen zu Halle," *Schweigger's J.*, (4), **48**, 108–12 (1826).

(*155*)   "Biographical memoirs," Vol. 6, National Academy of Sciences, Washington, D. C., **1909**, pp. 126 and 134–5. Memoir on S. L. Penfield.

(*156*)   "Gmelin's Handbuch der anorganischen Chemie," Vol. 5, Verlag Chemie, Leipzig-Berlin, **1926**, pp. 1–13. History and occurrence of fluorine.

(*157*)   MORICHINI, D. P., "Analisi di alcuni denti fossili di elefante trovati fuori della porta del popolo di Roma," Rome, **1802**; *Mem. math. fis. sci., Modena* **10**, 166 (1803); *ibid.*, **12**, 73 (1805); *Gehlen's J.*, **2**, 177 (1806).

(*158*)   KOPP, H., "Geschichte der Chemie," Vol. 3, Fr. Vieweg und Sohn, Braunschweig, **1845**, pp. 345–71; Vol. 4, pp. 82–9.

(*159*)   SÖDERBAUM, H. G., "Jac. Berzelius. Levnadsteckning," Vol. 1, K. Svenska Vet. Acad., Upsala, **1929**, p. 214.

(*160*)   WILLIS, L. G., Ref. (*153*), columns 357–66.

(*161*)   DEAN, H. T., "Fluorine and dental health," *A.A.A.S. Bull.*, **1**, 47–8 (Aug., 1942).

(*162*)   DANA, J. D., "Corals and coral islands," 3rd ed., Dodd, Mead and Co., New York, **1890**, pp. 99–100.

(*163*)   NICKLÈS, J., "On the presence of fluorine in the blood," *Am. J. Sci.*, (2), **23**, 101–2 (1857).

(*164*)   DELÉPINE, M., "Centenaire de la naissance d'Armand Gautier," *Bull. Soc. Chimique (France)*, (5), **5**, 117–48 (Feb., 1938).

(*165*) PROVENZAL, GIULIO, "Profili Bio Bibliografici di Chimici Italiani. Sec. XV–Sec. XIX," Istituto Nazionale Medico Farmacologico "Serono," Rome, **1937**, pp. 105–9.

(*166*) CARSON, RACHEL L., "The sea around us," Mentor Book published by The New American Library, New York, **1954**, pp. 144–54. Chapter on "Wealth from the salt seas."

(*167*) GERICKE, S. and B. KURMIES, "Fluorgehalt und Fluoraufnahme von Kulturpflanzen," *Die Phosphorsäure*, **1**, 50 (1955).

(*168*) PROUT, WILLIAM, "Chemistry, Meteorology, and the Function of Digestion Considered with Reference to Natural Theology," William Pickering, London, **1834**, pp. 113–14.

(*169*) BUNDY, HALL, STRONG, and WENTORF, *Nature*, **176**, 51–5 (July 9, 1955).

Sir William Ramsay, 1852–1916. Scottish chemist and physicist. Discoverer of the inert gases. Lord Rayleigh was a co-discoverer of argon, and M. W. Travis collaborated in the discovery of krypton, neon, and xenon. After F. E. Dorn had discovered radon, or radium emanation, Ramsay and Whitlaw Gray determined its density and proved it to be the heaviest member of the argon family.

Accurate and minute measurement seems to the non-scientific imagination a less lofty and dignified work than looking for something new. But nearly all the grandest discoveries of science have been but the rewards of accurate measurement and patient long-continued labor in the minute sifting of numerical results (1).

28

The inert gases

In 1894 Lord Rayleigh and Sir William Ramsay startled the scientific world by announcing the discovery of a new elementary, gaseous constituent of the atmosphere. Thorough investigation of the properties of the new element, which they called argon, has shown that it has scarcely any tendency whatsoever to form chemical compounds. Another closely related gas was revealed in a manner no less dramatic. In 1868 the astronomers Jules Janssen and Sir Norman Lockyer had independently observed in the sun's spectrum a yellow line, D_3, which did not belong to any element then known to exist on the earth, and Lockyer had therefore postulated the existence of a solar element, helium. In 1895 Ramsay in England and Cleve and Langlet in Sweden independently discovered helium in a radioactive mineral. The researches of Ramsay and Travers soon revealed three other gases, neon, krypton, and xenon, which, since they show almost no tendency to unite with other elements, are classified with argon and helium in the aristocratic family of the noble gases.* Radon, the heaviest member of the group, will be discussed in Chapter 29 with the natural radioactive elements.

Until the closing years of the nineteenth century chemists believed that the atmosphere had been thoroughly investigated, and no one thought for a moment of searching there for new elements. It is true however, that Mr. Henry Cavendish had long before predicted the discovery of an unknown gas in the atmosphere, for in 1785 he had passed electric sparks through a mixture of oxygen and common air in the presence of alkali ("soap-lees"), and had found that part of the "phlogisticated air" (nitrogen) had failed to be oxidized and absorbed. He had said that this residue was "certainly not more than $1/120$ of the bulk of the phlogisticated air let up into the tube; so that if there is any part of the phlogisticated air of our atmosphere which differs from the rest and cannot be reduced to nitrous acid, we may safely conclude that it is not more than $1/120$ part of the whole" (2). This important experiment had

---

* A few compounds of the elements of this group have been reported in chemical literature.

long been forgotten by chemists, but in 1882 Lord Rayleigh began a research on the densities of the gases in the atmosphere.

Robert John Strutt, the third Lord Rayleigh, was born at Terling on November 12, 1842. His ability for clear thinking and self-expression was evident in his student days, and when he was Senior Wrangler in the Tripos in 1865, one of his examiners remarked, "Strutt's papers were so good that they could have been sent straight to press without revision" (*41*).

Robert John Strutt, the Third Lord Rayleigh, 1842–1919. Professor of physics at Cavendish Laboratory, Cambridge. He made elaborate investigations of the electrochemical equivalent of silver and of the combining volumes and compressibilities of gases. His observation that nitrogen prepared from the atmosphere is heavier than nitrogen prepared from ammonia led to the discovery of argon, the first noble gas. He also contributed to optics and acoustics.

Courtesy of L. C. Newell

After the great physicist Clerk Maxwell died in 1879, Lord Rayleigh became his successor at the Cavendish Laboratory, Cambridge. During his professorship the classes increased in size, and women from Girton and Newnham colleges were for the first time admitted on the same terms as the men. Since he was allowed insufficient funds for the purchase of new apparatus, he contributed £500 of his own money and solicited his friends for similar contributions until he had collected £1500 (*3*).

In 1882 Lord Rayleigh told the British Association that he had begun an investigation of the densities of hydrogen and oxygen to find out whether or not the ratio is exactly 1 to 16 in accordance with William

Prout's hypothesis that all atomic weights are multiples of the atomic weight of hydrogen; ten years later he announced that the correct ratio is 1 to 15.882 (38). In the course of this elaborate research on the combining volumes and compressibilities of gases, made with a view to calculating their molar volumes under limiting conditions, Lord Rayleigh also measured the density of nitrogen (40).

Although the oxygen which he prepared by three different methods all had the same density, his results with nitrogen were puzzling. The nitrogen he prepared from ammonia was always lighter by about five parts in one thousand than that which he prepared by absorbing the oxygen, carbon dioxide, and moisture from the atmospheric air. He then wrote to the English magazine, *Nature*, asking the readers to submit explanations, but none were received (39).

Lord Rayleigh himself thought of four possible explanations: (1) the nitrogen he had prepared from the atmosphere might still contain some oxygen; (2) the nitrogen prepared from ammonia might be slightly contaminated with hydrogen; (3) the nitrogen from the atmosphere might contain some N_3 molecules analogous to ozone; or (4) some of the molecules in the nitrogen from ammonia might have decomposed and thus decreased the density of the gas (40, 45).

The first hypothesis was most improbable, for, because of the very slight difference in the densities of oxygen and nitrogen, the contamination would have had to be very great in order to account for the discrepancy of five parts in one thousand. Lord Rayleigh showed experimentally that the nitrogen prepared from ammonia was entirely free from hydrogen. The third hypothesis was not encouraging for he was unable to increase the density of his nitrogen by passing a silent discharge through it. It was then that Sir William Ramsay obtained permission to experiment with the atmospheric nitrogen (4, 40).

Since these experiments led to such surprising and important results, it may be well to devote a little time to the character and personality of the man who conceived them. William Ramsay's parents were both about forty years old when they married. When, in the following year (October 2, 1852), a son was born to them, the happiness of these good Scotch parents was complete. The child was fond of nature, music, and books, and soon developed a passion for learning new languages. Friends of the family often wondered how the active little fellow could sit so quietly through the long Calvinist sermons at Free St. Matthew's Church in Glasgow. Whenever they looked at him he was intently reading his Bible; but, if they had been close enough, they would have seen that it was never an English Bible, but always a French or German one. The English text was so familiar to him that he rarely needed to consult it, and in this way he gained his first knowledge of these foreign languages (5). He also worked out many of his propositions in geometry from the mosaics in the church windows (6).

Mr. H. B. Fyfe, one of his classmates at the Glasgow Academy, gave the following account of Ramsay's first chemical experiments:

At that time he knew nothing of chemistry theoretically, but he had for some time been working at home at various experiments as we called them. He worked in his bedroom, and there were a great many bottles always about, containing acids, salts, mercury, and so on. When we began to meet in this way, I found he was quite familiar with all the ways of getting the material and apparatus for working in chemistry. We used to meet at my house in the afternoons and do what practical work we could, making oxygen and hydrogen and various simple compounds, such as oxalic acid from sugar. We also worked a great deal with glass. . . . We used to work with mouth blowpipes and Bunsen gas burners which we made ourselves, and in this way he became exceedingly expert in working with glass. I think he found this practice very useful in after life. We made nearly all the apparatus we used except flasks, retorts, and beakers. . . .(6).

Rudolf Fittig, 1835–1910. Professor of organic chemistry at Tübingen and Strasbourg. He discovered the lactones, and devised a general method for synthesizing homologs of benzene. With Erdmann he established the constitution of phenanthrene, and with Remsen he proved the constitution of the alkaloid, piperine. Sir William Ramsay was one of his students.

William Ramsay always excelled in wholesome amusements such as walking, cycling, rowing, swimming, diving, skating, singing, whistling, and story-telling, and hence had a host of friends. Mr. Fyfe also gave a fine description of Sir William's graceful swimming and diving. "When we were in Paris in 1876," said he, "the four of us used to go to one of the baths in the Seine every forenoon and, after the first time, when Ramsay was ready to dive, the bathman would pass round the word that the Englishman was going to dive and every one in the establishment, including the washerwoman outside, would crowd in and take up positions to watch him" (6).

Sir William Ramsay studied at Heidelberg under Bunsen and also at Tübingen under Fittig, and it was at the latter place that he met his life-long American friend, Ira Remsen (49). Although Ramsay later acquired perfect command of the German language, his first words to

Ira Remsen, 1846–1927. Distinguished American chemist and professor of organic chemistry. President of The Johns Hopkins University. Author of excellent textbooks. Founder and editor of the *American Chemical Journal*. Friend of Sir William Ramsay. He investigated the composition of commercial saccharin.

Courtesy Alumni Office, The Johns Hopkins University

Remsen sounded like this: *"Können Sie sagen wo ist die Vorlesungs-zimmer?"* Remsen puzzled over this for a while, and said with a smile, "Oh, I guess you want the lecture room." In later years both Remsen and Ramsay loved to tell this incident, and the former always cherished the honor of having been the first "to open the big front door" for Sir William Ramsay (7).

After studying on the Continent, Ramsay taught chemistry and engaged in research at Glasgow and later at University College, Bristol, where at the early age of twenty-eight years he was appointed Principal of the College (63). In his researches on the physical properties of gases he acquired remarkable skill in manipulating them.

ARGON

After Ramsay had gained permission from Lord Rayleigh to investigate the atmospheric nitrogen, he passed it over red-hot magnesium to find out whether or not it would be completely absorbed. After the gas had been passed back and forth over the hot magnesium, only forty cubic centimeters of it remained, and this residual gas was about $^{15}/_{14}$ as heavy as the original "nitrogen." Professor Ramsay had, of course, taken precautions to exclude dust, water, and carbon dioxide. After prolonged treatment, everything was absorbed except $^1/_{80}$ of the original volume. (It will be recalled that Cavendish had obtained a residue amounting to $^1/_{120}$ of the original volume (2).)

The gas finally obtained had a density of 19.086, and Ramsay and Rayleigh still believed it to be a modification of nitrogen, similar to ozone. However, when Ramsay examined its spectrum, he saw not only the bands of nitrogen but also groups of red and green lines which had never before been observed in the spectrum of any gas. Sir William Crookes made a very thorough study of the spectrum and observed nearly two hundred lines (28).

Rayleigh and Ramsay then worked together, exchanging letters nearly every day. On May 24, 1894, the latter wrote, "Has it occurred to you that there is room for gaseous elements at the end of the first column of the periodic table?" On August 7, he wrote again, "I think that joint publication would be the best course, and I am much obliged to you for suggesting it, for I feel that a lucky chance has made me able to get Q in quantity (there are two other X's, so let us call it Q or *Quid?* . . ." (8).

When the British Association met at Oxford in the same month, Ramsay and Rayleigh astonished the members by announcing the discovery of the first inert gas, which, at the suggestion of Mr. H. G. Madan, the chairman, they proposed to call *argon, the lazy one* (9, 25, 30).

Lord Rayleigh died in 1919 (41). M. W. Travers said that in all the contemporary correspondence of Sir William Ramsay and Lord Rayleigh which still exists, "there is no indication . . . of suspicion or sense of injustice on either side" (40). Visiting scientists were always surprised at the simplicity of the latter's apparatus. Although the essential instruments were designed and constructed with the utmost skill, the less important parts were assembled with little regard for appearance. His papers were written in a clear, polished style with the mathematical portions in concise, elegant form. His five volumes of collected contributions are prefixed with the motto he himself chose: "The works of the Lord are great, sought out of all them that have pleasure therein" (*41, 42*).

Soon after Lord Rayleigh and Sir William Ramsay discovered argon in 1894, H. F. Newall and W. N. Hartley independently observed some new lines in old photographs of the low-pressure spectrum of the air (*66, 67*). "After their announcement at the Oxford meeting of the British Association," said Newall, "it seemed for many reasons natural to borrow the first letter of Lord Rayleigh's and Professor Ramsay's names to give to the unknown lines, and in the measurements of the photographs which showed the lines well, there appears an "R" against seventeen lines out of sixty-one measured, the remaining lines being known to belong to mercury, hydrogen, nitrogen, and nitrocarbons. It transpires now, as I learnt from reading the abstract of the paper in which Lord Rayleigh and Professor Ramsay describe their consummate researches on argon, that the symbol "A" should have been used instead of "R" to designate the lines on my photographs. For the lines are Argon lines" (*66*). The lines which Newall observed in these photographs of the spectrum of the air coincided closely in wave length with the ones Sir William Crookes had measured for the blue and red spectra of argon (*66*). The photographs in which W. N. Hartley observed the lines of argon were taken in 1882 (*67*).

Soon after hearing of the discovery of argon, Lecoq de Boisbaudran predicted that it might belong to a family of absolutely inert elements all of which were then unknown, and that their atomic weights* would be: 20.0945, 36.40 ± 0.08, 84.01 ± 0.20, and 132.71 ± 0.15. He also predicted that the first two of these elements would be more abundant than the others (*33, 34*).

In 1907 Lord Rayleigh showed that many rocks, such as Matopo granite and syenite from Mt. Sorrel in Leicestershire and from Norway, which contain helium also contain argon (*68*).

Although traces of argon are present in the gases of the blood, it does not appear to play any direct role in metabolism (*69*). Bacteria in the nodules of leguminous plants absorb argon with the nitrogen, but no fixation of the argon occurs (*69*).

HELIUM

In the year 1868 the French astronomer Pierre-Jules-César Janssen (*43, 44*) went to India to observe a total eclipse of the sun and to make

---

* The 1954 atomic weights of the noble gases are: helium, 4.003; neon, 20.183; argon, 39.944; krypton, 83.80; xenon, 131.3; and radon, 222.

the first spectroscopic study of its chromosphere (36). He noticed a yellow line, D_3, which did not quite coincide with the D-line of sodium, and which he could not reproduce in the laboratory. When the English astronomer Sir Norman Lockyer (22) found that the new line did not belong to hydrogen or to any element then known, he named it *helium* for the sun (50), and for a quarter of a century helium was regarded as a hypothetical element which might possibly exist on the sun, but which had never been found on the earth (10, 20, 35). In some of his researches leading up to the discovery of solar helium, Lockyer was assisted by Professor Edward Frankland (37). Frankland believed however that

Pierre-Jules-César Janssen,* 1824–1907. French astronomer who directed many astronomical expeditions. Member of the French Institute and of the Bureau of Longitude. In 1868 he observed in the sun's chromosphere a yellow line, D_3, which is now known to belong to the element helium. He was the director of the astrophysical observatory at Meudon.

From Lebon's "Histoire Abrégée de l'Astronomie"

the new yellow line might possibly be due to hydrogen and that with an extremely long tube of hydrogen it might be possible to detect the line (22). For more than a quarter of a century most spectroscopists doubted the existence of Lockyer's "helium" and some went so far as to ridicule it (22).

John W. Draper, first president of the American Chemical Society, however, appreciated the full import of Lockyer's prediction, and on November 16, 1876, declared in his inspiring presidential address:

"And now, while we have accomplished only a most imperfect ex-

* Reproduced from E. LEBON's "Histoire Abrégée de l'Astronomie" by permission of Gauthier-Villars et Cie., 55 Quai des Grands-Augustins, Paris.

French Medallion Cast in 1878 in honor of the French astronomer, Jules Janssen, and the English astronomer, Sir Norman Lockyer, for their method of analyzing the solar protuberances.

amination of objects that we find on the earth, see how, on a sudden, through the vista that has been opened by the spectroscope, what a prospect lies beyond us in the heavens! I often look at the bright yellow ray emitted from the chromosphere of the sun, by that unknown element, Helium, as the astronomers have ventured to call it. It seems trembling with excitement to tell its story, and how many unseen companions it has. And if this be the case with the sun, what shall we say of the magnificent hosts of the stars? May not every one of them have special elements of its own? Is not each a chemical laboratory in itself?" (*65*).

In the light of present knowledge however the name *helium* is a misnomer, for it has the suffix *-ium* which is characteristic of the names of the metals.

In 1881 L. Palmieri thought he detected helium in a yellow amorphous sublimation product from Vesuvius. When he heated it in the Bunsen flame, he was able to observe the D_3 spectroscopic line with a wave length of 5875 Ångström units (*69, 70*). Although R. Nasini and F. Anderlini were unable in 1906 to produce this line by similarly heating minerals known to contain helium, they believed that, if the helium in Palmieri's mineral was bound endothermally, he might possibly have observed its spectrum in this manner (*69, 71*).

In 1888–90 the great American mineralogical chemist William F. Hillebrand (*46*) noticed that, when the mineral uraninite is treated with a mineral acid, an inert gas is evolved, which he believed to be nitrogen.

---

* Reproduced from LOCKYER, T. MARY, AND WINIFRED L. LOCKYER, "The Life and Work of Sir Norman Lockyer," by permission of Macmillan and Co.

Sir Joseph Norman Lockyer,* 1836–1920. Director of the solar physics observatory of The Royal College of Science at South Kensington. Pioneer in the spectroscopy of the sun and stars. In 1868 Lockyer and Janssen independently discovered a spectroscopic method of observing the solar prominences in daylight. Such observations had previously been made only at the time of total eclipses of the sun.

When Sir William Ramsay read the paper, he disagreed with this explanation, and repeated the experiment, using, however, a related uranium mineral called cleveite (*11, 61*). He obtained a little nitrogen, as Hillebrand had done, but also argon and another gas with different spectral lines. Since Ramsay did not have a very good spectroscope, he sent some specimens of the unknown gas to Sir Norman Lockyer and to Sir William Crookes for examination. Lockyer said, "When I received it from him, the glorious yellow effulgence of the capillary, while the current was passing, was a sight to see" (*27*).

On March 17, 1895, Ramsay wrote to Mr. J. Y. Buchanan, "Crookes thinks its spectrum is new, and I don't see from the method of treatment how it can be anything old, except argon, and that it certainly is not. We are making more of it, and in a few days I hope we shall have collected enough to do a density. I suppose it is the sought-for krypton, an element which should accompany argon. . . ." Before a week had passed, the new gas was shown to be identical with Lockyer's solar element, helium (*21, 23, 24, 26, 52*).

On March 24 Sir William wrote to Lady Ramsay:

Let's take the biggest piece of news first. I bottled the new gas in a vacuum tube, and arranged so that I could see its spectrum and that of argon

* Reproduced from LOCKYER, T. MARY, and WINIFRED L. LOCKYER, "The Life and Work of Sir Norman Lockyer," by permission of Macmillan and Co.

in the same spectroscope at the same time. There is argon in the gas; but there was a magnificent yellow line, brilliantly bright, not coincident with, but very close to, the sodium yellow line. I was puzzled, but began to smell a rat. I told Crookes, and on Saturday morning when Harley, Shields, and I were looking at the spectrum in the dark-room, a telegram came from Crookes. He had sent a copy here and I enclose that copy. You may wonder what it means.

Helium is the name given to a line in the solar spectrum, known to belong to an element, but that element has hitherto been unknown on the earth. Krypton was what I called the gas I gave Crookes, knowing the spectrum to point to something new. 587.49 is the wave-length of the brilliant line. It is quite overwhelming and beats argon. I telegraphed to Berthelot at once yesterday: *Gas obtained by me cleveite mixture argon helium. Crookes identifies spectrum. Communicate Academy Monday . . . Ramsay"* (12, 29).

C. Runge and Paschen found, however, that the spectrum of the gas from cleveite gave a yellow line which was double. Not until the D_3 line of solar helium had also been conclusively proved to be double, did Runge and Paschen admit the existence of helium in cleveite (69, 72).

In 1895 II. Kayser discovered the presence of helium in the atmosphere of Bonn, Germany (73). This observation was soon confirmed by Siegfried Friedländer, who detected minute amounts of it spectroscopically in the atmosphere of Berlin, and also by E. C. C. Baly, who in 1898 demonstrated spectroscopically the existence of helium in crude neon, thus indirectly proving it to be a constituent of the atmosphere (74, 75).

When W. F. Hillebrand discovered the presence of nitrogen in uraninite he considered it well worthy of further study but because of urgent official duties was unable to investigate it thoroughly. In one of his letters to Sir William Ramsay he wrote: "It doubtless has appeared incomprehensible to you in view of the bright argon and other lines noticed by you in the gas from cleveite that they should have escaped my observation. They did not." As Edgar Fahs Smith once stated, "The modesty and nobility of Hillebrand shine forth in his beautiful letters to Ramsay" (64).

In the meantime Per Theodor Cleve, the Swedish chemist for whom the mineral cleveite had been named by its discoverer, A. E. Nordenskiöld, had his student Nils Abraham Langlet investigate it (53). Although Ramsay announced the discovery before Cleve and Langlet had completed their research, the Swedish chemists were independent discoverers of helium. Langlet's first helium was purer, in fact, than Ramsay's, for he obtained a much better value for its atomic weight (13, 31, 32). The spectroscopic measurements were made by Professor Robert Thalén (47).

Sir Norman Lockyer's "Story of helium," published in *Nature* on

February 6 and 13, 1896 and reprinted with additions in the biography by T. Mary Lockyer and Winifred L. Lockyer, is a masterpiece of clear, understandable scientific literature (22). In 1899 Sir Norman Lockyer detected helium in the water of the Harrogate springs (22).

Immediately after the discovery of argon and helium, Professor Raffaello Nasini of Padua and his collaborators began to search for them in the natural products of Italy, especially in the gaseous emanations. Traveling hour after hour by carriage, on horseback, by mule, or on foot, using portable improvised apparatus in the field, they devoted many years to careful analyses of the natural gases of Italy (54, 85). In 1898 they detected helium in the volcanic gases from Monte Irone and in the boric acid soffioni in Tuscany (55). It was found only in minute amounts, and in 1897 Clemens Winkler ranked it "among the rarest of elements" (56).

Per Theodor Cleve, 1840-1905. Professor of chemistry at Upsala. Chairman of the Nobel Committee for chemistry. Cleve and Nils Abraham Langlet were independent discoverers of terrestrial helium. Sir William Ramsay's announcement was made before their research was completed.

A few years later an abundant source of helium was found in natural gas. In 1903 a gas well was started near the town of Dexter, Kansas. In honor of the new well a dedication ceremony was planned at which a portion of the gas drawn off through a small pipe was to be lighted in presence of a large group of citizens and invited guests. At the appointed time they looked forward expectantly to the sight of a large jet of flame which would usher in prosperity for the little town of Dexter, but to their astonishment the torch that was supposed to light the gas was extinguished (62). An early account of this historic occasion reads:

"It was soon closed in, and an attempt was made to burn it, as natural gas is usually burned, for generating steam for drilling purposes. Much to the surprise of parties interested, it would not burn. Later it was found that when a fire was already kindled in a fire box or an engine and the gas turned on, . . . it would begin to burn and would develop sufficient heat to generate steam moderately well. But as soon as the coal or other fuel in the firebox was consumed, the gas would no longer burn.

A cylinder of the gas was shipped to the University of Kansas later during the summer and was partially examined by members of the chemical and geological departments. . . . The owners of the well . . . did not wish it given great publicity" (57).

Hamilton P. Cady, 1874–1943. Codiscoverer with D. F. McFarland of the presence of helium in the natural gases of Kansas; pioneer in research with liquid ammonia. A few years before the close of his life, Dr. Cady perfected an instrument for determining molecular weights rapidly and precisely. See ref. (60).

Courtesy Robert Taft

The strange gas was investigated by E. Haworth and D. F. McFarland of the University of Kansas (57, 58). McFarland's analysis of it showed the presence of about 15 per cent methane, 72 per cent nitrogen, 12 per cent inert residue, and small amounts of oxygen and hydrogen. In an analysis of natural gas it had been customary to report the nitrogen by difference, i.e., to determine the percentages of the other constituents separately and subtract the total from 100 per cent, reporting the difference as nitrogen. Because of the abnormally high inert residue from this gas, however, McFarland had determined the nitrogen directly and yet had found an appreciable residue that could not be gotten rid of chemically. Thinking that this inert residue might contain argon or some other member of the group of recently discovered gases, Dr. H. P. Cady and McFarland investigated it further (59) and found that it contained 1.84 per cent of helium (84).

With the aid of cocoanut charcoal chilled to the temperature of liquid air they were able to absorb the constituents other than helium and obtain the latter rather easily, especially after the University of Kansas purchased a small liquid air plant for that purpose. On examining many other natural gases from fields in Kansas and elsewhere they found helium in almost every specimen (59). The price of helium then fell from $2500 per cubic foot in 1915 to 3 cents a cubic foot in 1926 (62). Since helium is a light gas like hydrogen yet does not burn nor form explosive mixtures with air, it is used for inflating balloons and dirigibles, thus adding enormously to the safety of such ascensions and flights.

Using apparatus similar to that of Cady and McFarland, Emerich Czakó of Karlsruhe in 1913 detected helium in the natural gas from several Austrian, Hungarian, German, and Alsatian wells and measured the radioactivity of the gases. He also found helium in the gases from hot springs of the Wildbad health resort in the Black Forest, thus confirming H. Kayser's results of 1895 (73, 76).

KRYPTON

Since the atomic weights of argon and helium were found to be about 40 and 4, respectively, Ramsay thought that these gases might possibly belong to a new group of the periodic system and that there must be an intermediate member with an atomic weight of approximately 20 (63). In this search he was aided by his assistant Morris William Travers.

Dr. Travers, who was born in London on January 24, 1872, studied at University College, and received his doctorate in 1893. Soon after this he became intensely interested in Sir William Ramsay's remarkable new elements and in the possibility of discovering another one between helium and argon and two others of higher atomic weight than argon.

Ramsay and Travers tried in vain to find these new gases by heating rare minerals. Their next attempt, and, in fact, their only hope, was to diffuse argon to separate it, if possible, into two fractions of different density. Dr. William Hampson presented them with about a liter of liquid air, which they used, not for liquefying the argon, but for obtaining sufficient skill in manipulation so that they would not risk losing their precious fifteen liters of argon. They were careful, moreover, to save the residues of the liquid air in the hope that these might contain some higher-boiling constituents. The residue left after most of the liquid air had boiled away consisted largely of oxygen and nitrogen, which Ramsay and Travers removed with red-hot copper and magnesium (*18, 19*).

One day as the younger chemist returned to the laboratory after lunch, a colleague called gaily to him, "It will be the new gas this time, Travers," and with pretended self-confidence he replied, "Of course it will be." Ramsay and Travers then examined the twenty-five cubic centimeters of residual gas, and when they found it to be inert, they immediately placed it in a Plücker tube connected to an induction coil and observed its spectrum. There was a bright yellow line with a greener tint than that of the helium line and a brilliant green line that did not coincide with any line of argon, helium, mercury, or hydrogen (*14*).

Sir William Ramsay, 1852–1916. Scottish chemist and physicist who, with Lord Rayleigh and M. W. Travers, discovered the inert gases: helium, neon, argon, krypton, and xenon. He also made a remarkable determination of the atomic weight of radon (radium emanation), the heaviest of the inert gases.

They discovered this gas on May 30, 1898, and named it *krypton*, meaning *hidden* (*15*). After working until eleven o'clock that evening on a density determination of the new gas, Ramsay and Travers found that it belonged between bromine and rubidium in the periodic table, and so great was their excitement that the younger chemist almost forgot about his examination for doctor of science which had been scheduled for the next day (*14*).

NEON

Although krypton was undoubtedly a new element of the zero group, it was not the one for which they had been looking. The gas they had been *expecting* to find would have appeared in the more volatile portion of the argon. Continuing their search for this lighter gas, Professor Ramsay and Dr. Travers liquefied and solidified the argon by surrounding three liters of it with liquid air boiling under reduced pressure, allowed the argon to volatilize, and collected the portion that distilled off first. This had a complex spectrum which Ramsay described in his

Morris William Travers. Honorary professor at the University of Bristol. Formerly director of the Indian Institute of Science in Bangalore Co-discoverer with Sir William Ramsay of the inert gases, neon, krypton, and xenon. He is an authority on glass technology.

notes as follows: "Lightest fraction of all. This gave magnificent spectrum with many lines in red, a number of faint green, and some in violet. The yellow line is fairly bright, and persists at very high vacuum, even phosphorescence" (*16*).

The vacuum tube containing this most volatile fraction of the argon immediately convinced them that it must be a new gas, for, said Dr. Travers:

The blaze of crimson light from the tube told its own story, and it was a sight to dwell upon and never to forget. It was worth the struggle of the previous two years; and all the difficulties yet to be overcome before the research was finished. The *undiscovered gas* had come to light in a manner which was no less than dramatic. For the moment, the actual spectrum of the gas did not matter in the least, for nothing in the world gave a glow such as we had seen (*16*).

Willie Ramsay, Sir William's thirteen-year-old son, inquired, "What are you going to call the new gas? I should like to call it *novum*." His father liked the suggestion, but thought that the synonymous term, *neon*, would sound better, and it is by this name that the gas discovered in June, 1898, is now known (*16*). In the brilliant neon signs on every business street one may now see at night the "blaze of crimson light" that brought such deep satisfaction and contentment to Professor Ramsay and Dr. Travers.

Since Ramsay and Travers discovered neon in the most volatile portion of their argon (*69*), this immediately established the occurrence of neon in the atmosphere. In 1909 Armand Gautier showed that the fumaroles of Vesuvius and the gas which bubbled from the hot springs in an old crater at Agnano, near Naples, contained neon (*69, 77*).

XENON

With the aid of a new liquid-air machine, generously provided by Dr. Ludwig Mond, Professor Ramsay and Dr. Travers prepared larger quantities of krypton and neon, and by repeated fractionation of krypton, a still heavier gas was separated from it, which they named *xenon, the stranger* (*15*). It was discovered on July 12, 1898. Vacuum tubes containing it show forth a beautiful blue glow.

Sir William Ramsay (*48*) had a rare sense of humor. He once said of his visit to the Norwegian chemist, Peter Waage, "He speaks a little German, and with my knowledge of Norse, which as you know is surpassed by few and equalled by none of the natives of that country, we got on very well." In writing of a certain pleasure trip, he said, "I went to Paris with three spirits more wicked than myself, lawyers . . . a fearful compound, 3 lawyers and a chemist . . . just like NCl_3 for all the world, liable to explode at any moment" (*17*).

Sir William was also one of the finest linguists the scientific world ever produced. He could lecture in perfect German before a cultured German audience, or in French before an assembly of French scientists. When presiding in 1913 over the International Association of Chemical Societies, he astonished and delighted his cosmopolitan audience by speaking first in English, then in French, then in German, and occasionally in Italian, always with perfect grace and composure. In spite of his splendid command of languages, his sense of humor sometimes led him to write to members of his family in the following vein: *"Mi Car Dora, . . . Io hab recip vestr litr, ke era mult facil a comprendar . . ."* (17).

Ramsay's extended travels never dulled the enthusiasm with which he visited new scenes. Americans may read with pleasure his description of Great Falls, Montana:

It is a pretty town and perfectly civilized. By the way, in all American towns the electric car is the chief feature. There are overhead wires, and cars like our tram cars run at a prodigious rate, careless of life apparently, yet there are very few accidents. I suppose the fittest, i.e., those who don't get killed, survive. They are delightful as a form of motion and almost rival the bicycle. That creature, too, has penetrated everywhere, and is used even over the prairie (17).

Sir William Ramsay's later work on radioactivity is regarded as even more remarkable than his discovery of the inert gases. He died on July 23, 1916, about three years before the death of his distinguished collaborator, Lord Rayleigh.

Dr. Travers served from 1906 to 1914 as director of the Indian Institute of Science in Bangalore, and in 1921 he became president of the Society of Glass Technology (51). He is an honorary professor at the University of Bristol. In 1928 he wrote a book entitled "The Discovery of the Rare Gases," which is illustrated with pictures of apparatus and facsimile pages from Sir William Ramsay's notebooks (9).

In 1920 Charles Moureu and A. Lepape detected all of the noble gases in the natural gas of Alsace-Lorraine (69, 78). Moureu also found krypton and xenon in many French spring waters such as those of Aix-les-Bains, Audinac, Bagnères-de-Bigorre, Bagnères-de-Luchon, Balaruc, and Vichy (69, 79).

Charles Moureu was born on April 19, 1863, in the little village of Mourenx near Pau in southern France. In early infancy he had the great misfortune to lose his father. Since Charles was the youngest of seven children in a humble peasant home, his widowed mother had a great struggle to give him the education which his rapidly developing talents deserved. His affectionate brother Félix, who had become a successful pharmacist at Biarritz, helped and encouraged him in his secondary studies, however, and gave him practical instruction in pharmacy.

In his studies at the École Supérieure de Pharmacie in Paris, Charles Moureu made an outstanding record. In 1907 he became professor of pharmaceutical chemistry, and ten years later he accepted the chair of organic chemistry at the Collège de France as M. Berthelot's successor.

Although most of his work was done in the fields of organic and theoretical chemistry, Moureu and his assistants also devoted much thought to the rare gases of the atmosphere and their geological significance. In 1895 he detected argon and helium in a natural source of nitrogen (*80*). He investigated many subterranean gases from wells and mines and showed that they contain helium, neon, argon, krypton, xenon, and radon and its isotopes.

Since the rare gases are inert, they could not be detected by means of any chemical reaction. Since they were too highly diluted in the natural gases, it was impossible to detect the inert gases by direct spectroscopic examination. Preliminary removal of carbon dioxide, oxygen, and nitrogen by chemical means was therefore necessary. After measuring the total volume of the rare gases at a known temperature and pressure, Moureu and his collaborators subjected the mixture to fractionation, using cocoanut charcoal chilled with liquid air. As Sir James Dewar had shown, the charcoal absorbed the most easily condensable and heavier gases, xenon, krypton, and argon, while the lighter gases, neon and helium, remained free. After drawing off the light gases by suction, Moureu heated the cocoanut charcoal to disengage the heavy gases, thus separating the rare gases into two groups, which could be further fractionated.

In 1911 Moureu and Lepape found that, although the neon, argon, krypton, and xenon in natural gases are always present in a fixed proportion, the proportion of helium to the other gases (since helium is continually being created by disintegration of radioactive elements) varies within wide limits.

Since nitrogen, a "relatively inert" element, "always accompanies the rare gases, of which it is the constant diluant," it is easy to tell whether a given specimen of nitrogen is of mineral origin or the result of the decomposition of nitrogen compounds or of nitrogenous organic matter. According to Moureu, the nitrogen in fire damp is of mineral origin and always contains the rare gases.

Moureu and his collaborators, unfortunately, were never able to find any source of neon, argon, krypton, and xenon that would be easier to exploit than the atmosphere. M. Georges Claude however succeeded in tapping this difficult but limitless source of the rare gases and developed from it a wonderful new field of illumination (*81, 83*).

Charles Moureu was editor of the *Annales de chimie et de physique* and of the *Revue scientifique*. In spite of his many scientific honors and duties, he always maintained affectionate and sympathetic contacts with the humble workers with whom his childhood years had been spent. He died at Biarritz on June 13, 1929 (*82*).

LITERATURE CITED

(*1*) "Report of the British Association for the Advancement of Science," **41**, xci (1871). Quotation from Lord Kelvin.

(2)   RAMSAY, W., "The Gases of the Atmosphere. The History of Their Discovery,"
      Macmillan and Co., London, 1915, p. 144; T. E. THORPE, "Scientific Papers
      of the Honourable Henry Cavendish," Vol. 2, Cambridge University Press,
      Cambridge, England, 1921, p. 193.
(3)   "History of the Cavendish Laboratory, 1871–1910," Longmans, Green and Co.
      London, 1910, pp. 40–74.   Chapter on Lord Rayleigh's Professorship by
      Glazebrook.
(4)   RAMSAY, W., "The Gases of the Atmosphere," Ref. (2), p. 158.
(5)   TILDEN, W. A., "Sir William Ramsay, Memorials of His Life and Work," Mac-
      millan and Co., London, 1918, p. 12.
(6)   Ibid., pp. 20–5.
(7)   Ibid., p. 39.
(8)   Ibid., p. 131.
(9)   TRAVERS, M. W., "The Discovery of the Rare Gases," Edward Arnold and Co.,
      London, 1928, p. 22.
(10) VON MEYER, ERNST, "History of Chemistry," 3rd English ed. from 3rd German,
      Macmillan and Co., London, 1906, p. 245.
(11) CHAMBERLIN, R. T., "The Gases in Rocks." Carnegie Inst., Washington, D. C.,
      1908, p. 8.
(12) TILDEN, W. A., "Sir William Ramsay, Memorials of His Life and Work," Ref.
      (5), p. 137.
(13) EULER, H. and A. EULER, "Per Theodor Cleve," Ber., 38, 4221–38 (Part 4,
      1905).
(14) TRAVERS, M. W., "The Discovery of the Rare Gases," Ref. (9), pp. 90–1.
(15) RAMSAY, W., "The Gases of the Atmosphere," Ref. (2), pp. 251–5.
(16) TRAVERS, M. W., "The Discovery of the Rare Gases," Ref. (9), pp. 95–7.
(17) TILDEN, W. A., "Sir William Ramsay, Memorials of His Life and Work," Ref.
      (5), p. 62.
(18) "Rare gases of the atmosphere. A classic of science," Sci News Letter, 18, 70–2
      (Aug. 2, 1930).
(19) RAMSAY, W., "The recently discovered gases and their relation to the periodic
      law," Science [N. S.], 9, 273–80 (Feb. 24, 1899); Ber., 31, 3111–21 (1898).
(20) YOUNG, C. A., "The Sun," 3rd ed., D. Appleton and Co., New York City, 1897,
      pp. 88–9, 259–60.
(21) Ibid., pp. 344–50.
(22) LOCKYER, T. MARY and WINIFRED L. LOCKYER, "Life and Work of Sir Norman
      Lockyer," Macmillan and Co., London, 1928, 474 pp.
(23) Ibid., pp. 155–7.
(24) Ibid., pp. 266–91.
(25) RAMSAY, W. and W. COLLIE, "Helium and argon. Part III. Experiments
      which show the inactivity of these elements," Nature, 54, 143 (June 11,
      1896); Chem News, 73, 259–60 (June 5, 1896).
(26) RAMSAY, W., "The position of argon and helium among the elements," Chem.
      News, 73, 283 (June 19, 1896).
(27) LOCKYER, J. N., "On the new gas obtained from uraninite," Chem. News, 72,
      4–5 (July 5, 1895); 271–2 (Dec. 6, 1895).
(28) CROOKES, W., "On the spectra of argon," Chem. News, 71, 58–9 (Feb. 1,
      1895); 72, 66–9 (Aug. 9, 1895).
(29) CROOKES, W., "The spectrum of the gas from clèveite," Chem. News, 71, 151
      (Mar. 29, 1895); "The spectrum of helium," ibid., 72, 87–9 (Aug. 23, 1895).
(30) RAYLEIGH, LORD and W. RAMSAY, "Argon: A new constituent of the atmos-
      phere," Chem. News, 71, 51–8 (Feb. 1, 1895).
(31) CLEVE, P. T., "On the presence of helium in clèveite," Chem. News, 71, 212
      (May 3, 1895); Compt. rend., 120, 834 (Apr. 16, 1895).   Letter from Cleve
      to Berthelot, Apr. 8.
(32) CLEVE, P. T., "Sur la densité de l'hélium," Compt. rend., 120, 1212 (June 4,
      1895); Chem. News, 71, 283 (June 14, 1895).

(33)   REED, "A prediction of the discovery of argon," *Chem. News,* **71,** 213–15 (May 3, 1895).

(34)   DE BOISBAUDRAN, LECOQ, "Remarks on the atomic weights," *Chem. News,* **71,** 116 (Mar. 8, 1895); *Compt. rend.,* **120,** 361–2 (Feb. 18, 1895).

(35)   DE LA RUE, "Sur une méthode employée par M. Lockyer pour observer en temps ordinaire le spectre des protubérances signalées dans les éclipses totales de soleil," *Compt. rend.,* **67,** 836–8 (Oct. 26, 1868).

(36)   JANSSEN, P.-J.-C., "Indication de quelques-uns des résultats obtenus à Guntoor pendant l'éclipse du mois d'août dernier, et à la suite de cette éclipse," *Compt. rend.,* **67,** 838–9 (Oct. 26, 1868).

(37)   FRANKLAND, E. and N. LOCKYER, "Recherches sur les spectres gazeux dans leurs rapports avec l'étude de la constitution physique du soleil," *Compt. rend.,* **68,** 420–3 (Feb. 22, 1869).

(38)   RAYLEIGH, LORD, "On the relative densities of hydrogen and oxygen," *Proc. Roy. Soc.* (London), **43,** 356–63 (Feb. 9, 1888); *Nature,* **46,** 101–4 (June 2, 1892).

(39)   RAYLEIGH, LORD, "Letter to the Editor, Sept. 24, 1892," *Nature,* **46,** 512–3 (Sept. 29, 1892).

(40)   TRAVERS, M. W., "The Discovery of the Rare Gases," Ref. (9), pp. 1–7.

(41)   GLAZEBROOK, SIR R. T., "Lord Rayleigh," *Sci. Progress,* **14,** 286–91 (1919); J. J. T., "Lord Rayleigh," *Nature,* **103,** 365–6; R. T. G., "Lord Rayleigh," 366–8; C. H. L., "Lord Rayleigh," 368–9 (July 10, 1919).

(42)   "Scientific worthies. Lord Rayleigh," *Nature,* **70,** 361–3 (Aug. 18, 1904).

(43)   MACPHERSON, "Astronomers of Today," Gall and Inglis, London, **1905,** pp. 18–24. Chapter on Janssen.

(44)   LEBON, E., "Histoire Abrégée de l'Astronomie," Gauthier-Villars, Paris, **1899,** pp. 141–4.

(45)   RAMSAY, W., "The Gases of the Atmosphere," Ref. (2), pp. 126–7.

(46)   ALLEN, E. T., "Pen portrait of William Francis Hillebrand, 1853–1925," *J. Chem. Educ.,* **9,** 73–83 (Jan., 1932).

(47)   HASSELBERG, "Biografier. Tobias Robert Thalén," Kungl. Svenska Vetenskapsakademiens Årsbok, **1906,** pp. 219–40.

(48)   NEWELL, L. C., "Caricatures of chemists as contributions to the history of chemistry," *J. Chem. Educ.,* **8,** 2143–8 (Nov., 1931).

(49)   CLARK, F. E., "Remsen at the turn of the century," *J. Chem. Educ.,* **6,** 1282–5 (July–Aug., 1929).

(50)   LOCKYER, T. M. and W. L. LOCKYER, "Life and Work of Sir Norman Lockyer," Ref. (22), pp. 41–2.

(51)   BUGGE, G., "Das Buch der grossen Chemiker," Vol. 2, Verlag Chemie, Berlin, **1930,** pp. 250–63. Article on Ramsay by P. Walden.

(52)   TRAVERS, M. W., "Ramsay and helium," *Nature,* **135,** 619 (Apr. 20, 1935).

(53)   ANON., "Obituary of Nils Abraham Langlet," *Bihang till Göteborgs K. Vet.-och Vitterhets-Samhälles Handl.,* **55,** 87–9 (1936).

(54)   LEVI, M. G., "Raffaello Nasini," *Gazz. chim. ital.,* **62,** 727–45 (1932); GIULIO PROVENZAL, *La Chimica nell' Industria, nell'Agricoltura e nella Biologia,* **6,** 103–6 (Mar., 1930); ALDO MIELI, *Archeion,* **13,** 290–1 (1931).

(55)   NASINI, R., F. ANDERLINI, and SALVADORI, "Gas delle terme di Abano, dei soffioni boraciferi della Toscana, gas combustibili dell' Appennino bolognese," *Gazz. chim. ital.,* **28** (1), 81–153 (1898); *Nature,* **58,** 269 (July 21, 1898).

(56)   WINKLER, C., "The discovery of new elements within the last twenty-five years," *Annual Report,* Smithsonian Institution, Government Printing Office, Washington, D. C., 1897, pp. 243–4.

(57)   HAWORTH, E. and D. F. McFARLAND, "The Dexter, Kansas, nitrogen gas well," *Science,* **21,** 191–3 (Feb. 3, 1905).

(58)   McFARLAND, D. F., "Composition of gas from a well at Dexter, Kansas," *Trans. Kansas Acad. Sci.,* **19,** 60–2 (1903–4).

(59) CADY, H. P. and D. F. McFARLAND, "The occurrence of helium in natural gas," *J. Am. Chem. Soc.*, **29**, 1523–36 (Nov., 1907); *Science* (n. s.), **24**, 344 (Sept. 14, 1906); C. W. SEIBEL, "Helium and natural gas," *J. Chem. Educ.*, **3**, 45–9 (Jan., 1926).

(60) TAFT, ROBERT, "The beginning of liquid ammonia research in the United States," *J. Chem. Educ.*, **10**, 34–9 (Jan., 1933).

(61) BARTOW, VIRGINIA, "W. F. Hillebrand and some early letters," *J. Chem. Educ.*, **26**, 367–72 (July, 1949).

(62) SEIBEL, C. W., "Helium and natural gas," *J. Chem. Educ.*, **3**, 45–9 (Jan., 1926).

(63) TAYLOR, F. SHERWOOD, "The work of Sir William Ramsay; he discovered five new elements in six years," *Am. Scientist*, **41**, 449–52 (July, 1953).

(64) BROWNE, C. A. (editor), "A Half-Century of Chemistry in America, 1876–1926," Am. Chem. Soc., Philadelphia, **1926**, p. 84.

(65) DRAPER, JOHN W., "Science in America," Proc. Am. Chem. Soc., Vol. 1, Part 1, pp. 144–5; see also FLEMING, DONALD, "John William Draper and the Religion of Science," University of Pennsylvania Press, Philadelphia, **1950**, 205 pp.

(66) NEWALL, H. F., "Note on the spectrum of argon," *Proc. Roy. Soc.*, **57**, 346–50 (Feb. 21, 1895).

(67) HARTLEY, W. N., "On the spark spectrum of argon as it appears in the spark spectrum of air," *Proc. Roy. Soc.*, **57**, 293–6 (Jan. 31, 1895).

(68) STRUTT, R. J., "Helium and argon in common rocks," *Nature*, **75**, 271 (Jan. 17, 1907); *Proc. Roy. Soc.*, **A79**, 436–9 (May 31, 1907).

(69) "Gmelin's Handbuch der anorganischen Chemie," 8th ed., Vol. 1, Verlag Chemie, Leipzig-Berlin, **1926**, pp. 1–35. History and occurrence of the noble gases.

(70) PALMIERI, L., "La riga dell'Helium apparsa in una recente sublimazione vesuviana," *Rendic. Accad. Napoli*, **20**, 233 (1881); *Gazz. chim. ital.*, **12**, 556 (1882).

(71) NASINI, R. and F. ANDERLINI, "Esame spettroscopico col metodo del Bunsen di prodotti vulcanici," *Gazz. chim. ital.*, **36**, (2), 557–61, 563 (1906).

(72) RUNGE, C. and PASCHEN, "Terrestrial helium (?)," *Chem. News*, **71**, 283 (June 14, 1895); *Nature*, **52**, 128 (June 6, 1895); *Chem.-Ztg.*, **19**, 977 (1895).

(73) KAYSER, H., "Note on helium and argon," *Chem. News*, **72**, 89 (Aug. 23, 1895); *Chem.-Ztg.*, **19**, 1549 (1895).

(74) BALY, E. C. C., "Helium in the atmosphere," *Nature*, **58**, 545 (Oct. 6, 1898).

(75) FRIEDLÄNDER, SIEGFRIED, "Ueber Argon," *Z. phys. Chem.*, **19**, 657–67 (1896).

(76) CZAKÓ, E. and L. LAUTENSCHLÄGER, "A gaseous spring containing a high percentage of helium," *Chem. News*, **108**, 16 (July 11, 1913); CZAKÓ, E., "The helium content and radioactivity of natural gases," *Z. anorg. Chem.*, **82**, 249–77 (1913).

(77) GAUTIER, A., "Observations sur la nature et l'origine des gaz qui forment les fumerolles volcaniques ou qui sortent des cratères des anciens volcans," *Compt. rend.*, **149**, 84–91 (July 12, 1909).

(78) MOUREU, C. and A. LEPAPE, "Les gaz rares des gaz naturels d'Alsace-Lorraine," *Compt. rend.*, **171**, 941–7 (Nov. 15, 1920).

(79) MOUREU, C., "Les gaz rares des gaz naturels," *J. Chem. Soc.*, **123**, 1905–47 (1923).

(80) MOUREU, C., "Sur la présence de l'argon et de l'hélium dans une source d'azote naturelle," *Compt. rend.*, **121**, 819 (1895).

(81) CLAUDE, GEORGES, "Préparation industrielle du krypton et du xénon et applications à l'éclairage électrique par incandescence," *La Nature*, **62** (2), 90–1 (July 15, 1934).

(82) DUFRAISSE, CH., "Charles Moureu," *Bull. Soc. Chim. (Paris)*, (4), **49**, 741–825 (1931); NORRIS, J. F., *J. Am. Chem. Soc.*, **52**, 31–5 (May, 1930); URBAIN, G., *Ann. chim.*, (10), **12**, 3–8 (July, Aug., 1929).

(83) WRIGHT, MILTON, "Inventors who have achieved commercial success," *Sci. Am.*,
       (2), **136**, 396 (June, 1927); J. H. O'NEIL, "Purifying gases for neon signs,"
       Chem. Met. Eng., **36**, 143–4 (Mar., 1929); GEORGES CLAUDE, "Progress on
       luminous tubes containing rare gases," *La Nature*, **1932**, Aug. 1, pp. 121–3.
(84) "Necrology. D. F. McFarland," *Chem. Eng. News*, **33**, 1008 (Mar. 7, 1955).
(85) PROVENZAL, GIULIO, "Profili Bio-Bibliografici di Chimici Italiani. Sec. XV–
       Sec. XIX," *Istituto Nazionale Medico Farmacologico "Serono,"* Rome, **1937**,
       pp. 257–70.

Pierre and Marie Curie

Together, this famous couple, Pierre Curie, 1859–1906, and Mme. Marie Sklodowska Curie, 1867–1934, discovered radium and polonium, and founded the beneficent science of radioactivity. Pierre served as professor of physics at the Sorbonne, and collaborated with his brother, Jacques Curie, in the discovery and investigation of piezo-electricity. He introduced the concept of symmetry in physical phenomena and studied magnetic properties as a function of temperature. Marie served as professor of radioactivity at the University of Paris.

"Radium is not to enrich any one. It is an element; it is for all people" (**1**).

"So the atoms in turn, we now clearly discern,
Fly to bits with the utmost facility;
They wend on their way, and, in splitting, display
An absolute lack of stability" (2)

29

The natural radioactive elements

In 1898 there was discovered an element, radium, which continually and spontaneously emits light, heat, and other radiations. Investigation of these astonishing phenomena by the Curies and many others revealed about forty interrelated radioactive elements which, like radium, are unstable. They do not, however, occupy forty places in the periodic system, but are crowded into only ten places. The explanation for the existence of these numerous so-called "radioactive isotopes" and their genealogical descent from uranium and thorium were discovered independently by K. Fajans, F. Soddy, A. S. Russell, and A. Fleck. Since the original literature on the radioactive elements embraces such a vast field of research, the following account of their discovery is necessarily far from complete.

*A*ntoine-Henri Becquerel, a member of a family renowned for scientific achievement, noticed in 1896 that when a phosphorescent salt, such as potassium uranyl sulfate, is placed near a photographic plate protected by black paper, the plate becomes fogged as though it had been exposed to light (*51, 58*). His later work showed that all uranium compounds, even those which do not phosphoresce, give off penetrating rays which, like X-rays, darken a photographic plate and, by making the surrounding air a conductor, cause the gold leaves of a charged electroscope to lose their electrostatic charge and collapse. These radiations are now known to be of three kinds: alpha rays, which consist of helium atoms each bearing two units of positive electricity; beta rays consisting of streams of negative electrons; and gamma rays, which constitute a very penetrating radiation of extremely short wave length.

The amazingly rapid development of the science of radioactivity is largely due to the brilliant work of M. Pierre Curie and his wife, Mme. Marie Sklodowska Curie. The former was born in Paris on May 15, 1859, and was educated by his cultured parents. Many happy hours were spent on excursions to the country, and thus this city child grew up in intimate contact with nature, collecting plants and animals and enjoying them in quiet contemplation. While serving as director of the laboratory under Paul Schützenberger at the School of Physics and Chemistry, Pierre Curie carried on researches on condensers, magnetism, piezo-electrictiy, and the principle of symmetry in nature. When in 1895 he received the degree of *Docteur-ès-sciences* from the Sorbonne, Schützen-berger created a chair of physics for him (3).

Marie Sklodowska, a daughter of Dr. Sklodowski,* a professor of physics and mathematics at the Warsaw gymnasium, was born on November 7, 1867. Because of the early death of her gifted mother, the little girl grew up in her father's laboratory and under his instruction. She soon developed a passionate love of country and joined a secret society of students who organized evening classes for laborers and peasants. However, because of the limited opportunities for advanced study, she decided to leave her beloved motherland and go to Paris (99).

Antoine-Henri Becquerel, 1852–1908. French physicist and engineer. Discoverer of the rays emitted by uranium. He carried out important researches on rotatory magnetic polarization, phosphorescence, infrared spectra, and radioactivity. His grandfather Antoine-César-Becquerel (1788–1878), and his father, Alexandre-Edmond Becquerel (1820–1891), also made many important contributions to chemistry and physics.

During the four years of her student life, she lived in a chilly little attic room, carrying the coal herself up the six flights of stairs, and cooking her simple meals over an alcohol lamp. This was Marie Sklodowska's introduction to the city which became her permanent home (4, 68). When she enrolled at the Sorbonne, Henri Poincaré, the famous mathematical physicist, soon recognized her ability, and Professor Gabriel Lippmann also took great interest in her research.

Her first meeting with Pierre Curie was at the home of a Polish physicist in Paris. Because of their mutual interest in scientific, social, and humanitarian subjects, there gradually developed a singleness of

* The feminine ends in *-ska,* the masculine in *-ski.*

(Jules) Henri Poincaré, 1854–1912.
French mathematician, physicist, and
astronomer. Prolific and gifted writer
on mathematical analysis, analytical and
celestial mechanics, mathematical physics, and philosophy of science.

Gabriel Lippmann, 1845–1921. Professor of mathematical physics at the University of Paris. Inventor of the capillary electrometer and of a process of
direct color photography. The phenomenon of piezo-electricity in crystals predicted by Professor Lippmann was first
demonstrated experimentally by Pierre
and Jacques Curie.

purpose that caused M. Curie to say, "It would . . . be a beautiful thing
in which I hardly dare believe, to pass through life together hypnotized
in our dreams: your dream for your country; our dream for humanity;
our dream for science." After their marriage in 1895 Professor Schültzen-
berger arranged that they might work together in the laboratory, and

their mutual devotion to science once led M. Curie to remark, "I have got a wife made expressly for me to share all my preoccupations" (5).

George Jaffé, who carried out laboratory research under Pierre and Marie Curie, wrote "There have been, and there are, scientific couples who collaborate with great distinction, but there has not been a second union of woman and man who represented, both in their own right, a great scientist. Nor would it be possible to find a more distinguished instance where husband and wife with all their mutual admiration and devotion preserved so completely independence of character, in life as well as in science" (113).

POLONIUM

Professor Curie continued his researches on the growth of crystals, and his young wife prepared for her examinations. Many chemists consider her dissertation (55) to be the most remarkable thesis ever presented for the doctorate. She continued the work begun by Becquerel, and tested most of the known elements, including a number of rare ones loaned by E.-A. Demarçay and Georges Urbain, with Prof. Curie's piezo-electric quartz electrometer, and found that thorium and uranium were the only ones whose compounds produced appreciable ionization (26, 54, 55). The radioactivity of thorium was discovered independently by Gerhardt Carl Schmidt, professor of physics at the University of Münster (25).

Of much greater significance than this, however, was Mme. Curie's observation that the activity of the uranium mineral pitchblende is four or five times as great as one might expect it to be from its uranium content (24). She concluded that the ore must contain another radio-active element in addition to uranium, and that, since the composition of the ore was known, the active element must be present in extremely small amount and must therefore be very active indeed. Therefore it became necessary to work up large quantities of pitchblende and to make elaborate and tedious fractionations of this complex ore.

The pitchblende was supplied by the Austrian government from its uranium mines in the Joachimsthal, Bohemia. Mme. Curie explained that pitchblende was so expensive that they were unable to buy enough of it for their large-scale researches. Since the residues from the St. Joachimsthal uranium mine had not previously been put to use, M. and Mme. Curie, through the influence of the Academy of Sciences of Vienna, were able to obtain several tons of these residues at a moderate price (114).

As Mme. Curie examined each fraction with the electrometer, she found that a very active substance separated with the bismuth. After convincing herself in 1898 that this was a new element, she named it

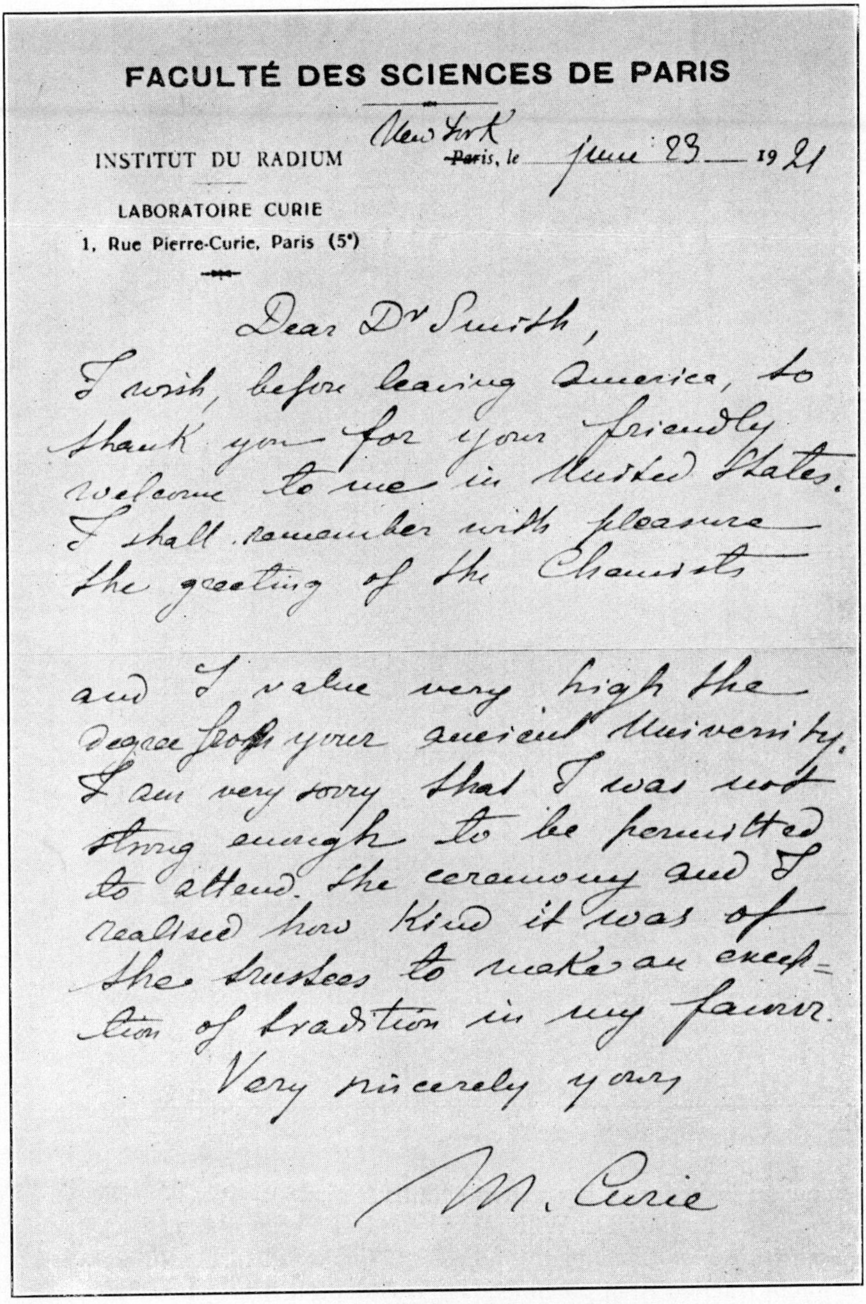

FACULTÉ DES SCIENCES DE PARIS

INSTITUT DU RADIUM

LABORATOIRE CURIE

1, Rue Pierre-Curie, Paris (5e)

New York, le June 23 1921

Dear Dr Smith,

I wish, before leaving America, to
thank you for your friendly
welcome to me in United States.
I shall remember with pleasure
the greeting of the Chemists
and I value very high the
degree from your ancient University.
I am very sorry that I was not
strong enough to be permitted
to attend the ceremony and I
realised how kind it was of
the trustees to make an exception of tradition in my favor.

Very sincerely yours

M. Curie

Edgar Fahs Smith Memorial Collection, University of Pennsylvania

Autograph Letter from Mme. Curie to Dr. Edgar F. Smith

From Z. Elektrochemie,
Courtesy Verlag Chemie

Left to Right: *Back row:* G. v. Hevesy, H. Geiger, J. Chadwick, K. Przibram, F. Paneth. *Front row:* O. Hahn, Lord Rutherford, Lise Meitner, Stefan Meyer.

polonium in honor of her native country (*27, 65*). It is also known as *radium F*. In 1902 Dr. Willy Marckwald of Berlin obtained a metallic deposit on a polished plate of bismuth immersed in a solution of the bismuth fraction from pitchblende. This deposit, which he called radio-tellurium, was later shown to be identical with Mme. Curie's polonium (*6, 29*).

After commenting on the discovery of gallium, scandium, and germanium (eka-aluminum, eka-boron, and eka-silicon), D. I. Mendeleev had written in 1891, "I foresee some more new elements, but not with the same certitude as before. I shall give one example, and yet I do not see it quite distinctly" (7). He had then proceeded to describe an undiscovered "dvi tellurium" with an atomic weight of about 212. Since polonium resembles tellurium and has an estimated atomic weight of about 210, it is probably the realization of Mendeleev's "dvi tellurium,"

A Non-radioactive Isotope of Polonium. In an examination of the X-ray spectra of the gold-tellurium minerals of Transylvania, Professor Horia Hulubei and Mlle. Yvette Cauchois discovered the existence of a non-radioactive isotope of polonium (element 84) (*115*). The ore they examined contained (in addition to the principal constituents: gold, lead, and tellurium) silver, arsenic, antimony, copper, nickel, zinc, sulfur, and a trace of selenium. After dissolving the ore and removing most of the gold, silver, and lead as chlorides, element 84 (along with other elements) was deposited electrochemically on silver. After dissolving the deposit and removing the silver by precipitation, Professor Hulubei and Mlle. Cauchois placed the remaining salts on an anticathode and subjected them to X-ray analysis with their curved-crystal focusing spectrograph (*115*). In this non-radioactive material they observed the lines of element 84, polonium. They estimated that the new isotope of polonium must be present in their sample in the proportion of about one part in a million.

RADIUM

After the Curies, with the assistance of M. G. Bemont, had carried out many laborious fractionations of barium chloride, they found that the most insoluble fractions were the most radioactive. In the course of her experiments Mme. Curie had learned that radioactivity is an atomic property depending solely on the quantity of active element present. For this reason the presence of another active element was suspected, and the radioactive barium chloride was therefore submitted to M. Demarçay for spectroscopic examination. He detected a new line in the ultraviolet region of the spectrum, and certain other lines, all of which were most distinct in the most radioactive preparations, and, as fractionation proceeded, the barium lines became fainter and fainter (*23, 28, 52*).

While tracing down the new element, the Curies often wondered how its salts would look, and hoped that perhaps they might display beautiful colors. The radium chloride which they finally obtained proved to be a white salt, however, but it was even more beautiful than their brightest dreams: it glowed in the dark!   Radium, like phosphorus, is a giver of light, and this property was to them, as it had been to Hennig Brand and Johann Kunckel, a source of surprise and delight.   "One of our joys," wrote Mme. Curie, "was to go into our workroom at night; we then perceived on all sides the feebly luminous silhouettes of the bottles or capsules containing our products.   It was really a lovely sight and always new to us.   The glowing tubes looked like faint fairy lights" (8, 60).

The Laboratory* in which M. and Mme. Curie discovered radium

The new substance was named *radium,* the giver of rays, and, were it not for this property, it might still be numbered among the missing elements.   Although it gives a distinct spectrum, the methods of detecting it with an electrometer is five hundred thousand times more sensitive than the spectroscopic method (9).

Professor Georges Urbain once said:

I was certainly privileged, for I saw with my own eyes the birth of radium. Pierre Curie, who was my teacher, rendered me the incomparable honor of according me his confidence and friendship.   I saw Mme. Curie work like a man at the difficult treatments of great quantities of pitchblende.   I saw the first fractionations of the bromides of barium-radium.   I saw the radium-bearing crystals shine in the dark before the radium spectrum could be observed in them.   Every Sunday we used to go with Langevin, Perrin, Debierne,

* Reproduced from an article by Jacques Danne, *La Nature,* **32** [1], 217 (Mar. 5, 1904) by permission of Masson et Cie., Paris.

Cotton, and Sagnac to the little Curie home, which was thus transformed into an intimate academy. There the master, with his customary simplicity, explained his ideas to us and deigned to discuss ours. . . . (74).

Wilhelm Ostwald (112) gave in his autobiography the following account of his visit to the birthplace of radium:

At my urgent request the Curie laboratory, in which radium was discovered a short time ago, was shown to me. The Curies themselves were traveling. It was a cross between a horse-stable and a potato-cellar, and, if I had not seen the worktable with the chemical apparatus, I would have thought it a practical joke (10).

When M. Curie was offered the decoration of the Legion of Honor, he wrote, "I pray you to thank the Minister, and to inform him that I do not in the least feel the need of a decoration, but that I do feel the greatest need for a laboratory." Nevertheless, Mme. Curie regarded the years spent in this dingy old shed as "the best and happiest" of her life (8).

THE URANIUM SERIES

In 1900 Sir William Crookes prepared a solution containing a uranium salt and a small amount of a ferric salt. When he added to this an excess of a solution containing ammonium hydroxide and ammonium carbonate, he found that the resulting ferric hydroxide precipitate was intensely radioactive. After studying the radioactive properties of the substance which precipitates with the iron, he said, "For the sake of lucidity the new body must have a name. Until it is more tractable I will call it provisionally UrX—the unknown substance in uranium" (30). It is now known as *uranium* X_1. H. N. McCoy and W. H. Ross, B. B. Boltwood, and R. B. Moore and H. Schlundt found independently that there are two uraniums, *uranium 1* and *uranium 2* (12, 48, 81, 108, 109, 110).

In 1913 Kasimir Fajans and O. H. Göhring of Karlsruhe showed that uranium X_1 disintegrates by β-ray emission into a very short-lived product which they called *brevium* (11, 48), but which is now known as *uranium* X_2. Professor Fajans taught physical chemistry for many years at the University of Munich and is now teaching at the University of Michigan (70). Like Mme. Curie he is a native of Warsaw. Mendeleev predicted the discovery of uranium X_2 in 1871 when he said, "There is a third vacant place at series 12 in group V between Th = 231 and U = 240 for an element which forms [the oxide] R_2O_5 and has an atomic weight of about 235" (71).

Since uranium X_1 gives two kinds of β-rays, it yields two radioactive products: *uranium X_2* and *uranium Z (12)*. The latter substance, which was discovered by Professor Otto Hahn in 1921, is a subordinate branch of the family, however, for the disintegration of uranium X_1 yields 99.65 per cent of uranium X_2 and only 0.35 per cent of uranium Z.

Professor Hahn is a native of Frankfort-on-the Main. He collaborated with Sir William Ramsay, and later with Miss Lise Meitner, and in 1944 was awarded the Nobel Prize in Chemistry for his work on atomic fission. He is a member of the German Atomic Weight Commission and director of the Kaiser Wilhelm Institute for Chemistry in Berlin-Dahlem. Miss Meitner, who was also on the staff of this Institute, is a native of Vienna.

Kasimir Fajans, 1887–   . American physical chemist, born in Poland. Professor at the University of Michigan. Codiscoverer with Göhring of uranium X_2 (brevium). In 1913 he discovered, simultaneously with Soddy, the law of radioactive displacement of elements in the periodic system as the result of α- and β-ray emission.

Courtesy Cornell University

There is also a sixth member of this series, known as *uranium Y* (*46, 50, 56, 59*), which was discovered in 1911 by G. N. Antonoff, who was working under Sir Ernest Rutherford at the University of Manchester. He afterward returned to St. Petersburg. Uranium Y, like uranium Z, belongs to a subordinate branch of the family. Frederick Soddy attributed Antonoff's success, not to the special chemical process adopted, but "to the lapse of a suitable period of time between successive separations" (*75*). Thus in the uranium series uranium 1 breaks down to form uranium X_1, and this in turn disintegrates to form the successive products: uranium X_2, uranium Z, uranium 2, and uranium Y.

THE RADIUM SERIES

In 1904 B. B. Boltwood, H. N. McCoy, and R. J. Strutt proved independently that radium is produced by spontaneous transmutation of uranium (107). Three years later Boltwood discovered an element which he named *ionium* and which he found to be the parent substance of radium (39). Professor Boltwood had acquired a broad cosmopolitan education in Munich, Leipzig, Manchester, and New Haven, and was a skilled laboratory technician, a sympathetic teacher, and a polished gentleman with "a certain courtliness of manner." He proved that there is a genetic relationship between uranium, ionium, and radium (13). Ionium was discovered independently at about the same time by Otto Hahn and by Willy Marckwald (14, 73, 77).

Bertram Borden Boltwood, 1870–1927. Professor of chemistry and physics at Yale University. Discoverer of the radioactive element ionium, the parent of radium. Ionium was discovered independently at about the same time by Hahn and by Marckwald.

The Edgar F. Smith Memorial Collection, University of Pennsylvania

The second member of the series is radium itself. The task of isolating it was most difficult, and involved risk of losing the precious product. In 1910, however, Mme. Curie and M. André Debierne finally succeeded in preparing the shining white metal; but, since they needed the radium in their researches, they did not keep it in this form.

Like all radioactive elements, it undergoes continuous, spontaneous disintegration into elements of lower atomic weight. M. and Mme. Curie had noticed that when air comes into contact with radium compounds it, too, becomes radioactive. The correct explanation was first given in

Condensation of the Radium Emanation on the occasion of Professor Cox's lecture on liquid air in the Macdonald Physics Building at McGill University, Nov. 6, 1902. The original coil of Rutherford and Soddy which appears in this picture and in which the first condensation was effected is still in the Physics Building at McGill University. The original photograph bears the initials F. S. [Soddy].* It was in the Macdonald Physics Building that Rutherford and Soddy proved that the radioactive elements undergo spontaneous transformation.

1900 by Friedrich Ernst Dorn, who was born on July 27, 1848, at Guttstadt in eastern Prussia. He studied at Königsberg and taught physics for many years at Darmstadt and at Halle. Professor Dorn showed that one of the disintegration products of radium is a gas (*15, 37*). This was at first called *radium emanation*, or *niton*, but, since it is an inert gas derived from radium the modern name *radon* is to be preferred. After showing that the highest temperatures obtainable had no effect on the rate of transformation of this emanation, Rutherford and Soddy decided to try the effect of extreme cold. According to Professor A. S. Eve, "Within a quarter of an hour after the first 100 cc. of liquid air were prepared, the emanation had been condensed, and the material nature of this gas had been proved beyond question" (*103*). It is the last mem-

* The writer wishes to thank Dr. William H. Barnes and Dr. A. S. Eve of McGill University for their kind assistance in procuring the photograph of the apparatus for condensing radon and the portraits of Miss Brooks (Mrs. Pitcher) (p. 815) and Professor Owens (p. 826).

ber of the group of noble gases previously discovered by Sir William Ramsay (62), and in 1910 the remarkable density determination of Ramsay and Robert Whytlaw Gray proved that it is the heaviest gas known (91).

In 1904 Miss Harriet Brooks of McGill University in Montreal studied the "active deposit of short life" which forms as a thin layer on all substances which have been exposed to radon (43), a phenomenon which Soddy compared to "a sort of continuous snowstorm silently going on covering every available surface with this invisible, unweighable, but intensely radioactive deposit" (83). From Miss Brooks's researches and

Harriet Brooks, 1876–1933 (Mrs. Frank Pitcher). In 1902 Rutherford and Miss Brooks studied the penetrating power of α-rays from various sources and made the first attempt to determine the density of radon by a diffusion method. Their study led to the discovery of radium A, B, and C. This photograph was taken in 1898 when Miss Brooks obtained her B.A., McGill University.

Photo by William Notman & Son, Ltd.

his own, Rutherford concluded that radon forms three successive disintegration products: radium A, B, and C. These were found and separated, and in "the active deposit of long life" there were discovered three additional elements: radium D, E, and F (polonium), which are products of further disintegration (11, 53).

Sir Ernest Rutherford was born in 1871 in Nelson, New Zealand. After studying at New Zealand University and Cambridge, he went to Canada in 1898 as a professor of physics at McGill University. After serving there for nine years and carrying out many remarkable researches in radioactivity, he became professor of physics at Manchester University, and in the following year he was awarded the Nobel Prize in chemistry. In 1919 he became a professor at Cambridge (72).

Lord Rutherford, 1871–1937. Professor of physics at McGill, Manchester, and Cambridge Universities.   He identified the three types of radiations from radioactive substances, and devised methods for counting alpha particles and for determining the number of free positive electrons in the nucleus of an atom.

Courtesy Mr. Sederholm, Nobelstiftelsen, Stockholm

His three greatest discoveries were the proof of the transmutation of radium into other elements (Rutherford and Soddy), the nuclear atom, and artificial transmutation. Lord Rutherford took his teaching duties very seriously and was exceedingly kind to his students and collaborators and most generous in sharing with them his ideas and his honors. Because of his remarkable genius for planning research and apportioning to every worker a task suited to his ability, he trained many of the physicists and chemists who are now working in the great research institutes throughout the world (*104*).

Professor H. Geiger stated that Lord Rutherford "threatened the severest penalties" for anyone who allowed emanation to escape, for it spread rapidly throughout the building and made it impossible to work with the electroscope. One day when Geiger's counting experiments were thus interrupted, he found that the emanation was coming from the room where Rutherford was working. When informed of the trouble, Rutherford replied, "Well, there you have further proof of the power inherent in this emanation." Thereupon he took Dr. Geiger for a ride in the country and "was soon discoursing on his own experiments and on all the problems that were yet to be solved. Nothing was so refreshing nor

Courtesy Ralph E. Oesper

Otto Hönigschmid, 1878– . Director of the German Atomic Weight Laboratory at the University of Munich. At the Radium Institute in Vienna he made the first accurate determination of the atomic weight of radium. His work on radioactive elements strikingly confirmed the hypothesis of atomic disintegration proposed by Rutherford and Soddy. See ref. (*135*).

so inspiring as to spend an hour in this way, alone with Rutherford" (*102*).

According to J. J. Thomson, Lord Rutherford's death on October 19, 1937, "just on the eve of his having in the High-Tension Laboratory means of research far more powerful than those with which he had already obtained results of profound importance, is, I think, one of the greatest tragedies in the history of Science" (*101, 102*). Lord Rutherford was the first scientist born in the overseas dominions to be buried in Westminster Abbey, beside the graves of Sir Isaac Newton, Lord Kelvin, Charles Darwin, and Sir John Herschel.

Hahn and Meitner (*82*) and Fajans (*33*) found that radium C disintegrates in two ways, forming radium C' and radium C''. K. A. Hofmann and Eduard Strauss noticed in 1900 that radium D has a strong resemblance to lead, and these two elements were later found to be inseparable (*38*). Karl A. Hofmann was associated with Adolf Baeyer at Munich.

Elster and Geitel also made pioneer researches on "radio-lead," of which radium D is the principal constituent (*42*).

Julius Elster was born on December 24, 1854, at Blankenburg, Germany (*85*), and studied at Berlin and Heidelberg. In 1881 he began his teaching career at the Wolfenbüttel Gymnasium, where he was destined to serve for nearly forty years and to carry out many brilliant researches with his intimate friend, Hans F. K. Geitel (1855–1923). They showed that the radioactivity of common lead is not a specific property of the element, but that it is always caused by admixture of some radioactive substance. Very old specimens of lead, which no longer contain radium D, are inactive (*85*). The friendship of Elster and Geitel lasted from childhood throughout life. During their first years at Wolfenbüttel, they lived with Geitel's mother. After her death, Elster married, and built a fine, hospitable home and private laboratory, where Geitel became a permanent member of the household and where they prepared more than a hundred joint papers. Together they proved that the electrical conductivity of the atmosphere is not caused by dust but by ions produced by radioactive substances present in the air. They also demonstrated the surprisingly wide distribution of radioactive substances. Simultaneously with Sir William Crookes, they observed the scintillations of Sidot blende when bombarded with alpha particles. As early as 1899 they recognized that the atom of a radioactive element is unstable and that it gradually breaks down into the stable atom of an inactive element. Since Elster and Geitel were of almost the same age and since their names are inseparable, German physicists chose an intermediate date for the observance of their sixtieth birthday (*96, 106*). Professor Elster died at Wolfenbüttel on April 8, 1920 (*96*).

Ramsay, Soddy, Fajans, and Georg Bredig were all greatly interested

Theodore William Richards, 1868–1928. Director of the Wolcott Gibbs Memorial Laboratory at Harvard University. The precision of his atomic weight determinations has never been surpassed. He discovered the anomalous atomic weights of lead from radioactive minerals.

Courtesy Harvard University

in the anomalous atomic weights of lead from various sources, and Fajans sent his assistant, Max E. Lembert, to America to work on this problem with Theodore William Richards at Harvard (*67, 78*). Fajans also provided Professor Richards with several radioactive ores containing lead. After studying ores from Ceylon, Colorado, England, Norway, and Bohemia, Richards and Lembert announced in 1914 that the atomic weight of lead from such minerals is much lower than 207.2, the value accepted for ordinary lead (*16, 78, 87*). O. Hönigschmid and Mlle. Stephanie Horovitz (*79*) of Vienna and Maurice Curie (*92*) made the same discovery independently at about the same time.

These two kinds of lead are now known to be *isotopes,* or inseparable elements which belong in the same space in the periodic table and yet differ in atomic weight and in radioactive properties. According to Frederick Soddy, the first clear recognition of isotopes as chemically inseparable substances was that of H. N. McCoy and W. H. Ross in 1907 (*75, 107*). Strictly speaking, the science of radioactivity has revealed only five naturally occurring new elements with distinctive physical and chemical properties: polonium, thoron, radium, actinium, and uranium X_2. All the other natural "radioactive elements" share previously occupied places in the periodic table.

Since the activity of polonium in time disappears completely, and since the ratio of lead to uranium is almost constant in all primary uranium minerals from a given geological formation, the last stage in the disintegration of uranium is believed to be a stable element, *uraniolead*, or *radium G*, which is inseparable from ordinary lead. The members of the radium series are: ionium, radium, radon, and radium A, B, C, C', C", D, E, F, and G.

THE ACTINIUM SERIES

F. Soddy, A. S. Russell, and K. Fajans independently predicted the existence of a new member of the uranium series of radioactive elements and that it would occupy the vacant place just below tantalum in the V*a* group of the periodic system. Protactinium, the patriarch of the actinium series of elements, was discovered in 1917 independently by Otto Hahn and Miss Lise Meitner, by K. Fajans, and by Frederick Soddy, John A. Cranston, and A. Fleck (*47, 49, 50*).

To remove radium and other radioactive constituents from pitchblende, Hahn and Meitner treated pulverized pitchblende repeatedly and for long periods of time with hot concentrated nitric acid. From the insoluble siliceous residue they separated a new radioactive substance, which they called protoactinium. This name has subsequently been shortened to protactinium. When they added a little tantalum salt to a solution containing protactinium, the reactions of the new substance so closely resembled those of tantalum that Hahn and Meitner were unable to separate the two substances (*118*). Since tantalum is not radioactive, the protactinium could thus be obtained free from other radioelements. Since protactinium is not an isotope of tantalum, it should be possible to separate them from each other (*119*). By working up large quantities of rich pitchblende residues from the Quinine Works at Braunschweig, Hahn and Meitner were able to extract more active preparations of the new element (*49*).

F. Soddy and J. A. Cranston concluded in 1918 that protactinium might possibly occupy the ekatantalum position (that of element 91 in the periodic system), a view which has since been confirmed (*50*). Their experiments were made on pitchblendes from India and the Joachimsthal.

In 1927, Dr. Aristid V. Grosse* succeeded in preparing two milligrams of a white powder which was shown to be the pentoxide of protactinium, Pa_2O_5 (*88*). Grosse and M. G. Agruss later worked up large quantities of radium residues from Joachimsthal, Czechoslovakia, at the Lindsay Light Company. The residues were extracted with hydrochloric acid, and the siliceous residue containing the protactinium was fused with sodium hydroxide. After leaching the basic oxides from the melt, Grosse and Agruss precipitated zirconium phosphate, which

---

* The process patented by Grosse and Hahn for preparing pure Pa_2O_5 is described in *Chem. Zentr.*, **102**, 3525–6 (1931).

carried down with it the protactinium. They succeeded in concentrating the protactinium from the original value of about 0.3 gram per metric ton in the Joachimsthal residues to 1 part per 1000 in the plant product, which they further concentrated in the laboratory by fractional crystallizations of zirconium oxychloride and repeated precipitation of zirconium phosphate. Most of the zirconium was finally separated by sublimation of the chlorides, after which the protactinium was precipitated with hydrogen peroxide. In this way they isolated 0.1 gram of pure protactinium pentoxide (95).

Dr. John A. Cranston. Member of the Council of the Society of Chemical Industry. Chairman of the Glasgow Section. He collaborated with Frederick Soddy in important researches on radioactivity, and is an independent discoverer of the element protactinium, Mendeleev's predicted eka-tantalum.

In the fall of 1934, Dr. Grosse reduced this pure oxide by two methods and obtained from it the metal protactinium, which is even rarer than radium, but much more permanent in air. In the first method, he bombarded the oxide on a copper target, in a high vacuum, with a stream of electrons. After a few hours, he obtained "a shiny, partly sintered, metallic mass, stable in air." In his second method, he converted the oxide to the iodide (or chloride or bromide) and "cracked" it in a high vacuum on an electrically heated tungsten filament, according to the reaction:

$$2PaI_5 = 2Pa + 5I_2$$

The metallic protactinium retained its bright luster for some time (95).

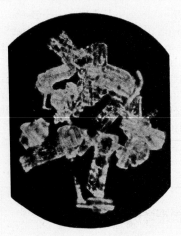 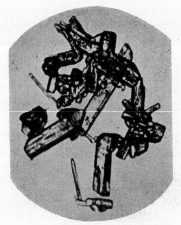

Proc. Roy. Soc. (London)

Crystals of Potassium Protactinium Fluoride—K_2PaF_7.   *Left:* Dark field illumination; $\times$ 60.

Dr. Grosse then converted part of his pure protactinium pentoxide into potassium protactinium fluoride, K_2PaF_7, which can easily be dried to constant weight.   Using the classical method which J.-C. G. de Marignac had used for determining the atomic weight of tantalum, he weighed the new element both as the pentoxide and as potassium protactinium fluoride.   His duplicate results for the atomic weight of protactinium, made on this very small sample but with precise technique and apparatus, are 230.4 and 230.8.*   These researches were especially important because they led to a much better understanding of the entire actinium series.   Protactinium is an isotope of uranium Z and of uranium X_2, and thus there are at least three radioactive elements all identical in chemical and physical properties with Mendeleev's predicted eka-tantalum (*17*).

In 1899 André Debierne, a young chemist who had served as *préparateur* under Charles Friedel and who was an intimate friend of the Curie family, discovered that another radioactive element is carried down with the precipitate of the rare earths produced by adding ammonium hydroxide to a solution obtained by dissolving pitchblende (*40*).   This element, which he named actinium, was discovered independently in 1902 by F. Giesel, who removed it with the lanthanum and cerium (*41*) and called it *emanium.*

In 1949, about half a century after the discovery of actinium, the International Rare Metals Refinery, Inc. produced it industrially (*134*). It is about 150 times as active as radium and is a valuable source of neu-

* The 1954 atomic weight of protactinium is 231.

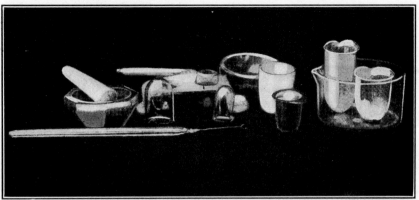

Apparatus used by Dr. Aristid V. Grosse in his researches on protactinium. This diminutive apparatus occupies a total length from left to right of about eleven centimeters.

trons.   Although actinium itself is a nearly pure beta-ray emitter, actinium in equilibrium with its decay products is also a powerful source of alpha-radiation (*134*).

The actinium series is very much like that of radium.   In 1904 and 1905 Giesel and T. Godlewski, while working independently, discovered the element actinium X, which is precipitated with the ferric hydroxide by adding an excess of ammonium carbonate solution to a solution containing actinium and iron (*41, 44*).

Friedrich O. Giesel (born 1852) was for many years a chemist at the quinine works of Braunschweig Buchler and Company, and in the early days he worked up large quantities of radioactive minerals and generously distributed his radium among investigators in all parts of the world (*56*).

Tadeusz Godlewski, the youngest son of Emil Godlewski, the famous plant physiologist, was born on January 4, 1878, at Lemberg, Poland. After graduating from the ancient Jagiellonian University at Cracow, he went to Stockholm for a year of graduate study under Svante Arrhenius. A year of research under Sir Ernest Rutherford at Montreal resulted in the publication of three papers on radioactivity.   After returning to Poland, Godlewski became professor of physics and rector at the Technische Hochschule of Lemberg, where he continued his original investigation in radioactivity and electrochemistry.   His life was all too short, and it is believed that his death in 1921 was caused by leakage of coal gas in his laboratory (*89*).

In 1906 Professor Otto Hahn discovered radioactinium between actinium and actinium X (*45*).   Actinium emanation, or *actinon,* which, like radon, is an inert gas, was discovered independently by F. Giesel and André Debierne (*40, 41*).   The other members of the series, actinium A, B, C, C′, C″, and D, are analogous to the corresponding members in the radium series (*43, 64*).   It was proved by B. B. Boltwood that there is a genetic relationship between the uranium, the radium, and the actinium series of elements, and in 1915 F. Soddy and Miss A. F. Hitchins measured the steady growth of radium in purified uranium preparations (*39, 57*).

THE THORIUM SERIES

The thorium series is apparently independent of the three just named. In 1905 Otto Hahn, working under Sir William Ramsay's direction, discovered *radiothorium* in the residues from a Ceylon mineral called thorianite, and two years later he showed that *mesothorium* is an intermediate disintegration product (*19, 35, 36*).

Since the radioactivity of thorium salts is smaller than that of the minerals, B. B. Boltwood (*93*) thought that some of the radiothorium must have been lost during the purification process.   On the assumption that radiothorium was formed directly from thorium, he computed that the half-life period of the former ought to be at least six years, whereas

Alexander Smith Russell. Scottish chemist who discovered the effect of a beta-ray change on the atomic number of an element.   Lecturer on inorganic chemistry at Oxford University.   He has carried on chemical research, especially in radioactivity, in the laboratories of Soddy in Glasgow, of Nernst in Berlin, and of Rutherford in Manchester. His publications include many research papers, literary contributions, and a book on the chemistry of radioactive substances.

Hahn obtained an experimental value of only two years. Hahn therefore assumed that there must exist between thorium and radiothorium an unknown rayless product, *mesothorium,* which can easily be separated from thorium in the purification process.

He found that freshly prepared thorium salts have a normal radioactivity which decreases to a minimum in 4.6 years. He computed that the undiscovered member ought to have a half-life period of five and one-half years, and two chemists at the University of Chicago, Herbert N. McCoy (*100*) and William H. Ross, later verified this prediction. The new element was at first called *mesothorium,* but is now known as *mesothorium 1* (*20, 63*), the name having been changed because Hahn

Alexander Fleck. Author of many research papers on the radioactive isotopes. He proved the inseparability of uranium X_1 and radioactinium from thorium, of thorium B and actinium B from lead, of mesothorium 2 from actinium, of radium E from bismuth, and of radium A from polonium, and confirmed the discovery of uranium X_2 by Fajans and O. H. Göhring. Chairman of Imperial Chemical Industries, Ltd.

afterward found that mesothorium 1 disintegrates into a short-lived product, *mesothorium 2.* Soddy's brilliant elucidation of the chemistry of mesothorium 1 led to his theory of radioactive isotopes, for which he was awarded the Nobel Prize (*66*).

Because of its lower cost, mesothorium 1 is frequently substituted for radium in therapy and in the manufacture of luminous watch-dials. The commercial process for extracting it from the by-products of monazite sand was long kept secret, but after Soddy and W. Marckwald independently discovered that it is chemically identical with radium, the process for extracting the latter element from pitchblende was adapted so that it could be used for recovering mesothorium 1 (*84, 94*).

In 1902 Rutherford and Soddy added ammonium hydroxide to a thorium solution, filtered off the thorium hydroxide precipitate, and found that, after they evaporated the thorium-free filtrate to dryness and fumed off the ammonium salts, the residue was much more active than the original thorium salt (*18*). This observation led them to the discovery of a new member of the thorium series, which they called *thorium X.*

R. B. Owens, Macdonald professor of electrical engineering at McGill University, and Sir Ernest Rutherford noticed that when a thorium compound is placed in an open vessel exposed to air currents, its radio-

R. B. Owens. He observed in 1899 that the ionization current through a confined volume of air exposed to the rays from thorium compounds decreased to a minimum when air was drawn through his apparatus. Rutherford showed that this effect is caused by the emission of thorium emanation, now known as thoron. This photograph was taken in about 1910 when Professor Owens was at McGill University.

Photo by William Notman & Son, Ltd.

activity is not constant, and a study of this anomaly led them to the discovery that thorium gives off a gas, or emanation (*21, 31*), which is now known as *thoron.* It is an isotope of radon and actinon, and was the first radioactive gas to be discovered (*20*).

Professor Hans Geiger and E. Marsden noticed that the alpha particles from thoron are expelled at such very short intervals that they seem to be double. They found, as Rutherford suggested, that this strange behavior is caused by the presence of a very short-lived decay product of thoron, which they named *thorium A* (*80*). Prof. Geiger was born in

Frederick Soddy, 1877– . Professor of chemistry at Glasgow, Aberdeen, and Oxford. Author of books on radioactivity and economics. He showed that when a radioactive element emits alpha particles, its position in the periodic table is shifted two spaces to the left, whereas a beta-ray change causes a shift of one space toward the right. This rule, which explains the existence of radioactive isotopes, was discovered independently by A. S. Russell, A. F. Fleck, F. Soddy, and K. Fajans.

Courtesy Ralph E. Oesper

Neustadt, Germany, was educated at Erlangen, Munich, and Manchester, and became director of the laboratory for Radium Research at Charlottenburg.

Thorium A quickly decays into *thorium B,* another rather short-lived product, which spontaneously disintegrates, as shown by Rutherford, into *thorium C (53).* By heating a lead-encased platinum wire charged with the mixture to 700°, Miss J. M. W. Slater, Bathurst student at Newnham College, Cambridge, succeeded in volatizing the thorium B* from the platinum and condensing it on the cold lead cylinder. At 1000° almost pure thorium C remained on the wire (*32*).

It was shown by E. Marsden and Thomas Barratt and independently by Hahn and Meitner that thorium C* breaks down into *thorium C'* and *thorium C'' (20, 34, 76).* The last member of this series, *thorium D,* or *thorio-lead,* ends what Soddy has called "the stately procession of element evolution" (*57*). Thus thorium "disintegrates in cascade" to form the successive products: mesothorium 1, mesothorium 2, radiothorium. thorium X, thoron, and thorium A, B, C, C', C'', and D.

The explanation of the radioactive isotopes was given independently by Alexander S. Russell, Frederick Soddy, and Kasimir Fajans in 1913 (*90*). With the aid of Alexander Fleck at Glasgow, who had devoted

---

* Before 1911 the elements now known as *thorium B* and *thorium C* were called, respectively, *thorium A* and *thorium B.*

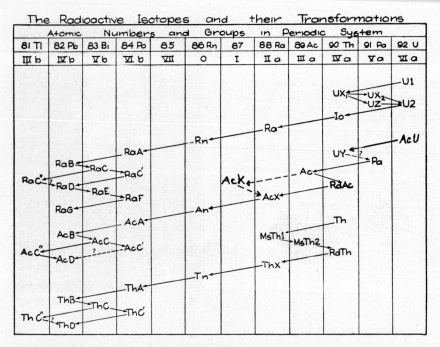

The Radioactive Isotopes and their Transformations

Atomic	Numbers	and	Groups	in	Periodic	System					
81 Tl	82 Pb	83 Bi	84 Po	85	86 Rn	87	88 Ra	89 Ac	90 Th	91 Pa	92 U
III b	IV b	V b	VI b	VII	0	I	II a	III a	IV a	V a	VI a

Long arrows pointing to the left represent α-ray transformations; short ones pointing to the right indicate β-ray changes.

three years to a thorough study of the chemical properties of the radio-active elements, Soddy deduced the following rule: The chemical properties of an alpha-ray product correspond with those of an element whose group number in the periodic system is *two less* than that of its parent.

A. S. Russell, Carnegie Research Fellow at the University of Glasgow, soon discovered the following corollary to this rule: The chemical properties of a beta-ray product correspond with those of an element whose group number is *greater by one* than that of its parent.

That is, in an alpha-ray change, or expulsion of a helium atom with double positive charge, the atomic number (serial number of the element in the periodic system) decreases by two, and the atomic weight by four, units, whereas in a beta-ray transformation or emission of a negative electron, the atomic number increases by one unit while the atomic weight remains unchanged. Thus the combined effect of two beta-ray changes and one alpha-ray transformation is to produce an element which, like uranium 2, is chemically identical with its great-grandparent. "Radio-active children," says Soddy, "frequently resemble their great-grand-parents with such complete fidelity that no known means of separating them by chemical analysis exists" (56).

The complete sequence of radioactive changes in the last twelve places in the periodic system which was worked out through the researches of A. S. Russell, K. Fajans, F. Soddy, A. Fleck, and others, is given in the table reproduced herewith.

Thus it is evident that there are three natural radioactive isotopes of thallium, seven of lead, four of bismuth, seven elements in the polonium pleiad, three inert radioactive gases, four isotopes of radium, two of actinium, six of thorium, three eka-tantalums, and three uraniums.

The Curie Family

From "The Sphere"

In 1903 M. and Mme. Curie, together with M. A.-H. Becquerel, were awarded the Nobel Prize in chemistry. The Curie household with its two bright little daughters was a most happy one, and the gifted parents looked forward to a lifetime of united efforts for science. That dream was not to be fulfilled. On April 19, 1906, as Pierre Curie was crossing a busy street in Paris, he was struck by a heavy vehicle and instantly killed (61).

As a result of this frightful shock, Mme. Curie suffered a long, serious illness, but, when she finally recovered she resolved to devote the rest of her life to her children and to science. She taught the little girls herself, and for a time had charge of a small private school (22). The elder

Mme. Curie and her daughter, Mme. Joliot-Curie. The latter published many papers on the radioactive elements. During World War I, while still very young, she assisted her mother in the radiological service to the wounded. With her husband, Dr. F. Joliot of the Institut de Radium in Paris, she prepared artificial radioactive elements.

daughter, Irène (Mme. Joliot), followed in the footsteps of her illustrious parents; while Ève, the younger one, has become a well-known concert pianist and has written a splendid biography which intimately reveals the great soul of Mme. Curie (*98, 105*).

Less than a year after her husband's death, Mme. Curie accepted a professorship at the University of Paris. With the able assistance of Professor André Debierne, who took charge of the laboratory and taught for many years an ever-increasing number of students from all parts of the world, she directed the instruction and research in radioactivity (*86*). When the university acquired new land, it laid out a street called the Rue Pierre Curie and built a laboratory for her. The Curie Institute and the Pasteur Institute work in close harmony, and Mme. Curie spent much of her time on researches dealing with the therapeutic properties of radium and radon (*69*). During World War I she had complete charge of the radiological service in French military hospitals.

In 1911 she was awarded the Nobel Prize in physics, and was thus the only person ever to have received the Nobel award twice. While radium with its dangerous yet beneficent radiations was prolonging countless lives, it was gradually undermining the health of its discoverer, and on July 4, 1934, her life of devotion to science and humanity came to a close (*97*).

Her years in the adopted country had given her a mode of expression that was truly French. She summarized her life story in these few words: "I was born in Warsaw of a family of teachers. I married Pierre Curie and had two children. I have done my work in France" (*1*).

After Julius Elster and Hans Geitel had noticed that the electrical conductivity of the air in caves and closed cellars is higher than that in the free atmosphere, they finally found that this was caused by the presence of emanations, or radioactive gases, in the ground. In a series of investigations from 1901 to 1906 they demonstrated the presence of radioactive elements in various kinds of rocks and soils, and showed that minute amounts of both radium and thorium are widely distributed in the earth's crust, in spring waters, in sea water, and in the atmosphere (*85, 96*).

J. J. Thomson, A. Sella, and I. Pochettino discovered independently in 1902 that certain natural waters are radioactive (*64*). The activity of most radioactive springs is due not to radium itself but to its disintegration product, radon, which the water has dissolved while flowing through rocks containing radium (*116*).

Radium is occasionally present in bone and teeth (*117*).

ARTIFICIAL RADIOACTIVITY[*]

The creation, by neutron bombardment of uranium, of the so-called "transuraniums" is based on the discovery of artificial radioactivity by M. and Mme. Joliot-Curie. Irène Curie was born in Paris in September, 1897, the elder daughter of M. and Mme. Pierre Curie of honored memory. Both in Poland and in France she had many relatives who were devoting their lives to science, and from her earliest childhood she lived in a scientific atmosphere, among distinguished chemists and physicists. When Irène was less than a year old, her mother discovered the radioactive element polonium, which was destined to play an important part in the later researches of both mother and daughter. A few months later M. and Mme. Curie discovered another element of even greater importance, which they named radium.

While they were patiently carrying out the laborious but brilliantly executed investigations on which the science of radioactivity is based, Irène was left under the affectionate care of her grandfather, Dr. Eugène Curie, a cultured physician, well versed in the sciences. When she was seven years old, her parents, together with Henri Becquerel, were awarded

[*] The section on artificial radioactivity was first published in April, 1936, for the Kansas City Meeting of the American Chemical Society.

Mme. Joliot-Curie, [*] **1897–1956.** Daughter of Pierre and Marie Curie. She made many original contributions to radioactivity and collaborated with her husband and her mother in many brilliant researches. M. and Mme. Joliot and J. Chadwick showed that when light elements like beryllium or boron are bombarded with swift α-particles, a highly penetrating stream of uncharged particles or neutrons, is emitted. Each neutron is believed to consist of one positive proton and one negative electron closely bound together.

the Nobel Prize in physics. Mme. Curie once said, "As our elder daughter grew up, she began to be a little companion to her father, who took a lively interest in her education and gladly went for walks with her in his free times, especially on his vacation days. He carried on serious conversations with her, replying to all her questions and delighting in the progressive development of her young mind" (*120*). When Irène Curie was only eight years old, however, she suffered the cruel loss of her affectionate father, who was killed in a traffic accident.

She received her earliest instruction from two Polish governesses, one of them a cousin of Mme. Curie. Thus she soon learned to understand and love the language and culture of her mother's native country. After studying for a time in a private school in Paris, she attended for two years a coöperative school in which Mme. Curie and other members of the university staff united to give their own children the advantages of a well-balanced literary, artistic, scientific, and physical education in which practical experiments played a large part. According to Mme. Curie, Irène "resembled her father in the form of her intelligence. She was not quick, but one could already see that she had a gift of reasoning power and that she would like science." As a girl of fourteen, Irène went to Stockholm to witness the solemn, inspiring ceremony in which her

[*] Courtesy M. Freymann, Hermann et Cie., Paris.

mother was awarded the Nobel Prize in chemistry.   Mlle. Curie later attended a Paris college, passed her bachelor's examination at an unusually early age, and continued her scientific studies at the Sorbonne.

During and after the World War, Mme. Curie established many radiological stations and radiologic motor cars, with which she taught volunteer helpers how to use Röntgen-ray equipment in the examination of the wounded.   This made it possible to determine the exact location of projectiles and to save many men from death or permanent disability. On several of her trips to the ambulance stations in the war zone, Mme. Curie was accompanied by Irène, who was then only seventeen years old. Although she was just beginning her advanced studies at the Sorbonne, Mlle. Curie, eager to be of service, studied nursing and radiology, and did ambulance work at the front, for which, at the close of the war, she was awarded a medal.   In 1916 a department of radiology was added to the Nurses' School, where, according to Mme. Curie, "a few persons of good will, among them my daughter" trained one hundred and fifty operators.   Throughout the entire duration of the war, Mme. Curie took almost no vacation.   "My older daughter," said she, "would scarcely take any, and I was obliged to send her away sometimes to preserve her health. She was continuing her studies in the Sorbonne, and . . . was helping me with my war work."

In 1921 Mme. Curie visited the United States, where she received many honors, including the gift of a gram of radium from the women of America.   Irène and her younger sister, Ève-Denise, accompanied their mother on this visit.

In the same year Mlle. Curie published in the *Comptes rendus* her first scientific paper, which was entitled "The atomic weight of the chlorine in certain minerals."   Upon examining three chlorine minerals (a Canadian sodalite, a Norwegian chlor-apatite, and a sample of sodium chloride from a Central African desert, which had probably been formed by the weathering of local Archaean granites), she found the chlorine in the first two to be identical within the experimental error of 0.02 atomic weight unit with that in an ordinary chloride.   "The results concerning the sodalite and the apatite lead one to think," said she, "that in general the atomic weight of the chlorine contained in ancient minerals scarcely differs from that of normal chlorine from sea water; if this result were generalized, one would be led to conclude that there was a very perfect mingling of the two isotopes before the formation of the mineral or rather that the two isotopes were formed from the beginning in a practically constant proportion."   The chlorine in the sodium chloride from the African desert apparently had a higher atomic weight, however, for Mlle. Curie obtained 35.60 for its atomic weight, even though bromine and iodine were absent (*121*).

Beginning in 1922 she published a long series of excellent researches on polonium, in which she determined the velocity of its alpha-rays and the distribution of their lengths, and observed their ionizing power, the oscillations in their paths, and the homogeneity of their initial velocity. In 1923 she used an original method to determine the range in air of its alpha-particles.

In the following year Mlles. Curie and C. Chamié measured the half-life period of radon by a method which is very simple in principle. If a *single* tube of radon placed in the ionization chamber yields at time t a

Jean-Frédéric Joliot.[°]   Physicist and chemist at the Curie Institute. He has made many important researches on the phenomenon of recoil and the conservation of momentum, on the electrochemical behavior of the radioelements, and on the expulsion of atomic nuclei and the existence of the neutron.

given current i, and the time t' is noted at which the same current i is obtained with *two* tubes of radon (the second of which is exactly equivalent to the first), then $t - t' = T$, the half-life period of radon. Since it is impossible to prepare two tubes of radon of exactly the same activity, Mlles. Curie and Chamié applied a correction. Their value for this constant was 3.823 days (*122*).

Mlle. Curie's doctor's dissertation in 1925 was entitled "Investigation regarding the alpha rays of polonium." With the help of various collaborators, including F. Behounek, Mlle. Chamié, J. d'Espine, G. Fournier,

[°] Courtesy M. Freymann, Hermann et Cie., Paris.

N. Yamada, and P. Mercier, she published a number of researches on other radioactive elements, including radium C, radium C′, radon, radium A, and radium E.

In 1926 Mlle. Curie married M. Frédéric Joliot, a young scientist whose tastes, interests, and intellectual attainments are entirely comparable to her own. He was born in Paris in 1900. In 1923 he completed the engineering course at the Ecole de Physique et de Chimie Industrielle. Upon the recommendation of his professor, M. Paul Langevin, he became *préparateur* under Mme. Curie and continued his studies at the Sorbonne. He succeeded M. André Debierne as lecturer at the Faculty of Sciences. So intimate is the collaboration between M. and Mme. Joliot that, when a new discovery is made, they themselves scarcely know in which mind the original concept first arose. In order that the honored name *Curie* might be handed down to their children and posterity, M. Joliot gladly consented, at the time of his marriage, to add this name to his own. Thus they are known either as M. and Mme. Joliot-Curie or simply as M. and Mme. Joliot.

Their joint papers on "The numbers of ions produced by alpha rays of radium C′ in air" were published in the *Comptes rendus* in 1928. In the following year they investigated the nature of the absorbable radiation which accompanies the alpha-rays from polonium. In 1930 M. Joliot presented his thesis for the doctorate, which was entitled "The electrochemistry of the radio-elements," and Mme. Joliot continued her study of polonium (*123*).

In speaking of the spontaneous disintegration of the natural radio-elements, Mme. Curie pointed out in her fine biography of her husband that "In many cases, up to the present, no exterior action has shown itself effective in influencing this transformation." This view remains unshaken even to the present day. Near the very close of her life, however, Mme. Curie witnessed the discovery by her own daugher and son-in-law of a wonderful new type of radioactivity, artificially produced (*124*). The transformation of one element into another stable, inactive one had already been accomplished. Lord Rutherford, in 1919, had bombarded nitrogen with swift alpha-particles, or helions, and liberated high-speed protons, and P. M. S. Blackett had shown that the nitrogen nucleus had captured the alpha-particle and that the resulting element was an isotope of oxygen. The nuclear reaction was therefore as follows:

$$_7N^{14} + {_2}He^4 = {_8}O^{17} + {_1}H^1$$

$$\text{helion} \qquad\qquad \text{proton}$$

Artificial transmutations into other *stable* elements had also been accomplished.

In 1930 W. Bothe and H. Becker observed a very penetrating radiation from beryllium which had been bombarded with helions. M. and Mme. Joliot-Curie found that when they placed paraffin or other hydrogen-containing substances before the window of an ionization chamber, the ionization produced by these new rays increased; for the protons which were ejected from the paraffin by the radiation from the beryllium had a higher ionizing power than the beryllium-radiation itself (125). Professor James Chadwick proved that the activity of the beryllium is not merely a hard gamma-radiation, as at first supposed, but that neutrons, or uncharged particles of mass one, are also ejected. Each neutron consists of one proton and one negative electron, or negatron, closely bound together; hence its atomic number is zero. The nuclear reaction for the change which occurs when beryllium is bombarded with helions is as follows:

$$_4\text{Be}^9 + {}_2\text{He}^4 = {}_6\text{C}^{12} + {}_0n^1 + \text{gamma rays}$$
$$\text{neutron}$$

M. and Mme. Joliot showed that boron and lithium, when they are bombarded with alpha-rays from polonium, also emit penetrating radiations (126). Their work gave early evidence of the probable existence of the neutron, a hypothesis which has since been fully verified by the researches of Professor James Chadwick, the 1935 Nobel laureate in physics (127).

Early in 1934, M. and Mme. Joliot-Curie observed that in some kinds of transmutation, *true radio-elements* are produced which, after their artificial creation, continue for a measurable period of time to emit positive or negative electrons as they disintegrate at last into stable elements (128). When M. and Mme. Joliot bombarded boron, aluminum, or magnesium with helions from polonium and photographed the fog-tracks which the ejected electrons made in a Wilson expansion chamber, they noted that, even after the removal of the alpha-ray source, an activity remained which, like that of the natural radioactive elements, decreased in geometrical proportion with the time. The radiations from the bombarded boron and aluminum consisted of positrons; irradiated magnesium, however, gave off a radiation consisting of both positrons and negatrons.

Since the alpha-ray impacts shattered only a minute proportion of the total number of atoms of boron, aluminum, or magnesium, the chemical identification of the products was extremely difficult. These indefatigable workers, however, accomplished even this. Although it would have been impossible to identify the products simply by ordinary chemical means, the Joliots were able to take advantage of the radioactive nature of the products formed. Since they had good reason to believe that the boron atom had captured a helion and ejected a neutron and that the new element was therefore probably an isotope of nitrogen, they heated some bombarded boron nitride with caustic soda and found that the liberated ammonia carried with it the new activity, leaving the residual boron inactive. The nuclear reaction which occurred during the alpha-ray bombardment was therefore as follows:

$$_5B^{10} + {}_2He^4 = {}_7N^{13} + {}_0n^1$$

The new product, which they named radionitrogen, is a hitherto unknown radioactive isotope of ordinary nitrogen. It disintegrates with a half period of fourteen minutes and expulsion of positrons, forming a stable, inactive isotope of carbon:

$$_7N^{13} = {}_6C^{13} + {}_1e^0$$
positron

Since the Joliot-Curies believed that a similar capture of the alpha-particle, with formation of an isotope of phosphorus, had occurred during the bombardment of the aluminum, they treated a piece of irradiated aluminum with hydrochloric acid. The liberated hydrogen carried with it the new activity, probably in the form of phosphine, leaving the aluminum residue inactive. The nuclear reaction which took place during the bombardment was therefore as follows:

$$_{13}Al^{27} + {}_2He^4 = {}_{15}P^{30} + {}_0n^1$$

The radio-phosphorus, a hitherto unknown isotope of ordinary phosphorus, disintegrates with a half period of three minutes and fifteen seconds, according to the following reaction:

$$_{15}P^{30} = {}_{14}Si^{30} + {}_1e^0$$

M. and Mme. Joliot-Curie showed that the magnesium atom, when similarly bombarded, also captures a helion and emits a neutron, as follows:

$$_{12}Mg^{24} + {}_2He^4 = {}_{14}Si^{27} + {}_0n^1$$

The resulting radio-silicon decays with a half-life period of two minutes and forty-five seconds, emitting both positrons and negatrons.

Since other projectiles, such as neutrons, protons, and deuterons, have also been used to produce artificial radioactivity, the number of active elements thus created already exceeds by far the number of naturally occurring radio-elements (*129, 130, 131*). By January, 1940, three hundred and thirty artificial radioactivities had been described; these include isotopes of every known element in the range of atomic numbers 1 to 85 inclusive, as well as isotopes of thorium (atomic number 90) and of uranium (atomic number 92) (*132*). Thus the work of M. and Mme. Joliot-Curie opened up vast avenues of research on the physical, chemical, and radioactive properties of these isotopes and on their therapeutic uses. In 1935 they were awarded the Nobel Prize in chemistry (*133*).

In recent years M. and Mme. Joliot-Curie have made further studies on the gamma-radiation of ionium, on chain reactions in a medium containing uranium, and on neutrons and artificial radioactivity. The elements discovered with the aid of this new science will be discussed in Part 31. Mme. Joliot-Curie died in Paris on March 17, 1956 (*136*) after distinguished service to France.

LITERATURE CITED

(1) CURIE, MME., "Pierre Curie," English translation by Charlotte and Vernon Kellogg, The Macmillan Co., New York City, 1926, pp. 24–6.
(2) RAMSAY, SIR WM., "The death-knell of the atom," *Ind. Eng. Chem., News Ed.*, 8, 18 (Jan. 20, 1930). Poem written in 1905.
(3) CURIE, MME., "Pierre Curie," ref. (1), pp. 54–72.
(4) HARROW, B., "Eminent Chemists of Our Time," D. Van Nostrand, Inc., New York City, 1920, p. 158.
(5) "Editor's outlook. Marie Sklodowska Curie," *J. Chem. Educ.*, 7, 225–7 (Feb., 1930).
(6) MARCKWALD, W., "Die Radioaktivität," *Ber.*, 41, 1524–61 (May, 1908). A review.
(7) MENDELEEV, D., "Principles of Chemistry," Vol. 2, English translation from 5th Russian edition, Longmans, Green and Co., London, 1891, p. 447, footnote.
(8) CURIE, MME., "Pierre Curie," ref. (1), pp. 133 and 186–7.
(9) JONES, HARRY C., "The Electrical Nature of Matter and Radioactivity," D. Van Nostrand Co., Inc., New York City, 1906, p. 56.
(10) OSTWALD, W., "Lebenslinien, eine Selbstbiographie," Vol. 3, Klasing & Co., Berlin, 1927, p. 158.
(11) FÄRBER, E., "Geschichtliche Entwicklung der Chemie," Springer, Berlin, 1921, p. 279.
(12) HAHN, O., "Über eine neue radioaktive Substanz im Uran," *Ber.*, 54, 1131–42 (June 11, 1921); "Über das Uran Z und seine Muttersubstanz," *Z. physik. Chem.*, 103, 461–80 (Hefte 5 and 6, 1923).
(13) "Editor's outlook. Bertram Borden Boltwood," *J. Chem. Educ.*, 6, 602–4 (Apr., 1929).
(14) HEVESY, G. and F. PANETH, "A Manual of Radioactivity," English translation by Lawson, Oxford University Press, London, 1926, p. 225.
(15) RUTHERFORD, E., "Radioactive Transformations," Charles Scribner's Sons, New York City, 1906, p. 70.
(16) HARROW, B., "Eminent Chemists of Our Time," ref. (4), pp. 73–5.
(17) GROSSE, A. V., "The analytical chemistry of element 91, ekatantalum, and its difference from tantalum," *J. Am. Chem. Soc.*, 52, 1742–7 (May, 1930).
(18) RUTHERFORD, E. and F. SODDY, "The radioactivity of thorium compounds. I. An investigation of the radioactive emanation," *Trans. Chem. Soc.*, 81, 321–50; "II. The cause and nature of radioactivity," *ibid.*, 837–60 (1902).
(19) HAHN, O., "Über ein neues die Emanation des Thoriums gebendes radioaktives Element," *Jahrb. der Radioaktivität*, 2, 233–66 (Heft 3, 1905); *Proc. Roy. Soc.* (London), 76A, 115–17 (Mar. 7, 1905).
(20) MELLOR, J. W., "Comprehensive Treatise on Inorganic and Theoretical Chemistry," Vol. 7, Longmans, Green and Co., New York City, 1927, pp. 184–203. Article on the "Radioactivity of thorium."
(21) JONES, H. C., "Electrical Nature of Matter and Radioactivity," ref. (9), p. 111.
(22) CURIE, MME., "Pierre Curie," ref. (1), pp. 195–6.

(23) DOLT, M. L., "Chemical French," Chemical Publishing Co., Easton, Pa., **1918**, pp. 282–312. Article by MME. CURIE, "Recherches sur les substances radio-actives."

(24) CURIE, MME., "Recherches sur les substances radioactives," *Ann. chim. phys.*, [7], **30**, 99–203 (Oct., 1903).

(25) SCHMIDT, G. C., *Wied. Ann.*, **65**, 141 (1898).

(26) CURIE, MME., "Rayons émis par les composés de l'uranium et du thorium," *Compt. rend.*, **126**, 1101–3 (Apr. 12, 1898).

(27) CURIE, P. and MME. CURIE, "Sur une substance nouvelle radioactive, contenue dans la pechblende," *Compt. rend.*, **127**, 175–8 (July 18, 1898).

(28) CURIE, P. and MME. CURIE, "Sur une nouvelle substance fortement radio active contenue dans la pechblende," *ibid.*, **127**, 1215–7 (Dec. 26, 1898).

(29) MARCKWALD, W., "Ueber den radioactiven Bestandtheil des Wismuths aus Joachimsthaler Pechblende," *Ber.*, **35**, 2285–8; 4239–41 (1902); **36**, 2662–7 (1903); "Ueber das Radiotellur," **38**, 591–4 (1905).

(30) CROOKES, W., "Radioactivity of uranium," *Chem. News*, **81**, 253–5 (June 1, 1900); 265–7 (June 8, 1900); *Proc. Roy. Soc.* (London), **66**, 409 (May 10, 1900).

(31) OWENS, R. B., "Thorium radiation," *Phil. Mag.*, [5], **48**, 360–87 (Oct. 1899); E. RUTHERFORD, "A radioactive substance emitted from thorium compounds," **49**, 1–14 (Jan., 1900); "Radioactivity produced in substances by the action of thorium compounds," *ibid.*, 161–92 (Feb., 1900); E. RUTHERFORD and F. SODDY, "An investigation of the radioactive emanation produced by thorium compounds," *ibid.*, [6], **4**, 569 (Jan. 16, 1902); *Chem. News*, **85**, 55–6 (Jan. 31, 1902); 261–2 (May 30, 1902); 271–2 (June 6, 1902); 282–5 (June 13, 1902); 293–5 (June 20, 1902); 304–8 (June 27, 1902).

(32) SLATER, J. M. W., "On the excited activity of thorium," *Phil Mag.*, [6], **9**, 628–44 (May, 1905); *Chem. Zentr.*, **76** [1], 1629 (June 21, 1905).

(33) FAJANS, K., "Ueber die komplexe Natur von Radium C," *Physik. Z.*, **12**, 369–77 (May 15, 1911); "Ueber die Verzweigung der Radiumzerfallsreihe," *ibid.*, **13**, 699–705 (Aug. 1, 1912); "Das Verzweigungsverhältnis und das Atomgewicht der C₁-Glieder der drei radioaktiven Umwandlungsreihen," *Physik. Z.*, **14**, 951–3 (Oct. 1, 1913).

(34) HAHN, O., "Ueber einige Eigenschaften der α-Strahlen des Radiothoriums," *Physik. Z.*, **7**, 412–19, 456–62 (1906).

(35) HAHN, O., "A new radioactive element which emits thorium emanation," *Chem. News*, **92**, 251–2 (Dec. 1, 1905).

(36) HAHN, O., "Ein neues Zwischenprodukt im Thorium," *Ber.*, **40**, 1462–9 (1907); "Ueber die Strahlung der Thorium-produkte," *ibid.*, 3304–8 (1907).

(37) DORN, F. E., "Von radioactiven Substanzen ausgesandte Emanation," *Abh. Naturf. Ges.*, Halle, 1900.

(38) HOFMANN, K. A. and E. STRAUSS, "Radioactives Blei und radioactive seltene Erden," *Ber.*, **33**, 3126–31 (1900); **34**, 8–11, 907–13 (1901); 3033–9 (1901).

(39) BOLTWOOD, B. B., "The production of radium from uranium," *Am. J. Sci.*, [4], **20**, 239–44 (No. 117, 1905); "Note on a new radioactive element," *ibid.*, **24**, 370–2 (No. 142, 1907); "On the ultimate disintegration products of the radioactive elements," *ibid.*, **20**, 253–67 (No. 118, 1905).

(40) DEBIERNE, A., "Sur une nouvelle matière radioactive," *Compt. rend.*, **129**, 593–5 (Oct. 16, 1899); "Sur un nouvel élément radioactif: l'actinium," **130**, 906–8 (Apr. 2, 1900); "Sur du baryum radioactif artificiel," **131**, 333–5 (July 30, 1900); **136**, 446–9 (Feb. 16, 1903); 671–3 (Mar. 16, 1903); "Sur l'émanation de l'actinium," **138**, 411–14 (Feb. 15, 1904); "Sur l'actinium," **139**, 538–40 (Oct. 3, 1904); "Sur les gas produits par l'actinium," **141**, 383–5 (Aug. 14, 1905).

(41) GIESEL, F. O., "Ueber Radium und radioactive Stoffe," *Ber.*, **35**, 3608–11 (1902); "Ueber den Emanationskörper aus Pechblende und über Radium," *ibid.*, **36**, 342–7 (1903); "Ueber den Emanationskörper (Emanium)," *ibid.*, **37**, 1696–9, 3963–6 (1904); **38**, 775–8 (1905); **40**, 3011–15 (1907).

(42) HÖNIGSCHMID, O., "Ueber Radioelemente," *Ber.*, **49**, 1835–65 (1917). A review.

(43) BROOKS, H., "A volatile product from radium," *Nature*, **70**, 270 (July 21, 1904); *Phil. Mag.*, [6], **8**, 373 (Sept., 1904).

(44) GODLEWSKI, T., "A new radioactive product from actinium," *Nature*, **71**, 294–5 (Jan. 26, 1905); "Actinium and its successive products," *Phil. Mag.*, [6], **10**, 35–45 (July, 1905).

(45) HAHN, O., "Ueber ein neues Produkt des Actiniums," *Ber.*, **39**, 1605–7 (1906).

(46) HAHN, O. and L. MEITNER, "Ueber das Uran Y," *Physik. Z.*, **15**, 236–40 (Mar. 1, 1914).

(47) HAHN, O. and L. MEITNER, "Ueber die Eigenschaften des Protoaktiniums," *Ber.*, **54**, 69–77 (1921).

(48) FAJANS, K. and O. H. GÖHRING, "Ueber das Uran X₂—das neue Element der Uranreihe," *Physik. Z.*, **14**, 877–84 (Sept. 15, 1913); *Naturwissenschaften*, **1**, 339 (1913).

(49) HAHN, O. and L. MEITNER, "Die Muttersubstanz des Actiniums, ein neues radioaktives Element von langer Lebensdauer," *Physik. Z.*, **19**, 208–18 (May 15, 1918); *Naturwissenschaften*, **6**, 324 (1918).

(50) SODDY, F. and J. A. CRANSTON, "The parent of actinium," *Nature*, **100**, 498–9 (Feb. 21, 1918); *Proc. Roy. Soc.* (London), **94A**, 384 (Feb. 7, 1918).

(51) BECQUEREL, A.-H., "Note sur quelques propriétés du rayonnement de l'uranium et des corps radioactifs," *Compt. rend.*, **128**, 771–7 (Mar. 27, 1899).

(52) DEMARCAY, E.-A., "Sur le spectre d'une substance radioactive," *Compt. rend.*, **127**, 1218 (Dec. 26, 1898).

(53) RUTHERFORD, E., "The succession of changes in radioactive bodies," *Phil. Mag.*, **8**, 636 (1904); *Phil. Trans.*, **204A**, 169–219 (1904); "Slow transformation products of radium," *Nature*, **71**, 341–3 (Feb. 9, 1905).

(54) "Classics of science: radioactive substances," *Sci. News Letter*, **14**, 137–8 (Sept. 1, 1928).

(55) CURIE, MME., "Recherches sur les Substances Radioactives," 2nd ed., Gauthier-Villars, Paris, **1904**, 155 pp. Thesis.

(56) SODDY, F., "The Interpretation of Radium," 4th ed., G. P. Putnam's Sons, New York City, **1922**, 260 pp.

(57) *Ibid.*, p. 134.

(58) LODGE, "Becquerel memorial lecture," *Trans. Chem. Soc.*, **101**, 2005–42 (1912).

(59) ANTONOFF, G. N., "The disintegration products of uranium," *Phil. Mag.*, [6], **22**, 419–32 (Sept., 1911); "On the existence of uranium Y," *ibid.*, **26**, 1058 (Dec., 1913).

(60) DANNE, J., "Les sels de radium," *La Nature*, **32**, [1], 214–18 (Mar. 5, 1904), 243–6 (Mar. 19, 1904).

(61) F. S., "Professor Pierre Curie," *Nature*, **73**, 612–13 (Apr. 26, 1906).

(62) RAMSAY, W., "Radium emanation," *Nature*, **76**, 269 (July 18, 1907).

(63) McCoy, H. N. and W. H. Ross, "The specific radioactivity of thorium and the variation of the activity with chemical treatment and with time," *J. Am. Chem. Soc.*, **29**, 1709–18 (Dec., 1907).

(64) KOVARIK, A. F. and L. W. MCKEEHAN, "Radioactivity. Report of Committee on X-rays and Radioactivity, National Research Council," National Academy of Sciences, Washington, D. C., **1925**, 203 pp.

(65) "Madame Marie Curie dedicates Hepburn Hall of Chemistry at St. Lawrence University," *J. Chem. Educ.*, **7**, 268–76 (Feb., 1930).

(66) "Editor's outlook. Frederick Soddy," *ibid.*, **8**, 1245–6 (July, 1931).

(67) "Editor's outlook. Theodore William Richards," *ibid.*, **5**, 783–4 (July, 1928).

(68) CURIE, MME., "Pierre Curie," ref. (1), p. 170.
(69) W. R. W., "Anniversaries of science," J. Chem. Educ., 4, 400 (March, 1927).
(70) "Local activities. Cornell University," ibid., 7, 707 (March, 1930).
(71) MENDELEEV, D., "Die periodische Gesetzmässigkeit der chemischen Elemente," Ann., Suppl. VIII, 191 (1871).
(72) "Editor's outlook. Sir Ernest Rutherford (1871–   )," J. Chem. Educ., 7, 493–4 (Mar., 1930).
(73) HAHN, O., "The mother substance of radium," Chem. News, 96, 272–3 (Dec. 6, 1907); Ber., 40, 4415–20 (1907).
(74) URBAIN, G., "Discours sur les Éléments Chimiques et sur les Atomes. Hommage au Professeur Bohuslav Brauner," Rec. trav. chim., 44, 285 (1925).
(75) "Les Prix Nobel en 1921–1922," P. A. Norstedt & Söner, Imprimerie Royale, Stockholm, 1923, pp. 1–29. Soddy on "The origins of the conception of isotopes."
(76) MARSDEN, E. and T. BARRATT, "The α-particles emitted by the active deposits of thorium and actinium," Proc. Physical Soc., 24, [1], 50–61 (1911); Physik. Z., 13, 193–9 (Mar. 1, 1912).
(77) MARCKWALD, W. and KEETMAN, "Notiz über das Ionium," Ber., 41, 49–50 (1908).
(78) RICHARDS, T. W. and M. E. LEMBERT, "The atomic weight of lead of radioactive origin," J. Am. Chem. Soc., 36, 1329–44 (July, 1914).
(79) HÖNIGSCHMID, M. E. and S. HOROVITZ, "Sur le poids atomique du plomb de la pechblende," Compt. rend., 158, 1796–8 (June 15, 1914).
(80) GEIGER, H. and E. MARSDEN, "Number of alpha particles emitted by actinium and thorium emanations." Physik. Z., 11, 7–11 (Jan. 1, 1910).
(81) HÖNIGSCHMID, M. E. and S. HOROVITZ, "Zur Kenntnis des Atomgewichtes des Urans," Monat., 37, 185–90 (Dec. 9, 1916).
(82) HAHN, O. and L. MEITNER, "Nachweis der komplexen Natur von Radium C," Physik. Z., 10, 697–703 (Oct. 15, 1909).
(83) SODDY, F., "The Interpretation of Radium," ref. (56), p. 138.
(84) Ibid., pp. 192–3.
(85) BERGWITZ, "Julius Elster," Chem.-Ztg., 44, 457 (June 19, 1920).
(86) SZILARD, B., "Die diesjährigen Träger der Nobelpreise für Chemie und Physik. Frau Pierre Curie und ihr Werk," Chem.-Ztg., 35, 1361–2 (Dec. 9, 1911).
(87) H. B. D., "Theodore William Richards," Proc. Roy. Soc. (London), 121A, xxix–xxxiv (1928).
(88) GROSSE, A. V., "The rarest metal yet obtained," Sci. Am., 142, 42–4 (Jan., 1930). Protactinium.
(89) R. W. L., "Prof. Tadeusz Godlewski," Nature, 110, 361 (Sept. 9, 1922).
(90) RUSSELL, A. S., "The periodic system and the radio-elements," Chem. News, 107, 49–52 (Jan. 31, 1913); F. SODDY, ibid., 107, 97–9 (Feb. 28, 1913); K. FAJANS, "Die radioaktiven Umwandlungen und das periodische System der Elemente," Ber., 46, 422–39 (1913).
(91) RAMSAY, W. and R. W. GRAY, "La densité de l'émanation du radium," Compt. rend., 151, 126–8 (July 11, 1910).
(92) CURIE, MAURICE, "Sur les écarts de poids atomiques obtenus avec le plomb provenant de divers minéraux," Compt. rend., 158, 1676–9 (June 8, 1914).
(93) BOLTWOOD, B. B., "The radioactivity of thorium minerals and salts," Am. J. Sci. [4], 21, 423 (June, 1906); ibid., 24, 95 (Aug., 1907).
(94) SCHLUNDT, H., "The refining of mesothorium," J. Chem. Educ., 8, 1267–87 (July, 1931).
(95) GROSSE, A. V., "Metallic element 91," J. Am. Chem. Soc., 56, 2200–1 (Oct., 1934).
(96) WIECHERT, E., "Julius Elster," Nachrichten Gesellsch. Wiss. Göttingen, pp. 53–60 (1921); R. POHL, "Hans Geitel," ibid., pp. 69–74 (1923–24).
(97) RUSSELL, A. S., "Mme. Curie memorial lecture," J. Chem. Soc., 1935, 654–63.

(98)   CURIE, EVE, "Marie Curie, my mother," *Saturday Evening Post*, **210** (Sept. 4–Oct. 23, 1937); Doubleday, Doran and Co., Garden City, New York, **1937**, 393 pp.

(99)   RAMSTEDT, EVA, "Marie Curie och radium," P. A. Norstedt & Söner, Stockholm, **1932**, 58 pp.; "Marie Sklodowska Curie," *Svenska Fysikersamfundets Kosmos*, **12**, 10–44 (1934).

(100)   STIEGLITZ, J., "Herbert Newby McCoy," *Ind. Eng. Chem.*, *News Ed.*, **13**, 280 (July 10, 1935).

(101)   EVE, A. S., J. CHADWICK, J. J. THOMSON, W. H. BRAGG, NIELS BOHR, F. SODDY, E. N. DA C. ANDRADE, and F. E. SMITH, "The Right Hon. Lord Rutherford," *Nature*, **140**, 746–54 (Oct. 30, 1937).

(102)   GEIGER, H., "Memories of Rutherford at Manchester," *Nature*, **141**, 244 (Feb. 5, 1938).

(103)   EVE, A. S., "The Macdonald Physics Building, McGill University, Montreal," *Nature*, **74**, 272–5 (July 19, 1906).

(104)   MEYER, STEFAN, A. N. SHAW, N. BOHR, G. VON HEVESY, M. LE DUC DE BROGLIE, J. STARK, O. HAHN, E. FERMI, WERTENSTEIN, and N. KAPITZA, "Further tributes to the late Lord Rutherford," *Nature*, **140**, 1047–54 (Dec. 18, 1937).

(105)   MAUROIS, ANDRÉ, "Mlle. Ève Curie," *Vogue*, **91**, 74–7, 172 (Apr. 15, 1938).

(106)   VON SCHWEIDLER, E., "Julius Elster und Hans Geitel als Forscher," *Naturw.*, **3**, 372–7 (July 16, 1915); KARL BERGWITZ, "Julius Elsters und Hans Geitels Bedeutung für die atmosphärische Elektrizität," *ibid.*, **3**, 377–83 (July 16, 1915).

(107)   "Award of the Willard Gibbs Medal to H. N. McCoy," *Chem. Bull.*, **24**, 207–24 (June, 1937).

(108)   McCoy, H. N. and W. H. Ross, "The specific radioactivity of uranium," *J. Am. Chem. Soc.*, **29**, 1698–1708 (1907).

(109)   BOLTWOOD, B. B., *Nature*, **75**, 223 (1906–7); *Am. J. Sci.* (4), **25**, 298 (1908).

(110)   GEIGER, H. and E. RUTHERFORD, "The number of alpha-particles emitted by uranium and thorium and by uranium minerals," *Phil. Mag.*, **20**, 691–8 (1910).

(111)   KLICKSTEIN, H. S., "Pierre Curie. An appreciation of his scientific achievements," *J. Chem. Educ.*, **24**, 278–82 (June, 1947).

(112)   WALL, FLORENCE E., "Wilhelm Ostwald," *J. Chem. Educ.*, **25**, 2–10 (Jan., 1948).

(113)   JAFFÉ, GEORGE, "Recollections of three great laboratories," *J. Chem. Educ.*, **29**, 236–8 (May, 1952).

(114)   CURIE, MARIE, "Pierre Curie," ref. (*1*), pp. 98–100.

(115)   HULUBEI, H. and Y. CAUCHOIS, "A stable element of atomic number 84," *Compt. rend.*, **210**, 761–3 (June 3, 1940).

(116)   "Gmelin's Handbuch der anorganischen Chemie," Vol. 31, Verlag Chemie, Berlin, **1928**, pp. 1–27. History and occurrence of radium.

(117)   SHOHL, A. T., "Mineral Metabolism," Reinhold Publishing Corporation, New York, **1939**, pp. 32–3, 96, 141, 145.

(118)   MELLOR, J. W., "Comprehensive Treatise on Inorganic and Theoretical Chemistry," Vol. 4, Longmans, Green and Co., London, **1923**, pp. 135–6.

(119)   HEVESY, G. and F. PANETH, ref. (*14*), pp. 163–4.

(120)   CURIE, MME., ref. (*1*), p. 129.

(121)   CURIE, I., "The atomic weight of the chlorine in certain minerals," *Compt. rend.*, **172**, 1025–8 (1921); "Nuclear gamma rays from beryllium and lithium, excited by alpha rays from polonium," *ibid.*, **193**, 1412–4 (1931); "Nuclear structure and radioactivity," *Rev. sci.*, **73**, 357 (1935).

(122)   CURIE, I. and C. CHAMIÉ, "The radioactive constant of radon," *Compt. rend.*, **178**, 1808–10 (1924).

(123)   JOLIOT, F., "Electrochemical study of the radioelements," *J. chim. phys.*, **27**, 119–62 (1930).

(124) CROWTHER, J. G., "Mme. Curie and her successors," The Nineteenth Century and After, 116, 194–205 (Aug., 1934).

(125) CURIE, I. and F. JOLIOT, "The emission of high-speed protons by hydrogen compounds under the influence of gamma rays of high penetration," Compt. rend., 194, 273–5 (1932); "The effect of the absorption of gamma rays on the projection of nuclear radiation," ibid., 194, 708–11 (1932); "The projection of atoms by very penetrating radiation excited in light nuclei," ibid., 194, 876–7 (1932); "The nature of the penetrating radiation excited in light nuclei by alpha particles," ibid., 194, 1229–32 (1932); "Evidence for the neutron," Nature, 130, 57 (1932); "Conditions of emission of neutrons by the action of alpha particles on the light elements," Compt. rend., 196, 397–9 (1933); "Positive electrons," ibid., 196, 1105–7 (1933); "The origin of positive electrons," ibid., 196, 1581–3 (1933); "Positive electrons of transmutation," ibid., 196, 1885–7 (1933); "The complexity of the proton and the mass of the neutron," ibid., 197, 237–8 (1933); "Experimental proofs of the existence of the neutron, J. phys. radium, (7), 4, 21–33 (1933); "Recent researches on the emission of neutrons," ibid., (7), 4, 278–86 (1933); "Electrons of materialization and of transmutation," ibid., (7), 4, 494–500 (1933); "Chemical separation of new radioelements emitting positive electrons," Compt. rend., 198, 559–61 (1934); "Mass of the neutron," Nature, 133, 721 (1934); "Artificial production of radioactive elements. Chemical proof of the transmutation of elements," J. phys. radium, (7), 5, 153–6 (1934); "Neutrons and positrons, Artificial radioactivity," Rev. gén. sci., 45, 229–35 (1934).

(126) CURIE, I., F. JOLIOT, and P. SAVEL, "Radiations excited by alpha rays in light elements," Compt. rend., 194, 2208–11 (1932).

(127) SHADDUCK, H. A., "The neutron," J. Chem. Educ., 13, 303–8 (July, 1936).

(128) JOLIOT, F. and I. CURIE, "Un nouveau type de radioactivité," Compt. rend., 198, 254–6 (Jan. 15, 1934); "Artificial production of a new kind of radio-element," Nature, 133, 201–2 (Feb. 10, 1934); "Les nouveaux radio-éléments. Preuves chimiques des transmutations," J. chim. phys., 31, 611–20 (Dec. 25, 1934).

(129) CURIE, I., F. JOLIOT, and P. PREISWERK, "Radioelements produced by bombardment with neutrons. New type of radioactivity," Compt. rend., 198, 2089–91 (1934).

(130) CURIE, I., H. VON HALBAN, and P. PREISWERK, "Artificial formation of elements of an unknown radioactive family by irradiation of thorium with neutrons," Compt. rend., 200, 1841–3 (1935); "Radioactive elements formed by irradiation of thorium with neutrons," ibid., 200, 2079–80 (1935).

(131) JOLIOT, F., A. LAZARD, and P. SAVEL, "Synthesis of radio-elements by deuterons accelerated by means of an impulse generator," ibid., 201, 826–8 (1935).

(132) SEABORG, G. T., "Artificial radioactivity," Chem. Revs., 27, 199–285 (Aug., 1940).

(133) BOYER, "Les Prix Nobel de 1935. Une visite à M. et Mme. Joliot-Curie, lauréats du Prix Nobel de Chimie," La Nature, 63, 585–6 (Dec. 15, 1935).

(134) ANON., "Actinium isolated," Chem. Eng. News, 27, 3240 (Oct. 31, 1949).

(135) OESPER, RALPH E., "Otto Hönigschmid," J. Chem. Educ., 17, 562 (Dec., 1940).

(136) Chem. Eng. News, 34, 1584 (Apr. 2, 1956).

Henry Gwyn Jeffreys Moseley, 1887–1915. English physicist who studied the X-ray spectra of more than fifty elements and discovered the relation existing between the atomic number of an element and the frequency of the X-rays which it emits when bombarded by cathode rays. At the age of twenty-seven years he was killed while in active service at the Dardanelles.

Beyond the violet seek him, for there in the dark he dwells,
Holding the crystal lattice to cast the shadow that tells
How the heart of the atom thickens, ready to burst into flower.
Loosing the bands of Orion with heavenly heat and power.
He numbers the charge on the center for each of the elements.
That we named for gods and demons, colors and tastes and
  scents . . . (1).

Atom from atom yawns as far as moon from earth, as star from
  star . . . (2).

30

Discoveries by X-ray spectrum analysis

When H. G. J. Moseley discovered the simple relationship which exists between the X-ray spectrum of an element and its atomic number, there were seven unfilled spaces in the periodic table. Elements 43, 61, 72, 75, 85, 87, and 91, were yet to be revealed. Element 91 (protactinium) was discussed with the radioactive elements in Chapter 29. In 1923 D. Coster and G. von Hevesy showed that element 72, hafnium, is widely distributed but that it had escaped detection because of its close resemblance to zirconium. Element 75 (rhenium) was announced by W. and I. Noddack in 1925, and is now a commercial article.

*A*lthough Mendeleev's periodic system was a great aid in the search for new elements, there were some anomalies that it did not explain. The practical atomic weight of argon, for example, is higher than that of potassium, yet argon must precede potassium in the table, for there is no doubt whatever that it is an inert gas like helium and that potassium is an alkali metal like sodium. Tellurium and iodine present a similar discrepancy, and the radioactive isotopes were also the cause of much perplexity.

A much better basis of classification for the elements was finally found by a young English physicist in the course of his researches on X-rays. Henry Gwyn Jeffreys Moseley was born at Weymouth on November 23, 1887. While he was still a very young child he had the misfortune to lose his father, a distinguished zoölogist and professor at Oxford University. Moseley studied at Eton and at Trinity College, Oxford, and received his master's degree in 1910. A year before his graduation he went to Manchester to discuss with Sir Ernest Rutherford the possibility of undertaking original research in physics (3).

After serving the University of Manchester for two years as lecturer and demonstrator in physics, he resigned his position in order to devote all his time to research, and was awarded the John Harling Fellowship. His colleagues soon recognized his superiority as an experimenter, and admired him because of his marvelous technique, broad knowledge of physics, cheerfulness, and friendly coöperation. When the British Association met in Australia in 1914, he entered enthusiastically into the discussion of atomic structure and gave an excellent report of his own researches on the X-ray spectra of the rare earths (4).

No scientist of the first rank ever had a shorter career. When Great Britain entered the war he immediately returned to England, entered the military service as a signaling officer, and on June 13, 1915, left for the Dardanelles. On the 10th of August, when he was telephoning an order to his division, a Turkish bullet passed through his head. His will, made while he was in active service, bequeathed all his apparatus and much of his private fortune to the Royal Society. Although Moseley was not quite twenty-eight years old at the time of his death, his researches had so revolutionized the study of atomic structure that his name will endure forever in the annals of science (5, 6, 7, 8).

Before entering the military service he had become intensely interested in Professor Max von Laue's discovery that "the ordered arrangement of the atoms in a crystal would do the same for X-rays that a diffraction grating does for light" (9). When a target, or anticathode, is bombarded with cathode rays, it emits a beam of X-rays which is characteristic of the substance of which the target is made. With the help of Mr. C. G. Darwin, a grandson of the famous biologist, Moseley mapped the high-frequency spectrum of an X-ray tube provided with a platinum anticathode (9).

In the hope of finding some relationship between the frequency of the rays and the atomic number, or ordinal number of the element in the periodic table, he then carried out an elaborate investigation in which many different elements served as anticathodes. Upon examining these rays by diffracting them through a crystal, he found the following simple and beautiful relationship: When all the known elements are numbered in the order of their positions in the periodic system, the square root of the frequency of the X-rays emitted is directly proportional to the atomic number.

Thus Moseley's series is almost the same as Mendeleev's series of increasing atomic weights. When, however, the elements are arranged, not according to their atomic weights, but according to their atomic numbers (Moseley numbers), the discrepancies between argon and potassium and between iodine and tellurium disappear (10).

Moseley's work not only shed much light on the periodic system and the relationships between known elements and the radioactive isotopes, but was also a great stimulus in the search for the few elements remaining undiscovered (11). One of the first chemists to utilize the new method was Professor Georges Urbain of Paris, who took his rare earth preparations to Oxford for examination. Moseley showed him the characteristic lines of erbium, thulium, ytterbium, and lutetium, and confirmed in a few days the conclusions which Professor Urbain had made after twenty years

Max von Laue, 1879– . German physicist who in 1912 discovered the interference of X-rays diffracted by crystals, measured the wave lengths of X rays, and studied the structure of crystals. In 1914 he was awarded the Nobel Prize for physics.

of patient research. The latter was greatly surprised to find that a scientific contribution of such fundamental importance had been made by one so young, and immediately began to teach Moseley's method of X-ray analysis. "His law," said he, "substituted for the rather romantic classification of Mendeleev a precision entirely scientific" (6).

A. V. Grosse (12) has shown, however, that, when one substitutes for the practical atomic weight of each element the *arithmetic mean* of the atomic weights of all its isotopes, "the row of increasing atomic weights is identical with the sequence of increasing nuclear charges" and the discrepancies formerly presented by argon and potassium, cobalt and nickel, tellurium and iodine, and thorium and protactinium no longer exist.

HAFNIUM (Element 72)

Moseley stated that, within the limits of his researches, which covered all the elements between aluminum (number 13) and gold (number 79), there were spaces for three missing ones: numbers 43, 61, and 75, and that, since their X-ray spectra can be accurately predicted, it ought to be rather easy to find them. It was then believed that the *celtium* whose arc spectrum Professor Urbain had described in 1911 was element 72 (6, 13, 14).

However, when Moseley and Urbain examined the rare-earth residues supposed to contain the new element, they found only about ten lines, all of which could be attributed to lutetium and ytterbium. In 1922, after a long period of interruption because of military duties, Professor Urbain resumed his search for element 72 in the same rare-earth residues which he and Moseley had examined before the war. At his suggestion M. A. Dauvillier used de Broglie's improved method of X-ray analysis and observed two faint lines which almost coincided with those predicted for element 72 (15, 16).

After titanium was discovered in 1791 by the Reverend William Gregor in Cornwall, its atomic weight was determined by such able chemists as H. Rose, C. G. Mosander, and J.-B.-A. Dumas, but the results showed such great discrepancies that Mendeleev predicted that another element would be found in titanium ores (17).

When Edgar Fahs Smith was investigating monazite sand under the direction of F. A. Genth (1820–1893), the latter always appropriated the zirconium sulfate that was extracted, and would say as he carried it away, "Zirconium is not simple; there is another element concealed in it, and when I have leisure I shall endeavor to isolate it" (18). It was in zirconium ores that large quantities of element 72 were first revealed (19, 20, 21).

Since zircon often contains small amounts of other elements in addition to the zirconium, silicon, and oxygen which are essential to its composition, announcements appeared from time to time of the complexity of zirconium, and several "new elements" were announced which were later proved to be false (*22*).

On the basis of his quantum theory of atomic structure, Niels Bohr believed that, since Urbain's *celtium* had been obtained from the rare earths, it could not be element 72, for the latter must be quadrivalent rather than trivalent and must belong to the zirconium family. He showed that the chemical properties of an atom are determined by the number and arrangement of the electrons within it and especially by the number

Georg von Hevesy. Hungarian chemist who, with Dr. Dirk Coster of the University of Groningen, discovered the element hafnium in zirconium ores and made a thorough study of its properties. Author of many papers on chemical analysis by X-rays, radioactivity, the rare earths, and electrolytic conduction. In 1943 he was awarded the Nobel Prize in Chemistry.

Courtesy Cornell University

and arrangement of the outermost ones, the so-called "valence electrons." Since there is usually an appreciable difference in the outer electrons of two adjacent elements in the periodic system, there is also, as a rule, a marked difference in chemical properties. In the rare-earth group, however, and in the triads of the iron and platinum families, the only structural differences are in the deeper shells of the atoms, and therefore these elements are more difficult to separate. According to Bohr's theory these deep-seated differences in the rare earths lie in the interval between lanthanum (element 57) and lutetium (element 71). Element 72 should, however, according to his theory, be quite different from lutetium in the constitution of its outer group of electrons, and should therefore exhibit properties entirely different from those of the rare earth elements (*16*), but closely resembling those of zirconium. Bohr therefore advised Dr. Georg von Hevesy to search for this element in zirconium ores (*23, 24*).

It was in January, 1923, that Dirk Coster and Georg von Hevesy in Copenhagen brought their search for the new member of the zirconium family to a successful conclusion. Its discovery in a Norwegian zircon and later in all the zirconium minerals and all the commercial zirconium preparations they investigated, even those which had previously been believed to be pure, was made possible by Moseley's method of X-ray analysis, and it was Coster's previous work in the same field that enabled him to recognize the new element (*5*).

Dirk Coster. Professor of physics and meteorology at the Royal University of Groningen. Co-discoverer with Georg von Hevesy of the element hafnium. Author of many papers on X-rays and atomic structure.

Although they named it *hafnium** for the city of Copenhagen, neither of these investigators is Danish. Professor Coster is a professor of physics and meteorology at the Royal University of Groningen and director of the physical laboratory. The Dutch, French, English, German, and American journals contain many of his papers on such subjects as X-ray spectra, theory of atomic structure, Stokes's law in the L-series of X-rays, and the rotational oscillation of a cylinder in a viscous liquid.

Professor von Hevesy was born in Budapest in 1885 and was educated in the universities of Budapest, Berlin and Freiburg. His researches

* Both sides of the controversy regarding the name of element 72 are presented in the English journals, *Nature* and *Chemistry and Industry* (*16, 24*).

have brought him into close contact with such famous scientists as Fritz Haber at Karlsruhe, Lord Rutherford at Manchester, and F. G. Donnan at Liverpool, and the X-ray investigation with Dr. Coster which resulted in the discovery of hafnium was carried out while both were connected with Bohr's Institute of Theoretical Physics at Copenhagen. Professor von Hevesy taught for a time as professor of physical chemistry at the University of Freiburg. In 1930 he served as the George Fisher Baker Non-Resident Lecturer in Chemistry at Cornell University. His researches have been carried out in the fields of physical chemistry, electrochemistry, radioactivity, and the separation of isotopes (25).

Hafnium had lain hidden for untold centuries, not because of its rarity but because of its close similarity to zirconium (16), and when Professor von Hevesy examined some historic museum specimens of zirconium compounds which had been prepared by Julius Thomsen, C. F. Rammelsberg, A. E. Nordenskjöld, J.-C. G. de Marignac, and other experts on the chemistry of zirconium, he found that they contained from 1 to 5 per cent of the new element (26, 27). The latter is far more abundant than silver or gold. Since the earlier chemists were unable to prepare zirconium compounds free from hafnium, the discovery of the new element necessitated a revision of the atomic weight of zirconium (24, 28). Some of the minerals were of nepheline syenitic and some of granitic origin (20). Hafnium and zirconium are so closely related chemically and so closely associated in the mineral realm that their separation is even more difficult than that of niobium (columbium) and tantalum (29). The ratio of hafnium to zirconium is not the same in all minerals.

Professor von Hevesy and Thal Jantzen separated hafnia from zirconia by repeated recrystallization of the double ammonium or potassium fluorides (20, 26). Metallic hafnium has been isolated and found to have the same crystalline structure as zirconium. A small specimen of the first metallic hafnium ever made is on permanent display at the American Museum of Natural History in New York City. Dr. von Hevesy, who prepared it, presented it to the Museum for the collection of chemical elements (29). A. E. van Arkel and J. H. de Boer prepared hafnium by passing the vapor of the tetraiodide over a heated tungsten filament (26, 30).

RHENIUM (Element 75)

Two new elements of the manganese group, numbers 43 (eka-manganese) and 75 (dwi-manganese), were announced in June, 1925, by the German chemists Dr. Walter Noddack and Dr. Ida Tacke of the Physico-Technical Testing Office in Berlin and Dr. Otto Berg of the Werner-Siemens Laboratory. The discovery was not accidental, but the result of a long search begun in 1922 in platinum ores and later in sulfide ores and in the mineral columbite (*31*).   Platinum ores contain the elements 24 to 29, 44 to 47, and 76 to 79 (chromium to copper, ruthenium to silver, and osmium to gold), whereas columbite contains numbers 39 to 42 and 72 to 74 (yttrium to molybdenum, and hafnium to tungsten). Hence it was hoped that one or both of these sources might yield the missing elements, 43 and 75.

Upon studying the relative frequencies of known elements in the earth's crust, Noddack, Tacke, and Berg found that those of odd atomic number are less common than those of even number, and from the known frequency of occurrence of platinum ores and of columbite they obtained an approximate idea of the extent to which they would have to carry their processes of extraction.   Moreover, since elements 43 and 75 were believed to belong to the manganese group, many of their physical and chemical properties could be predicted.   In May, 1925, Noddack and Tacke and Dr. O. Berg of the Siemens and Halske Company accomplished a 100,000-fold concentration of element 75 in a gadolinite, and by careful measurement of five lines of the L-series of its X-ray spectrum established the existence of this new element (*36*).   Element 75 was finally separated from columbite, and named *rhenium* in honor of the German Rhine (*32*, *33*).   The difficult concentration processes were carried out by Drs. Noddack and Tacke alone, but Dr. Berg assisted in making the observations with the X-ray spectroscope (*34*).   They also observed some X-ray lines which they attributed to element 43, which they named *masurium* for Masurenland, East Prussia.   The history of element 43 will be given in Chapter 31.   Before the discovery of rhenium, manganese had no companions in sub-group *VIIa* of the periodic system.

On September 5, 1925, Fräulein Tacke lectured on the new elements before the Verein deutscher Chemiker in Nuremberg (*35*).   After thanking her for the address, the president mentioned that this was an historic occasion, for it was the first time that a woman had ever spoken before the Verein.   He also expressed the hope that other *"Chemikerinnen"* might soon follow her example.   Fräulein Tacke and Dr. Noddack have since been united in marriage and have continued their joint researches. Largely through their efforts, the knowledge of rhenium has rapidly increased, and the chemical, physical, and analytical properties of a large number of its compounds have been accurately determined.   In recognition of their discoveries they were awarded the Liebig Medal.   They found that Scandinavian sulfide ores of iron, copper, and molybdenum are a far more suitable source of rhenium than are native platinum ores (*36*).   Because of its scarcity, rhenium could not be detected by direct physical or chemical means in ores, minerals, or technical products.   By working up 660 kilograms of molybdenite, the discoverers of rhenium nevertheless succeeded in 1928 in preparing a gram of it. In the following year they extracted an additional 1.7 grams of it from pyrrhotite (magnetic pyrites) and molybdenite, which enabled them to investigate its properties. Since the process of extracting rhenium from minerals was too expensive to permit production on a larger scale, the Noddacks investigated a number of technical products in search of one which might contain rhenium in higher concentrations. Near the end of 1929 W. Feit presented them with a molybdenum sulfide solution containing 1.5 per cent

Jaroslav Heyrovský, 1890– . Professor of physical chemistry at Charles University, Prague. Author of an "Introduction to Radioactivity." With E. Votoček he founded the *Collection of Czechoslovak Chemical Communications*, a monthly journal published in French and English to make the contributions of Czechoslovakian and Russian chemists accessible to those who do not read the Slavonic languages.

of rhenium. Since the raw material, a residue already in technical use, contained ten times as much rhenium as the richest ore, Feit soon developed a commercial process which made possible the production of several hundred grams of potassium perrhenate (36).

Molybdenite from a mine at Middle Inlet, Marinette County, in northern Wisconsin was found to contain relatively large amounts of rhenium (37).

In 1925 F. H. Loring and J. G. F. Druce in England and V. Dolejšek and J. Heyrovsky in Czechoslovakia independently announced that commercial manganese salts and even so-called "pure" preparations contain small amounts of element 75 (38, 39, 40). While searching for an element of atomic number 93, the English chemists removed manganese and other heavy metals by precipitation as the sulfides, and evaporated the filtrate to dryness. X-ray analysis of the residue apparently revealed lines of element 75.

Dr. J. Heyrovský, professor of physical chemistry at the Charles University of Prague, and Dr. Dolejšek of the Prague Academy of Sciences thought they detected element 75 in manganese salts by a different method. They examined some manganese solutions with their dropping mercury cathode, plotted the current intensity as ordinates against the applied electromotive force as abscissas, and notice a peculiar "hump" in the curve in the region between −1.00 and −1.19 volts from the potential of the calomel electrode. After showing that zinc, nickel, cobalt, and

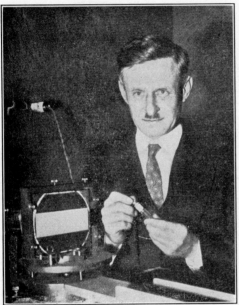

William Frederick Meggers. Physicist at the U. S. Bureau of Standards since 1914. Chief of the spectroscopy section. Author of many papers on optics, astrophysics, photography, measurement of wave-length standards, and description and analysis of spectra. The instrument in the foreground is a concave grating spectrograph, used for photographing the emission spectrum of rhenium (*41*).

Courtesy Scientific Monthly

iron were absent, Heyrovský and Dolejšek suspected the presence of the undiscovered eka-manganeses, elements 43 and 75. Using their dropping mercury cathode in conjunction with a polarograph, they obtained automatically a permanent record of the electrolytic reaction.

After dipping strips of zinc into concentrated solutions of manganese salts, they scraped off a deposit containing zinc, lead, cadmium, nickel, and cobalt. After complete removal of these heavy metals by precipitation as the sulfides, they found no evidence of element 43, but thought they found the X-ray lines of number 75 (*42*). When Dr. Druce took his dwi-manganese preparation to the Charles University in Prague for polarographic examination, the Czechoslovakian chemists confirmed his conclusions.

In response to criticism by the Noddacks and by L. C. Hurd (43), who was unable to detect rhenium in any of the various manganese salts which he studied, Dr. Heyrovský himself afterward worked out a sensitive polarographic test for the *absence* of rhenium in manganese salts. Although potassium perrhenate gives a polarographic step at −1.2 volts from the normal calomel zero, this is not conclusive evidence for rhenium in presence of cobalt, iron, nickel, or zinc. When, however, he added sodium acetate, acetic acid, and hydrogen sulfide to precipitate these metals, the perrhenate was changed to Re_2S_7 or thioperrhenate, without precipitating, and the "step" was shifted. In the absence of perrhenate, this shift does not occur. Upon testing various commercial manganese salts in this manner, Professor Heyrovský found that they contain less than one part of rhenium per million parts of manganese and that the polarograph steps at −1.0 and −1.2 volts shown on polarograms of manganese solutions, as well as the lines of the X-ray spectrum, must be due to elements other than rhenium (44). Although the polarograms were at first misinterpreted in this case, the polarographic method has nevertheless been used successfully in other analyses (45).

According to the well-founded rules of Josef Mattauch, no stable isotopes of element 43 are to be expected. This may explain why it has never been prepared and concentrated from natural products (46).

Colin G. Fink and P. Deren of Columbia University in 1934 perfected a process for electroplating rhenium as a bright, hard deposit which is surprisingly resistant to hydrochloric acid (47). Dr. William F. Meggers of the United States Bureau of Standards has made a thorough study of the arc spectrum of rhenium (41).

LITERATURE CITED

(1) LEWIS, E. H., "Ballad of Ryerson," *J. Chem. Educ.*, **2**, 610 (July, 1925). Poem in memory of Moseley.

(2) Journals of R. W. Emerson, Centenary Ed., Vol. VI, Houghton, Mifflin Co., p. 207; See also C. A. BROWNE, "Emerson and chemistry," *J. Chem. Educ.*, **5**, 269–79 (Mar., 1928); **5**, 391–403 (Apr., 1928).

(3) RUTHERFORD, E., "Henry Gwyn Jeffreys Moseley," *Nature*, **96**, 33–4 (Sept. 9, 1915).

(4) "Discussion on the structure of atoms and molecules," *Brit. Assoc. Reports*, **84**, 293–301 (Aug. 18, 1914).

(5) POGGENDORFF, J. C., "Biographisch-Literarisches Handwörterbuch zur Geschichte der exakten Wissenschaften," 6 vols., Verlag Chemie, Leipzig and Berlin, **1863–1937**. Articles on Moseley and Coster.

(6) E. R., "H. G. J. Moseley, 1887–1915," *Proc. Roy. Soc.*, (*London*), **93A**, xxii–xxviii (1917).

(7) LANKESTER, SIR E. RAY, "Henry Gwyn Jeffereys Moseley," *Phil. Mag.*, **31**, 173–6 (Feb., 1916).

(8) SARTON, G., "Moseley. The numbering of the elements," *Isis*, **9** (1), 96–111 (1927).

(9)   MOSELEY, H. G. J., and C. G. DARWIN, "The reflexion of the X-rays," *Phil. Mag.*, (6), **26**, 210–32 (July, 1913); *Sci. News Letter*, **15**, 203–4 (Mar. 30, 1929).

(10)   MOSELEY, H. G. J., "The high-frequency spectra of the elements," *Phil. Mag.*, (6), **26**, 1024–34 (Dec., 1913); **27**, 703–13 (Apr., 1914).

(11)   HEVESY, G., "The use of X-rays for the discovery of new elements," *Chem. Revs.*, 3, 321–9 (Jan., 1927).

(12)   GROSSE, A. V., "The row of increasing atomic weights and the periodic law," *J. Chem. Educ.*, **14**, 433–44 (Sept., 1937).

(13)   RUTHERFORD, E., "Moseley's work on X-rays," *Nature*, **116**, 316–17 (Aug. 29, 1925).

(14)   URBAIN, G., "Sur un nouvel élément qui accompagne le lutécium et le scandium dans les terres de la gadolinite: le celtium," *Compt. rend.*, **152**, 141–3 (Jan. 16, 1911).

(15)   URBAIN, G., "Les numéros atomiques du néo-ytterbium, du lutécium, et du celtium," *ibid.*, **174**, 1349–51 (May 22, 1922).

(16)   ANON., "The new element hafnium," *Chem. & Ind.* (N. S.), **42**, 67 (Jan. 26, 1923); D. COSTER and G. HEVESY, *ibid.*, 258 (Mar. 16, 1923); Editorial, *ibid.*, 763–4 (Aug. 10, 1923); G. URBAIN, "Should the element of atomic number 72 be called celtium or hafnium?" *Chem. & Ind.* (N. S.), **42**, 764–9 (Aug. 10, 1923); ANON., *ibid.*, 784–8 (Aug. 17, 1923); B. BRAUNER, "Hafnium or celtium," *ibid.*, 884–5 (Sept. 14, 1923); G. HEVESY, "On the chemistry of hafnium," *ibid.*, 929–30 (Sept. 28, 1923); HEVESY, G. VON, "Ueber die Auffindung des Hafniums und den gegenwärtigen Stand unserer Kenntnisse von diesem Element," *Ber.*, **56**, 1503–16 (1923); A. DAUVILLIER, "On the high-frequency lines of celtium," *Chem. & Ind.*, 1182–3 (Dec. 7, 1923); Editorial, *ibid.*, **44**, 619–20 (June 19, 1925).

(17)   THORPE, T. E., "Hafnium and titanium," *Nature*, **111**, 252–3 (Feb. 24, 1923).

(18)   BROWNE, C. A. (editor), "A Half-Century of Chemistry in America, 1876–1926," "Am. Chem. Soc., Philadelphia, **1926**, p. 72.

(19)   COSTER, D., "Hafnium, a new element," *Chem. Weekblad*, **20**, 122–3 (1923).

(20)   HEVESY, G., "The discovery and properties of hafnium," *Chem. Reviews*, **2**, 1–41 (Apr., 1925).

(21)   "The newer metals of group IV. A classic of science," *Sci. News Letter*, **21**, 166–8 (Mar. 12, 1932).

(22)   VENABLE, F. P., "Zirconium and Its Compounds," Chem. Catalog Co., New York, **1922**, 173 pp.

(23)   HOPKINS, B. S., "Building blocks of the universe," *Sci. Am.*, **136**, 87–9 (Feb., 1927).

(24)   URBAIN, G., and A. DAUVILLIER, "On the element of atomic number 72," *Nature*, **111**, 218 (Feb. 17, 1923); D. COSTER and G. HEVESY, "On the new element of atomic number 72," *ibid.*, **111**, 79 (Jan. 20, 1923); 182 (Feb. 10, 1923); 252 (Feb. 24, 1923).

(25)   Biographical sketch of Hevesy, *J. Chem. Educ.*, **7**, 2739–40 (Nov., 1930).

(26)   MELLOR, J. W. "Comprehensive Treatise on Inorganic and Theoretical Chemistry," Vol. 7, Longmans, Green and Co., New York, **1927**, pp. 166–70 (article on Hf); G. HEVESY, "The hafnium content of some historical zirconium preparations," *Nature*, **113**, 384–5 (Mar. 15, 1924).

(27)   HEVESY, G., "Recherches sur les propriétés du hafnium," Kgl. Danske Videnskab. Selskab, Mat.-fys. Medd., **6**, 3–149 (1925). In French.

(28)   "Hafnium," *Sci. Mo.*, **25**, 285–8 (Sept., 1927).

(29)   LEE, O. IVAN, "The mineralogy of hafnium," *Chem. Reviews*, **5**, 17–37 (Feb., 1928).

(30)   VAN ARKEL, A. E., and J. H. DE BOER, "Darstellung von reinen Titanium-, Zirkonium-, Hafnium-, and Thoriummetall," *Z. anorg. Chem.*, **148**, 345–50 (Oct. 29, 1925).

(31)   Noddack, W., I. Tacke, and O. Berg, *Naturw.*, 10, 567 (1925), I. and W.
          Noddack, "Die Sauerstoffverbindungen des Rheniums," *Z. anorg. Chem.*,
          181, 1–37 (Heft 1, 1929); *Chem. News*, 131, 84–7 (Aug. 7, 1925).

(32)   "Two new elements of the manganese group," *Nature*, 116, 54–5 (July 11,
          1925).

(33)   Noddack, W., and I. Noddack, "Über den Nachweis der Ekamangane," *Z.
          angew. Chem.*, 40, 250–4 (Mar. 3, 1927).

(34)   Berg, O., Über den röntgenspektroskopischen Nachweis der Ekamangane," *Z.
          angew. Chem.*, 40, 254–6 (Mar. 3, 1927).

(35)   Tacke, I., "Zur Auffindung der Ekamangane," *Z. angew. Chem.*, 38, 794
          (Sept. 10, 1925); 1157–60 (Dec. 17, 1925).

(36)   Noddack, I., and W. Noddack, "Das Rhenium," Leopold Voss, Leipzig, 1933,
          86 pp.

(37)   Works, Mrs. L. P., "A rhenium-bearing molybdenite in northern Wisconsin,"
          Rocks and Minerals, 16, 92–3 (March, 1941).

(38)   Bligh, N. M., "Newly discovered chemical elements," Smithsonian Report
          for 1929, pp. 245–51; *Sci. Progress*, 20, 109–14 (July, 1926); *Scientia*, 43,
          4 (Apr. 1, 1928).

(39)   Dolejšek, V., J. G. F. Druce, and J. Heyrovský, "The occurrence of
          dwimanganese in manganese salts," *Nature*, 117, 159 (Jan. 30, 1926).

(40)   Druce, J. G. F., "Examination of crude manganese compounds and the
          isolation of the element of atomic number 75," *Chem. News*, 131, 273–7
          (Oct. 30, 1925); F. H. Loring and J. G. F. Druce, "Examination of crude
          dwimanganese," *ibid.*, 337–8 ,Nov. 27, 1925).

(41)   Meggers, W. F., "Rhenium," *Sci. Mo.*, 33, 413–18 (Nov., 1931); "The arc
          spectrum of rhenium," *Bur. Standards J. Research*, 6, 1027–50 (June, 1931).

(42)   Dolejšek, V., and J. Heyrovský, "The occurrence of dwimanganese (at. no.
          75) in manganese salts," *Nature*, 116, 782–3 (Nov. 28, 1925); J. Heyrovsky,
          ibid., 117, 16 (Jan. 2, 1926); *Science* (N. S.), 62, Suppl. xiv (Nov. 20,
          1925); "Researches with the dropping mercury cathode," *Rec. trav. chim.*,
          44, 488–502 (May, 1925); V. Dolejšek and J. Heyrovský, "Über das
          Vorkommen von Dvimangan in Manganverbindungen," *ibid.*, 46, 248–55
          (Apr., 1927).

(43)   Hurd, L. C., "The discovery of rhenium," *J. Chem. Educ.*, 10, 605–8 (Oct.,
          1933); J. G. F. Druce, *ibid.*, 11, 59 (Jan., 1934).

(44)   Heyrovský, J., "A sensitive polarographic test for the absence of rhenium in
          manganese salts," *Nature*, 135, 870–1 (May 25, 1935).

(45)   Herman, J. "The polarograph, a valuable tool in quantitative chemical
          analysis," *Eng. Mining J.* 135, 299–300 (July, 1934).

(46)   Segrè, E., "Artificial radioactivity and the completion of the periodic system
          of the elements," *Sci. Mo.*, 57, 12–16 (July, 1943).

(47)   Fink, C. G., and P. Deren, "Rhenium plating," *Trans. Electrochem. Soc.*,
          66, 471–4 (1934).

Courtesy Chemical and Engineering News

**E. O. Lawrence, G. T. Seaborg, and J. R. Oppenheimer
at controls of Cyclotron**

Ernest O. Lawrence, 1901– . Inventor of the cyclotron, with which he and his collaborators have investigated the structure of atoms, produced artificial radioactivity, effected transmutations of certain elements, and applied artificial radioactive elements to the study of biological and medical problems. In 1939 he was awarded the Nobel Prize for Physics. **Glenn T. Seaborg, 1912–** . Professor of chemistry at the University of California. Codiscoverer of element 94, plutonium, and its fissionable isotope, and later of elements 95 (americium) and 96 (curium). At the "Metallurgical Laboratory" at the University of Chicago he had charge of the ultramicrochemical research for working out methods for the separation and manufacture of plutonium which were later used on a large scale at Hanford, Washington, and Clinton, Tennessee. **J. Robert Oppenheimer, 1904–** . Director of the laboratories at Los Alamos, New Mexico, where American and European scientists worked secretly to produce the first atomic bombs. Director of the Institute for Advanced Study at Princeton, New Jersey.

31

Elements discovered by atomic bombardment

All methods tried by 1937 had failed to reveal elements number 43, 61, 85 and 87, and no element was known beyond uranium, number 92. Then came the discovery of the cyclotron and later the atomic pile. With these it was possible to bombard elements with positive particles or neutrons to create new elements. Soon after this work was begun the empty spaces of the periodic table were filled. Only element number 87, francium, discovered by Mlle. Perey, was found among natural decay products of actinium without help of atomic bombardment. This powerful method was needed for Perrier and Segrè to discover technetium, Marinsky and Glendenin to find promethium, and Segrè, Mackenzie, and Corson to prepare astatine. The table was apparently complete, but this was not the end. In 1940 McMillan and Abelson obtained the first transuranium element, neptunium. Under the stimulus of the atomic bomb project Seaborg and his group synthesized plutonium and guided its preparation in large amounts. They went on to obtain americium and curium. After the war their work was continued at the University of California. Berkelium and californium were announced in 1950, elements 99 and 100 in 1954, and element 101, mendelevium, in 1955.

The discovery by Frédéric and Irène Joliot-Curie* of artificial radioactivity induced by neutron bombardment opened the way for completion of the periodic table. Spaces still remained for elements number 43, 61, 85, and 87 before the apparent end was reached with uranium, number 92. Although a number of investigators believed that they had found one or more of the missing elements, and several had even proposed names for them, positive proof of their existence was lacking. On theoretical grounds it was suggested that these elements might not exist in nature in amounts sufficient for their identification even by such delicate means as spectrum analysis. It would be expected that these substances might be radioactive, and so might have disappeared from the earth even if they had once been present on it. Now, however, came

---

This chapter was written by Dr. Henry M. Leicester.
* See Chapter 29.

the possibility of creating them anew, and, what was even more exciting, of preparing elements with atomic numbers greater than 92, the so-called transuraniums.

Experimental studies soon confirmed all these expectations. The most powerful tool in achieving these results was the cyclotron. Ernest O. Lawrence, its inventor, was born in Canton, South Dakota, on August 8, 1901. He was educated at St. Olaf College and the University of South Dakota, and did graduate work in physics at Minnesota, Chicago, and Yale. The latter university gave him his doctorate in 1925. He remained at Yale until 1928, and was then called to the University of California at Berkeley, where he still remains as Director of the Radiation Laboratory. He received the Nobel Prize in Physics in 1939. It was due to Lawrence and the cyclotron that California became the outstanding center for the synthesis of new elements, which it still remains (1).

In 1929, while glancing through a German periodical, Lawrence noticed a diagram of an apparatus for the multiple acceleration of positive ions by applying radiofrequency oscillating voltages to a series of cylindrical electrodes in line. Almost at once he thought of modifying this idea by circulating the positive particles back and forth through the electrodes in a magnetic field. The first crude cyclotron based on this idea was constructed by Lawrence's student, Nils Edlefsen, in 1930. From this the development was steady up to the enormously powerful bevatron now in operation at Berkeley (2). This apparatus is capable of furnishing tremendous amounts of energy either directly, in the form of positive particles such as deuterons or helium ions, or of directing these onto suitable targets such as beryllium to produce equally powerful beams of neutrons. Almost all the elements discussed in this chapter were obtained from such beams.

The quantity of any given element which could be synthesized in the cyclotron was not great. In most cases only unweighable amounts of the new substances were obtained in it. Specialized techniques had to be developed to identify the traces of the elements by carrying them through a series of reactions with elements which they resembled chemically. This tracer technique has yielded a surprising amount of information as to the chemistry of the new elements, and has made possible the positive identification of substances which are present in amounts too small even to give an X-ray spectrum.

The discovery of uranium fission by Enrico Fermi and L. Szilard at Columbia University opened the way for further advances. This work was done under the cloak of wartime secrecy and led directly to the atomic bomb, but its significance for the discovery of new elements was very great.

Fermi was born in Rome on September 29, 1901. He took his

Enrico Fermi, 1901–1954. Naturalized Italian-American physicist. Professor of physics at Columbia University and the University of Chicago. In 1938 he was awarded the Nobel Prize for Physics in recognition of his work on artificial radioactivity induced by bombardment with neutrons. He found that the effectiveness of neutron bombardment is much greater in presence of water or paraffin and concluded that the neutrons are slowed down by collisions with the hydrogen nuclei in these substances and therefore have a greater probability of disrupting nuclei. The citation accompanying his Congressional Medal for Merit, awarded in 1946, states that he was "the first man in all the world to achieve nuclear chain reaction."

Courtesy Chemical and Engineering News

doctor's degree at the University of Pisa in 1922 and then studied with Max Born at Göttingen and at Leiden. In 1924 he returned to Italy, to the University of Florence, and in 1927 he became professor of theoretical physics at Rome. In 1939 he came to Columbia University and began work on the atomic pile. After the war he was named professor of physics at the University of Chicago. He was awarded the Nobel Prize in Physics in 1938. He died at the height of his career in 1954 (*3*).

The operation of the atomic pile is based on the fact that natural uranium, chiefly the isotope U^{238}, contains some U^{235} which under the impact of neutrons undergoes fission to produce a number of lighter elements and also neutrons. These neutrons can be slowed down in their paths by graphite. If pieces of uranium are distributed in a more or less regular arrangement through a graphite lattice, the slowed neutrons can be captured by the U^{238} and new and higher elements can be formed. The atomic pile is a source of many of these (*4*). Because of the large scale on which the piles were built in the manufacture of the atomic bomb, relatively large supplies of the new substances could be obtained. Thus the cyclotron served as a source in which new elements could first be prepared and identified, and the pile then furnished them in amounts which could be used for detailed study. The combination of these methods has been responsible for striking advances in the last decade.

TECHNETIUM

Following the recognition that two vacant spaces existed in the manganese column of the periodic table, a number of attempts were made to isolate the eka- and dvi-manganese. Various workers believed they had succeeded in isolating eka-manganese, and such names as davyum, illmenium, lucium, and nipponium were suggested (5). None of these claims was confirmed. With the discovery of atomic numbers it was recognized that eka-manganese was number 43. In 1925 Noddack, Tacke, and Berg at the time they described the properties of rhenium (Chapter 30) also claimed to have isolated number 43, which they named masurium. In spite of a great deal of work, and of the isolation of rhenium in large amounts, the existence of masurium was never positively established.

Work on this element was then begun by Emilio Gino Segrè in Italy. Segrè was born at Tivoli, Italy, in 1905. He took his doctorate in Rome in 1928 and remained there until 1935. At that time he was named professor of physics at the Royal University of Palermo, where he remained until 1938. He then came to the Radiation Laboratory of the University of California at Berkeley, where he remained, except for the years from 1943 to 1945, which he spent at Los Alamos. He is now professor of physics at the University of California.

In December, 1936, Ernest Lawrence sent to Segrè and C. Perrier at Palermo a sample of molybdenum which had been bombarded in the cyclotron for several months with a strong deuteron beam. The sample showed considerable radioactivity. Perrier and Segrè found that the activity was not due to niobium, zirconium, or molybdenum, but it did accompany carrier samples of manganese and rhenium, in chemical separations. The active material resembled rhenium more closely in its properties than it did manganese. It could be separated from its carrier only by volatilization in a current of hydrochloric acid (6). Later these investigators found that it could be extracted by boiling the bombarded molybdenum with ammonium hydroxide containing a little hydrogen peroxide (7).

All the preliminary studies on the chemical properties of element 43 were conducted with unweighable amounts of material. Segrè estimated that the amount they used was about 10^{-10} gram (8). In 1940 Segrè and C. S. Wu (9) found element 43 among the fission products of uranium. Much larger amounts were obtained from this source.

In 1947 F. A. Paneth (10) pointed out that there was no justification in considering artificially prepared elements as different from those which occurred naturally. He therefore laid down the rule that the discoverers of such elements had the same right to name them as did the discoverers of any element. Perrier and Segrè at once proposed the name technetium, symbol Tc, for element 43, deriving the name from the Greek word for "artificial" (*11*).

The reaction of formation of technetium by the original process was

$$_{42}Mo^A + {}_1H^2 = {}_{43}Tc^A + {}_0n^1.$$

Subsequently it was prepared by bombardment of molybdneum by neutrons, and of niobium with helium ions, as well as by uranium fission (*5*).

When larger amounts of technetium became available, studies of its chemical properties became easier. Pertechnate salts of tetraphenylarsonic acid were found to be useful for its separation (*12*). At the Oak Ridge Laboratory, weighable amounts were obtained by co-precipitating the pertechnate with tetraphenyl arsonium perchlorate and electrolyzing the homogeneous solution of the mixture in sulfuric acid. The black solid which was deposited was dissolved in a mixture of nitric, perchloric, and sulfuric acids. The technetium was co-distilled with perchloric acid and collected under dilute ammonium hydroxide. Tc_2S_7 was precipitated with hydrogen sulfide and dissolved in ammoniacal hydrogen peroxide. Evaporation to dryness gave a mixture of NH_4TcO_4 and $(NH_4)_2SO_4$ which was reduced by hydrogen to give 0.6 gram of spectroscopically pure technetium metal as a silver gray, spongy mass which tarnished slowly in moist air (*13*). It burned in air to give pure Tc_2O_7. When this was dissolved in water and the solution evaporated, long, red-black, hygroscopic crystals of $Tc_2O_7 \cdot H_2O$, or $HTcO_4$, were formed (*14*).

PROMETHIUM

The properties of the rare earths were so similar, and the various discoveries of new elements in this group so confusing (Chapter 26), that no one could be sure of how many such elements actually existed until Moseley derived the rules for determining atomic numbers. It was then seen that one rare earth remained undiscovered, occupying the place of number 61, between neodymium and samarium. Fractionation of concentrates of these elements from monazite sands by J. A. Harris and B. S. Hopkins in 1926 (*15*) gave a preparation in which they believed they found spectral lines of element 61. They named this "illinium." The announcement was promptly challenged by L. Rolla and L. Fernandes of the Royal University of Florence, who had deposited a sealed packet with the Accademia dei Lincei in 1924. In this they had described a rare earth concentrate which they believed contained element 61. They gave it the name "florentium" (*16*). None of the work of either group was successfully repeated, though many polemics on the subject appeared in the literature in the next few years. Other groups also claimed to have isolated the element, but with no more success than their predecessors. Hopkins himself suggested that the element might be radioactive and short-lived (17).

When the cyclotron bombardment method became available, H. B. Law, M. L. Pool, J. D. Kurbatov, and L. L. Quill at Ohio State University bombarded samples of neodymium and samarium and obtained radioactive preparations which they believed might contain some 61 (18). C. S. Wu and E. Segrè confirmed this (19). F. A. Paneth pointed out that they probably actually had obtained 61 in their mixtures, but the cyclotron method was not sufficiently powerful to give conclusive evidence of its existence (10). Nevertheless, the Ohio State group proposed the name "cyclonium" for the element.

Charles D. Coryell, 1912– . Professor of chemistry at the Massachusetts Institute of Technology. Consultant to the Brookhaven and Oak Ridge National Laboratories of the United States Atomic Energy Commission. The studies of J. A. Marinsky and L. E. Glendenin in his group led to the chemical identification of the missing element 61, which in 1949 was officially named promethium. Dr. Coryell participates actively in the scientific efforts of the Federation of American Scientists and of the United World Federalists toward peace and world stability.

Courtesy Record of Chemical Progress

The final answer came from the atomic pile. J. A. Marinsky, L. E. Glendenin, and C. D. Coryell at the Clinton Laboratories at Oak Ridge (20) obtained a mixture of fission products of uranium which contained isotopes of yttrium and the entire group of rare earths from lanthanum through europium. Using a method of ion-exchange on Amberlite resin worked out by E. R. Tompkins, J. X. Khym, and W. E. Cohn (21) they were able to obtain a mixture of praseodymium, neodymium, and element 61, and to separate the latter by fractional elution from the Amberlite column with 5 per cent ammonium citrate at pH 2.75. Neutron irradiation of neodymium also produced 61.

Since they could find no convincing evidence that 61 had ever been detected in nature, Marinsky and Glendenin, having isolated the element in milligram amounts, claimed its discovery and named it prometheum, symbol Pm, after the Titan in Greek mythology who stole fire from heaven for the use of mankind. The name was suggested to them by Grace Mary Coryell (22). They pointed out that the name not only symbolized the dramatic method of producing the metal by harnessing the energy of nuclear fission, but also warned of the impending danger of punishment by the vulture of war. Their claim was accepted by the International Union of Chemistry in 1949, but the spelling was changed to promethium to make the name conform to those of other metals (23).

One study has been made on the biological effects of promethium. Its injection results in its localization on the surfaces of bones, from which it is removed extremely slowly (24).

ASTATINE

Search for the missing halogen, eka-iodine, was actively pursued for many years. One of the most widely publicized claims for its discovery was that of F. Allison who developed a magneto-optical method by which he believed he had identified the element. He named it "alabamine" (25). The claim was not subsequently verified, and the element was actually found only after use of the cyclotron began.

In 1940 D. R. Corson, K. R. Mackenzie, and E. Segrè at the University of California bombarded bismuth with alpha particles (26, 27). Preliminary tracer studies indicated that they had obtained element 85, which appeared to possess metallic properties. The pressure of war work prevented a continuation of these studies at the time. After the war, the investigators resumed their work, and in 1947 proposed the name astatine, symbol At, for their element. The name comes from the Greek word for "unstable," since this element is the only halogen without stable isotopes (28). The longest lived isotope is At^{210} with a half-life of 8.3 hours and a very high activity.

Tracer studies of the chemical properties showed that astatine was soluble in organic solvents, could be reduced to the -1 state, and had at least two positive oxidation states. These studies were made on solutions of 10^{-11} to 10^{-15} molar astatine (29). The similarity between astatine and iodine was found to be less close than that between technetium and rhenium or that between promethium and the other rare earths (30).

Like iodine, astatine tends to accumulate in the thyroid gland of the living animal (31). The radioactivity of the element thus concentrated seems to cause severe damage to thyroid tissue without affecting the adjacent parathyroid glands. It may therefore be useful in cases of hyperthyroidism (32). Therefore it is important to determine the amount of astatine in living tissue. This can be done by perchloric-nitric acid digestion of the organic matter. No loss of astatine occurs during this digestion. The astatine can then be co-precipitated with metallic tellurium or deposited on silver foil (33). Thus, an element which does not occur in nature, and which can be obtained only in unweighable amounts, may still have important therapeutic uses.

FRANCIUM

As in the case of astatine, many attempts were made to isolate the heaviest alkali metal, eka-cesium. The various names suggested by those who believed that they had isolated the element indicate the amount of work in various countries which was done in this field. These include russium, alcalinium, virginium, and moldavium (34). In no case were these claims confirmed.

The actual discovery was made by Mlle. Marguerite Perey at the Curie Institute in Paris. In 1939 she purified an actinium preparation by removing all the known decay products of this element. In her preparation she observed a rapid rise in beta activity which could not be due to any known substance. She was able to show that, while most of the actinium formed radioactinium, an isotope of thorium, by beta emission, 1.2 ± 0.1 per cent of the disintegration of actinium occurred by alpha emission and gave rise to a new element, which she provisionally called actinium K, symbol AcK (35, 36). This decayed rapidly by beta emission to produce AcX, an isotope of radium, which was also formed by alpha emission from radioactinium. Thus AcK, with its short half-life, had been missed previously because its disintegration gave the same product as that from the more plentiful radioactinium.

Mlle. Perey was able to purify AcK by dissolving an actiniferous lanthanum ore in hydrochloric acid and treating the solution with a slight excess of sodium carbonate to precipitate most of the contaminants, followed by a little barium chloride to remove all AcX. This left a solution containing only AcK and AcC″, an isotope of thallium. The latter disintegrates faster than AcK, but if its chemical removal was desired, it could be precipitated by NH_4HSO_4, tartrates, or chromates. The AcK could then be co-precipitated with cesium perchlorate, or various cesium double salts (37). It was later shown that the element could also be co-precipitated with silicotungstic acid (38) or separated from most of its contaminants by paper chromatography (39).

The properties of this new element left no doubt that it was the missing alkali, eka-cesium, number 87. In 1946 Mlle. Perey suggested that the name actinium K be kept for the naturally occurring isotope which resulted from the decay of actinium, but that element 87 in general be called francium, symbol Fa, from the name of her native France (*34, 40*). The name was accepted, though her suggested symbol was changed to Fr (*41*).

The failure to discover francium earlier is easy to understand when it is remembered that the half-life of the longest lived isotope is only 21 minutes. This gives the element the distinction of being the most unstable to radioactive disintegration of all elements up to number 98 (*38*). It is also noteworthy that this is the only element in the group discussed in this chapter which was not discovered by artificial preparation in the laboratory. Nevertheless, the rarity of actinium in nature is so great that this element is best prepared artificially when its properties or those of its daughter elements are to be studied.

Mlle. Perey has recently shown that when francium is injected into rats, it is found in greatest concentration in the excretory organs, the kidneys, saliva, and liver (*42*). In rats suffering from sarcoma, the francium activity was higher in the tumor tissue than in normal muscular tissue (*43*). Thus the element may eventually have medicinal uses.

THE TRANSURANIUM ELEMENTS

In 1934, Fermi (*44*) found that when uranium was bombarded with neutrons, it showed evidence of neutron capture and the production of

Otto Hahn, 1879– . President of the Max Planck Society for the Promotion of Science. Discoverer with F. Strassmann, in 1938, of the splitting of uranium and of thorium by neutron irradiation into two elements of medium weight. Discoverer of radioactinium, radiothorium, mesothorium, uranium Z, and (with Miss Lise Meitner) protactinium. He has devised radioactive methods for determining the geologic and biologic age of materials. In 1945 he received the Nobel Prize for Chemistry for the year 1944.

Courtesy Chemical and Engineering News

artificial radioactivity. Fermi and his co-workers, knowing that beta emission produces an element of higher atomic number than its parent, expected to find element number 93 among the radioactive products of uranium bombardment. They expected the transuranium elements in general to have properties similar to the elements below them in the periodic table, such as rhenium, osmium, and so on. When they did not find any elements with atomic numbers from 86 to 92 in their products, they believed they had synthesized elements beyond uranium. This view prevailed for several years, but as further experiments were performed, it became less and less probable. In 1939 O. Hahn and F. Strassmann (45) discovered that under these conditions, fission was occurring, and the products of neutron bombardment of uranium were elements of approximately half its atomic number (46).

NEPTUNIUM

Among the fission products of uranium, one unidentified substance remained. O. Hahn, Lise Meitner, and F. Strassmann (47) had found a substance with a half-life of 23 minutes which they considered an isotope U^{235}. In 1940 Edwin McMillan at the University of California in Berkeley, while investigating the properties of this isotope, discovered another substance associated with it which had a half-life of 2.3 days. He at once suspected that this might be the element with atomic number 93. A chemical study of the substance was made by E. Segrè (48). This showed that the substance did not have properties similar to those of rhenium, as was expected of 93. Rather, the substance resembled the rare earths. In spite of this, McMillan did not lose interest in this material.

Edwin M. McMillan was born on September 18, 1907, in Redondo Beach, California. He graduated from the California Institute of Technology in Pasadena and took his doctorate in physics at Princeton University in 1932. He then went to Berkeley as a National Research Fellow and has remained on the faculty there ever since, except for a period of war research from 1940 to 1945. He received the Nobel Prize in Chemistry jointly with Seaborg in 1951 (49, 50).

In the spring of 1940 Philip Abelson came to Berkeley for a short vacation. He had been a graduate student in the Radiation Laboratory at the time when fission was announced, and was now at the Carnegie Institution of Washington, where, unknown to McMillan, he had also begun to work on the 2.3-day substance. When McMillan and Abelson discovered their mutual interest, they decided to work together on the problem (51). They soon established the fact that the substance could exist in a reduced and an oxidized state, with valences of four and six, like uranium, which it resembled also in other respects. Using these properties, McMillan and Abelson were able to demonstrate that they were dealing with the first transuranium element, number 93 (52). McMillan subsequently decided to name it neptunium, symbol Np, since it was the element next to uranium, just as the planet Neptune was next to Uranus (53).

The existence of this element was later confirmed in Germany by K. Starke (54) and by F. Strassmann and O. Hahn (55). At this point in his work, however, McMillan left Berkeley to undertake war research on radar. He turned the investigation of the new element over to his colleague, Glenn T. Seaborg (51).

Seaborg and his co-workers continued the work actively, and sent a number of communications to the *Physical Review* during 1940 and 1941, but these were not published until 1946. The impending war threw a curtain of secrecy over all their program. Discovery of the fission of element 94 (56) had much to do with this. By 1942 the full impact of the Manhattan Project for making atomic bombs was felt and the various workers scattered to laboratories of the project in Chicago, Los Alamos, and elsewhere. They continued to coöperate closely in their investigations, however. Nothing was known to the public of the feverish activities under way in all these institutions. The unknowing even expressed regret that such a promising field of research had been abandoned (57).

After the war security restrictions were gradually lifted, though by no means all the information which was obtained has been released even in 1955. It was learned in 1948 (58) that the first pure compounds of neptunium had been prepared in June and July of 1944. Bombardment of 64 pounds of uranium in the Berkeley cyclotron yielded about two parts of neptunium per billion parts of uranium by weight. In addition the atomic pile was also yielding neptunium by this time. In all, 45 micrograms of Np^{237} were obtained. From this the hydroxide of the lower oxidation state was prepared and ignited to give NpO_2. This was shown by its diffraction pattern to be isomorphous with the dioxides of thorium, uranium, and plutonium, proving the tetravalent state of the element. The oxide was converted to the hexavalent state as sodium neptunium dioxytriacetate. The manipulation of these minute amounts of material required special techniques which will be discussed under plutonium. Neptunium exists in the oxidation states III, IV, V, and VI with a shift in stability toward the lower valences (58, 59). It has been prepared as a silvery metal by heating the trifluoride to 1200° in the presence of barium vapors. The metal is not much affected by air (60).

The neptunium isotope first prepared by McMillan was Np^{239}, but the atomic pile yielded larger amounts of Np^{237} which has a half-life of 2.25×10^6 years and a relatively low specific alpha-particle activity, only about one thousand times that of uranium. This isotope can be handled in an ordinary laboratory without too great difficulty, and Seaborg believes that it may some day be used sparingly in university laboratory courses in qualitative analysis and advanced inorganic chemistry (61).

Neptunium is also interesting because it can be considered the parent of the so-called "missing disintegration series." Th^{232} begins a series in which the masses of all the members can be distinguished by a formula 4n, where n is an integer. U^{238} begins a (4n + 2) series and U^{235} a (4n + 3) series. There is no natural (4n + 1) series, but Np^{237} supplies this gap (62).

This element has not been found in any naturally occurring mineral but Seaborg believes it may exist in minute amounts as the result of neutron bombardment in uranium ores (63). Neptunium is not absorbed from the digestive tract of animals, but when it is injected it tends to accumulate in the bones. Subsequent loss from this site is very slow (64, 65).

PLUTONIUM

When McMillan left Berkeley in November 1940 he turned over his transuranium studies to Seaborg. Glenn Theodore Seaborg was born on April 19, 1912, at Ishpeming, Michigan. When he was ten his family moved to Los Angeles, where he attended school and graduated in 1934 from the University of California at Los Angeles. He then went to the Berkeley campus of the University, where he received his doctorate in 1937 with a thesis on the inelastic scattering of fast neutrons. He joined the faculty at Berkeley in 1939. From 1942 to 1946 he was chief of the section on transuranium elements at the Manhattan Project Metallurgical Laboratory at the University of Chicago. In 1946 he returned to Berkeley and has since carried on his work there. He and McMillan shared the 1951 Nobel Prize in Chemistry (50, 66).

McMillan had been sure that another element was present in his neptunium fractions. In December, 1940, Seaborg, A. C. Wahl, and J. W. Kennedy separated from neptunium a fraction which had alpha activity and which showed at least two oxidation states. It required stronger oxidizing agents to oxidize this substance than were needed for neptunium. The new element was identified as 94. The notes reporting this discovery were submitted to the journals early in 1941, but were not published until 1946 (67, 68).

The isotope first isolated resulted from beta emission by Np^{238}. In the spring of 1941 Seaborg's group isolated a new isotope, prepared by neutron bombardment of U^{238}. The series of reactions was:

Courtesy Chemical and Engineering News

G. T. Seaborg and E. M. McMillan. The Nobel Prize for Chemistry for 1951 was awarded jointly to Glenn T. Seaborg and Edwin M. McMillan, both of the University of California, for "their discoveries in the chemistry of the transuranium elements." Dr. Seaborg is chairman of the Division of Physical and Inorganic Chemistry at the University of California. Dr. McMillan worked at the Massachusetts Institute of Technology in connection with radar development, collaborated with J. Robert Oppenheimer in organizing the Los Alamos Scientific Laboratory, and did the initial work that led to the discovery of elements heavier than uranium.

$$\beta-$$
$$U^{238} + n \rightarrow U^{239} \xrightarrow{\quad\quad} Np^{239} \rightarrow Pu^{239}$$

decay

This isotope had a half-life of about 24,000 years. It proved to be fissionable (56) and was the basis for the plutonium atomic bomb. Concentrated work on the new element was now begun by the Manhattan Project. The main work was done at Chicago. At this time it became desirable to have names for the elements which had previously been called simply 93 and 94 by the men who worked with them. The name suggested by McMillan, neptunium, was therefore adopted for 93, and by analogy 94 was named plutonium from the planet Pluto, next beyond Neptune in the solar system (53, 69).

It is interesting that this name, plutonium, had once before been suggested for an element. About 1817 Edward Daniel Clarke (1769–1822), professor of mineralogy at Cambridge University, suggested that this name be used instead of barium, since barium metal was not unusually heavy. He suggested this name because barium, isolated by electrolysis, "owed its existence to the dominion of fire" (70).

All the early work on plutonium was done with unweighable amounts on a tracer scale. When it became apparent that large amounts would be needed for the atomic bomb, it was necessary to have a more detailed knowledge of the chemical properties of this element. Intensive bombardment of hundreds of pounds of uranium was therefore begun in the cyclotrons at Berkeley and at Washington University in St. Louis. Separation of plutonium from neptunium was based on the fact that neptunium is oxidized by bromate while plutonium is not, and that reduced fluorides of the two metals are carried down by precipitation of rare earth fluorides, while the fluorides of the oxidized states of the two elements are not. Therefore a separation results by repeated bromate oxidations and precipitations with rare earth fluorides.

This work was carried on by B. B. Cunningham and L. B. Werner. On August 18, 1942, they isolated about one microgram of a pure compound. This was the first sight of a synthetic element and the first case of the isolation of a weighable amount of an artificially produced isotope (71, 59, 69). In September, 30 micrograms of the element were obtained and the iodate, hydroxide, peroxide, and ammonium plutonium fluoride were prepared in a pure state.

The work had now progressed from the tracer to the microgram stage. Normally, this stage could have lasted for many years. At this time, however, plans were being made for the construction of a plant to produce plutonium on a large scale, and it was necessary to know the behavior of plutonium compounds in the concentrations which would be used in the plant. This problem was brilliantly solved by the use of ultramicrochemical methods. The apparatus used was so small that all operations had to be carried out on the stage of a microscope. Actual chemical reactions were conducted with micrograms of material in solutions with volumes on the order of 10^{-1} to 10^{-5} ml. They soon revealed much of the chemistry of plutonium (4, 71, 72). The information obtained in this way made possible the almost simultaneous construction of the plutonium plant at Hanford, Washington, a step up of 10^{10}-fold, "surely the greatest scale up factor ever attempted," as Seaborg later said (72). Yet this scale up was entirely successful. After large amounts of plutonium became available, ordinary chemical methods could be used, but because of the extreme radioactivity of the element, there was the further complication of having to perform all manipulations at a distance and behind shielded walls. Many further remarkable devices were designed to overcome these difficulties. Radiochemistry has become a highly specialized field.

The chemistry of plutonium is now well known. It has valence states of III, IV, V, and VI and many of its compounds have been prepared

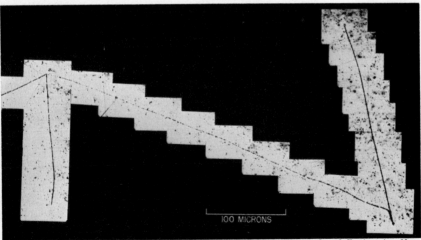

100 MICRONS

Courtesy Chemical and Engineering News

A nuclear agent caused by 270-Mev protons accelerated in the 184-inch cyclotron at the Radiation Laboratory, University of California. A neutron (leaving no trail because it carries no electrical charge) strikes an emulsion atom at upper left, producing a negative heavy meson and two heavier particles, probably protons. The meson moves to the right, stopping in another emulsion atom and giving up its energy by knocking out another heavy particle, probably an alpha particle.

(59, 73). The lower oxidation states are more stable than those of neptunium (59). Much that is known has not been disclosed, but the information is slowly emerging. Thus, only in 1954 was it revealed that the metallurgists at Los Alamos in 1945 knew that plutonium metal had the unique property of possessing at least five allotropic modifications at atmospheric pressure (74).

Plutonium is the only transuranium element which has been found in nature. Until its properties were known it would have been impossible to detect it in the minute amounts in which it occurs, but when its behavior was understood, Seaborg and his co-workers were able to find it in pitchblende, monazite ores, and carnotite in concentrations of about one part in 10^{14} (63, 75, 76). Peppard and his group found it in somewhat greater amounts in pitchblende from the Belgian Congo (77). Seaborg believes that most of this plutonium arises by fission of the uranium in the ore, though other processes may also be involved (77, 78).

Plutonium is not readily absorbed from the animal intestine (65), though on long continued low-level feeding some is taken up (79). There is some absorption through the lungs, and when it enters the body by this path or by injection, it localizes in the bones (64, 65). It is probably more toxic than radium under these conditions (65). It is not actually incorporated into the mineralized matter of the bone as is radium, but seems to concentrate in the cartilaginous portion (24).

AMERICIUM AND CURIUM

One of the characteristics of the production of new radioactive elements is that each new one which is found at once opens the possibility of advancing one place in the periodic table if beta emission occurs. Thus there is always a higher element to beckon the investigator on. Added to this is the fact that each of the radioactive elements has a large number of isotopes, and that there are various types of particles with which these isotopes can be bombarded. Besides neutrons, deuterons, and helium ions which have been mostly used up to the present, the future holds promise of the use of still larger particles such as ions of oxygen or nitrogen. Thus the number of possible transuranium elements is limited only by their own stability and by the possibility of their chemical or physical identification.

Since this is so, it was inevitable that as soon as Seaborg and his collaborators had clearly established the identity and properties of neptunium and plutonium, they would look for the next higher elements, numbers 95 and 96. The general similarity in chemical properties of uranium, neptunium, and plutonium led Seaborg to believe that these new elements could be isolated by methods similar to those already used.

In the summer of 1944, Seaborg realized that in the transuranium elements he was dealing with a group resembling the rare earths. The higher transuranium elements should have properties similar to the heavier rare earths. Thus the predominant valence should be three. When these ideas were applied element 96 was found almost at once in a sample of Pu^{239} which had been bombarded with helium ions in the Berkeley cyclotron. In the late fall of 1944 element 95 was found as a result of neutron bombardment of Pu^{239}. For nearly a year, however, attempts at chemical separation and identification failed. During this period the elements remained unnamed, though Seaborg reports that one disgusted member of his group insisted on referring to them as "pandemonium" and "delirium" (69). Since these elements resemble the rare earths so closely, they can best be separated by the very efficient method of adsorption on cation exchange resins and selective elution with suitable solvents. This method, which has replaced the old, tedious fractional crystallizations of the salts, has made the rare earth chemistry much clearer than it has ever been. It will be recalled that promethium was isolated by this procedure. The similarity of the transuranium elements to the rare earths extends to this process also, and it is so accurate that the conditions for the elution of a given substance can be predicted in advance and can be used as evidence in identifications (80).

The first pure compound of element 95 was obtained by B. B. Cunningham in the fall of 1945, and the first of 96 by L. B. Werner and I. Perlman at Berkeley in the fall of 1947 (69). The elements were named by analogy with the corresponding rare earths. Number 95, the analogue of europium, was named americium, symbol Am, and number 96, the analogue of gadolinium which was named for the famous investigator of rare earths Johan Gadolin, was named for the investigators of radioactivity, the Curies. It was called curium, symbol Cm. Chemical studies of these elements have been difficult because of their intense radioactivity. Curium is so active that solutions of its salts decompose water (61, 81). Nevertheless, many compounds have been prepared, and the pure metals have been obtained by reduction of the trifluorides with barium vapors at 1100–1300° in a vacuum. Americium is a silvery, very malleable and ductile metal with a very low density, a property also possessed by europium. It tarnishes in air and forms a hydride with hydrogen (82). Curium is a silvery metal, almost as malleable as plutonium, but more reactive than either plutonium or americium, since it tarnishes even in dry nitrogen (83).

Americium and curium injected into animals are distributed to the extent of about 25 per cent in bone, but unlike neptunium and plutonium, about 70 per cent of the injected dose is found in the liver. Loss from the latter organ occurs fairly soon (64). The part of the americium that enters bone is deposited on the surfaces, like promethium and plutonium (24).

THE ACTINIDE SERIES

A hypothesis which has been of the greatest value in isolating and identifying the transuranium elements was set forth by Seaborg in 1944 and has been described frequently since (69). This is based on the analogy of the transuraniums with the rare earths. The latter group begins with lanthanum, and may be considered a group of lanthanides. The analogue of lanthanum is actinium, and so the transuranium elements can be considered to belong to an actinide group. The similarity in chemical properties of the members of the lanthanides depends upon the fact that in them the 4d electron shell is being progressively filled as the series advances. In the actinides it is the 5f shell which is filling. The lanthanides end with lutetium, number 71. The actinides should end with element 103. The actinide theory has served as a valuable guide in separating the members of this series (84, 85). Some chemists have questioned it on chemical grounds, since the properties of the first members of the series up to plutonium seem to differ greatly from the characteristic trivalent compounds of the lanthanides (86, 87, 88). This appears to be a somewhat formal distinction, however.

BERKELIUM AND CALIFORNIUM

Continuation of the study of the radioactive elements produced by cyclotron bombardment of lower elements led in 1950 to isolation by tracer techniques of numbers 97 and 98. Bombardment of Am^{241} with helium ions by S. G. Thompson, A. Ghiorso, and G. T. Seaborg produced 97^{243} which resembled its analogue, terbium, in its elution from ion-exchange resins. Since terbium was named from the city of Ytterby, 97 was named from the city in which so many new elements had been discovered, Berkeley, and the name berkelium and symbol Bk have been accepted (89, 90).

Helium ion bombardment of Cm^{242} by S. G. Thompson, K. Street, Jr., A. Ghiorso, and G. T. Seaborg produced 98^{244}. At this point naming by analogy with the rare earths broke down, since no good analogy with the name dysprosium was available. The discoverers therefore chose to honor the university and state in which the discovery was made, and the name californium, symbol Cf, was chosen. The discoverers remarked, however, that "the best we can do is to point out, in recognition of the fact that dysprosium is named on the basis of a Greek word meaning 'difficult to get at,' that the searchers for another element a century ago found it difficult to get to California" (91). Only a few thousand atoms of californium were isolated in any of the experiments on this element (92). Tracer experiments have indicated a predominant trivalent state for both berkelium and californium, with evidence for a tetravalent state in the former and less clear evidence for this state in the latter (93, 94).

Courtesy Chemical and Engineering News

University of California Bevatron. A section of the giant Bevatron financed by the Atomic Energy Commission at the University of California Radiation Laboratory, Berkeley. At far right is the Cockroft-Walton, which starts particles on their 300,000 mile journey through the machine. The large tube-shaped instrument at right center is the linear accelerator, which boosts particles to 10 million electron volts. At left is the giant Bevatron magnet in which particles are accelerated to cosmic ray energies.

Shortly after the announcement of the naming of berkelium A. P. Znoiko in Russia, who had made earlier predictions of the properties of element 97, suggested that Mendeleev should be honored by giving his name to this element, calling it mendelevium (95). The name berkelium had already been adopted, but, as will be seen, at the first opportunity the Berkeley group did honor the father of the periodic table.

EINSTEINIUM, FERMIUM, AND MENDELEVIUM

Still the search continued. In 1954 several laboratories reported the isolation and study of elements 99 and 100. A group at Berkeley gave some details of the discovery of 99 (96), and soon afterwards of 100 (97). Only minute amounts of these substances were obtained, but the elution sequences on ion-exchange resins served to identify them. Physical properties were reported from both Berkeley (98) and the Argonne Laboratories at Arco, Idaho (99). The authors of all these papers added notes to their reports stating that unpublished information still remained, and that no attempt should be made to prejudge questions of priority of discovery on the basis of the published papers.

The reason for these cautions became apparent when more details could be given. In the summer of 1955 it was revealed that these elements had actually been discovered among the substances produced in uranium which had been subjected to a very high instantaneous neutron flux in the thermonuclear explosion of November, 1952. Groups at the University of California, the Argonne Laboratories, and the Los Alamos Laboratories had worked simultaneously on the identification of the new elements and had established their existence and elution properties. Later intense neutron irradiation of Pu^{239} confirmed their results. Until the secrecy surrounding the thermonuclear explosion was lifted, only guarded reports of this work could be given. With fuller details the investigators suggested the names einsteinium (symbol E) for element 99 and fermium (symbol Fm) for element 100. Thus the fundamental studies of Albert Einstein and Enrico Fermi will be perpetuated (102).

The complexity of the reactions involved in the bombardment of plutonium and the production of higher transuranium elements can be seen from the following scheme which indicates the method of synthesis of einsteinium and fermium:

$$Pu^{239} + 2n \rightarrow Pu^{241} \xrightarrow[\text{decay}]{\beta^-} Am^{241} + n \rightarrow Am^{242} \xrightarrow[\text{decay}]{\beta^-} Cm^{242}$$

$$Cm^{242} + 7n \rightarrow Cm^{249} \xrightarrow[\text{decay}]{\beta^-} Bk^{249} + n \rightarrow Bk^{250} \xrightarrow[\text{decay}]{\beta^-} Cf^{250}$$

$$Cf^{250} + 3n \rightarrow Cf^{253} \xrightarrow[\text{decay}]{\beta^-} E^{253} + n \rightarrow E^{254} \xrightarrow[\text{decay}]{\beta^-} Fm^{254} \ (100)$$

In 1955 the next step was announced. Very intense helium ion bombardment of tiny targets of E^{253} produced a few spontaneously fissionable atoms which eluted from ion-exchange resins in the eka-thulium position. This was evidence that element 101 had been found. Only seventeen atoms of this element were produced. It showed a half-life of between one-half and several hours. The name mendelevium (symbol

Mv) was proposed by the discoverers, A. Ghiorso, B. G. Harvey, G. R. Choppin, S. G. Thompson, and G. T. Seaborg, in honor of the basic ideas of D. I. Mendeleev on which have depended all discoveries of elements since his day (*100, 101*).

The coöperation of Mr. James M. Crowe, Executive Editor of *Chemical and Engineering News*, in procuring illustrations for this chapter is gratefully acknowledged.

LITERATURE CITED

(1) BIRGE, R. T., "Presentation of the Nobel Prize in Physics," *Science*, **91**, 323–9 (1940).

(2) LAWRENCE, E. O., "The Evolution of the Cyclotron," Les Prix Nobel en 1951, Imprimerie Royale, Stockholm, **1952**, pp. 127–40.

(3) HEATHCOTE, N. H. DE V., "Enrico Fermi," Nobel Prize Winners in Physics, 1901–1950, Henry Schuman, New York, **1953**, p. 369.

(4) SEABORG, G. T., "The heavy elements," *Chem. Eng. News*, **24**, 1193–8 (1946).

(5) HACKNEY, J. C., "Technetium—element 43," *J. Chem. Educ.*, **28**, 186–90 (1951).

(6) PERRIER, C. and E. SEGRÈ, "Some chemical properties of element 43," *J. Chem. Phys.*, **5**, 712–16 (1937).

(7) PERRIER, C. and E. SEGRÈ, "Chemical properties of element 43. II," *ibid.*, **7**, 155–6 (1939).

(8) SEGRÈ, E., "Element 43," *Nature*, **143**, 460–1 (1939).

(9) SEGRÈ, E. and C. S. WU, "Some fission products of uranium," *Phys. Rev.*, **57**, 552 (1940).

(10) PANETH, F. A., "The making of the missing chemical elements," *Nature*, **159**, 8–10 (1947).

(11) PERRIER, C. and E. SEGRÈ, "Technetium: element of atomic number 43," *Nature*, **159**, 24 (1947).

(12) TRIBALAT, S. and J. BEYDON, "Isolement du technétium," *Anal. Chim. Acta* **6**, 96–7 (1952).

(13) COBBLE, J. W., C. M. NELSON, G. W. PARKER, W. T. SMITH, JR., and G. E. BOYD, "Chemistry of technetium. II. Preparation of technetium metal," *J. Am. Chem. Soc.*, **74**, 1852 (1952).

(14) BOYD, G. E., J. W. COBBLE, C. M. NELSON, and W. T. SMITH, JR., "Chemistry of technetium. I. Preparation of technetium heptoxide," *J. Am. Chem. Soc.*, **74**, 556–7 (1952).

(15) HARRIS, J. A. and B. S. HOPKINS, "Element 61. Isolation," *J. Am. Chem. Soc.*, **48**, 1585–94 (1926).

(16) ROLLA, L. and L. FERNANDES, "Ricerche sopra l'elemento a numero atomico 61. Nota I," *Gazz. chim. ital.*, **56**, 435–6 (1926).

(17) GOULD, R. F., "The naming of element 61," *Chem. Eng. News*, **25**, 2555–6 (1947).

(18) LAW, H. B., M. L. POOL, J. D. KURBATOV, and L. L. QUILL, "Radioactive isotopes of Nd, Il, and Sm," *Phys. Rev.* **59**, 936 (1941).

(19) WU, C. S. and E. SEGRÈ, "Artificial radioactivity of some rare earths," *Phys. Rev.* **61**, 203 (1942).

(20) MARINSKY, J. A., L. E. GLENDENIN, and C. D. CORYELL, "The chemical identification of radioisotopes of neodymium and element 61," *J. Am. Chem. Soc.*, **69**, 2781–5 (1947).

(21) TOMPKINS, E. R., J. X. KHYM, and W. E. COHN, "Ion exchange as a separation method. I. The separation of fission-produced radioisotopes, including individual rare earths, by complex elution from Amberlite resins," *J. Am. Chem. Soc.*, **69**, 2769–77 (1947).

(22)   MARINSKY, J. A. and L. E. GLENDENIN, "A proposal of the name prometheum for element 61," *Chem. Eng. News*, **26**, 2346–8 (1948).

(23)   "Names of new elements confirmed by International Union of Chemistry," *Chem. Eng. News*, **27**, 2990 (1949).

(24)   ASLING, C. W., J. G. HAMILTON, D. AXELROD-HELLER, and B. J. LOUIE, "The localization of certain alkaline and rare earth elements in the costochondral junction of the rat," *Anat. Rec.*, **113**, 285–300 (1952).

(25)   ALLISON, F., E. J. MURPHY, E. R. BISHOP, and A. L. SOMMER, "Evidence of the detection of element 85 in certain substances," *Phys. Rev.* **37**, 1178–80 (1931).

(26)   CORSON, D. R., K. R. MACKENZIE, and E. SEGRÈ, "Possible production of radioactive isotopes of element 85," *Phys. Rev.* **57**, 459 (1940).

(27)   SEGRÈ, E., K. R. MACKENZIE, and D. R. CORSON, "Some chemical properties of element 85," *Phys. Rev.*, **57**, 1087 (1940); **58**, 672–8 (1940).

(28)   CORSON, D. R., K. R. MACKENZIE, and E. SEGRÈ, "Astatine: element of atomic number 85," *Nature*, **159**, 24 (1947).

(29)   JOHNSON, G. L., R. F. LEININGER, and E. SEGRÈ, "Chemical properties of astatine. I," *J. Chem. Phys.*, **17**, 1–10 (1949).

(30)   ATEN, A. H. W., JR., T. DOORGEEST, U. HOLLSTEM, and H. P. MOLKEN, "Analytical chemistry of astatine," *Analyst*, **77**, 774–8 (1952).

(31)   HAMILTON, J. G. and M. H. SOLEY, "Comparison of the metabolism of iodine and of element 85 (eka-iodine)," *Proc. Natl. Acad. Sci.*, **26**, 483–9 (1940).

(32)   HAMILTON, J. G., C. W. ASLING, W. M. GARRISON, K. G. SCOTT, and D. AXELROD-HELLER, "Destructive action of astatine[211] (element 85) on the thyroid gland of the rat," *Proc. Soc. Exptl. Biol. Med.*, **73**, 51–3 (1950).

(33)   GARRISON, W. M., J. D. GILE, R. D. MAXWELL, and J. G. HAMILTON, "Procedure for radiochemical determination of astatine in biological material," *Anal. Chem.*, **23**, 204–5 (1951).

(34)   PEREY, M., "L'élément 87," *J. chim. phys.*, **43**, 155–68 (1946).

(35)   PEREY, M., "Sur un élément 87, dérivé de l'actinium," *Compt. rend.*, **208**, 97–9 (1939).

(36)   PEREY, M., "Propriétés physiques de l'élément 87: actinium K et son emploi dans le dosage de l'actinium," *J. chim. phys.*, **43**, 269–78 (1946).

(37)   PEREY, M., "Propriétés chimiques de l'élément 87: actinium K," *ibid.*, **43**, 262–8 (1946).

(38)   HYDE, E. K., "Radiochemical methods for the isolation of element 87 (francium)," *J. Am. Chem. Soc.*, **74**, 4181–4 (1952).

(39)   PEREY, M. and J. P. ADLOFF, "Séparation chromatographique du francium," *Compt. rend.*, **236**, 1163–5 (1953).

(40)   PEREY, M., "Le francium: élément 87," *Bull. soc. chim. France*, **1951**, 779–85.

(41)   CRANE, E. J., "Names of elements recommended by IUPAC," *Chem. Eng. News*, **27**, 3779 (1949).

(42)   PEREY, M. and A. CHEVALLIER, "Sur la répartition de l'élément 87: francium dans les tissus du rat normal," *Compt. rend. soc. biol.*, **145**, 1205–7 (1951).

(43)   PEREY, M. and A. CHEVALLIER, "Sur la fixation de l'élément 87: francium dans le sarcome expérimental du rat," *ibid.*, **145**, 1208–11 (1951).

(44)   FERMI, E., "Radioactivity induced by neutron bombardment," *Nature*, **133**, 757 (1934).

(45)   HAHN, O. and F. STRASSMANN, "Zur Frage nach der Existenz der 'Trans-Urane.' I. Endgültige Streichung von Eka-platin und Eka-iridium," *Naturwiss.*, **27**, 451–3 (1939).

(46)   SEABORG, G. T. and E. SEGRÈ, "Transuranium elements," *Nature*, **159**, 863–5 (1947).

(47)   HAHN, O., L. MEITNER, and F. STRASSMANN, "Neue Umwandlungs-Prozesse bei Neutronen-Bestrahlung des Urans; Elemente jenseits Uran," *Ber.*, **69**, 905–19 (1936).

(48) SEGRÈ, F., "An unsuccessful search for transuranium elements," *Phys. Rev.* **55**, 1104–5 (1939).

(49) "Edwin M. McMillan," Les Prix Nobel en 1951, Imprimerie Royale, Stockholm, **1952**, p. 91.

(50) "Nobel Prize awarded to Seaborg and McMillan," *Chem. Eng. News*, **30**, 238 (1952).

(51) McMILLAN, E. M., "The trans-uranium elements; early history," Les Prix Nobel en 1951, Imprimerie Royale, Stockholm, **1952**, pp. 165–73.

(52) McMILLAN, E. M. and P. ABELSON, "Radioactive element 93," *Phys. Rev.*, **57**, 1185–6 (1940).

(53) SEABORG, G. T., and A. C. WAHL, "The chemical properties of elements 94 and 93," *J. Am. Chem. Soc.*, **70**, 1128–34 (1948).

(54) STARKE, K., "Abtrennung des elements 93," *Naturwiss.*, **30**, 107 (1942).

(55) STRASSMANN, F. and O. HAHN, "Über die Isolierung und einige Eigenschaften des Elements 93," *Naturwiss.*, **30**, 256–60 (1942).

(56) KENNEDY, J. W., G. T. SEABORG, E. SEGRÈ, and A. C. WAHL, "Properties of 94^{239}," *Phys. Rev.*, **70**, 555–6 (1946). (Article originally received May 29, 1941.)

(57) FOSTER, L. S., "Synthesis of the new elements neptunium and plutonium," *J. Chem. Educ.*, **22**, 619–23 (1945).

(58) MAGNUSSON, L. B. and T. J. LaCHAPELLE, "The first isolation of element 93 in pure compounds and a determination of the half life of $_{93}Np^{237}$," *J. Am. Chem. Soc.*, **70**, 3534–8 (1948).

(59) SEABORG, G. T., "The chemical and radioactive properties of the heavy elements," *Chem. Eng. News*, **23**, 2190–3 (1945).

(60) HULL, W. Q., "The transuranium elements," *Chem. Eng. News*, **30**, 232–7 (1952).

(61) SEABORG, G. T., "Plutonium and the other transuranium elements," *Chem. Eng. News*, **25**, 358–60 (1947).

(62) "Seaborg tells of isotope synthesis at Nichols Medal award," *Chem. Eng. News*, **26**, 740–1 (1948).

(63) LEVINE, C. A. and G. T. SEABORG, "Occurrence of plutonium in nature," *J. Am. Chem. Soc.*, **73**, 3278–83 (1951).

(64) HAMILTON, J. G., "The metabolism of the fission products and the heaviest elements," *Radiology*, **49**, 325–43 (1947).

(65) HAMILTON, J. G., "Metabolism of radioactive elements created by nuclear fission," *New Engl. J. Med.*, **240**, 863–70 (1949).

(66) "Glenn Theodore Seaborg," Les Prix Nobel en 1951, Imprimerie Royale, Stockholm, **1952**, pp. 89–90.

(67) SEABORG, G. T., E. M. McMILLAN, J. W. KENNEDY, and A. C. WAHL, "Radioactive element 94 from deuterons on uranium," *Phys. Rev.*, **69**, 366–7 (1946). (Article originally received Jan. 28, 1941.)

(68) SEABORG, G. T., A. C. WAHL, and J. W. KENNEDY, "A new element: radioactive element 94 from deuterons on uranium," *Phys. Rev.*, **69**, 367 (1946). (Article originally received March 7, 1941.)

(69) SEABORG, G. T., "The transuranium elements: present status," Les Prix Nobel en 1951, Imprimerie Royale, Stockholm, **1952**, pp. 141–64.

(70) WEBB, K. R., "Naming the elements: a former suggested use of 'plutonium,'" *Nature*, **160**, 164 (1947).

(71) CUNNINGHAM, B. B. and L. B. WERNER, "The first isolation of plutonium," *J. Am. Chem. Soc.*, **71**, 1521–8 (1949).

(72) SEABORG, G. T., "The transuranium elements," *Science*, **104**, 379–86 (1946).

(73) HARVEY, B. G., H. G. HEAL, A. C. MADDOCK, and E. L. ROWLEY, "The chemistry of plutonium," *J. Chem. Soc.*, **1947**, 1010–21.

(74) SMITH, C. S., "Properties of plutonium metal," *Phys. Rev.*, **94**, 1068–9 (1954).

(75) SEABORG, G. T. and M. L. PERLMAN, "Search for elements 94 and 93 in nature. Presence of 94^{239} in pitchblende," *J. Am. Chem. Soc.*, **70**, 1571–3 (1948).

(76) GARNER, C. S., N. A. BONNER, and G. T. SEABORG, "Search for elements 94 and 93 in nature. Presence of 94²³⁹ in carnotite," *J. Am. Chem. Soc.*, **70**, 3453–4 (1948).

(77) PEPPARD, D. F., M. H. STUDIER, M. W. GERGEL, G. W. MASON, J. C. SULLIVAN, and J. F. MECH, "Isolation of microgram quantities of naturally occurring plutonium and examination of its isotopic composition," *J. Am. Chem. Soc.*, **73**, 2529–31 (1951).

(78) CORVALEN, M. I., "Concentration of plutonium in pitchblende," *Phys. Rev.*, **71**, 132 (1947).

(79) KATZ, J., H. A. KORNBERG, and H. M. PARKER, "Absorption of plutonium fed chronically to rats," *Am. J. Roentgenol., Radium Therapy, Nuclear Med.*, **73**, 303–8 (1955).

(80) STREET, K., JR. and G. T. SEABORG, "The separation of americium and curium from the rare earth elements," *J. Am. Chem. Soc.*, **72**, 2790–2 (1950).

(81) SEABORG, G. T., "Plutonium and other transuranium elements," *Chem. Eng. News*, **24**, 3160–1 (1946).

(82) WESTRUM, C. F., JR. and L. EYRING, "The preparation and some properties of americium metal," *J. Am. Chem. Soc.*, **73**, 3396–8 (1951).

(83) WALLMANN, J. C., W. W. T. CRANE, and B. B. CUNNINGHAM, "The preparation and some properties of curium metal," *J. Am. Chem. Soc.*, **73**, 493–4 (1951).

(84) PEPPARD, D. F., P. R. GRAY, and M. M. MARKUS, "The actinide-lanthanide analogy as exemplified by solvent extraction," *J. Am. Chem. Soc.*, **75**, 6063–4 (1953).

(85) EMELIUS, H. J., "Transuranium and other newly discovered elements," *Science Progr.*, **38**, 609–21 (1950).

(86) PANETH, F. A., "The making of the elements 97 and 98," *Nature*, **165**, 748–9 (1950).

(87) HAÏSSINSKY, M., "The position of the cis- and trans-uranic elements in the periodic system: uranides or actinides?" *J. Chem. Soc.*, **1949**, S 241–3.

(88) HAÏSSINSKY, M., "La place des éléments transuraniens dans le système périodique," *Experientia*, **9**, 117–20 (1953).

(89) THOMPSON, S. G., A. GHIORSO, and G. T. SEABORG, "Element 97," *Phys. Rev.*, **77**, 838–9 (1950).

(90) THOMPSON, S. G., A. GHIORSO, and G. T. SEABORG, "The new element berkelium (atomic number 97)," *ibid.*, **80**, 781–9 (1950).

(91) THOMPSON, S. G., K. STREET, JR., A. GHIORSO, and G. T. SEABORG, "Element 98," *Phys. Rev.*, **78**, 298–9 (1950).

(92) THOMPSON, S. G., K. STREET, JR., A. GHIORSO, and G. T. SEABORG, "The new element californium (atomic number 98)," *ibid.*, **80**, 790–6 (1950).

(93) THOMPSON, S. G., B. B. CUNNINGHAM, and G. T. SEABORG, "Chemical properties of berkelium," *J. Am. Chem. Soc.*, **72**, 2798–801 (1950).

(94) STREET, K., JR., S. G. THOMPSON, and G. T. SEABORG, "Chemical properties of californium," *J. Am. Chem. Soc.*, **72**, 4832–5 (1950).

(95) ZNOIKO, A. P. and V. I. SEMISHIM, "The problem of elements numbered 97 and 98" (in Russian), *Doklady Akad. Nauk S.S.S.R.*, **74**, 917–19 (1950).

(96) THOMPSON, S. G., A. GHIORSO, B. G. HARVEY, and G. R. CHOPPIN, "Transcurium isotopes produced in the neutron irradiation of plutonium," *Phys. Rev.*, **93**, 908 (1954).

(97) HARVEY, B. G., S. G. THOMPSON, A. GHIORSO, and G. R. CHOPPIN, "Further production of transcurium nuclides by neutron irradiation," *Phys. Rev.*, **93**, 1129 (1954).

(98) CHOPPIN, G. R., S. G. THOMPSON, A. GHIORSO, and B. G. HARVEY, "Nuclear properties of some isotopes of californium, elements 99 and 100," *Phys. Rev.*, **94**, 1080–1 (1954).

(99)   STUDIER, M. H., P. R. FIELDS, H. DIAMOND, J. F. MECH, A. M. FRIEDMAN, P. A. SELLERS, G. PILE, C. M. STEVENS, L. B. MAGNUSSON, and J. R. HUIZENGA, "Elements 99 and 100 from pile-irradiated plutonium," *Phys. Rev.*, **93**, 1428 (1954).

(100) "99, 100, and now 17 atoms of 101," *Chem. Eng. News*, **33**, 1956–7 (1955).

(101) GHIORSO, A., B. G. HARVEY, G. R. CHOPPIN, S. G. THOMPSON, and G. T. SEABORG, "New element mendelevium, atomic number 101," *Phys. Rev.*, **98**, 1518–19 (1955).

(102) GHIORSO, A., S. G. THOMPSON, G. H. HIGGINS, G. T. SEABORG, M. H. STUDIER, P. R. FIELDS, S. M. FRIED, H. DIAMOND, J. F. MECH, G. L. PYLE, J. R. HUIZENGA, A. HIRSCH, W. M. MANNING, C. I. BROWNE, H. L. SMITH, and R. W. SPENCE, "New elements einsteinium and fermium, atomic numbers 99 and 100," *Phys. Rev.*, **99**, 1048–9 (1955).

A list of the chemical elements

Atomic No.	Name	Symbol	1955 Atomic Wt.
0	neutron	n	
1	hydrogen	H	1.0080
2	helium	He	4.003
3	lithium	Li	6.940
4	beryllium	Be	9.013
5	boron	B	10.82
6	carbon	C	12.011
7	nitrogen	N	14.008
8	oxygen	O	16.0000
9	fluorine	F	19.00
10	neon	Ne	20.183
11	sodium	Na	22.991
12	magnesium	Mg	24.32
13	aluminum	Al	26.98
14	silicon	Si	28.09
15	phosphorus	P	30.975
16	sulfur	S	32.066±0.003
17	chlorine	Cl	35.457
18	argon	A	39.944
19	potassium	K	39.100
20	calcium	Ca	40.08
21	scandium	Sc	44.96
22	titanium	Ti	47.90
23	vanadium	V	50.95
24	chromium	Cr	52.01
25	manganese	Mn	54.94
26	iron	Fe	55.85
27	cobalt	Co	58.94
28	nickel	Ni	58.71
29	copper	Cu	63.54
30	zinc	Zn	65.38
31	gallium	Ga	69.72
32	germanium	Ge	72.60
33	arsenic	As	74.91
34	selenium	Se	78.96
35	bromine	Br	79.916
36	krypton	Kr	83.80
37	rubidium	Rb	85.48
38	strontium	Sr	87.63
39	yttrium	Y	88.92
40	zirconium	Zr	91.22
41	niobium (columbium)	Nb (Cb)	92.91
42	molybdenum	Mo	95.95
43	technetium	Tc	99*
44	ruthenium	Ru	101.1
45	rhodium	Rh	102.91

* Mass number of the isotope of longest known half-life

Atomic No.	Name	Symbol	1955 Atomic Wt.
46	palladium	Pd	106.4
47	silver	Ag	107.880
48	cadmium	Cd	112.41
49	indium	In	114.82
50	tin	Sn	118.70
51	antimony	Sb	121.76
52	tellurium	Te	127.61
53	iodine	I	126.91
54	xenon	Xe	131.30
55	cesium	Cs	132.91
56	barium	Ba	137.36
57	lanthanum	La	138.92
58	cerium	Ce	140.13
59	praseodymium	Pr	140.92
60	neodymium	Nd	144.27
61	promethium	Pm	145*
62	samarium	Sm	150.35
63	europium	Eu	152.0
64	gadolinium	Gd	157.26
65	terbium	Tb	158.93
66	dysprosium	Dy	162.51
67	holmium	Ho	164.94
68	erbium	Er	167.27
69	thulium	Tm	168.94
70	ytterbium	Yb	173.04
71	lutetium	Lu	174.99
72	hafnium	Hf	178.50
73	tantalum	Ta	180.95
74	tungsten	W	183.86
75	rhenium	Re	186.22
76	osmium	Os	190.2
77	iridium	Ir	192.2
78	platinum	Pt	195.09
79	gold	Au	197.0
80	mercury	Hg	200.61
81	thallium	Tl	204.39
82	lead	Pb	207.21
83	bismuth	Bi	209.00
84	polonium	Po	210
85	astatine	At	210*
86	radon	Rn	222
87	francium	Fr	223*
88	radium	Ra	226.05
89	actinium	Ac	227
90	thorium	Th	232.05
91	protactinium	Pa	231
92	uranium	U	238.07
93	neptunium	Np	237*
94	plutonium	Pu	242*
95	americium	Am	243*
96	curium	Cm	245*
97	berkelium	Bk	249*
98	californium	Cf	249*
99	einsteinium	E	
100	fermium	Fm	
101	mendelevium	Mv	256*

Chronology of element discovery

Sixteenth Century

1524	Hernando Cortés mentions coins made of tin from Taxco that were in use in Mexico.
1541	Francisco Vazquez de Coronado observes a copper ornament worn by an Indian chief, in what is now the southwestern part of the United States.
1570	Pedro Fernándes de Velasco demonstrates his cold amalgamation process for the recovery of silver from the ores of Mount Potosí (Bolivia).
1590	The Chinese encyclopedia of materia medica, the Pen Ts'ao Kan-Mu, describes the uses of arsenic.
1590	Father José de Acosta describes the metallurgy of silver and mercury in the New World.

Seventeenth Century

1602	John Brereton describes the copper artifacts of the Indians of Virginia.
1604	The "Triumphal Chariot of Antimony" by Pseudo-Basilius Valentinus is published.
1604	Birth of J. R. Glauber.
Jan. 25, 1627	Birth of Robert Boyle in Ireland. Independent discoverer of phosphorus.
1630	Birth of Johann Kunckel, early writer on phosphorus.
1637	A Chinese book entitled "Tien kong kai ou" describes the metallurgy and uses of zinc.
1640	Father A. A. Barba of Potosí publishes the first treatise on American metallurgy.
1641	Birth of Dr. John Mayow in London. Author of an early theory of combustion.
Nov. 17, 1645	Birth of Nicolas Lémery at Rouen.
1649	Johann Schroeder describes two methods of preparing metallic arsenic.
1652	Birth of Wilhelm Homberg.
1660	Birth of G. E. Stahl.
1665	Robert Hooke gives a theory of combustion in his book "Micrographia."
1668	Birth of Herman Boerhaave.
1669	The alchemist Brand of Hamburg discovers phosphorus; but see footnote on p. 110.

1670	Heinrich Schwanhard etches glass with a mixture of fluorspar and a concentrated acid.
1670	Death of J. R. Glauber.
1671	Robert Boyle prepares hydrogen ("inflammable solution of Mars") by dissolving iron in dilute hydrochloric or sulfuric acid.
1672	Birth of E.-F. Geoffroy.
1674	Dr. John Mayow recognizes that the air has two constituents.
1677	Birth of Louis Lémery
1679	Death of Dr. Mayow.
1683	Johann Bohn distinguishes between "cubic saltpeter" (sodium nitrate) and ordinary "prismatic saltpeter."
1683	Birth of Caspar Neumann.
1688	Bernard S. Albinus (Weiss) mentions the presence of phosphorus in the ash of mustard and cress.
1691	Death of Robert Boyle.
June 26, or July 21, 1694	Birth of Georg Brandt, the discoverer of cobalt, at Riddarhytta, Vestmanland, Sweden.
1695	Nehemiah Grew publishes a dissertation on Epsom salt.
1700	Nicolas Lémery describes hydrogen.
1700	Birth of H.-L. du Hamel du Monceau.

Eighteenth Century

1701	A posthumous edition of Turquet de Mayerne mentions the inflammability of hydrogen.
1702	Death of Kunckel.
1702	Wilhelm Homberg prepares "sedative salt" (boric acid).
1702	G. E. Stahl distinguishes between the natural and the artificial alkali (soda and potash).
1705	Birth of Vincenzo Menghini, the first to demonstrate the presence of iron in red blood corpuscles.
1707	Nicolas Lémery publishes his "Treatise on Antimony."
Mar. 3, 1709	Birth of Andreas Sigismund Marggraf at Berlin.
June 19, 1715	Death of Nicolas Lémery.
1715	Death of Wilhelm Homberg.
1716	Birth of Don Antonio de Ulloa.
1718	Birth of P.-J. Macquer.
Dec. 23, 1722	Birth of Axel Fredrik Cronstedt, the discoverer of nickel, in Södermanland, Sweden.
1731	Death of E.-F. Geoffroy.
Oct. 10, 1731	Birth of Henry Cavendish at Nice.
(old style) Mar. 13, 1733	Birth of Joseph Priestley at Fieldhead, Yorkshire, near Leeds.
1734	Death of G. E. Stahl.

1735	Birth of Torbern Bergman.
1736	H.-L. du Hamel du Monceau demonstrates that the mineral alkali (soda) is a constituent of common salt, of Glauber's salt, and of borax, and prepares sodium carbonate from salt.
1737	Death of Caspar Neumann.
1737	Jean Hellot prepares a button of metallic bismuth and makes public the secret process for preparing phosphorus.
1737–38	Georg Brandt isolates cobalt.
1738	Death of Herman Boerhaave.
1740	J. H. Pott states that pyrolusite contains the calx of a new metal.
July 1, 1740	Birth of Müller von Reichenstein, the discoverer of tellurium, at Nagyszeben, Transylvania.
1740–41	Charles Wood finds in Jamaica some platinum which has come from Carthagena, New Spain.
1742	Anton von Svab distills zinc from calamine.
1742	Birth of Baron Ignaz Edler von Born.
Dec. 9 (or 19), 1742	Birth of Carl Wilhelm Scheele at Stralsund, Swedish Pomerania.
1743	Death of Louis Lémery.
Aug. 26, 1743	Birth of Lavoisier in Paris.
Dec. 1, 1743	Birth of Martin Heinrich Klaproth at Wernigerode in the Harz. One of the first to investigate uranium, titanium, and cerium.
1745	V. Menghini detects iron in red blood corpuscles.
Aug. 19, 1745	Birth of Johan Gottlieb Gahn, the discoverer of manganese, at Xoxna, South Helsingland, Sweden.
1746	Marggraf prepares metallic zinc by reduction of calamine.
Oct. 2, 1746	Birth of Peter Jacob Hjelm, the discoverer of molybdenum, at Sunnerbo Härad, Sweden.
1748	Don Antonio de Ulloa describes platinum.
Nov. 3, 1749	Birth of Daniel Rutherford, the discoverer of nitrogen, at Edinburgh.
1750	Dr. William Brownrigg describes platinum.
1751	Cronstedt isolates nickel.
1752	H. T. Scheffer fuses platinum with the aid of arsenic.
1753	Claude-François Geoffroy's research on "The Chemical Analysis of Bismuth" is published.
1754	Marggraf prepares and characterizes alumina.
June 15, 1754	Birth of Juan José de Elhuyar.
Oct. 11, 1755	Birth of Don Fausto de Elhuyar at Logroño, Spain. With his brother, Don Juan José he isolated tungsten (wolfram).
1755	Dr. Joseph Black of Edinburgh recognizes magnesia alba to be distinct from lime.

1758–59	Marggraf independently recognizes the distinction between magnesia and lime, and uses flame tests to distinguish between the nitrates of sodium and potassium.
June 5, 1760	Birth of Johan Gadolin, the discoverer of yttria, at Åbo, Finland.
Nov. 30, 1761	Birth of Smithson Tennant, the discoverer of osmium and iridium, at Wensleydale, Yorkshire.
Dec. 25, 1761	Birth of the Reverend William Gregor, the discoverer of titanium, in Trewarthenick, Cornwall.
May 16, 1763	Birth of N.-L. Vauquelin, the discoverer of chromium and beryllium, at St. André des Berteaux.
Nov. 10, 1764	Birth of A. M. del Río, discoverer of vanadium (erythronium), in Madrid.
Jan. 2, 1765	Birth of Charles Hatchett, the discoverer of columbium (niobium), in London.
Aug. 19, 1765	Death of Cronstedt in Säters parish, near Stockholm.
Aug. 6, 1766	Birth of Dr. William Hyde Wollaston, the discoverer of palladium and rhodium, at East Dereham, Norfolkshire.
Dec., 1766	Birth of Wilhelm Hisinger, the discoverer of the earth ceria. Berzelius, Hisinger, and Klaproth all investigated this earth, the latter independently.
Jan. 16, 1767	Birth of Anders Gustaf Ekeberg, the discoverer of tantalum, at Stockholm.
Apr. 29, 1768	Death of Georg Brandt at Stockholm.
1769	Scheele and Gahn isolate phosphorus from bones.
1770	P. S. Pallas describes the "red lead of Siberia" (crocoite), in which Vauquelin later discovered chromium. This mineral had been analyzed four years earlier by J. G. Lehmann.
1771	Scheele describes hydrofluoric acid.
1772	Daniel Rutherford discovers nitrogen. (Scheele, Priestley, and Cavendish discover it independently at about the same time.)
1772–82	Baron Carl von Sickingen devises a process for making platinum malleable.
1774	Birth of J.-F. Coindet.
Apr., 1774	Pierre Bayen prepares oxygen by heating mercuric oxide.
1774	Scheele publishes his famous treatise "Concerning Manganese and its Properties," which led to the discovery of three elements: manganese, barium, and chlorine.
Aug. 1, 1774	Priestley prepares oxygen. (Scheele prepared it before this, but his results were not published until 1777.)
1774	Gahn isolates manganese.
1775	Johan Arvidsson Afzelius publishes his doctor's dissertation defending Bergman's belief in the elementary nature of nickel. (He sometimes signed his name Johan Afzelius Arvidsson.)

Aug. 2, 1776	Birth of Friedrich Stromeyer, the discoverer of cadmium, at Göttingen.
Feb. 8, 1777	Birth of Bernard Courtois, the discoverer of iodine, at Dijon.
1777	Lavoisier overthrows the phlogiston theory and demonstrates the true nature of combustion.
May 4, 1777	Birth of Louis-Jacques Thenard.
Aug. 14, 1777	Birth of Hans Christian Oersted.
1778	Scheele distinguishes between graphite and the ore then known as "molybdenum."
Dec. 6, 1778	Birth of Gay-Lussac at Saint-Léonard.
Dec. 17, 1778	Birth of Sir Humphry Davy at Penzance, Cornwall.
1779	Scheele distinguishes between lime and baryta.
Aug. 20, 1779	Birth of Berzelius at Wäfversunda, Sweden.
1780	Birth of J. W. Döbereiner, the discoverer of the "triads."
1781	Scheele discovers tungstic acid.
1781	Hjelm isolates molybdenum.
Aug. 7, 1782	Death of Marggraf.
1783	Discovery of tellurium by Müller von Reichenstein.
1783	Discovery of tungsten by the de Elhuyar brothers.
1783	P.-F. Chabaneau patents a process for making platinum malleable.
1784	Death of Torbern Bergman.
1784	Death of P.-J. Macquer.
1785	R. E. Raspe shows that tungsten hardens steel.
May 21, 1786	Death of Scheele.
June 2, 1787	Birth of Nils Gabriel Sefström, the rediscoverer of vanadium, in Ilsbo Socken, Sweden. Although vanadium is now known to be identical with del Río's "erythronium," the latter chemist did not distinguish clearly between chromium and the new element.
1789	Klaproth observes uranium in pitchblende, but does not isolate it. In the same year he discovers the earth zirconia.
1790	Hjelm publishes his first paper on molybdenum. He had isolated it as early as 1781.
1790	Adair Crawford recognizes strontia as a new earth.
1791	The Rev. William Gregor discovers the oxide of a new metal, titanium.
1791	Death of Baron von Born.
Jan. 12, 1792	Birth of Johan August Arfwedson, the discoverer of lithium, at Skagerholms-Bruk, Skaraborgs Län.
May 8, 1794	Death of Lavoisier on the guillotine.
1794	Gadolin discovers the earth yttria.
May 29, 1794	Birth of A.-A.-B. Bussy at Marseilles. He obtained magnesium in coherent form.

1795	Klaproth rediscovers titanium, but does not succeed in isolating it.
1795	Death of Don Antonio de Ulloa.
Jan. 23, 1796	Birth of Karl Karlovich Klaus, the discoverer of ruthenium, at Dorpat, Estonia.
1796	Smithson Tennant proves that the diamond consists solely of carbon.
Sept. 10, 1797	Birth of Carl Gustav Mosander, the discoverer of lanthanum and didymium, at Kalmar, Sweden.
1797–98	Vauquelin recognizes beryllium (glucinum) and isolates chromium. Beryllium was first isolated in 1828 by Wöhler.
Jan. 25, 1798	Klaproth brings Müller von Reichenstein's discovery of tellurium to the attention of German chemists.
Feb. 19, 1799	Birth of Ferdinand Reich, the discoverer of indium, at Bernburg.
July 31, 1800	Birth of Friedrich Wöhler at Eschersheim, Germany.
1800	J. B. de Andrada describes petalite and spodumene, minerals in which J. A. Arfwedson afterward discovered lithium.

Nineteenth Century

1801	Robert Hare fuses platinum. Two years later he volatilizes it.
1801	Del Río recognizes the presence of a new metal "erythronium" (vanadium) in a lead ore from Zimapán, Mexico. He afterward confuses it with chromium.
1801	Hatchett observes columbium (niobium) in an ore from New England.
1802	Ekeberg discovers the earth tantala.
Sept. 30, 1802	Birth of A.-J. Balard, the discoverer of bromine, at Montpellier.
Mar. 17, 1803	Birth of Carl Löwig, independent discoverer of bromine.
1803	Klaproth, Berzelius, and Hisinger analyze cerite and discover the earth ceria.
1803	Wollaston discovers palladium and rhodium.
Feb. 6, 1804	Death of Priestley at Northumberland, Pa.
1804	Smithson Tennant discovers osmium and iridium.
Oct. 6, 1807	Davy isolates potassium. A few days later he isolates sodium.
1808	Davy isolates barium, strontium, calcium, and magnesium.
1808	Gay-Lussac and Thenard isolate boron. Davy isolates it independently.
1809	Gay-Lussac and Thenard prove that sulfur is an element.
1809	Dr. Wollaston makes the erroneous conclusion that tantalum and columbium are identical.
Feb. 24, 1810	Death of Cavendish.

Nov. 15, 1810	Davy announces his proof of the elementary nature of chlorine to the Royal Society.
1811	Bernard Courtois discovers iodine.
Mar. 24 (or Feb. 24), 1811	Birth of Eugène-Melchior Peligot, the first to isolate uranium.
Mar. 31, 1811	Birth of Robert Bunsen at Göttingen.
Feb. 11, 1813	Death of Ekeberg at Upsala.
Oct. 7, 1813	Death of Hjelm at Stockholm.
1813	Clément confirms the discovery of iodine by Courtois.
1814	Fraunhofer discovers the dark lines in the sun's spectrum.
1814	Gay-Lussac publishes his classical research on iodine.
Feb. 22, 1815	Death of Tennant at Boulogne-sur-Mer.
Jan. 1, 1817	Death of Klaproth at Berlin.
Apr. 24, 1817	Birth of Jean Galissard de Marignac, the discoverer of ytterbia and gadolinia, at Geneva, Switzerland.
June 11 (or July 11), 1817	Death of William Gregor.
1817	Arfwedson discovers lithium.
1817	Stromeyer discovers cadmium
1818	Berzelius discovers selenium.
Mar. 11, 1818	Birth of Henri Sainte-Claire Deville on the island of St. Thomas in the Antilles.
Dec. 8, 1818	Death of Gahn at Stockholm.
Dec. 15, 1819	Death of Daniel Rutherford.
1820	J.-F. Coindet prescribes iodine in goiter therapy.
1820	Birth of Beguyer de Chancourtois, the discoverer of the "telluric screw."
July 15, 1820	Birth of Claude-August Lamy at Néry, France. He prepared thallium in the metallic state.
1822	Discovery of platinum in the Urals.
1823	William Prout detects free hydrochloric acid in the stomach.
1824	Berzelius isolates amorphous silicon.
Mar. 12, 1824	Birth of Gustav Kirchhoff at Königsberg.
Nov. 21, 1824	Birth of Hieronymus Theodor Richter, the first to observe the indigo line of indium.
1824	Berzelius isolates impure zirconium.
1825	Oersted isolates impure aluminum.
Oct. 12, 1825 (1826?)	Death of Müller von Reichenstein at Vienna.
1825	Berzelius prepares impure amorphous titanium.
1825	Carl Löwig isolates bromine.
1826	P. G. Sobolevskiĭ and V. V. Liubarskiĭ prepare malleable platinum.

1826	Balard isolates bromine. His results were published before those of Löwig.
1827	Wöhler isolates aluminum.
1828	Wöhler isolates beryllium. Bussy isolates it independently.
Dec. 22, 1828	Death of Dr. Wollaston in London. His specifications for making platinum malleable were circulated at the same time as the news of his death.
1829	Berzelius separates the earth thoria from thorite.
1829	Döbereiner observes the triads.
May 29, 1829	Death of Davy at Geneva, Switzerland.
Nov. 14, 1829	Death of Vauquelin at the Château des Berteaux.
1830	Sefström rediscovers vanadium.
Aug. 19, 1830	Birth of Lothar Meyer at Varel on the Jade.
1831	Bussy obtains magnesium in compact form. (Davy had isolated it in 1808.)
June 17, 1832	Birth of Sir William Crookes.
Jan. 6, 1833	Death of Don Fausto de Elhuyar at Madrid.
Jan. 7, 1833	Birth of Sir Henry E. Roscoe, the first to liberate metallic vanadium.
1834	Death of J.-F. Coindet.
Feb. 8 (Jan. 27), 1834	Birth of Mendeleev at Tobolsk, Siberia.
Aug. 18, 1835	Death of Stromeyer at Göttingen.
1837	Birth of J. A. R. Newlands, the discoverer of the law of octaves.
Apr. 18, 1838	Birth of Lecoq de Boisbaudran at Cognac.
Sept. 27, 1838	Death of Bernard Courtois in Paris.
Dec. 26, 1838	Birth of Clemens Winkler, the discoverer of germanium, at Freiberg.
1839	Mosander discovers lanthana.
Feb. 10, 1840	Birth of Per Theodor Cleve, the discoverer of thulium, at Stockholm.
May 27, 1840	Birth of Lars Fredrik Nilson, the discoverer of scandium, in Östergötland, Sweden.
1841	Peligot isolates uranium.
1841	Mosander discovers didymia.
Oct. 28, 1841	Death of J. A. Arfwedson at his Hedensö estate.
Nov. 12, 1842	Birth of Robert John Strutt, Lord Rayleigh, at Terling, England.
1843	Mosander separates terbia and erbia from gadolinite.
1844	Klaus discovers ruthenium.
Nov. 30, 1845	Death of Sefström at Stockholm.
1847	E. Harless detects copper in the blood of the octopus *Eledone*.
Mar. 10, 1847	Death of Hatchett at Chelsea.

Aug. 7, 1848	Death of Berzelius at Stockholm.
Mar. 23, 1849	Death of del Río in Mexico.
Mar. 24, 1849	Death of Döbereiner.
May 9, 1850	Death of Gay-Lussac in Paris.
Mar. 9, 1851	Death of Oersted.
Jan. 1, 1852	Birth of E.-A. Demarçay, the discoverer of europium.
June 28, 1852	Death of Hisinger.
Aug. 15, 1852	Death of Gadolin.
Sept. 28, 1852	Birth of Henri Moissan in Paris.
Oct. 2, 1852	Birth of Sir William Ramsay at Glasgow.
1854	David Alter observes that each element has a characteristic spectrum.
1854	Henri Sainte-Claire Deville perfects an industrial process for aluminum and prepares the first crystalline silicon.
June 21, 1857	Death of Thenard.
Sept. 1, 1858	Birth of Carl Auer, Baron von Welsbach.
Oct. 15, 1858	Death of Mosander.
May 15, 1859	Birth of Pierre Curie.
1859	Invention of the spectroscope by Kirchhoff and Bunsen.
1859	The first petroleum well in the United States is drilled at Titusville, Pennsylvania.
May 10, 1860	Bunsen and Kirchhoff announce the discovery of cesium.
Feb. 23, 1861	Bunsen and Kirchhoff announce the discovery of rubidium.
Spring, 1861	Crookes observes the green line of thallium.
Spring, 1862	Lamy prepares an ingot of metallic thallium.
1862	Beguyer de Chancourtois draws his "telluric screw."
1863	Birth of P.-L.-T. Héroult and of Charles Martin Hall, independent discoverers of the electrolytic process for preparing metallic aluminum.
Summer, 1863	Reich and Richter discover indium.
1864	Newlands and Lothar Meyer independently arrange the elements in series and families.
Mar. 24, 1864	Death of Klaus.
Nov. 7, 1867	Birth of Marie Sklodowska (Mme. Curie) at Warsaw, Poland.
1868	Janssen and Lockyer independently observe the D line of helium in the sun's chromosphere.
July 9, 1868	Birth of N. A. Langlet.
June 16, 1869	Roscoe announces the isolation of vanadium.
1869	Lothar Meyer and Mendeleev independently discover the periodic system.
1870	Birth of B. B. Boltwood, the discoverer of ionium.
Jan. 24, 1872	Birth of Morris William Travers at London.
April 12, 1872	Birth of Georges Urbain, the discoverer of lutetium.

1873	Dennis Searle and E. M. Skillings discover the borax deposits of California.
Aug. 27, 1875	Boisbaudran discovers gallium, the first element to be discovered with the aid of the spark spectrum.
Oct., 1875	Lewis Reeve Gibbes presents his "Synoptical Table of the Elements."
Mar. 30, 1876	Death of Balard at Paris.
1878	Marignac separates ytterbia from erbia.
Mar. 20, 1878	Death of Lamy at Paris.
1879	Boisbaudran discovers samaria.
1879	Nilson discovers scandium (eka-boron).
1879	Cleve discovers holmia and thulia. The former had been discovered independently by Soret in 1878.
Apr. 27, 1880	Birth of Charles James near Northampton, England.
Jan. 1, 1881	Death of Henri Sainte-Claire Deville at Boulogne-sur-Seine.
Feb. 1, 1882	Death of Bussy at Paris.
Apr. 27, 1882	Death of Ferdinand Reich.
Sept. 23, 1882	Death of Wöhler.
1885	Birth of Georg von Hevesy in Budapest. Co-discoverer with Dirk Coster of the element hafnium.
June 18, 1885	Auer von Welsbach announces his separation of didymia into praseodymia and neodymia.
1886	Death of Beguyer de Chancourtois.
1886	Boisbaudran discovers dysprosia and gadolinia, but finds that the latter is identical with an oxide discovered by Marignac in 1880.
Feb. 6, 1886	Winkler discovers germanium.
Feb. 23, 1886	Charles Martin Hall produces electrolytic aluminum. Dr. Héroult made the same discovery independently at about the same time.
June 26, 1886	Moissan isolates fluorine.
Oct. 17, 1887	Death of Kirchhoff.
Nov. 23, 1887	Birth of Moseley at Weymouth, England.
Apr. 15, 1890	Death of Peligot in Paris.
1892	Lord Rayleigh finds that atmospheric nitrogen is heavier than nitrogen from the decomposition of ammonia.
1894	Ramsay and Rayleigh announce the discovery of argon.
Apr. 15, 1894	Death of Marignac.
1895	Ramsay and Cleve independently discover helium.
Apr. 11, 1895	Death of Lothar Meyer.
May 30, 1898	Ramsay and Travers discover krypton.
June, 1898	Ramsay and Travers discover neon.
July 12, 1898	Ramsay and Travers discover xenon.
July, 1898	Mme. Curie discovers polonium.

July 29, 1898	Death of J. A. R. Newlands.
Sept. 25, 1898	Death of Hieronymus Richter.
Dec., 1898	M. and Mme. Curie discover radium.
1898	Mme. Curie and G. C. Schmidt independently discover the radioactivity of thorium.
May 14, 1899	Death of Nilson.
Aug. 16, 1899	Death of Bunsen.
1899	Debierne discovers actinium.
1900	Dorn discovers radon (radium emanation).
1900	Sir William Crookes discovers uranium X_1.

Twentieth Century

1901	Demarçay discovers europium.
1902	Rutherford and Soddy discover thorium X.
1904	B. B. Boltwood, H. N. McCoy, and R. J. Strutt prove independently that radium is produced by spontaneous transmutation of uranium.
Oct. 8, 1904	Death of Winkler.
1904	Death of Demarçay at Paris.
1904–5	Giesel and Godlewski independently discover actinium X.
1905	L. B. Mendel and H. C. Bradley discover zinc in the liver and respiratory protein of the snail *Sycotypus*.
1905	Hahn discovers radiothorium and mesothorium I.
June 18, 1905	Death of Cleve at Upsala.
1906	Hahn discovers radioactinium.
1906	Richard Willstätter detects magnesia in the ash of pure chlorophyll.
Apr. 19, 1906	Death of Pierre Curie.
1907	H. N. McCoy and W. H. Ross clearly recognize the existence of isotopes, or chemically inseparable elements.
1907	Boltwood discovers ionium. This element was independently discovered by Hahn and Marckwald.
Feb. 2, 1907	Death of Mendeleev.
Feb. 20, 1907	Death of Moissan.
1907	Urbain discovers lutetium.
1907	Von Bolton prepares a columbium (niobium) regulus.
1909	E. Weintraub prepares pure fused boron.
1910	Mme. Curie and M. Debierne isolate radium metal.
1910	M. A. Hunter prepares titanium 99.9 per cent pure.
1911	Antonoff discovers uranium Y.
May 28, 1912	Death of Boisbaudran.
1913	Fajans and Göhring discover uranium X_2 (element 91, ekatantalum).

Dec., 1913, and Apr., 1914	Moseley publishes his papers on "The High Frequency Spectra of the Elements."
1914	T. W. Richards discovers a radioactive isotope of lead.
1914	Death of P.-L.-T. Héroult and C. M. Hall.
Aug. 10, 1915	Moseley killed at the Dardanelles.
Dec. 18, 1915	Death of Sir Henry E. Roscoe.
July 23, 1916	Death of Ramsay.
1917	Hahn and Meitner discover protactinium. Soddy and Cranston discover it independently.
Apr. 4, 1919	Death of Sir William Crookes.
June 30, 1919	Death of Lord Rayleigh.
1921	Hahn discovers uranium Z.
Jan., 1923	Coster and Hevesy discover hafnium (element 72).
June, 1925	Noddack, Tacke, and Berg discover rhenium (element 75).
July 1, 1926	Death of F. F. Jewett in Honolulu.
1927	Death of Boltwood.
1928	E. B. Hart et al. discover the importance of copper in nutrition.
Dec. 10, 1928	Death of Charles James in Boston.
Aug. 4, 1929	Death of Auer von Welsbach at Welsbach Castle in Carinthia.
1930	Nils Edlefsen, a student of Ernest O. Lawrence, constructs the first crude cyclotron.
1932	H. C. Urey, F. G. Brickwedde, and G. M. Murphy discover the hydrogen isotope of mass 2.
1932	J. Chadwick and M. and Mme. Joliot-Curie demonstrate the existence of the neutron, which W. D. Harkins regards as the atom of an element "neuton" of atomic number zero.
1934	Colin G. Fink and P. Deren perfect a process for electroplating rhenium.
Jan. 15, 1934	M. and Mme. Joliot-Curie produce artificial radioactive elements by a-ray bombardment of light elements.
July 4, 1934	Death of Mme. Curie.
Sept., 1934	A. V. Grosse liberates metallic protactinium.
March 30, 1936	Death of N. A. Langlet.
Oct. 19, 1937	Death of Lord Rutherford.
Nov. 5, 1938	Death of Georges Urbain.
1939	Mlle. Marguerite Perey detects element 87 (francium) which is formed by the alpha-disintegration of a small percentage of the atoms of actinium.
1939	Hahn and Strassmann split the nucleus of the uranium atom.
1939	C. Perrier and E. G. Segrè discover technetium (element 43) among the fission products of molybdenum which has been bombarded with deuterons in the Berkeley cyclotron.
1940	Edwin McMillan and Philip Abelson obtain the first transuranium element, neptunium (element 93), by bombardment of uranium with neutrons.

1940	D. R. Corson, K. R. Mackenzie, and F. G. Segrè prepare element 85 (astatine) by bombarding bismuth with helions. W. Minder and Hulubei and Cauchois independently give evidence for the existence of element 85 in the decay products of radon.
1940	McMillan and Abelson prepare element 93 by bombarding uranium with neutrons, and find that it bears a closer resemblance to uranium than to rhenium.
1940	G. T. Seaborg, Edwin McMillan, J. W. Kennedy, and A. C. Wahl prepare plutonium (element 94) in the cyclotron.
1941	The Dow Chemical Company produces an ingot of magnesium from sea water.
Jan. 17, 1941	Death of Sven Otto Pettersson at Göteborg.
Dec. 2, 1941	Death of Thomas H. Norton.
1944–45	Americium (element 95) is prepared by Seaborg, R. A. James, and L .O. Morgan, curium (element 96) by Seaborg, James, and A. Ghiorso.
1945	J. A. Marinsky and L. E. Glendenin discover promethium (element 61).
1950	S. G. Thompson, A. Ghiorso, and G. T. Seaborg discover berkelium (element 97). S. G. Thompson, K. Street, Jr., A. Ghiorso, and G. T. Seaborg discover californium (element 98).
1954	Elements 99 and 100 (einsteinium and fermium) are announced.
1955	Mendelevium (element 101) is announced by A. Ghiorso, B. G. Harvey, G. R. Choppin, S. G. Thompson, and G. T. Seaborg.

Index

Page numbers in italics indicate portraits

Abelson, Philip, 868, 869
Abildgaard, Peder Christian, 460
Achard, F. C., 417
Acid of salt, 186, 187
Acosta, Joaquín, 422
Actinide series, 876–879
Actinium series, 820–824
Afzelius, Johan Arvidsson, 313
Afzelius, Pehr, 346
Agricola, Georgius, 11 37, 98, 105, 677, 755
Agruss, M. G., 820
Alabaster, 505
Albert the Great, *93*, 186
Alchemistic symbols, 95
Alchemists, elements of, 91; paintings of, 91, 107, 120
Aldrovandi, Ulisse, 511, *512*
Allen, William, 482, 741
Alter, David, *623*, 624
Alum, 588–608; potash in, 458, 459
Aluminum, 588–610; in plants and animals, 610; isolation of by Wöhler, 598, 600
Alunite (see Alum)
Amalgamation process, 50, 51
American Philosophical Society, 375, 400, 403
Americium, 874–876
Ammonia, 190
Ampère, André-Marie, *741*
Animal nutrition, 151, 152; calcium in, 510; carbon in, 83
Animals, aluminum in, 610; barium in, 516, 517; beryllium in, 570; boron in, 585, 586; bromine in, 755; cerium in, 558; copper in, 28; effect of thallium on, 641; fluorine in, 770; hydrogen in, 187, 188; iron in, 38; lithium in, 489, 490; magnesium in, 527, 528; manganese in, 174; potassium in, 460; silica in, 588; sodium in, 467, 468; strontium in, 521; sulfur in, 57; titanium in, 549–551; vanadium in, 364
Antimony, 95–103; calcination of, 97; early uses of, 103; native, 103
Antonoff, G. N., 812
Aqua regia, 186
Arfwedson, Johan August, 267, 485–488, *494*–503, 687, *701*
Argon, 784, 785

Argyrodite, 688, 689
Aristotle, 3
Armstrong, Eva, 403
Arrhenius, Carl Axel, 495, 695, *697*
Arrhenius Svante, 550
Arsenic, 92–95; investigation of by Brandt, 156; isolation of, 92; metallic nature of, 95
Artificial diamonds, 768
Asphalt, 76–77
Astatine, 865, 866
Auer, Carl, Baron von Welsbach, 713, 714, *715*–717
Azurite, 23

Baas-Becking, L. G. M., 461
Bagge, C., 465
Bailey, E. H. S., 517
Balard, Antoine-Jérôme, 733, 744, 747, 749–754
Balfour, I. B., 246
Balke, C. W., 344
Balloon ascensions by Gay-Lussac and Biot, 576, 577
Bancroft, H. H., 297, 398
Banks, Sir Joseph, *201*
Barba, Padre Alvaro Alonso, 10, 18, 45, 50, 51, 106, 188, 293
Barium, 510–517; in plants and animals, 516, 517; metallic, 516
Baryta, 507, 514, 515
Basalt, sodium in, 466, 467
Baskerville, Charles, 364
Bauch, Martin Anders, 221
Baumé, Antoine, *415*
Bayen, Pierre, 212
Beccari, Jacopo Bartolomeo, 514
Beccaria, Giovanni Battista, 40
Becher, Johann Joachim, 197, *199*
Beckmann, Johann, 144, 160
Becquerel, Antoine-Henri, 803, *804*
Beddoes, Thomas, 478, *479*
Bell, Alexander Graham, 318
Berg, Otto, 851, 852
Bergman, Torbern, 159, 164, *167*, 169, 223, 255–257, 260, *261*, 286, 288, 304, 326, 473, 515, 516, 522, 528, 544, 551; his statement on sedative salt, 575
Berkelium, 876, 877
Bernhardt, Johann Christian, 185

Berthelot, Pierre-Eugène-Marcelin, 407, 767

Berthollet, Claude-Louis, 286, 420, 421, 433, 486, 729, 730, 734, 735

Beryllium, 565–570; first preparation of pure, by electrolytic process, 569, 570; in plants and animals, 570

Berzelius, Betty, 707

Berzelius, Jöns Jacob, 135, 171, 184, 302, 306–315, 342, 349, 350, 353, 354, 357, 358, 362, 376, 385, 386, 423, 431–434, 438, 440, 444, 485–487, 497–499, 501, 502, 509, 510, 516, 533, 545, 549, 550, 552–554, 556, 558–560, 678, 685, 733; his friendship with Mosander, 700–706, 707, 711; his friendship with Wöhler, 597, 598, 602; his work with silicon, 586, 587

Bible, elements mentioned in the, 5–8, 14–16, 19–22, 30–31, 41–43, 52, 53, 76, 96, 183, 462, 464

Bicquet, Jean-Baptiste-Michel, 467

Biot, Jean-Baptiste, his balloon ascension with Gay-Lussac, 576, 577

Biringuccio, Vannoccio, 153, 154

Bishop, Joachim, 423

Bismuth, 103–109, 157, 158; recipes for making it, 107

Bitumen, 76–77

Björkbom, Carl, 502

Black, Joseph, 205, 206, 237, 243, 456, 523, 524

Blake, W. P., 305

Bleaching, with chlorine, 734, 735

Blomstrand, C. W., 343

Blood, iron in, 39; red color of, 39

Boerhaave, Herman, 189, 192, 236, 237, 456, 462, 466, 474

Böttger, Rudolph Christian, 640, 646

Bohn, Johann, 473, 474

Bohr, Niels, 849

Bolívar, Simón, 423

Bologna stone, 510–515

Bolton, Werner von, 344

Boltwood, Bertram Borden, 813

Boracite, 583

Borax, 570–580; early process of recovering, 584; in California, 583, 584

Borch, Ole, 211

Boric acid, decomposition of by Gay-Lussac and Thenard, 579, 580; in sea water, 584, 585; natural, 581–583

Boron, 570–586; Davy's method of isolating, 580; in plants and animals, 585, 586

Born, Baron Ignaz Edler von, 264, 290, 321, 322, 323, 326, 632

Bostock, John, 370, 383

Boulduc, Gilles-Egide-François, 522

Bourdelin, Louis-Claude, 574

Boussingault, Jean-Baptiste, 86, 187, 422, 423

Bowen, George, 189

Boyle, Robert, 4, 112, 114, 122, 123, 125, 126, 188, 197, 198

Brand, Hennig, 108, 109, 121–124; process of making phosphorus, 126

Brande, William Thomas, 371, 428, 437, 439, 487

Brandes, R., 745

Brandt, Georg, 156–160, 476, 671

Brass, 19, 141, 142

Brauner, Bohuslav, 660, 661, 716, 717

Braunstein (see Pyrolusite)

Breislak, Abbé Scipione, 590

Brewster, Sir David, 622, 623

Brodie, Sir Benjamin, 385

Bromide mineral, 754, 755

Bromine, 747–755; from sea water, 754; in animals, 755

Bronze, 43

Brooke, H. J., 502

Brooks, Harriet (see Pitcher, Mrs. Frank)

Brown, Samuel, 193

Browne, C. A., 387

Brownrigg, William, 83, 214, 409, 412–415, 462

Bruce, Archibald, 150

Bunge, G., 467

Bunsen, Robert Wilhelm, 488–490, 618, 624–629, 632–634

Bussy, Antoine-Alexandre-Brutus, 526, 527, 569

Butlerov, Alexander Mikhaïlovich, 445, 446

Cabezas, Joaquín, 420

Cadmium, 529–535; from zinc ores, 534, 535

Cady, Hamilton P., 791

Cailliaud, F., 565

Calamine, 147–149

Calcium, 505–510; in plant and animal nutrition, 510

Caley, Earle R., 47, 264

California, borax in, 583, 584

California gold rush, 13

Californium, 876, 877

Calomel, 52

Cap, Paul-Antoine, 102

Carbon, 58, 75; as an element, 59; in plant and animal nutrition, 83–87

Carbon dioxide, 237, 238

Cardano, Girolamo, 408
Carstanjen, E., 641
Carter, Howard, 506
Casciarolo, Vincenzo, 510
Cassiterite, 43
Cathcart, Charles Murray, 535
Cavendish, Henry, 200–204, 208, 214, 235, 238, 380, 779
Caycedo, Bernardo J., 290, 299
Celli, Marco Antonio, 511
Ceria, 699
Cerium, 551–558; in plants and animals, 558
Cesium, 626–631
Chabaneau, Pierre-François, 289, 417–420
Chadwick, James, 836
Chameleon mineral, 172, 173
Chaptal, Jean-Antoine-Claude, 294, 295, 382, 739
Charlotte, Elisabeth, her character sketch of Homberg, 573
Chenevix, Richard, 382, 383, 430, 431
Chevillot, Pierre-François, 173
Chevreul, Michel-Eugène, 173, 383, 384
Children, J. G., 534
Chilean nitrate, 193
Chile, selenium in, 315
Chinese, as originators of large-scale zinc production, 142–144; in discovery of oxygen, 209; knowledge of arsenic possessed by, 92–94; salt industry, 461
Chlorine, 729–736; bleaching with, 734, 735; disinfecting with, 735; in the human body, 736
Choke damp, 83
Choppin, G. R., 879
Christison, Sir R., 246
Chromite, 278, 279
Chromium, 270–279, 394; in meteorites, 279; in the emerald and ruby, 278
Chronology, 886–898
Chrysoberyl, Arfwedson's analysis of, 500
Cinnabar, 47–49
Clarke, Edward Daniel, 171, 263, 485, 486, 534, 558
Clayton, Reverend John, 81
Clément, Nicolas, 738, 740
Cleve, Per Theodor, 709–712, 789, 790
Cloud, Joseph, 430, 431
Coal, 75; description of, 75; in Pennsylvania, 75
Coal gas, 81
Cobalt, 152–161; discoverer of, 156; elemental nature of, 159; in meteorites, 160, 161; in nutrition, 161; metallic,

accurate description of, 157; roasted, 153
Cock, Thomas, 426
Coindet, Jean-François, 742–744
Coleridge, Samuel Taylor, 478
Colin, Jean-Jacques, 744
Collet-Descotils, H.-V., 394, 437
Columbite, 375–380
Columbium (see Niobium)
Columbus, Christopher, 9, 22
Combes, A., 482
Combustion, doctrine of, 228
Condorcet, M.-J.-A.-N. de Caritat, his eulogy on Marggraf, 591, 592
Conti, Prince Piero Ginori, 582, 583
Conybeare, Reverend J. J., 386
Copley Medal, 83
Copper, 19–29, 141, 142; in plants and animals, 28; in spring waters, 25
Copper mines, 26
Cornwall, H. B., 647
Corrosive sublimate, 52
Corson, D. R., 865
Cortenovis, Father Angelo Maria, 407
Coryell, Charles D., 864
Coster, Dirk, 850
Courtois, Bernard, 192, 736–740
Courtois, Jean-Baptiste, 192
Cramer, Johann Andreas, 109, 146–148
Crampton, C. A., 585
Cranston, John A., 820, 821
Crawford, Adair, 517, 518
Crell, Lorenz von, 133, 134, 528, 551
Cronstedt, Axel Fredrik, 161, 163–165, 416, 417, 551, 553
Crookes, Sir William, 316, 635–637, 638, 639, 811; discoveries in radioactivity, molecular physics, uranium X₁, 637; inventor of radiometer and spinthariscope, 637
Crookesite, 316, 641
Crowe, James M., 879
Cryolite, 608–610
Cunningham, B. B., 872, 875
Curie-Joliot, Irène (see Joliot, Irène Curie)
Curie, Marie Sklodowska, 560, 802–811, 813, 829, 830
Curie, Pierre, 802–811, 813, 829
Curium, 874–876
Cyclotron, 860

Dains, Frank Burnett, 403, 609
Dalton, John, 399
da Vinci, Leonardo, 91, 209, 210

Davy, Sir Humphry, 55, 202, 276, 370, *472*, 478–484, 487, 498, *507–510*, 545, 730, *732–734*
de Acosta, Father José, 10, 17, 49, 106; his description of Peruvian emeralds, 566
de Andrada e Silva, Jozé Bonifácio, *484*, 485
de Beaumont, Louis-Léonce Elie, *603*
Debierne, André, 813
de Blancourt, Haudicquer, 154, 455
de Boisbaudran, Paul-Émile Lecoq, 671, 672–676, 712, 717
de Bourdelin, Louis-Claude, 456
Debray, J. Henri, *446*
Debus, Heinrich, *625*
de Carvalho, M. Herculano, 270
de Castro, Giovanni, 589
de Chancourtois, Alexandre-Emile Beguyer, 654–656
de Condorcet, Marquis, 475
de Elhuyar, Fausto, 255, *256*, 257, *284*, 285–298, 299, 391, 392, 418
de Elhuyar, Juan José, 255–257, 285–299, 391, 418, 551
de Figueiredo Neiva, Venâncio, 485
de Fontenelle, B. Le Bovier, 99, 102, 513; his eulogy of Homberg, 573, 574
de Fourcroy, A.-F., 271, 273, 276, 279, 341, 382, 394, 458–460, 515, 567
de Gálvez-Cañero, A., 297, 299, 403
Déhérain, Pierre-Paul, 467
Delafontaine, Marc, *705*, 712
de Larderel, Francesco Giacomo, 582
de León, Joaquín Velázquez, 402
del Río, Andrés Manuel, 254, *292*, 293, 299, 316, 352, 359, 391–405, 434; regarding iodine as a mineral, 745, 746
de Mayerne, Turquet, 200
de Medina, Bartolomé, 291, 293
de Menonville, N.-J. Thiery, 411
Demarçay, Eugène-Anatole, 717, *718–720*
de Marignac, Jean-Charles Galissard, *708*
de Morveau, Louis-Bernard Guyton, 185, 192, 258, *544*, 735
de Respour, P. M., 147
Derham, W., 511
Desgrez, Alexandre, 490
Desormes, Charles-Bernard, 738, 740
de Tournefort, J.-P., 524, 590
de Ulloa, Antonio, *406*, 409–412, 420, 423
Deuterium, 205
de Velázquez Cárdenas y León, Joaquín, 289, 299
de Viera y Clavijo, Father José, 218
Deville (see Sainte-Claire Deville)

Diamonds, 60; artificial, 768
Didymia, 699–705
Digitalis, 516
Disinfecting, with chlorine, 735
Döbereiner, Johann Wolfgang, 519, 653, *654*
Domeyko, Ignaz, 315
Dorn, Friedrich Ernest, 814
Dossie, Robert, 186, 189
Draper, John W., 786
Duhamel du Monceau, Henri-Louis, 474
Dumas, Jean-Baptiste-André, 187, 639, *640*, 742
Dumoulin, G., 462
Dwight, Timothy, 463
Dysprosia, 717

Edwards, William Frederic, 173
Eggertz, Hans Peter, 184, 309, 310
Egyptians, sal ammoniac preparation of, 188, 189
Einsteinium, 878, 879
Ekeberg, Anders Gustaf, 307, *345–350*
Element, conception of, 3; first man to discover, 109
Elements, Lavoisier's list of, 477; mentioned in the Bible, 5–8, 14–16, 19–22, 30, 31, 41–43, 52, 53, 76, 96, 183, 462, 464; modern list, 884, 885; of the alchemists, 91
Elsholtz, Johann Sigismund, 755, 757
Elster, Julius, 818, 831
Emerald, chromium in the, 278
Epsom salt, 521, 522
Erbia, 705–712
Erythronium, 353, 394
Esmark, Jens, 558
Esmark, Reverend Hans Morten Thrane, 559
Estner, Abbé Franz Joseph Anton, 327, 329, 331–333
Europia, 717–720
Euxenite, 677, 680; discovery of, 678
Eye paints, ancient, 96

Fages y Virgili, Juan, 288, 289, 420
Fajans, Kasimir, 811, *812*, 820
Fajardo, Clavijo, 420
Fang, Lien-Che Tu, 461
Faulkner, Thomas, 386
Ferber, J. J., 459
Fermi, Enrico, 860, *861*, 867, 868
Fermium, 878, 879
Fiala, František, 336
Fink, Colin G., 13
Fire damp, 83

Fittig. Rudolf, 782
Flame test, for lithium, 516
Fleck, Alexander, 825, 827
Flink, Gustaf, 488
Fluorescent lighting, 535
Fluorine, 755–770; in plants and animals, 770
Fluorine gas, victims of, 762, 763
Forbes, Allyn B., 387
Forchhammer, Johan Georg, 161, 517, 584, 585
Forster, Georg, 323
Fourcroy, Antoine-François (see de Fourcroy)
Francium, 866, 867
Frankland, Edward, 786
Franklin, Benjamin, 214, 415
Franklinite, 151
Frasch, Herman, 56; process of mining Louisiana sulfur, 464
Fraunhofer, Josef, 620
Fremy, Edmond, 763
Friedrich, Duke Johann, 122, 123, 124
Fuchs, Johann Nepomuk von, 485
Fyfe, Andrew, 743

Gadolin, Johan, 696, 698, 699
Gadolinia, 712, 713
Gadolinite, 696
Gahn, D. Heinrich, 134
Gahn, Johan Gottlieb, 133, 134, 136, 137, 168, 169–172, 184, 223, 260, 309–311, 313, 458, 514, 515, 556
Gallium, 671–677
Garbett, Samuel, 186
Gas fixtures, 82
Gas lighter, automatic, 715, 716
Gas lighting, 81–82
Gaultier, Henri-François, 744
Gay-Lussac, Louis-Joseph, 482, 496, 575–580, 730, 732, 733, 744; his balloon ascension with Biot, 576, 577
Geiger, Hans, 826
Geitel, Hans F. K., 818, 831
Genth, F. A., 305
Geoffroy, Claude-François, 108
Geoffroy, Claude-Joseph (Geoffroy the Younger), 36, 188, 382
Geoffroy, Étienne-François (Geoffroy the Elder), 12, 24, 25, 36, 77, 168, 189, 191, 192, 464, 589
Germanite, 677, 690
Germanium, 683–690
Gesner, Johann Albrecht, 160
Ghiorso, A., 876, 879

Gibbes, Lewis Reeve, 664–667, synoptical table of, 665
Giesel, Friedrich O., 823
Gilbert, L. W., 534
Glass, 465, 466, 586–588; etching, 756, 760; gold ruby, 11; Macquer's account of etching, 760, 761; pyrolusite in manufacture of, 168
Glassmaking, use of cobalt in, 153
Glauber, Johann Rudolph, 12, 144, 172, 183, 184, 186, 100, 466, 528
Glauber's salt, 183, 466
Glendenin, L. E., 864
Glueck, Nelson, 21
Gmelin, C. G., 487
Gmelin, Johann Friedrich, 568
Gmelin, Leopold, 597
Godfrey, Ambrose (see Hanckwitz, Ambrose Godfrey)
Godlewski, Tadeusz, 823
Göhring, O. H., 811
Goethe, J. W. von, 514, 745
Gold, 6; in California, 13; in sea water, 13; potable, 12; ruby glass, 11
Gore, George, 764
Gray, Daniel, 648
Greenockite, 535
Green Vitriol, 33
Gregor, Reverend William, 545–548
Gren, F. C., 258, 382
Grew, Nehemiah, 521
Grill, Johan Abraham, 571
Grosse, Aristid V., 820–822, 848
Guericke, Otto von, 114, 571
Guettard, Jean-Étienne, 462
Gunther, R. T., 264

Hafnium, 848–851
Hahn, Otto. 812, 820, 823–826, 867, 868
Haidinger, Karl, 327
Hales, Stephen, 212, 238, 241
Half-metals, 157, 163
Hall, Charles Martin, 606, 607
Hall, Sir James, 382
Hamburger, L., 560
Hampe, Dr. J. H., 129, 130
Hanckwitz, Ambrose Godfrey, 113, 114, 128
Hare, Robert, 423, 424
Harvey, B. G., 879
Hasselqvist, Fredrik, 189
Hatchett, Charles, 264, 338–343, 368–389
Hausmann, Johann Friedrich, 356
Haüy, René-Just, 485, 488, 498, 564, 566, 567
Haworth, E., 791
Hayyan, Abu Musa Jabir ibn, 188

Helium, 785–792; discovery of, 637
Hellot, Jean, 108, 114
Helmholtz, Hermann (Ludwig Ferdinand) von, 634
Helmont, Jan Baptist van, 206, 207
Hematite, 33
Henckel, J. F., 147
Henry, Thomas, 526, 528, 735
Henry, William, 731
Henze, M., 364
Heraclitus, 4
Herapath, William, 534
Hermann, K. S. L., 532
Hermbstädt, Sigismund Friedrich, 224
Héroult, Louis-Toussaint, 606, 608
Hess, Gertrude D., 375, 387
Hevesy, Georg von, 849–851
Hewson, William, 40
Heyrovsky, Jaroslav, 853–855
Hiärne, Urban, 162
Hillebrand, William Francis, 555, 557, 787, 788
Hirsch, Alcan, 557
Hisinger, Wilhelm, 313, 485, 497, 502, 551–554, 555, 557
Hjelm, Peter Jacob, 171, 172, 261–264, 551
Höfer, Hubert Franz, 581
Hönigschmid, Otto, 817
Hoffmann, Friedrich, 75, 474, 522
Hofmann, August Wilhelm von, 635, 636
Holmia, 709–712, 717
Homberg, Willem, 112, 513, 571–574; character sketch of, 573
Home, Sir Everard, 370
Hooke, Robert, 210
Hope, John, 244, 245
Hope, Thomas Charles, 504, 518–521, 741
Hopkins, B. Smith, 724
Howard, Edward, 382
Howe, James Lewis, 418
Human body, chlorine in the, 736
Humboldt, Baron Alexander von, 293, 294, 298, 360, 390, 391, 394, 396, 422, 428
Hunter, M. A., 550
Hussak, Eugen, 431
Hydrochloric acid, 186, 187; in the stomach, 187
Hydrogen, 183–188, 197–205; density of, 780, 781; in plants and animals, 187, 188

Ilsemann. J. C., 171
Incandescent gas mantle, 714, 715

Indium, 641–648; commercial development of, 647, 648; description of first metallic, 645, 646; detection of in zinc blendes, 647
Ingenhousz, Jan, 74, 85, 86
Iodide mineral, 745, 746
Iodine, 736–747; in spring water, 744, 745; diffusion of in nature, 746, 747
Iridium, 436–440
Iron, in animals, 38; in the blood, 39; in vegetable ash, 36; meteoric, 32; mines, 35; seventeenth century symbol, 15; smelted, 33

Jackson, C. T., 305
James, Charles, 721, 722, 723
Janssen, Pierre-Jules-César, 785, 786
Jeanety, M., 420
Jewett, Frank Fanning, 604
John, Johann Friedrich, 496
Johnson, Percival Norton, 426, 431, 432
Johnston, James Finlay Weir, his description of Berzelius and his laboratory, 559, 560
Joliot, Jean-Frédéric, 834–838
Joliot, Mme. Irène Curie, 830, 831, 832–838
Joss, J. R., 754
Juan y Santacilia, Jorge, 409, 410
Jungfleisch, Emile-Clément, 674, 675

Kaim, Ignatius Gottfried, 168
Kalm, Per, 462, 525, 526
Karsten, C., 532
Kennedy, Robert, 459, 460, 466, 467
Kersten, Carl, 317
Kircher, Father Athanasius, 512
Kirchoff, Gustav Robert, 490, 624, 626, 627, 628, 629, 632
Kirwan, Richard, 520
Kitaibel, Paul, 305, 320, 326–336, 735
Klaproth, Martin Heinrich, 258, 262, 263–267, 276, 277, 288, 304, 305, 313, 326–336, 407, 459, 460, 467, 500, 542–544, 548, 549, 566, 567, 632
Klaus, Karl Karlovich, 440, 441–447
Kopp, Hermann, 186, 474
Krafft, Johann Daniel, 116, 122–125
Krypton, 792, 793
Kunckel, Johann (see Löwenstern, Johann Kunckel von)
Kupfernickel, 162, 163, 164

Lac, 382
Lampadius, Wilhelm August, 254
Lamy, Claude-Auguste, 638, 639, 640
Lanthana, 699–705

Larson, Mary, 427
Laue, Max von, 846, *847*
Laugier, André, 279
Lava, sodium in, 466, 467
Lavoisier, Antoine-Laurent, 5, 55, 192, *196*, 225–227, 243, 244, 294, 457, 476, 507; his list of elements, 477
Lawrence, Ernest O., 858, 860
Lawson, Isaac, 148
Lead, 41; resemblance to bismuth, 108
Lead mines, 42
Lebeau, P., 569
Leblanc, Nicholas, 465
Leclerc, Georges-Louis, *435*
Lely, D., Jr., 560
Lehmann, Johann Gottlob, 253, 272
Leibniz, Gottfried Wilhelm, *121–123*, 124
Lémery, Louis, 36–38, 190
Leméry, Nicolas, 13, 38, 45, *99*, 100, 102, 103, 106, 107, 126, 198, 200, 512, 513
Lentilius, Rosinus, 75
Lenz, Johann Georg, 327
Lepape, A., 796, 797
Lepidolite, 487, 631, 632
Leucite, analysis of by Arfwedson, 495; potash in, 459
Levy, Armand, 151
Lewis, William, 417, 422, 527, 528
Liebig, Justus von, *599*, 600, 753
Li Jung, 461
Lime, 507
Linck, Johann Heinrich, *131*, 162
Linnaeite, 160
Linné, Carl von, 26, 159
Li-Ping, 461
Lippmann, Edmund Oskar von, 104, 407
Lippmann, Gabriel, *805*
Lithium, 484–490; discoverer of, 485; in natural waters, 489; in plants and animals, 489, 490
Liubarskiĭ, V. V., 428
Lockyer, Sir Joseph Norman, 637, 786, *788*, 789
Lodestone (Magnetite), 33
Lomonosov, M. V., 210
Louisiana, sulfur in, 56
Louyet, Paulin, *760*
Lovits, Toviĭ, Egorovich, 277–279
Löwenstern, Johann Kunckel von, 12, 110, *111*, 154, 190; experiments of, 112
Löwig, Carl, 747, *748, 750*
Lowitz, Tobias (see Lovits, Toviĭ Egorovich)
Lucas, Alfred, 407
Lucas, Anthony F., 79
Lulio, Raimundo, 190
Lumb, A. D., 423

Lutetia, 720–724

McCollum, E. V., 528
McCoy, Herbert Newby, *714*
McCutcheon, F. G., 676
McFarland, D. F., 791
Mackenzie, K. R., 865
McMillan, Edwin M., 868, *869–871*, 872
MacNeven, William James, 481
McPherson, William, 663
Macquer, Pierre-Joseph, 60, 114, 130, 185, 187, 190, 457, 570, 571
Madács, Petrus, 159
Magdeburg miracles, 571, 572
Magini, Giovanni Antonio, 511
Magnesium, 521–528; from sea water, 528; in plants and animals, 527
Magnetite (Lodestone), 33
Magnus, Albertus (see Albert the Great)
Magnus, Gustav, *308*
Malachite, 23
Malpighi, Marcello, 521
Manganese, 168–174; discoverer of, 168; in animals, 174; in plants, 173, 174; metallic, 169
Mao-Khóa, 209, 210
Marcet, Alexandre, *312*, 350, 386, 425, 433, 434, 438, 487, 496
Marden, J. W., 363
Marggraf, Andreas Sigismund, 132, *140*, 148, 149, 456, 476, 514, 523–525, 591, 592, 619, 756
Marinsky, J. A., 864
Marsden, E., 827
Mascagni, Paolo, 581, 582
Matches, phosphorus, 135, 136
Matthiessen, A., 488
Maxson, R. N., 193
Mayow, John, 210, *212*, 244
Meerschaum, 526
Meggers, William Frederick, *854*
Meionite, analysis of by Arfwedson, 495
Meissner, W., 532
Meitner, Lise, 812, 820, 868
Mendeleev, Dmitri Ivanovich, 653, 657, *660–665*, 688, 689; elements predicted by, 663; periodic table of the elements of, 652, *670*
Mendelevium, 878, 879
Mendez, Dr., 522
Menghini, Vincenzo, 39
Menschutkin, B. N., 428
Mephitic air, 241, 242
Mercury, 47; freezing of, 52
Metals, ancient, 5; Swedish, 152–174
Meteorites, chromium in, 279; cobalt in, 160, 161; nickel in, 165, 166

Meunier, J., 490
Mexico, first ironworks in, 396
Meyer, J. K. F., 133, 165
Meyer, Julius Lothar, 653, 657, 658–661
Meyer, Kirstine, 595
Miller, C. F., 490
Mine accidents, frequent causes of, 83
Mineral, iodide, 745, 746
Mineral waters, uranium in, 270
Mineralogy, chemical system of, 165
Mines, ancient silver, 16; copper, 26; iron, 35; lead, 42; nickel, 166 Potosí, 17; zinc, 150
Mitchill, Samuel Latham, 374, 375, 421, 506
Moissan, Ferdinand-Frédéric-Henri, 343, 550, 764–766, 768, 769, 770
Moles, Enrique, 288, 392, 393, 394, 403
Molybdenum, 258–264
Molybdic acid, 369
Monnet, Antoine-Grimoald, 458, 459
Mosander, Carl Gustav, 556, 699, 700–706
Moseley, Henry Gwyn Jeffreys, 844–848
Moureu, Charles, 796, 797
Mudge, B. F., 464
Müller, Franz Joseph, Baron von Reichenstein, 303–305, 325–327, 548
Münchausen, Baron von, 257
Murray, William S., 647
Musin-Pushkin, Apollos Apollosovich, 277, 278, 426
Mutis, José Celestino, 289, 419, 423
Muwaffaq, Abu Mansur, 506

Nagy, Julius, 336
Nasini, Raffaello, 572, 790
Natural gas, 79–81
Natural soda, 464, 465
Natural waters, lithium in, 489
Nature, diffusion of iodine in, 746, 747
Neodymia, 713–717
Neptunium, 868–870
Neri, Father Antonio, 154
Neumann, Caspar, 107, 145, 146, 508, 522; on alum, 590
Newlands, John Alexander Reina, 656, 657, 683
Niccolite, 163, 164
Nicholson, William, 164, 382
Nickel, 161–167; accepting the new element, 164, 165; discoverer of, 161; early alloys, 166, 167; famous mines and smelters, 166; first pure malleable, 167; history of, 162; in meteorites, 165, 166
Nilson, Lars Fredrik, 550, 677–683

Niobium, 339–345; discovery of, 371
Niter, 190–193
Nitric acid, 184, 185
Nitrogen, 205–208; as distinct from carbon dioxide, 238; compounds, 188–193; discoverer of, 235; elementary nature of, 208
Nobel Prize, awarded to Chadwick, 836; to Mme. Curie, 830; to the Curies, 829; to Fermi, 861; to Hahn, 812, 867; to von Hevesy, 849; to Joliot-Curies, 837; to von Laue, 847; to Lawrence, 860; to Seaborg and McMillan, 870; to Soddy, 825
Noddack, Walter, 851–853
Nollet, Abbé Jean-Antoine, 130, 513
Nordenskiöld, Baron Nils Adolf Erik, 316, 346, 347, 516, 533, 552, 641
Norton, Thomas H., 556, 557
Nutrition, cobalt in, 161
Nuttall, Thomas, 489

Ocher, 33
Oersted, Hans Christian, 592, 594, 595
Oesper, Ralph E., 465
Oil of vitriol, 185, 186
Oppenheimer, J. Robert, 858
Orfila, Mateo-José-Buenaventura, 276 277, 295
Osann, G. W., 440
Osmium, 436–440
Ostwald, Wilhelm, visit to Curie laboratory, 811
Owens, R. B., 826
Oxides of manganese, Arfwedson's research on, 495, 496
Oxygen, 208–229; density of, 780, 781

Paints, ancient eye, 96
Palcani, Luigi, 465
Palissy, Bernard, 154, 155
Palladium, 429–432; discoverer of, 171
Pallas, Peter Simon, 272–274
Paneth, F. A., 862
Paracelsus, 144, 153, 197
Patronite, 364
Pauli, Matthäus, his glass-etching fluid, 756
Pedanios, Dioscorides, 455
Peligot, Eugène-Melchior, 267, 268, 269, 270, 501
Pelletier, Bertrand, 264, 416, 420, 421, 516
Peñaflorida, Count of, 285
Pennsylvania, coal discovery in, 75
Perdix, Bartholomew, 589

Pereira-Forjas, A., 270
Perey, Marguerite, 866
Periodic law, discovery of, 653–669
Periodic table of the elements, Mendeleev's, 652; Meyer's, 659
Perlman, I., 875
Peroni, G., 490
Perrier, C., 862
Petalite, 485–489; Arfwedson's work on, 496, 497
Petroleum, 77–79
Petroleum well, the first U. S., 79
Petrov, Vasilii Vladimirovich, 228, 229
Pettersson, Sven Otto, 550, 677, 679, 680
Pharmacopoeia, Schroeder's, 94, 101
Phelps, Almira Hart Lincoln, 80
Phlogiston, 197, 206, 212, 227, 242
Phosphorus, 109–116; chemical nature, incorrect views of, 130, 131; constituent of bone, 133; description of Brand's process of making, 126; discovery of, 121; elemental, discoverer of, 121; Hanckwitz's recipe for, 129; matches, 135; new method of preparation, 132; preparation of, from vegetable and animal matter, 133; presence of, 132, 133; rediscovery of, 125; red modification of, 135; secret processes of making, 112, 114
Pisani, Félix, 631
Pitchblende, 266–270
Pitcher, Mrs. Frank, 815
Plant nutrition, calcium in, 510; carbon in, 83–87; zinc in, 151, 152
Plants, aluminum in, 610; barium in, 516, 517; beryllium in, 570; boron in, 585, 586; cerium in, 558; copper in, 28; effect of thallium on, 641; fluorine in, 770; hydrogen in, 187, 188; lithium in, 489, 490; magnesium in, 527, 528; manganese in, 173; origin of potash in, 456–458; silica in, 588; sodium in, 467, 468; strontium in, 521; sulfur in, 57; titanium in, 549–551; vanadium in, 364
Plaster of Paris, 506
Platinum, 407–429
Plattner, Carl Friedrich, 630
Pliny the Elder, 8, 9, 141, 407, 465, 565
Pliny the Younger, 466
Poda, Abbé Nicolaus, 631
Poincaré, Henri, 805
Polo, Marco, 77, 141
Polonium, 806–809; a non-radioactive isotope of, 809
Pomet, Pierre, 155, 156
Pontin, M. M. af, 509, 510

Potash, from vegetable ash, 455; in alum, 458, 459; in leucite, 459; in pumice, 459, 460; origin in plants, 456–458
Potassium, 473–484; in animals, 460
Potassium permanganate, 172, 173
Potosí mines, 17
Pott, J. H., 169, 173, 457, 590
Praseodymia, 713–717
Priestley, Joseph, 40, 83–85, 208, 213–215, 216–221, 238–240, 242, 423; his apparatus, 217; his laboratory, 219
Promethium, 863–865
Proust, Joseph-Louis, 165, 286, 291, 420
Prout, William, 182, 187; regarding iodine, 741, 742
Pseudo-Geber, 184–186
Pumice, potash in, 459, 460
Pumping engine, del Río's, 396
Pyrite, 33; thallium in, 641
Pyroligneous acid, 183, 184
Pyrolusite, 168, 170–173

Quartz, 586–588
Quennessen, Louis, 418
Qvist, Bengt (Andersson), 259, 260

Radioactivity, artificial, 831–838
Radium, 809–811
Radium series, 813–820
Ramacsaházy, Colonel Joseph, 324
Rammelsberg, Carl Friedrich, 361
Ramsay, Sir William, 242, 637, 778, 781–785, 788, 792, 793–796
Raspe, Rudolf Erich, 257
Rayleigh, Lord, the Third (see Strutt, Robert John)
Regnault, Henri-Victor, 662
Reich, Ferdinand, 254, 641, 642, 643–646
Remsen, Ira, 783
Retzius, Anders Jahan, 222
Rey, Jean, 210
Rheinboldt, Heinrich, 593
Rhenium, 851–855
Rhodium, 432–436; discoverer of, 171
Rich, M. N., 363
Richards, Theodore William, 819
Richter, Hieronymus Theodor, 254, 641, 644–646
Ridgeway, William, 566
Rinman, Sven, 150, 159
Ritthausen, H., 490
Robinson, W. O., 490
Robottom, Arthur, his explorations of borax in Nevada and California, 583, 584
Roebuck, Dr. John, 186
Roloff, J. C. H., 532

Roscoe, Sir Henry Enfield, *360*–363, 619, 626, *629*, 634
Rose, Heinrich, 316, 341, *347*, 348
Rose, Valentin the Younger, *265*
Rouelle, Guillaume-François, *115*, 456, 467
Rouelle, Hilaire-Marin, 467
Rubidium, 631–634
Ruby, chromium in the, 278
Rückert, G. C. A., 528
Rumford (see Thompson, Benjamin)
Rupprecht, Anton von, 324, 526
Russell, Alexander Smith, *824*, 828
Ruthenium, 440–447
Rutherford, Daniel, 205, 206, 208, *234*–249
Rutherford, John, 235, 236
Rutherford, Sir Ernest, 815, *816*, 818
Rydén, Stig, 290, 299

Sage, Balthasar-Georges, *164*
Sainte-Claire Deville, Charles, *602*
Sainte-Claire Deville, Henri, 550, 587, 588, *602*–606
Sal ammoniac, 188–190
Salt, 461–464; Glauber's, 466
Saltpeter, 190–193, 211, 212; as distinguished from sodium carbonate, 192
Samaria, 712, 713, 717–720
Sassolite (see Boric acid, natural)
Sayre, L. E., 517
Scaliger, Julius Caesar, *408*, 409
Scandia, 708, 709
Scandium, 677–683
Scheele, Carl Wilhelm, 133, 170, 173, 208, 213, 221, 222–225, 243, 252, 254–256, 260–262, 264, 456, 458, 514–517, 551, 552, 729, 756, 758
Scheelite, 254–258
Scheerer, C. J. A. Theodor, 678
Scheffer, Henric Theophil, 416, 417
Schiapparelli, C., 490
Schmidt, G. C., 560
Schoolcraft, Henry R., 151
Schroeder, Johann, 94
Schrötter, Anton von, 135, 136
Schürer, Christoph, 158
Schultze, M. O., 161
Schwanhard, Heinrich, 756
Schweigger, J. S. C., 530, 531
Scott, Sir Walter, 235, 236, *239*, 247–249
Seaborg, Glenn Theodore, *858*, 869–*871*, 875–879
Searle, Dennis, co-discoverer of borax in California, 583
Sea water, boric acid in, 584, 585; bromine from, 754; magnesium from, 528

Sedative salt, 574, 575
Sefström, Nils Gabriel, 353, *354*, 355, 357–359, 684
Segrè, Emilio Gino, 862, 865
Selenium, 306–318; in Chile, 315; other sources of, 316, 317; uses of, 317, 318
Selenium poisoning, 317
Sempere y Guarinos, J., 412
Serpentine, 523, 524
Shepard, Charles Upham, 377
Shu-Sha, 461
Sicard, Father, 188
Sickingen, Baron Carl von, 417
Silica, in plants and animals, 588
Silicon, 586–588; preparation of first crystalline, 587
Silliman, Benjamin, 78, 376, *519*
Silliman, Benjamin, Jr., 376
Silver, 14; mines, 16; symbol, 15, 16; trees, 18
Skillings, E. M., co-discoverer of borax in California, 583
Slevogt, Johann Adrian, 522
Sloane, Sir Hans, *342*, 372, *373*, 377
Smalt, 158, 159
Smelters, nickel, 166
Smith, Edgar Fahs, 377; his picture of Wöhler, 600
Smith, J. Lawrence, 387, 459, *706*
Smith, Thomas P., 375
Smithson, James, 382
Sobolevskii, P. G., 428
Soddy, Frederick, 812, 820, 825–*827*, 828
Sodium, 473–484; in basalt and lava, 466, 467; in plants and animals, 467, 468; some compounds, 460–468
Sodium carbonate, as distinguished from saltpeter, 192
Söderbaum, H. G., 497
Soret, Louis, 711
Southey, Robert, 478
Sowerby, James, 166
Spallanzani, Abbé Lazaro, 590
Spectroscope, Kirchhoff-Bunsen, 626
Spectroscopic analysis, 624
Speter, Max, *129*, 137, 336, 717
Sphalerite, 151
Spodumene, 485, 489
Stahl, Georg Ernst, 197, *198*, 474, 507, 590
Steinkoenig, L. A., 490
Stibick-stone, 96
Stock, Alfred E., 768
Stomach, free hydrochloric acid in the, 187
Strabo of Amasia, 141
Strassmann, F., 868